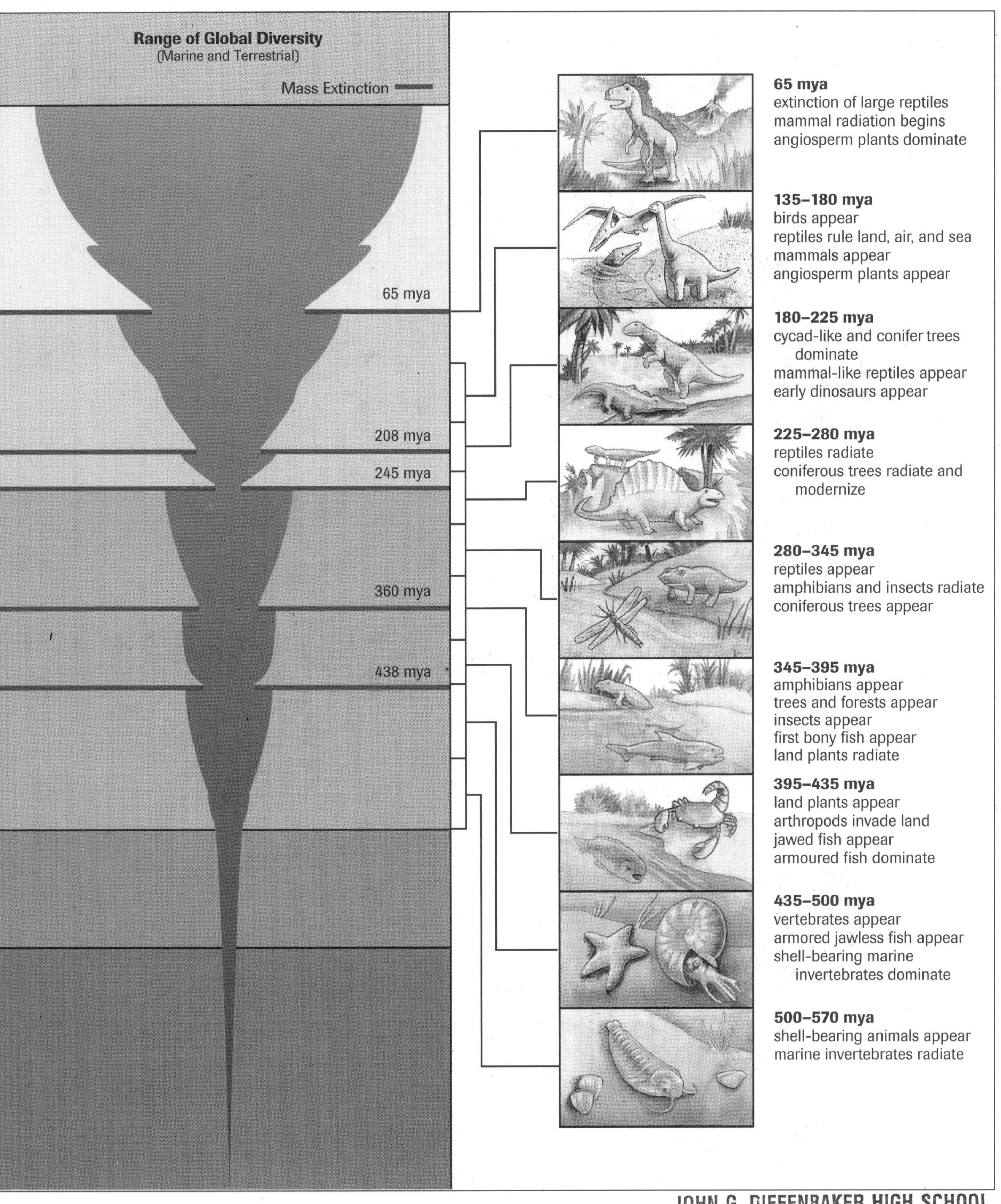
Range of Global Diversity
(Marine and Terrestrial)
Mass Extinction
65 mya
208 mya
245 mya
360 mya
438 mya
65 mya
extinction of large reptiles
mammal radiation begins
angiosperm plants dominate
135–180 mya
birds appear
reptiles rule land, air, and sea
mammals appear
angiosperm plants appear
180–225 mya
cycad-like and conifer trees dominate
mammal-like reptiles appear
early dinosaurs appear
225–280 mya
reptiles radiate
coniferous trees radiate and modernize
280–345 mya
reptiles appear
amphibians and insects radiate
coniferous trees appear
345–395 mya
amphibians appear
trees and forests appear
insects appear
first bony fish appear
land plants radiate
395–435 mya
land plants appear
arthropods invade land
jawed fish appear
armoured fish dominate
435–500 mya
vertebrates appear
armored jawless fish appear
shell-bearing marine invertebrates dominate
500–570 mya
shell-bearing animals appear
marine invertebrates radiate

Nelson

Biology

Alberta 20–30

Authors

Dr. Bob Ritter
Edmonton Catholic Separate School District No. 7

K.L. Burley
Red Deer Public School District No.104

Douglas Fraser
District School Board Ontario North East

Contributing Writers

Lorraine Lastiwka
Science Consultant, Edmonton School District No.7

Jennifer Halia MacLean
(Formerly) Holy Trinity High School, Edmonton Catholic Separate School District No.7

Australia Canada Mexico Singapore Spain United Kingdom United States

THOMSON™

Biology Alberta 20–30

Authors
Dr. Bob Ritter
K.L Burley
Douglas Fraser

Contributing Writers
Lorraine Lastiwka
Jennifer Halia MacLean

Director of Publishing
Beverley Buxton

General Manager, Mathematics, Science, and Technology
Lenore Brooks

Publisher, Science
John Yip-Chuck

Executive Managing Editor, Development
Cheryl Turner

Managing Editors, Development
Susan Ball
Lois Beauchamp

Product Manager
Paul Masson

Program Manager
Jackie Dulson

Developmental Editors
Barbara Booth
Kelly Davis
Jackie Dulson
Jenna Dunlop
Barb Every
Christy Hayhoe
Louise MacKenzie
Lisa McManus
Tom Shields
Rosemary Tanner

Editorial Assistants
Jacquie Busby
Christina D'Alimonte
Aisha Hammah
Alisa Yampolsky

Executive Director, Content and Media Production
Renate McCloy

Director, Content and Media Production
Linh Vu

Senior Content Production Editors
Deborah Lonergan
Lisa McManus
Sue Selby

Content Production Editor
Cheryl Tiongson

Copy Editor
Susan Till

Proofreaders
Christine Hobberlin
Wendy Thomas

Indexer
Noeline Bridge

Production Manager
Cathy Deak

Production Coordinators
Sharon Latta Paterson
Helen Locsin
Kathrine Pummell

Design Director
Ken Phipps

Art Management
Suzanne Peden

Illustrators
AMID Studios
ArtPlus Ltd.
Greg Banning
Andrew Breithaupt
Steven Corrigan
Deborah Crowle
Kyle Gell Design
Imagineering
Irma Ikonen

Interior Design
Kyle Gell
Allan Moon

Cover Design
Johanna Liburd

Cover Image
Sarah Spencer/ShutterStock

Compositors
Zenaida Diores
Nelson Gonzalez

Photo/Permissions Researcher
Karen Becker

Printer
Transcontinental Printing Inc.

ISBN-13: 978-0-17-6289188
ISBN-10: 0-17-6289186

Printed and bound in Canada
1 2 3 4 09 08 07 06

For more information contact Thomson Nelson, 1120 Birchmount Road, Toronto, Ontario, M1K 5G4. Or you can visit our Internet site at http://www.nelson.com

Reviewers and Advisors

Teacher Reviewers

Peggy Au
Winston Churchill High School, Lethbridge School District No.51

Barry Hertz
St. Mary's High School, Calgary Roman Catholic Separate School District No. 1

Shannon Mitchell
Lindsay Thurber Composite High School, Red Deer Public School District No.104

Narsh Ramrattan
Peace River High School, Peace River School Division No.10

Sandy Shields
Winston Churchill High School, Lethbridge School District No.51

Tim Trentham
Hunting Hills High School, Red Deer Public School District No. 104

Aboriginal Education Reviewers and Consultants

Leith Campbell
Edmonton Catholic Separate School District No. 7

Dean Cunningham
Consultant, Edmonton

Accuracy Reviewers

Dr. Keith M. Bagnall
Professor, Division of Anatomy, University of Alberta

Dr. Ralph Cartar
Associate Professor, Department of Biological Sciences, University of Calgary

Dr. Steve Harvey
Professor, Department of Physiology, University of Alberta

Dr. Robin E. Owen
Instructor, Department of Chemical, Biological & Environmental Science, Mount Royal College

Dr. Michael Pollock
Instructor, Department of Chemical, Biological & Environmental Science, Mount Royal College

Assessment Reviewers

Jayni Caldwell
Foothills Composite High School, Foothills School Division No. 38

Kelly Dunn
Bishop Grandin High School, Calgary Roman Catholic Separate School District No. 1

Barry Hertz
St. Mary's High School, Calgary Roman Catholic Separate School District No. 1

Mary McDougall
Secondary Science Consultant, Calgary Roman Catholic Separate School District No. 1

David Milne-Ives
Strathcona-Tweedsmuir School, Private

Audio Clip Writers

Pat Adams
Strathcona-Tweedsmuir School, Private

Careers Consultant

Art Bauer
Science Coordinator, Living Waters Catholic Regional Division No. 42

Investigations Reviewers

Greg Voigt
Archbishop Oscar Romero, Edmonton Catholic Separate School District No.7

T.J. Sadler
Harry Ainlay School, Edmonton School District No.7

Literacy Reviewers

Mary McDougall
(Formerly) Secondary Science Consultant, Calgary Roman Catholic Separate School District No. 1

Janice Ritter
St. Francis High School, Calgary Roman Catholic Separate School District No. 1

Safety Reviewer

Art Bauer
Science Coordinator, Living Waters Catholic Regional Division No. 42

Web Quest Writers

Dr. Norma Nocente
Associate Professor, Faculty of Education, University of Alberta

Technology Reviewers and Consultants

Pat Adams
Strathcona-Tweedsmuir School, Private

Dan Braun
Kingsville District High School, Greater Essex County District School Board

William Konrad
Boreal-Northwest

Dr. Norma Nocente
Associate Professor, Faculty of Education, University of Alberta

T.J. Sadler
Harry Ainley School, Edmonton School District No.7

International Baccalaureate Advisors

David Milne-Ives
Strathcona-Tweedsmuir School, Private

Dr. Bob Ritter
Assistant Superintendent, Edmonton Catholic Separate School District No. 7

David Rose
John G. Diefenbaker High School, Calgary School District No.19

Field Test Schools

Alberta Education Field Test Schools

Battle River Regional Division No.31: Camrose Composite High School

Calgary Roman Catholic Separate School District No.1: Bishop Grandin High School

Chinook's Edge School Division No.73: Spruce View School

East Central Alberta Catholic Separate Schools Regional Division No.16: St. Jerome's School

Edmonton Catholic Separate School District No.7: Archbishop O'Leary, St. Francis Xavier

Fort McMurray Public School District No.2833: Westwood Community High School

Grande Prairie School District No.2357: Grande Prairie Composite High School

Grasslands Regional Division No.6: Brooks Composite High School

Thomson Nelson Field Test Schools

Buffalo Trail Public Schools Regional Division No.28: Kitscoty Junior Senior High School

Calgary Roman Catholic Separate School District No.1: St. Mary's High School

Calgary School District No.19: Centennial High School, James Fowler High School, John G. Diefenbaker High School

Edmonton Catholic Separate School District No.7: Archbishop Oscar Romero, Holy Trinity, Louis St. Laurent High School

Edmonton School District No.7: Amiskwaciy Academy, J. Percy Page School, McNally School

Elk Island Public Schools Regional Division No.14: Salisbury Composite High School

Foothills School Division No.38: Foothills Composite High School

Grande Prairie Roman Catholic Separate School Division No.28: St. Joseph Catholic High School

Holy Spirit Roman Catholic Separate Regional Division No.4: Catholic Central High School

Lethbridge School District No.51: Lethbridge Collegiate Institute, Winston Churchill High School

Medicine Hat School District No.76: Crescent Heights High School

Parkland School Division No.70: Spruce Grove Composite High School

Peace River School Division No.10: Grimshaw Junior Senior High School

Pembina Hills Regional Division No.7: Barrhead Composite High School, Fort Assiniboine School, Richard F. Staples Secondary School

Red Deer Catholic Regional Division No.39: Notre Dame High School

Red Deer Public School District No.104: Hunting Hills High School

Rocky View School District No.41: Bert Church High School, Bow Valley High School

Sturgeon School Division No.24: Sturgeon Composite

Wolf Creek School Division No.72: Lacombe Composite High School, Rimbey Junior Senior High School

CONTENTS

Unit 30 B Reproduction and Development 506

Unit 30 C Cell Division, Genetics, and Molecular Biology 552

Your Guide to this Textbook

Each unit begins with a two-page set of questions: **Are You Ready?** These questions will help you assess which concepts you should review before you begin the unit.

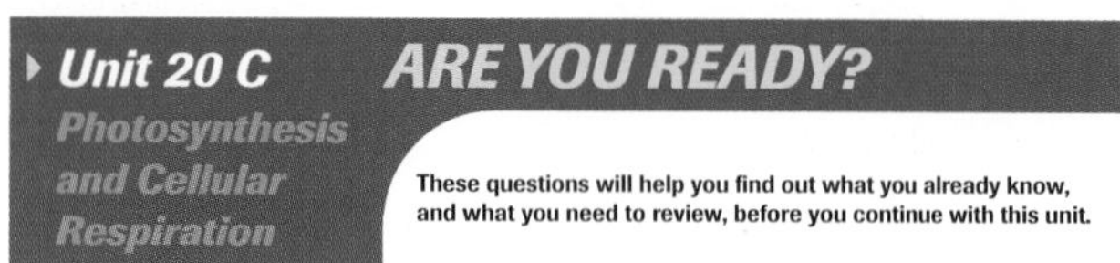

You can review prerequisite concepts and skills on the Nelson Web site and in the Appendices. The **Appendices** are useful resources for your reference throughout the course.

Each chapter begins with **Starting Points** questions, helping you assess what you already know about the concepts for that chapter. Continue to consider these as you go through the chapter.

Throughout the chapters are activities that have one of the following icons on the left-hand side of their banner. Icons indicate the curriculum emphasis to which the activity relates.

Icon	Curriculum emphasis of activity
	Nature of Science
	Science and Technology
	Social and Environmental Contexts

Investigations are labs in which you will make predictions, form hypotheses, gather and record evidence, then analyze, evaluate, and communicate your results. **Report Checklists** in Investigations show you the parts of lab reports you will need to complete.

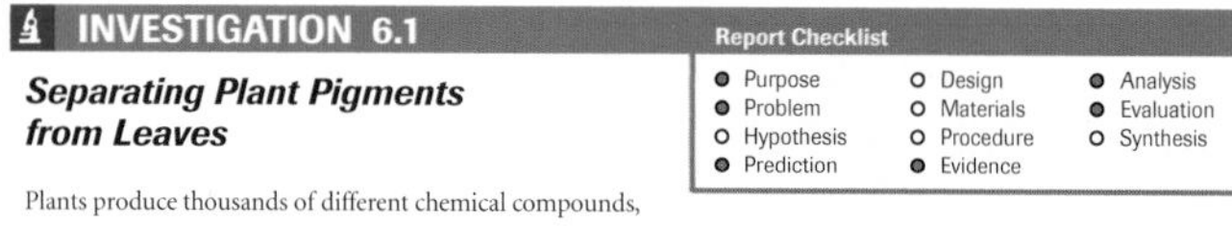

You will see an **Investigation Introduction** at the point in the chapter where you will most likely perform each Investigation.

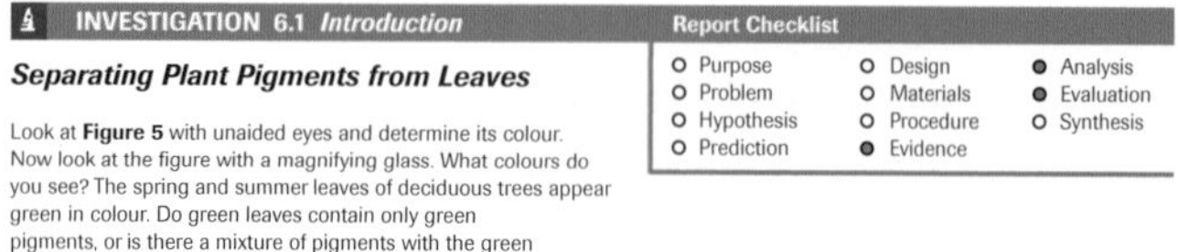

A **Case Study** provides you with information or data, and then guides you in analyzing, decision making, or problem solving by a series of questions.

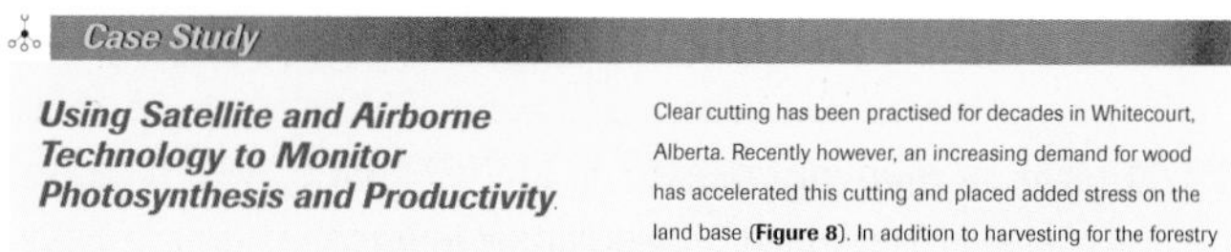

In an **Explore an Issue** feature, you have the opportunity to define, research, analyze, and report on issues affecting our planet. The **Issue Checklist** shows you the parts of the decision-making process you will need to complete.

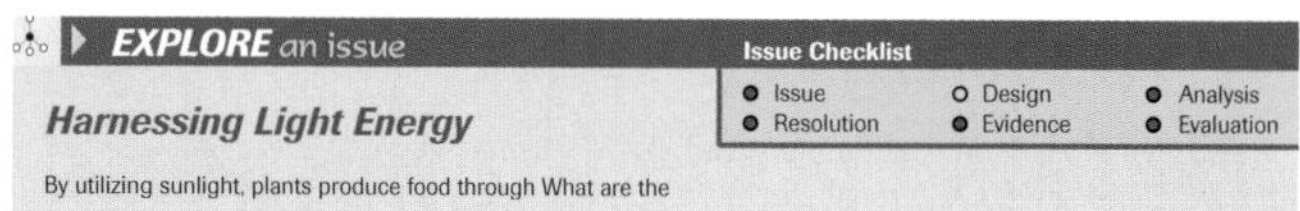

Sample Exercises guide you step-by-step through a solution.

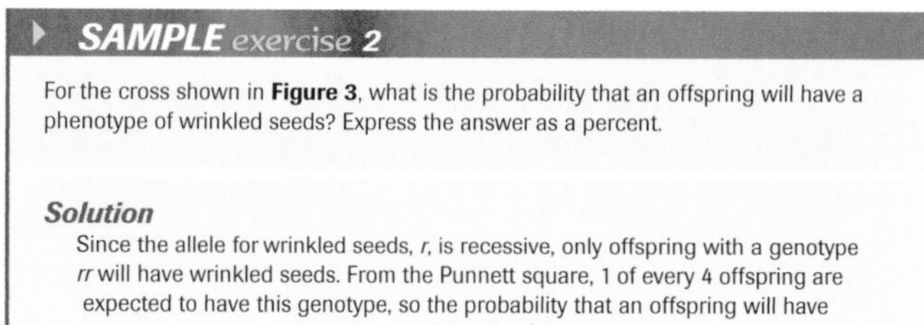

You will have many opportunities throughout each unit for practice and review. **Practice** questions are found after all Sample Exercises and at other points throughout the chapter, and will help you to assess your understanding as you work.

Practice

1. A student working with *Drosophila* makes the following cross:

   E^1E^2 (wild-type eye colour) $\times$ E^2E^4 (apricot eye colour)

   What will be the phenotypic ratio of the offspring?

You can review and demonstrate your understanding of the concepts and skills in each section using the **Summaries** and **Section Questions**.

The **Chapter Summary** lists the outcomes that you should have mastered as you worked through the chapter, as well as equations and key terms. There is also a box of questions—**Make a Summary**—to help you consolidate your understanding of the concepts addressed.

The **Chapter Reviews** and **Unit Reviews** give you practice in answering questions similar to those on the Alberta Diploma Exam. **Appendix A5** provides diploma exam tips and **Appendix D** contains numerical answers and short answers for questions throughout your textbook.

Other icons throughout the textbook will direct you to features to aid you in your learning.

Icon	Explanation
	• an invitation to go to the **Nelson Web site** for research, additional information, or to reach an activity
	Starting Points • questions for you to check your knowledge of upcoming concepts, and to revisit at the end of the chapter to assess your learning
	Lab Exercise • data from an experiment for you to analyze and/or evaluate
	Career Connection • online information about a science-related career
	Audio • an audio file on the Student CD and the Nelson Web site that may be a walk-through of a Sample Exercise, an Extension, or pronunciation of Key Terms
	Video • a video or animation on the Nelson Web site that demonstrates a technique or illustrates a concept

Icon	Explanation
	Caution • a warning of particular safety concerns
	Explorations and Mini Investigations • brief activities that introduce new concepts or skills and help you to explore concepts being discussed
	Extension • reading material or an activity related to concepts or skills beyond the Alberta Biology 20-30 curriculum
	Chemistry Connection • online information about a related topic in your chemistry course
	Web Activity • activities on the Nelson Web site that are an integral part of your Biology textbook - Web Quests (investigations in which you gather, analyze, and use online information); - Case Studies (activities that provide information and then ask you to analyze it and draw conclusions); - Simulations (interactive online activities or investigations); and - Canadian Achievers (explorations of science-related careers of exceptional Canadians)

Preparation for Alberta Diploma Exams

We hope that your interest in science will grow and deepen as you work through your Biology course with the aid of this textbook. As your knowledge, skills, and attitudes develop, you will also be working toward the Biology Diploma Exam. This resource has been developed to help you achieve your best on the Alberta Biology 30 Diploma Exam. **Appendix A5** provides specific tips on writing the exam. Part 1 of the Chapter and Unit Reviews contain multiple choice and numerical response questions like you will find on the Diploma Exam. Your teacher can provide you with additional questions we have provided to her/him. The Case Studies provide practice in answering closed-response written questions based on a scenario. In completing an Explore an Issue, you will develop skills for answering open-response written questions on the Diploma Exam. Here you will find and read information about a science-related issue and then formulate and communicate your ideas, supported by your research. You will apply these skills to the written-response (Part 2) questions in the Chapter Reviews and Unit Reviews, and in the **additional Diploma Exam-style Review Questions** on the Nelson Web site. These questions are longer scenario-based questions, sometimes using published articles.

unit

20 A

Energy and Matter Exchange in the Biosphere

About 50 years ago, the first photographs taken from space allowed us to see our planet as a whole. Traditional Western thought saw Earth's natural resources as infinite and viewed nature as a force to be dominated for our benefit. Such views are now linked to many environmental problems. Satellite images often reveal scars on our planet from human activities, such as forests that are burned away to create agricultural land or the silting of waterways, such in the Mississippi River Delta shown in the photograph. However, we have now learned that the best way to correct and prevent these problems is to ensure our activities are carried out in ways that help to maintain the natural balance of the biosphere. When we view humanity as an integral part of the biosphere, connected to all living things, we begin to consider not only the ways that science and technology can change natural ecosystems, but also how those changes will impact us.

As you progress through the unit, think about these focusing questions:

- How are carbon, oxygen, nitrogen, and phosphorus cycled in the biosphere?
- How is the flow of energy balanced in the biosphere?
- How have human activities and technological advances affected the balance of energy and matter in the biosphere?

UNIT 20 A PERFORMANCE TASK

Environmental Effects of Human Communities

In this Performance Task, you will choose one of three tasks that will demonstrate your understanding of how ecosystems are sustained, and the effects of human activities. The first task considers golf. In many areas, new courses are appearing in what was farmland or forest. How might you create a golf course with minimum impact on local ecosystems? The second task considers community water quality. We use water for many purposes, such as for drinking, building, making chemicals, and transporting goods. How could you monitor the impact of human activities on a local body of water? Finally, you might create an educational board game that will help players learn about ecosystems and how they can be sustained.

www.science.nelson.com 

GENERAL OUTCOMES

In this unit, you will

- explain the constant flow of energy through the biosphere and ecosystems
- explain the cycling of matter through the biosphere
- explain the balance of matter and energy exchange in the biosphere as an open system, and how this maintains equilibrium

Unit 20 A Energy and Matter Exchange in the Biosphere

ARE YOU READY?

Prerequisites

Concepts

- biotic and abiotic factors
- producers, consumers, and, decomposers
- food chains and food webs
- the water cycle
- open and closed systems
- thermal energy transfer in the biosphere

Skills

- select and use appropriate vocabulary to communicate scientific ideas
- use graphs to compile, organize, and interpret data

You can review prerequisite concepts and skills on the Nelson Web site and in the Appendices.

A Unit Pre-Test is also available online.

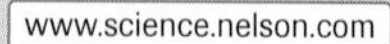

These questions will help you find out what you already know, and what you need to review, before you continue with this unit.

Knowledge

1. Use **Figure 1** to identify the following:
   (a) two biotic and two abiotic factors
   (b) a producer, a consumer, and a decomposer
   (c) three different food chains of at least three organisms each

Figure 1
An ecosystem

2. Describe the role of producers in an ecosystem.
3. Could an ecosystem continue if all the decomposers were removed? Why or why not?
4. Describe how water is cycled within ecosystems.
5. Identify two ways that thermal energy (heat) is transferred from one region of Earth to another.
6. Distinguish between an open system and a closed system.

Skills

7. Using a diagram, describe the greenhouse effect.
8. In your notebook, sketch **Figure 2** or write labels to represent the organisms. Draw arrows to complete a food web.

Figure 2

STS Connections

9. Why should we be concerned with air and water pollution that is happening on the side of Earth opposite to where we live?
10. Attitudes toward the environment have changed over time. Using specific examples, describe evidence that Canadians' attitudes have changed over time. Is there still a need for changes in attitude? Explain your answer.
11. Different cultures often look differently at the relationships between living organisms and their ecosystems.
    (a) Using the wolf as an example, explain the different worldviews of Aboriginal people and early European settlers.
    (b) Is there any evidence that the view of the early European settlers is no longer held by Canadians?

chapter

1 The Biosphere as a Closed System

In this chapter

- Exploration: Earth under a Microscope
- Web Activity: Dr. David Suzuki
- Web Activity: Creating a Database of At-Risk Species
- Explore an Issue: What Is the Value of Wolves?

In the traditional knowledge of Canada's Aboriginal peoples, nature is full of interconnections and complexities. Spiritual stories describe how animals are connected to living things such as plants and other animals, non-living things such as air or water, and natural events such as storms. For example, the Sandy Lake Cree tell of the thunderbird Binay-sih, who protects other animals from the sea serpent, Genay-big. Binay-sih's anger is expressed through black clouds, thunder, and lightning. Humans are just one of the many connected elements.

In contrast, a traditional Western view is that nature is a source of raw materials or products to be exploited for human needs. This narrow viewpoint has sometimes lead us to damage the environment and, in turn, damage ourselves. For example, the recent oil spill at Wabamun Lake can be seen as a conflict between our need for oil and the needs of the organisms in that environment.

Today, scientists from various cultures recognize that they must look at the world differently to meet our need and sustain our planet. Although Western scientific thought and traditional Aboriginal culture have different starting points, both offer important insights into how ecosystems work.

STARTING Points

Answer these questions as best you can with your current knowledge. Then, using the concepts and skills you have learned, you will revise your answers at the end of the chapter.

1. Explain this statement: "An ecosystem is constantly changing, yet it remains the same."
2. Describe a typical food web in your region. Be sure to include producers, consumers, and decomposers.
3. Do you think that Earth's ecosystems can withstand the current negative impacts of human activity? What evidence supports your opinion?
4. A commonly held stereotype is that traditional Aboriginal lifestyles had/have no negative impact on the environment. Recently, writers and researchers have acknowledged that buffalo jumps (which killed more buffalo than were needed) and the burning of forests for agricultural land are inconsistent with this perception. Explain why even positive stereotypes can be dangerous.

Career Connection: Photographer (Scientific)

Figure 1
On August 3rd, 2005, a train derailed at Lake Wabamun, Alberta. More than 1 million litres of oil were spilled, causing severe environmental damage.

Exploration — Earth under a Microscope

Purpose
To investige how living things interact in a closed system on a small and simple scale, by observing microscopic organisms

Materials: tap water; medicine dropper; microscope slides; microscope; cultures of yeast, *Paramecium*, and *Didinium*

Use gloves while making and observing the slides. Dispose of slides and gloves as directed by your teacher. Wash your hands before leaving the lab.

Using the Light Microscope
Listen to a review of the proper use a light microscope.

www.science.nelson.com 

- Using a medicine dropper, prepare separate wet mounts from each of the three cultures. Examine each slide under a light microscope.

(a) For each slide, how many different kinds of living things do you see?
(b) Sketch and describe the organism(s) on each slide.
(c) Describe the behaviour of the organism(s) on each slide.

- Combine the living organisms to observe how they interact. Prepare the following wet mounts:

  1 drop *Paramecium* culture + 1 drop yeast culture
  1 drop *Paramecium* culture + 1 drop *Didinium* culture

(d) Describe the interactions between the organisms.
(e) How would an ecosystem that contained all three organisms be different from one that contained only *Paramecium*?

1.1 Equilibrium in the Biosphere

Figure 1
Interactions among biotic components: **(a)** a plant and an insect, **(b)** an insect and an amphibian, **(c)** an amphibian and a bird

"We do not inherit the Earth from our grandparents; we borrow it from our grandchildren."—Chief Seattle

Imagine how the Apollo astronauts felt when they first set foot on the Moon and saw the spectacle of the living Earth rising above the lifeless lunar rock. From that viewpoint, one might think of our planet as a spaceship. Travelling around the Sun in a slightly elliptical orbit, Earth carries with it the only forms of life confirmed in the universe. As you learned in your previous studies, Earth is a closed system, which is any system in which *matter* is not exchanged with its surroundings. A closed system exchanges *energy* with its surroundings, however. Life is totally dependent on incoming solar energy and the matter available on Earth.

When we see the whole planet from a distance, we can see that everything on Earth is connected. There are no real boundaries. The atmosphere that envelops Earth is continuous and free to flow. The oceans are continuous, even though we have given the oceans separate names.

This distant view of Earth shows us the big picture. It does not allow us to see the countless continuous interactions among living and non-living components that take place in this system. We do not see the insect feeding on the leaves of a tree, or the frog feeding on the insect, or the bird eating the frog (**Figure 1**), or any other details of a complex web of activity that keeps the system running. Neither can we see the impacts of human activity—the treeless hills; the smog hanging over cities, and the polluted rivers, lakes, and oceans—or the efforts of humans to prevent species extinction or to preserve the natural environment.

J.E. Lovelock, a British scientist, compares Earth to a living body. The metaphor is referred to as the *Gaia* (pronounced "gay-ah") *hypothesis*, named after the Greek goddess of Earth. Although a controversial idea in the scientific community, it serves to emphasize that all living things interact with each other and with the non-living components of our planet. In much the same way that the brain requires oxygen and nutrients from the circulatory system to function properly, each component of Earth's environment must be in a state of balance or equilibrium with every other component. What affects one part affects all parts. The expression **dynamic equilibrium** is used to describe any system in which changes are continuously occurring but whose components have the ability to adjust to these changes without disturbing the entire system.

dynamic equilibrium describes any system with constant change in which the components can adjust to the changes without disturbing the entire system

Today's ecologists have evidence to suggest that Earth is facing a crisis in which its dynamic equilibrium is being upset. However, scientists have not reached a consensus about the magnitude of the predicament or what can be done. The problems appear to result from the activities of a single dominant species: humans. We humans can also be a positive force in preserving the dynamic equilibrium of Earth. We have the ability to understand natural processes and act on this knowledge. As a member of Earth's community, you can become a knowledgeable decision maker by studying some of the well-established principles of ecology. The decisions you make will, in part, determine the future direction of life on this small and fragile planet.

The Biosphere

Earth has three basic structural zones: the lithosphere (land), the hydrosphere (water), and the atmosphere (air). Living organisms are found in all three zones. Together, these three zones make up the **biosphere**, the narrow zone around Earth that harbours life.

biosphere the narrow zone around Earth that harbours life

The limits of the biosphere extend from the ocean depths all the way to the atmosphere. Most terrestrial animals are confined to a narrow band where the atmosphere meets the surface of the earth. The regions that are not within the biosphere, such as the upper atmosphere and Earth's core, are also important because they affect living organisms.

Life forms are referred to as the **biotic**, or living, components of the biosphere. Chemical and geological factors, such as rocks and minerals, and physical factors, such as temperature and weather, are referred to as the **abiotic**, or non-living, components. It is the interactions within and between the biotic and abiotic components that the ecologist endeavours to understand and explain.

When biologists investigate how a complex organism functions, they must study its various levels of organization. Moving from the simple to the more complex, these levels are individual cells; then tissues; organs and organ systems; and finally the integrated, functioning body. Ecologists investigating the biosphere proceed in a similar manner. By examining its individual parts, ecologists are able to bring together the various data and provide a picture of how the biosphere operates as an integrated unit.

Ecological studies begin at the organism level. Investigations are designed to determine how the individual interacts with its biotic and abiotic environment. However, an organism does not live in isolation. It tends to group with others of the same species into **populations**. A population influences, and is influenced by, its immediate environment. When more than one population lives in an area, a **community** of organisms is established. An **ecosystem**, the functional unit of the biosphere, has both biotic and abiotic components. The physical and chemical environment, as well as the community of organisms, interact with each other in an ecosystem.

biotic components the biological or living components of the biosphere

abiotic components the non-living components of the biosphere. They include chemical and physical factors.

population a group of individuals of the same species occupying a given area at a certain time

community the populations of all species that occupy a habitat

ecosystem a community and its physical and chemical environment

biodiversity the number of species in an ecosystem

food chain a sequence linking organisms that feed on each other, starting with a food source and continuing in order with each consumer

producer an autotroph; an organism that makes its own food

consumer a heterotroph; an organism that must eat producers or other consumers to survive

Biodiversity

The number of species in an ecosystem is described as the biological diversity or **biodiversity** of the ecosystem. Because every organism in an ecosystem is connected to all the other organisms, the reduction in biodiversity caused by the extinction of a single species can cause a domino effect. The loss of one part from an ecosystem, like the removal of a moving part from a car, can cause the collapse of an entire food chain. A **food chain** is a step-by-step sequence linking organisms that feed on each other, starting with a food source such as plants (**producers**), and continuing with animals and other living things that feed on the plants and on each other (**consumers**). When a species acts as a predator, it keeps the population of its prey in check; when it acts as prey, it provides an important food source.

For example, the overhunting of sea otters along the Pacific coasts of Asia and North America removed the main predator of the sea urchin. Predictably, the number of sea urchins grew rapidly. Sea urchins eat kelp, a form of seaweed. As the number of sea urchins grew, the amount of kelp declined, and so did the fish that relied on the kelp-bed ecosystem for habitat and food. Sea otters very nearly became extinct as a result of hunting pressure. From the point of view of humans, killing sea otters for their fur resulted in the decline of a valuable fishery. Where the sea otter has been reintroduced, sea urchin populations have fallen, kelp beds are being re-established, and the number of fish is increasing.

The story of the whooping crane (**Figure 2**) is another example of an attempt to restore a natural balance. In spring, whooping cranes fly north to live in the marshes and swamps of the prairies and the Canadian north, where they eat crayfish, fish, small mammals, insects, roots, and berries. Efforts by conservationists have helped increase the population from a low of 14 individuals in 1940 to 213 in 2004. Chemical pesticides were the original human threat to the crane, but it was already struggling. Cranes fly a

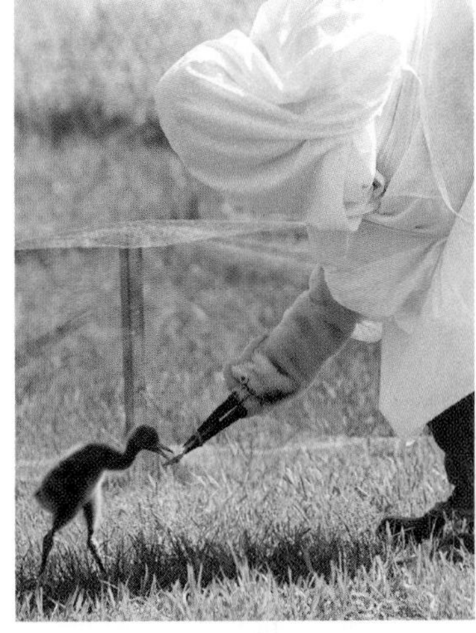

Figure 2
The efforts of wildlife biologists are preventing the whooping crane from becoming extinct. Some young birds are hand-raised but, to prevent the chicks from associating humans with safety, the caregivers disguise themselves as adult cranes.

EXTENSION 

Why is Biodiversity a Good Thing?
Learn more about how species' survival is connected to the biodiversity of a region.

www.science.nelson.com 

long way during their migration, and are vulnerable to hunting and accidents along the way. In addition, the whooping crane reproduces very slowly. Each year females produce two eggs; however, only one will mature. The first fledgling to emerge from its egg kills its brother or sister. This ensures there will be enough food for the survivor, but it also reduces the rate at which the population can increase.

We do not fully understand all the relationships between species in many ecosystems, so we cannot predict reliably what will happen to an ecosystem if its biodiversity is reduced, even by one species.

 WWW **WEB Activity**

Canadian Achievers—Dr. David Suzuki

Dr. David Suzuki (**Figure 3**) is perhaps Canada's most recognizable living scientist. Through his many books and his popular CBC television show "The Nature of Things," Suzuki has taken science out of the laboratory and into people's day-to-day lives. One of Dr. Suzuki's main interests is environmental issues. Explore David Suzuki's contributions to environmental studies further, and find out his opinions on Canada's ecosystems. Think about the following questions:

Which ecosystems in Canada are most at risk?

How does the level of risk relate to biodiversity?

What role does human activity play in loss of biodiversity?

What can you do to reverse this trend?

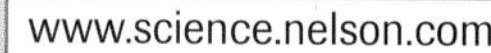
www.science.nelson.com 
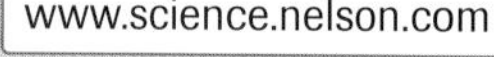

Figure 3
Dr. David Suzuki

SUMMARY Equilibrium in the Biosphere

- Earth supports the only confirmed life forms in existence. Living organisms are found in a limited region of Earth known as the biosphere.
- The expression *dynamic equilibrium* is used to describe any system in which changes are continuously occurring but the components have the ability to adjust to these changes without disturbing the entire system.
- The number of species in an ecosystem is described as the biological diversity or biodiversity of the ecosystem. Since organisms interact with each other in potentially important and unique ways, the reduction in biodiversity caused by the extinction of a single species can cause a "domino effect."

Section 1.1 Questions

1. How can the metaphor of a spaceship be used to describe Earth?
2. What is a closed system?
3. What are the abiotic and biotic components of the biosphere?
4. In what way does a community differ from an ecosystem?
5. Name the levels of organization in the biosphere.
6. Using the organisms in **Figure 1**, on page 8, as an example, explain how ecosystems are in a state of dynamic equilibrium.
7. (a) In your own words define the term *biodiversity.*
   (b) Explain why diversity is important for ecosystems.
   (c) Give two examples of ecosystems that have high biodiversity, and two that have low biodiversity. Explain your classification.
8. Canadian wildlife biologists have been attempting to preserve the whooping crane. Are they succeeding? In a short essay, evaluate the success of their program.

www.science.nelson.com 

Equilibrium Unbalanced 1.2

The first bald eagle born and raised on the shores of Lake Erie in nearly 30 years took flight in 1983. Wildlife officers had moved the parent birds to Long Point peninsula in an attempt to re-introduce the birds to the natural ecosystem in the lower Great Lakes.

During the 1700s and 1800s the bald eagle was common along the northern shores of Lake Erie. By the early 1900s, biologists began to see a decline in their numbers. Early settlers and farmers regarded the birds as a threat to livestock and often killed them. A second, and even more deadly, threat followed. Toxic chemical waste, produced by the many industrial plants that bordered the Great Lakes, entered the eagles' food chain. The high levels of toxins caused eggshells of the bald eagle and some other birds, such as the double-crested cormorant and the herring gull, to become unusually thin. Eggs broke more easily, and many eagles were born with abnormalities. Their birth rate declined significantly.

Eagles depend directly or indirectly on all of the other members of their food chain (**Figure 1**). The health of top-level consumers like eagles indicates whether toxins are entering an ecosystem. When the dynamic equilibrium of an ecosystem becomes unbalanced for any reason, the health or numbers of organisms in that ecosystem are affected. If the changes are large enough, some organisms may even become extinct. Eagles are one of many species that are providing evidence that changes in ecosystems are affecting the natural equilibrium in a negative way. In Canada, more than 450 species of plants and animals are at various degrees of risk, and 12 species have become extinct.

At-risk species are classified depending on the degree of risk. An *endangered* species is one that is close to extinction in all parts of the country or in a significantly large location. An *extirpated* species is one that no longer exists in one part of the country, but can be found in others. A *threatened* species is any species that is likely to become endangered if factors that make it vulnerable are not reversed. The term *special concern* refers to any species that is at risk because of low or declining numbers at the fringe of its range or in some restricted area. **Figure 2** gives some examples of at-risk species across Canada.

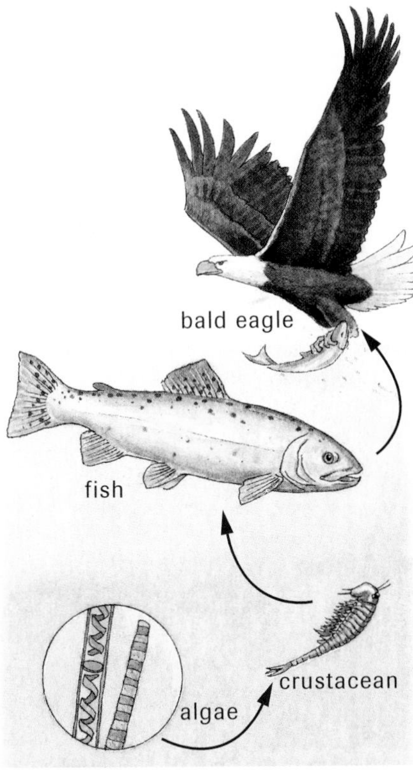

Figure 1
The bald eagle has been reintroduced to the shores of Lake Erie, in an attempt to re-establish a natural ecosystem.

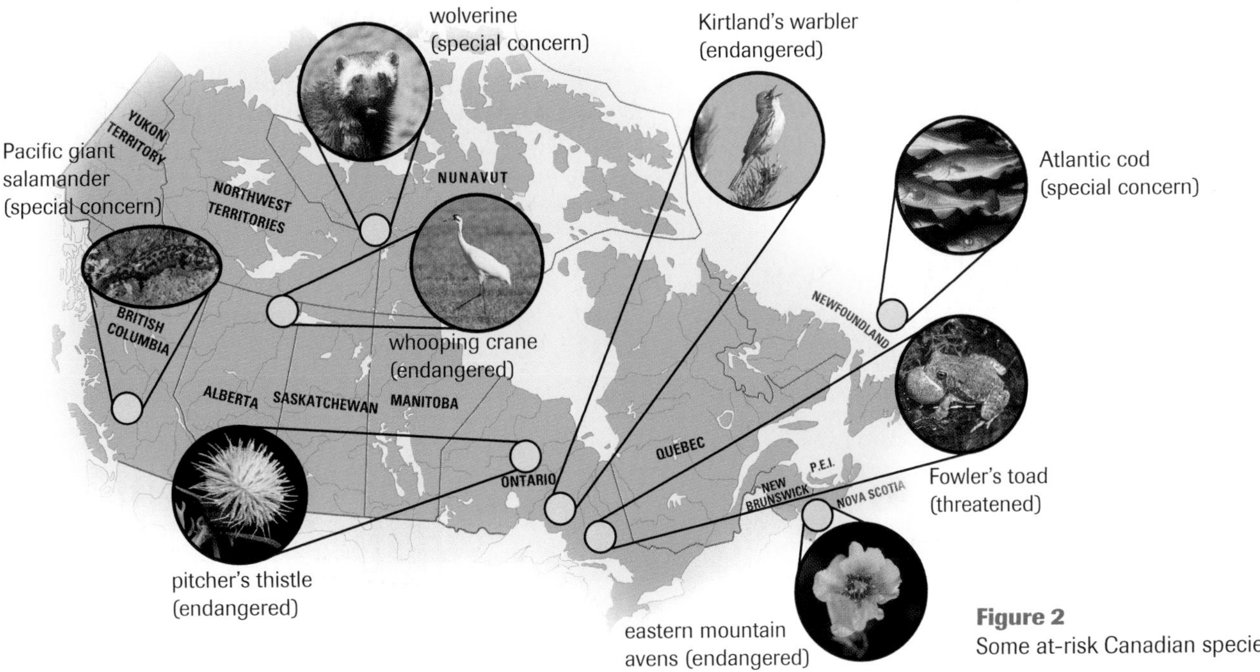

Figure 2
Some at-risk Canadian species

Web Quest—Creating a Database of At-Risk Species

Create an electronic database of endangered species in Canada. First, decide on the categories you will use to describe the information (e.g., type of species, level of risk, and habitat). Then, create a table to define the categories that you want to use to record your data. Include different types of organisms in your database. After you have finished your database, test it by searching according to different categories. Show another group how your database works. Import the data recorded by the other group to make a larger database.

www.science.nelson.com 

The Disappearance of Frogs

indicator species a species sensitive to small changes in environmental conditions

Some species are particularly sensitive to changes in an ecosystem. These **indicator species** can provide an early warning that the balance in an ecosystem is being negatively affected. Some amphibians may be especially important indicator species. Why might this group of animals play such an important role?

The word *amphibian* is a clue. The word comes from two Greek words, *amphi* ("on both sides") and *bios* ("life"). Amphibians literally have two lives (**Figure 3**). Frogs begin as eggs and grow to tadpoles in ponds, and then enter their second life as adults in forest and grassland areas. This means they are exposed to hazards in both ecosystems, instead of only one. Any decline in the health of either of the two ecosystems in which they live will have an impact on frogs.

herbivore an animal that eats only plants

carnivore an animal that feeds only on other animals

omnivore an animal that eats both plants and other animals

Not only do frogs occupy two different ecosystems, they are also parts of two very different food chains. Adult frogs eat mostly insects and a few small fish. In turn, large fish, predatory birds, reptiles, and small mammals eat frogs. This makes the adult frog a member of a food chain (**Figure 4**, next page) that includes producers (plants), **herbivores** (animals that eat plants), and **carnivores** (animals, like the frog, that feed on other animals). Animals that eat both plants and animals, such as humans, raccoons, and bears, are called **omnivores**.

If frogs became extinct, insect populations would soar. This has already happened in Bangladesh, where frog populations have been decimated to supply restaurants with delicacies. The result is a rise in the number of mosquitoes, and a dramatic rise in cases of malaria among humans. Malaria is a disease that is transmitted by mosquitoes, which are eaten by frogs. The increase in malaria can be traced back to the disappearance of frogs from the local ecosystems.

(a)

(b)

Figure 3
The northern leopard frog, native to Alberta, is one of the threatened amphibian species. **(a)** Leopard frogs lay their eggs in ponds, and tadpoles develop. **(b)** Adult leopard frogs live in fields and around ponds.

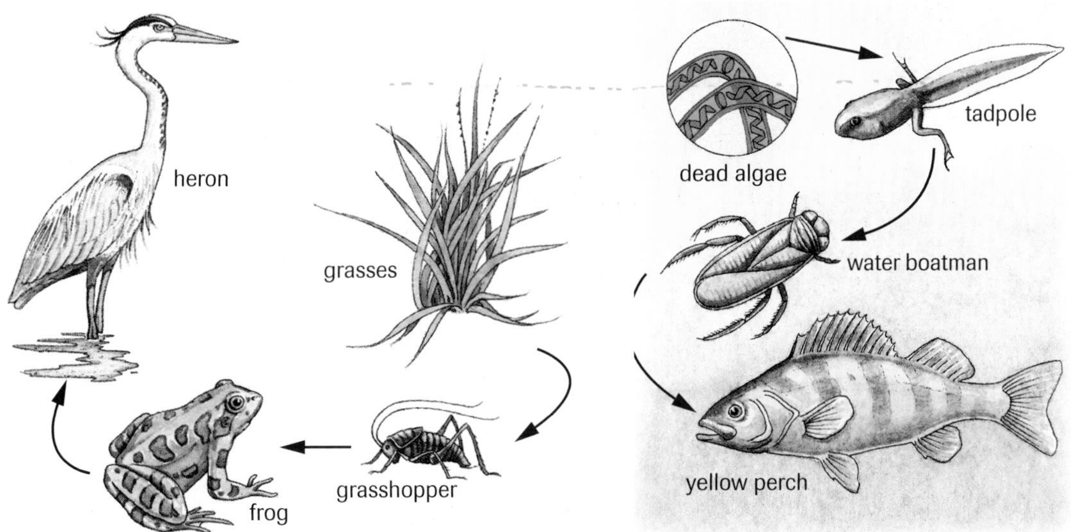

Figure 4
The adult frog is part of a food chain that includes producers (plants) that make food and consumers (animals) that feed either directly or indirectly on the plants.

Figure 5
Waste is recycled within a detritus food chain. Organisms in the chain include fungi, bacteria, insects and other invertebrates, and, in ponds, tadpoles.

Tadpoles eat large amounts of algae (small plantlike organisms), both living and dead. The tadpole is a herbivore, not a carnivore, and is part of a different food chain than that of its parents (**Figure 5**). In this food chain, there are two food sources—producers (the algae) and **detritus** (waste from plants and animals, including their dead remains). Detritus food chains are critical in the recycling of matter in ecosystems. They include **decomposers**, organisms that break down detritus to get nutrients for their own use, but in the process also release nutrients to the soil and water. Plants and algae use those nutrients to grow.

detritus waste from plants and animals, including their dead remains

decomposer an organism that feeds on detritus

Why Are Frogs Disappearing?

Amphibians have been around for more than 400 million years. They survived the catastrophe that killed all the dinosaurs 65 million years ago. They have adapted to ice ages and extended periods of global warming, withstanding drought, flood, and winter ice. They can be found in most ecosystems that include water. Amphibians live on the peaks of the Canadian Rockies, in the city parks of Winnipeg, and in the swamps of Newfoundland. They have even done well dealing with the growth of the human population, at least until recently. Biologists have become aware of the gradual disappearance of amphibians such as frogs, toads, and salamanders. These animals seem to be dying at unprecedented rates. About 30 % of North America's frogs and toads are in trouble. The worldwide disappearance of frogs is puzzling scientists around the globe. In some areas, they have identified a few probable causes.

Loss of Habitat

In Canada, frogs in more heavily populated areas seem to be in great danger. The loss of **habitat**, places where a species can live, is usually thought to be the main cause. Frogs need wetlands, ponds, or lakes with clean water so they can breed and lay their eggs. As adults, they need a place where they can catch insects, such as a forest or a field. They also need a safe path between the two. The growth of cities, and human activities such as

habitat a place or type of environment with conditions suitable for the survival of an organism or population of organisms

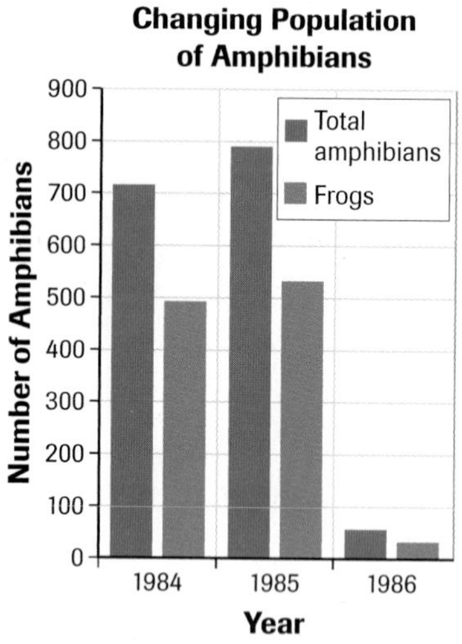

Changing Population of Amphibians

Number of Amphibians (0–900) by Year (1984, 1985, 1986); legend: Total amphibians, Frogs

Figure 6
In the first year of the study, researchers counted 716 amphibians, 493 of which were frogs. After the trees were cut in 1986, they found very few.

farming and industry, take away all of these things. Humans drain wetlands, cut down trees, build on fields, and build roads between ponds and woods.

A highway separating a woodlot from a pond or lake can claim the lives of many frogs as they move between their feeding and breeding areas. Cutting down some of the trees that surround a lake creates problems for amphibians by exposing them to increased UV radiation and predation. **Figure 6** shows data from one study, carried out from 1984 to 1986, in which scientists studied an area where a swamp and a forest were separated by a road. When trees bordering the road were cut in 1986, researchers noticed a huge decline in the number of frogs and other amphibians.

Air and Water Quality

A second cause for the decline in frog numbers is pollution. This is because frog skin is thin and is not protected by feathers, fur, or scales. Frogs have lungs, but they also breathe through their skin, which must be thin to allow oxygen through. Pollutants can also pass through their thin, moist skin. The pollutants in acid rain are known to harm frogs.

Acidity also affects frogs' ability to reproduce. Researchers have noted that if the water in which eggs are laid is even slightly acidic, it reduces the mobility of frog sperm cells. This makes it less likely that eggs will be fertilized. Even if mating is successful, acid affects the frog's development. Embryos, if they develop at all, grow slowly in acidic water. Some ponds may dry up before tadpoles can become adult frogs, and the tadpoles die. Acidic water can cause other problems, such as deformed limbs. Tadpoles with such limbs do not survive for very long.

Climate Change

Climate change may be another factor in the disappearance of frogs. Evidence of global warming is growing. Increasing global temperatures have been linked to the increased use of fossil fuels such as coal, oil, and gasoline. Climate change can cause important changes in local ecosystems. For example, if the climate becomes drier, frog populations will decline. No frog can stay in direct sunlight too long or completely separate itself from fresh water.

Ultraviolet Radiation

The thin skin of the frog is also susceptible to **ultraviolet** (UV) **radiation**. This invisible radiation from the Sun causes sunburns, but it has also been linked with more serious cell damage. The amount of UV radiation reaching Earth's surface is increasing because of damage to the protective **ozone** layer surrounding our planet. A thin layer of ozone (O_3) blocks harmful solar radiation. The layer is getting thinner. Atmospheric scientists believe that chlorofluorocarbons (CFCs), which were widely used in spray cans and refrigerators, are at least partly responsible for the thinning.

Frog species that live at higher altitudes, where the UV radiation is greater, seem to be most vulnerable to changes in the ozone layer. Many of these species have adaptations to protect them from high levels of UV radiation. For example, some species lay black eggs and have a black covering lining their internal organs. However, biologists are concerned that these adaptations may not be enough if change in the ozone layer continues to increase UV radiation levels in this habitat.

The frog is not the only animal whose skin is exposed to UV radiation. Humans also have a delicate skin and are affected by the increase in UV rays. Areas of thinning ozone have been identified above Antarctica and the Canadian Arctic. The concurrent increase in skin cancers and eye problems associated with ultraviolet radiation are raising much concern among ecologists and the general public. The fact that the rate of human skin cancer is rising all over the world underscores the importance of studying the frog as a "bioindicator" of the health of the planet.

CAREER CONNECTION

Photographer (Scientific)

Scientific photographers use high-tech equipment to take specialized photographs, such as photomicrography and time-lapse photography. Forensic photography is one specialization that is used to provide evidence for criminal investigations. If using computers, high-tech cameras, and media equipment interests you, research more about this career.

www.science.nelson.com 

ultraviolet radiation electromagnetic radiation from the Sun that can cause burning of the skin (sunburn) and cellular mutations

ozone O_3, an inorganic molecule. A layer of ozone found in the stratosphere helps to screen out ultraviolet radiation.

EXPLORE an issue

What Is the Value of Wolves?

Issue Checklist

- ○ Issue
- ● Resolution
- ○ Design
- ● Evidence
- ● Analysis
- ● Evaluation

Few animals stir as many emotions as the wolf (**Figure 7**). Some Aboriginal peoples saw the wolf as a traveller, a guide, and a teacher, capable of appearing and disappearing at will. People saw many similarities to humans in the way wolves co-operate.

In contrast, the wolf of European stories chased three little pigs, disguised itself in the fleece of a lamb, and ate the grandmother of Little Red Riding Hood. Unlike the Native peoples of the plains, Europeans saw the wolf as a sharp-toothed villain that preyed on livestock and people.

The Decline of the Wolf

When European settlers reached central North America and found plains covered in bison, they were not willing to compete with the wolf for valuable hides. Thousands of wolves died after they ate poisoned bison carcasses that had been laid out as bait.

After the bison hunters left, having killed most of the bison, there was a break of a few years before ranchers began to kill wolves in the 1880s and 1890s. In both the United States and Canada, anyone bringing a wolf skin to a local government office was paid. In Montana alone, more than 80 000 wolves were destroyed between 1883 and 1918.

However, the effects of removing the wolves were dramatic. It was followed by an increase in the population of the next dominant predator, the coyote. The coyote, a close relative of the wolf, is smaller and rarely forms packs. Bison and elk are much too large for single coyotes to hunt. The coyote eats mostly small mammals, such as mice, voles, and ground squirrels, and the eggs and fledglings of ground-nesting birds. It competes with foxes, badgers, and martens, who eat similar things. As the number of coyotes grew, the numbers of these smaller predators declined.

Wolves frequently left remains from their kills. These leftovers were taken by scavengers such as magpies, ravens, and vultures. Without the wolf, these species began to decline.

Meanwhile, large herbivores such as the elk were safe. The population of elk in the highlands grew so large that they stripped the hills of plants. Diseases spread rapidly within their large herds, causing the population to decline.

The Return of the Wolf

The wildlife managers of Yellowstone National Park in the United States saw these signs and recognized that something was seriously wrong. In 1987 they put together a plan: they were going to import wolves from Canada.

Despite continuing resistance from local ranchers, who feared for their sheep and cattle, 35 wolves were transplanted from Alberta in 1996. More have since been added. Signs of change are already evident. Where wolves have been introduced, elk have moved from open fields (where they are more vulnerable), and now stick to tree-covered areas. Vegetation is recovering, and the number of small predators, such as the kit fox, is increasing. As ranchers feared, some of the new wolves have killed livestock. Five cows and 53 sheep were killed by wolves in Idaho in the spring of 1997. Ranchers are compensated for losses to wolves, but they are still not happy about the reintroduction of wolves.

Figure 7
In 1996, wolf packs were relocated from Alberta to Yellowstone National Park in an attempt to restore an ecological balance.

Understanding the Issue

1. Classify the at-risk status of the wolf in and around Yellowstone National Park
   (a) before European settlers arrived,
   (b) during the bison hunt,
   (c) after ranchers arrived, and
   (d) in 1996.
2. How might the views of Aboriginal people about the wolf lead them to treat wolves differently than European settlers and hunters did?
3. Make a concept map showing how the removal of the wolf caused problems in the local ecosystem.

Different Views

The following are three views on what should have been done about wolves in Yellowstone Park.

The Frontier View: To feed ourselves and the hungry of the world, we must open up, clear, and claim wilderness areas for ranching and other forms of agriculture. Wolves endanger that effort. They kill cattle and sheep. They must be removed wherever they interfere with farming and ranching, and they should not be reintroduced once they have been extirpated.

The Stewardship View: Humans are the most intelligent animals on the planet. It is our duty to take care of other species and preserve our world. Once we recognize that we have damaged an ecosystem, we must try to repair the damage using whatever resources are available to us. Wolves must be preserved in all ecosystems where they are now found, and reintroduced to ecosystems where they once lived.

The Ownership View: Canadians do not own wild animals or plants just because they live in Canada. We have no right to move them around whenever we feel like it. It may have been a mistake to kill the wolves of Yellowstone, but we have no right to take Alberta wolves and move them to a place they've never been before. It is better to let the ecosystem in the park find a new balance. Perhaps one day wolves will find their own way to the park.

Take a Position

- Should we have captured wolves in Alberta and shipped them to Yellowstone National Park? After a group discussion, decide which views you support, or develop an alternative view.
- Using libraries, the Internet, and CD-ROMs, research to find information that will support your position and write a report on the results of your research.

www.science.nelson.com 

SUMMARY Equilibrium Unbalanced

- The frog can serve as an indicator species whose decline signals an unhealthy environment.
- Detritus food chains are critical in the recycling of matter in ecosystems. They include decomposers, organisms that break down detritus to get nutrients for their own use, but in the process also release nutrients to the soil and water. Plants and algae use those nutrients to grow.
- In Canada, 12 species are extinct, while over 450 species are at risk. Some are extirpated (extinct in some former ranges), while others are endangered, threatened, or of special concern.

Section 1.2 Questions

1. Explain how each of the following factors could lead to the extinction of a species. With each explanation include an example of a species threatened by that factor.
   (a) poor reproductive success
   (b) competition from a species newly introduced into an ecosystem
   (c) change in climate
   (d) hunting by humans
2. Choose one of the species listed in **Figure 2**, on page 11, for further research. Why is the species at risk? Are there any initiatives underway to improve the status of the species? What could you do to help? Report on the results of your research.

   www.science.nelson.com 

3. (a) Explain why the life cycle and skin of the frog make it a good indicator species if you want to determine the health of local ecosystems.
   (b) Construct a concept map that links the decline in the number of frogs to factors that may cause the decline.
4. (a) Design a scientific experiment that would assess the impact of acid rain on one species of frog.
   (b) If you actually carried out such an experiment, what would happen to the animals on which you experimented? From an ethical perspective, discuss your experimental design.
5. (a) Predict which area of Canada has the greatest number of organisms at risk. Provide a hypothesis that explains why wildlife in this area would have more problems.
   (b) Do national and provincial parks help alleviate this problem? Explain.
6. The peregrine falcon was once considered endangered. Research Canadian efforts to restore this predator and report on their success.

   www.science.nelson.com 

Chapter 1 SUMMARY

Outcomes

Knowledge

- explain the structure of ecosystem trophic levels, using models such as food chains and webs (1.1, 1.2)

STS

- explain that the process of scientific investigation includes analyzing evidence, and providing explanations based upon scientific theories and concepts (1.2)
- explain that science and technology have both intended and unintended consequences for humans and the environment (1.2)

Skills

- analyze data and apply mathematical and conceptual models by: analyzing data on the diversity of plants, animals, and decomposers of an endangered ecosystem and predicting a future outcome (1.2)
- work as members of a team and apply the skills and conventions of science (all)

Key Terms

1.1

dynamic equilibrium
biosphere
biotic components
abiotic components
population
community
ecosystem
biodiversity
food chain
producer
consumer

1.2

indicator species
herbivore
carnivore
omnivore
detritus
decomposer
habitat
ultraviolet radiation
ozone

MAKE a summary

1. Using as many key words from the chapter as possible, construct a concept map that links key ideas within the chapter. The following Key Terms must appear in your concept map.

   abiotic components
   biotic components
   consumer
   dynamic equilibrium
   population
   community
   detritus
   ecosystem
   producer

2. Revisit your answers to the Starting Points questions at the start of the chapter. Would you answer the questions differently now? Why?

Go To

The following components are available on the Nelson Web site. Follow the links for *Nelson Biology Alberta 20–30*.

- an interactive Self Quiz for Chapter 1
- additional Diploma Exam-style Review Questions
- Illustrated Glossary
- additional IB-related material

There is more information on the Web site wherever you see the Go icon in the chapter.

EXTENSION

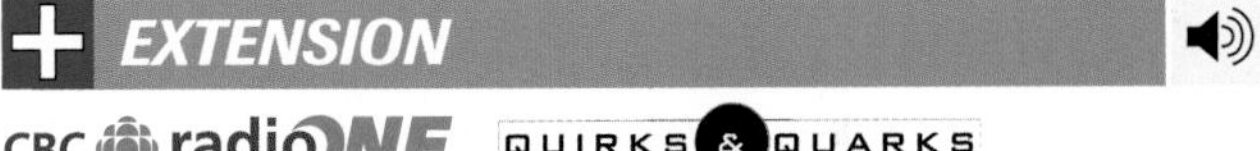

Does a Bear Shed in the Woods?

Grizzly bears in western North America have a restricted range. Dr. Micheal Procter (University of Alberta) is working on bear DNA, and has found that the southernmost bears are isolated, making them more prone to local extinction. Dr. Proctor conducted his research while studying at the University of Calgary.

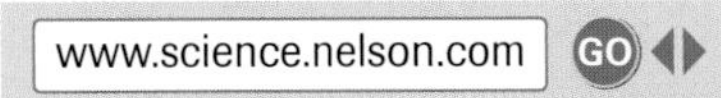

EXTENSION

Bye, Bye, Blue Bayou

This short video discusses the loss of wetlands in the Gulf Coast area of United States. The wetlands in this area are one example of how human activities, including those that contribute to climate change, can affect ecosystems and lead to extinction of species. The loss of the wetlands also has consequences to human life.

Many of these questions are in the style of the Diploma Exam. You will find guidance for writing Diploma Exams in Appendix A5. Science Directing Words used in Diploma Exams are in bold type. Exam study tips and test-taking suggestions are on the Nelson Web site.

www.science.nelson.com 

DO NOT WRITE IN THIS TEXTBOOK.

Part 1

Use the following information to answer questions 1 to 4.

Figure 1 is a diagram of an ecosystem.

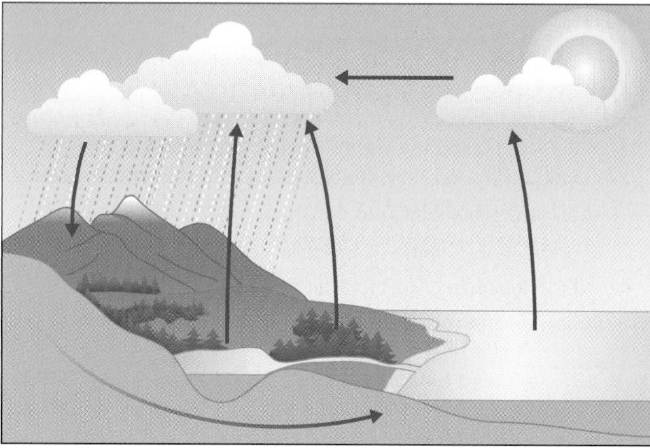

Figure 1

1. Identify three abiotic factors of the ecosystem shown in **Figure 1**.
   A. rain, sunlight, and soil quality
   B. water temperature, water lilies, and minnows
   C. poplars, grasses, and earthworms
   D. soil quality, bacteria, and earthworms

2. Explain how two members of the biotic community affect an abiotic factor.
   A. Pine trees and poplar trees affect the growth of grasses.
   B. Beavers and shrubs affect the number of poplar trees.
   C. Water temperature and pond oxygen levels affect the amount of plankton in the lake.
   D. Poplar trees and shrubs lose their leaves, which are decomposed and improve soil quality.

3. Identify the statement that lists two decomposers and correctly explains their role in the ecosystem.
   A. Clams and algae improve soil quality by returning organic nutrients to the soil.
   B. Bacteria and earthworms improve soil quality by returning organic nutrients to the soil.
   C. Pine trees and shrubs perform photosynthesis and add oxygen to the ecosystem.
   D. Algae and bacteria perform photosynthesis and add oxygen to the ecosystem.

4. What is the ultimate source of energy for the ecosystem shown in **Figure 1**? NR
   A. water
   B. sunlight
   C. producers
   D. consumers

5. Air temperatures were measured various distances above and below the soil in two different communities, a grassland community and a woodland community. Data was plotted on the graph in **Figure 2**.

   Statements:
   1. Woodland communities offer more shade and lower soil temperatures.
   2. Woodland communities have more animals because of lower soil temperatures.
   3. Temperatures increase below the soil surface, so burrowing animals must protect themselves against the heat.
   4. The greatest variation between temperature readings for the two communities occurs at the soil surface.
   5. Warmer air temperatures nearer the soil surface indicate that some radiant energy is reflected by the soil.
   6. An animal could escape the heat by burrowing underground.

   Which of these statements are supported by the data in **Figure 2**? (Record all three digits of your answer in lowest-to-highest numerical order.)

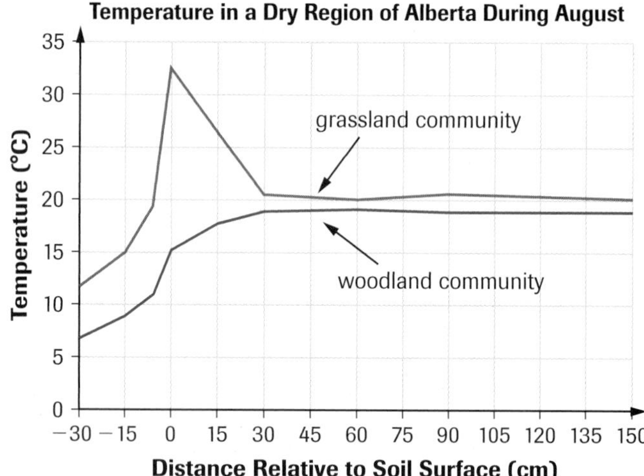

Figure 2

6. Biodiversity can be explained as
   A. the number of different species found in an ecosystem
   B. the different traits found within a species
   C. the number of organisms of the same species within a population
   D. the number of organisms of different extinct species within a population

7. Identify which choice gives two correct reasons why scientists are concerned about a reduction in the frog population.
   A. Frogs are indicator species because they are interconnected to all species in an ecosystem. Frogs are sensitive to changes in sunlight.
   B. Frogs have survived more than 400 million years. Frog populations cannot withstand the coming of an ice age.
   C. Frogs are a part of two different ecosystems (fresh water and terrestrial). Frogs belong to two different food chains.
   D. Frog populations have been slowly decreasing for the past 100 million years and now the population is increasing. Frogs are indicator species used to predict changes in the ozone layer.

8. Identify the choice in which the terms *organism, population, community, ecosystem,* and *biosphere* are all correctly defined.
   A. An organism is a distinct form of life, classified as a separate species. A population is a group of organisms of the same species, occupying a given area at a certain time. A community is the populations of all species that occupy a habitat. An ecosystem is the biotic community and its physical environment. The biosphere is the area of Earth in which life is found.
   B. An organism is the biotic community and its physical environment. A population is a group of organisms of the same species, occupying a given area at a certain time. A community is the populations of all species that occupy a habitat. An ecosystem is a distinct form of life, classified into separate species. The biosphere is the area of Earth in which life is found.
   C. An organism is the populations of all species that occupy a habitat. A population is a group of organisms of the same species, occupying a given area at a certain time. A community is a population of the same species, occupying a given area at a certain time. An ecosystem is the biotic community and its physical environment. The biosphere is the area of Earth in which life is found.
   D. An organism is a distinct form of life, classified as a separate population. A population is a group of organisms of different species, occupying a given area at a certain time. A community is the populations of all species that occupy a habitat. An ecosystem is the biotic community and its physical environment. The biosphere is the area of Earth in which life is found.

Part 2

9. Human interference often causes ecosystems to change. **Illustrate** with an example
   (a) how human interference has caused an increase in the population of a species.
   (b) how human interference has caused a decrease in the population of a species.
   (c) how the rapid increase in the population of a species has affected another species.

10. **Why** might a species be classified as endangered?

11. (a) In your own words, **describe** the classification system for at-risk species.
    (b) **Why** is a classification system like this useful?

12. **Identify** whether each of the following species is extinct, endangered, extirpated, threatened, or vulnerable. **Explain** your classification.
    (a) The wood turtle is found in pockets throughout southern Ontario, southern Quebec, New Brunswick, and Nova Scotia. The number of wood turtles in Canada seems to be stable, but in the United States their numbers are decreasing as many are being taken from the wild into homes as pets.
    (b) Furbish's lousewort is a tall herb that grows on riverbanks. In Canada, it grows only on a 200-km stretch of the Saint John River in New Brunswick. Forestry, farming, and flooding caused by hydroelectric dams all affect the area in which it lives.
    (c) The greater prairie chicken has not been seen in Ontario, Manitoba, or Alberta for many years. It was last seen in Saskatchewan in 1977. It can still be found in the prairie states of the United States.

13. (a) A decline in the number of frogs would affect other species. Using the term *food chain,* explain how the decline would affect insects and algae.
    (b) In a paragraph, **explain** the differences between the two food chains to which the frog belongs. **Describe** the role of the frog in each chain.

14. **Outline** in a list things that you could do, or avoid doing, that might help frogs to survive. Identify the things that would be easy for you, and those that would demand sacrifices. Would you be willing to do the hard things to save frogs? **Explain** your answer.

15. The common cockroach is not at risk of extinction. In fact, it is one of the species that have benefited from human activities.
    (a) **Hypothesize** about which human activities benefit the cockroach.
    (b) If a chemical company invented a spray that could kill all cockroaches, would it be acceptable to use the spray to make the cockroach extinct? **Explain** your position in a letter to the chemical company.

16. The bald eagle is not listed as at risk in Canada. Should resources be used to help restore this bird in the prairie provinces? **Justify** your answer.

17. Research the disappearance of the whooping crane from Wood Buffalo National Park along the Alberta–Saskatchewan border and **summarize** your findings in a report.

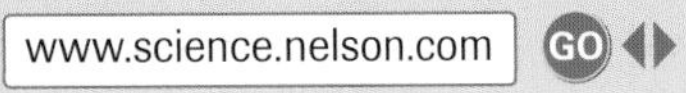

chapter

Energy Flow in the Biosphere

In this chapter

- Exploration: Competition between Plants
- Chemistry Connection: Chemical Bonds
- Investigation 2.1: Constructing Food Webs
- Web Activity: Designing Food Webs
- Investigation 2.2: Light Intensity and Plant Biomass
- Career Connection: Geographer

The source of almost all of the energy on Earth is the Sun. Much of the energy that reaches Earth's atmosphere is filtered out before it reaches the surface (**Figure 1**). Only a tiny portion is actually used by green plants for photosynthesis (**Figure 2**). However, as this chapter will discuss, almost all organisms on Earth depend on this energy.

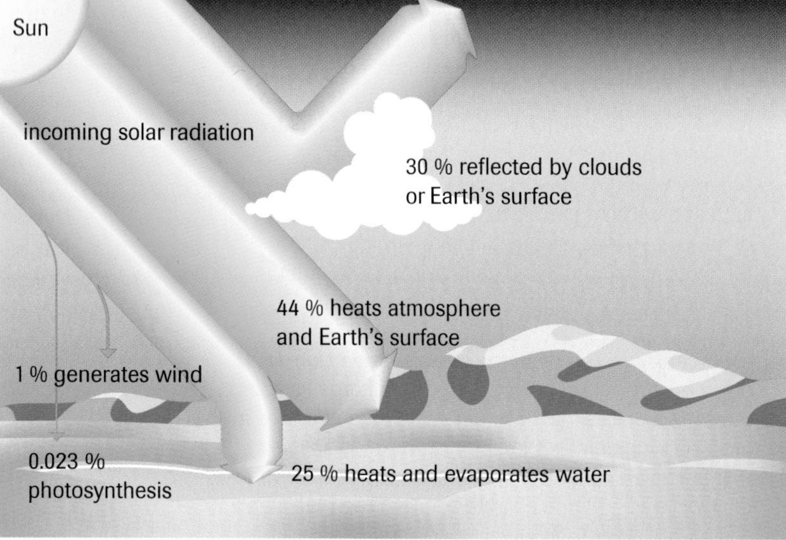

Figure 1
A model of the flow of energy from the Sun, to Earth, and back into space

STARTING Points

Answer these questions as best you can with your current knowledge. Then, using the concepts and skills you have learned, you will revise your answers at the end of the chapter.

1. Predict how increased cloud cover or pollution haze would affect a forest ecosystem.
2. The text above states that the Sun is "the source of almost all of the energy on Earth." What other source(s) can you think of? How important is each energy source?
3. Is it possible for food chains to exist in a cave or the ocean depths where no sunlight can penetrate? Explain why or why not. 

Figure 2
Photosynthesis is the process by which green plants use solar energy to produce carbohydrates (sugars), which can then be used as food by other organisms. Plants compete for solar energy. In this mixed forest, the various plant species have adaptations that allow them to avoid or tolerate the shade of the plants around them.

Exploration — Competition between Plants

Changes in the biotic or abiotic factors within an ecosystem often cause one plant community to replace another. In turn, changes in the plant community are accompanied by changes in the animal community. In this activity, you will determine which plant species has an advantage under certain conditions. Each research group can study a different set of variables.

Materials: apron, milk cartons, 9 kinds of vegetable or flower seeds, potting soil, water

 **Always wash your hands after handling soil.**

- As a class, decide on the types of seeds you will plant in each milk carton.
- Fill milk carton with moist potting soil. Divide the soil surface into nine squares.
- In each square, plant two seeds of one of the species according to the instructions on the packets. Water each carton with the same amount of water every second day. Record the amount of water used.
- Once seeds start to germinate, store each carton in a different environment. You could use amount of sunlight, temperature, or amount of water as variables.
- Measure the growth of each plant daily. Record any other observations.

(a) Does one type of plant begin to dominate the community? Is it the same type of plant in all cartons?

(b) Choose the most successful plant you grew. Do research to answer these questions: In what environment is this plant naturally found? What does this environment have in common with the conditions you set in the exploration?

(c) Speculate about why one plant might be better adapted for a specific environment than another.

2.1 Energy Transfer and Food Webs

trophic level a category of living things defined by how it gains its energy; the first trophic level contains autotrophs, and each higher level contains heterotrophs

autotroph an organism that uses the Sun's energy and raw materials to make its own food; a producer

primary consumer in a food chain or food web, an organism that relies directly on autotrophs for its source of energy; organisms at the second trophic level

secondary consumer in a food chain or food web, an organism that relies on primary consumers for its principal source of energy; organisms at the third trophic level

heterotroph an organism that is incapable of making its own food, and so must feed on other organisms to gain energy

You can begin to understand how energy flows through ecosystems by categorizing living things by their **trophic level**, according to how they gain their energy. The term *trophic* comes from a Greek word meaning "feeder."

Organisms that can make their own food from basic nutrients and sunlight or some other non-living energy source are placed in the first trophic level (**Figure 1**). Not surprisingly, these organisms are also referred to as producers or **autotrophs** (from Greek words meaning "self-feeders"). Plants, algae, and some types of bacteria are in the first trophic level.

The second trophic level contains organisms that feed on the producers. These organisms are referred to as **primary consumers**. Primary consumers rely on autotrophs directly for their source of energy.

Secondary consumers are animals in the third trophic level. They rely on primary consumers for their source of energy, but they are still dependent on the autotrophs in the first trophic level. Although a wolf eats other animals, it still relies indirectly on the photosynthesis of plants for energy. The deer that the wolf eats has eaten grass or the buds of a spruce tree.

Consumers, at whatever trophic level, are sometimes called **heterotrophs.** Heterotrophs cannot make their own food, and so must obtain their food and energy from autotrophs or other heterotrophs. Human beings are heterotrophs.

DID YOU KNOW ?

An Alternative View

One Aboriginal approach to trophic levels is to rank them according to dependence. Primary consumers depend on autotrophs, and secondary consumers depend on the primary ones. Humans are the most dependent consumers.

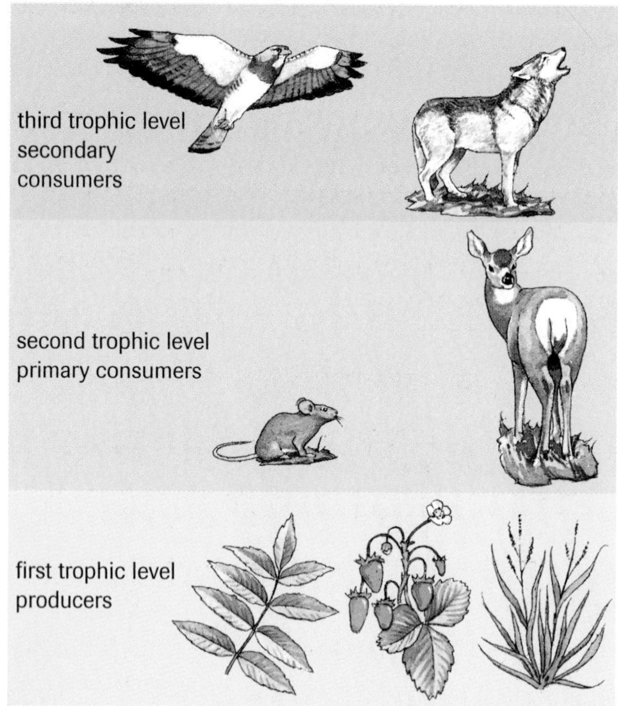

Figure 1
Trophic levels, showing producers and consumers. An ecosystem may contain more than three trophic levels.

Energy and Food Chains

Every organism within an ecosystem provides energy for other organisms. Food chains are a way of showing a step-by-step sequence of who eats whom in an ecosystem. The sequence in **Figure 2** shows a one-way flow of energy in a simple food chain from producer to secondary consumer. The deer does not make its own energy; instead, it relies on the spruce tree. The deer is a heterotroph. Since the deer receives its energy two steps away from the original source (sunlight), it is in the second trophic level. Using the same reasoning, the wolf, also a heterotroph, is a member of the third trophic level.

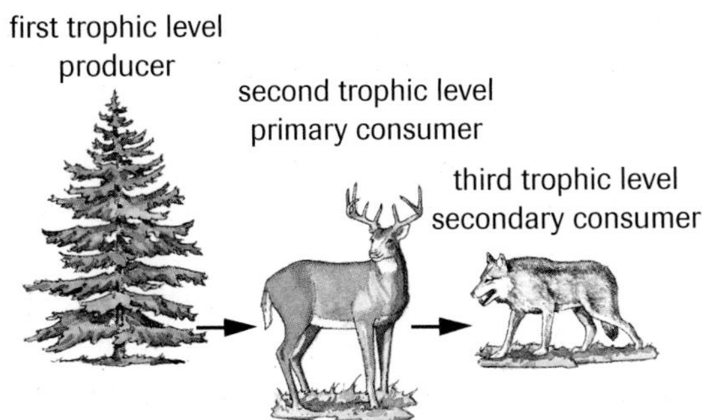

Figure 2
In this food chain, energy flows from a producer (the spruce tree), to a primary consumer (the deer), to a secondary consumer (the wolf).

Consumers are placed in categories based on their trophic level in a food chain. A carnivore directly feeding on a primary consumer is a secondary consumer. However, if the carnivore eats a secondary consumer (another carnivore), it is now a tertiary consumer—it is at the fourth trophic level. The final carnivore in any food chain is called a top carnivore. Top carnivores are not eaten by other animals (at least, while they are alive). In the example above, the wolf is both a secondary consumer and a top carnivore, since it obtains its energy from the deer and no other animal eats the wolf.

EXTENSION

Decomposers

Decomposers do not always fit neatly into one position in food webs or trophic levels. Listen to this clip to learn more about the role of decomposers in ecosystems.

www.science.nelson.com 

Food Webs

The food chain shown in **Figure 2** would be highly unlikely to include all the organisms in a natural ecosystem. In reality, deer also eat buds, stems, bark, and grasses. The wolf includes in its diet many different animals, such as rabbits, ground-nesting birds and their eggs, beavers, and muskrats. Each individual organism in an ecosystem is involved in many food chains. The chains all interlock with each other to form a feeding relationship called a **food web** (**Figure 3**).

food web a representation of the feeding relationships among organisms in an ecosystem

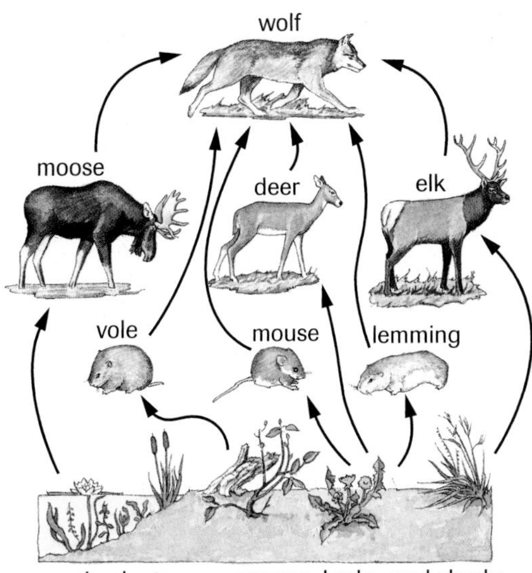

Figure 3
A simplified food web shows the wolf as the top carnivore and plants as producers. Notice that both the vole and the deer belong in the second trophic level of this web. Of course, in a real ecosystem, the food web would be much more complicated. It would include most of the organisms in the ecosystem.

CHEMISTRY CONNECTION

Chemical Bonds

Your Chemistry textbook has more information on the nature of chemical bonds, and energy changes during bond-making and bond-breaking.

www.science.nelson.com 

The most stable ecosystems, those with the greatest biodiversity, have such complex and well-developed food webs that the reduction in numbers or even the complete removal of one type of organism may have only a small effect on the overall web. Predict what would happen to the organisms in **Figure 2**, on the previous page, if deer depended exclusively on the buds of spruce trees for food, and spruce budworm were introduced. Spruce budworms also eat the buds of spruce trees. What would happen to the deer and the wolves if spruce budworms ate most of the spruce buds? If this food chain showed all the organisms in the ecosystem, you would predict that the deer and wolves would be deprived of food and would die. In fact, if spruce budworms eat most of the spruce buds, deer may switch to another tree or grass, and wolves may not be much affected.

However, where abiotic factors limit the number of organisms, the webs begin to look more like food chains. This is particularly true in the Arctic, where the number of producers is small. Because there is less energy available from the Sun and temperatures are often low, producers in the Arctic cannot photosynthesize as rapidly as they do in the south. Less energy is available, so fewer organisms can live in that ecosystem. The limited number of organisms means that their relationships with each other are more direct. In these situations, the loss of any one member will have a profound effect on all the remaining organisms. The lower the biodiversity of an ecosystem, the simpler the food web, and the more vulnerable each organism is to changes in the ecosystem.

Photosynthesis and Respiration

Food webs always begin with autotrophs, such as plants. All living things use some form of chemical energy for food. Green plants make their own food by using carbon dioxide (CO_2) and water (H_2O), plus energy from sunlight, to make molecules of a sugar, glucose ($C_6H_{12}O_6$). This process, called **photosynthesis**, captures solar energy and stores it in the chemical bonds of glucose. You can read more about photosynthesis in Chapter 6. The reaction below summarizes photosynthesis.

photosynthesis the process by which green plants and some other organisms use solar energy, carbon dioxide, and water to produce carbohydrates

carbon dioxide + water + energy → glucose + oxygen

$$CO_2(g) + H_2O(l) + \text{energy} \rightarrow C_6H_{12}O_6(s) + O_2(g)$$

Since photosynthetic organisms are at the first trophic level, photosynthesis ultimately provides the energy required by the entire ecosystem. Photosynthesis absorbs energy from an abiotic component of an ecosystem (sunlight) and moves it into biotic components (green plants). As one moves up through the trophic levels of an ecosystem, this energy is then transferred to different organisms through the food they eat.

All organisms, including plants, undergo **cellular respiration** in order to use the energy in their food. Cellular respiration breaks down glucose, releasing the energy stored in its bonds. Some of this energy is used to fuel cell processes, and some is released in the form of thermal energy. You can read more about cellular respiration in Chapter 7. The reaction below summarizes cellular respiration.

cellular respiration the process by which cells break down glucose into carbon dioxide and water, releasing energy

chemosynthesis the process by which non-photosynthetic organisms convert inorganic chemicals to organic compounds without solar energy

chemoautotroph an organism that can synthesize organic compounds from inorganic chemicals without using solar energy

glucose + oxygen → carbon dioxide + water + energy

$$C_6H_{12}O_6(s) + O_2(g) \rightarrow CO_2(g) + H_2O(l) + \text{energy}$$

If you look at the two reaction equations, you will see that they are the reverse of one another. The processes of photosynthesis and cellular respiration are therefore said to be complementary. Since these two processes are complementary, a balance of oxygen and carbon dioxide is maintained within any ecosystem. The plants produce oxygen and glucose during photosynthesis, while all organisms produce carbon dioxide and water during cellular respiration (**Figure 4**). Since plants carry out both photosynthesis and respiration, you might think that plants could maintain the balance between oxygen and carbon dioxide themselves. However, plants produce about nine times the amount of oxygen by photosynthesis that they use up in cellular respiration.

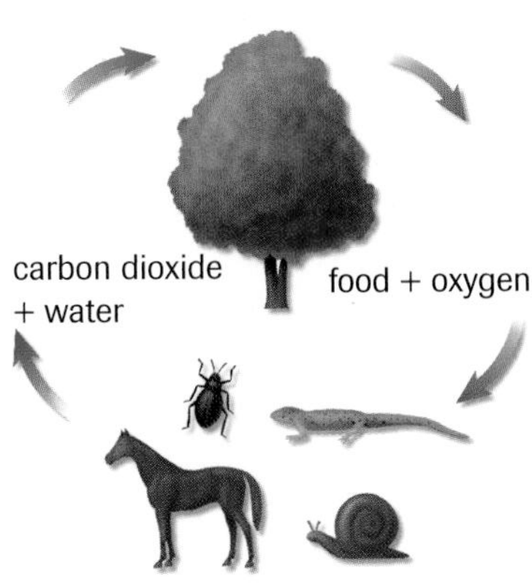

Figure 4
The byproducts that plants release in photosynthesis support animals. The waste products that both animals and plants produce in cellular respiration support plants.

Chemosynthesis

Not all food webs begin with photosynthetic organisms. In a few ecosystems, such as in caves or the deep oceans, producers convert simple molecules into more complex compounds without solar energy, by a process called **chemosynthesis**. These bacteria are **chemoautotrophs**, which are organisms that require only carbon dioxide, water, and an energy source (other than solar energy) to make nutrients. Chemical energy is extracted from inorganic chemicals such as hydrogen sulfide (H_2S), ammonia (NH_3), ferrous ions (Fe^{2+}), or sulfur (S_8).

In sulfur hot springs, such as those in Banff National Park, thermal energy generated within Earth's crust heats underground water, which is then released through vents in the rock. Some bacteria use the thermal energy to convert dissolved hydrogen sulfide and carbon dioxide into organic compounds. These bacteria, as producers, become a food source for tiny consumers in this ecosystem. **Figure 5** shows a food chain that depends on chemosynthesis.

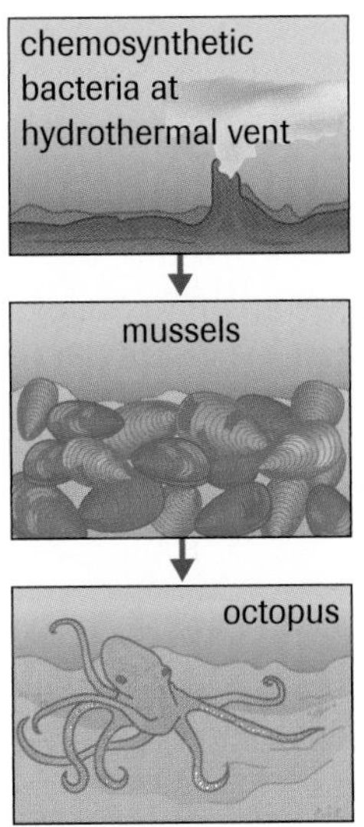

Figure 5
In this food chain, bacteria use the thermal energy from hydrothermal vents on the ocean floor to make nutrients.

Limits on Energy Transfer

Every time energy is transferred between the components of an ecosystem, the amount of energy available to the next trophic level is reduced. Why? One reason is that whenever energy is transferred, some of the energy is transformed to a different form. Some energy is released as thermal energy during cellular respiration. Some of it is converted to other chemical energy in molecules other than glucose. The organisms at the next trophic level may not be able to use all these molecules as a source of energy. Let's return to the simple spruce → deer → wolf food chain.

- Through photosynthesis, producers such as the spruce tree use solar energy to make molecules of glucose. The plant then uses most of that energy to carry out the processes it needs to live and to manufacture the chemicals it needs to grow. Therefore, not all of the chemical energy captured during photosynthesis is available to an animal that eats the spruce tree.
- Primary consumers, such as the deer, rely on the chemical energy produced by plants to sustain their lives. A deer does not digest all of a meal of spruce buds. Some is eliminated in the deer's feces (wastes). Some of the remaining energy is lost as thermal energy during the chemical transformations of digestion. Some of the remainder is used to fuel the deer's cells through cellular respiration, which also releases thermal energy. Some of that thermal energy is used to maintain the deer's body temperature, but eventually all of the thermal energy released is lost to the surrounding air. Only about 10 % of the energy in the spruce buds is transferred to the deer. It uses this energy to move its limbs, pump its blood, and manufacture the molecules it needs to carry out its life processes and grow.
- Like the deer, the wolf loses some of the energy in its meal during digestion and body maintenance. Therefore, only about 10 % of the energy in the wolf's meal is transferred to the wolf.

Chemosynthetic Food Chains

Listen to a discussion of energy sources that may be used by chemoautotrophs.

www.science.nelson.com 

In all food chains, whether the producers are photosynthetic organisms or chemoautotrophs, the farther up the chain you travel, the less energy is available (**Figure 6**). In every ecosystem, less energy is available to secondary consumers than to primary consumers. In general, the overall loss of energy at each step limits the number of trophic levels in a food chain to about five. This is supported by the laws of thermodynamics.

Laws of Thermodynamics

thermodynamics a scientific study of energy transformations, described by laws

Thermodynamics is the study of energy transformations. The energy flowing from the Sun through ecosystems illustrates the laws of thermodynamics.

- The *first law of thermodynamics* states that although energy can be transformed (changed) from one form to another, it cannot be created or destroyed.
- The *second law of thermodynamics* states that during any energy transformation, some of the energy is converted into an unusable form, mostly thermal energy, which cannot be passed on. Each time energy is transformed, some energy is lost from the system. As a result, the amount of energy available in each step of a chain of transformations is always less than the amount of energy available at the previous step. This applies to all systems, including food chains (**Figure 7**).

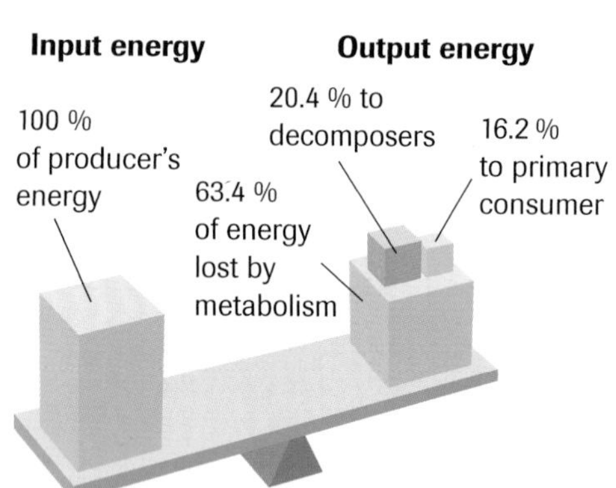

Figure 6
Most of the energy transformed from solar energy to chemical energy by a plant is used to maintain the plant and to grow. Every time the plant uses some of its energy store, it also loses energy as thermal energy. As a result, when the plant is eaten, only a small amount of energy is available for the primary consumer and decomposers.

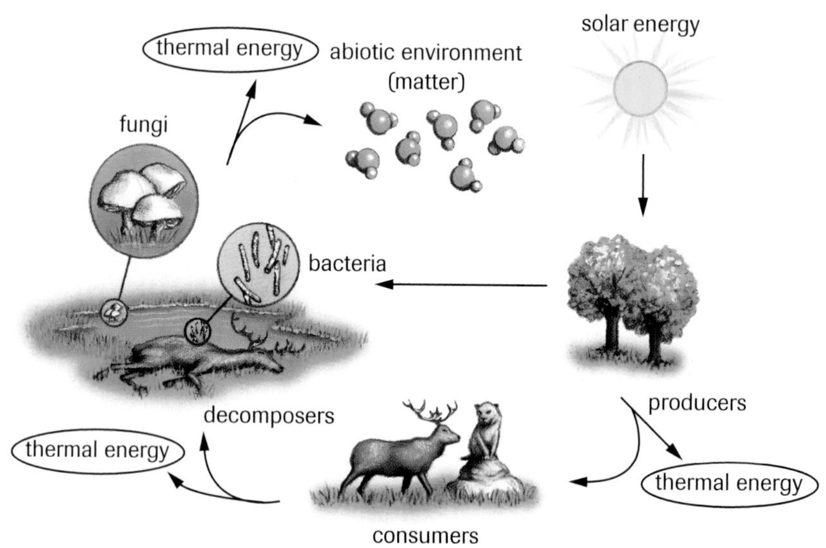

Figure 7
According to the second law of thermodynamics, energy is lost each time energy is transferred from one organism to another, and inside each organism as it uses the energy to survive.

INVESTIGATION 2.1 ***Introduction***

Constructing Food Webs

In Part 1 of this Investigation, you will research an Antarctic ecosystem and connect the organisms in a food web. In Part 2, you will construct a food web of organisms found in your community.

Report Checklist

○ Purpose	● Design	● Analysis
○ Problem	○ Materials	○ Evaluation
○ Hypothesis	● Procedure	○ Synthesis
○ Prediction	● Evidence	

To perform this investigation, turn to page 35.

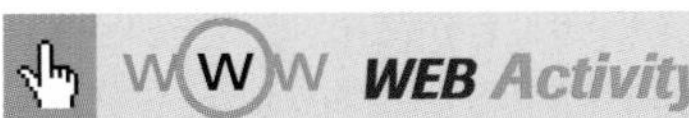

Web Quest—Designing Food Webs

There are many different food webs in our world, some containing familiar organisms, others filled with exotic species. Drawing food webs by hand and analysing them can be difficult. In this Web Quest, you will use the computer to build a food web. You can then easily study the interactions by adding and removing organisms and seeing the result.

www.science.nelson.com 

SUMMARY Energy Transfer and Food Webs

- Food chains describe relationships between lower and higher trophic levels and describe the flow of energy within an ecosystem.
- Energy is transferred to organisms at the next trophic level in a food chain or food web. At each transfer, some energy is transformed into thermal energy and is no longer available.
- During photosynthesis, plants use solar energy to combine carbon dioxide and water. Photosynthesis can be summarized by the equation:

  carbon dioxide + water + energy $\rightarrow$ glucose + oxygen
- The energy required for almost all living organisms originates with solar radiation, which is converted to chemical energy during photosynthesis and stored in the chemical bonds of sugars such as glucose. In the cells, cellular respiration breaks down the chemical bonds, releasing the energy to be used for growth and metabolism. Cellular respiration can be summarized by the equation:

  glucose + oxygen $\rightarrow$ water + carbon dioxide + energy
- Chemoautotrophic organisms produce chemical energy without solar energy, and provide the base of food pyramids in those rare ecosystems with little or no sunlight.

Section 2.1 Questions

1. In your own words, explain what is meant by the term *trophic level.*
2. What type of food would be consumed by a secondary consumer? Explain your answer.
3. Distinguish between a food chain and a food web. Give examples of each.
4. Identify the reactants and products for the chemical reaction of photosynthesis.
5. Identify the reactants and products for the chemical reaction of cellular respiration.
6. What source of energy is used by chemosynthetic bacteria to make organic compounds?
7. In your own words, explain the first and second laws of thermodynamics.
8. Explain why only about 10 % of the energy available in a plant is transferred to the primary consumer.

2.2 Scientific Models

Scientists often construct models to help them understand how living things function. Models are theoretical descriptions or analogies that help us visualize something that has not been directly observed. For example, a scientist might reconstruct the climatic conditions of 65 million years ago to uncover what might have happened to the dinosaurs. Indirect fossil evidence is used to gather information on weather patterns and vegetation cover in an ecosystem. Plants such as ferns are unable to live in hot, arid conditions or in extreme cold. When fossils of ferns are found, scientists are able to make inferences about climate range.

The advantage of scientific models is that they provide a pathway for making predictions. Scientists often use mathematical models, which exist only as equations, to help them understand biological observations. There are three essential steps in formulating a mathematical model:

1. making an estimate and developing an equation based upon indirect data and background information;
2. computing the prediction implied by the equation; and
3. comparing the prediction with future or past events. Supporting evidence is gathered to make sure that the mathematical model does not support just one situation. If this is ever shown to be the case, then the model is rejected.

A good mathematical model can be used to test and predict the implications of many different courses of action. By being tested on past events, the model gains acceptance in predicting future events.

DID YOU KNOW ?

Speed and the Dinosaur

From fossil evidence, some scientists suggested that *Tyrannosaurus rex* was capable of speeds in excess of 70 km/h. However, by using mathematical models, other scientists have calculated that *T. rex* would be killed if it ever tripped. The tiny forelimbs were much too small to offer protection to such a heavy animal at such speeds. They calculated that *T. rex* would skid for more than 40 metres after tripping if it ran at such speeds. Falling would create a force on the chest equivalent to a 36 tonne mass (352 800 N), easily crushing the dinosaur's ribs. Even greater damage would occur to the head. A fall would apply a force equivalent to a 13.6 tonne mass (133 820 N), enough to snap its neck. These new calculations have caused scientists to estimate that *T. rex* likely didn't run any faster than 15 km/h.

www.science.nelson.com 

Ecological Pyramids

Graphs called **ecological pyramids** can be used to represent energy flow in food chains and food webs or the populations of organisms in a food chain. These graphs help the ecologist visualize more clearly the relationships in an ecosystem and compare ecosystems.

ecological pyramid a representation of energy flow in food chains and webs

Pyramids of Numbers

A pyramid of numbers can be drawn by counting the number of organisms at each trophic level in an ecosystem. When these numbers are then represented on a vertical graph, with the volume of each level representing the number of organisms at that level, the graph sometimes takes on the general shape of a pyramid (**Figure 1**, next page). However, ecologists have found that, in some cases, the shape is not like a pyramid because of the physical size of the members of a food chain. For example, many tiny aphids (an insect that feeds by sucking sap from plants) may be found feeding off a single plant (**Figure 2**, next page).

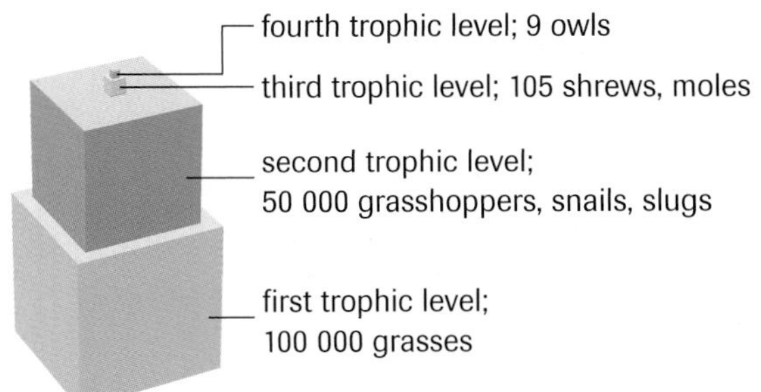

Figure 1
A pyramid of numbers for a grassland ecosystem. In this ecosystem, the number of producers is greater than the number of primary consumers.

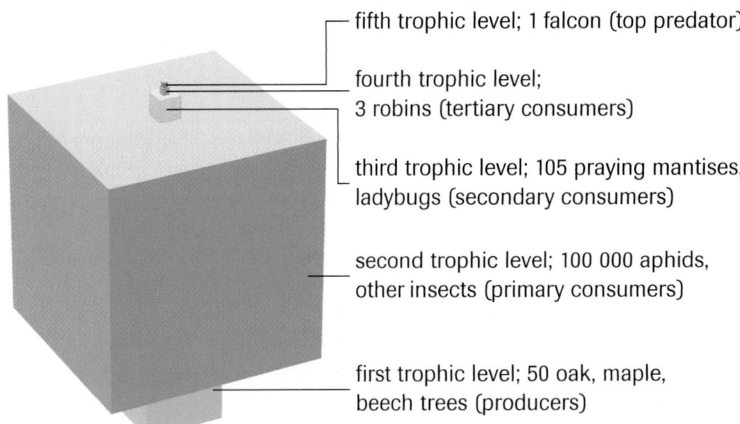

Figure 2
A pyramid of numbers for a deciduous forest ecosystem. Because an aphid is much smaller than a tree, a single plant may provide food for thousands of aphids.

Pyramids of Biomass

biomass the total dry mass of all the living material in an ecosystem

Biomass is the total dry mass of all the living material in an ecosystem. Since organisms store energy as organic molecules, biomass is a measure of stored energy content. To understand this idea, compare a rainforest ecosystem with a tundra ecosystem. Rainforest ecosystems are located in tropical areas with intense sunlight. A rainforest ecosystem would be able to store large amounts of energy from the Sun. As a result, it would contain a large amount of organic material and have a large total biomass. In contrast, tundra ecosystems are located in northern areas with less intense sunlight and long, dark winters. A tundra ecosystem would be able to store less energy, and thus would contain a smaller amount of organic material and have a lower total biomass.

A pyramid of biomass is a useful way to represent an ecosystem. To make such a pyramid, the dry mass (after water has been removed) of the tissue in the plants or animals is measured and graphed (**Figure 3**). Occasionally, a graph of biomass is not a regular pyramid. Such ecosystems, however, are rare.

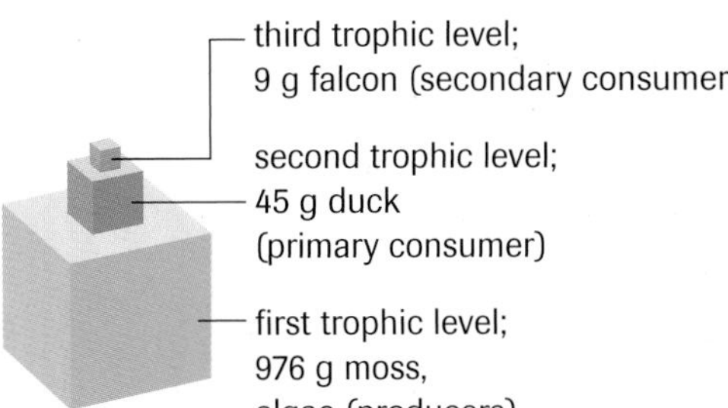

Figure 3
A pyramid of biomass for a Newfoundland peat bog. The numbers represent the dry mass (g) for all organisms at that trophic level found in 1 m^2. As you can see, there is less biomass at each trophic level.

Pyramids of Energy

It is possible to measure the amount of energy available at each trophic level. Creating a pyramid graph allows us to better understand the relationships and energy flow (**Figure 4**, next page). The comparatively larger mass of the individual tertiary consumers and the vast amount of energy that they expend while hunting limits the number of individuals that can be supported at the top position of the pyramid.

Figure 4
A pyramid of energy for a grassland ecosystem. At each level, the energy found in the bodies of the organisms is graphed. The larger the volume of the level, the greater the energy at that level. As you can see, only about one-thousandth of the chemical energy from photosynthesis stored in the producers in this food web actually reaches the top predator (the owl) at the fourth trophic level. Energy is measured using joules (1000 joules (J) = 1 kilojoule (kJ)).

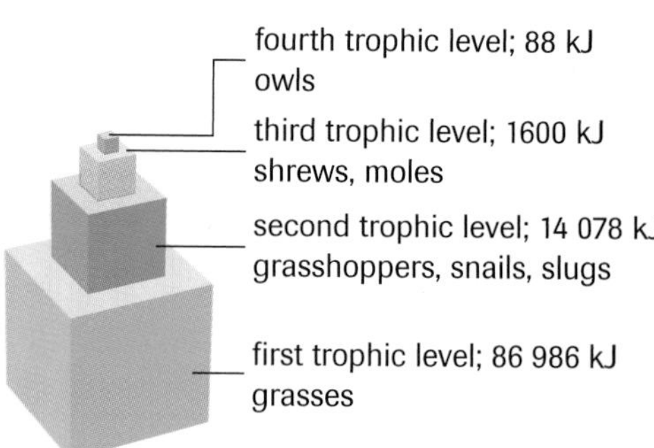

As you learned in the previous section, most of the energy at each level of a food chain is used and/or lost as heat. Only a fraction of the energy passes from one level of a food chain to the next. This fraction is often said to be about $\frac{1}{10}$, or 10 %. Although this number is just an approximation, it can be useful for making estimations. For example, if the grasses in an ecosystem produce 1×10^{10} kJ of energy per year, you can estimate that the primary consumers in that ecosystem can only obtain 1×10^{9} kJ per year by eating the grasses. Secondary consumers will only obtain about 1×10^{8} kJ per year. (Note that these estimations are extremely simplified. Calculations are more often done for energy per gram, or per square metre, rather than for an entire ecosystem.)

Look at the sample exercise below to learn how to create two- and three-dimensional pyramids. The second sample exercise shows how to calculate energy loss through a food chain.

SAMPLE exercise 1

Pyramids of energy are graphical representations that show energy flow in food chains and webs. As energy is lost, fewer organisms can be supported at each successive level. The base of the pyramid always indicates the total amount of energy held by producers. Use the data in **Table 1** to construct a two-dimensional energy pyramid.

Table 1 Energy Pyramid Data

Trophic level	Energy (kJ)	Area of the box (mm^2)
producers (first trophic level)	100 000	1 000
consumer (second trophic level)	15 000	
consumer (third trophic level)	1 000	

Solution

1. Establish a ratio between the area of the box and the amount of energy held by the producers. For two-dimensional pyramids, the amount of energy held by producers is displayed as a ratio of the area of the box at the base of the pyramid.

   energy = area of the box at the base of the pyramid
   100 000 kJ = 1000 mm^2

2. Determine length and width of the producer box.

   1000 mm^2 = width × length
   1000 mm^2 = 20 mm × 50 mm

   Draw the box with these dimensions (**Figure 5 (a)**, next page).

3. Use the ratio for producers to establish the size of the box for second-level consumers.

$$\frac{\text{area of box for producer}}{\text{energy of producer}} = \frac{\text{area of box for second-level consumer}}{\text{energy of second-level consumer}}$$

$$\frac{1000 \text{ mm}^2}{100\,000 \text{ kJ}} = \frac{x}{15\,000 \text{ kJ}}$$

$$x = \frac{1000 \text{ mm}^2 \times 15\,000 \text{ kJ}}{100\,000 \text{ kJ}}$$

$$x = 150 \text{ mm}^2$$

4. Determine the length and width of the second-level consumer box.

$150 \text{ mm}^2 = \text{width} \times \text{length}$
$150 \text{ mm}^2 = 30 \text{ mm} \times 5 \text{ mm}$

Draw the box with these dimensions on top of the producer box (**Figure 5 (b)**).

5. Repeat for the third-level consumer box.

$$\frac{\text{area of box for producer}}{\text{energy of producer}} = \frac{\text{area of box for third-level consumer}}{\text{energy of third-level consumer}}$$

$$\frac{1000 \text{ mm}^2}{100\,000 \text{ kJ}} = \frac{x}{1000} \text{ kJ}$$

$$x = \frac{1000 \text{ mm}^2 \times 1000 \text{ kJ}}{100\,000 \text{ kJ}}$$

$$x = 10 \text{ mm}^2$$

6. Determine the length and width of the third-level consumer box.

$10 \text{ mm}^2 = \text{width} \times \text{length}$
$10 \text{ mm}^2 = 5 \text{ mm} \times 2 \text{ mm}$

Draw the box (**Figure 5 (c)**).

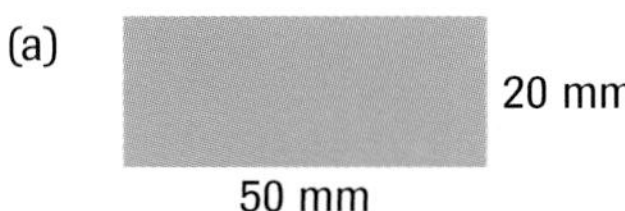

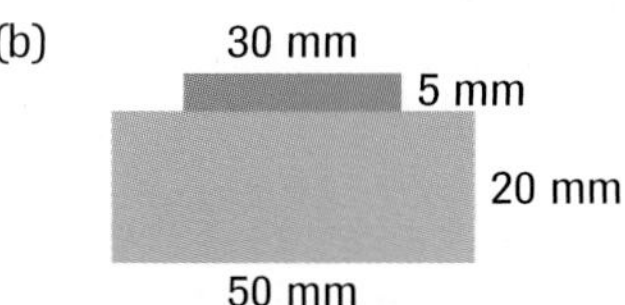

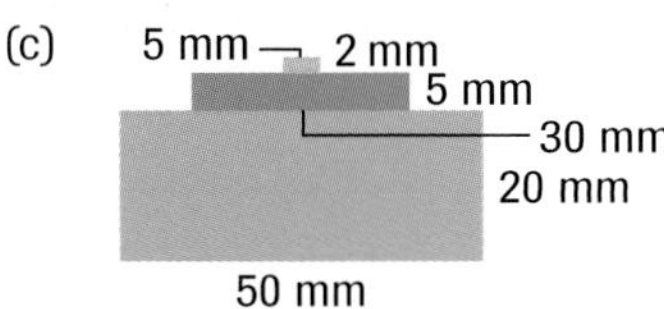

Figure 5
Constructing an energy pyramid

Practice

1. Draw two-dimensional and three-dimensional pyramids using the data in **Table 2**, of an Alberta mixed woodland ecosystem.

Table 2 Pyramid of Numbers

Trophic level	Number of organisms
producers (trees and shrubs) first trophic level	100
consumers (insects, slugs, snails) second trophic level	9800
consumers (ladybugs, praying mantises) third trophic level	500
consumers (shrews, moles, robins) fourth trophic level	10
consumers (hawks, falcons, snakes) fifth trophic level	3

SAMPLE exercise 2

As shown below, phytoplankton are at the base of an ocean food chain.

phytoplankton → zooplankton → herring → salmon

(a) If the phytoplankton in an ecosystem produce 20 000 000 kJ of energy per day, how much energy is available for the salmon?

(b) Suppose each herring requires 1000 kJ of energy per day to survive. How many herring can this ecosystem support?

Solution

(a) Assume that 10 % of the energy passes from each level of the food chain to the next. Calculate the amount of energy that reaches the top level of the food chain.

20 000 000 kJ $\times$ 0.10 = 2 000 000 kJ (energy that will reach the zooplankton)

2 000 000 kJ $\times$ 0.10 = 200 000 kJ (energy that will reach the herring)

200 000 kJ $\times$ 0.10 = 20 000 kJ (energy that will reach the salmon)

Thus, 20 000 kJ of energy is available for the salmon each day.

(b) You know that 200 000 kJ of energy is available for the herring each day. Divide this number by the amount of energy required by each herring.

200 000 kJ $\div$ 1000 kJ/herring = 200 herring

The ecosystem can support 200 herring.

Practice

2. Draw a two-dimensional energy pyramid for the following food chain. Use the data from the sample exercise and solution.

   phytoplankton → zooplankton → herring → salmon

3. An ecosystem contains 1000 bushes and grasses. Each produces about 10 000 kJ of energy per day.
   (a) How many rabbits can be supported by this ecosystem, if each rabbit requires 5 000 kJ of energy per day?
   (b) How many foxes can be supported by this ecosystem, if each fox requires 10 000 kJ of energy per day?
   (c) Draw a pyramid of numbers for this ecosystem.

INVESTIGATION 2.2 *Introduction*

Light Intensity and Plant Biomass

Through photosynthesis, plants capture solar energy and use it to combine water and oxygen into glucose. Glucose is then used to fuel its cellular activities and to build other molecules required by the plant. These molecules are used in plant growth, which increases the mass and size of the plant. How does light intensity affect plant biomass? In this investigation, you will design and carry out your own experiment to address this problem.

Report Checklist

○ Purpose	○ Design	● Analysis
● Problem	○ Materials	● Evaluation
○ Hypothesis	● Procedure	○ Synthesis
● Prediction	● Evidence	

To perform this investigation, turn to page 36. 

Human Use of Energy in Ecosystems

Like all other living things, humans are dependent on the energy flow through ecosystems. We are part of many food chains at different levels. For example, a person eating vegetables is a primary consumer; a person eating steak is a secondary consumer; and a person eating salmon may be a tertiary consumer, depending on the salmon's diet. Unlike most other living things, humans also use the energy in ecosystems in other ways. For example, we burn wood for fuel, obtaining the energy trapped in it by photosynthesis.

Human use of the energy in an ecosystem often changes the ecosystem itself. Most ecosystems can adapt to small changes, such as the removal of a few salmon. Large-scale changes in ecosystems, however, often permanently change the types and sizes of populations of organisms found in that ecosystem. For example, humans have permanently changed many ecosystems in order to grow and hunt food. Hunting, fishing, and extensive crop growth have impacted many large ecosystems (**Figure 6**).

Figure 6
Cultivation of the land has disrupted many food chains. In Alberta, European settlers who selected monocultures of wheat and barley in favour of natural grasses contributed to a decline in the populations of mule deer, bison, elk, and moose, while increasing the range and number of whitetail deer.

Hunting and Fishing

The science of wildlife management involves the manipulation of populations of wild species and their habitats for the benefit of humans. In the past, over-hunting of wild species such as wolves and buffalo have led to extirpation and large changes in ecosystems. Today, however, conservation groups like the Sierra Club and the Defenders of Wildlife recognize hunting and fishing as acceptable management tools.

A confrontation between technology and nature is unfolding in Canadian coastal waters. Improved factory ships, larger nets, improved technology for fish detection, and more boats have dramatically increased the harvest of marine fish. As a result, prized fish such as cod, halibut, and salmon have been drastically reduced. The pursuit of short-term economic gain at the expense of long-term economic collapse from overfishing is an important issue that governments must address.

CAREER CONNECTION

Geographer

Geographers study physical aspects of particular biological or physical regions. They often use satellite and imagery technologies to provide information on environmental issues, study the large-scale effects of human activity, or coordinate development plans with land-use planners. Learn more about geographer specializations and decide if this career direction is right for you.

www.science.nelson.com

Monocultures

Fossil records tell us that biological diversity has increased over time. About 150 different families of animals existed at the end of the Cambrian period 500 million years ago. Since then the number has increased to nearly 800 (**Figure 7**). This represents over two million species. However, most biologists will argue that this number is very conservative. There may be as many as 15 million different species of organisms now living on Earth.

Historically, humans have used about 700 different species of plants. According to the noted biologist Edward Wilson, today we rely heavily on about 20 species—wheat, rice, cotton, barley, and corn being the most important. Most human agriculture has

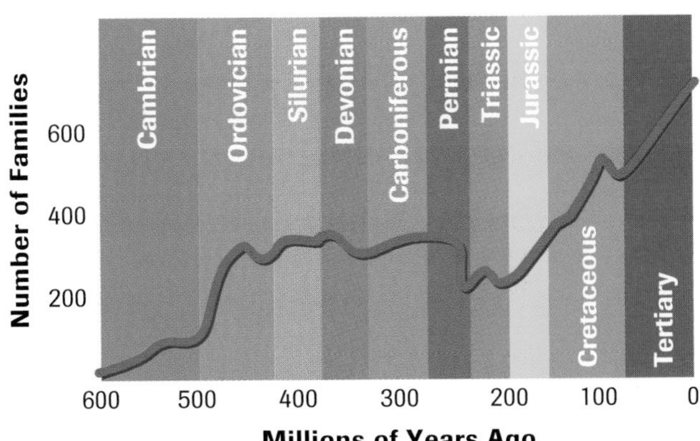

Figure 7
The graph shows a trend toward greater biodiversity.

monoculture cultivation of a single species

Figure 8
Many different species of plants can be found in a rain forest.

been directed at producing food crops. However, many wild plants are also important to humans. For example, the rosy periwinkle, a plant native to Madagascar, produces two important chemicals that are useful in treating Hodgkin's disease, a form of leukemia, or cancer of the white blood cells. Unfortunately, many wild plants have already been destroyed to grow food crops, especially in tropical rain forests.

The nutrient-poor soil of the tropical rain forests is not well suited for **monocultures** of cereal grains such as wheat and barley. These soils require the renewal of decomposed matter to maintain adequate levels of nitrogen and phosphorus. Nitrogen and phosphorus cycles should not be disrupted in the delicate rain forests (**Figure 8**). A few seasons after planting, the soil will no longer support the growth of crops. What makes the situation even more critical is that the greatest biodiversity exists in the tropical rain forests. Many species have yet to be classified, let alone investigated for possible medicines.

SUMMARY Scientific Models

- Mathematical models are theoretical models that exist as equations. These models are used to make non-intuitive and testable predictions that follow from simple assumptions.
- Environmental models allow scientists to study what could happen to organisms in an ecosystem if changes occurred. The models help check predictions without disrupting a large area.
- Pyramids of energy measure the amount of energy available at each trophic level.
- Pyramids of numbers can be drawn by counting the number of organisms at each trophic level in an ecosystem.
- Pyramids of biomass can be drawn by determining the dry mass of organisms.

Section 2.2 Questions

1. What data would you need to collect to create an ecological pyramid of numbers?
2. What problem might you encounter if you tried to show energy flow through an ecosystem using a pyramid of numbers?
3. How might a pyramid of energy for a grassland community differ between summer and winter? Think about the effects the different abiotic conditions of each season might have on the ecosystem. Use your conclusions to draw a pyramid of energy for each season. Explain any differences between the two pyramids.
4. **Figure 9** shows pyramids of biomass and numbers for a deciduous forest. Explain why the two pyramids are different shapes.

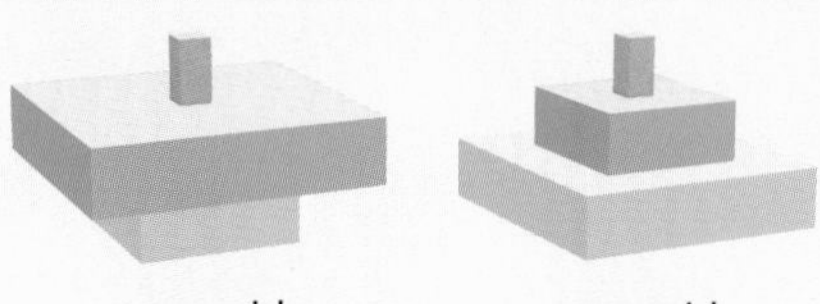

Figure 9

5. Why do energy pyramids have their specific shape?
6. What would be the best source of energy for an omnivore: the plant or animal tissue it feeds on? Explain.
7. A field mouse eats 10 000 g of leaves each year, among other things. If each gram of leaves has absorbed 150 kJ of energy from the Sun, about how much energy is available for the mouse?
8. The producers in a closed ecosystem capture 1.5×10^9 kJ of energy from the Sun each year. The main food chain in the ecosystem has four levels.
   (a) How much energy is available for the consumers at the top level?
   (b) Draw a pyramid of energy for the food chain.
9. Despite warnings about future shortages and the pollutants released, we continue to burn oil and coal for energy. What evidence, if any, suggests that attitudes toward conservation are changing? Are they changing quickly enough?

INVESTIGATION 2.1

Constructing Food Webs

Report Checklist

○ Purpose	● Design	● Analysis
○ Problem	○ Materials	○ Evaluation
○ Hypothesis	● Procedure	○ Synthesis
○ Prediction	● Evidence	

Part 1: Antarctic Ecosystem

Research each of the organisms shown in the diagram (**Figure 1**) and connect them with a food web. Your teacher will provide you with an outline diagram of the organisms. Cut them out and stick them on another piece of paper. Use arrows to connect consumers with their food. Be prepared to explain how the organisms are interrelated.

www.science.nelson.com 

Part 2: Food Webs in Your Community

Using field guides, identify the organisms found in one of the following ecosystems within your community, and construct a food web:

- forested area
- park
- natural grassland
- lake or pond

Figure 1

INVESTIGATION 2.1 *continued*

Design

(a) What area did you choose to study?

(b) How did you define the area of study?

Procedure

(c) Provide your procedure.

Evidence

(d) What organisms did you identify?

Analysis

(e) Find out more about each organism. How does it fit into the food ecosystem? What does it eat? Which organisms prey on it?

(f) Construct a food web.

INVESTIGATION 2.2

Light Intensity and Plant Biomass

Through photosynthesis, plants capture solar energy and use it to combine water and carbon dioxide to make glucose. Glucose is then used to fuel its cellular activities and to build other molecules required by the plant. These molecules are used in plant growth, which increases the mass and size of the plant.

Does plant biomass increase with light intensity? Make a prediction. Then, using the materials listed and the design given, write a procedure to address this problem. Make sure you include safety procedures in your design. When your teacher has approved your procedure, carry out the experiment. Ensure you collect the evidence in a clear manner that will allow you to evaluate it later. Your analysis should indicate whether your prediction was correct.

Purpose

To determine how light intensity affects plant biomass

Report Checklist

- ○ Purpose
- ● Problem
- ○ Hypothesis
- ● Prediction
- ○ Design
- ○ Materials
- ● Procedure
- ● Evidence
- ● Analysis
- ● Evaluation
- ○ Synthesis

Materials

algae culture
filter paper
light source or access to sunlight
balance (mechanical or electronic)
funnel
two 250 mL beakers
light meter

Design

Plant biomass can be determined by filtering a given quantity from an algae culture and allowing the filter paper and algae to dry.

EXTENSION

Constructing Scientifically Valid Procedures

Do you remember how to conduct investigations so that your data are reliable and valid? Listen to this audio clip for a quick review.

www.science.nelson.com GO

Chapter 2 SUMMARY

Outcomes

Knowledge

- explain, in general terms, the one-way flow of energy through the biosphere and how stored biological energy in the biosphere is eventually "lost" as thermal energy (2.1, 2.2)
- explain how biological energy in the biosphere can be perceived as a balance between both photosynthetic and chemosynthetic, and cellular respiratory activities, i.e., energy flow in photosynthetic environments and; energy flow in deep sea vents (chemosynthetic) ecosystems and other extreme environments (2.2)
- explain the structure of ecosystem trophic levels, using models such as food chains and webs (2.1, 2.2)
- explain, quantitatively, energy exchange in ecosystems, using models such as pyramids of energy, biomass, and numbers (2.2)
- explain the interrelationship of energy, matter and ecosystem productivity (biomass production) (2.2)
- explain how the equilibrium between gas exchanges in photosynthesis and cellular respiration influences atmospheric composition (2.2)

STS

- explain that scientific investigation includes analyzing evidence and providing explanations based upon scientific theories and concepts (2.1, 2.2)

Skills

- ask questions about observed relationships and plan investigations (2.1, 2.2)
- conduct investigations and use a broad range of tools and techniques by: performing an experiment to demonstrate solar energy storage by plants (2.2)
- analyze data and apply mathematical and conceptual models by: describing alternative ways of presenting energy flow data for ecosystems: pyramids of energy, biomass, or numbers (2.2)
- work as members of a team and apply the skills and conventions of science (all)

Key Terms

2.1

trophic level
autotroph
primary consumer
secondary consumer
heterotroph
food web
photosynthesis
cellular respiration
chemosynthesis
chemoautotroph
thermodynamics

2.2

ecological pyramid
monoculture

MAKE a summary

1. Using scientific models, such as a pyramid of energy, draw a diagram that shows the one-way flow of energy through the biosphere. Briefly describe how stored energy in the biosphere is eventually lost as heat.
2. Revisit your answers to the Starting Points questions at the start of the chapter. Would you answer the questions differently now? Why?

The following components are available on the Nelson Web site. Follow the links for *Nelson Biology Alberta 20–30.*

- an interactive Self Quiz for Chapter 2
- additional Diploma Exam-style Review Questions
- Illustrated Glossary
- additional IB-related material

There is more information on the Web site wherever you see the Go icon in the chapter.

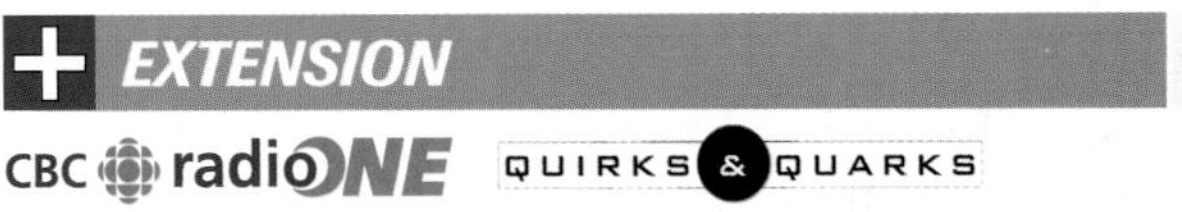

Lovin' a Lichen

Dr. Irwin Brodo describes lichens—tiny creatures, part algae and part fungus, that are found in all parts of the globe. They are an integral part of the global food web.

Many of these questions are in the style of the Diploma Exam. You will find guidance for writing Diploma Exams in Appendix A5. Science Directing Words used in Diploma Exams are in bold type. Exam study tips and test-taking suggestions are on the Nelson Web site.

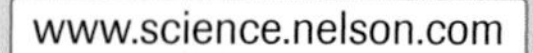

DO NOT WRITE IN THIS TEXTBOOK.

Part 1

1. Bracket fungi, mushrooms, and bread mould can be classified by ecologists as
   A. producers
   B. herbivores
   C. carnivores
   D. decomposers

2. An example of an ecosystem in equilibrium would be
   A. a grassland community in which the number of producers and consumers remains relatively constant over a number of years
   B. a naturally occurring grassland community in which fire is prevented
   C. a pond ecosystem in which the water temperature changes little throughout the year
   D. a pond ecosystem in which the population of algae remains constant throughout the year

3. Photosynthesis can best be explained by the following simplified equation.
   A. $CO_2 + H_2O + O_2 \rightarrow \text{energy} + C_6H_{12}O_6$
   B. $CO_2 + H_2O + \text{energy} \rightarrow C_6H_{12}O_6 + O_2$
   C. $\text{energy} + C_6H_{12}O_6 \rightarrow CO_2 + H_2O + O_2$
   D. $C_6H_{12}O_6 + O_2 \rightarrow CO_2 + H_2O + \text{energy}$

Part 2

4. In your own words, **explain** what is meant by the term *top carnivore.* **Illustrate** your explanation by giving three examples of a top carnivore. **Identify** the ecosystem in which you would find each one.

5. **Sketch** a food web for a freshwater ecosystem in a dark cave.

6. Using the example of a cat and a mouse, **explain** the factors that account for the loss of energy in the transfer from mouse to cat.

Use the following information to answer questions 7 to 9.

Figure 1 shows the flow of energy in an ecosystem.

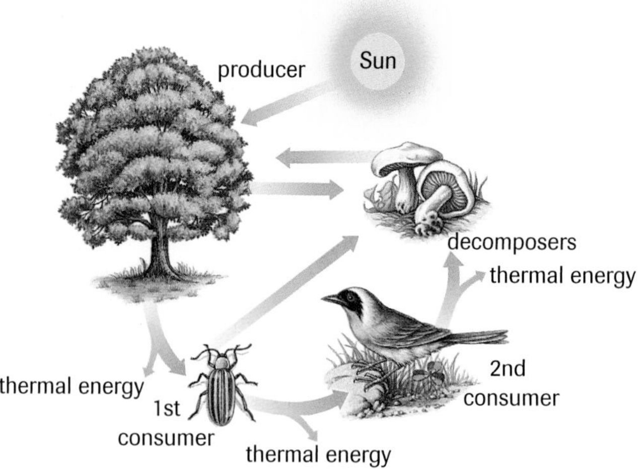

Figure 1

7. **Illustrate** the first and second laws of thermodynamics using the components of **Figure 1**. DE

8. **Sketch** the predicted shape of an ecological pyramid of numbers using the organisms in **Figure 1**. DE

9. **Sketch** the predicted shape of an ecological pyramid of energy. DE

10. **Predict** whether each of the four ecosystems listed in **Table 1** can be sustained. A check mark indicates that the type of organism is present. Write a paragraph to **justify** each answer.

Table 1 Four Ecosystems

System	Autotrophs	Heterotrophs	Decomposers
1	✓		
2		✓	✓
3	✓		✓
4	✓	✓	

11. In your own words, **explain** why photosynthesis and cellular respiration are considered to be complementary processes.

12. Around the world, habitats available for wild animals have become smaller and smaller as the human population grows. Write a unified response addressing the following aspects of habitat loss. DE
    - Using an energy flow argument, explain why this shrinkage would affect animals in the highest trophic levels more severely than those in lower levels.
    - **Describe** a way to protect wild habitat. How would your solution affect humans?
    - **Identify** the type of habitat that might be at the greatest risk of collapse.

13. Wolves often prey upon cattle or sheep as well as on natural species, such as deer. Earlier in the century it was considered beneficial to eliminate predators. **Describe** two harmful outcomes of this approach to managing predator populations.

14. In underground caves, where there is permanent darkness, a variety of organisms exist. In terms of energy flow, **explain** how this is possible.

15. Based on what you have learned about energy pyramids, **criticize** the practice of cutting down rainforests to grow grain for cattle.

16. **Sketch** complex food webs for a tundra ecosystem and a middle-latitude woodland ecosystem. Conduct additional research to determine the members of the food web, if necessary.

www.science.nelson.com GO

(a) Which ecosystem has the greatest biomass? **Explain**.
(b) Which ecosystem has the greatest number of organisms? **Explain**.
(c) Which ecosystem has the greatest energy requirement? **Explain**.

17. By law in Canada, the cutting of forests must be followed by replanting. **Why** do some environmentalists object to monoculture replanting programs?

18. **Illustrate** the two laws of thermodynamics with examples of some common, everyday events.

19. Of the three basic energy pyramids, which best illustrates energy transfer in a food chain? **Explain**.

20. Assuming a 90 % loss of energy across each trophic level, **determine** how much energy would remain at the fourth trophic level if photosynthesis makes available 100 000 kJ of potential energy. **Justify** your answer. **Sketch** a properly labelled pyramid to represent this situation. Could a fifth-level organism be added to the chain? **Explain**.

21. Assume that a ski resort is proposed in a valley near your favourite vacation spot. **Describe** the type of environmental assessment that should be done before the ski resort is built. In providing an answer, pick an actual location you are familiar with and give specific examples of studies that you would like to see carried out.

22. Insect-eating plants such as the sundew are commonly found in bogs across the country. Although referred to as "carnivorous" plants, they are still considered to be members of the first trophic level. Is this the proper trophic level to assign to these plants? Research carnivorous plants, then state the trophic level you think is most appropriate. **Explain** your choice.

www.science.nelson.com GO

23. Some ecologists have stated that, to maximize the food available for Earth's exploding human population, we must change our trophic level position. **Describe** the probable reasoning behind this statement. **Predict** any potential biological problems that might occur if this switch were actually made.

24. The sea otter was once an extirpated species in Canada. This species was reintroduced to the west coast from 1969 to 1972. There are now well over a thousand sea otters on the west coast of Canada, but they are still listed as a threatened species. The sea otter eats sea urchins, which in turn eat algae, such as kelp. When the sea urchin population is kept in control, kelp populations increase. This improves the health of the ecosystem. Higher kelp populations also result in a decrease of barnacles and mussels.
(a) **Sketch** a food chain that includes the sea otter.
(b) Sea otters are threatened by oil spills. If the population of sea otters decreases, **predict** what will happen to the population of kelp.
(c) If the population of sea otters increases, what will happen to the populations of barnacles and mussels?
(d) Kelp provides shelter for fish. **Predict** how higher populations of kelp might impact fish-eating birds, such as eagles and osprey.
(e) **Sketch** a concept map showing the impact a decrease in sea otters would have on each species in this ecosystem.

25. The Banff longnose dace, *Rhinichthys cataractae smithi*, now extinct, was found only in Banff National Park, in a marsh into which the Cave and Basin Hot Springs drain. **Summarize** the factors that contributed to the extinction of this species.

www.science.nelson.com GO

26. **Figure 2** shows a food web.
(a) Make a chart classifying the species shown into producers, consumers, and trophic levels.
(b) Use the information in **Figure 2** to **sketch** a pyramid of energy that shows the level of each species. (Since you do not have energy data, just estimate the size of each level.)
(c) **How** might an increase in the population of snowshoe hares affect the owl over a short period of time? over a long period of time? **Explain** your reasons.
(d) **Predict** what would happen to the population of owls if hawks were introduced to the ecosystem.

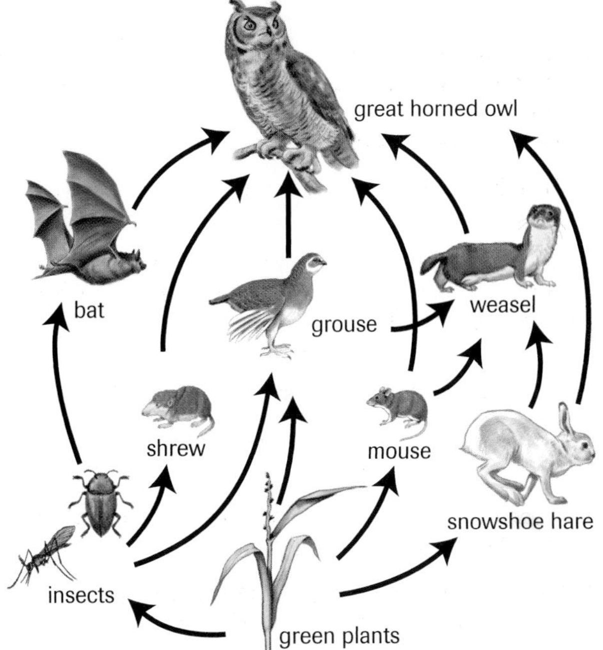

Figure 2

chapter 3 The Cycling of Matter in the Biosphere

In this chapter

- Exploration: Recycling Matter
- Investigation 3.1: Nutrient Cycling and Plant Growth
- Mini Investigation: Measuring Water Loss from Leaves
- Web Activity: Pesticides: Pro or Con?
- Lab Exercise 3.A: Carbon Dioxide Production by Plants and Animals
- Mini Investigation: Greenhouse Effect Simulation
- Investigation 3.2: The Albedo Effect
- Case Study: Technological Solutions for Global Warming
- Web Activity: Biosphere 2
- Investigation 3.3: Environmental Models
- Mini Investigation: Effects of Nitrogen on Algal Growth
- Investigation 3.4: Phosphate Identification
- Web Activity: Persistent Pesticides and Matter Flow

Ecosystems are always changing. Trees in a forest die and are replaced by new trees. Lakes change greatly in temperature and oxygen levels throughout the year. Grasslands are burned by wildfires, and new plants appear. By changing constantly, ecosystems can remain stable, in a dynamic equilibrium, or balance.

The rusting truck in **Figure 1**, on the next page, reminds us of some of the ways that ecosystems respond to change. In time, the weeds growing around the truck will be replaced by shrubs, and the small trees will grow tall. Pieces of the truck will fall off and be buried under detritus. Eventually, even the iron atoms in the truck will return to the soil.

Where will the atoms and molecules of the truck go? Recall that the biosphere is a closed system. Energy can pass into and out of the biosphere but, other than small amounts in meteorites, matter neither enters nor leaves the biosphere. Instead, all the atoms that make up matter in the biosphere are transformed from one form to another through different cycles. The cycling of matter helps to maintain the environmental conditions that support the organisms in that ecosystem. Any large changes may cause an irreversible shift in the dynamic equilibrium, and a new balance must be established. If changes are too large or too fast, some species may not survive.

STARTING Points

Answer these questions as best you can with your current knowledge. Then, using the concepts and skills you have learned, you will revise your answers at the end of the chapter.

1. One truck abandoned in a forest probably won't affect the ecosystem too much. However, humans produce far more than one waste truck every year. Estimate the number of trucks and cars that are abandoned each year in Canada. What problems might be caused by this volume of waste?
2. Western thought often describes humans as being at the centre of change. In this worldview, the ideal human acts as a protector for an ecosystem. By contrast, Aboriginal peoples describe humans as belonging to an ecosystem, living in harmony with it. How would a description of a grassland ecosystem written by a typical scientist differ from a description written by an Aboriginal elder?
3. Low oxygen levels in landfills limit the number of bacteria that can decompose foods.
   (a) Explain why slow rates of decomposition are a concern.
   (b) Why is reducing wastes so important?

Career Connection: Environmental Auditor

Figure 1
If left here, this truck will slowly disappear, leaving little behind.

Exploration Recycling Matter

Materials: scissors, shoe box, masking tape, soil, magnifying lens, plastic (e.g., garbage bag), spoon, rubber gloves, beaker, items for testing (newspaper, orange peel, aluminum foil, plastic bottle cap, coffee grounds, lettuce, metal tab from pop can)

- Line a shoe box with plastic from a garbage bag. Tape the plastic along the top edge of the box.
- Place about 8 cm of soil in the shoe box and add enough water to make the soil moist. Arrange different items for testing on the surface of the soil. Cover each item with a layer of moist soil.
- Place the shoe box in a warm, sunny place for the next month. Keep the soil moist by adding water when needed.
- Examine each item once a week. Each time, put on rubber gloves and use a spoon to remove the top layer of soil. Put the soil in a beaker. Examine each sample using a hand lens. Cover the materials with the soil after you examine them.

(a) Explain why you lined the box with plastic.
(b) Record your observations in a chart.
(c) Why should you wear rubber gloves to examine the materials?

3.1 The Hydrological Cycle

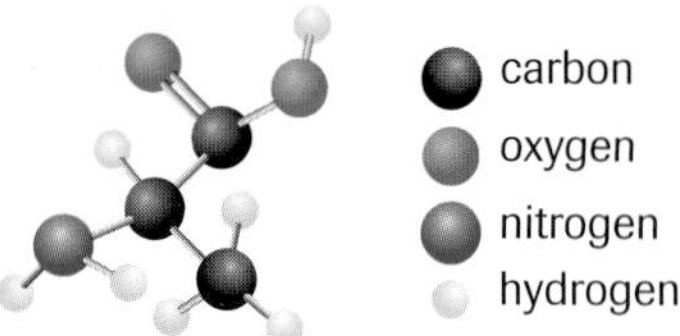

(a) alanine, an amino acid. Amino acids are used to build proteins, which regulate the chemistry of the cell and make up most of its structures.

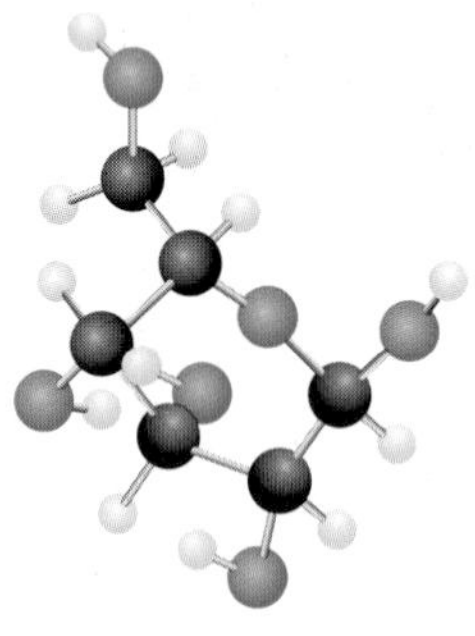

(b) glucose, a sugar. Sugars are used to store energy.

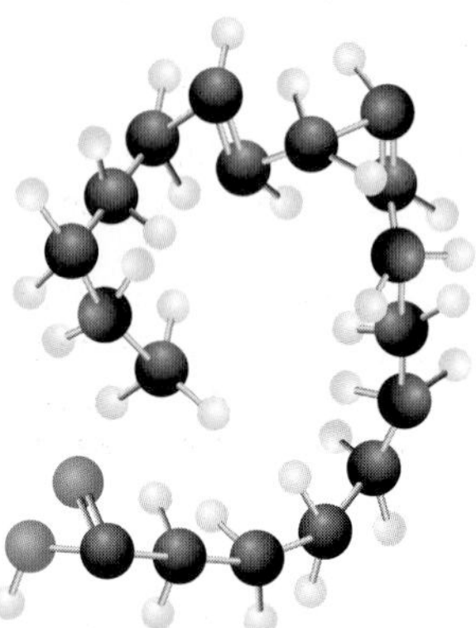

(c) linoleic acid, a fatty acid. Fatty acids are combined to form fats, which are used to store energy and to build cell membranes.

Figure 1
Three organic molecules. Note that they all contain carbon and hydrogen atoms. Some organic molecules are extremely complex. A DNA molecule, for example, contains millions of atoms.

To understand how matter cycles through ecosystems, we must also understand the cycling of organic substances within living things. Living organisms contain many organic compounds, which are substances that contain atoms of carbon and hydrogen. Proteins, sugars, and fats, the important chemicals that make up your body, are all organic (**Figure 1**). Organic compounds undergo changes within living things and within ecosystems. Their complex structures are broken and rebuilt in a continuous cycling of matter.

Cycling of Organic Matter

The materials used in building the bodies of living organisms are limited to the atoms and molecules that make up the planet. There is no alternative source of matter. Therefore, to maintain life on Earth, matter must be recycled.

Incredible as it may sound, every carbon atom is recycled time and time again into new life forms. Because of this cycling, it is possible that somewhere in your body are atoms that once made up a *Tyrannosaurus rex*, one of the giant carnivorous dinosaurs that lived 70 million years ago.

Food is organic matter. Every time you eat, organic matter that was once part of other living things passes into your body. Through the process of digestion, complex organic molecules are broken down into simpler molecules. Cells use these simple molecules to build the complex molecules that become part of your own structure.

Another process involved in the cycling of matter is decay. Organic materials are held temporarily in the bodies of living organisms, but after death, decomposer organisms make the materials available to other living things. Decomposers break down the organic matter in dead bodies and feces into small, inorganic molecules. These small molecules pass into the soil or water, where they can become part of the living world at some future time (**Figure 2**).

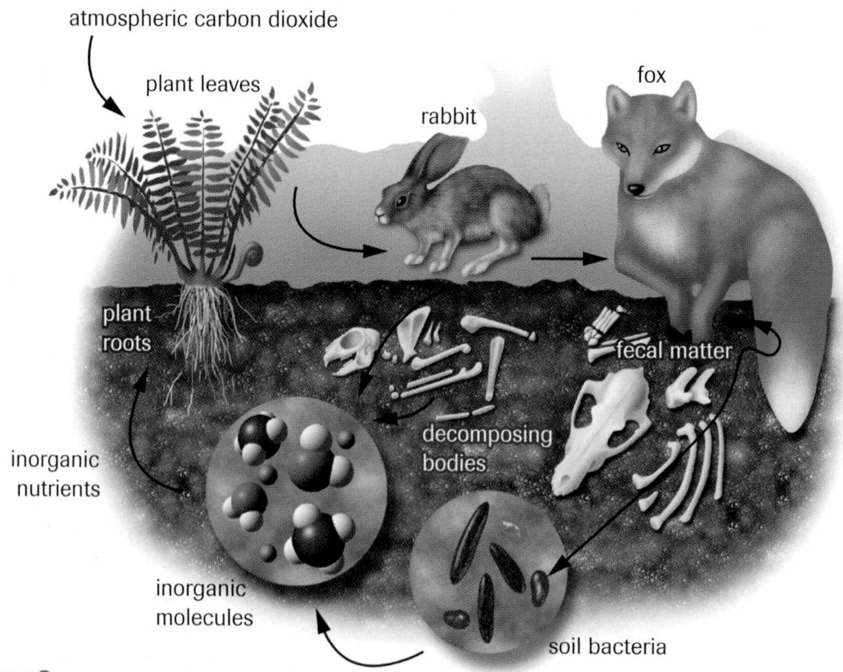

Figure 2
Decomposers break down complex organic molecules into inorganic matter, which may be used by plants. Plants reassemble these inorganic substances (also called nutrients) to make food for themselves. In turn, animals may eat the plants, continuing the cycling of matter.

 **INVESTIGATION 3.1** *Introduction*

Nutrient Cycling and Plant Growth

Humans often add nutrients to soil to promote plant growth. In natural ecosystems, soil nutrients are recycled between decomposing matter and growing plants. In this investigation, you will determine which of three samples of different soil types delivers the most nutrients to plants.

Report Checklist

- ○ Purpose
- ● Problem
- ○ Hypothesis
- ○ Prediction
- ● Design
- ○ Materials
- ○ Procedure
- ● Evidence
- ● Analysis
- ● Evaluation
- ● Synthesis

To perform this investigation, turn to page 67.

Properties of Water

All living organisms need water (**Table 1**). Water is the solvent in which most metabolic reactions take place. It is the major component of a cell's cytoplasm. Many organisms live within its stable environment, while others depend on water to carry dissolved nutrients to their cells. The volume of water in the biosphere, including its solid phase (snow or ice) and gaseous phase (vapour), remains fairly constant; however, the specific amount in any one phase can vary considerably. It is continuously entering and leaving living systems.

Table 1 The Importance of Water to Organisms

• Absorbs and releases thermal energy and moderates temperature fluctuations
• Is the medium in which metabolic reactions take place
• Is an excellent solvent
• Makes up over 60 % of the cell's mass
• Supplies hydrogen atoms to producers during the metabolism of key organic molecules during photosynthesis and oxygen atoms to all organisms during cellular respiration
• Is a reactant in some metabolic activities and a product in others

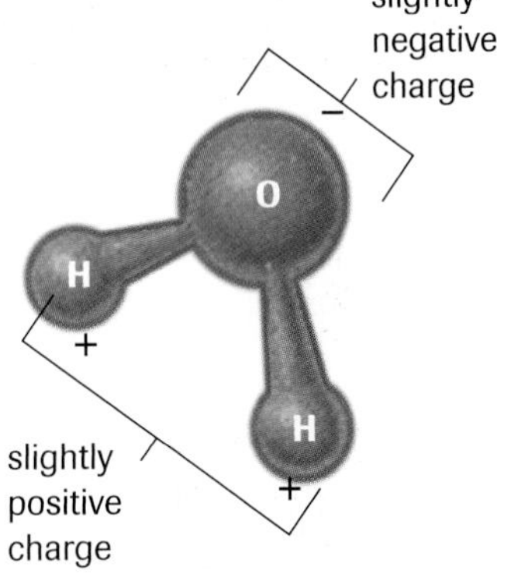

Figure 3
The electrons are pulled closer to the oxygen end of the molecule. The single proton of each hydrogen atom causes a positively charged end.

polar molecule a molecule that has a positive and a negative end

hydrogen bond the type of bond that is formed between the positive end of one water molecule and the negative end of another water molecule

Water: A Polar Molecule

Water molecules are held together by covalent bonds that join one oxygen and two hydrogen atoms (**Figure 3**). The electrons are drawn toward the oxygen atom, creating a region of negative charge near the oxygen end of the molecule and a positive charge near the hydrogen end of the molecule. Although the positive and negative charges on the molecule balance each other out, the molecule has a positive pole and a negative pole. It is for this reason that water is referred to as a **polar molecule**. The negative end of a water molecule repels the negative end of another water molecule, but attracts its positive end. Attraction between opposing charges of different molecules creates a special **hydrogen bond**. Hydrogen bonds pull water molecules together (**Figure 4**).

Hydrogen bonding helps explain some of the physical properties of water. Water boils at 100 °C and freezes at 0 °C. By comparison, sulfur dioxide, a molecule of similar size, boils at 62 °C and freezes at −83 °C. The higher boiling point and melting point of water can be explained by the hydrogen bonds. Consider the boiling point of water. Before water molecules can escape into the air, hydrogen bonds must be broken. This requires additional energy. Molecules like sulfur dioxide and carbon dioxide do not have hydrogen bonds. Consequently, they require less energy to boil and have lower boiling points.

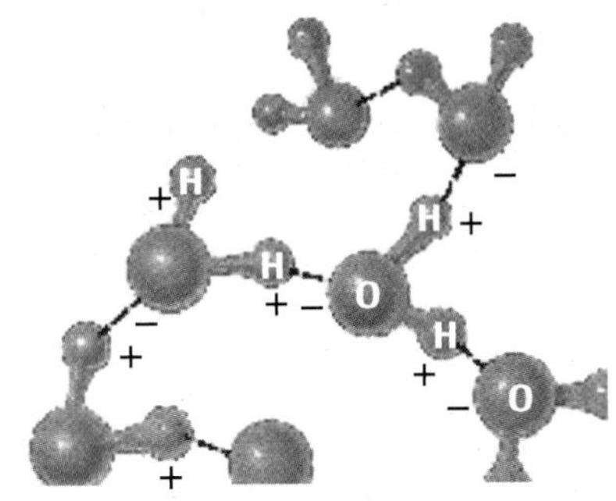

Figure 4
A hydrogen bond is formed between the oxygen end of one water molecule and the hydrogen end of another water molecule.

hydrological cycle (water cycle) the movement of water through the environment from the atmosphere to Earth and back

+ EXTENSION

Dissociation of Water

Water exists as two atoms of hydrogen attached to an atom of oxygen. However, a small number of water molecules dissociate into two separate ions: a positive hydrogen ion and a negative hydroxide ion. Solutions in which the concentration of hydrogen ions is greater than the number of hydroxide ions are acids. Bases are formed when the concentration of hydroxide ions is greater than the concentration of hydrogen ions. Complete this Extension to review acids, bases, and the pH scale.

www.science.nelson.com 

The Hydrological Cycle

The movement of water through the biosphere is called the **hydrological** or **water cycle**, shown in **Figure 5**. Water reaching Earth's surface as precipitation (rain, snow, sleet, hail, or any combination of these forms) can enter a number of pathways. It may remain on the surface as standing water (lakes, swamps, sloughs) or form rivers and streams that eventually flow to the oceans, which form the bulk of the water reserves. Some of the precipitation sinks into the soil and subsurface rock, forming ground water. If the rock is permeable, some of this ground water may seep to the surface, forming springs or adding water to existing lakes and streams. The movement of water through rock is slow but measurable.

By absorbing energy from the Sun, some of the surface water evaporates and becomes water vapour. The water vapour rises upward in the atmosphere until it reaches a point where the temperature is low enough for the water vapour to condense into tiny droplets of liquid water. These droplets are so light that they remain suspended in the atmosphere as clouds, supported by rising air currents and winds. When conditions are right (e.g., the temperature drops), the droplets join together, forming larger drops or ice crystals. Once the mass of the droplet or ice crystal can no longer be supported by air currents, precipitation occurs. This cycle repeats itself endlessly.

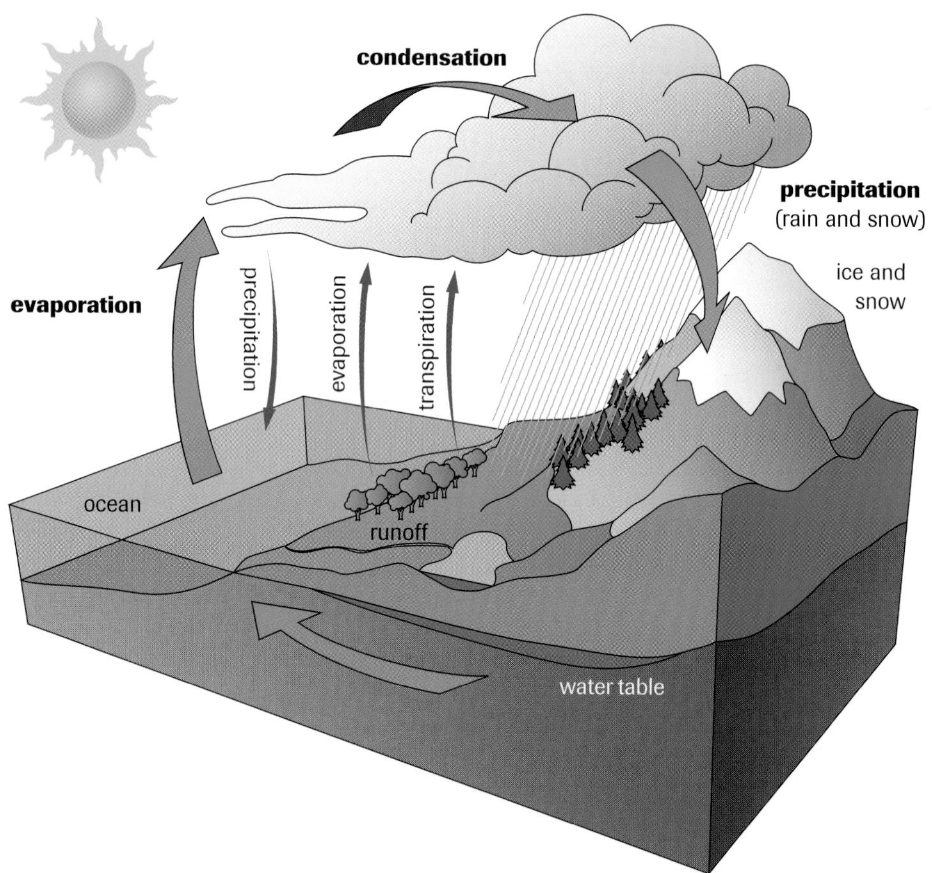

Figure 5
The water cycle

Living organisms also play a vital role in the water cycle. Water enters all organisms and is used by them in various ways during their metabolic activities. You may think that living things tend to remove water from the environment, thus interfering with the cycle. However, through such processes as cellular respiration and the decay of dead organisms, water is released back to the land or atmosphere. Plants, particularly broad-leaf trees and shrubs, play a major role in water recycling through the process of **transpiration**. In fact, where forests have been removed by logging or burning, there is less water in the atmosphere, along with noticeable climate changes. Surface runoff patterns become disturbed and the water-holding capability of the soil may be reduced. This helps explain why the destruction of Brazilian rainforests provides only temporarily usable land for agriculture.

transpiration the loss of water through plant leaves

Water beneath the Soil

The fresh water that we use comes from two sources: ground water and surface water. Precipitation that collects above the ground, such as the water in lakes, ponds, and rivers, is called surface water. Precipitation increases surface runoff, making lakes and rivers rise. In addition, rainfall seeps into the soil. The water filters downward because of gravity. The downward pull of water is called **percolation**. The larger the soil particles are, the greater the size of the pores between the particles and the faster the percolation rate. Eventually, water fills the lower levels of soil, which are composed of sand and gravel. The **water table** forms above a layer of relatively impermeable bedrock or clay. The greater the rainfall, the higher the water table will be.

As water seeps downward, it carries dissolved organic matter and minerals to the lower layers of the soil. The process is called **leaching**. Removing these chemicals from the upper layers of the soil is a serious problem because plants require these nutrients for growth and development. In many ways, plants help correct the problem of leaching. Long branching roots extend deep into soil and help bring minerals and other chemicals from the lower levels of the soil back to the surface.

percolation the movement of a liquid through a porous material, such as soil particles

water table the top level of the region below the ground that is saturated with water

leaching the removal of soluble minerals by percolation

mini *Investigation* — *Measuring Water Loss from Leaves*

Plants contribute to the water cycle by moving water from their roots to the atmosphere, through pores in their leaves. Do all plant species contribute at the same rate?

- Find the mass of two small plastic bags. Place one bag around a leaf of a growing deciduous tree and another around a small branch from a coniferous tree (**Figure 6**).
- Gently tie off the bags and collect water for 24 hours.
- Find the mass of the bags.

(a) In which bag was the most water collected?

(b) Provide reasons to explain the difference.

(c) Design an activity to measure water consumption and loss in animals.

(i) Identify the responding and manipulated variables.

(ii) What variables must be controlled?

(iii) Write a possible laboratory procedure.

Figure 6

CAREER CONNECTION

Environmental Auditor

Environmental auditors work to make sure that industries and corporations are meeting environmental standards and regulations. They help to detect potential environmental concerns and to monitor business activities that might have environmental impacts. These specialists also oversee remediation activities and make recommendations to environmental organizations.

Find out more about this important and meaningful career, including the educational requirements.

www.science.nelson.com 

Acid Deposition and the Water Cycle

Although society obtains many benefits from technology, there is almost always an environmental price to pay. Nowhere is this more evident than with the technologies that contribute to acid deposition. Smokestacks of coal-burning generating stations, metal smelters, and oil refineries provide energy and products for the industrial world, but at the same time produce oxides of sulfur and nitrogen, some of the most dangerous air pollutants.

When fossil fuels and metal ores containing sulfur are burned, the sulfur is released in the form of sulfur dioxide (SO_2), a poisonous gas. Combustion in automobiles and fossil fuel-burning power plants, along with the processing of nitrogen fertilizers, produce various nitrous oxides (NO_x). Sulfur dioxide and nitrous oxides enter the atmosphere and combine with water droplets to form acids. The acids return to the surface of Earth in the form of snow or rain, called "acid rain" (**Figure 7**).

Acid rain has been measured to be as much as 40 times more acidic than normal rain. The devastation of acid rain on ecosystems has been well documented. Acid precipitation kills fish, soil bacteria, and both aquatic and terrestrial plants, as shown in **Figure 8**, on the next page. It leaches nutrients from the soil by dissolving them in the ground water. The devastation is rarely uniform; some ecosystems are more sensitive than others. Alkaline soils neutralize the acids, minimizing their impact. The moun-

Figure 7
Wet and dry acid deposition

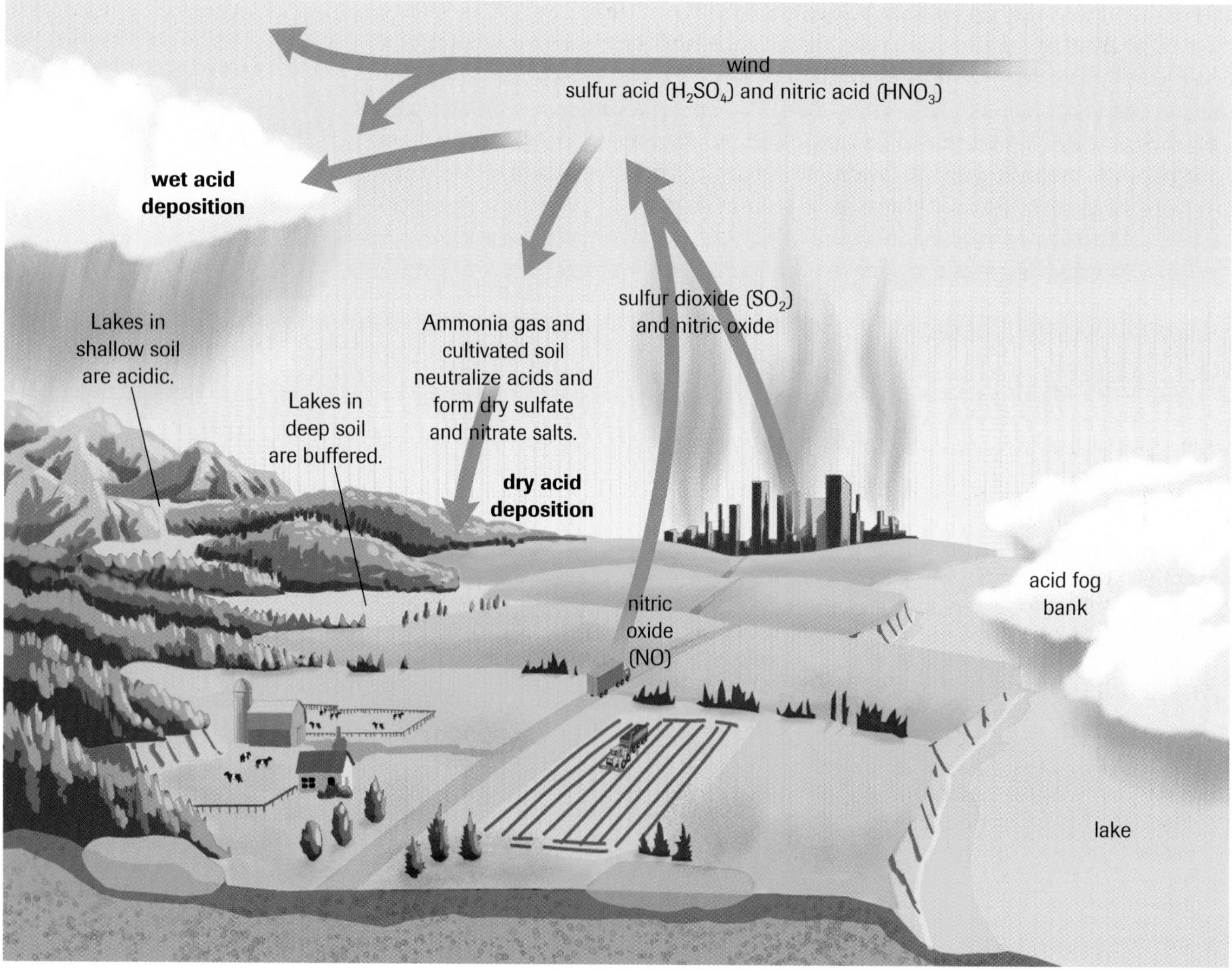

tains of British Columbia are limestone, which help to counter the effect of the acid. Thus, Alberta's rivers are not very acidic. Soils in much of southeastern Canada, however, lie over a solid granite base, which does little to balance the acid.

The sulfur and nitrous oxides released from smokestacks do not always enter the water cycle in the atmosphere. Depending on weather conditions, particles of sulfur and nitrogen compounds may remain airborne and then settle out in the dry state, or as "dry deposition." These dry pollutants, then, form acids when they combine with moisture on a surface, such as the dew on a lawn, the surface of a lake, or the water inside your respiratory tract.

Technology offers some solutions to the problems that have been caused by emitting oxides of sulfur and nitrogen. "Scrubbers" in smokestacks now remove much of the harmful emissions, and lime has been added to lakes in an attempt to neutralize acids from the atmosphere. However, both of these solutions are expensive. The prospect of improving smelters is equally difficult. Mining companies are already battling to remain operational and compete in a world market. Many developing countries are producing ores at a much lower cost because of cheaper labour and more relaxed environmental standards. Tougher legislation could result in higher levels of unemployment.

Figure 8
Devastation of forests caused by long-term exposure to acid rain. Conifers are particularly susceptible to acid, which makes them vulnerable to a variety of infections.

The Role of Water in Nutrient Cycling

As you have just seen, many harmful substances are transported when dissolved in water. In the next two sections, you will see that water also plays an essential role in the cycling of other substances throughout the biosphere. Since it is such an excellent solvent, water can dissolve nutrients such as nitrates and phosphates, enabling plant roots to absorb them. Because of hydrogen bonding, water can move against gravity, carrying nutrients up plant stems and trunks to cells throughout the plant. This upward motion of water is called "capillary action." Water has a role in the cycling of carbon and oxygen as well. For example, water dissolves carbon dioxide and oxygen, bringing these gases to organisms in aquatic ecosystems. Because water can dissolve carbon dioxide, the ocean stores vast amounts of carbon. Water is also an essential factor in photosynthesis and cellular respiration, two processes that form the backbone of carbon and oxygen cycling in the biosphere.

Web Quest—Pesticides: Pro or Con?

Pesticides are chemicals that protect our crops from damage by insects and disease-causing organisms. Although they were developed to improve human life, this protection also has a price. Instead of contributing to the cycling of matter, many pesticides persist in the environment for long periods. Many people now believe that pesticides cause more harm than good. In this Web Quest, you will explore the costs and benefits of pesticides, and then make a well-supported decision about where you stand on this issue.

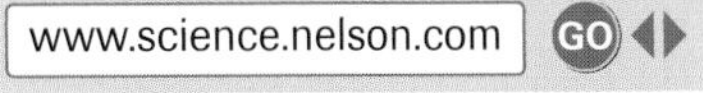

SUMMARY The Hydrological Cycle

- Polar molecules, such as water, are molecules with a positive and a negative end. Hydrogen bonds are formed between the positive end of one water molecule and the negative end of another water molecule.
- The hydrological cycle or water cycle is the movement of water through the environment from the atmosphere to Earth and back.
- The hydrological cycle traces the phase changes of water in the abiotic environment and follows its role in living organisms.
- Sulfur dioxide and nitrous oxides enter the atmosphere and combine with water droplets to form acids. The acids return to the surface of Earth in the form of snow or rain, called "acid precipitation."
- Water plays an important role in the cycling of nutrients in the biosphere.

Section 3.1 Questions

1. (a) What two types of atoms are contained in all organic compounds?
   (b) Oxygen atoms are part of many organic compounds. How might these atoms enter the body of a living thing?
   (c) Many organic compounds also contain nitrogen and phosphorus atoms. How might these atoms enter the body of a living thing?
   (d) What are three ways that matter leaves the bodies of living things?
2. Using diagrams, show two different ways that a carbon atom that was once in a cell in a grass leaf could become part of a cell in your ear.
3. In a few paragraphs, explain the diagram in **Figure 9**.

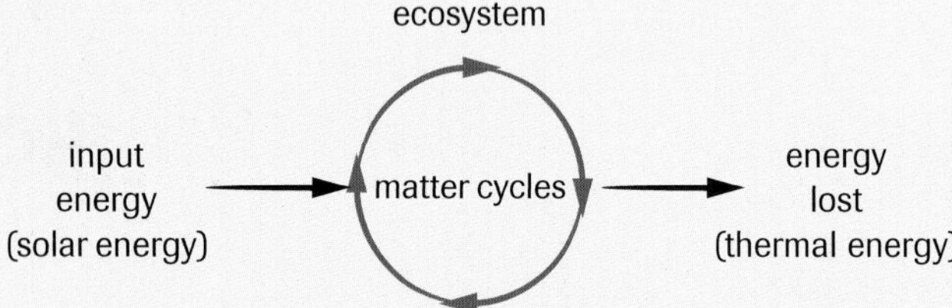

Figure 9

4. When space probes were sent to the Moon and Mars, soil samples were collected and analyzed for organic compounds. Why would scientists want to know if organic matter were present in these soil samples?
5. The following sentence is found in the opener of of this chapter: "By changing constantly, ecosystems can remain stable, in a dynamic equilibrium, or balance." Using a grassland ecosystem as an example, explain what is meant by dynamic equilibrium.
6. Predict what would happen to a deciduous forest ecosystem if an agent were released that destroyed decomposing bacteria found in the soil.
7. Why is water important to living things?
8. Using water as an example, define polar molecules.
9. What is a water table?
10. How does the water cycle purify water samples?
11. Why do minerals leach from the soil?
12. Identify and describe two factors that would alter the amount of ground water in an area.
13. How do the roots of plants help prevent the leaching of important minerals?
14. Describe the danger of digging a hole for an outhouse at a beach cottage.
15. How could a landfill site contaminate ground water?
16. Natural and genetically engineered bacteria and fungi can be used to either destroy toxic chemicals or convert them to harmless forms. The process, referred to as bioremediation, mimics nature by using decomposers to recycle matter. Research how bioremediation is used to clean up various pollutants, and report on your findings.

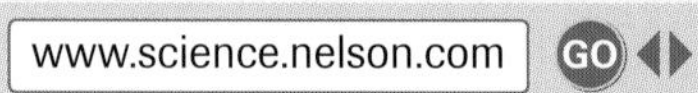

17. List abiotic characteristics of an ecosystem that make it particularly vulnerable to the effects of acid deposition. Predict the long-term effects of such deposition.

The Carbon Cycle and the Oxygen Cycle 3.2

Carbon is the key element for living things. Carbon can be found in the atmosphere and dissolved in the oceans as part of the inorganic carbon dioxide (CO_2) molecule. Each year, 50 to 70 billion tonnes of carbon from inorganic carbon dioxide are cycled into more complex organic substances. This is done through photosynthesis (see Chapter 2). Some of the organic carbon is released back to the atmosphere through cellular respiration as carbon dioxide.

Because photosynthesis and cellular respiration are complementary processes, and because the carbon that they use is repeatedly cycled through both processes, this relationship is often called the **carbon cycle**. This cycle is actually much more complex than a simple exchange of carbon-as-carbon-dioxide and carbon-as-glucose (**Figure 1**). Most of the carbon in living organisms is returned to the atmosphere or water as carbon dioxide from body wastes and decaying organisms. However, under certain conditions the decay process is delayed and the organic matter may be converted into rock or fossil fuels such as coal, petroleum, and natural gas. This carbon is then unavailable to the cycle until it is released by processes such as uplifting and weathering, or by burning as fuels. The burning process (**combustion**) releases carbon dioxide into the atmosphere.

carbon cycle the cycle of matter in which carbon atoms move from an inorganic form to an organic form and then back to an inorganic form

combustion the chemical reaction that occurs when a substance reacts very quickly with oxygen to release energy

Reservoirs for Inorganic Carbon

When it is not in organic form, carbon can be found in three main reservoirs (storage areas): the atmosphere, the oceans, and Earth's crust. The smallest of these reservoirs is the atmosphere. Carbon dioxide makes up a very small percentage (about 0.03 %) of the gases that we breathe in. However, there is plenty of atmospheric carbon dioxide for land plants to use in photosynthesis.

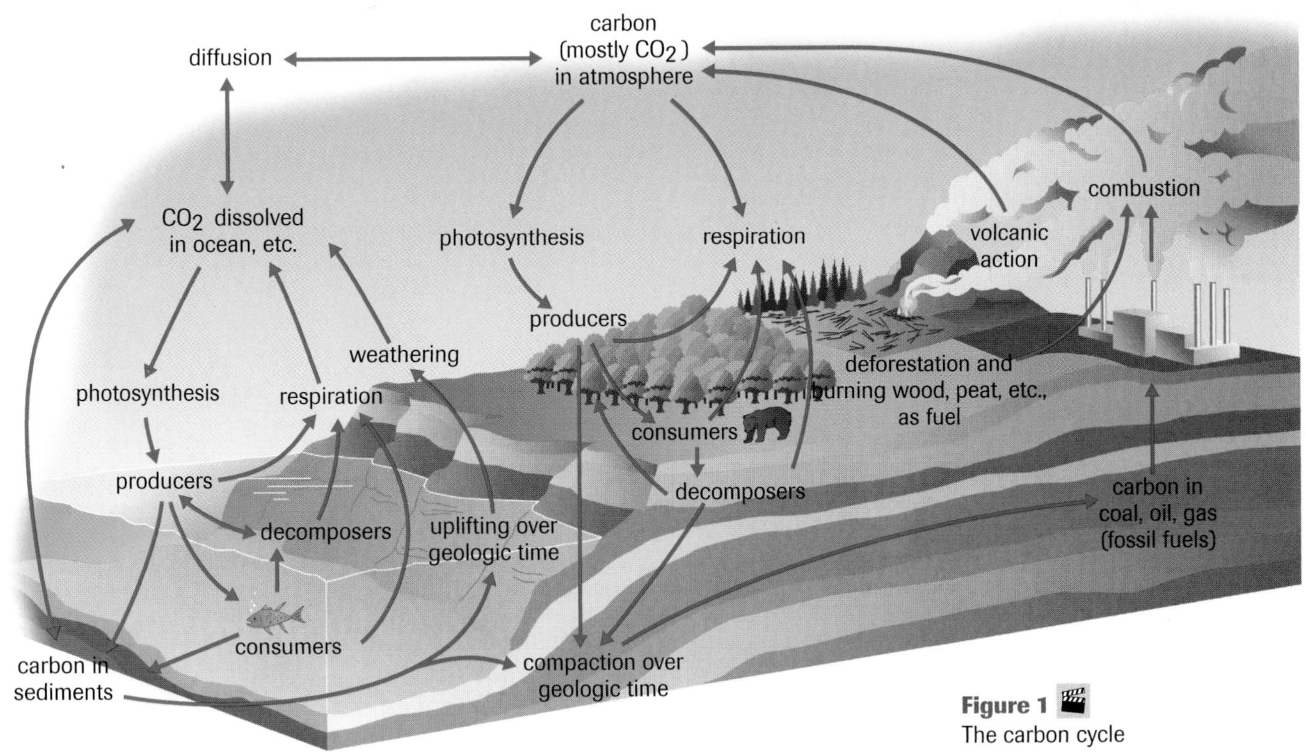

Figure 1
The carbon cycle

Inorganic Carbon Reservoirs

Approximate Time (years)

Location

atmosphere	soil	oceans
3	25–30	1500

Figure 2
The average carbon atom is held in inorganic form much longer in the ocean than in the atmosphere. The time for carbon held in rocks (millions of years) would not fit well in this graph.

A tremendous amount of inorganic carbon is held as dissolved carbon dioxide in the oceans, where it is available to algae and other water plants for photosynthesis. However, some carbon dioxide reacts with sea water to form the inorganic carbonate ion (CO_3^{2-}) and the bicarbonate ion (HCO_3^-). Combined with calcium, these ions become calcium carbonate ($CaCO_3$), which is used by living things to make shells and other hard structures. The carbon in carbonates can be recycled, but in the ocean much of it ends up as sediment. As layers of sediment form, the carbonates are crushed and heated and eventually become rock. Limestone is made from the discarded shells and bones of living things. This explains why by far the largest reservoir of Earth's carbon is in sedimentary rocks. Carbon can be trapped in rock for millions of years until geological conditions bring it back to the surface. Volcanic activity can break down carbonate-containing rocks such as limestone, releasing carbon dioxide. Acid rain falling on exposed limestone will also cause the release of carbon dioxide into the atmosphere.

Figure 2 shows how long, on average, a carbon dioxide molecule will remain in each reservoir.

Reservoirs for Organic Carbon

Organic carbon is also held in reservoirs—the bodies of living things. However, all living things die, and decomposition eventually returns the carbon to the cycle in inorganic form. There is one important exception to this rule: some ecosystems, such as bogs, store huge quantities of carbon in organic form. Bogs contain very little oxygen, and under these conditions decomposition is very slow. Carbon atoms may remain locked away in dead plant matter (**peat**) for many years in a bog. Occasionally these deposits are overlaid with sediment. As more layers of sediment are piled on top, the slowly decaying organic matter can end up trapped between layers of rock. The result is the formation of a carbon-containing fossil fuel, coal (**Figure 3**).

peat slowly decomposing plant matter produced in low-oxygen environments such as bogs

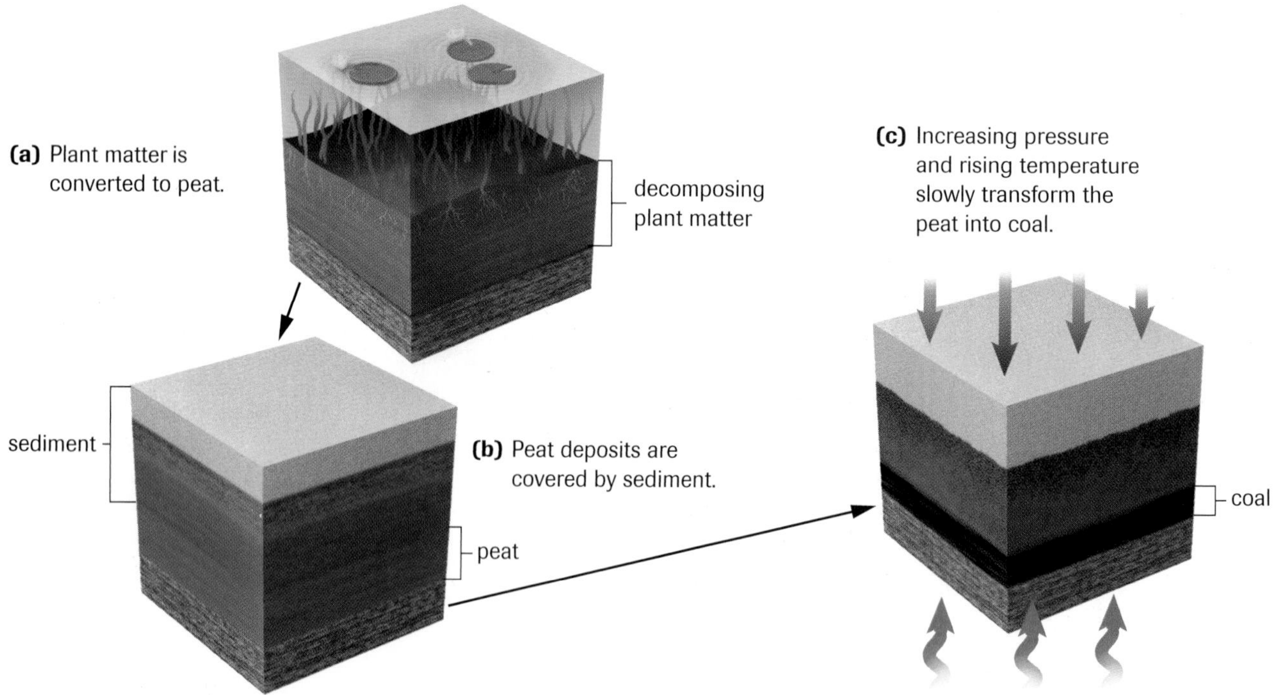

(a) Plant matter is converted to peat.
decomposing plant matter
(c) Increasing pressure and rising temperature slowly transform the peat into coal.
sediment
(b) Peat deposits are covered by sediment.
peat
coal

Figure 3
Coal is a reservoir of organic carbon that can be stored in Earth's crust for millions of years before cycling again into carbon dioxide.

Conditions similar to those in a bog also exist on the floors of oceans; organic carbon can also be trapped there for long periods. Oil is formed in a process similar to the formation of coal, when decaying aquatic animals and plants are trapped under sediment in a low-oxygen environment.

In the form of fossil fuels in Earth's crust, organic forms of carbon can be held out of the carbon cycle for many millions of years.

LAB EXERCISE 3.A

Carbon Dioxide Production by Plants and Animals

Through photosynthesis, plants take up carbon dioxide and release oxygen. Both plants and animals carry out cellular respiration, which uses oxygen and releases carbon. Plants and animals, therefore, could have very different effects on the cycling of carbon. Carbon dioxide produced by aquatic species dissolves in the water in which they live. Bromothymol blue is an indicator used to show the presence of carbon dioxide in solution. Low levels of carbon dioxide will result in the bromothymol blue solution remaining blue, while higher levels of carbon dioxide will cause the dye to change to yellow. In this lab exercise, you will use the given list of materials to design an investigation to compare the carbon dioxide production of plants and animals.

Report Checklist

○ Purpose	● Design	○ Analysis
○ Problem	○ Materials	○ Evaluation
○ Hypothesis	○ Procedure	○ Synthesis
○ Prediction	○ Evidence	

Purpose

To compare carbon dioxide production of plants and animals

Problem

Do plants and animals contribute similar amounts of carbon dioxide to the carbon cycle?

Materials

8 test tubes
water
4 aquatic snails
8 stoppers
bromothymol blue solution
4 stalks of *Elodea*
light source
timer

Design

Design an experiment to address the Problem. Ensure you include the manipulated variable and controlled variables in your design.

The Oxygen Cycle

Since oxygen is an integral part of both photosynthesis and cellular respiration, the cycling of oxygen in the biosphere is closely linked to the cycling of carbon. In general, the oxygen cycle on Earth consists of the movement of oxygen gas, O_2, from living things into the atmosphere through photosynthesis, and then back into living things through cellular respiration. However, this description of the oxygen cycle is very simplified. Oxygen atoms cycle in the atmosphere between oxygen gas and ozone, O_3. Oxygen atoms are also present in carbon dioxide, water, glucose, and many other important substances. In addition, oxygen gas plays a part in many reactions. As a result, the oxygen cycle is extremely complex. Oxygen can be found in living things, in the atmosphere, in water, and in many types of rock. In fact, most of Earth's oxygen is stored in the rock of the lithosphere. Oxygen is needed by most living things for cellular respiration, and as part of the decomposition process.

+ EXTENSION

Interpreting Changes in the Ozone Layer from Satellite Images

Human industry has also affected the amount of ozone in our atmosphere. In this Extension, you will investigate the ozone layer and its changes over time.

www.science.nelson.com

Figure 4
The burning of the rain forest disrupts the balance between photosynthesis and cellular respiration. Many human activities affect the carbon cycle.

Human Impact on the Carbon Cycle

Over the past century, humans have mined fossil fuels trapped in Earth's crust and burned them. This has modified the global carbon cycle by releasing carbon from organic reservoirs faster than would normally occur.

Humans are also increasing the amount of carbon dioxide in the inorganic reservoir of the atmosphere by clearing away vegetation in order to build or farm. The destruction of vegetation reduces the amount of photosynthesis, and so reduces the amount of carbon dioxide removed from the atmosphere (**Figure 4**). Most carbon dioxide released into the air eventually becomes dissolved in the oceans, but the oceans can hold only so much. The amount of carbon dioxide in the atmosphere is rising.

The Greenhouse Effect

Have you ever noticed how hot it can get in a car on a sunny day? Every year, dogs and cats are killed when their owners leave them in closed cars. The heating is caused by the greenhouse effect. The shorter wavelengths of sunlight (primarily infrared) enter the car (acting just like a greenhouse) through the glass. These are absorbed and re-radiated as longer wavelengths. The reflected light is prevented from escaping by the glass. The car (or greenhouse) heats up.

Many of the atmospheric gases that surround Earth, such as CO_2 and CH_4, act like the glass of the greenhouse shown in **Figure 5**. The gases trap the heat from the Sun and warm Earth's surface. A certain amount of "greenhouse gas" is essential for the survival of life on Earth. Without greenhouse gases, the average temperature of the planet would fall from 15 °C to −18 °C.

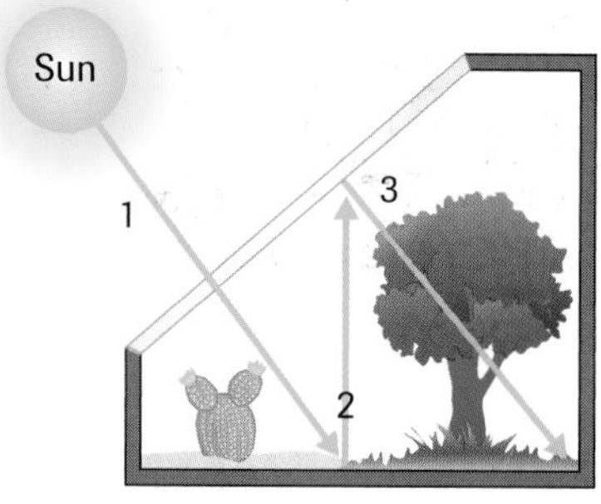

Figure 5
The greenhouse effect: 1. Shorter wavelengths of sunlight enter the greenhouse. 2. Light is reflected and wavelengths become longer. 3. The longer wavelengths are trapped by the glass.

Global Warming

The increased energy demands of an industrialized world have brought about more factories that produce smoke and more automobiles that release exhaust. Carbon dioxide is released during combustion. Scientists estimate that the burning of wood and fossil fuels (coal, oil, and gas) has caused carbon dioxide levels to triple over the past 40 years. Global temperatures have increased by 1 °C over that same time. The rising levels of carbon dioxide, one of the main greenhouse gases, have changed the balance between photosynthesis and cellular respiration (**Figure 7**, next page).

mini *Investigation* — *Greenhouse Effect Simulation*

The greenhouse effect can be simulated by the following experiment.

Materials: ice cubes, 2 plastic bags, 2 small thermometers, 1 large glass jar, clock or timer, 100 mL graduated cylinder

- Put the same mass of ice cubes in two separate plastic bags.
- Place a small thermometer inside each bag to record the air temperature.
- Place one of the bags inside a large glass jar and allow it to sit in sunlight. Put the second bag beside the first, but not enclosed in glass (**Figure 6**).

Figure 6

- After 10 min, remove the first bag from the glass jar. Record the air temperatures inside both bags.
- Use a graduated cylinder to measure the amount of melting that has occurred.

(a) Present your data.
(b) State your conclusions.

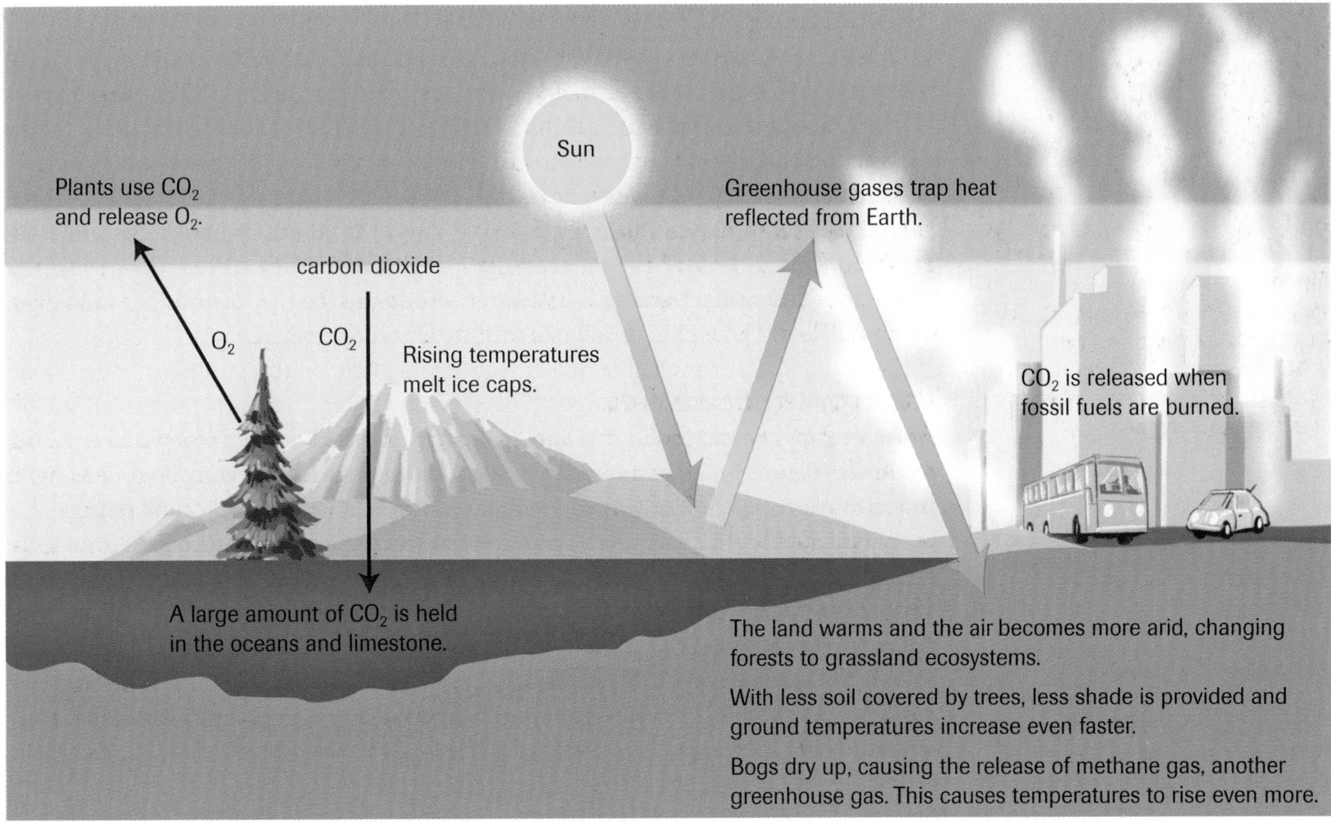

Sun
Plants use CO_2 and release O_2.
Greenhouse gases trap heat reflected from Earth.
carbon dioxide
O_2
CO_2
Rising temperatures melt ice caps.
CO_2 is released when fossil fuels are burned.
A large amount of CO_2 is held in the oceans and limestone.
The land warms and the air becomes more arid, changing forests to grassland ecosystems.
With less soil covered by trees, less shade is provided and ground temperatures increase even faster.
Bogs dry up, causing the release of methane gas, another greenhouse gas. This causes temperatures to rise even more.

Figure 7
Effects of increases in carbon dioxide levels in the atmosphere

A Warmer Climate

The prospect of increased temperatures may seem appealing to most Canadians. However, increased temperatures can bring several ecological problems. In Canada's high Arctic, the layer of ground that remains permanently frozen would thaw, causing the collapse of many roads and buildings that rely on frozen ground for support. Snowcaps would melt and rivers would overflow, causing flooding in many of our cities. The melting snow and glaciers would also raise the level of the world's oceans, causing drastic changes in coastal areas.

Port cities like Halifax and Vancouver would find much of their waterfront real estate under water. Cities that border large lakes or have rivers would experience greater fluctuations in water levels. The city of Winnipeg has many neighbourhoods that are regularly affected by flood waters from the Red and Assiniboine Rivers (**Figure 8**). This flooding could become worse.

Figure 8
Because so many Canadians live close to large bodies of water, scientists believe that global warming could cause enormous property damage.

The Albedo Effect

If global warming continues to increase, scientists fear that much of the world's permanent ice and snow cover will melt. As mentioned earlier, the melting of polar ice caps will increase the level of Earth's oceans. What other effects could the loss of ice and snow have on the biosphere?

albedo a term used to describe the extent to which a surface can reflect light that strikes it. An albedo of 0.08 means that 8 % of the light is reflected.

As radiation from the Sun reaches Earth, it is reflected back by Earth's surface. Some surfaces reflect radiation more than others. The term **albedo** is used to describe the extent to which a surface can reflect radiation. The higher the albedo, the greater the ability to reflect radiation. This principle can be applied to the solar radiation striking Earth's surface. The higher the albedo of the surface, the less energy will be absorbed.

Snow and ice have a valuable role in maintaining temperatures on Earth. The albedo of snow and ice cover is extremely high. During winter, the Sun's energy reflects off snow, keeping temperatures low. Snow is part of a cycle known as snow-temperature feedback (**Figure 9**). To picture this cycle, think of an area that is covered in snow. If that area warms up, the snow will melt. Less of the sun's radiation will be reflected, so more radiation will be absorbed. The temperature in the area will increase even more.

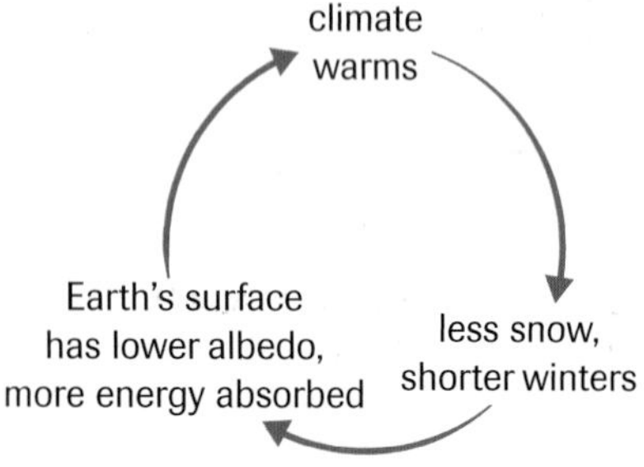

Figure 9
The snow-temperature feedback cycle

Some parts of Earth are permanently covered in snow or ice. If Earth's overall snow and ice cover decreases due to global warming, Earth's surface could absorb more heat, and warm up even more. The snow-temperature feedback cycle works the opposite way, as well. For example, if Earth's temperature were to drop during an ice age, more snow would cover Earth's surface, reflecting more of the Sun's radiation. The temperature would continue to drop.

INVESTIGATION 3.2 *Introduction*

The Albedo Effect

The albedo of a surface is affected by various factors, including colour and surface conditions. In this investigation, you will measure the amount of light reflected when the colour and texture of a surface is varied.

Report Checklist

○ Purpose	○ Design	● Analysis
○ Problem	○ Materials	● Evaluation
○ Hypothesis	○ Procedure	● Synthesis
○ Prediction	● Evidence	

To perform this investigation, turn to page 68.

Equilibrium and Earth's Atmosphere

The levels of carbon dioxide and oxygen change little from year to year. However, when these levels are examined over the life of the planet, dramatic changes in the carbon cycle show how living things, Earth's crust, and the atmosphere interact to alter the biosphere. Initially, Earth contained exceedingly high concentrations of CO_2, causing the planet to warm. About 3.5 billion years ago, microscopic marine life began consuming CO_2 and releasing methane. Fossils of these bacteria can be found in rocks called **stromatolites**. Stromatolites are banded limestone structures that contain colonies of marine bacteria.

stromatolite a banded limestone structure containing fossilized bacteria

Many researchers believe that the methane-producing bacteria poured about 600 times the amount of methane into the skies as is found today. That amount of methane, another greenhouse gas, would have increased the temperature of the planet even more. According to this theory, the warmer conditions of the planet in turn increased the population of methane-producing bacteria, causing more methane to be produced and the temperature to rise even more, in a positive feedback loop (**Figure 10**).

Warmer conditions intensified the water cycle and accelerated the weathering of rocks, a process that pulls CO_2 from the atmosphere. The CO_2 concentrations began to fall and methane production continued to rise. Eventually, the methane gas formed a haze over the planet, deflecting incoming sunlight, and causing temperatures to drop. This made conditions less favourable for the methane-producing bacteria.

DID YOU KNOW 

The Kyoto Accord

The Kyoto Accord is an international agreement to reduce greenhouse gas emissions. It calls for Canada to reduce emissions to 6 % below 1990 levels over a period of 10 years. Why does the government of Alberta oppose Kyoto's targets? What is your own opinion? Visit the Nelson Web site to learn more about Alberta's response to the Kyoto Accord.

www.science.nelson.com GO

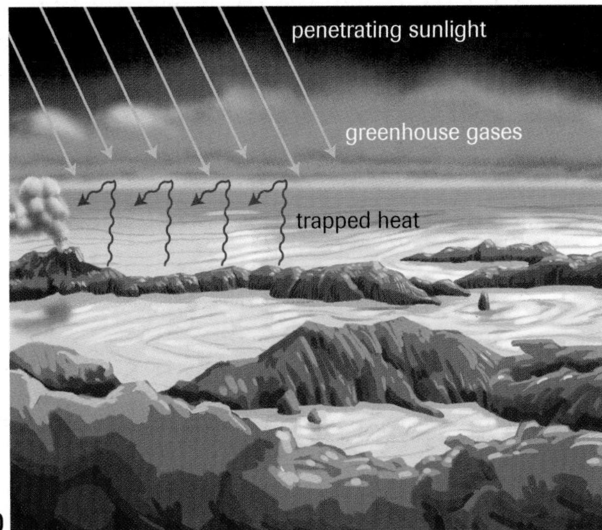

(a)

(b)

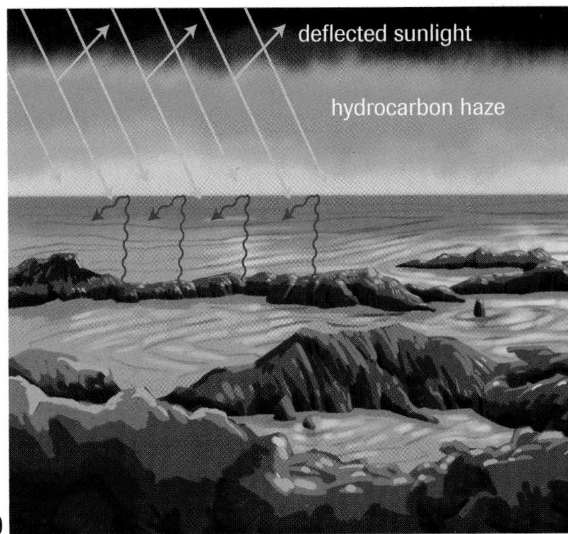

(c)

Figure 10
Earth's early atmosphere.
(a) The greenhouse gases carbon dioxide (from volcanoes) and methane (from bacteria) trapped heat while allowing sunlight to penetrate.
(b) Warmer temperatures accelerated the water cycle and increased the weathering of rocks. The process caused CO_2 to be absorbed from the atmosphere. CO_2 levels dropped and methane increased.
(c) A methane haze blocked sunlight and lowered temperatures. Lower temperatures made conditions less favourable to methane-producing bacteria.

Causes of the Greenhouse Effect

This audio clip provides some deeper information about the causes and global impacts of the greenhouse effect.

www.science.nelson.com 

The decline in methane-producing bacteria, approximately 2.3 billion years ago, was accompanied by the appearance of another life form capable of withstanding the cooler temperatures. These photosynthetic bacteria released oxygen. Eventually, the hardier oxygen-producing bacteria overtook the methane-producing bacteria. As oxygen levels began to increase, more complicated life forms could be supported.

Deforestation and the Atmosphere

In the distant past, changes in the populations of living things resulted in changes to Earth's atmosphere. Large-scale changes are happening to populations of trees and other plants at the present time. How will these changes affect the atmosphere?

Human activities are reducing the number of organisms on Earth that carry out photosynthesis. For example, logging reduces the amount of forested area, and land development decreases the space available for plants to grow. Photosynthesis is the source of oxygen in our atmosphere, and also removes carbon dioxide gas from the atmosphere. With less photosynthesis happening on Earth, oxygen levels will decrease, and carbon dioxide levels will increase even more. Protecting forests on Earth is, therefore, essential to preserving our atmosphere.

INVESTIGATION 3.3 *Introduction*

Environmental Models

Report Checklist

○ Purpose	● Design	● Analysis
● Problem	○ Materials	● Evaluation
● Hypothesis	● Procedure	○ Synthesis
● Prediction	● Evidence	

Environmental models allow scientists to study what could happen to the plants and animals in an ecosystem if changes occur. Models help check predictions without disrupting a large area.

In this investigation, you will build an ecocolumn to research an environmental problem. An ecocolumn is an ecological model that is especially designed to cycle nutrients. You must investigate one of three different environmental problems in the ecocolumn. You must design your own procedure, collect your own data, and draw your own conclusions.

To perform this investigation, turn to page 69. 

 *Case Study*

Technological Solutions for Global Warming

More than 200 years ago, Earth's atmosphere contained about 280 parts per million (ppm) of carbon dioxide. By 1993, the burning of fossil fuels had raised the level of carbon dioxide to 355 ppm. At our present rate, the projected concentration of carbon dioxide could be 700 ppm by 2050.

The vast majority of scientists believe that this increase in atmospheric carbon dioxide is increasing the greenhouse effect and contributing to global warming. However, indirect evidence suggests that global fluctuations in temperature and carbon dioxide levels occurred even before humans appeared on the planet. About 135 million years ago, the levels exceeded 1000 ppm, considerably higher than current levels.

As the effects of global warming become more apparent, scientists have developed several potential solutions, using mini-ecosystems and computer models to test various hypotheses. This Case Study presents several suggested solutions. However, no plan is without problems. Think about each technological fix below, and consider its consequences.

Using "Sun Block"

The eruption of Mount Pinatubo in 1991 shot a plume of ash and debris 20 km into the atmosphere. Within three years, even the smallest particles had returned to Earth. Climatologists estimate that this ash blanket cooled global temperatures by about 0.7 °C, at least in tropical areas.

Putting more particles into the atmosphere was suggested by Dr. S.S. Penner, a retired professor from the University of California at San Diego, as a way to cool the planet. Running jet engines on a richer mixture of fuels would add particles to the atmosphere (**Figure 11**). Burning coal also adds soot to the air. This partial screen would be inexpensive. Eventually, the particles would fall to Earth so the air would not remain polluted.

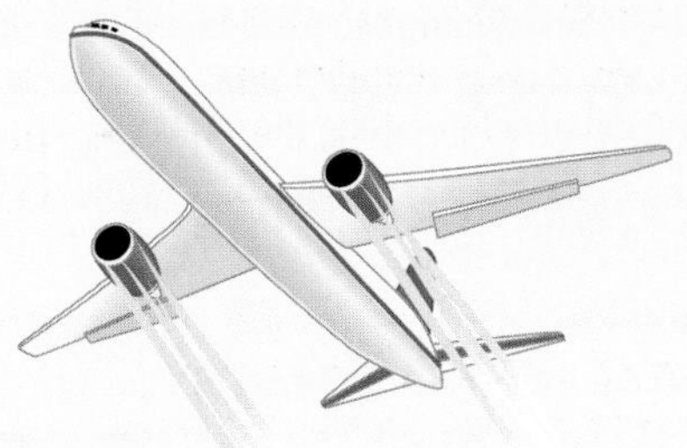

Figure 11

Adding Iron to Sea Water

For many years, naturalists have observed that certain areas of the open ocean are rich in life, while other areas appear barren. After a 7 km^2 patch of ocean off the coast of South America was sprayed with half a tonne of iron, it soon turned green with phytoplankton (**Figure 12**). The experiment, conducted in 1995, caused a bloom of marine plants that perform photosynthesis. Adding iron to seawater could increase photosynthesis and use up some of the CO_2 in the atmosphere.

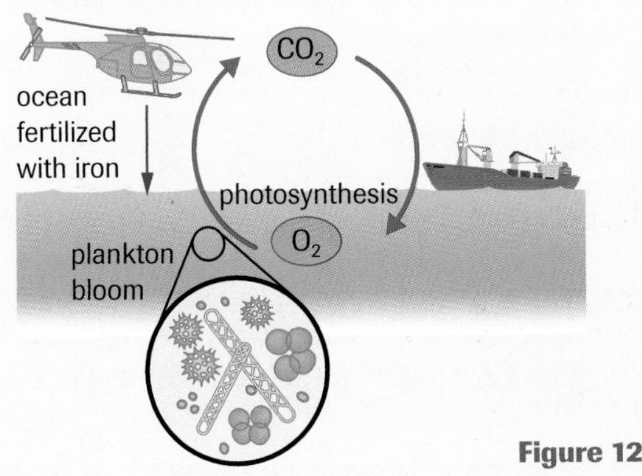

Figure 12

Creating a Deep-Water "Grave" for Carbon Dioxide

An oil company in Norway came up with a revolutionary method to reduce CO_2 levels. Normally, the CO_2 that escapes during the processing of natural gas is released into the air. In 1991, a new carbon tax made this very expensive in Norway. Norwegian companies had to find alternatives.

Natural gas is pumped into a tall tower where the carbon dioxide is removed (**Figure 13**). Almost 1 km below the seafloor, a pipe carries the CO_2 to a layer of shale. The CO_2 displaces seawater from the porous shale, forming a gas bubble in the rock. The CO_2 takes several hundred years to move through the shale to the seafloor.

Scientists point out that most of the floor of the North Sea is sandstone, capped with a layer of shale. This is ideal for the storage of excess carbon dioxide. On a large scale, it could soak up all of the excess CO_2 produced by countries of the European Union. One of the main dangers is that the CO_2 will combine with water to form a weak acid around the pipe.

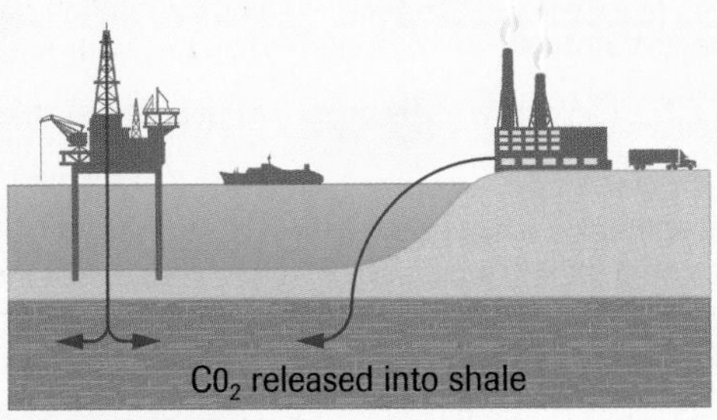

Figure 13
The shale acts as a sink for carbon dioxide gas.

Case Study Questions

1. What groups in Canada might not favour reducing carbon emissions? Provide at least one concern that might be voiced.
2. Why would ash and other particles in the atmosphere cool temperatures?
3. What are some of the possible problems with adding ash and other particles to Earth's atmosphere?
4. How could more algae in Earth's oceans lower global temperatures?
5. What negative effects could increasing the ocean's algae population have on the ecosystem?
6. Why would the formation of weak acids around pipes used to carry carbon dioxide beneath the ocean floor be dangerous?
7. Passing a bylaw saying that people must car pool or take public transportation could reduce fossil fuel usage. Make a list of benefits and problems if this law were instituted.
8. What are the major sources of carbon dioxide in Canada? And what are Canadians doing about the problem of carbon dioxide production? Do research, and then write a short paragraph answering these questions.

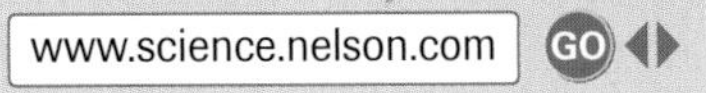

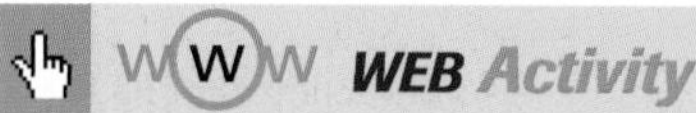

Case Study—Biosphere 2

On September 26, 1991, four men and four women entered a gigantic dome near Tucson, Arizona, that contained 3800 species of plants and animals. The dome was sealed after they entered. They were to live there for one year. Nothing was to be brought in and nothing, and no one, would be allowed out. All raw materials and waste products were to be recycled by humans, animals, and plants living together. Named Biosphere 2, the dome was the largest and most expensive artificial ecosystem ever created.

Unfortunately, the experiment demonstrated in a fairly short time that we do not know everything we need to know about Earth's ecosystems to fulfill this goal. Despite careful planning to ensure the right numbers of plants and animals, and the use of computer simulations and electronic monitoring devices, the amount of carbon dioxide in the air inside the dome kept increasing. Scientists were not able to establish a workable balance between the number of plants and animals. On November 12, the team running the experiment gave up and pumped in purified air from the outside.

In this Web Activity, you will explore what caused the initial failure of the Biosphere 2 experiment, and find out how the facility is being used today to increase our understanding of the interactions among biotic and abiotic factors in ecosystems.

www.science.nelson.com

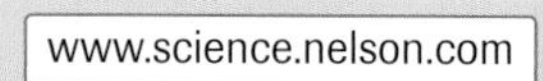

EXTENSION

CBC radiONE

QUIRKS & QUARKS

A Carbon Sinking Feeling

Dr. Werner Kurz (team leader at Essa Technologies and an adjunct professor at the University of British Columbia and Simon Fraser University) discusses the idea that carbon can be absorbed by forests and natural ecosystems.

www.science.nelson.com

SUMMARY The Carbon Cycle and the Oxygen Cycle

- Most of the carbon in living organisms is returned to the atmosphere or water as carbon dioxide when wastes and the bodies of dead organisms decay. Carbon cycles rapidly through the atmosphere or when dissolved in water, but can be held for many years in living things such as trees.
- A tremendous amount of carbon is held in the oceans. Some of the carbon dioxide is dissolved in water, another portion reacts with seawater to form carbonate ions (CO_3^{2-}) and bicarbonate ions (HCO_3^-), and yet another portion is used by algae and plants that perform photosynthesis.
- The largest reservoir for Earth's carbon is in sedimentary rocks, such as limestone ($CaCO_3$), found on the ocean floor and continents.
- Oxygen cycles between living things and the atmosphere via photosynthesis and cellular respiration. Oxygen is stored in the atmosphere, in water, and in rock.
- Humans have modified the global carbon cycle through the increasing use of fossil fuels and by the burning of forests. These cause the release of carbon dioxide at a rate well above natural cycling. In addition, the destruction of vegetation reduces the amount of photosynthesis and thus the volume of carbon dioxide removed from the atmosphere.
- The term albedo is used to describe the extent to which a surface can reflect light that strikes it. The albedo of ice and snow is extremely high, so ice and snow reflect considerable amounts of radiation from the Sun. Changes in Earth's snow and ice cover may affect equilibrium in the biosphere.

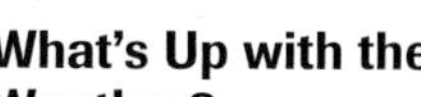

EXTENSION

What's Up with the Weather?

FRONTLINE and NOVA take on a complex and critical phenomenon—global warming.

www.science.nelson.com

Section 3.2 Questions

1. Explain the importance of decomposers in the carbon cycle.
2. The oceans are often described as a carbon reservoir. In what ways is carbon held within the oceans?
3. Explain how the burning of fossil fuels by humans affects the carbon cycle.
4. Carbon cycles more quickly through some ecosystems than others.
   (a) Explain why carbon is cycled more slowly in northern ecosystems than in the tropics.
   (b) Explain why carbon is cycled more rapidly in grassland communities than in peat bogs and swamps.
5. Study **Table 1**.

Table 1 Carbon Cycle

Carbon movement	Mass of carbon per year (10^{13} kg)
from atmosphere to plants	120
from atmosphere to oceans	107
to atmosphere from oceans	105
to atmosphere from soil	60
to atmosphere from plants	60
to atmosphere from burning of fossil fuels	5
to atmosphere from net burning of plants	2
to oceans from runoff	0.4

   (a) Calculate the amount of carbon entering the atmosphere as carbon dioxide every year and the amount of carbon leaving the atmosphere. Is atmospheric carbon dioxide increasing or decreasing?
   (b) Draw a bar graph showing factors that increase and decrease atmospheric carbon dioxide levels.
   (c) The burning of forests contributes 2×10^{13} kg of carbon yearly, but its impact on creating a carbon imbalance is even greater than the carbon dioxide released from the burning plants. What other factor would be affected by burning forests?
   (d) Provide a list of suggestions that would reduce the flow of carbon dioxide into the atmosphere. How would the suggestions affect your life? Which of your suggestions do you think you could help with?
6. Scientists have expressed concerns about the burning of the rainforests to clear land for farming.
   (a) Explain how the burning of the forests could change oxygen levels in the atmosphere.
   (b) What impact would the change in oxygen levels have on living things?
7. In 1998, the federal government of Canada proposed a "carbon tax" on gasoline.
   (a) Would a carbon tax reduce the amount of carbon dioxide entering the atmosphere? Give reasons for your answer.
   (b) What businesses would be affected by the tax? Explain how they would be affected.
   (c) What other groups or individuals would be affected by the tax? Would it apply equally and fairly to everyone?
   (d) Based on your analysis, who would you expect to oppose the tax? Who would you expect to support the tax?
   (e) What are emission credits and how do these affect the amount of CO_2 produced globally? Do research to find out.

www.science.nelson.com 

8. A number of different factors affect the balance of oxygen and carbon dioxide on the planet. Some of these are listed below. Research a factor and draw a poster. Use text to help explain the poster.

www.science.nelson.com 

   A. Deforestation means less oxygen is available.
      - Tropical rain forests are being cleared and burned for farming and ranching.
      - Temperate rain forests are being cut for lumber.
   B. Agricultural land is being used for housing developments, new factories, and landfill sites. An overall decrease in plant life will lower oxygen levels.
   C. Increased combustion in factories is increasing the amount of CO_2 in the atmosphere. The increased level of CO_2 elevates temperatures, which;
      - causes the ice caps and glaciers to melt;
      - expands the size of deserts; and
      - changes the types of crops and food supply.
9. As ice and snow cover on Earth decreases, what effect do you think this may have on the equilibrium of Earth's atmosphere?

3.3 The Nitrogen Cycle and the Phosphorus Cycle

nitrogen cycle a cycle of matter in which nitrogen atoms move from nitrogen gas in the atmosphere, to inorganic forms in the soil, to organic forms in living things, and then back to inorganic forms in the soil and nitrogen gas in the atmosphere

Life depends on the cycling of nitrogen. Nitrogen atoms are required so that cells can make proteins. Nitrogen is also required for the synthesis of deoxyribonucleic acid or DNA, the hereditary material found in all living things. The movement of nitrogen through ecosystems, the soil, and the atmosphere is called the **nitrogen cycle**.

When you consider that nitrogen gas (N_2) makes up nearly 79 % of Earth's atmosphere, you would expect nitrogen to be easy for organisms to access. Unfortunately, this is not the case. Nitrogen gas is a very stable molecule, and reacts only under limited conditions. To be useful to plants, nitrogen must be supplied in another form, the nitrate ion (NO_3^-). The nitrogen cycle is exceptionally complex. A simplified description is shown in **Figure 1**.

Nitrogen Fixation

nitrogen fixation two processes in which atmospheric or dissolved nitrogen is converted into nitrate ions

There are two ways in which atmospheric nitrogen can be converted into nitrates, in a process called **nitrogen fixation**. The first method is through lightning, and the second is through bacteria in the soil.

A small amount of nitrogen is fixed into nitrates by lightning. The energy from the lightning causes nitrogen gas to react with oxygen in the air, producing nitrates. The nitrates

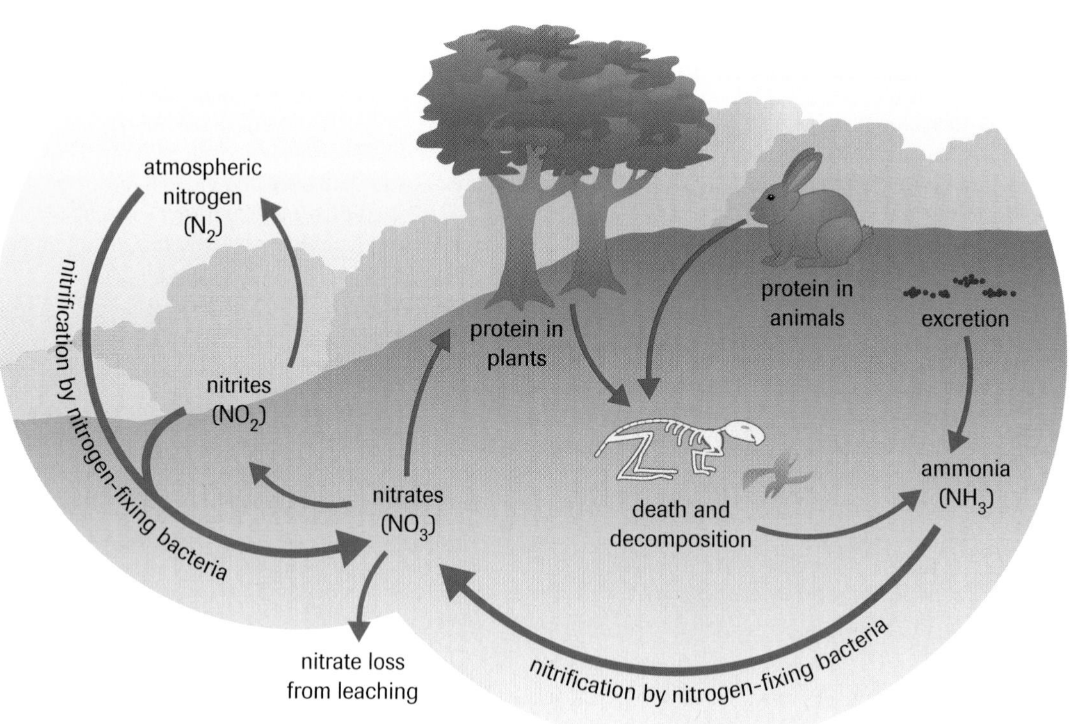

Figure 1 Like carbon, nitrogen moves in a cycle through ecosystems, passing through food chains and from living things to their environment and back again.

dissolve in rain or surface water, enter the soil, and then move into plants through their roots. Plant cells can use nitrates to make DNA, and convert nitrates into amino acids, which they then string together to make proteins. When a plant is consumed by an animal, the animal breaks down the plant proteins into amino acids and then can use the amino acids to make the proteins it needs.

Some bacteria are capable of fixing nitrogen. These bacteria provide the vast majority of nitrates found in ecosystems. They are found mostly in soil. Nitrogen-fixing bacteria can also be found in small lumps called nodules on the roots of legumes such as clover, soybeans, peas, and alfalfa (**Figure 2**). The bacteria provide the plant with a built-in supply of usable nitrogen, while the plant supplies the nitrogen-fixing bacteria with the sugar (energy) they need to make the nitrates. This plant–bacteria combination usually makes much more nitrate than the plant or bacteria need. The excess moves into the soil, providing a source of nitrogen for other plants.

Figure 2
A clover root: the swollen nodules contain nitrogen-fixing bacteria

Traditional agricultural practices of including legumes in crop rotation and mixed planting, capitalize on bacterial nitrogen fixation. For example, the Iroquois traditionally planted corn, beans, and squash together. Known as the "Three Sisters," these crops help each other and protect the soil. Corn provides scaffolding for the other plants, while beans add nitrate to the soil. Squash prevents water evaporation and erosion, and helps control the growth of weeds.

Nitrogen and Decomposers

All organisms produce wastes and eventually die. When they do, a series of decomposers break down the nitrogen-containing chemicals in the waste or body into simpler chemicals such as ammonia (NH_3). Other bacteria convert ammonia into nitrites, and still others convert the nitrites into nitrates. These bacteria all require oxygen to function. The nitrates, then, continue the cycle when they are absorbed by plant roots and converted into cell proteins and DNA.

Farmers and gardeners who use manure and other decaying matter as fertilizer take advantage of the nitrogen cycle. Soil bacteria convert the decomposing protein in the manure into nitrates. Eventually, the nitrates are absorbed by plants.

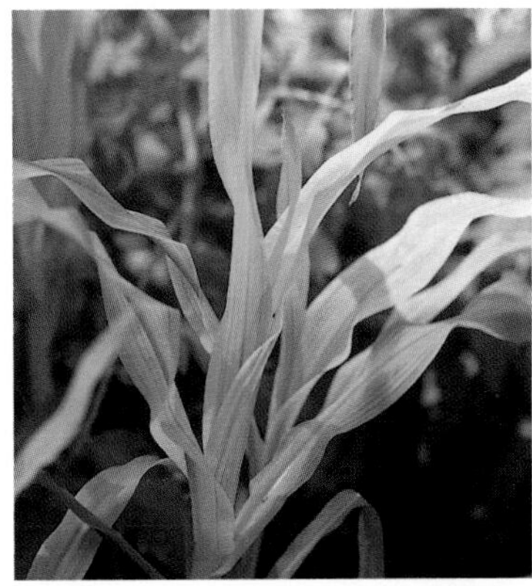

Figure 3
Plants that grow in nitrogen-poor soils can form only a limited amount of chlorophyll. The yellowness of this plant's leaves indicates that the plant is starving for nitrogen.

Denitrification

At various stages in the decay process, bacteria can break down nitrates into nitrites, and then nitrites into nitrogen gas. Eventually, the nitrogen gas is released back into the atmosphere. This process, called **denitrification**, is carried out by bacteria that do not require oxygen. Denitrification acts to balance nitrates, nitrites, and atmospheric nitrogen in the soil, and completes the nitrogen cycle.

denitrification the process in which nitrates are converted to nitrites and then to nitrogen gas

Older lawns often have many denitrifying bacteria. The fact that denitrifying bacteria grow best where there is no oxygen may help to explain why gardeners often aerate their lawns in early spring. Exposing the denitrifying bacteria to oxygen reduces the breakdown of nitrates into nitrogen gas. Nitrates will then remain in the soil, where they can be drawn in by grass roots and used to make proteins.

This information may also help you understand why the leaves of some plants may not be a rich green colour. Chlorophyll is a protein, and plants require nitrates to make it. The colour of a plant's leaves may tell you the nitrate content of the soil (**Figure 3**).

The denitrification process speeds up when the soil is acidic or water-logged (oxygen content is low). Bogs, for example, are well known for their lack of useful nitrogen. They can support only a few types of plants—those able to live with low levels of nitrogen. Insect-eating plants, such as sundews and pitcher plants (**Figure 4**), are commonly found in bogs. In an interesting reversal of roles, these plants obtain their nitrogen by digesting trapped insects.

Figure 4
Insect-eating plants like this pitcher plant can grow in nitrogen-poor soil.

Agriculture and Nutrient Cycles

The seeds, leaves, flowers, and fruits of plants all contain valuable nutrients, which is why we eat them. However, as crops are harvested, much of the valuable nitrogen and phosphorus in these plants is removed and does not return to the field or orchard. This diversion of nitrates and phosphate from the local cycles would soon deplete the soil unless the farmer replaced the missing nutrients. **Fertilizers** are materials used to restore nutrients and increase production from land. Some estimates suggest that fertilizers containing nitrogen and phosphates can double yields of cereal crops such as wheat and barley. However, fertilizers must be used responsibly. More is not necessarily better.

fertilizer a material used to restore nutrients to plants

Soil bacteria convert the nitrogen content of fertilizers into nitrates, but the presence of high levels of nitrates may result in an increase in the amount of nitric acids in the soil. Changes in the levels of acidity can affect all organisms living in the soil, including decomposer bacteria.

Depending on the soil and the other chemicals in the fertilizer, a typical annual application of between 6 and 9 kg/ha of nitrogen fertilizer can, in 10 years, produce a soil that is 10 times more acidic. This can have devastating effects on food production. Most grassland soils in Canada's prairies have a pH near 7 (neutral). If the soil becomes more acidic, some sensitive crops like alfalfa and barley will not grow as well. Acid rain and snow only add to the problem.

Fertilizer and Ecosystems

The accumulation of nitrogen and phosphate fertilizers produces an environmental problem. As spring runoff carries decaying plant matter and fertilizer-rich soil to streams and then lakes, the nutrients allow algae in the water to grow more rapidly (**Figure 5**) in what is called an algal bloom. When the algae die, bacteria use oxygen from the water to decompose them. Because decomposers flourish in an environment with such an abundant food source, oxygen levels in lakes drop quickly, so fish and other animals may begin to die. Dying animals only make the problem worse, as decomposers begin to recycle the matter from the dead fish, allowing the populations of bacteria to grow even larger, and use still more oxygen.

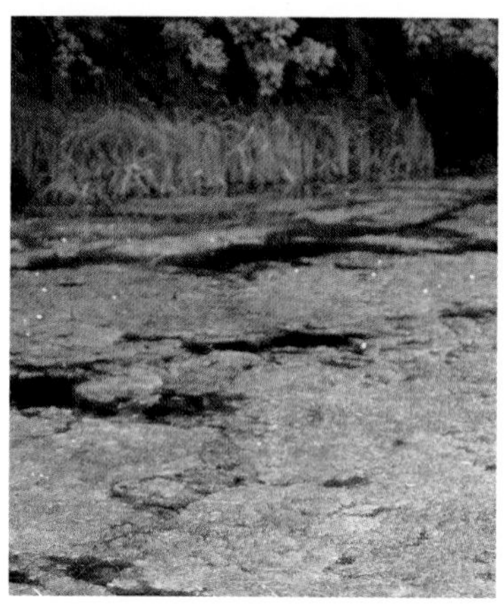

Figure 5
Spring runoff of nitrogen and phosphorus fertilizers promotes the growth of algae.

Nitrates present another problem. As you have seen, there are bacteria that convert nitrates into nitrites (NO_2^-). But nitrites are dangerous to animals that have hemoglobin in their blood, such as humans and other mammals, fish, reptiles, and amphibians. Nitrites can attach to the hemoglobin in blood, reducing its ability to carry oxygen to tissues.

The problem of nitrates in drinking water is especially serious for young animals, including human infants. Humans and other animals usually have bacteria that convert nitrates into nitrites in their large intestines. For adults, the presence of these bacteria in the digestive system is not harmful, because the stomach of an adult is so acidic that the bacteria cannot survive. But the stomach of an infant is much less acidic, so the bacteria can move up into the stomach, where they will convert nitrates into nitrites. The nitrites can then pass into the blood of the infant.

The question of how much nitrate should be allowed in drinking water and food is important, but we also need to know more about the nitrogen cycle in order to properly evaluate the environmental impact of nitrates.

mini Investigation — Effects of Nitrogen on Algal Growth

Spring runoff of nitrogen fertilizers causes algae to grow rapidly in neighbouring lakes. In some lakes, a film of algae coats the entire surface of the water. This makes the lake a lot less appealing to swim in. More importantly, the resulting lack of oxygen places other organisms in the ecosystem in peril.

By passing pond water through a filter and then allowing the filter and algae to dry, you can measure the mass of algae collected.

(a) Using this technique, design a controlled investigation to measure how a fertilizer affects growth of algae.

- Have your design, safety precautions, materials, and written procedure approved by your teacher before beginning the procedure. Conduct your investigation and collect your results.

(b) Report on the results of your investigation. Include an evaluation of your design, as well as suggestions for improvement.

The Phosphorus Cycle

Phosphorus is a key element in cell membranes, in molecules that help release chemical energy, in the making of DNA, and in the calcium phosphate of bones. The **phosphorus cycle** has two parts: a long-term cycle involving the rocks of Earth's crust, and a short-term cycle involving living organisms (**Figure 6**).

phosphorus cycle the cycling of phosphorus between the biotic and abiotic components of the environment; consists of a biological and geochemical cycle

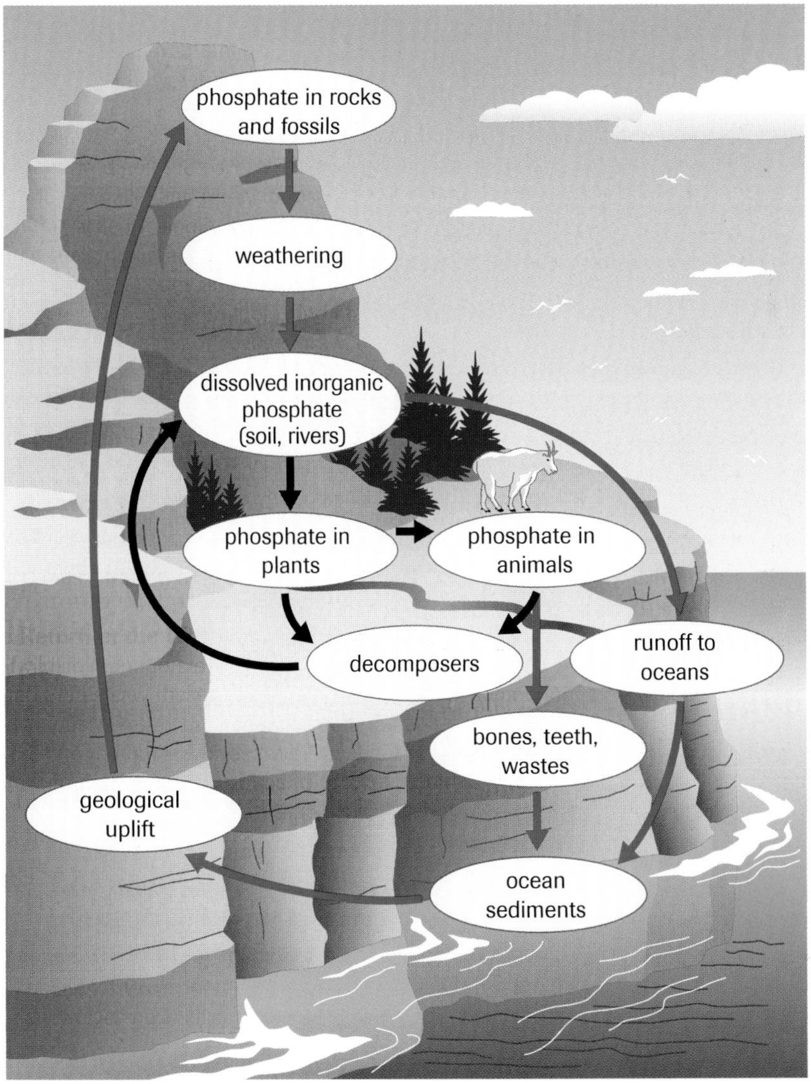

Figure 6 Phosphates cycle in both long (red arrows) and short (black arrows) cycles.

DID YOU KNOW ?

Matter Cycling in a Closed System

In the International Space Station, carbon dioxide, oxygen, water, and other materials must be recycled. How does matter cycling work in a closed system? Research the life support systems of the ISS to answer this question.

www.science.nelson.com 

Living things divert phosphates from the normal (long) rock cycle. Phosphorus is found in bedrock in the form of phosphate ions (PO_4^{3-}), combined with a variety of elements. Phosphates are soluble in water and so can be dissolved out of rock. While dissolved, phosphates can be absorbed by photosynthetic organisms and so pass into food chains.

Phosphates eroded from rock are also carried by water from the land to rivers, and then to the oceans. In the ocean, phosphates are absorbed by algae and other plants, where they can enter food chains. Marine animals use phosphates to make bones and shells. When they die, these hard remains form deposits on the ocean floor. Covered with sediment, the deposits eventually become rock, ready to be brought to the surface again. The long cycle can take millions of years to complete.

In the short cycle, wastes from living things are recycled by decomposers, which break down wastes and dead tissue and release the phosphates. The short cycle is much more rapid.

Variations in Nutrient Cycling

nutrient a chemical that is essential to living things

Nitrates and phosphates are both nutrients. **Nutrients** are chemicals that are essential to living things. Potassium, calcium, and magnesium are other examples of nutrients. The rate at which nutrients cycle through an ecosystem is linked to the rate of decomposition. Organic matter decomposes relatively quickly in the tropical rain forests. Warmth, moist soil, and the vast number of diverse and specialized decomposers permit a cycle to be complete in as little as a few months. Cycling in cooler forests takes an average of between four and six years. In the even cooler tundra, nutrient cycling takes up to 50 years. In the oxygen-poor environment of most lakes, cycling may take even longer. Temperature and oxygen levels are the two most important abiotic factors regulating decomposition. Other factors, such as soil chemistry and the frequency of fire, also affect decomposition and cycling.

INVESTIGATION 3.4 *Introduction*

Phosphate Identification

Phosphate is a common pollutant that may arise from human activity. The presence of phosphates in water can be detected by adding magnesium sulfate. In this investigation, you will use this salt to test various water samples for the presence of this pollutant.

Report Checklist

○ Purpose	○ Design	● Analysis
○ Problem	○ Materials	● Evaluation
○ Hypothesis	○ Procedure	● Synthesis
○ Prediction	● Evidence	

To perform this investigation, turn to page 71. 

Case Study—Persistent Pesticides and Matter Flow

Pesticides are chemicals designed to kill pests. A pest is an organism that people consider harmful or inconvenient, such as weeds, insects, fungi, and rodents. In many situations, pesticides are used to protect species that are beneficial to humans from a competitor or predator that is less useful. One estimate suggests that as much as 30 % of the annual crop in Canada is lost to pests such as weeds, rusts and moulds (both forms of fungi), insects, birds, and small mammals. The cost to consumers can be staggering. For example, in 1954 three million tonnes of wheat from the Prairies was destroyed by stem rust, a fungus that grows inside the leaves and stems of the wheat and other plants, feeding on the plant's stores of food.

In 1998, a total of 9 300 497 kg of pesticides were sold in, or shipped into, Alberta. By far the greatest amount, approximately 96 %, can be linked to agriculture. Persistent pesticides are those that break down very slowly, and so affect the environment for a long period. This activity is a case study of the use of persistent pesticides in Alberta and other regions.

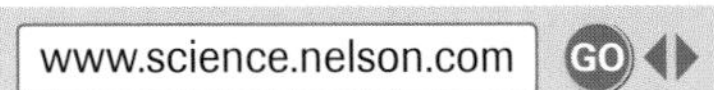

The Nitrogen Cycle and the Phosphorus Cycle

- Life depends on the cycling of nitrogen, which is required for the synthesis of proteins and DNA. The movement of nitrogen through ecosystems, the soil, and the atmosphere is called the nitrogen cycle.
  - Atmospheric nitrogen is converted into nitrates by nitrogen fixation, either by lightning or by bacteria in the roots of legumes.
  - Decomposers break down nitrogen compounds in wastes or dead bodies into simpler compounds such as ammonia (NH_3). Other bacteria convert ammonia into nitrites, and still others convert the nitrites back into nitrates.
  - Denitrifying bacteria break down nitrates into nitrites, and then nitrites into nitrogen gas, which is released back into the atmosphere.
- Phosphorus is found in cell membranes, in energy-containing molecules, in DNA, and in bones.
- Phosphorus cycles in two ways: a long-term cycle involving the rocks of Earth's crust, and a short-term cycle involving living organisms.
- The rate of cycling of nutrients is linked to the rate of decomposition.

Section 3.3 Questions

1. Why do the levels of nitrogen and phosphorus in fields decline when crops are harvested?
2. Explain how excess fertilizers might affect decomposing organisms.
3. (a) Why do algal blooms usually occur in spring?
   (b) Explain how algal blooms affect other organisms in freshwater ecosystems.
4. What dangers do high levels of nitrates in the drinking water present for infants?
5. If a farmer does not plant a crop in one field, and then plows the field in the fall, how would this help restore nitrogen and phosphorus levels in the soil?
6. Explain why nitrogen is important to organisms.
7. If nearly 79 % of the atmosphere is nitrogen, how could there be a shortage of nitrogen in some soils?
8. How do animals obtain usable nitrogen?
9. Nitrogen-fixing bacteria are found in the roots of bean plants. Explain how the bacteria benefit the plant and how the plant benefits the bacteria.
10. Draw a diagram of the nitrogen cycle for a farm or garden where manure is used.
11. Explain why it is a good practice to aerate lawns.
12. Explain why phosphorus is important to living things.
13. Some farmers alternate crops that require rich supplies of nitrogen, such as corn, with alfalfa. Alfalfa is usually less valuable in the marketplace than corn. Why would farmers plant a crop that provides less economic value?
14. Explain why bogs and swamps are usually low in nitrogen.
15. Speculate about why clover would begin to grow in an older lawn. How would the presence of clover benefit the lawn?
16. Nitrate levels were analyzed from living material and soil samples in three different ecosystems (grassland, temperate rain forest, and tropical rain forest) in the same month. To determine the mass of nitrates in living things, all living plant matter was collected in a study area and the levels of nitrates were determined. The same analysis was conducted for the top layer of soil. The results are listed in **Table 1**, where each ecosystem is identified by a number.

Table 1 Nitrate Content of Three Ecosystems

Study area	Soil nitrates (kg/ha)	Biomass nitrates (kg/ha)	Soil temperature (°C)
1	30	90	25
2	10	175	19
3	2	270	30
tundra	?	?	?

   (a) In which community does nitrogen cycle most rapidly? Explain your conclusion.
   (b) Which ecosystem (grassland, temperate rain forest, and tropical rain forest) is study area 1, 2, and 3? Give reasons for your answers.
   (c) Speculate about the data that might be collected from a tundra ecosystem. Explain your prediction.
17. The phosphorus cycle has been described as having two components—a long cycle and a short cycle. The carbon cycle can be described the same way. Draw a diagram that splits the carbon cycle into "short" and "long"components.
18. Human waste contains nitrates and nitrites. Before the arrival of municipal sewers, the backyard outhouse was standard for collection of human waste. Outhouses can still be found at some cottages. Outhouses consist of a small building over a hole in the ground. Explain why outhouses pose a risk to neighbouring lakes, using information that you have gained about the nitrogen cycle.
19. How is the water cycle important in the cycling of nitrogen and phosphorus?
20. The use of nitrogen-rich fertilizers has allowed farmers to abandon crop rotation.
   (a) What advantages are gained from planting wheat year after year?
   (b) New strains of crops have been especially bred to take up high levels of nitrogen. These strains produce more grain. Speculate about some possible long-term disadvantages that these crops might present for ecosystems.
21. People have used fertilizers for a long time. Explain why we must begin changing our views on the use of fertilizers so the ecosystems we live in will be sustainable. Why is it so difficult to change practices?
22. Crop rotation is an effective way of restoring nitrogen to the soil; however, the planting of legumes is not always popular with farmers. Legume crops may provide less income, because they are more costly to plant, difficult to tend and harvest, and worth less in the marketplace. Farmers must continually balance short-term gains and long-term results in this way. Provide some examples of how you balance short-term gains with long-term results in decisions that you make.

INVESTIGATION 3.1

Nutrient Cycling and Plant Growth

In a natural setting, plants grow without benefit of artificial fertilizers. The continuous recycling of nutrients between decomposing matter and growing plants, together with changes in the species of plants growing in the soil, ensures that the soil remains productive. However, not all soils are equal. In this investigation, you will determine whether nutrients leached from different soils can promote plant growth. Since many of these nutrients are water-soluble, they are carried downward to the lower levels of the soil by percolation.

Report Checklist

○ Purpose	● Design	● Analysis
● Problem	○ Materials	● Evaluation
○ Hypothesis	○ Procedure	● Synthesis
○ Prediction	● Evidence	

Design

This is a controlled experiment to determine which of three soil samples yields the most dissolved nutrients. Seeds are planted in standard potting soil and watered using leachate from three soil samples.

(a) Identify the dependent and independent variables in this experiment.

(b) What control is used in the experiment? Explain your answer.

Materials

safety goggles
apron
250 mL clay soil (sample A)
250 mL silt soil (sample B)
250 mL sandy soil (sample C)
soil-less potting mixture such as vermiculite
food colander
cheesecloth
distilled water
250 mL beaker
bucket or other large container
3 plastic storage bottles
marking pen
pots or other containers
pea, corn, or bean seeds (presoaked for 24 h)
100 mL graduated cylinder

CAUTION: Always wash your hands thoroughly after handling soil.

Procedure

1. Line a colander with cheesecloth. Place 250 mL of soil sample A in the colander. Position a large container under the colander and pour 250 mL of distilled water over the soil (**Figure 1**). Allow the water to collect in the container.

Figure 1

2. Repeat step 1 twice, reusing the water in the container. After the final filtering, pour the filtered water into a plastic storage bottle and label it "leachate from soil sample A."
3. Repeat steps 1 and 2 for soil samples B and C, using clean cheesecloth and fresh water .
4. Pour a 20-cm depth of soil-less potting mixture into each of four plant pots. Label the pots A, B, C, and control.
5. Plant five seeds in each pot.
6. Using a 100 mL graduated cylinder, add 50 mL of leachate from soil sample A to the pot labelled A, from soil sample B to pot B, and from soil sample C to pot C.
7. Add 50 mL of distilled water to the seeds in the pot labelled "control."
8. Put the pots in a warm, well-lit location.
9. Each day, check the pots for moisture (they should be moist, but not wet). If water must be added, add the same amount of water to each pot from its leachate bottle.

INVESTIGATION 3.1 *continued*

Evidence

(c) Record the height of each plant every day. Make notes on the colour, health, and appearance of each of the plants.

Analysis and Evaluation

(d) Calculate the mean height for the control and experimental plants each day. (If one seed in a group fails to germinate and grow, do not count it when you calculate the mean).

(e) Why is it useful to report the mean height for all five plants, rather than the height of each individual plant?

(f) Plot a line graph of the mean height over time for the control and experimental groups.

(g) Read the comments you kept about the plants as they grew and review your growth data. Does the evidence that you collected in this experiment support or contradict your prediction? Explain your answer.

Synthesis

(h) Grain farmers may burn the stubble (the stalks of the grain plants) after harvest. List the advantages and disadvantages of burning stubble for
  (i) the farmer
  (ii) soil organisms
  (iii) neighbours

(i) Suggest gardening techniques that could help reduce the amount of artificial fertilizer used in a garden.

INVESTIGATION 3.2

The Albedo Effect

Report Checklist

- ○ Purpose
- ● Problem
- ○ Hypothesis
- ● Prediction
- ○ Design
- ○ Materials
- ○ Procedure
- ● Evidence
- ● Analysis
- ● Evaluation
- ● Synthesis

Purpose

To examine the ability of selected colours and surface conditions to reflect light

Materials

desk lamp	dissecting pan
ring stand	sand
extension clamp	gravel
light sensor	soil
coloured card stock	water
(including black and white)	snow and/or ice

Procedure

1. Aim the desk lamp at the bench surface.
2. Attach the light sensor to the ring stand so that it is higher than the light source. Its active surface must face down and have a clear path to the surface of the bench. (**Figure 1**).
3. Place the sheet of white card stock directly under the lamp.

Figure 1
The experimental setup

INVESTIGATION 3.2 *continued*

Evidence

4. Turn on the lamp and record the reading from the light sensor.
5. Repeat the experiment, using the other coloured sheets. Remember to control all your variables.
6. Set the dissecting pan directly under the lamp.
7. Record the reflective value of the pan when empty. Repeat, using a sand surface, a gravel surface, soil, water, and snow and ice.

Analysis and Evaluation

(a) Why is it necessary to keep the light sensor out of the direct line of light?

(b) What variable must be controlled?

(c) Why are black and white card stock colours used in this experiment?

(d) List the coloured surfaces in order from least to greatest reflected light.

(e) Use your data to make comments on the albedo effect of the materials used.

(f) What variable were you unable to control in Step 7 of the laboratory procedure? How could you redesign these steps to account for the variable?

(g) Design an experiment to measure the effect of colour or surface conditions on the absorption of heat. State your hypothesis and the predictions resulting from it.

(h) Perform the investigation you designed (approval of instructor required) and draw conclusions based on the collected data.

Synthesis

(i) In order to melt a pile of snow more quickly, a researcher sprayed dye-coloured water on it. Which colour was probably selected and why?

INVESTIGATION 3.3

Environmental Models

Environmental models allow scientists to study what could happen in an ecosystem if changes occurred. Models help check predictions without disrupting a large area. In this investigation, you will build an ecocolumn, an ecological model that is especially designed to cycle nutrients. You will then design and carry out an experiment to investigate one of three environmental problems.

Report Checklist

○ Purpose	● Design	● Analysis
● Problem	○ Materials	● Evaluation
● Hypothesis	● Procedure	○ Synthesis
● Prediction	● Evidence	

Problem

(a) Choose from one of the three ecological problems below:

A. How would an oil spill affect an aquatic ecosystem? (You will be allowed to use motor oil to test the environmental impact.)

B. How would acid rain affect an ecosystem? (You will be allowed to use household vinegar only.)

C. How would rapid changes in climate affect an ecosystem?

(b) Research the problem and provide at least one page explaining the environmental problem.

www.science.nelson.com GO

Prediction

(c) Make a prediction.

Design

(d) Based on the materials and instructions below for building an ecocolumn, design your experiment. Include materials, a procedure, and any needed safety precautions. Present your design for approval before beginning.

INVESTIGATION 3.3 *continued*

Materials

2 or more 2 L plastic pop bottles with caps (remove labels)
pond water, soil compost
representative organisms (moss, flies, spiders, snails, etc.)
scissors
duct tape or binding tape (wide width) or silicone sealant

Instructions for Building the Ecocolumn

1. Using scissors, remove the top and bottom of a 2-L plastic bottle, as shown in **Figure 1.**
2. Cut a second bottle just before the point at which the bottle narrows (**Figure 2**).

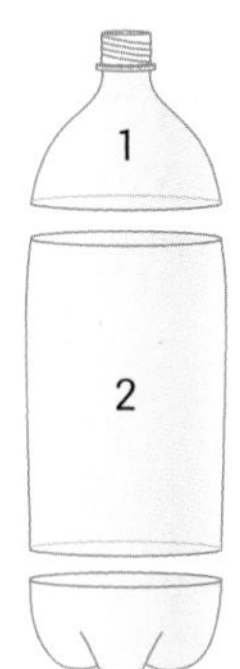

Figure 1

Figure 2

3. Slide part 1 into part 2, as shown in **Figure 3**. Seal the two together with silicone or tape. Next stack the structure on top of part 4.
4. A example of a more complex ecocolumn is shown in **Figure 4**. You decide on the design.

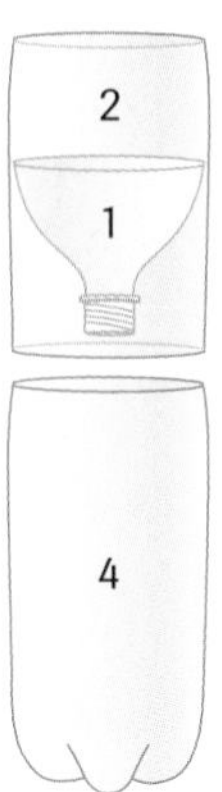

Figure 3

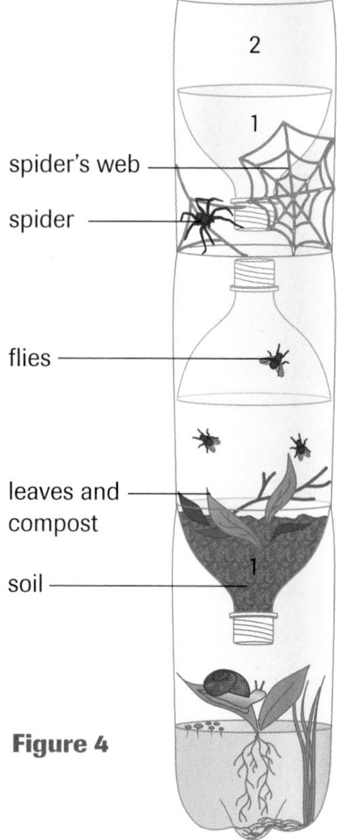

Figure 4

INVESTIGATION 3.4

Report Checklist

○ Purpose	○ Design	● Analysis
○ Problem	○ Materials	● Evaluation
○ Hypothesis	○ Procedure	● Synthesis
○ Prediction	● Evidence	

Phosphate Identification

Algae populations increase rapidly in response to phosphate pollution. There is a quick, simple test for detecting this form of pollution. The presence of phosphates in a water sample can be detected by adding the salt magnesium sulfate. The magnesium in the compound combines with phosphates in the water to form the insoluble salt magnesium phosphate. As crystals of magnesium phosphate form, they turn the clear solution in the test tube cloudy.

Wear gloves throughout the procedure, and wash your hands thoroughly.

Materials

goggles
safety gloves
apron
4 large test tubes
test-tube rack
waterproof marker
distilled water (A)
water samples from your local area (B, C, and D)
10 mL graduated cylinder
medicine dropper
dilute ammonium hydroxide solution
magnesium sulfate solution
watch glass
hand lens
pH paper, pH probe, or pH meter

Procedure

1. Obtain four large test tubes and label them A, B, C, and D. Place the tubes in a test-tube rack. Using a graduated cylinder, pour 10 mL of distilled water into tube A. Pour 10 mL each of samples B, C, and D into the test tube with the corresponding letter label. Rinse and dry the cylinder after each sample.
2. Measure and record the pH of each sample.
3. Using a medicine dropper, add 25 drops of dilute ammonium hydroxide to each sample. This will ensure that the samples will be basic (have a pH greater than 7).
4. Using the graduated cylinder, add 2 mL of magnesium sulfate solution to each of the samples in the test tubes. Let the test tubes stand for 5 min. Record your observations over the 5 min.
5. Pour a small sample of the solution from test tube A into a clean watch glass. Using a hand lens, examine the sample for crystals. Record your observations. Repeat this step for each of the other samples.
6. Wash your hands, first with your gloves on and then without.

Analysis and Evaluation

(a) Based on your results, which of the samples contained phosphates?

(b) Speculate about the source of phosphates in each of the samples that tested positive. What is the most likely source? Make a plan to determine the source of the phosphates.

(c) Was pH related to the amount of phosphate in the samples? Explain.

Synthesis

(d) The pH of lakes and streams can change as a result of acid rain. Predict how acidification of a lake would affect its phosphate levels.

(e) Predict how lake acidification would affect the biomass of a lake ecosystem. Explain your reasoning, using a food chain or food web.

▸ Chapter 3 SUMMARY

Outcomes

Knowledge

- explain and summarize the cycling of carbon, oxygen, nitrogen, and phosphorus, and relate to reuse of all matter in the biosphere (3.2, 3.3)
- explain water's role in the matter cycles, using its chemical and physical properties (3.1)
- explain how the equilibrium between gas exchanges in photosynthesis and cellular respiration influences atmospheric composition (3.2)
- describe the geological evidence (stromatolites) and scientific explanations for change in atmospheric composition, with respect to O_2 and CO_2, and the significance to current biosphere equilibrium (3.2)

STS

- explain that science and technology are developed to meet societal needs and expand human capabilities (all)
- explain that science and technology have both intended and unintended consequences for humans and the environment (all)

Skills

- ask questions and plan investigations by: designing an experiment to compare the carbon dioxide production of plants with that of animals (3.2); hypothesizing how alterations in the carbon cycle as a result of the burning of fossil fuels might interact with other cycling phenomena (3.2); predicting disruptions in the nitrogen and phosphorus cycles that are caused by human activities (3.1, 3.3); and predicting the effects of changes in carbon dioxide and oxygen concentration due to factors such as a significant reduction of photosynthetic organisms, combustion of fossil fuels, agricultural practices (3.2)
- conduct investigations and gather and record data and information by measuring and recording the pH and the amount of nitrates, phosphates, iron or sulfites in water samples within the local area (3.3)
- analyze data and apply mathematical and conceptual models by: analyzing data collected on water consumption and loss in plants and animals (3.1); and designing and evaluating a model of a closed biological system in equilibrium with respect to carbon dioxide, water, and oxygen exchange (3.2)
- work as members of a team and apply the skills and conventions of science (all)

Key Terms

3.1

polar molecule
hydrogen bond
hydrological cycle (water cycle)
transpiration
percolation
water table
leaching

3.2

carbon cycle
combustion
peat
albedo
stromatolite

3.3

nitrogen cycle
nitrogen fixation
denitrification
fertilizer
phosphorus cycle
nutrient

▸ MAKE a summary

1. Draw a diagram of a terrestrial or an aquatic ecosystem that shows how matter is cycled. Pay particular attention to the carbon and nitrogen cycles.
2. Revisit your answers to the Starting Points questions at the start of the chapter. Would you answer the questions differently now? Why?

▸ Go To

The following components are available on the Nelson Web site. Follow the links for *Nelson Biology Alberta 20–30.*

- an interactive Self Quiz for Chapter 3
- additional Diploma Exam-style Review Questions
- Illustrated Glossary
- additional IB-related material

There is more information on the Web site wherever you see the Go icon in the chapter.

▸ UNIT 20 A PERFORMANCE TASK

Environmental Effects of Human Communities

In this Performance Task, you will use the knowledge and skills you gained in this Unit to study the impact of humans on natural ecosystems. You will choose one of the following tasks: (1) design a golf course; (2) assess community water quality; or (3) design a game that teaches about the effects of human activities on the environment. Go to the Unit 20 A Performance Task link on the Nelson Web site to complete the task.

www.science.nelson.com 

Chapter 3 REVIEW

Many of these questions are in the style of the Diploma Exam. You will find guidance for writing Diploma Exams in Appendix A5. Science Directing Words used in Diploma Exams are in bold type. Exam study tips and test-taking suggestions are on the Nelson Web site.

www.science.nelson.com GO

DO NOT WRITE IN THIS TEXTBOOK.

Part 1

1. Which statements accurately describe photosynthesis and cellular respiration?
   A. Photosynthesis is carried out by plants and animals and uses glucose as the energy source. Cellular respiration is carred out by plants only and uses solar energy as the energy source.
   B. Photosynthesis is carried out by plants only and uses glucose as the energy source. Cellular respiration is carred out by plants and animals and uses solar energy as the energy source.
   C. Photosynthesis is carried out by plants only and uses solar energy as the energy source. Cellular respiration is carred out by plants and animals and uses glucose as the energy source.
   D. Photosynthesis is carried out by plants and animals and uses solar energy as the energy source. Cellular respiration is carred out only by plants and uses carbon dioxide as the energy source.

2. At various stages in the decay process, bacteria can break down nitrates to nitrites, and then nitrites to (1) _________. The process called (2) _________ releases nitrogen gas back into the atmosphere.
   A. (1) nitrate, (2) denitrification
   B. (1) nitrogen gas, (2) denitrification
   C. (1) nitrate, (2) nitrogen fixation
   D. (1) nitrogen gas, (2) nitrogen fixation

3. The term *albedo* is used to describe the extent to which a material can reflect sunlight. Which substance has the highest albedo?
   A. Dark soil: It absorbs sunlight, which warms the surface of the biosphere and stimulates plant growth.
   B. Water: It holds the heat from solar energy and serves as a heat source for the land.
   C. Snow: It is a contributing factor to low temperatures experienced during winter. It also delays spring, even though there is more solar radiation available per unit area.
   D. Clouds: They ensure that less incoming radiant energy is reflected directly back into space. Clouds decrease solar radiation, thereby increasing the warming of the air, which in turn decreases plant growth.

Use the following information to answer questions 4 and 5.

Four different soil samples with varying amounts of water were used to measure the conversion of ammonia to nitrates. The results are shown in **Figure 1**. The coloured lines show the percent of ammonia in each soil sample that was converted to nitrates. The labels for each line give the percent of water present in the sample.

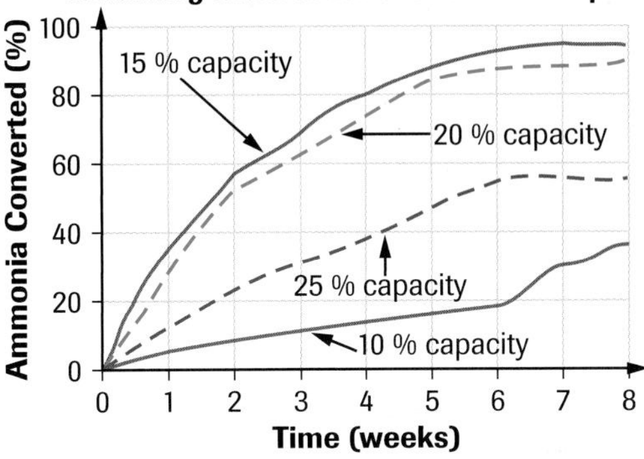

Figure 1

4. According to the data presented, the amount of ammonia converted to nitrates after 4 weeks would be approximately
   A. 80 % in the soil sample that contained 15 % of its water capacity.
   B. 80 % in the soil sample that contained 10 % of its water capacity.
   C. 20 % in the soil sample that contained 20 % of its water capacity.
   D. 20 % in the soil sample that contained 25 % of its water capacity.

5. According to the data presented, the best amount of water within the soils for conversion of ammonia to nitrates is
   A. 10 % capacity
   B. 15 % capacity
   C. 20 % capacity
   D. 25 % capacity

Part 2

6. **Describe** two ways in which the carbon cycle and oxygen cycle are connected.

7. In your own words, **define** *matter cycle.*

8. In your own words, **define** *biomass.*

Use the following information to answer questions 9 to 12.

Figure 2 is a diagram of an ecosystem.

Figure 2

9. Using the organisms in the ecosystem, **explain** the carbon cycle. DE

10. **Sketch** a flow chart that shows how nitrogen in the air reaches the caterpillar. DE

11. **Figure 2** doesn't show any bacteria, but they are always present in ecosystems. **Identify** the roles that bacteria have in the ecosystem. DE

12. **Identify** the organism that would end up with the highest concentration of the insecticide in its body, if DDT were used to control mosquitoes in the ecosystem. **Justify** your choice. DE

---

13. (a) In your own words, **define** *nutrient.*
(b) **Why** do nutrients cycle faster in a tropical rainforest than in the tundra?

14. In your own words, **define**
(a) nitrogen fixation
(b) denitrification

15. Nitrogen is cycling through the ecosystems near your home and school. Choose a local natural wooded area and **sketch** a diagram to show how nitrogen cycles within this area.

Use the following information to answer questions 16 to 20.

A researcher carried out an experiment in a deciduous forest near Rocky Mountain House to determine the rate of decay of fallen leaves. At three times during a year, all the dead leaves were collected from 100 1 m^2 plots on the ground. The leaves were sorted by species, and the dry mass of each species' leaves was recorded. Data is provided in **Table 2**. In the table, the numbers in brackets indicate the percentage of the mass of the leaves of each species remaining.

Table 2 Leaves in a Deciduous Forest

	Dry mass (g) and percentage (%) of mass remaining		
Type of leaf	**Nov.**	**May**	**Aug.**
aspen poplar	4200 g (100 %)	2422 g (58 %)	1100 g (26 %)
balsam poplar	3700 g (100 %)	3110 g (89 %)	1540 g (42 %)
willow	2980 g (100 %)	1001 g (34 %)	6 g (<1 %)
birch	5700 g (100 %)	3987 g	1121 g

16. **Determine** the percentage of the dry mass remaining of the birch leaves in May and August. DE

17. **Identify** the species that decays fastest between November and May. DE

18. **Identify** the species that decays fastest between May and August. DE

19. **Infer** the abiotic factor(s) that could accelerate the amount of decay between November and May and between May and August. DE

20. **Infer** the biotic factor(s) that could accelerate the amount of decay between November and May and between May and August. DE

---

21. **Why** do farmers add nitrogen fertilizers but not carbon fertilizers to fields?

22. **Explain** why every ecosystem must have some continuous supply of energy to survive but can do quite well without a continuous influx of nutrients.

Use the following information to answer questions 23 to 26.

An experiment studied the effects of various factors on photosynthesis. *Elodea,* a water plant, was placed in a test tube of water. The test tube was supported upright on a stand and a light was shone at the side of the test tube. The number of oxygen bubbles produced by the plant was counted for 5 min. **Table 3** shows the collected data.

Part 1: Distance of the light source: The light source was placed 5 cm and 20 cm away from the *Elodea*. Data was collected for two trials for each distance.

Part 2: Sodium bicarbonate added: A small amount of sodium bicarbonate ($NaHCO_3$) was added to the test tube. Data was collected for two trials with the lamp 5 cm from the test tube.

Table 3 Data from *Elodea* Experiment

Experimental condition	Number of oxygen bubbles produced in 5 min		
	Trial 1	Trial 2	Average
lamp 5 cm from plant	50	62	56
lamp 20 cm from plant	27	24	25.5
plant in $NaHCO_3$, lamp 5 cm away	78	84	81

23. Write a hypothesis for Part 1 of the experiment.
DE

24. **Identify** the manipulated (independent) variable and responding (dependent) variable in Part 1.
DE

25. **Identify** variables that must be controlled in Part 1.
DE

26. Sodium bicarbonate undergoes the following reaction in water. **Explain** the results obtained from Part 2 of the experiment.
DE

$$2\,NaHCO_3(aq) \rightarrow Na_2CO_3(aq) + CO_2(g) + H_2O(l)$$

27. A forest fire destroyed a 25 ha forest in the Swan Hills area of northwestern Alberta. Years after the fire, the forest had been regrown. A field biologist noted that pine and spruce trees in the area that had been burned appeared more lush than trees in forest areas that had not been affected by the fire. **How** is it possible that the vegetation appeared more lush in the area that had been burned?

28. Fire is a decomposer. It turns complex organic molecules into inorganic nutrients. Fire can be used to release inorganic nutrients from the stalks remaining after grain is harvested. This process is faster than normal decomposition, but much of the carbon in the stalks escapes to the air as carbon dioxide. Should fire be used to return nutrients to the soil? **Criticize** this position. Include both benefits and risks in your answer.

29. (a) **Describe** some of the ways oxygen cycles through the biosphere?
(b) **Sketch** your own diagram of the oxygen cycle.

30. **How** might changes in the carbon cycle, due to burning fossil fuels, affect the cycling of water in the biosphere?

Use the following information to answer questions 31 to 35.

Under controlled laboratory conditions, a research team from Environment Alberta monitored the solubility of oxygen and carbon dioxide in water samples taken from Lake Wabamun. Their data are shown in **Table 4**.

Table 4 Changes in Solubility of Carbon Dioxide and Oxygen with Temperature

Temp (°C)	CO_2 solubility (ppm)	O_2 solubility (ppm)
0	1.00	14.6
5	0.83	12.7
10	0.70	11.3
15	0.59	10.1
20	0.51	9.1
25	0.43	8.3
30	0.38	7.5

31. **Sketch** a graph of the solubility of oxygen in the water.
DE

32. **Relate** oxygen solubility in water to temperature.
DE

33. Using the data collected by the researchers, **predict** the consequences of prolonged warming of a shallow lake.
DE

34. Using the data from the table, **explain** why carbon dioxide levels can become dangerously high in an Alberta lake in winter.
DE

35. **Explain** why solubility of oxygen in water is so much greater than that for carbon dioxide at all temperatures.
DE

36. The albedo of the planet Venus is very high. At the same time, the atmosphere of the planet has an exceptionally high concentration of greenhouse gases. **How** might these two factors affect the surface temperature of Venus?

37. A plowed field is adjacent to the fairway of a golf course. During the winter, equal depths of snow cover the field and the fairway. Assuming that both fields are level and there is no disturbance to the snow pack, **explain** why the plowed field loses most of its snow before the fairway even begins to lose its cover. Is there a danger associated with the early loss of snow cover on the plowed field?

38. In this chapter, you have studied the cycling of carbon, oxygen, nitrogen, and phosphorus. In one or two paragraphs, **explain** how each cycle is part of the general reuse of all matter in the biosphere.

▸ Unit 20 A REVIEW

Many of these questions are in the style of the Diploma Exam. You will find guidance for writing Diploma Exams in Appendix A5. Science Directing Words used in Diploma Exams are in bold type. Exam study tips and test-taking suggestions are on the Nelson Web site.

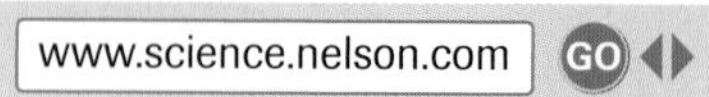

DO NOT WRITE IN THIS TEXTBOOK.

Part 1

1. Place the following organisms in order as they would be in NR a food chain. (Record all four digits of your answer.)
1. salmon
2. shark
3. plankton
4. small herring

2. Place the following levels in order, from the level with the NR most energy available to the level with the least energy available. (Record all four digits of your answer.)
1. tertiary consumers
2. producers
3. secondary consumers
4. primary consumers

3. In a food web, organisms that break down organic matter, returning nutrients to the ecosystem for further growth, can be classified as _____.
A. herbivores
B. omnivores
C. detritus
D. decomposers

4. A species that is doing well in one part of Canada but has been eliminated from another region is classified as ______, while a species that is close to extinction in all parts of Canada is classified as _____.
A. extinct, vulnerable
B. threatened, endangered
C. extirpated, endangered
D. vulnerable, extinct

5. A group of organisms of the same species, located in the same area, is called a _____.
A. population
B. community
C. ecosystem
D. biome

6. Decomposers break down the nitrogen-containing chemicals in the wastes or body tissues (proteins) into
A. simpler chemicals such as ammonia (NH_3), then decomposing bacteria convert ammonia into nitrites and eventually to nitrates.
B. more complex chemicals such as ammonia (NH_3), then other decomposing bacteria convert ammonia into nitrates and eventually to nitrites.
C. simpler chemicals such as nitrites, then other decomposing bacteria convert nitrites into free nitrogen.
D. more complex chemicals such as nitrates, then other decomposing bacteria convert nitrates into free nitrogen.

7. In a bog you would expect
A. higher levels of usable nitrogen, since the denitrification process speeds up when the soil is acidic or becomes water-logged.
B. lower levels of usable nitrogen, since the nitrification process speeds up when the soil is acidic or becomes water-logged.
C. lower levels of methane, since methane-producing bacteria require anerobic conditions to grow, and bogs are high in oxygen.
D. low levels of carbon dioxide, since low levels of decomposing bacteria are found in bogs because of a lack of vegetation.

8. Predict what will happen if fertilizers are carried from the land to an aquatic ecosystem with spring runoff.
A. Algae populations will decrease, since nitrogen and phosphorus fertilizers inhibit all plant growth, including algae.
B. Algae populations will increase, since nitrogen and phosphorus fertilizers promote all plant growth, including algae.
C. Fish populations will increase, since increased plant growth will provide more carbon dioxide for fish.
D. Fish populations will be unaffected, since fish do not use nitrates found in fertilizers.

9. A step-by-step sequence showing how organisms feed on each other is referred to as
A. an ecosystem
B. a food chain
C. a population
D. an ecological pyramid

10. Agriculture is affecting ecosystems in Alberta because
A. wheat fields help cycle phosphates and nitrates in the soil.
B. crops in Alberta produce carbon dioxide, which contributes to global warming.
C. taiga soil is not fertile enough for wheat crops.
D. monoculture crops are replacing the biodiversity of prairie ecosystems.

11. An example of an endangered Canadian species is
A. passenger pigeon
B. whooping crane
C. elk
D. grizzly bear

12. Which of the following describes an abiotic factor in an ecosystem?
A. competition between species
B. predator–prey relationships
C. amount of sunlight
D. birth rate

Use the following information to answer questions 13 to 16.

Figure 1 shows a food chain.

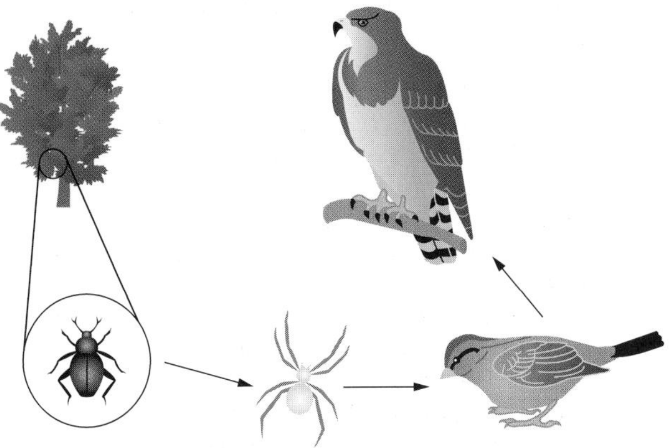

Figure 1

13. Which organism would be classified as the producer?
A. aspen tree
B. beetle
C. spider
D. sparrow

14. Which organism would be part of a population that would have the least biomass?
A. beetle
B. spider
C. sparrow
D. hawk

15. Based on your knowledge of number and biomass pyramids, which organism would you expect to have the greatest population?
A. aspen tree
B. beetle
C. spider
D. sparrow

16. Which level of organism has the least energy available to it?
A. beetle
B. spider
C. sparrow
D. hawk

Use the following information to answer questions 17 to 20.

The temperature of the air, the litter, the topsoil (10 cm below the surface), and the subsoil (30 cm below the surface) were monitored in one location in a temperate deciduous forest through the day. Use the data in **Figure 2** to answer questions 17 to 20.

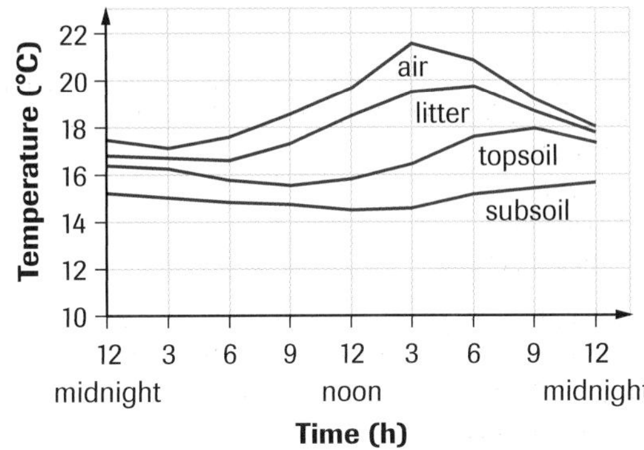

Figure 2

17. In which area of the forest did the greatest variation in temperature occur?
A. air
B. litter
C. topsoil
D. subsoil

18. Using a 24-h clock, at what time of day was the maximum ambient air temperature obtained?
A. 18:00
B. 3:00
C. 24:00
D. 15:00

19. What abiotic factor would account for the greatest difference in temperature readings in the litter?
A. wind
B. exposure to sunlight
C. moisture of the soil
D. thickness of the blanket of leaves

20. For the experiment described above, the dependent variable (responding variable) and independent variable (manipulated variable) are, respectively,
A. temperature and type of soil
B. type of soil and time
C. temperature and time
D. time and temperature

Part 2

21. Use the Great Slave Lake food web in **Figure 3** to **sketch** an ecological pyramid of numbers.

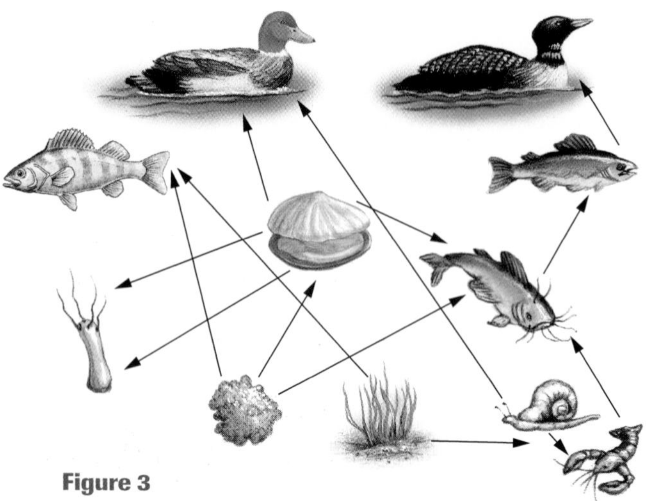

Figure 3

Use the following information to answer questions 22 to 27.

Two different experiments were carried out to determine the effects of different factors on photosynthesis. A freshwater plant, *Elodea*, was placed in a test tube of water. A light was placed at various distances from the plant for 5 min, then the number of oxygen bubbles produced by the plant were counted for 1 min. Different colours of light bulbs were used as well. The data are shown in **Table 1**.

22. **Identify** the two questions that the researcher is attempting to answer. DE

23. Write a hypothesis for both questions being investigated. DE

24. Represent the results of the experiment **graphically**. DE

25. **Identify** the two variables that affect the rate of photosynthesis. DE

26. **Why** are oxygen bubbles counted? DE

27. State the conclusions for the experiment. DE

28. The removal of a predator often has consequences that extend beyond the immediate food chain. In Bangladesh, where frog populations have been decimated to supply restaurants with delicacies, the number of mosquitoes has increased. In turn, this has caused a dramatic rise in cases of malaria among humans. Write a unified response addressing the following aspects of frog and mosquito populations in Bangladesh. DE
    - **How** has the decline in frog populations affected human health?
    - **Describe** a technological approach and an ecological approach for controlling malaria. **Describe** one advantage and one disadvantage for each approach.

29. The worldwide disappearance of frogs is a puzzle. In some areas, scientists don't really know what is causing the problem. **Illustrate** each of the following hypotheses regarding the causes of the disappearance of frogs with a supporting example. **Describe** things that the average citizen could do to remedy the problem implied by each hypothesis.
    (a) Hypothesis: loss of habitat
    (b) Hypothesis: decreasing quality of air and water
    (c) Hypothesis: increase in ultraviolet radiation
    (d) Hypothesis: climate change

30. There are a number of different reasons for extinction. Use Canadian examples to **illustrate** why extinction has occurred for each of the causes described below.
    (a) the competition between naturally occurring species and exotic species introduced into the area
    (b) the reduction of natural habitats
    (c) climate change
    (d) over-hunting

Use the following information to answer questions 31 to 33.

The water entering the ocean from the river in **Figure 4**, on the next page, is polluted with nitrates. A group of scientists decided to identify the sources of pollution. They chose five different testing sites to measure nitrate concentration in the water.

Table 1 Data from *Elodea* Experiment

Distance of light from test tube (cm)	Number of O_2 bubbles produced (1 min), white light bulb	Number of O_2 bubbles produced (1 min), red light bulb	Number of O_2 bubbles produced (1 min), green light bulb
5	25	10	4
10	20	8	2
15	15	6	1
20	10	4	0
25	5	2	0

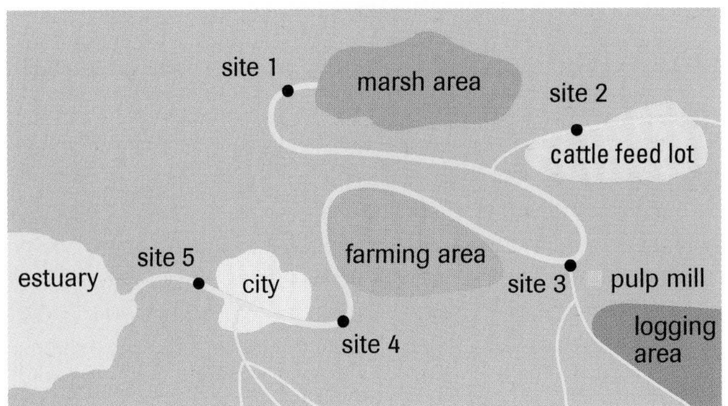

Figure 4

31. Choose two sites in **Figure 4** and **explain** why these two sites might show a local source of nitrates. DE

32. **Describe** two effects of severe nitrate pollution. DE

33. Choose one site in **Figure 4** and **describe** how the level of nitrates in the water could be reduced. DE

34. As the available natural wildlife habitats are reduced worldwide, scientists have expressed concerns about animals that occupy the highest trophic levels of energy pyramids. Using energy flow as an argument, **explain** why these animals would be most severely affected.

Use the following information to answer questions 35 to 37.

In 1965, NASA scientists compared the atmosphere of Earth with those of Mars and Venus. Their data are shown in **Table 2**.

Table 2 Chemical Composition of Venus, Earth, and Mars

Chemical composition	Venus	Earth	Mars
carbon dioxide	95 %	0.03 %	95 %
nitrogen	2 %	77 %	3 %
oxygen	none	21 %	none
chemical equilibrium	yes	no	yes

35. There are very high levels of carbon dioxide in the atmospheres of Mars and Venus. **How** might this affect the temperature of these planets? DE

36. Of these three planets, oxygen is only found in Earth's atmosphere. **Why** is this an important fact? DE

37. Suggest some reasons **why** Earth's atmosphere is not in equilibrium. DE

Use the following information to answer questions 38 to 42.

Figure 5 shows an apparatus that was used to measure water consumption by a plant.

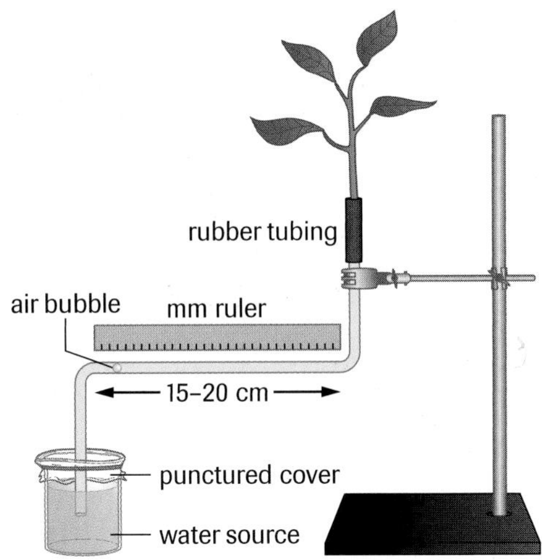

Figure 5

38. **Identify** the problem being investigated by this experiment. DE

39. **Identify** two variables that would affect water loss by transpiration. DE

40. **Sketch** a graph of the data provided in **Table 3**. DE

41. **Predict** how placing a plastic bag over the leaves would affect transpiration. DE

42. **Identify** two adaptations of the plant that reduce water loss by transpiration. DE

Table 3 Change in Mass of Plant Over Time

Time (min)	Mass of potometer + plant (g)	Change in mass of potometer + plant (g)
0	150.2	0
10	143.6	6.6
20	137.2	13.0
30	131.4	18.8
40	125.4	24.8

43. Review the focusing questions on page 2. Using the knowledge you have gained from this unit, briefly **outline** a response to each of these questions.

unit

20 B

Ecosystems and Population Change

The biosphere is constantly undergoing change. The conditions in an ecosystem and the organisms that live there can change, sometimes in unexpected ways. For example, University of Calgary researcher Dr. Dennis Parkinson says there is no evidence that earthworms lived in the Kananaskis area in the past. However, earthworms have been found in Kananaskis country since the mid-1980s. Most likely, they were introduced into the region by tourists. Earthworm eggs easily stick to hiking boots, all-terrain vehicles, and horses' hooves, and drop off during trail-rides. In 2004, the environmental impact of the invasion of earthworms into the Kananaskis country was assessed. In some locations, researchers have found as many as 2500 earthworms per square metre.

As you progress through the unit, think about these focusing questions:

- What are the major biotic and abiotic characteristics that distinguish aquatic and terrestrial ecosystems?
- What data would one need to collect in a field study to illustrate the major abiotic characteristics and diversity of organisms?
- What mechanisms are involved in the change of populations over time?

UNIT 20 B PERFORMANCE TASK

The Sixth Extinction

The dinosaurs disappeared about 65 million years ago in a "mass extinction" event. Investigate past mass extinction events, and compare and contrast them to species extinctions that are occurring in the present day. You will consider the biotic and abiotic factors that influence such extinction rates, both historically and today.

www.science.nelson.com  

GENERAL OUTCOMES

In this unit, you will

- explain that the biosphere is composed of ecosystems, each with distinctive biotic and abiotic characteristics
- explain the mechanisms involved in the change of populations over time

Unit 20 B Ecosystems and Population Change

ARE YOU READY?

These questions will help you find out what you already know, and what you need to review, before you continue with this unit.

Prerequisites

Concepts

- ecosystems and biomes
- biological diversity
- adaptations
- inheritance of traits

Skills

- identify variables
- create hypotheses
- draw and interpret graphs

You can review prerequisite concepts and skills on the Nelson Web site and in the Appendices.

A Unit Pre-Test is also available online.

Knowledge

1. In your notebook, indicate whether the statement is true or false. Rewrite a false statement to make it true.
   (a) Ecosystems with greater biodiversity tend to be less fragile.
   (b) Natural ecosystems usually have greater biodiversity than artificial ecosystems.
   (c) A biome is geographical region with a particular climate, and the organisms that are adapted to that climate.
   (d) Introducing exotic species into an ecosystem helps improve biodiversity, and helps all organisms within an ecosystem.
   (e) An organism's physical traits are affected by both its genetic makeup and the environment.
   (f) Virtually all large populations exhibit genetic variation among individuals.
2. Each of the organisms in **Figure 1** exhibits special adaptations. For each species, describe two obvious adaptations and state how they enhance the biological success of the organism.

Figure 1
(a) morning glory; (b) kangaroo; (c) sea nettle; (d) bull elk; (e) luna moth; (f) blue-footed booby

Skills

3. A field study of temperatures throughout the day in a forest produced the observations in **Table 1** on the next page.
   (a) Identify the variables being measured in this study.

Table 1 Temperature Readings (°C) Taken over a 24-h Period in a Forest

Location	Time of day								
	12 midnight	3 a.m.	6 a.m.	9 a.m.	12 noon	3 p.m.	6 p.m.	9 p.m.	12 midnight
air	17.5	17.0	17.5	18.5	19.5	21.5	21.0	19.0	18.0
litter	17.0	17.0	16.5	17.0	18.5	19.5	20.0	19.0	18.0
topsoil	16.5	16.5	16.0	15.5	16.0	16.5	17.5	18.0	17.5
subsoil	14.0	14.0	13.5	13.5	13.5	13.0	13.5	14.0	14.0

(b) Propose a hypothesis to explain the variation in temperature among the locations.
(c) Use these data to produce a line graph illustrating the observations.

4. Use **Table 1** or the graph from question 3 to answer the following questions:
   (a) Which location in the forest showed the greatest variation in temperature?
   (b) Which location in the forest showed the least variation in temperature?

5. The graph in **Figure 2** shows the growth in the world human population over the last 50 years.
   (a) Describe the trend in population growth.
   (b) Is the rate of population growth increasing, decreasing, or staying the same? Explain your answer.
   (c) Predict human population growth for the next 30 years. Do you think it is very likely that the population will actually reach that number? Explain.
   (d) At the current population growth rate, in approximately what year will the world population reach 12 billion?

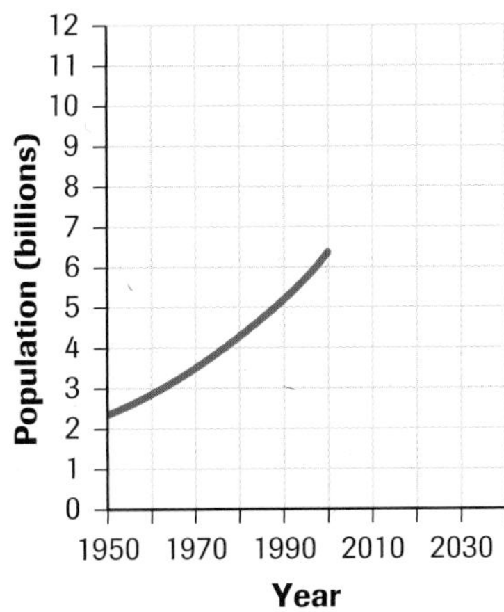

Figure 2

STS Connections

6. For each of the following, list two examples—one that is not genetically inherited and one that might have been genetically inherited:
   (a) physical characteristics
   (b) diseases and medical conditions
   (c) behaviours, and likes and dislikes

7. **Table 2** shows energy requirements per person per day for different societies.

Table 2 Energy Requirements for Humansin Different Societies

Society	Energy expenditure (kJ per person per day)
industrialized (e.g., Canada)	961 400
early industrialized	251 200
advanced agricultural	83 700
early agricultural	50 200
hunter-gatherer	20 900

   (a) Why would early agricultural societies require more energy per person than hunter–gatherer societies?
   (b) What activities require the enormous energy usage by the modern world?
   (c) Which society is able to support the greatest number of people? Why?

chapter

Characteristics of Ecosystems

In this chapter

- Exploration: Establishing Ecosystems in Space
- Investigation 4.1: A Schoolyard Ecosystem
- Web Activity: Mary Thomas
- Case Study: Natural and Artificial Ecosystems
- Web Activity: The Zebra Mussel
- Explore an Issue: Genetically Modified Crops
- Web Activity: Critical Ecoregions of the World
- Investigation 4.2: A Forest Ecosystem
- Mini Investigation: How Does Temperature Affect Seed Germination?
- Mini Investigation: Measuring Undissolved Solids
- Investigation 4.3: Biological Oxygen Demand and Organic Pollutants
- Investigation 4.4: Biological Indicators of Pollution in Streams
- Web Activity: Whose Lake Is It?
- Explore an Issue: Selling Water

It is often difficult to place a value on sustaining the ecosystems around the world. Wetlands are drained to make way for more farmland to feed people, and forests are cut to supply wood for housing and industries. But at what cost? A sustainable ecosystem survives and functions over a long time. Long-term sustainability is not sacrificed for short-term gains. Similarly, a sustainable human society manages its economy and population size without exceeding the planet's ability to replenish resources.

If you think of a balance sheet of deposits and withdrawals, living sustainably means living within your means and not depleting your savings. Failure to conserve the capital of the planet jeopardizes current and future generations. We have a limited supply of resources on Earth. The use of non-renewable resources, such as coal, oil, iron, and sulfur, must be budgeted so that future generations will also have enough. Potentially renewable resources, such as water, topsoil, forests, wildlife, and food, must be monitored so that use does not exceed the rate at which they are replenished.

In this chapter, you will discover how ecosystems remain in balance and how they change. You will learn how the organisms within an ecosystem interact and then you will examine the characteristics of ecosystems. You will look at the factors that characterize and affect ecosystems.

STARTING Points

Answer these questions as best you can with your current knowledge. Then, using the concepts and skills you have learned, you will revise your answers at the end of the chapter.

1. Examine the photographs in **Figure 1**, on the next page. For each photograph, answer the following questions.
   (a) What are some of the resources in this ecosystem? Explain.
   (b) Which of these resources are renewable?
   (c) What are some factors that affect the ecosystem?
   (d) Explain how each factor you identified in Part (c) affects the ecosystem.
   (e) Is the ecosystem sustainable? If you answer no, identify the factor(s) that would prevent the ecosystem from being sustainable.
   (f) Identify the main environmental problem shown. Can this environmental problem be solved by technology? Why or why not?

Career Connections:
Fish and Wildlife Officer; Wildland Firefighter; Environmental Education Specialist

Figure 1
Human activity plays a role in each of these ecosystems.

Exploration — Establishing Ecosystems in Space

The colonization of other planets or the Moon will require the establishment of ecosystems able to support humans. Using a terrarium, construct a model ecosystem that might be able to support life if it were transported to the Moon. Think about the following when you construct your model.

- How will you provide a continuous supply of oxygen?
- How will you provide a continuous supply of food?
- What will happen to the waste?

(a) Make a list of plants and animals that are essential to humans.

(b) Describe the things that would be needed for the survival of each plant and animal you mentioned on your list.

4.1 Interactions within Ecosystems

ecology the study of interactions between organisms and their living and non-living environment

abiotic factor a non-living factor that influences an organism

biotic factor a living factor that influences an organism

Ernst Haeckel, a German biologist, first coined the word **ecology** in 1866, to describe the study of how organisms interact with each other. Ecology combines the Greek words *oikos*, meaning "the place where one lives," with *logos*, meaning "study of."

Ecological studies can begin at the level of a single organism. For example, an investigation could be designed to determine how the individual interacts with its environment, and how factors in the environment affect its growth, feeding habits, and reproduction. Non-living factors or influences on organisms, such as amount of sunlight and temperature are called **abiotic factors**. Factors caused by the presence and roles of other living things are called **biotic factors**.

Organisms do not live in isolation however; they usually group with others of the same species. All of the members of the same species, living in the same ecosystem or habitat, are referred to as a population. For example, all the pike in a lake form a population.

Since there is usually more than one species in an ecosystem, there is also more than one population. The collection of all the populations of all the species in an ecosystem or habitat is called the community of organisms. For example, the community in a lake might include populations of pike, perch, tadpoles, mosquito larvae, and algae, among others.

When studying a community, an ecologist might determine how biotic factors affect each population. For example, an ecologist studying a forest community might examine the interactions between different types of plants and animals in the area.

Ecologists can extend their study beyond the community of organisms to the physical environment. When they do so, they begin investigating ecosystems. An ecosystem includes the community of living things and its physical environment. For example, in studying a forest ecosystem, an ecologist could measure how much sunlight reaches the forest floor, and how the amount of sunlight affects the plants and animals that live in the ecosystem.

Practice

1. In your own words, define the term *ecology*.
2. Describe how a population differs from a community, using your own examples.
3. Describe how an ecosystem differs from a community, using your own examples.

INVESTIGATION 4.1 *Introduction*

A Schoolyard Ecosystem

Ecosystems are constantly changing in response to changes in biotic and abiotic factors. In this investigation, you will make observations on the differences in biotic and abiotic factors at different locations in your schoolyard, and relate these to the number and types of weeds.

Report Checklist

○ Purpose	○ Design	● Analysis
○ Problem	○ Materials	● Evaluation
○ Hypothesis	○ Procedure	● Synthesis
● Prediction	● Evidence	

To perform this investigation, turn to page 123. 

Ecotones and Biodiversity

Ecosystems rarely have sharp boundaries, and organisms can move back and forth from one ecosystem to another. There is often a grey area between ecosystems where organisms from both ecosystems interact with each other. These transition areas or **ecotones** (**Figure 1**) contain species from both bordering ecosystems, so they often contain greater biodiversity (more species) than either ecosystem.

Ecosystems with greater biodiversity tend to be less fragile. For example, if a predator has to rely on a single species as a food source, its very existence is tied to the survival of the prey. In ecotones and other diverse areas there are more species, and a predator may have an alternative prey if something happens to the population of its main prey. By providing alternative food sources, ecotones help guard against extinction.

ecotone a transition area between ecosystems

DID YOU KNOW ?

Biodiversity in Quebec

Quebec is home to many different types of ecosystems. Within these ecosystems live almost 40 000 species of plants and animals. Quebec was one of the first Canadian provinces to propose a strategy to protect biodiversity.

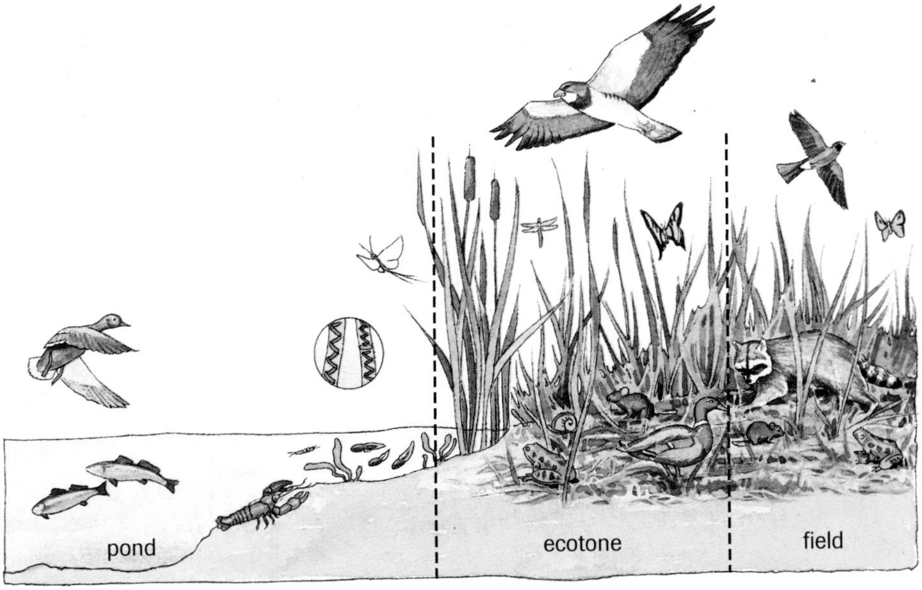

Figure 1
In the ecotone between the pond and the field, species from both ecosystems meet.

Canadian Achievers—Mary Thomas

Mary Thomas (**Figure 2**) has spent her lifetime educating people of all cultures about the need for environmental awareness and the relevance of the traditional ways to preserve ecosystems. She received the National Aboriginal Achievement Award in 2001, for her work as an educator and environmentalist. In 1997, she became the first Aboriginal in North America to receive the Indigenous Conservationist of the Year award from the Seacology Foundation. In 2000, she received an honorary doctorate from the University of Victoria. Find out more about Mary Thomas' contributions to protecting ecosystems and preserving traditional knowledge.

www.science.nelson.com GO

Figure 2
Mary Thomas

Case Study

Natural and Artificial Ecosystems

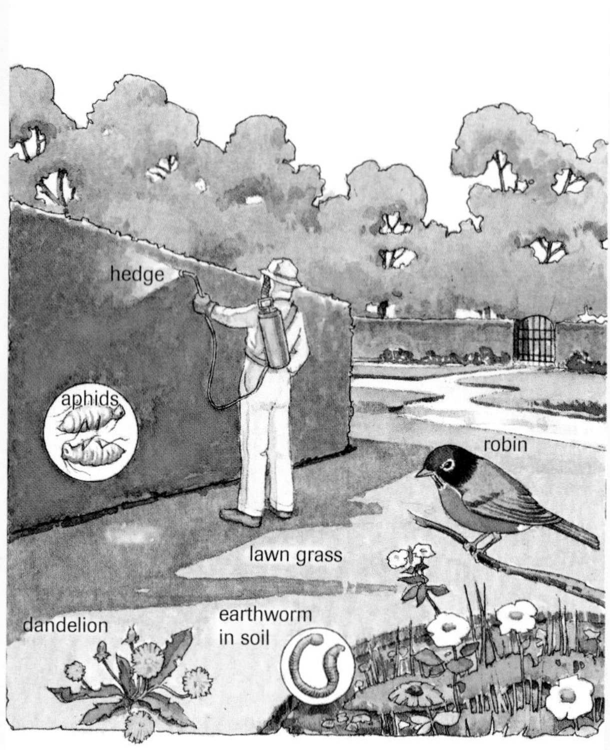

Figure 3
A park ecosystem

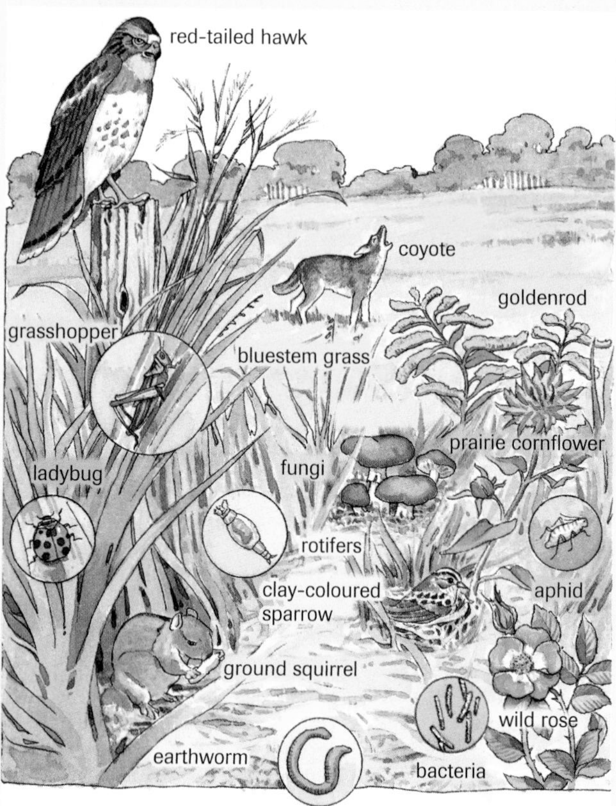

Figure 4
A prairie ecosystem

Your schoolyard, local parks, farms, and managed forests are artificial ecosystems. An **artificial ecosystem** is planned or maintained by humans. Lakes, rivers, forests, deserts, and meadows can all be classified as natural ecosystems. In a **natural ecosystem**, the living community is free to interact with the physical and chemical environment (see **Figure 4**). However, this does not mean that the area is untouched by humans: humans are a natural part of many ecosystems. Natural ecosystems haven't been planned or maintained by humans. In this case study, you will compare a prairie grassland (natural) and a park (artificial).

Change within a park is limited because of human interference. Although the trees grow, most parks look somewhat the same from year to year (**Figure 3**). Humans manage change. Natural ecosystems undergo subtle changes as one plant or animal species gradually replaces another. In natural ecosystems, only plants suited for the environment flourish. In an artificial ecosystem, plants selected by humans have an advantage.

Case Study Questions

Study **Figures 3** and **4**.

1. What human activities prevent the artificial ecosystem of the city park from changing?
2. Which ecosystem demonstrates the greater biodiversity? Explain your conclusion.
3. Speculate about why clay-coloured sparrows, found in the prairie, are less likely to be found in a city park.
4. Speculate about why coyotes are not common in city parks.

Table 1, on the next page, provides data collected from a city park and a prairie ecosystem. All measurements were taken on the same day at the same times. Relative humidity is the percentage of the amount of water vapour in a mass of air compared with the maximum amount of vapour that could be held at that temperature. Evaporation rate measures the volume of water lost from soil in one day. "Soil litter" is a

Table 1 Abiotic and Biotic Factors in Two Ecosystems

Abiotic factors	City park	Prairie
temperature (maximum)	28 °C	26 °C
temperature (minimum)	12 °C	10 °C
wind speed at ground	22 km/h	15 km/h
evaporation rate	10 L/day	3.5 L/day
relative humidity	85 %	64 %
light at ground (% of sunlight available)	95 %	91 %
soil nitrogen rating	very high	low
soil phosphorus rating	high	low
Biotic factors		
soil litter	56 g/m^2	275 g/m^2
robin density	3/100 m^2	1/100 m^2
ground squirrel density	0/100 m^2	14/100 m^2

measure of the mass of decomposing organic matter found above the soil.

5. Why is it important to take measurements on the same day and at the same time?
6. Why might the wind velocity at ground level differ in the two ecosystems?
7. Why might you expect the temperature to be higher in the park than in the prairie?
8. Explain the differences in the evaporation rate in the two ecosystems.

Table 2 provides detailed counts for some species in the two ecosystems.

9. Suggest reasons why goldenrod is found in the prairie but not the city park.
10. Provide a hypothesis that explains why more earthworms are in the prairie than the park.
11. Why are more spiders found in the prairie?
12. List abiotic factors of the city park and prairie.
13. Explain how human interference influences each of the factors you listed in question 12.
14. Which of the two ecosystems, the prairie or the park, would provide a better habitat for a fox? Give reasons for your answer.
15. Not all natural ecosystems have more biodiversity than all artificial ecosystems. Give two examples of an artificial ecosystem that might have more biodiversity than a natural ecosystem. Provide an explanation of each example.
16. **Tables 1** and **2** provide some data on two ecosystems. What additional data would be useful in making a comparison of an artificial and a natural ecosystem?
17. Some animals, such as the raccoon and the tree squirrel, do very well in artificial ecosystems. What special adaptations or behaviours make these two animals successful in human-dominated environments? Report on the results of your research.

Table 2 Inventory of Species in 10 m × 10 m Study Areas

	City park		Prairie	
Types of organism	**Number of species**	**Population of all species**	**Number of species**	**Population of all species**
grass	1	100 000/m^2	3	40 000/m^2
goldenrod	0	0	1	51
plants considered weeds	3	6	17	459
earthworms	1	25	8	210
beetles	4	7	22	39
spiders	1	2	2	13
birds	3	10	11	39
rodents	0	0	3	45

Roles in Ecosystems

Each organism has its own place within an ecosystem. The organism's place in the food web, its habitat, breeding area, and the time of day that it is most active constitute its **ecological niche**. The niche that an organism fills in an ecosystem includes everything it does to survive and reproduce.

ecological niche an organism's role in an ecosystem, consisting of its place in the food web, its habitat, its breeding area, and the time of day at which it is most active

Each species in an ecosystem tends to have a different niche, or a different role to play. This helps reduce competition between species for the same territory and resources.

Owls and hawks (**Figure 5**) feed on many of the same organisms, but they occupy distinctly different niches. The owl, with its short, broad wings, is well adapted to hunt down prey within forests. The longer wings of the hawk are ideal for soaring above grasslands and open fields but present problems for flight through dense brush. Owls are active during dusk and at night, while hawks hunt by daylight. Although the two birds do prey on some of the same species, different prey are active during the night and the day.

Figure 5
Even though the red-tailed hawk and the great grey owl eat some of the same food, they are not in competition because they have different ecological niches.

To support their roles, owls and hawks have different adaptations. In addition to their different wing shapes, they also differ in their senses, particularly their eyes. Hawk eyes are excellent at detecting changes in colour patterns, which helps them see rodents even when they are well hidden by their camouflage. Owl eyes see colour poorly, but are excellent at detecting motion, even in the dark. Owls also have excellent hearing, so they can detect the tiniest rustling noises of mice and other rodents as they move.

Competition is further reduced because owls and hawks nest in different areas. Many owls seek the deep cover of trees; hawks nest near the tops of the taller trees of a forest, overlooking grassland.

The different species of warblers that inhabitant forests of Atlantic and central Canada make up one of the best examples of how species reduce competition by occupying different niches. Each species of insect-eating bird feeds in a different part of the tree (**Figure 6**). Even though all warblers eat insects, they don't compete much with each other because different species of insects are found in the feeding area of each warbler species.

In general, the higher the number of different niches in an ecosystem, the more organisms that will be found. For example, a natural forest will have trees of many different ages and sizes than a planted forest in which all the trees are the same age and size. The natural forest therefore has more niches, and also has more biodiversity than the planted forest.

Figure 6
Competition is reduced because each species of warbler prefers to feed in a different section of the tree.

Competition for Niches

When a new species enters an ecosystem, it causes a disturbance. The new species comes into competition for a niche with one or more of the species already in the ecosystem. The introduction of new species (often called "exotic species" because they are not native to the ecosystem) happens naturally. Animals are mobile and can move from one ecosystem to another. Plant seeds can be carried by the wind or animals and take root in new areas. Sometimes a completely new route to an area is opened up, allowing organisms that were separated from each other to mix.

The results of opening up a new route can be dramatic. For example, when North and South America came together about 5 million years ago, animals could move freely from north to south. This was devastating for ecosystems in South America, where many of the native species came into competition with invaders from the north, and lost. Only a few animals from the south managed to cross over to northern ecosystems and find a niche. One of these animals is the opossum (**Figure 7**).

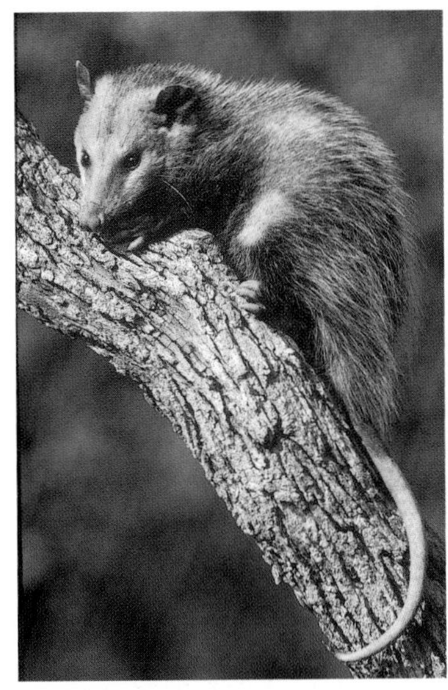

Figure 7
The opossum, once native to South America, can now be found in North America. It competed for, and established, its own niche in forest ecosystems.

Introduction of Exotic Species

The introduction of new species to an ecosystem by humans is one of the main causes of species depletion and extinction, second only to habitat loss. The ecosystem may lack the natural population controls of the introduced species, such as predators or diseases. When a population is unchecked by predators or disease, it has an advantage over the native (indigenous) populations and can increase very quickly. Native species might not be able to compete successfully for space, food, or reproductive sites. If the introduced species is a predator, prey organisms may not have defence mechanisms against it.

For example, in the 1890s, a misguided fan of Shakespeare brought all of the birds mentioned in his plays from the United Kingdom and released them in Central Park in New York City. One of the birds was the starling (**Figure 8 (a)**). A single pair of starlings multiplied so rapidly that starlings are now one of the most abundant and widespread birds in North America. In Alberta, starlings settle in prime nesting sites long before the mountain bluebird (**Figure 8 (b)**) returns from the south. Starlings even evict swallows and mountain bluebirds from their nesting sites. As a result, the population of indigenous bluebirds has declined.

The actual number of introduced species that have established themselves in Canada is widely debated, but even the most conservative estimates are well over 3000 species. Exotic species change natural ecosystems and cost Canadians billions of dollars annually just to control their numbers. Many of the weeds we struggle to control, such as Canada thistle (**Figure 9 (a)**), are exotic species.

Figure 8
The niches of the starling **(a)** and the mountain bluebird **(b)** overlap. The naturally occurring bluebird is losing its range to the invading starling.

Figure 9
Canada thistle **(a)** and purple loosestrife **(b)** are exotic species in Canada.

Fox versus Skunk
Dr. Gary Roemer (New Mexico State University) unravels the complex interactions between foxes and skunks on the Californian island of Santa Cruz. The ecosystems had been in balance for hundreds of years, but the introduction of exotics (in the form of feral pigs) has changed everything.

www.science.nelson.com 

Cattle, goats, and pigs were intentionally imported to North America. Other species, such as purple loosestrife, (**Figure 9 (b)**, previous page) which was mixed in contaminated grain seeds, have entered North America accidentally. Purple loosestrife spread so quickly and is so common that early settlers believed it was an indigenous (native) plant. Since it is well-suited for marshes, purple loosestrife has choked out many species of native plants in wetlands.

Case Study—The Zebra Mussel

The identification of the zebra mussel in Lake Erie in the early 1990s set off a series of alarms. Biologists believe that this tiny bivalve, a native of the Caspian Sea in western Asia, entered the Great Lakes from bilge water discharged from ships. In 1991, there were extensive colonies of zebra mussels in Lake Ontario and only small groups in Lake Huron. By 1994, the zebra mussel was common in southern Ontario's rivers and lakes. By 1995, zebra mussels had moved through the Ohio River to the Mississippi, and were found all the way to the Gulf of Mexico. In this activity, you will read and assess information on the effects of the zebra mussels on the ecosystems in these waterways. You will also conduct your own research on another exotic species that has been introduced to the Western Hemisphere.

www.science.nelson.com 

EXPLORE an issue

Genetically Modified Crops

Issue Checklist

- ● Issue
- ○ Resolution
- ○ Design
- ● Evidence
- ● Analysis
- ● Evaluation

In the biotechnology field called genetic engineering, scientists remove small segments of DNA from one organism and insert them into the chromosomes of another. This transfers highly desired characteristics from one species to another, unrelated organism. Organisms treated with this technology are called genetically modified (GM) organisms (GMOs). Many GMOs are crop plants. The first GM crops were planted in North America in the early 1990s. By 2000, more than 40 % of the corn, 45 % of the soybeans, and 50 % of the cotton crop were GM plants. On our grocery shelves, about 70 % of the processed foods contain some GM ingredients.

When a GMO is introduced to an ecosystem, it is new to the entire biosphere. A few of its genes are not found in related natural organisms. The competitive advantage of a GMO over a non-GMO could alter an ecosystem in ways that are difficult to predict.

Benefits of GM crops

- Decreased fertilizer use: the genes added to some GM plants allow them to produce their own nitrate or phosphate nutrients, reducing fertilizer use and saving money.
- Herbicide resistance: the genes in some GM plants make them resistant to herbicides, so the herbicide kills only the weeds. Crop yield is increased and herbicide use is reduced.
- Resistance to cold and disease-causing agents: some GM plants grow faster in cooler temperatures or are more resistant to disease than their non-GM counterparts.

Concerns about GM crops

- Allergies: GM plants could contain proteins that trigger allergies in people.
- Nutrient levels: do GM foods have the same nutritional value as non-GM foods?
- Interbreeding: can GM plants breed with non-GM plants? If so, what might result?

With your group, conduct research to find out more on the benefits and concerns of GM crop plants in Canada.

www.science.nelson.com 

When research is complete, use an appropriate method to communicate your ideas on the appropriate use of this technology.

SUMMARY Roles in Ecosystems

- Ecosystems contain abiotic and biotic components. The biotic components can be grouped into populations and communities.
- Ecotones, transition areas between ecosystems, often have more biodiversity than the ecosystems do themselves.
- An ecological niche refers to an organism's place within the ecosystem—its place in the food web, living quarters, breeding area, oxygen requirements, etc.
- Each species has a different niche or role to play in an ecosystem. This helps reduce competition between species for the same territory and resources.
- The introduction of a foreign species to an ecosystem is a primary cause of species depletion and extinction. The introduced species can have advantages over the native species, since natural population controls, such as predators or diseases, may be lacking in the ecosystem.

Section 4.1 Questions

1. List four biotic and four abiotic factors in:
   (a) a freshwater ecosystem, such as a lake
   (b) a terrestrial ecosystem, such as a forest
2. Predict whether you would find more species in a forest, an open field, or the forest-grassland ecotone between them. Explain your prediction.
3. **Figure 10** shows changes in the size of the populations of paramecia (single-cell organisms) placed in three different beakers.
   (a) Compare the growth of Species 1 in Beaker A with the growth of Species 2 in Beaker B.
   (b) What evidence suggests that the populations of paramecia affect each other?
   (c) Suggest a conclusion that can be drawn from the population changes in Beaker C.
4. In your own words, define the term *ecological niche.*
5. Give examples illustrating the problems that can be created when a new species is introduced into an ecosystem.
6. Describe your ecological niche. Consider your habitat and your place in food webs.
7. Human interference often causes ecosystems to change.
   (a) Provide an example of how human interference has caused an increase in the population of a species.
   (b) Provide an example of how human interference has caused a decrease in the population of a species.
   (c) Provide an example of how the rapid increase in a species has affected another species.
8. For many years, ecologists have argued about whether all niches within ecosystems are occupied. Present examples that support both sides of the argument.
9. Do lions and tigers occupy the same niche? Research and give reasons for your answer.

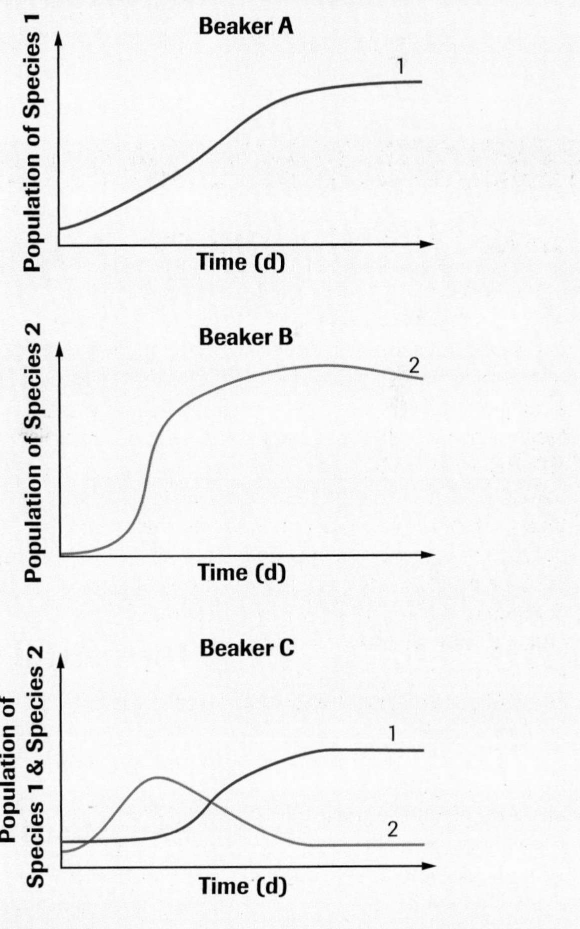

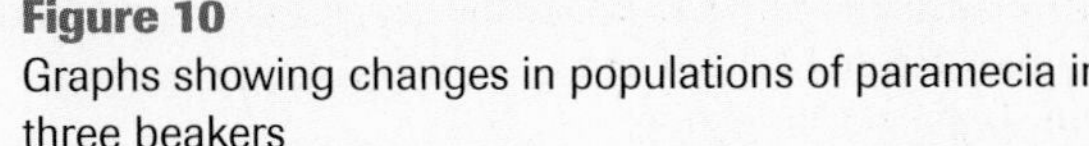
Figure 10
Graphs showing changes in populations of paramecia in three beakers

www.science.nelson.com 

4.2 Terrestrial and Aquatic Ecosystems

Ecological systems or ecosystems are smaller regions within the biosphere. The scale and complexity of ecosystems varies, depending not only on the organisms that live in them but also on abiotic factors such as climate and local geology. By studying a variety of ecosystems and comparing the data gathered from them, ecologists can get an overall picture of the biosphere as a whole.

One way of organizing the interactions between biotic and abiotic components is to divide the biosphere into biomes. A **biome** is a large geographical region with a specific climate, and the plants and animals that are adapted to that climate. Biomes have particular dominant species, such as the coniferous trees of the taiga biome or the prairie grasses of the grassland biome. However, each biome also contains many different ecosystems, each defined by the particular local biotic and abiotic factors. Some of these ecosystems support organisms that are found nowhere else in the biosphere.

biome a large geographical region with a specific range of temperatures and precipitation, and the organisms that are adapted to those conditions of temperature and precipitation

Canada has four major terrestrial biomes (**Figure 1**). We also have contact with two major aquatic biomes: the freshwater biome composed of lake, river, and pond ecosystems, and the marine or salt water biome that contains all ocean ecosystems. In this section, you will explore some of the ecosystems that are found in Alberta's terrestrial biomes. You will also look at the aquatic ecosystems found in Alberta's lakes. In the next section, you will revisit these terrestrial and aquatic ecosystems to look more closely at the biotic and abiotic factors that define an ecosystem.

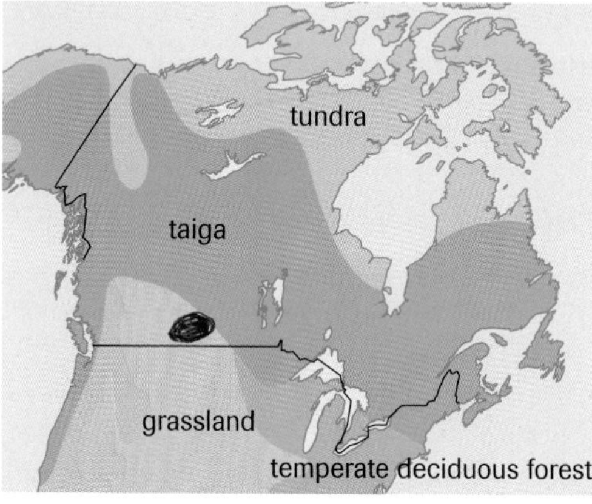

Figure 1 
Canadian terrestrial ecosystems can be grouped into four main biomes: tundra, taiga, temperate deciduous forest, and grassland. Mountains are shown in purple.

(a)

(b)

Figure 2
Snow slides off conifer trees. **(a)** The flexible branches bend, causing the snow to tumble down the tapering boughs. By comparison, deciduous trees **(b)** are shaped more like an inverted cone, with many branches at the top. Although well-suited for collecting sunlight, they also easily collect snow or freezing rain.

Terrestrial Ecosystems

Terrestrial ecosystems are ecosystems that are found anywhere on Earth that is not covered by water. Alberta's terrestrial ecosystems are found within two major biomes: taiga and grassland.

Ecosystems of the Taiga Biome

Most of the taiga biome (also called the boreal forest biome) can be found throughout northern Alberta and along the Rocky Mountains. Dominated by conifers (cone-bearing trees that have needles, instead of leaves), taiga is found in every province in Canada. Approximately 80 % of all our forested regions are taiga. Conifers are especially well-adapted to the warm, moist summers and the cold, dry winters found in most parts of this biome. The thin needle-like leaves provide less surface area for water loss during winter. A thick cuticle of wax coats the needles, preventing water loss and protecting against frost damage. The pyramid shape of the tree and its flexible branches shed the crushing weight of a heavy snowfall. Unlike deciduous trees, the tiny needles trap comparatively little snow (**Figure 2**, previous page).

Although taiga forests may appear uniform from a distance, they are actually a mosaic of different ecosystems. Each ecosystem is composed of organisms with adaptations that make them suited to the *local* differences in abiotic and biotic factors that occur in different regions in the biome.

Different ecosystems can also be found in the same small geographic area. In any forest, the amount of sunlight varies depending on the height above the ground. The parts of the trees that reach up into the forest **canopy** receive the most sunlight. In taiga, these are usually mature conifer trees, such as spruces and pines. Conifers are suitable as food for only about 50 species of birds, including seed-eaters such as crossbills (**Figure 3 (a)**), which have thick, strong beaks capable of cracking the cones. Some other species, such as red and flying squirrels, can feed on pine seeds.

canopy the upper layer of vegetation in a forest

In contrast, the forest floor is in almost continuous shade. Little sunlight filters through the canopy. As a result, vegetation on the forest floor is restricted to shade-loving plants such as shrubs, mosses, and ferns. The primary consumers of this ecosystem, including moose, voles, and white-tailed deer, depend on these shade-loving plants for their food. The available shelter is also determined by these shade plants. Nesting sites on the forest floor are unsuitable unless the animal has effective camouflage, such as that of the spruce grouse (**Figure 3 (b)**). Predators in this type of ecosystem include black and grizzly bears, weasels, owls, and wolverines.

(a)

(b)

Figure 3
Birds found in taiga ecosystems: white-winged crossbill **(a)** and spruce grouse **(b)**

Muskeg Ecosystems

Climate is the average conditions of temperature and precipitation of a region, and is one of the main factors that determine biomes. Temperature and water are important factors to any ecosystem. Within the taiga biome of Alberta, there is a range of climate conditions and thus, a range of ecosystems. In areas with warmer ground temperatures, there is relatively rapid decomposition of organic matter, resulting in good soil. The decomposition of needles produces acidic soils, in which only certain plants grow, such as black spruce trees.

As you move north, Alberta's climate becomes colder. The most northern regions are sufficiently cold that there is a layer of **permafrost** beneath the soil that never melts. Rain and melted snow cannot drain away in this part of the taiga, and the water soaks the decomposing plants and peat moss. This forms **muskeg**, ground that is swampy or boggy in the summer (**Figure 4**). Muskeg supports different organisms than are found in conifer forest ecosystems.

permafrost permanently frozen soil

muskeg soil above the permafrost that is swampy or boggy in summer

Figure 4
Muskeg has proved challenging for exploration companies searching for oil. Vehicles often sink into the spongy muskeg.

Figure 5
Caribou are more commonly found in muskeg ecosystems of taiga.

Decomposition of plant and animal matter is slow in muskeg ecosystems, since the low temperatures limit the growth and reproduction of soil bacteria and fungi. This in turn limits the amount of organic matter in the soil. Since soil formation is extremely slow, any damage to the fragile ecosystem takes years to repair. The plants best adapted to this ecosystem grow close to the ground and have fibrous root systems that can anchor the plant in the shifting soil. Plants include lichens, mosses, tall grasses, small shrubs, and stunted conifers. Numerous pools provide abundant water for plants, as well as ideal breeding conditions for black flies and mosquitoes. Muskeg also provides habitat for some larger animals, such as caribou (**Figure 5**).

Ecosystems of the Grassland Biome

The black earth of grassland ecosystems is said to be the most fertile in the world. Short-lived grasses with deep roots provide a large biomass for decomposition. The warm temperatures cause rapid decay and the formation of a rich layer of humus. Not surprisingly, grass length is controlled by precipitation. Unlike forests, grassland ecosystems have only one layer in which to support the biotic community, limiting the number and diversity of organisms.

Producers in Alberta's grasslands include rough fescue, wheat grass, and spear grass. Deer, squirrels, and rabbits graze on the grasses. Birds such as the yellow-bellied sapsucker, and snakes such as the prairie rattlesnake, also live in the grassland ecosystems.

Deciduous Forest Ecosystems

At the edges of the grassland biome of Alberta, before it turns into taiga, are ecosystems dominated by trees. Aspen, balsam poplar, and birch are the most common trees in these deciduous forest ecosytems (**Figure 6**). They require lower amounts of water than coniferous trees, and are found in areas where the rainfall is intermediate between the taiga and the true grasslands. Deciduous trees can also be found near rivers (such as the Bow River in Calgary), lakes, and ponds.

Figure 6
Of all the ecosystems in Canada, deciduous forests have the greatest plant and animal diversity.

Warmer temperatures, more precipitation, and the large amount of humus from the leaves provide a rich soil in deciduous forests. In the early spring, most of the sunlight reaches the forest floor and the **understorey**. By summer, the canopy is in full leaf and only about 6 % of the sunlight that strikes the canopy reaches the understorey. However, by this time the undergrowth is well-established. The broad leaves of deciduous trees maximize light capture for photosynthesis, promoting rapid growth.

Deciduous forests support a great diversity of animals. The thick layer of leaf litter provides an ideal environment for many types of insects. Not surprisingly, insect-eating birds and mammals, such as fly-catchers and shrews, live in deciduous forest ecosystems. The rich vegetation of the understorey shrubs and the lower branches of the trees support large browsers such as deer and moose. The canopy is home to many species of birds and some climbing mammals.

Alberta has a rich diversity of terrestrial ecosystems. **Table 1** summarizes the ecosystems that have been discussed.

understorey below the canopy layer; usually shrubs and smaller trees

Table 1 Terrestrial Ecosystems in Alberta

Name	Abiotic factors	Biotic community
taiga ecosystems	• northern and central Alberta forests • changeable weather • soil contains some water and is acidic • precipitation 50-250 cm/a	black and grizzly bears wolverines weasels moose deer grouse owls spruce and pine shrubs, ferns, mosses, and lichens
muskeg ecosystems	• cold temperatures • short growing season • permafrost layer beneath soil • low precipitation: 50-150 cm/a	black bear caribou ptarmigans rapidly flowering plants moss and lichens
grassland ecosystems	• central and southern Alberta • increased sunlight and warmer temperatures than muskeg or boreal forest ecosystems • rich fertile soil • precipitation 25-100 cm/a	bison deer rabbits hawks yellow-bellied sapsuckers fescue grasses grasshoppers
deciduous forest ecosystems	• central Alberta • increased sunlight and warmer temperatures than muskeg or taiga forest ecosystems • rich fertile soil • precipitation 75-250 cm/a	black bears weasels moose deer woodpeckers deciduous trees shrubs

DID YOU KNOW ?

Fire and Deciduous Trees in Alberta

Intermittent fires once swept across the Prairies, killing any saplings, thus ensuring that trees did not encroach on the grasslands. In addition, the fires acted as decomposers, returning nutrients back to the soil faster than by bacterial decomposition. Some of the Aboriginal peoples of the Prairies recognized the importance of the fires and set fires to maintain the grassland ecosystem. Today, most grassland fires are controlled by human actions.

+ EXTENSION

Biogeography

Why do different types of grasses grow in different parts of the Canadian Prairie? Why does Canada have different types of forests? In this activity, you will look at various abiotic factors and how they vary in regions across Canada. You will then relate these abiotic factors to the adaptations of the biotic components of the ecosystems in those regions.

www.science.nelson.com 

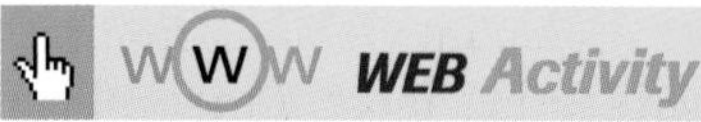

Case Study—Critical Ecoregions of the World

The Sierra Club has identified critical ecoregions in North America, and has developed strategies to restore and maintain each ecosystem. The objective of this plan is to re-establish the "web of life" on Earth. Choose an ecosystem of interest and find out the details of the plan to sustain that ecosystem, and identify underlying assumptions on which that strategy is based.

www.science.nelson.com GO

INVESTIGATION 4.2 ***Introduction***

A Forest Ecosystem

A variety of abiotic factors affect terrestrial ecosystems. Soil quality, temperature, and sunlight amounts determine which plants will populate an area. In this investigation, you will identify types of vegetation and calculate plant density in a selected study site. You will explore how environmental conditions interact with the plant community studied.

Report Checklist

● Purpose	○ Design	● Analysis
○ Problem	○ Materials	● Evaluation
○ Hypothesis	○ Procedure	● Synthesis
○ Prediction	● Evidence	

To perform this investigation, turn to page 125.

Practice

1. What is permafrost?
2. Why is soil quality poor in the muskeg ecosystem and rich in grasslands?
3. Why can a spruce tree grow in a taiga ecosystem but not in a grassland ecosystem?
4. Why do few trees grow on grasslands?

Aquatic Ecosystems

Water covers more than two-thirds of our planet. Ninety-seven percent of that water is saltwater. These great reserves of ocean water are of tremendous value to all living things. Millions of organisms live in many different ecosystems on and under the ocean's surface. In addition, the oceans control the weather patterns on our planet to a large extent. They also provide a constant supply of freshwater through evaporation. Most freshwater on Earth exists as snow and ice. However, there are still vast amounts of liquid freshwater on Earth's surface, housing millions of organisms in many different ecosystems.

Aquatic ecosystems are found in ponds, rivers, lakes, and oceans. In Alberta, the major aquatic ecosystems are freshwater ecosystems. The rest of this section will focus on lake ecosystems in particular.

Lake Ecosystems

On the surface, a lake may appear to be similar everywhere, but below the surface, the amount of light available, the water temperature, and oxygen levels can all vary. Not surprisingly, the organisms you can find in each area also differ greatly.

littoral zone the area from the shore of a lake or pond to the point where no more plants grow in the lake bottom

Figure 7 shows a cross section of a typical lake. The **littoral zone** is the area extending out from the lakeshore to the point where you can no longer find plants rooted in the bottom of the lake. Aquatic plants that grow to the surface, such as bulrushes and water lilies, take hold where the littoral zone is shallow. In slightly deeper areas, plants that are rooted to the bottom but completely submerged may thrive.

DID YOU KNOW ?

Comparing Productivity

With some important exceptions, aquatic ecosystems are less productive than terrestrial ecosystems. For example, a cubic metre of ocean water might contain 5 kg of biomass, while the same volume of fertile soil would contain about 50 kg of biomass.

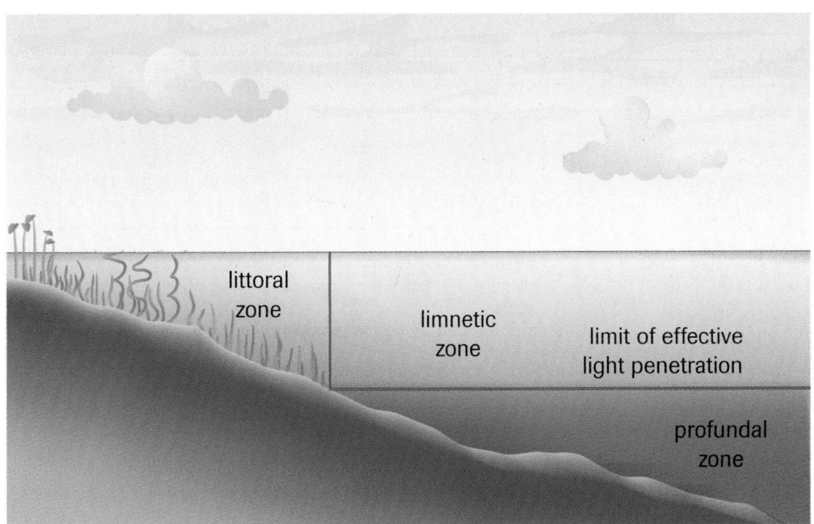

Figure 7 A cross section showing the three main zones of a lake. Note that the depth of the boundary between the limnetic zone and the profundal zone varies in each lake. Plankton and undissolved solids can block the light.

The littoral zone is the most productive part of a lake, the area where algae and plants take advantage of the sunlight to carry out photosynthesis. The size of the littoral zone is determined by the depth of a lake and the slope of its lakebed, both of which are individual to each lake.

Beyond the littoral zone is the **limnetic zone**, the area of the open lake where there is enough light for photosynthesis to occur. The most common form of organism within the limnetic zone is called plankton. The word **plankton** is used to describe both autotrophic and heterotrophic microorganisms. Heterotrophic plankton (invertebrate animals) feed on the autotrophic plankton (tiny plants and algae). Both kinds of plankton are food for consumers in the higher trophic levels, such as fish, tadpoles, and birds.

limnetic zone the area of a lake or pond in which there is open water and sufficient light for photosynthesis to occur

plankton autotrophic and heterotrophic microorganisms found in the limnetic zone of a lake or pond

The region beneath the limnetic zone, where there is not enough light for photosynthesis to occur, is called the **profundal zone**. (This zone is not usually found in ponds.) In most lakes, the only source of nutrients in the profundal zone is the rain of dead plants and animals that falls from the limnetic zone. This detritus is slowly broken down by bacteria or consumed by other bottom-dwelling invertebrates and fish, called detritus feeders.

profundal zone the region of a lake beneath the limnetic zone, in which there is insufficient light for photosynthesis to occur

The decay of this falling organic matter has important consequences for the ecosystem. Bacteria use oxygen to decompose detritus, reducing the amount of oxygen available in the water. In the absence of sunlight and plants to replenish the oxygen, oxygen levels could be reduced to very low levels. The only larger organisms that survive are those that can tolerate low oxygen levels; they include some invertebrates, and a very few fish species such as carp.

Terrestrial and Aquatic Ecosystems

- Alberta has two major terrestrial biomes, taiga and grassland. In these biomes, there are many different ecosystems.
- Alberta's terrestrial ecosystems experience a wide range of seasonal conditions. Organisms in these ecosystems are adapted to these conditions.
- Alberta's aquatic ecosystems are found in lakes, ponds, and rivers. Lake ecosystems vary depending on depth and the resulting amount of light available for photosynthesis.

Section 4.2 Questions

1. Hypothesize why the moose is often found in taiga and in deciduous forests but not in muskeg ecosystems.
2. What adaptations make conifers well-suited for taiga?
3. Rank the ecosystems discussed (muskeg, taiga, deciduous forest, grassland) in descending order according to each abiotic factor below. Give reasons for your rankings.
   (a) precipitation
   (b) cold temperatures
   (c) length of growing season
   (d) diversity of organisms
   (e) biomass
4. Copy **Table 2** (below) in your notes and fill in the blank cells.
5. Draw a map of Alberta, and locate regions that can be classified as muskeg, coniferous forest, deciduous forest, and grassland.
6. Identify the profundal zone, according to the data in **Table 3**.

Table 3 Abiotic Factors in a Lake

Zone	Temp. (°C)	Depth (m)	Light conditions
1	25	1	bright
2	20	5	medium
3	15	20	dim
4	10	25	dark

7. Explain why you would expect to find different organisms in the limnetic, littoral, and profundal zones of a lake. In your answer, refer to the abiotic factors in each zone.
8. Using the terms you've learned in this section, describe a local lake or pond.

Table 2 Components of Biomes

Ecosystem			Grassland	Deciduous forest
soil	acidic	permafrost		rich, fertile
biotic factor (vegetation)	spruce trees	lichens and moss		
annual mean precipitation (cm)	50-250		25-100	75-250

Factors Affecting Ecosystems 4.3

In the previous section, you looked at several terrestrial and aquatic ecosystems. Each ecosystem was defined not only by the organisms that live in it, but also by abiotic factors such as temperature, amount or type of water, and amount of light. In this section, you will take a closer look at the factors that affect ecosystems.

litter the upper layer of soil, composed mainly of partially decomposed leaves or grasses

topsoil the soil layer beneath the litter, composed of small particles of rock mixed with humus

humus decaying plant and animal matter

subsoil the soil layer beneath the topsoil, usually containing more rock particles and less organic matter than the topsoil

bedrock the layer beneath the soil, composed of rock

Factors Affecting Terrestrial Ecosystems

Despite their many differences, terrestrial regions such as coniferous forests, deserts, and grasslands are alike in one way: each region functions as a system. Within each ecosystem, the biotic and abiotic factors are interdependent. These factors can limit the size of populations and can also determine the number of species that can survive in each ecosystem.

Soil

Soil is so familiar that its importance can go unnoticed. A thin layer of soil, rarely more than two metres thick and often much thinner, provides nutrients for all plants that grow on land. The quality and amount of soil available are crucial factors in determining the size and health of the plant community, and thus, the biodiversity of the ecosystem. Entire civilizations have collapsed because the topsoil was depleted or overused (**Figure 1**).

Soil can be viewed as a series of layers, each of which can be identified by its distinct colour and texture (**Figure 2**, next page). As you move downward, deeper into the soil, less organic matter can be detected. The upper layer, known as the **litter**, is mostly made up of partially decomposed leaves or grasses. The litter acts like a blanket, limiting temperature variations in the soil and reducing water loss by evaporation.

Beneath the litter is the **topsoil** layer, made up of small particles of rock mixed with decaying plant and animal matter (**humus**). Humus is black, so topsoil is often dark. Topsoil usually contains a rich supply of minerals and other nutrients that plants require for growth. Nutrients from dead and decaying matter are recycled as new plants grow. Also present in the topsoil, in the spaces between the rock particles, are air and water. For dead material to decompose completely, oxygen is needed. This is because the microbes that cause decay use oxygen for respiration. For example, if oxygen is present in small amounts, dead plant material decays slowly and can build up into a layer of peat which is characteristic of muskeg.

Below the topsoil is the **subsoil**, a layer that usually contains more rock particles, mixed with only small amounts of organic matter. The subsoil is usually lighter in colour because of the lack of humus. Subsoil may contain relatively large amounts of minerals such as iron, aluminum, and phosphorus. Beneath the soil lies a layer of rock, the **bedrock**, which marks the end of the soil.

As you saw in Section 4.2, different ecosystems in a biome can have different types of soil. The type of soil affects the biotic components of the ecosystem. For example, taiga ecosystems with well-drained soil tend to have many white spruce and jack pine trees. Birds that feed on these trees are found more often in these ecosystems, as are the predators that depend on these birds for food. In contrast, muskeg soil in the northern taiga has relatively poor drainage and lower amounts of oxygen. As a result, muskeg ecosystems have more species that are adapted to water-soaked soil, such as black spruce and larch. The other biotic components of this ecosystem depend on the black spruce and larch for their food.

Figure 1
There are many possible explanations for the disappearance of the civilization that created these statues on Easter Island. One theory is that the islanders removed too many trees, causing the topsoil of the island to erode. With their soil depleted, the people could not grow as much food as before.

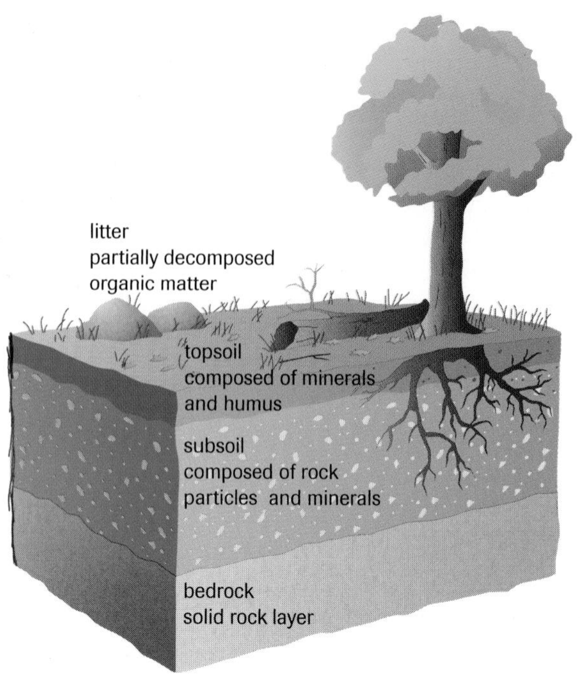

Figure 2
The soil can be divided into layers. Each layer can be identified by colour and the presence of stones. Roots from trees help break up large stones in the subsoil and the bedrock itself, helping to deepen the soil.

Soil can be acidic, neutral, or basic. Basic soils are often referred to as alkaline soils. The pH of the soil is determined by the nature of the rock from which it was formed, and by the nature of the plants that grow in it. (The decomposition of organic matter from dead plants and discarded leaves can cause the accumulation of acids in the soil.) The acidity of rain, snow, and groundwater that enters the soil, also plays a role. Humans have been contributing to higher levels of acidity in many soils by burning fossil fuels such as coal, oil, and gasoline. The burning of fossil fuels releases sulfur doxide and nitrogen oxides into the air. These gases form acidic compounds in the atmosphere, resulting in acidic rain and snow.

The pH of the soil determines which plants will grow best. For example, coniferous trees do poorly in strongly acidic soils, even though they are well adapted to mildly acidic soil. Mosses often flourish in acidic soils because of decreased competition from other plants that require more nutrients.

Available Water

The amount of available water in an ecosystem is another important abiotic factor. This factor is part of the overall climate of the region. All organisms depend on water to survive. Some organisms have adaptations that allow them to live in regions with extremely low levels of available water, such as deserts and extremely cold regions. For example, Alberta's rough fescue grass has long, thin leaves that reduce moisture loss. As a result, this organism can survive in dry areas.

The amount of available water is determined by the amount and the type of precipitation (e.g., rain or snow). The amount of available water is also affected by how long it stays in the upper layers of soil, and how much collects beneath the soil. Precipitation collects in lakes, ponds, and rivers, but it also seeps into the soil and the porous rock below the soil. Once in the soil or rock, water is called **groundwater**. The water that flows down through the soil eventually reaches a layer that is saturated with water. The boundary between this saturated layer and the unsaturated soil above it is called the water table. The depth of the water table in an area affects the organisms that grow there.

groundwater water in the soil or rock below Earth's surface

For example, if a region has little precipitation but a water table that is close to the surface, plants can reach down with their roots to obtain water, even though there is little rain or snow. If the water table is very close to the surface, the area will be marshy or swamp-like.

As water seeps downward, it dissolves organic matter and minerals from the soil and carries them deeper in a process called leaching. Leaching is a serious problem because plants require these nutrients for growth and development. In many ways, plants help to correct the problem themselves. Their branching roots extend deep into the soil and help pump minerals and other chemicals from the lower levels back to the surface.

DID YOU KNOW ?

Aboriginal Technologies

Aboriginal peoples have developed many technologies to cope with abiotic factors, including temperature, in their environments. Some of these technologies, such as snowshoes, kayaks, and canoes, are still in use today.

Temperature

Like available water, temperature is part of the overall climate of a region. Temperature can vary significantly throughout the year in an ecosystem, which affects both biotic and abiotic factors. For example, organisms such as cacti are not able to survive the temperature conditions in Northern Alberta, and so do not form part of food webs in ecosystems in this region. Similarly, the rate at which water evaporates is affected by the temperature. At cooler temperatures, it takes longer for water to evaporate, and so it is available to plants with shallow roots for a longer time.

Albertan ecosystems experience extreme summer and winter conditions. However, the organisms that live here are adapted to their ecosystems, which means that either they can cope with abiotic factors such as low moisture, cold temperatures, and decreased sunlight, or they migrate from the area before winter sets in.

For example, by keeping their leaves (the needles) throughout the winter, conifers are better able to survive in regions with a short growing season. These trees do not expend large amounts of time, energy, and nutrients to grow a complete new set of leaves each year.

Grassland populations are highly adapted to winter climates. A large proportion of the grasses' biomass exists underground in their root systems (**Figure 3**). Although the above-ground grass freezes off during the winter, the roots survive to regrow in spring.

Animals adapt in several different ways to the cold winters. Some birds, such as loons, ducks, and some species of hawk, migrate to warmer climates, while some mammals, such as black bears, hibernate (become inactive). Many insects enter a state of low metabolic activity or overwinter as eggs. Other animals, however, are active throughout the winter. For example, small animals such as mice and voles dig tunnels in the snow, protecting themselves from predators and cold temperatures.

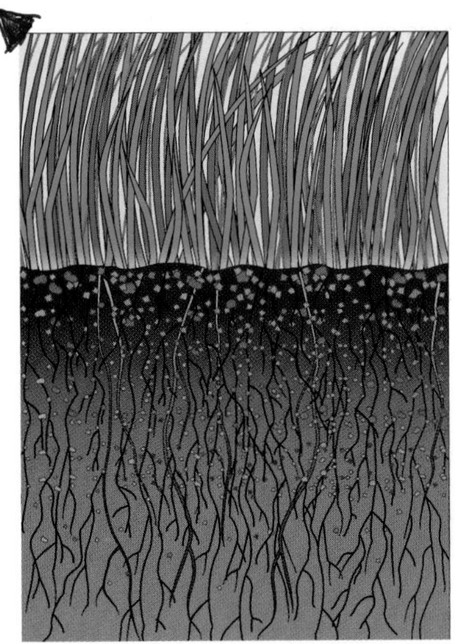

Figure 3
Most of the biomass of native prairie grasses is in the root system.

mini *Investigation* ***How Does Temperature Affect Seed Germination?***

Using the following materials, design an experiment that determines the effect of temperature on seed germination. The materials listed are per group.

Materials: 30 radish seeds, 3 Petri dishes, 3 plastic bags, paper towel, 100 mL graduated cylinder, water

(a) Construct a hypothesis for the experiment.

(b) Identify your independent and dependent variables, and which factors must be controlled.

(c) Write a procedure. Make sure you include any safety precautions and describe how you will record your data. Have your procedure checked by your teacher.

- Perform your investigation.

(d) Analyze your data and communicate your conclusions.

Sunlight

Finally, all terrestrial ecosystems are affected by the amount of sunlight they receive. In ecosystems close to the equator, the amount of sunlight received every day is more or less constant throughout the year. Regions at more southern or northern latitudes experience changes in the amount of sunlight during different times of the year. For example, in Canada, we receive fewer hours of sunlight in winter than in summer.

Ecosystems within any geographic region can also receive different amounts of sunlight. For example, an area that is shaded by a large outcrop of rock will support a different ecosystem than an area close by but in full sunlight. As plants in an ecosystem grow, they can affect the amount of sunlight received by other areas in their vicinity. For example, you saw in Section 4.2 how taller trees in a forest form a canopy blocking sunlight from shorter trees and shrubs in the understorey.

Practice

1. If you were to dig a hole in local soil, what layers would you expect to see? Explain your answer.
2. Describe two factors that would alter the amount of ground water in an area.
3. Using a diagram, explain how minerals leach from the soil and how plants help to correct this process.

Factors Affecting Aquatic Ecosystems

Like terrestrial ecosystems, aquatic ecosystems are limited by three main abiotic factors: the chemical environment, light levels, and temperature. Water pressure is a fourth abiotic factor that affects only aquatic ecosystems.

Figure 4
Aquatic ecosystems, such as this stream in the Kanaskis, will have more dissolved oxygen when the water is cold than when it is warm.

Chemical Environment

In aquatic ecosystems, the chemical environment naturally includes the type of water, whether freshwater or saltwater. Organisms that live in freshwater ecosystems can seldom survive in saltwater ecosystems, and vice versa. A second component of the chemical environment in aquatic ecosystems is the amount of oxygen that is dissolved in the water. Like terrestrial organisms, aquatic organisms require oxygen, but they must get their oxygen from the water. The amount of oxygen that is dissolved in a body of water depends on a number of factors, including temperature (**Figure 4**), pressure (determined by the depth of the water), and the amount of salt and other substances dissolved in the water. Finally, the chemical environment of aquatic ecosystems includes any other dissolved substances. For example, lake water might contain naturally occurring minerals, such as phosphorus and nitrogen, as well as organic pollutants.

Temperature and Sunlight

As in terrestrial ecosystems, the light and temperature of an aquatic ecosystem may vary over the course of a year. This is particularly true in Canada, where we have four seasons. However, in aquatic ecosystems, these factors are also affected by the depth of the water.

Ecosystems near the surface of an ocean will obtain far more light and experience warmer temperatures than ecosystems in the depths. Surprisingly, life can exist even in the dark regions of the ocean. As you learned in Chapter 2, oceanographers have discovered fascinating ecosystems existing around hydrothermal vents on the ocean floor. These ecosystems contain organisms such as tube worms, crabs, and mussels, forming food chains based on bacteria that produce food through chemosynthesis.

Water Pressure

Water pressure is another important abiotic factor in aquatic ecosystems. Plants and animals in aquatic ecosystems have adapted to conditions that are dramatically different from those on land. Water is about 800 times denser than air, making it more difficult to move through. This factor is particularly important in ocean ecosystems. Although sea animals can travel widely without obstruction, they are limited by how much they can move up and down. At a depth of 10 m, the pressure is roughly double what it is at the surface, and the pressure increases by 100 kPa for every 10 m of depth. The average depth of the ocean is about 4000 m. Very few organisms are adapted to survive both near the surface and under the crushing pressure at the ocean bottom.

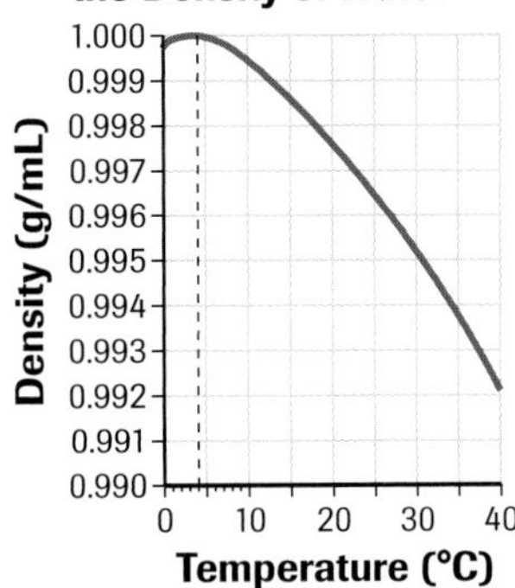

Figure 5
Unlike most substances, pure water becomes less dense as it cools below 4 °C.

Seasonal Variations in Canadian Lakes

In Canada, the changing of the seasons causes significant changes in the abiotic factors in freshwater ecosystems found in our lakes. As water cools, it becomes more dense, just like other substances. However, as water cools below 4 °C a strange thing happens—it starts becoming less dense (**Figure 5**). This is why ice floats, forming a layer on top of cold water, and why the lowest layer of water in a lake often has a temperature of 4 °C. Seasonal variations in a lake are shown in **Figure 6**.

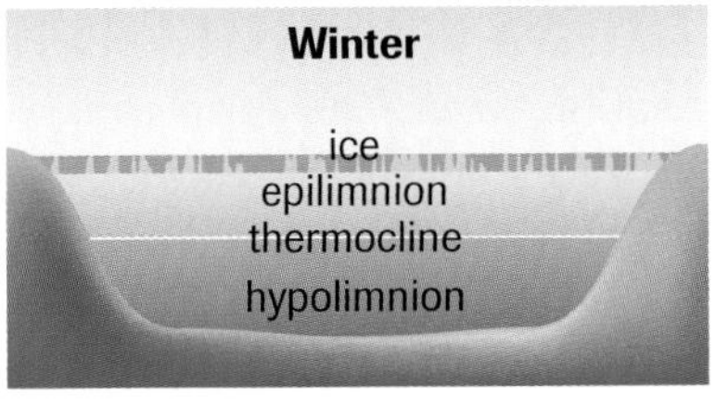

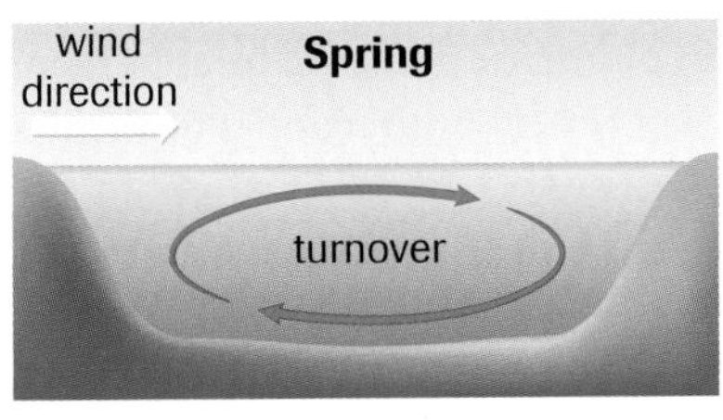

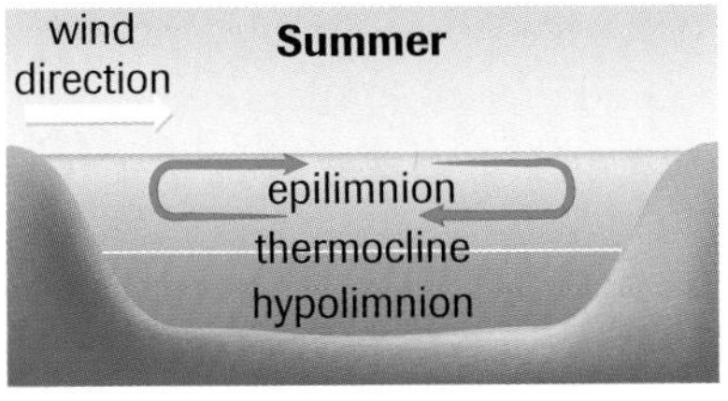

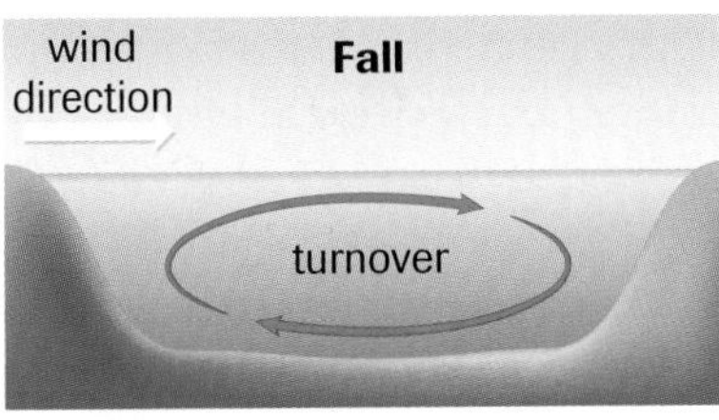

Figure 6
Temperature and the variable density of water both play important roles in seasonal changes in Canadian lakes.

Winter

During the winter, many of our lakes are covered by ice and snow. This prevents atmospheric oxygen from dissolving in the water and acts as an insulator. Under the ice the water is arranged in layers, according to its density. The least dense water, at or slightly above 0 °C, is near the surface. The densest water, at 4 °C, is found at the bottom. No matter how cold the air becomes above the ice, this structure remains the same, although the ice will get thicker if the air remains cold.

If the ice is wind-blown and transparent, light can penetrate into the water, supporting photosynthesis in the liquid water below. However, if the ice freezes to a greater thickness than normal, or is covered in thick snow, light can no longer penetrate, and the organisms under the ice are in trouble. The level of dissolved oxygen in the water may drop until it is not high enough to support some organisms. Because fish are particularly sensitive to dissolved oxygen concentrations, the result could be a massive die-off of some fish species. In shallow lakes, particularly in the Arctic, ice may form right to the bottom, virtually eliminating most life forms every winter.

+ EXTENSION

Thermal Stratification of Lakes

Listen to this audio clip to get a better understanding of how the properties of water relate to the process of thermal stratification. Find out how surface warming becomes an abiotic limiting factor.

www.science.nelson.com 

epilimnion the upper level of a lake, which warms up in summer

hypolimnion the lower level of a lake, which remains at a low temperature year round

thermocline the zone between the epilimnion and hypolimnion, in which temperature changes rapidly

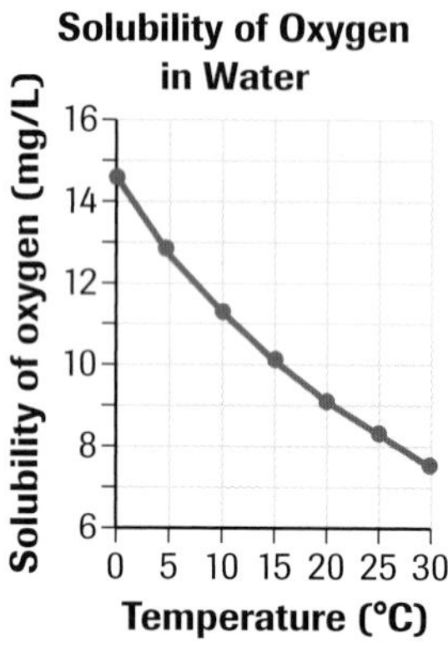

Figure 7
Solubility of oxygen in water

Spring

Spring brings storms and the melting of the ice. Oxygen can now pass from the air into the water. Wind stirs the water, creating waves that increase the surface area and so the rate at which oxygen can dissolve. As the cold surface water warms, it eventually reaches a temperature of 4 °C. At this point, it begins to sink through the less dense water beneath it, carrying its precious supply of oxygen with it. The mixing process that results is called the spring turnover.

Summer

As the surface water warms above 4 °C, it will no longer sink because it is less dense than the cooler water below. Just as in winter, layers of water are set up, with the densest water at the bottom. If you swim in a lake during summer you can experience these layers. By allowing your feet to sink slowly through the water, you will encounter colder regions.

The upper level of a lake, which warms up in summer, is called the **epilimnion**. The lower level, which remains at a low temperature, is called the **hypolimnion**. Between these two levels is the **thermocline**, a narrow zone in which the temperature drops rapidly from warm to cold.

Because the epilimnion and hypolimnion do not mix, there is little movement of oxygen from the surface to the depths during summer. Organisms living in the hypolimnion must rely on oxygen reserves brought down during the spring turnover.

The epilimnion has a different oxygen problem. The ability of water to hold dissolved gases is inversely proportional to the temperature of the water: The warmer the water, the less dissolved oxygen it can hold (**Figure 7**). During a hot spell, a lake that is fairly shallow may lose so much oxygen that some species, such as lake trout, will die.

Fall

As temperatures begin to drop in the fall, the surface water begins to cool. Once again, as the surface water reaches a temperature of 4 °C, it sinks down through the lake. This fall turnover renews oxygen levels at lower levels, and breaks up the summer thermal layers.

Practice

4. Explain why a shallow lake tends to be warmer than a deep lake in summer.
5. In your own words, describe the changes that happen in a lake from summer to winter.

mini Investigation — Measuring Undissolved Solids

Rain carries soil and other solids into surface water where they can remain suspended, creating turbidity (cloudiness or murkiness) that limits the penetration of sunlight and reduces photosynthesis. Solids that are deposited as sediment on the bottom of the body of water can also affect ecosystems. Large volumes can bury bottom-feeding animals and the eggs of fish. Large amounts of falling sediment also make life generally unpleasant for filter feeders such as clams.

(a) Using filter paper and other materials, design a procedure (including safety precautions) to determine the amount of undissolved solid material in water samples from three different sources.

- Have your materials list and procedure approved by your teacher before starting. (Shake each of the samples before each test.)

(b) Present your results (including your data) in a written report.

SUMMARY Factors Affecting Ecosystems

- The quality and amount of soil are critical factors in determining the size and health of the plant community and the biodiversity of an ecosystem.
- Terrestrial ecosystems can experience large changes in temperature and precipitation. Organisms must adapt to these changes.
- The amount of sunlight in a terrestrial ecosystem can vary with geographic location, time of year, and biotic and abiotic factors that change the amount of shade.
- Organisms in aquatic ecosystems are limited by the abiotic factors of that ecosystem: the chemical environment, light levels, and temperature.
- The solubility of oxygen in water increases as the water temperature decreases.
- The amount of sunlight and the temperature of aquatic environments are determined by the depth of the water, as well as any seasonal changes.
- Temperature and the density of water play important roles in seasonal changes in lakes in Canada. As water cools, it becomes more dense. However, below 4 °C, it becomes less dense.

Section 4.3 Questions

1. List some ways in which the amount of organic matter in an ecosystem can increase.
2. Why is it possible that two ecosystems, with identical conditions of temperature and precipitation, could support different plants?
3. Describe what you would expect to happen to oxygen levels in the hypolimnion of a lake over the summer months.
4. Cold water holds more dissolved gas than warm water. Cold water also tends to collect in the lower levels of a lake. However, in summer, oxygen levels in a lake can be highest in the warm surface water of a lake. Explain why.
5. Predict what would happen to a lake that experienced no seasonal changes in temperature. Make a diagram showing the temperature and oxygen levels in the water of the lake after many years of little change in surface air temperatures.
6. (a) Using soda pop, beakers, water, and other materials you choose, design a demonstration (including safety precautions) that shows the relationship between water temperature and the amount of dissolved gas. Have your teacher approve your materials list and design before you begin.
   (b) How did you measure the amount of dissolved gas in the soda pop?
   (c) Present your data in a graph and interpret your findings.
7. A good fisher knows where to find fish. Catfish are less active than trout. In the summer months, which of these fish would you expect to find in the hypolimnion and the epilimnion? Give your reasons.

4.4 Limits on Populations and Communities in Ecosystems

Field mice can have litters with six or more pups, and they can reproduce every six weeks. It takes only six weeks for a mouse to become sexually mature. In six months, a population of 20 mice could become a population of 5120 mice. What keeps the population of field mice under control? Predators, available amounts of food and water, disease, changing temperatures, and other factors all prevent mice populations from growing exponentially.

In the previous section, you examined specific factors that affect ecosystems. In this section, you will see how these and other factors limit populations and communities within ecosystems.

Biotic Potential

biotic potential the maximum number of offspring that a species could produce with unlimited resources

Species vary in their capacity to reproduce. **Biotic potential** is the maximum number of offspring that a species could produce if resources were unlimited. You have seen how quickly field mice reproduce, but many animals have a much lower biotic potential. For example, mature female black bears give birth to one or two cubs after a gestation period of 7.5 months. Generally, bears take at least two years to mature, during which time their mother will not give birth again. Biotic potential is regulated by four important factors, shown in **Figure 1**.

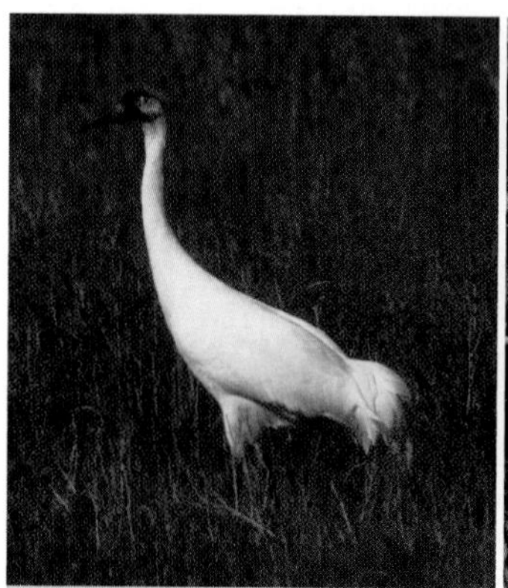

Factor: birth potential

Description: The maximum number of offspring per birth

Example: Whooping crane females lay two eggs per year, and usually only one chick survives.

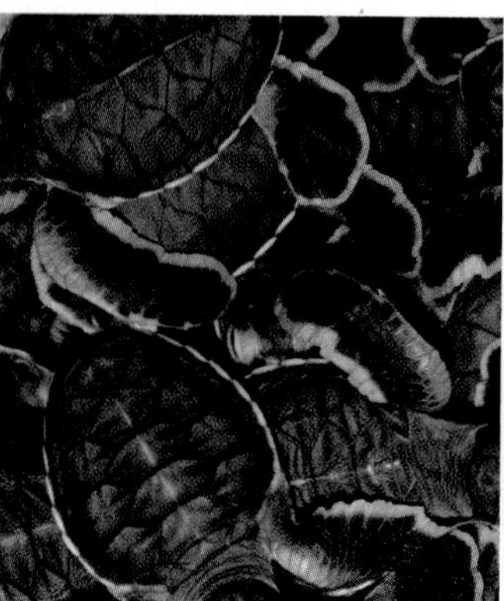

Factor: capacity for survival

Description: The number of offspring that reach reproductive age

Example: The female sea turtle lays many eggs, but only a few of her offspring even reach the sea, and fewer still reach maturity.

Factor: breeding frequency

Description: The number of times that a species reproduces each year

Example: Elk mate only once per year, during the fall.

Factor: length of reproductive life

Description: The age of sexual maturity and the number of years the individual can reproduce

Example: African elephants reach sexual maturity at about 15 years of age, but may reproduce until they are 90.

Figure 1
Factors that determine biotic potential

Limiting Factors

Factors in the environment can prevent populations from attaining their biotic potential. Any resource that is in short supply is a limiting factor on a population. Food, water, territory, and the presence of pollutants and other toxic chemicals are all limiting factors, as shown in **Table 1**.

Table 1 Factors That Limit Populations

	Factors that cause a population to increase	Factors that cause a population to decrease
Abiotic	favourable light	too much or too little light
	favourable temperature	too cold or too warm
	favourable chemical environment	unfavourable chemical environment
Biotic	sufficient food	insufficient food
	low number or low effectiveness of predators	high number or high effectiveness of predators
	few or weak diseases and parasites	many or strong diseases and parasites
	ability to compete for resources	inability to compete successfully for resources

For example, a fern plant produces more than 50 000 spores in a single year (**Figure 2**). If all fern spores germinated, fern plants would cover all of North America within two generations of the first plant. This doesn't happen because of the limiting biotic and abiotic factors. If the weather is wetter than usual, the soil is moist, and many fern spores will germinate, so the fern population will increase. A return to drier weather will not only prevent spores from germinating, but will also kill plants in exposed areas, so the population declines. The presence of many grazing animals will reduce the population of ferns, and if there are few grazers the population will grow. Fluctuations like these, caused by one factor, can occur in natural ecosystems; however, most populations are affected by more than one factor at a time.

Figure 2
Abiotic and biotic factors limit the number of ferns in an ecosystem.

Carrying Capacity

Populations commonly fluctuate because of an interaction of the many biotic and abiotic limiting factors. However, communities are often stable. Stability is achieved when an ecosystem is in equilibrium, when none of the populations exceeds the carrying capacity of the ecosystem. The **carrying capacity** is the maximum number of individuals of a species that can be supported at the time by an ecosystem. The carrying capacity for any species is determined by the availability of resources, such as food and water.

A population can exceed the carrying capacity of the ecosystem, but not for long. Consider the field mouse again. Imagine that the population of predators is lower than usual. Suddenly, the mouse population can grow. However, the extra mice will eat all the available food. Hungry rodents soon become sickly—making them easy prey for the hawks, owls, and foxes that are present. The mouse population will decline again, to or below the carrying capacity. Ecosystems soon re-establish equilibrium.

carrying capacity the maximum number of individuals of a species that can be supported by an ecosystem

DID YOU KNOW ?

Acting Like Lemmings?

The "lemming mass suicides" you may have seen or read about don't really happen. When Arctic lemming populations grow larger than the local carrying capacity, many of the lemmings migrate to neighbouring territories. They always try to arrive alive when they migrate.

Limits of Tolerance

You have seen that the survival and reproduction of an organism depend on the presence of nutrients and the ability of the organism to withstand the abiotic factors in the environment. Our understanding of this fact has developed over many years.

In the mid-1800s, Justus von Liebig noted that certain substances must be present if plants are to grow. If any one of these substances is present in low amounts, the growth

law of the minimum states that the nutrient in the least supply is the one that limits growth

law of tolerance states that an organism can survive within a particular range of an abiotic factor

of the plant is reduced, regardless of the quantity of other substances that are present. This observation became known as the **law of the minimum**: the nutrient in least supply is the one that limits growth.

In 1913, Victor Shelford added to von Liebig's work by noting that too much of a factor can harm an organism. This principle is often called Shelford's **law of tolerance**: an organism can survive within (tolerate) a certain range of an abiotic factor; above and below the range it cannot survive. The greater this range of tolerance, the greater the organism's ability to survive.

As seen in **Figure 3**, the maximum population size is possible when the abiotic factor is at an optimum level within the range of tolerance. However, many abiotic factors act on a species at any given time. Most species have a broad range of tolerance for some factors, and a narrow range for others.

Competitive Exclusion and Resource Partitioning

Listen to a discussion of competitive exclusion, resource partitioning, and Shelford's Law of Tolerance.

www.science.nelson.com

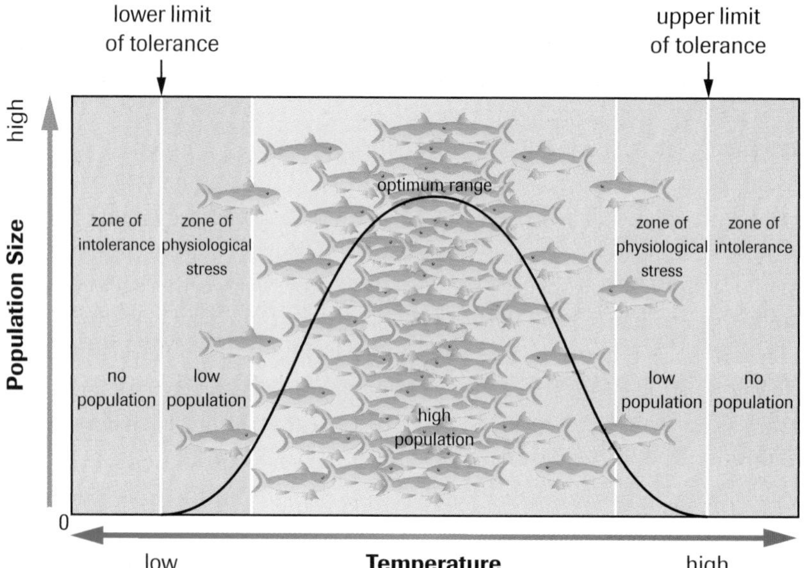

Figure 3
The population of a fish species is likely to increase as the water temperature gets closer to the optimum. None of the fish can survive if the water gets too hot or too cold.

Density-Independent and Density-Dependent Factors

The number of organisms in an ecosystem is important when considering the effects of some abiotic and biotic factors. A population is said to be dense when there is a large number of organisms in a small area.

density-independent factor a factor in an ecosystem that affects members of a population regardless of population density

density-dependent factor a factor in an ecosystem that affects members of a population because of the population density

Density-independent factors affect members of a population regardless of population density. Fire and flood are two naturally occurring events that are density-independent. They will affect a population regardless of its size.

When the density of a population increases, other factors may limit further growth or reduce population numbers. **Density-dependent factors** affect a population *because* of the density of the population. Food supply, water quality, sunlight, disease, and territory are density-dependent factors. For example, when a tree in a dense forest becomes infected with a fungal blight, the infection will spread more quickly than it would in a forest where trees are separated by larger distances.

Similarly, individuals in more densely populated areas are more prone to starvation, as food is in lower supply. Competition for food may leave animals weak and more susceptible to predation. The density-dependent factors listed in **Table 2**, on the next page, will cause higher mortality rates, lowering the population density. When the population density is reduced, the effects of the density-dependent factors are also reduced.

Table 2 Factors That Cause Changes in Populations

Density-independent factors	Density-dependent factors
• flood	• food shortage
• fire	• competition for mates, breeding areas (habitat)
• spraying with pesticides	• disease caused by a microorganism or parasite
• change in climate or temperature	• introduction of an exotic species
• destruction of habitat	• increased predation
• drought	• competition for water and other resources

CAREER CONNECTION

Fish and Wildlife Officer

Wildlife management and hunting have a long association. Concerned that the populations of game species were declining, hunters lobbied governments to regulate hunting. Each year, some game animal populations produce more offspring than can survive. Populations that exceed their carrying capacity are susceptible to disease and starvation. How does game regulation assist farmers and ranchers? What role does the Fish and Wildlife division of Alberta Environment play in game regulation?

www.science.nelson.com 

SUMMARY Limits on Populations and Communities

- Biotic potential is the maximum number of offspring that a population could produce if its resources were unlimited. It is determined by birth potential, capacity for survival, breeding frequency, and length of reproductive life.
- Carrying capacity is the maximum number of individuals in a population that can be supported at the time by an ecosystem.
- Populations that temporarily exceed their carrying capacity reduce their biotic resources.
- The law of the minimum states that the factor in lowest supply is the one that limits population growth. The law of tolerance describes the minimum and maximum limits for essential factors that control the population size.
- Density-independent factors affect members of a population regardless of population density. Fire and flood are density-independent.
- Density-dependent factors affect a population because of the actual density of the population. Food supply and territory are density-dependent factors.

Section 4.4 Questions

1. Four factors regulate population growth. Using an example of a nonhuman population, explain how each factor would affect the population size.
2. Cedar waxwings are one of the few birds that can withstand the cold and lack of available food during our winters. To ease the strains of winter, bird watchers in Lethbridge provide cedar waxwings with seeds during winter months.
   (a) Would the seeds alter the carrying capacity of the ecosystem? Explain.
   (b) Provide a hypothesis that explains why bird watchers have noted an increase in the falcon population in recent years.
3. A scientist studying wolves near Canmore notices a steady decline in the population of wolves for four consecutive years.
   (a) Make a prediction about how the population of wolves will affect the population of moose. Give your reasons.
   (b) Assuming that humans are not the cause of the wolf population decline, would it be reasonable to conclude that the wolf population will continue to decline until there are no more wolves left in the area? Give your reasons.
   (c) What might cause the wolf population to begin increasing again?
   (d) Using a flow chart, explain how changes in the wolf population would affect the plant community surrounding Canmore.

4. (a) Create a table like **Table 3** and classify the following information within it.
   - Larger mammals generally live longer than smaller ones.
   - Pregnant female elephants carry their young for nearly 18 months.
   - Elephants reach sexual maturity at 15 years.
   - Elephants usually produce one offspring each birth.
   - Most elephants wait more than 5 years between births.
   - Female elephants care for their young for more than 10 years.
   - Mice often produce litters of 6 or more.
   - After about 6 weeks, mice reach sexual maturity.
   - In a natural setting few mice are older than 2 years.
   - A pregnant female mouse will carry her young for 22 days.
   - Mice will breed every 6 weeks or less.

   (b) Refer to your table and write a paragraph comparing the biotic potentials of elephants and mice.

Table 3 Biotic Potential of Elephants and Mice

Biotic potential	Elephant	Mouse
birth potential		
capacity for survival		
breeding frequency		
maturity		

5. A researcher conducts a study to find a possible biological control for pine bark beetles, an insect considered a pest by the forestry industry. The researcher sets up four different studies of predators and the pine bark beetle. The populations of prey and predator are monitored over many different generations. The graphs in **Figure 4** show changes in populations over time.
   (a) Which species is most likely the best controlling agent? Give your reasons.
   (b) Sometimes the eggs of a predator are eaten by its prey. Which predator might serve as a food source for its prey? Give your reasons.
   (c) Why is the population of predator A consistently lower than that of the pine bark beetle?
   (d) Predict what would happen to the population of pine bark beetles if predator species C exceeds the carrying capacity of the environment after year 9.

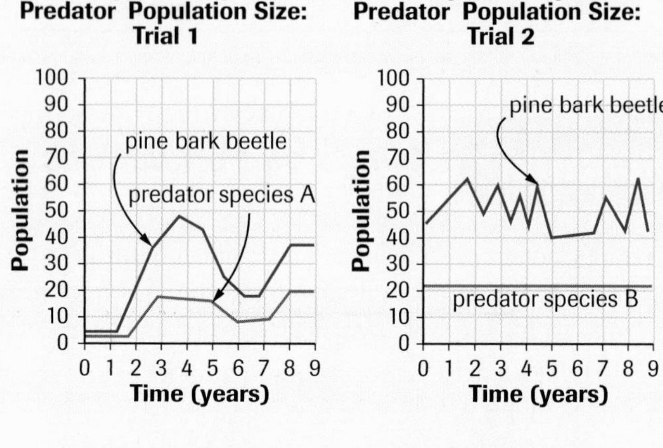

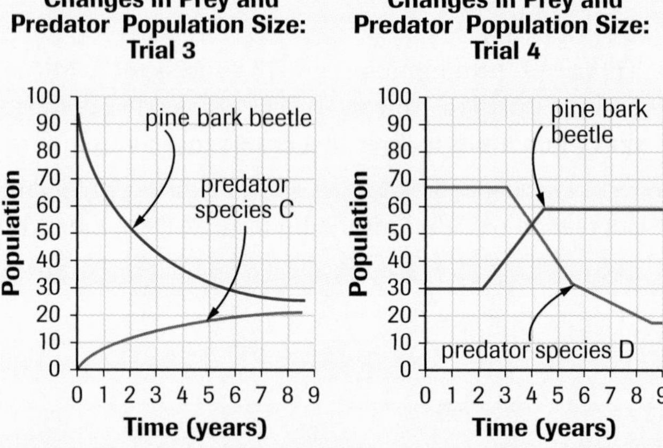

Figure 4
Changes in populations over time of pine bark beetles and four different potential control species

Changes in Ecosystems 4.5

Changes in terrestrial and aquatic ecosystems happen naturally, over time, as biotic and abiotic factors gradually shift. In addition, natural events such as floods and fires can cause sudden, dramatic changes. However, one of the most common sources of change for ecosystems is human activity. In this section, you will examine some natural and human-caused changes in terrestrial and aquatic ecosystems.

Changes in Terrestrial Ecosystems

Prior to the Industrial Revolution, there were approximately 6 billion hectares of forest on Earth. Today, an estimated 4 billion hectares remain. Approximately 33 % of Earth's forests have been cleared to make way for agricultural land or urban areas (**Figure 1**).

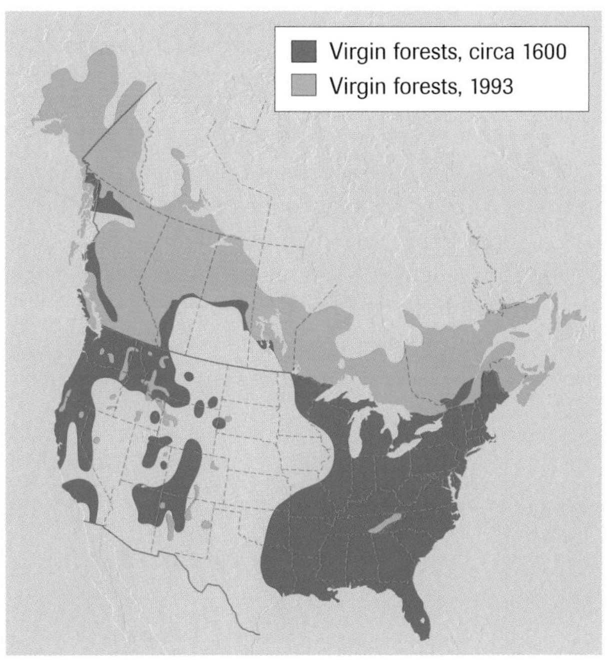

Figure 1
In Canada, more than 60 % of the virgin forest has been lost to logging since European settlers arrived.

Forests are important resources. They affect climate by recycling water and carbon dioxide. On a hot day, a large tree may absorb 5.5 T of water from the soil and release it into the atmosphere. Forests also affect the physical environment of ecosystems by acting as a giant sponge—controlling water runoff, holding groundwater, and preventing soil erosion. They act as shelters for wildlife, providing nesting sites and food for many different animals. According to one estimate, a typical tree provides $196 250 in long-term ecological value, compared with about $590 as timber.

Forestry Practices

In Canada, deforestation is one of the most controversial ways in which humans change ecosystems. Deforestation falls under three categories. **Slash-and-burn** is most commonly used in tropical areas to clear forests for agriculture. Bulldozers are often used to remove all existing vegetation. The debris is piled and ignited in a controlled burn to

slash-and-burn the complete clearing of a forest by felling and burning the trees

clear-cutting the removal of all trees in an area

selective cutting the harvesting of only certain trees from an area

provide soil nutrients for future crops. **Clear-cutting** involves the removal of all trees in an area for use in timber or pulp. In Canada, this practice is followed by replanting the dominant species. **Table 1** lists some effects of clear-cutting. In **selective cutting**, only certain trees are harvested from an area, leaving the others to regenerate the area.

Table 1 Effects of Clear-Cutting

Positive effects	Negative effects
• Clear-cutting is less expensive than selective cutting. This provides timber or pulp at more competitive prices. • If a site is teeming with pests, clear-cutting can eliminate the hazard without infecting surrounding areas. • Clear-cutting permits the replacement of less valuable trees with ones that are more valuable. • Some wildlife, such as moose, benefit from clear-cuts. Low vegetation, such as fruit-bearing shrubs, provide a stable food source.	• Soil erosion and runoff into the streams increase. • Nitrates and other nutrients are carried into streams and ponds, increasing algal growth. • Sediment is carried into streams, affecting fish spawning areas. • The removal of vegetation on the ground exposes dark soils and increases the warming of the area. In turn, this increases water loss from the soils. • Replanting with a monoculture decreases biodiversity in the ecosystem. • Some wildlife, such as owls, are negatively affected by clear-cuts. Nesting sites are destroyed in mature forest areas.

CAREER CONNECTION

Wildland Firefighter

A unique combination of training and mentoring equips wildland firefighters to deal safely and effectively with the dangers associated with wildfires in remote locations. Some firefighters are given specialized training, for example Helitack (helicopter attack) crews.

Alberta Environment has a specific program that handles the recruitment and training of these people. Explore the career of a wildland firefighter. How well are these jobs being filled in Canada?

www.science.nelson.com 

Used for pulp and paper, softwoods such as spruce and fir are often considered more valuable than hardwoods, which grow much more slowly. Two or three years after clear-cutting, herbicides are used to prevent the more valuable softwood trees from being crowded by hardwood trees (**Figure 2**). At about 10 years, the underbrush is removed. At about 35 years, the trees are checked for diseases and pests, such as the spruce budworm. Monocultures are much more susceptible to disease than natural forests are. After about 80 to 90 years, the softwood trees are large enough to harvest.

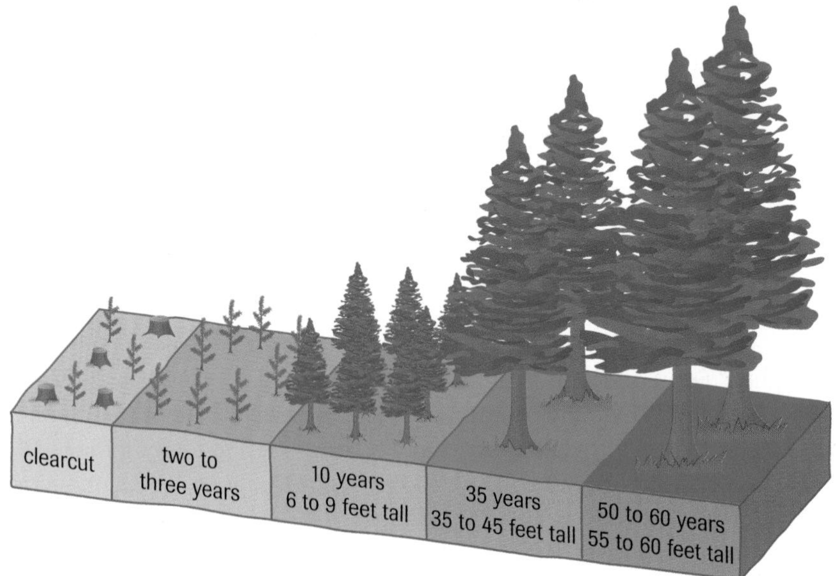

Figure 2
Forest succession after clear-cutting

The Effects of Fire

Fire is an important and often helpful cause of change in ecosystems. Elk Island National Park provides a good example of the important role fire has in ecosystems. This beautiful area in the Beaver Hills, designated as a National Park in 1906, is home to herds of free-roaming plains bison, wood bison, moose, deer, elk, and more than 250 species of birds. Located less than an hour east of Edmonton, this natural aspen parkland is one of the most endangered habitats in Canada.

Fires have occurred in the Beaver Hills for thousands of years. Fire creates and maintains a mosaic of different vegetation types, such as grassland, wetland, shrub area, and aspen parkland. Lightning causes some fires. In the past, Sarcee and Plains Cree intentionally set fires to discourage the expansion of forests and maintain a food supply for large animals like bison. More recently, settlers set fires to clear land and burn stubble.

Traditionally, all fires within the boundaries of all national parks have been suppressed. Therefore, since 1906, no fires were deliberately set in Elk Island and any wildfires were extinguished as quickly as possible. During the 1970s, however, Parks Canada realized that the absence of natural fires was upsetting the ecological integrity of the area. Park managers recognized the need for prescribed burns to maintain and enhance the Elk Island ecosystem. **Prescribed burns** are fires set intentionally in defined areas of the park (**Figure 3**). The fires are carefully controlled. Many park workers are involved and the fire is carefully put out after the prescribed area is burned.

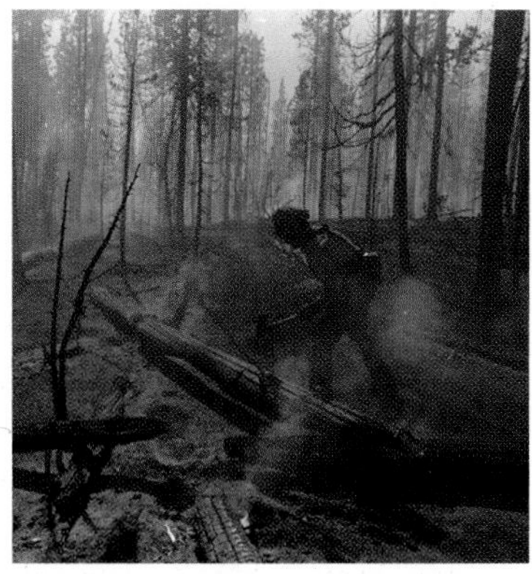

Figure 3
A prescribed burn

prescribed burn a controlled fire set intentionally in a designated area

Practice

1. Why are forests important?
2. What are three methods used for deforestation?
3. What problems could be created by clear-cutting an old-growth forest?

Changes in Lake Ecosystems

Like terrestrial ecosystems, aquatic ecosystems are sustained by the dynamic equilibrium among biotic and abiotic factors. When one or more of these factors changes, it can have profound effects on the ecosystem as a whole.

There are two kinds of lake. **Oligotrophic** lakes are typically deep and cold. Nutrient levels are low in such lakes, limiting the size of producer populations. Because there are limited numbers of only a few kinds of organisms, the water is usually very clear. **Eutrophic** lakes are generally shallow and warmer, and have an excellent supply of nutrients. Many species of photosynthetic organisms find these abiotic conditions very favourable. As a result, the water of eutrophic lakes is often murky.

oligotrophic having low nutrient levels

eutrophic having high nutrient levels

In general, oligotrophic lakes gradually become eutrophic over time. Eutrophic lakes become increasingly shallow, eventually filling in and becoming dry land. This evolution from oligotrophic, to eutrophic, to land is called eutrophication and may take hundreds or even thousands of years. **Figure 4**, on the next page, shows the eutrophication of a lake.

Water Pollution

Humans sometimes accelerate eutrophication by adding to lakes nutrient-rich substances such as human wastes, fertilizers in the runoff from agricultural land, other household and industrial products, and thermal energy (raising the temperature).

Water pollution is any physical or chemical change in surface water or groundwater that can harm living things. Biological, chemical, and physical forms of water pollution can be grouped into five categories:

Figure 4 The eutrophication of a lake, as seen through changes in the community (summer conditions)

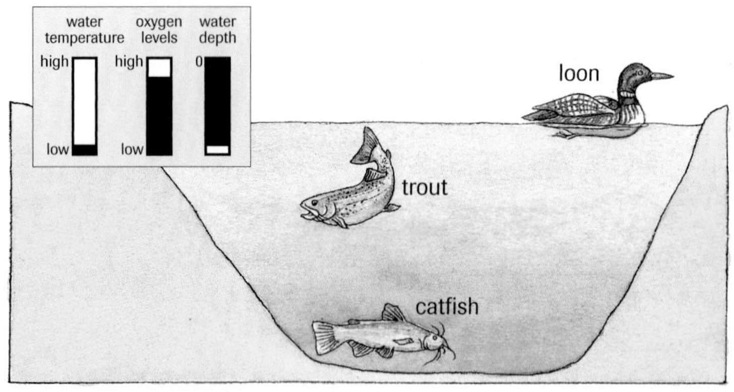

(a) An oligotrophic lake. Deeper lakes tend to be cooler. Cold water can hold more dissolved gases (including oxygen) than warm water.

(b) Soil sediment and organic material falling to the bottom of the lake gradually make the lake shallower. As it becomes shallower, its profundal zone slowly disappears, until eventually sunlight can reach the lakebed. Lake temperatures rise and oxygen levels drop. Organisms that require higher levels of oxygen begin to disappear.

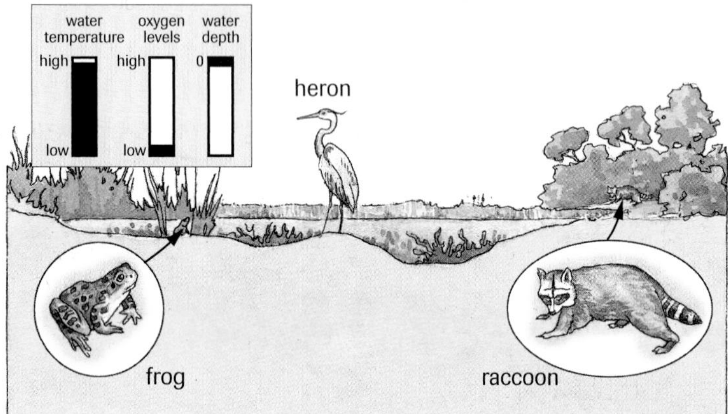

(c) The lake continues to become shallower and warmer. Plants can grow at all levels, and the warmth encourages the growth of plankton. When the plants die, decomposers return their nutrients to the lake, using oxygen in the process. Later in the eutrophication process, the lake will become a marsh and then dry land.

- *Organic solid waste* includes sewage and waste from food processing. As this matter is decomposed by bacteria, oxygen in the water is used up.
- *Disease-causing organisms* come from sewage and animal wastes that enter aquatic ecosystems with runoff. These organisms can trigger an outbreak of a waterborne disease such as typhoid.
- *Inorganic solids and dissolved minerals* include waste from mining, fertilizers, and salts from road runoff in winter.
- *Thermal energy* comes from electricity generating plants and other industries. Heating the water in aquatic ecosystems decreases the solubility of oxygen in the water.
- *Organic compounds* include oil from roads, pesticides, and detergents (organophosphates). Road oil is toxic to fish and waterfowl. Pesticides are toxic to various organisms, and accumulate through the food chain. Phosphates promote algae growth, resulting in a loss of oxygen during decomposition.

Indicators of Water Quality

When studying water pollution, researchers classify the quality of the water according to its intended use. For example, water too polluted to drink is often considered acceptable for industrial processes or watering lawns. There are three main indicators of water quality: bacteria count, the concentration of dissolved oxygen, and the biological oxygen demand (BOD).

Bacteria

The detection of disease-causing bacteria is both difficult and expensive. However, there is an indirect way to discover if these bacteria are present in water. Detecting **coliform bacteria**, a type of bacteria that occurs naturally in the intestines of humans and many other animals, is fairly easy (**Figure 5**). The presence of coliform bacteria indicates that animal wastes are polluting the water. Since many of the dangerous disease-causing bacteria are transmitted in wastes, the presence of coliform bacteria indicates that more dangerous bacteria may also be present. Some lakeside beaches are frequently closed to swimming in summer because of high counts of coliform bacteria.

coliform bacteria a type of bacteria that occurs naturally in the intestines of humans and other animals, and indicates the presence of fecal contamination in water

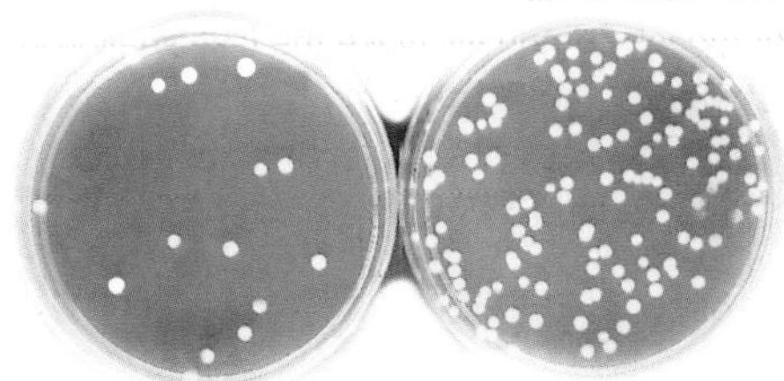

Figure 5
Agar nutrient medium, which contains minerals and a source of energy, is used to grow bacteria. Each bacterium in a water sample divides into many cells, forming colonies that can be seen on the agar plate. The greater the number of colonies, the more polluted the water sample is. Drinking water must produce no colonies of coliform bacteria per 100 mL. In contrast, swimming pools are permitted 200 colonies per 100 mL.

Dissolved Oxygen

A second indicator of water quality is dissolved oxygen. Several different solutions can be used to test for oxygen. The solutions change colour when they react with oxygen dissolved in a water sample. Lakes that are cooler and have fewer pollutants have levels of dissolved oxygen of between 8 and 14 mg/L. As dissolved oxygen begins to drop, fewer organisms can be supported.

Another way to determine dissolved oxygen levels is to examine the living things found in the water. Healthy trout indicate a high oxygen level; carp and catfish indicate a low level. A complete absence of fish may indicate that oxygen levels are very low, but it is also possible that there are toxins in the water that kill fish.

DID YOU KNOW?

River Rivals
The word *rival* comes from the Latin word *rivus* (stream). The first rivals were people who lived along the same stream—and competed for the same water.

INVESTIGATION 4.3 *Introduction*

Biological Oxygen Demand and Organic Pollutants

Thermal energy and nutrients can deplete the levels of dissolved oxygen in aquatic systems, and this can have dramatic effects on the community of organisms in an aquatic ecosystem. In this investigation, you will determine the biological oxygen demand (BOD) of an artificial aquatic ecosystem and observe how changes in thermal energy and nutrient levels affect BOD.

Report Checklist

○ Purpose	● Design	● Analysis
● Problem	○ Materials	● Evaluation
● Hypothesis	○ Procedure	○ Synthesis
● Prediction	● Evidence	

To perform this investigation, turn to page 126. 

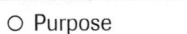

biological oxygen demand (BOD) the amount of dissolved oxygen needed by decomposers to completely break down the organic matter in a water sample at 20 °C over five days

Biological Oxygen Demand

To narrow down the causes of low dissolved oxygen levels, it is possible to test the **biological oxygen demand (BOD)**. The BOD is a measure of the amount of dissolved oxygen needed by decomposers (bacteria) to break down the organic matter in a sample of water over a five-day period at 20 °C. The BOD indicates the amount of available organic matter in a water sample. As the number of organisms in an ecosystem increases, so does the biological oxygen demand. A cold, less productive lake with fewer organisms might have a BOD near 2 mg of oxygen per litre, while a more productive lake with many living things might have a BOD as high as 20 mg/L.

It is important to note that, as the number of organisms increases and biological oxygen demand increases, more organisms use oxygen from the water. This causes the level of dissolved oxygen to decrease.

Too many nutrients can create problems for a lake. Consider the problems when cities release sewage into aquatic ecosystems without treatment. (Montreal releases untreated solid wastes into the St. Lawrence River. Victoria, St. John's, and Halifax release wastes into their harbours.) The greater the amount of decaying matter introduced into the water, the greater will be the population of decomposing bacteria. Unfortunately, both bacteria and fish use oxygen. While some species of fish have greater oxygen requirements than others, all fish eventually die if oxygen levels drop too low. Moreover, the death of fish adds detritus to the ecosystem. That detritus further promotes growth of the bacterial population. In turn, this causes oxygen levels to drop even more. To make matters even worse, human wastes act much like fertilizers by introducing nitrogen and phosphates into the ecosystem. The added nutrients promote the growth of plants and algae, which will eventually die and be decomposed. Each time organic matter is returned or added to an aquatic ecosystem, oxygen levels are further reduced.

CAREER CONNECTION

Environmental Education Specialist

Environmental education specialists encourage others to make responsible decisions about our environment by designing and delivering educational programs. They may be employed as guides and naturalists by both public and private sector organizations.

Do your personal characteristics match those of an environmental education specialist?

www.science.nelson.com 

INVESTIGATION 4.4 *Introduction*

Biological Indicators of Pollution in Streams

Ecologists use "indicator species" to determine the health of a stream. In this activity, you will collect organisms from a stream to provide indirect evidence of pollution.

Report Checklist

- ○ Purpose
- ○ Problem
- ○ Hypothesis
- ● Prediction
- ○ Design
- ○ Materials
- ● Procedure
- ● Evidence
- ● Analysis
- ● Evaluation
- ○ Synthesis

To perform this investigation, turn to page 127. 

Practice

4. List types of pollution that cause reduced levels of dissolved oxygen in aquatic ecosystems. For each type of pollution, explain in your own words how dissolved oxygen is affected.
5. Which would show a higher biological oxygen demand: a sample of water from a cold lake or a sample of water from a warm lake? Explain your answer.
6. Describe two ways in which phosphates can get into surface water.

Figure 6
Muriel Lake

Changes in Alberta Lakes

Cottage owners throughout Alberta have become aware that some shorelines are receding at an alarming rate. One of Alberta's receding lakes is Muriel Lake (**Figure 6**), located just south of Bonnyville in north-central Alberta. The water level has dropped more than 3 m between 1975 and 2005 (**Figure 7**, next page). At the same time, the salt content

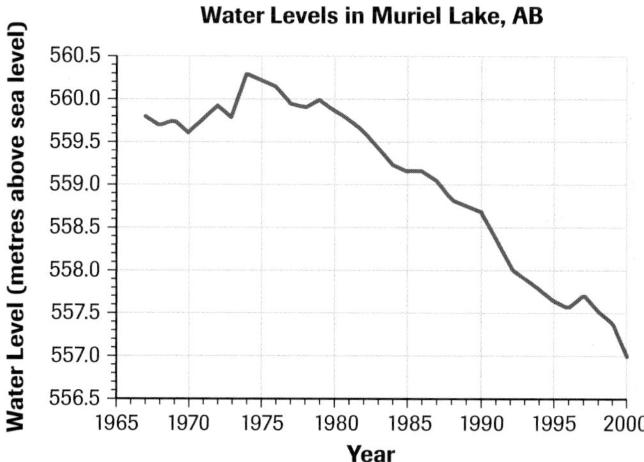

Figure 7
Muriel Lake's water level has steadily declined.

("salinity") has increased and the lake is now classified as slightly saline. As the concentration of dissolved solids has increased, oxygen levels have fallen.

The area of land that drains toward a lake is called the lake's **watershed**. Over time, a waterfront environment develops a natural balance among biotic and abiotic factors along the shoreline. This delicate equilibrium can easily be disrupted. Cottage dwellers have altered shorelines in many ways. Making a sandy beach increases erosion, while planting lawns increases nitrogen and phosphate runoff from fertilizers.

watershed the land that drains toward a lake or other body of water

Even removing shoreline plants profoundly affects the aquatic environment. These plants act as a filtering system by slowing the movement of potentially harmful chemicals from the land into the lake. Soil bacteria have more time to break down these chemicals, and the roots of many aquatic plants absorb them. In addition, shoreline plants provide shade, which keeps the water cooler, allowing it to hold more oxygen gas. Because shorelines are so vital to the existence of a lake, they remain crown land around most lakes. In Alberta, you need a permit to build a pier on a shore bed or alter the shoreline for most lakes.

One of the most serious problems presented by cottages is caused by sewage from outhouses seeping into lakes. The high levels of nutrients that are released cause eutrophication of the lake and declining dissolved oxygen levels (**Figure 8**).

Water and Farmland

Human activities have caused soil to deteriorate and deserts to expand. Globally, about 21 million hectares of farmland are lost every year. According to Bill Rees, a resource ecologist at the University of British Columbia, we produced 14 % less grain per capita in 1990 than we did in 1984.

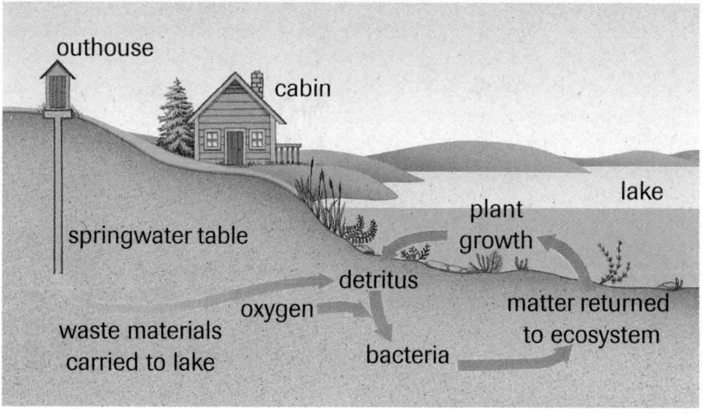

Figure 8
Human wastes are broken down by bacteria, which function as decomposers in the lake's ecosystem.

Increased erosion and the accelerated flow of nutrients into lakes speed the aging process of lakes. Enhanced plant growth along the shoreline can produce dense mats of organic matter that decompose during hot summer days. The decomposing plants release distinctive odours and change the taste of the water.

DID YOU KNOW ?

Alberta's Fish Populations

Alberta has very few fish-bearing lakes (800) compared with lakes in many other provinces. Only 2.5 % of the province is covered by water. By comparison, Ontario has 250 000 fish-bearing lakes, while Saskatchewan has 94 000.

Changes in Alberta's lakes have also been linked to climate change. Higher temperatures increase evaporation rates but do not increase precipitation. This lowers water levels and raises lake temperatures, creating problems for coldwater fish. Trout, for example, lose parts of their habitat and are replaced by fish such as perch, which can withstand warmer temperatures. As the global temperature increases, droughts will become more frequent and river and stream flows will slow down. As a result, the movement of water into and out of lakes will decrease. Minerals in lakes will have time to settle, and the concentration of sodium and chloride ions in lakes will increase. Nitrogen and phosphorus concentrations will also increase.

Practice

7. Indicate some factors that would cause a dramatic change in the shoreline of a lake.
8. How could the removal of plants from along the shoreline have a negative impact upon a lake?
9. Drilling companies pump water into oil wells to increase oil extraction. Because the oil is less dense than fresh water, the oil is pushed closer to the surface, making extraction less expensive. Indicate both positive and potentially negative impacts of this practice.
10. Alberta's lakes are a valuable recreational resource. Should the number of cottages built along the shoreline be restricted?

WWW WEB Activity

Web Quest—Whose Lake Is It?

Alberta's natural resources are highly valued by many different stakeholders. Have you ever thought about all of the different ways that people see resources such as lakes and rivers? This Web Quest explores issues surrounding Sylvan Lake. You will research how one lake can be so many different things to so many different people. You will then take a stand and participate in a town hall meeting concerning Sylvan Lake.

www.science.nelson.com 

EXPLORE an issue

Issue Checklist

● Issue ○ Design ● Analysis
● Resolution ● Evidence ● Evaluation

Selling Water

Have you ever thought of water as money? In many respects it may become our most precious natural resource. Water is essential to human life, both for drinking and in the production of our food. In 1960, the world's human population was only 3 billion. Today, it is over 6 billion. By 2030 it will increase to 8 billion and by 2200 to 10 billion. The world faces major food shortages, as more than 800 million people remain hungry around the world. Food production must be increased.

One technological solution involves diverting fresh water from remote northern lakes and rivers to the parched farmlands and cities of the south. The Republic of Uzbekistan was the first to employ giant engineering schemes that changed the pathways of rivers and created new lakes. With 75 % of its population living in the southwest but more than 80 % of its rivers draining into less populated regions of the Arctic, a plan was devised to distribute water to greater advantage. Irrigation systems supported by the diverted water sources changed millions of hectares of marginal land into farms. Unfortunately, the increase in productive land has not been without problems. For example, two large rivers were diverted away from the Aral Sea, once the world's fourth largest body of inland water. Deprived of this water, the Aral Sea has shrunk dramatically. Experts predict it will disappear altogether by 2010. The last fish was caught in 1983.

To make matters worse, the irrigation techniques have gradually made the soil salty. More than 26 000 km^2 are no longer arable. Crop production increased dramatically after the irrigation systems were built, but since then it has has fallen sharply.

Two similar projects have been proposed for North America. The GRAND project would dam James Bay, slowly converting it into a large freshwater lake. The water would be diverted southward to the Great Lakes where it could be exported south of the border. The second proposal, referred to as NAWAPA, is even more grandiose. The scheme would divert water from the Mackenzie River basin southward, flooding a trench along the Rocky Mountains. The huge freshwater canal would carry water to the vegetable farmers and vine growers of California. **Figure 9** outlines the two proposed projects.

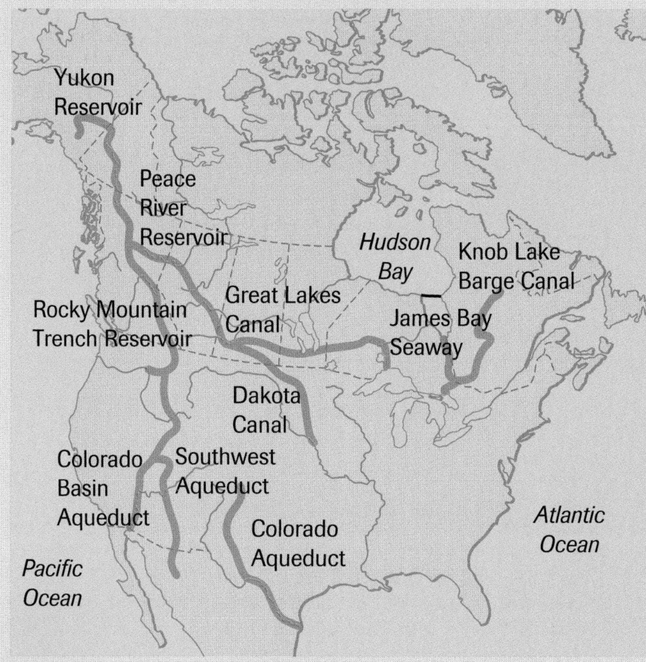

Figure 9
Several huge projects have been proposed to divert water southward.

The Benefits

Opinion of a taxpayer and concerned citizen: Fresh water could be diverted to the rich farmlands of the Midwest and the expanding cities of the United States. This would provide Canada with many economic benefits. We sell other resources such as oil and coal, so why not water?

Opinion of California vegetable grower: Canada and the United States are part of a free-trade agreement that is designed to benefit both countries. Resources must be looked at beyond that of boundaries. Having water carry fish to the Arctic will not help feed people. Water must be diverted to where it can do the most good.

The Risks

Wildlife biologist: Projects like GRAND will have a major impact on wildlife. Many species of marine organisms will be destroyed. In addition, the channel between the new lake and the Great Lakes will serve as a highway for many new predators and parasites. This could change the food chain in the Great Lakes and cause the destruction of certain fish stocks.

Climatologist: Water from southern rivers warms the Arctic Ocean. Diverting these waters southward would change Canada's climate. Removal of this important heat source would mean longer winters and shorter growing seasons in the north. There is no telling what the impact would be.

1. How would irrigation of farmlands benefit consumers?
2. Why have water diversion projects been proposed?
3. What are the two main proposals for diverting water?
4. Should large-scale irrigation projects be initiated?
5. Should Canada consider selling water?

SUMMARY *Changes in Ecosystems*

- Forests affect climate by recycling water (by transpiration) and carbon dioxide and help to control water runoff, hold groundwater, and prevent soil erosion. Old-growth forests contain many fallen trees that slowly decompose, providing a constant source of nutrients for the soil.
- Three methods of deforestation are slash and burn, clear-cutting, and selective cutting. Each has positive and negative environmental effects.
- Fires help maintain and rejuvenate forest and grassland ecosystems.
- Oligotrophic lakes are usually cold and have low nutrient levels. Eutrophic lakes tend to be warmer and have higher nutrient levels. Oligotrophic lakes often become eutrophic as they age and warm.
- Five categories of water pollution are organic solid waste, disease-causing organisms, inorganic solids wastes and dissolved minerals, thermal energy, and organic chemicals.

- High bacteria counts and falling oxygen levels indicate water pollution.
- Biological oxygen demand (BOD) is a measure of the amount of dissolved oxygen needed by decomposers to break down the organic matter in a sample of water over a five-day period at 20 °C. As the amount of organic matter increases, so does the BOD.

Section 4.5 Questions

1. Perform a risk–benefit analysis report for clear-cutting.
2. In British Columbia alone, more than twice as many trees are harvested than from all U.S. national forests. During a protest staged against the clear-cutting of an old-growth forest in the Clayoquot Sound area on Vancouver Island, environmentalists blocked a logging road. Do you believe that such protests are justified? Give your reasons.
3. By law, national parks in Canada are areas that are protected for public understanding, appreciation, and enjoyment.
   (a) Identify specific regulations that pertain to national parks.
   (b) Discuss why these regulations need to be in place.
   (c) Propose a regulation that you think would protect national parks even more than they are protected today.
   (d) Make a list of things that you need to take into consideration when you go to a national park.

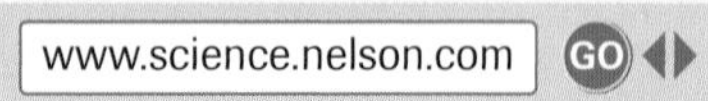

4. Use **Figure 4**, on page 116, to answer the following questions.
   (a) What happens to the depth of a lake over time?
   (b) Explain how the mean water temperature is related to the depth of the lake.
   (c) How would a change in lake temperature affect the types and numbers of plants found in the area?
   (d) Describe the changes in the species and populations of fish you would expect to find in a lake that progresses through the three stages of eutrophication.
   (e) Explain why turtles might be found in the second stage but not the first.
5. After complaints were received from fishers on a river (**Figure 10**), the data in **Figure 11** were collected from three sites.
   (a) What is the source of nitrates and phosphates?
   (b) In which area of the river would you find the highest level of eutrophication? Explain your answer.
   (c) Why does the BOD increase from site A to site B?
   (d) Why does the BOD decrease from site B to site C?
   (e) Sewage treatment plants are supposed to remove organic waste. Is the plant doing a good job?
6. Design and conduct an investigation to determine how water temperature affects algal growth. Based on your results, how would you expect surface thermal pollution to affect dissolved oxygen levels in the epilimnion and hypolimnion of a lake? Draw diagrams illustrating your hypothesis.

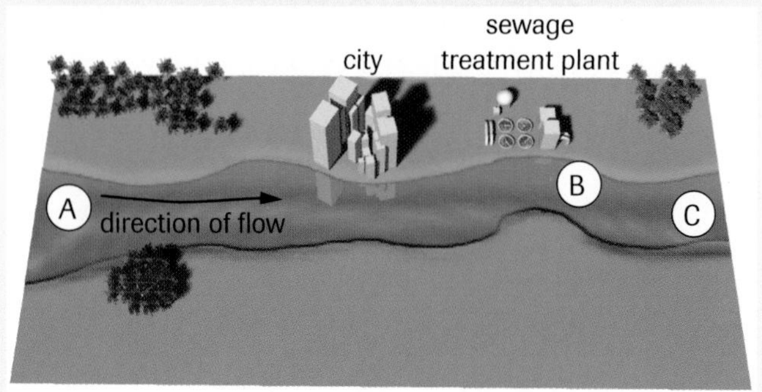

Figure 10
A polluted river with test sites

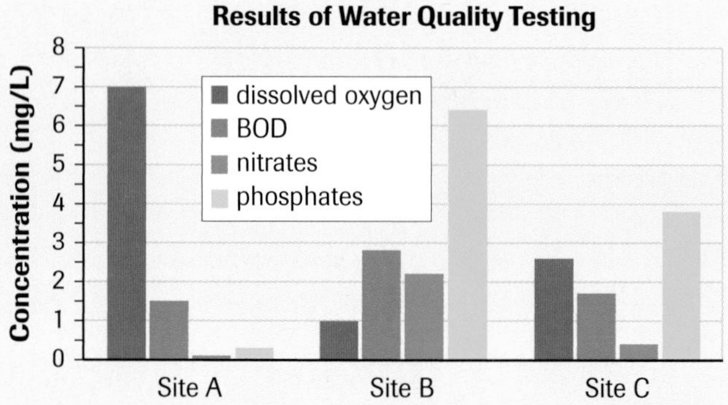

Figure 11

7. (a) Identify aquatic systems in your own area that you would expect to contain high levels of phosphates. Explain your prediction.
   (b) Take water samples from the identified systems and test for phosphates. Evaluate your prediction.
8. Small communities often discharge sewage into fields. Bacteria break down the organic wastes, releasing nutrients such as phosphates and nitrogen. Plants growing in the fields absorb the nutrients.
   (a) What advice would you give a small community investigating this approach to waste treatment?
   (b) Identify potential problems if the field is located in a valley that floods every spring.

INVESTIGATION 4.1

Report Checklist

- ○ Purpose
- ○ Problem
- ○ Hypothesis
- ● Prediction
- ○ Design
- ○ Materials
- ○ Procedure
- ● Evidence
- ● Analysis
- ● Evaluation
- ● Synthesis

A Schoolyard Ecosystem

To gain a better understanding of the impact of environmental change on living things within ecosystems, you do not have to go far. You can begin by investigating your schoolyard, and how living things there respond to local biotic and abiotic factors. A weed is classified as any plant the human caretaker does not want. Location can affect the distribution of common weeds.

Problem

To determine how abiotic factors affect the distribution of plants commonly considered weeds

Prediction

Abiotic factors play an important role in determining which plants can succeed in a given area. In this investigation you will study sites on the north and south sides of your school building.

(a) Predict which site will contain the most weeds. Explain your prediction.

Materials

string
8 sticks
tape
table-tennis ball
field guides for common weeds
protractor
metre stick or measuring tape
plastic bottle cap
light meter
thermometer
thread

Procedure

1. Set up equal study sites on the north and south sides of the school. Using string and 4 sticks mark off each study site as shown in **Figure 1**. Make sure you push the sticks completely into the ground. Calculate and record the area of each study site.

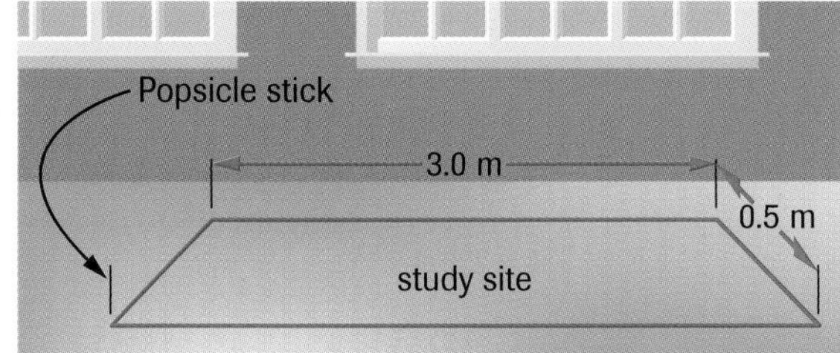

Figure 1

2. Toss a plastic bottle cap into a study site. Using the light meter, determine the amount of light reaching the soil next to the bottle cap. Repeat the procedure at least twice more. Record your observations in a table similar to **Table 1**.

Table 1 Light Readings

Measurement	North study site (lux)	South study site (lux)
1		
2		
3		
mean		

(b) Why was the bottle cap tossed before light readings were taken?

3. Repeat the light measurements in the second study area. Calculate the mean for each set of measurements.
4. Using a thermometer, measure the soil surface temperature in the north and south study sites. Throw the bottle cap, as in step 5, to choose measurement locations. Record your observations in a table.
5. Construct an anemometer (a device to measure wind speed), as shown in **Figure 2**.

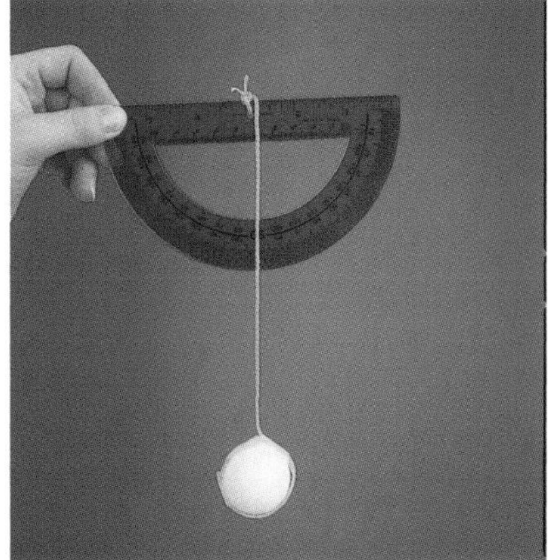

Figure 2
An anemometer

6. Make sure you are not blocking the wind. Point the thin edge of the anemometer into the wind. To measure wind speed, record how many degrees from vertical the thread is at the edge of the protractor. Take three readings in each study site and record them in a table. Record the time of day.
7. Using the conversion scale in **Table 2**, convert the degree readings to wind speeds.

Table 2 Conversion from Degrees to Wind Speed

Angle (°)	90	85	80	75	70	65	60
Wind speed (km/h)	0	9	13	16	19	21	24
Angle (°)	55	50	45	40	35	30	25
Wind speed (km/h)	26	29	32	35	38	42	46

8. Survey each study site by counting and recording the number and type of weeds in each site. Use the field guide to identify and name the species.
9. Within each of the study sites, record the coverage by each type of weed. Use a measuring tape or a metre stick to measure the diameter of each of the larger weeds in the study area.
10. Calculate the area covered by each weed using the formula

$$\text{area} = \frac{\pi d^2}{4}$$

For small weeds such as wild oats, you can measure the entire area covered by a grouping of weeds rather than the area covered by each individual plant.

Analysis and Evaluation

(c) Calculate the density of each kind of weed in the north and south study sites using the following formula:

$$\text{density} = \frac{\text{number of weeds}}{\text{area of the study side}}$$

(d) Determine the total number of weeds in each study site. Calculate the area covered by weeds in each study site.

(e) Comment on the accuracy of each instrument you used to take measurements. In each case, did the accuracy affect the reliability of your data? Explain.

(f) Was your prediction correct? Explain why or why not, based on your observations.

(g) Which abiotic factor do you think is most important for the growth of dandelions? Use your observations to create a hypothesis, and design an experiment that would allow you to test your hypothesis.

Synthesis

(h) You may have noticed that there are more weeds close to a building than in the open field. How would wind help explain that difference?

(i) How would the light meter help explain differences in weed distribution between the two study areas? Based on this investigation, could you tell if light or soil temperature is more important?

(j) Explain why unfavourable growing conditions for grass could increase the number of weeds in a study area.

(k) In which of the two study sites would you expect to find a larger animal population? Explain your answer.

(l) How do humans affect the distribution of weeds in your study areas?

(m) Examine a map of a new housing development. Provide some reasons that help explain the difference in selling price between two lots that are the same size but on different sides of the street.

(n) One biotic factor that affects distribution of plants is competition between plants. Design an experiment that would determine how competition from other plants affects the area covered by dandelions.

(o) You made several measurements and calculations in this investigation, including the density of each type of weed. Why would it be important for an ecologist to calculate the density of plants in an ecosystem?

INVESTIGATION 4.2

Report Checklist

● Purpose	○ Design	● Analysis
○ Problem	○ Materials	● Evaluation
○ Hypothesis	○ Procedure	● Synthesis
○ Prediction	● Evidence	

A Forest Ecosystem

Soil quality, air temperature, and amount of sunlight determine which plants will populate a region. Similarly, environmental conditions are affected by the distribution of plant life in an ecosystem. For example, soil quality affects the type and number of trees growing in a forest. However, the trees also affect the soil quality. The more leaves in an area, the greater the amount of decomposing organic matter and the better the soil quality. The number of trees also affects wind and shade, which in turn affect soil quality and the growth of smaller plants on the forest floor.

Purpose

To identify trees in a study site, and determine the relationships between environmental conditions and the plant community and between the plants and the physical factors in the site

Materials

4 craft sticks
graph paper
light meter
measuring tape
felt pen
notebook
string
thermometer

Procedure

1. Tie four 10 m sections of string between craft sticks. Put the craft sticks in the ground to make a study area as shown in **Figure 1**.

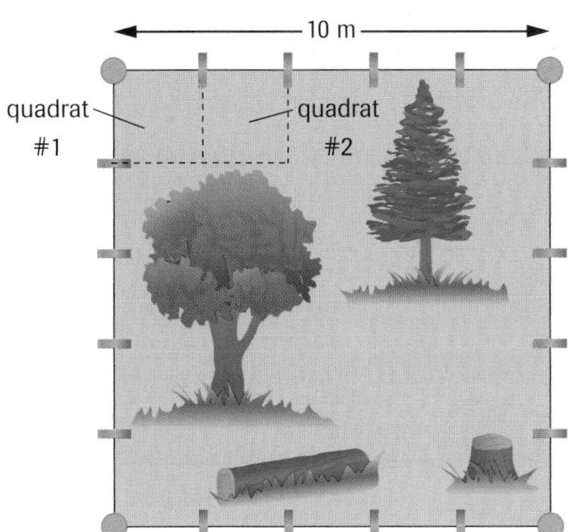

Figure 1

2. Using a measuring tape and felt pen, make a mark every 2 m along the strings. Use these marks to divide the study site into sections or quadrats. Record the number of quadrats in your study site.

(a) Make a map of the study area on graph paper. Use the quadrats to help you draw the map. Indicate the dominant plant or plants found in each quadrat. Locate the positions of trees, shrubs, paths, fences, and other objects. Include a legend, such as the legend shown in **Table 1**.

Table 1 Legend for Study Site

Letter symbol	Description of vegetation	Map symbol
D	deciduous trees such as maple, aspen, and poplar	D (in square)
C	coniferous trees such as spruce, pine, hemlock, cedar, and fir	C (in circle)
S	shrubs such as pin cherry, dogwood, and willow. These woody plants grow under the canopy of the trees.	S (in oval)
G	wild grasses, such as crab grass	G (in triangle)
W	non-grass weeds, such as ragweed, thistle, dandelions, and stink weed	W (in diamond)
L	leaves, moss, lichens, and other litter	L (in rectangle)

3. Count and record the number of large (over 3 m tall) deciduous trees, large (over 3 m tall) coniferous trees, and shrubs in the study area.

(b) Use plant guidebooks to determine the types of trees, shrubs, and smaller plants in the study area.

4. With a measuring tape, determine the amount of shade provided by each tree. Take and record measurements on at least two sides of the tree.

(c) On your map, indicate the shade provided by each large tree.

5. Take soil temperature readings at 0 m, 2 m, 4 m, 6 m, 8 m, and 10 m in your study area, by placing the bulb

INVESTIGATION 4.2 *continued*

of the thermometer on the surface of the forest floor. Do not hold the bulb of the thermometer with your fingers.

(d) Record the soil temperatures on your map, at the exact locations.

Analysis

(e) Calculate the area of the study site.

(f) Determine the density of deciduous trees, coniferous trees, and shrubs in the study site, using the following formula.

$$\text{density} = \frac{\text{number of trees}}{\text{area used in the study}}$$

(g) Using the quadrats on your map to help, estimate the percentage of your study site that is shaded by the trees.

(h) Present your temperature data in table format.

Evaluation

(i) In step 5, you were instructed not to hold the bulb of the thermometer. Explain why this instruction was given.

(j) Did you find a greater number of shrubs and weeds in the shaded areas or the open areas of your study site? Provide a theory that helps explain your observation.

Synthesis

(k) Why do dense forests usually have moist soil?

(l) How do dead leaves on the forest floor help increase soil moisture?

(m) Why are the shrubs and small plants of dense forests less affected by wind than the grasses of the open prairies?

(n) Describe how sunlight affects soil temperature and soil moisture.

INVESTIGATION 4.3

Biological Oxygen Demand and Organic Pollutants

As you have seen, thermal energy and nutrients can deplete dissolved oxygen in aquatic ecosystems. As oxygen levels drop, the community that can survive in the ecosystem changes. In this investigation, you will use methylene blue indicator to detect a change in oxygen levels. The indicator turns from blue to colourless when the oxygen content of the sample drops below a threshold level. The time taken for this colour change indicates the BOD.

The biological oxygen demand (BOD) is the amount of dissolved oxygen needed by decomposers to break down organic matter in the water. If more organic matter is introduced into an ecosystem, the population of decomposing bacteria will increase. This large population of bacteria requires more oxygen.

Purpose

To determine how nutrients and heat affect dissolved oxygen

Report Checklist

- ○ Purpose
- ● Problem
- ● Hypothesis
- ● Prediction
- ● Design
- ○ Materials
- ○ Procedure
- ● Evidence
- ● Analysis
- ● Evaluation
- ● Synthesis

Prediction

(a) Predict which sample will have the greatest BOD.

Always handle hot plates and heated items with care.

Materials

safety goggles
safety apron
water
500 mL beaker
hot plate
thermometer
brewer's yeast
mass balance
10 mL graduated cylinder
two 50 mL flasks
stirring rod
waterproof marker
11 mL homogenized milk
four 20 mL test tubes
test-tube rack
medicine dropper
methylene blue indicator
timing device
beaker clamp

INVESTIGATION 4.3 *continued*

Procedure

1. Make a hot-water bath by pouring about 400 mL of water into a 500 mL beaker and placing the beaker on a hot plate. Heat the water until the temperature reaches 40 °C . Using a thermometer, periodically check that the water temperature is maintained near 40 °C.
2. While the water is heating, measure 5 g of brewer's yeast with a mass balance. Pour 20 mL of water into a 50 mL flask, then add the yeast. Gently stir until the yeast dissolves. Label the flask "yeast."
3. Prepare a 25 % milk solution: mix 5 mL of milk and 15 mL of water in a 50 mL flask. Label the flask "25 % milk solution."
4. Label four test tubes 1, 2, 3, or 4 and put them in the test-tube rack. Add 3 mL of 100 % milk to test tubes 1 and 2. Add 3 mL of 25 % milk solution to test tubes 3 and 4.
5. When the temperature of the hot-water bath reaches 40 °C, add two drops of methylene blue indicator to each of the test tubes (**Figure 1**).

Figure 1

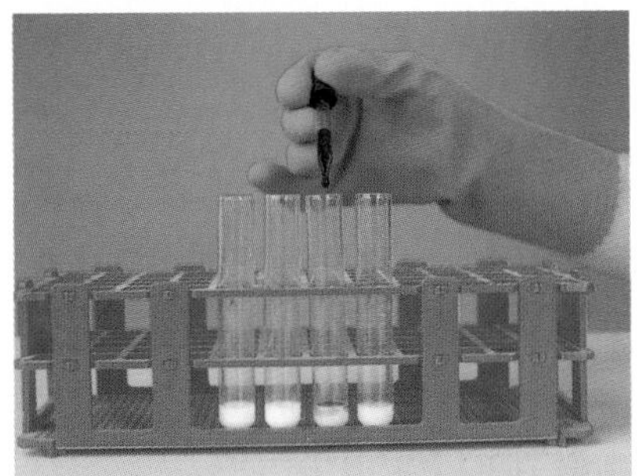

6. Rinse the graduated cylinder with tap water. Add 2 mL of the yeast solution to each of the test tubes. Place test tubes 1 and 3 in the hot-water bath and leave test tubes 2 and 4 in the test-tube rack. Record the time at which you put the tubes in the bath as time 0. Note the time when the methylene blue indicator turns colourless in each tube.

Analysis and Evaluation

(b) What was the source of organic matter used in this investigation?

(c) Yeast is a living organism. What purpose did the yeast serve in this investigation?

(d) A control was not used for the effect of nutrients on BOD levels. Devise such a control.

(e) Suggest some sources of error that might affect the outcome of this investigation.

(f) How does the concentration of nutrients affect the BOD?

(g) How does water temperature affect the BOD?

INVESTIGATION 4.4

Biological Indicators of Pollution in Streams

Report Checklist

○ Purpose	○ Design	● Analysis
○ Problem	○ Materials	● Evaluation
○ Hypothesis	● Procedure	○ Synthesis
● Prediction	● Evidence	

Many different pollutants can affect water quality. No single test can be used to assess water quality; however, an examination of the plants and animals found in the system can be used as a useful indicator of pollution in streams. Species that are active, such as trout, have high oxygen demands, while those that are less active, such as slugworms, need much less oxygen.

When aquatic ecosystems contain high levels of oxygen, the active species gain the advantage in the competition for food and territory. When oxygen levels are low, however, less active species gain the advantage. **Table 1**, on the next page, correlates oxygen level with species expected in freshwater systems.

Table 1 Oxygen Levels and Species

Oxygen level (mg/L)	Description	Species present
8 and above	high level of dissolved oxygen is positive for most species, resulting in high biodiversity	Fish: trout, jackfish, whitefish Invertebrates: mayfly larvae, caddis fly larvae, beetles, waterboatman
6 and above	level of dissolved oxygen sufficient for most species, although presence of active fish such as trout is less likely	Fish: perch, bottom feeders such as catfish Invertebrates: few mayfly larvae, some beetles, more worms (including leeches), slugworms.
4 and below	critical level for most fish; invertebrate populations increase	Fish: few Invertebrates: freshwater shrimp, many midge larvae, slugworms, leeches
2 and below	too low for fish	Invertebrates: some midge larvae, some slugworms, many small protozoans (amoebae)

It is important to note that the presence of a species usually identified with low levels of oxygen, such as the slugworm, does not mean that the water is polluted or even that oxygen levels are low. Slugworms can be found in well-oxygenated waters; however, their numbers tend to be lower.

Prediction

If a stream contains only organisms that do well when dissolved oxygen content is low, then the amount of dissolved oxygen in the stream will be low.

(a) Examine the stream you will investigate and the territory it flows through. Predict whether dissolved oxygen levels in the water will be high or low.

Materials

field guides to birds, fish, and invertebrates
high boots
plankton net
hand lens
bottom dredger
shovel
pan
bucket with lid
forceps
dissolved oxygen kit

Procedure

1. Before entering the stream, watch for fish and birds such as ducks and wading birds. Identify those you see, or record their colouring and shape for later identification.
2. Use a plankton net to take samples from the surface water. Examine the plankton with a hand lens. Record the type and population of the organisms you find.
3. Using a bottom dredger and a shovel, collect a sample from the streambed (**Figure 1**). Place the sample in a large pan and examine the organisms using the forceps and a hand lens. Be careful not to injure any organisms. Record your observations. Return the sample to the stream.

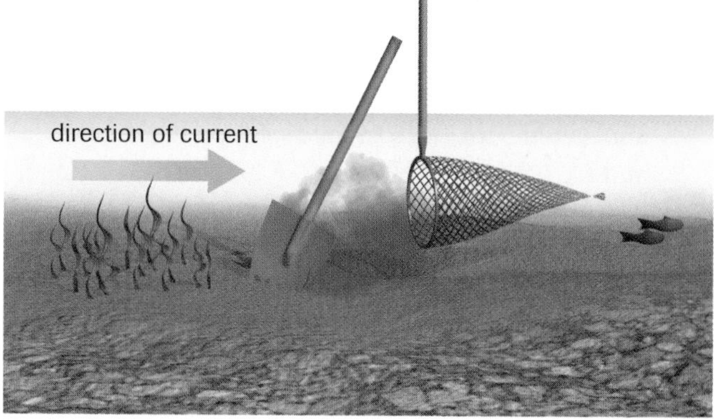

Figure 1

4. Use a bucket to collect a water sample from the stream. Using a dissolved oxygen kit, measure the amount of oxygen in the water.

Analysis and Evaluation

(b) Was your prediction correct? How do you account for any discrepancy between your observations and your prediction?

(c) Identify potential sources of pollution for this ecosystem.

(d) Suggest a method for determining the amount of plankton collected. How could one test site be compared with another?

(e) Using **Table 1** and your observations, rate the effects of pollution on the ecosystem you analyzed.

(f) Make a food web of the organisms you found.

(g) Make a pyramid of numbers for the organisms you found in the stream according to the following classification: producers; primary consumers; secondary consumers; decomposers.

Chapter 4 SUMMARY

Outcomes

Knowledge

- define and explain the interrelationship among species, population, community, and ecosystem (4.1)
- explain how a terrestrial and an aquatic ecosystem supports a diversity of organisms through a variety of habitats and niches (4.1, 4.2)
- identify biotic and abiotic characteristics and explain their influence in an aquatic and a terrestrial ecosystem in a local region (4.1, 4.2, 4.3, 4.5)
- explain how limiting factors influence organism distribution and range (4.4)

STS

- explain that science and technology have both intended and unintended consequences for humans and the environment (4.1, 4.5)

Skills

- ask questions by hypothesizing the ecological role of biotic and abiotic factors (4.1, 4.2, 4.3, 4.4)
- conduct investigations and gather and record data and information by: performing a field study to measure, quantitatively, abiotic characteristics of ecosystems and to gather evidence for analysis of the diversity of life of the ecosystem(s) studied (4.1, 4.2)
- analyze data and apply mathematical and conceptual models by: analyzing the interrelationship of biotic and abiotic characteristics that make up the ecosystem(s) studied in the field (4.1, 4.2) and; evaluating the accuracy and reliability of instruments used for measurement and identifying the degree of error in the field study data (4.1, 4.2, 4.5)
- work as members of a team and apply the skills and conventions of science (all)

Key Terms

4.1

ecology
abiotic factor
biotic factor
ecotone
artificial ecosystem
natural ecosystem
ecological niche

4.2

biome
canopy
permafrost
muskeg
understorey
littoral zone
limnetic zone
plankton
profundal zone

4.3

litter
topsoil
humus
subsoil
bedrock
groundwater
epilimnion
hypolimnion
thermocline

4.4

biotic potential
carrying capacity
law of the minimum
law of tolerance
density-independent factor
density-dependent factor

4.5

slash-and-burn
clear-cutting
selective cutting
prescribed burn
oligotrophic
eutrophic
coliform bacteria
biological oxygen demand (BOD)
watershed

MAKE a summary

1. Use as many key words as possible in the chapter to complete a fish bone diagram.
2. Revisit your answers to the Starting Points questions at the start of the chapter. Would you answer the questions differently now? Why?

Go To www.science.nelson.com GO

The following components are available on the Nelson Web site. Follow the links for *Nelson Biology Alberta 20–30.*

- an interactive Self Quiz for Chapter 4
- additional Diploma Exam-style Review Questions
- Illustrated Glossary
- additional IB-related material

There is more information on the Web site wherever you see the Go icon in the chapter.

▸ Chapter 4 REVIEW

Many of these questions are in the style of the Diploma Exam. You will find guidance for writing Diploma Exams in Appendix A5. Science Directing Words used in Diploma Exams are in bold type. Exam study tips and test-taking suggestions are on the Nelson Web site.

www.science.nelson.com 

DO NOT WRITE IN THIS TEXTBOOK.

Part 1

1. Write the numbers for the four factors that can cause a population to increase. (Record all four digits of your answer in lowest-to-highest numerical order.)
NR
1. low reproductive rate
2. ability to adapt to change
3. favourable light
4. highly specific niche
5. generalized niche
6. ability to compete

Use the following information to answer questions 2 and 3.

Yellow-headed blackbirds are typically found in marshes from the Great Lakes to the Pacific Ocean. Their population size is influenced by water levels and vegetation density. **Table 1** shows the yellow-headed blackbird population and the amount of rainfall from 1992 to 1999 in a marsh area.

Table 1 Yellow-headed Blackbird Populations and Amount of Rainfall

Year	Number of birds, site 1	Number of birds, site 2	Amount of rainfall (cm)
1992	24	28	13
1993	80	88	38
1994	75	86	35
1995	55	74	30
1996	70	98	43
1997	105	186	62
1998	90	130	50
1999	21	22	16

2. According to the data, what is the relationship between water level and population?
A. As water levels decrease, the bird population declines.
B. As water levels increase, the bird population declines.
C. As water levels decrease, the bird population increases.
D. There is no relationship between water levels and the bird population.

3. According to the data in **Table 1**, which statement is correct?
A. Site 1 had the greater number of birds, due to the area being protected from predators.
B. Site 1 had the greater number of birds, due to the area having more water.
C. Site 2 had the greater number of birds, due to the area being protected from predators.
D. Site 2 had the greater number of birds, due to the area having more water.

Use the following information to answer questions 4 to 6.

The temperatures of the air, in the litter (dead leaves on the ground), in the humus (topsoil 10 cm below the surface) and in the mineral layer (30 cm below the surface) were monitored in a deciduous forest throughout a day. The data appear in **Figure 1**.

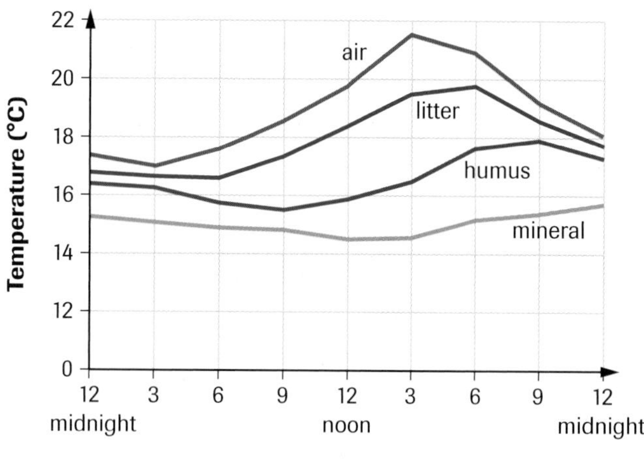

Figure 1

4. In which area of the forest did the greatest variation in temperature occur?
A. air
B. litter
C. humus
D. mineral

5. Which abiotic factor would account for the greatest difference in temperature readings in the litter?
A. wind
B. exposure to sunlight
C. soil moisture
D. thickness of litter

6. For the experiment described above, the dependent variable (responding variable) and independent variable (manipulated variable) are, respectively:
A. temperature and type of soil
B. type of soil and time
C. temperature and time
D. time and temperature

7. Forest fires have a beneficial role in ecosystems because they
   A. clear the ground so water can be absorbed into the soil.
   B. enrich the soil by returning nutrients.
   C. drive exotic plants out of ecosystems where they don't belong.
   D. reduce the number of predators in an area by destroying their homes.

8. Increased algae growth in a lake can occur because of
   A. decreased pH
   B. decreased water temperatures
   C. increased carbon levels
   D. increased nitrogen or phosphate levels

Part 2

Use the following information to answer questions 9 to 12.

Figure 2 is a Venn diagram showing species overlapping between a pond and a grassland.

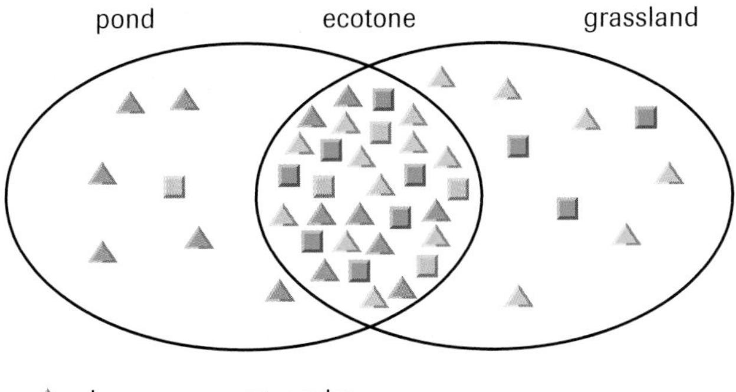

Figure 2

9. **Identify** producers within the ecosystem. DE

10. **Describe** the abiotic conditions that are likely in the ecotone between the pond and the grassland. DE

11. **Why** is the greatest number of species found in the ecotone? DE

12. **Predict** how pollution of the ecotone might affect the grassland and pond ecosystems. DE

13. Using the field mouse or the lemming as an example, **explain** the limits on the size of a population.

14. **Describe** the evidence you have gathered in this chapter that supports the statement that ecosystems must change to remain stable.

15. **Identify** the factors affect the distribution of small shrubs in a dense forest.

16. Using a chart, **compare** the abiotic factors in oligotrophic and eutrophic lakes.

17. **Compare** dissolved oxygen levels and light intensity in the epilimnion and hypolimnion of eutrophic and oligotrophic lakes.

18. (a) **Describe** the spring and fall turnovers as they occur in most Canadian lakes.
    (b) Costa Rica is a Central American country that is much closer to the equator than Canada. **Explain** how the process of turnover in a deep lake in Costa Rica might differ from that in a deep lake in Canada.

19. **Sketch** food webs in a lake as the lake changes from oligotrophic to eutrophic.

20. When the population of white-tailed deer becomes large, they destroy the vegetation, drastically altering the entire ecosystem and placing other populations, both plants and animals, in peril. Once food supplies decline, the deer herd becomes more prone to disease and starvation. This problem is developing in the foothills of Alberta. Controlled hunting has been proposed as a solution. There are several different opinions on whether hunting of white-tailed deer should be allowed in the foothills.
    (a) **Identify** the perspective for each of the statements below.
    (b) Do you agree with each statement? **Explain** your reasons for agreeing or disagreeing.
    - Once deer populations increase beyond the food supply, the herd will become ill. Some will die, and others will be taken by predators, removing the weak from the population. This will eventually strengthen the herd—only the strong remain. Generally, hunters shoot only the largest and healthiest animals. Hunting will weaken the deer.
    - The Alberta foothills are visited regularly by the general public, and camping is allowed in some campgrounds. Hunting might create dangers for tourists.
    - If deer eat too much of the local vegetation, there will be no more food left and they will begin to starve. It is more humane to allow hunting than to allow the deer to starve.

21. In an attempt to compare the amount of undissolved solids at two different sites in a lake, the following procedure is followed at each site.

    Procedure
    - The mass of a cheesecloth is measured using a triple-beam balance.
    - The cheesecloth is placed over the opening of a kitchen sieve.
    - The sieve is moved back and forth in water for 5 minutes.
    - The cheesecloth is removed from the sieve and the mass of the cheesecloth is measured using the triple-beam balance.

    (a) **Identify** potential sources of error in the procedure described above.
    (b) **Describe** how the procedure might be improved.

chapter

5 Evolution

In this chapter

- Exploration: Curiosity Generates Questions
- Chemistry Connection: Classifying Chemicals
- Mini Investigation: Classifying Organisms
- Investigation 5.1: Using a Classification Key
- Mini Investigation: Puzzling over Evidence
- Web Activity: Finding Fossils and Famous Footprints
- Mini Investigation: Variations on a Theme
- Lab Exercise 5.A Evidence from Genetics
- Web Activity: Were Neanderthals Humans?
- Mini Investigation: Genetic Shuffle
- Investigation 5.2: Measuring Inherited Variation
- Web Activity: Lactose Intolerance and Evolution
- Web Activity: Natural Selection

Black widow spider females (**Figure 1**) often consume their partners during mating. How can such unusual behaviour be explained? To answer this question, biologists have to understand and apply of the theory of evolution.

Researcher Dr. Maydianne Andrade believes she has found the answer. Some male black widow spiders intentionally offer their abdomens as food to the females. The females normally mate with several males, store their sperm, and use it to fertilize as many as 3000 eggs. Males who do not sacrifice themselves rarely mate with more than one female. Males who volunteer their bodies as food during mating extend their mating time and transfer more sperm to the female, increasing their chances of fertilizing eggs. Thus, males who are eaten have more offspring than those who are not. These findings support the conclusion that the volunteering-for-cannibalism behaviour has evolved because it increases the reproductive success of males who perform such behaviour.

Evolution is a compelling scientific theory that explains not only how organisms change over time, but also the diversity of species. To appreciate and judge the significance and validity of this theory, it is important to examine the evidence and to review the nature of science as a way of gaining knowledge. As you will learn, evolutionary biology is a modern science that provides answers about the past and has present-day applications in many fields of study, from medicine to conservation biology.

STARTING Points

Answer these questions as best you can with your current knowledge. Then, using the concepts and skills you have learned, you will revise your answers at the end of the chapter.

1. Domesticated animals such as dogs, cats, horses, and cattle are descended from wild animals. Why do many different domesticated breeds now exist? How could breeders have produced animals with traits that their wild ancestors did not have?
2. Penguins, ostriches, and eagles share many similar features, while fish, antelopes, and bats do not. Offer an explanation for such findings.
3. Why are some bacteria becoming immune to antibiotics?
4. The vast majority of fossil species are no longer alive today, and many species that are alive today are not found as fossils. Why?

Career Connections: Paleontologist; Breeder

Figure 1
A male of the black widow spider increases his reproductive success when he allows the female, shown here, to consume his body during mating.

Exploration — Curiosity Generates Questions

Most humans are curious by nature, and scientists particularly so. Whenever someone witnesses an unusual event or discovers an unusual object, questions immediately arise. What caused the event? Where did the object originate? When we try to answer such questions, we start with the knowledge and beliefs we already have.

Carefully examine the puzzling images in **Figure 2**.

(a) Generate two questions about each image.
(b) Based on background knowledge and understanding you already have, write short answers to your own questions.
(c) Exchange your question set with a fellow student. Record and respond to his or her questions.
(d) Was it difficult to generate questions about the images in **Figure 2**?
(e) Was it difficult to answer the questions? How confident do you feel about the accuracy of your answers?
(f) What specific steps would you take to better answer these questions?
(g) Would you describe your approach as a "scientific method?" Why?

(a)

(b)

(c)

(d)

Figure 2

5.1 Classification of Organisms

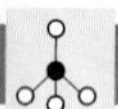

CHEMISTRY CONNECTION

Classifying Chemicals

Classification also plays an important role in chemistry. For example, scientists can predict the behaviour of elements in chemical reactions based on their position in the Periodic Table. Your chemistry textbook has more information on the use of classification in chemistry.

www.science.nelson.com 

Scientists estimate that there are at least 10 million different species alive today. However, this number is only a small part of the hundreds of millions of species that have existed on Earth over time. Understanding the dramatic history of Earth's changing biological diversity is the goal of evolutionary biology. Before studying how populations change over time (evolve), it is useful to understand Earth's current biological diversity. Biological diversity is usually a sign of a healthy ecosystem. When an ecosystem is biologically diverse, there is a higher chance that some organisms will survive changes in the ecosystem that arise.

There are two levels of biological diversity: (1) species diversity, which describes the number of different species; and (2) genetic diversity, which refers to the amount of variation in inherited traits between individuals of the same species. In this section, you will consider species diversity, by looking at how scientists use a classification system to understand the similarities and differences between species.

mini *Investigation* — Classifying Organisms

It is not always easy to classify an organism. To decide, a scientist makes careful observations. Clues are compiled based on organizing similarities and differences. Eventually, the clues can be linked and a conclusion can be drawn. Scientists then look for ways of testing their conclusions.

Examine the organisms in **Figures 1** to **6**.

(a) Speculate about which organisms are plants and which are animals. Give your reasons. *Hint:* recall the cellular differences between plants and animals.

(b) What test would you conduct on each of these organisms to determine whether they are plants, animals, or something else?

Figure 1
Fucus, a seaweed

Figure 2
Sponge

Figure 3
Brittle star

Figure 4
Coralina, a red alga

Figure 5
Sea anemone

Figure 6
Coral

Taxonomic Systems

Estimates of the number of living plant and animal species range somewhere between 2 and 4.5 million. Bacteria and other microorganisms add several more million species to this total. Many scientists believe that there may be up to four times this number, including many species that are now extinct. Is it any wonder, given the numbers and diversity of living things on this planet, that classification is a major field of biology? The science of classifying organisms is called **taxonomy**. Scientists who carry out this work are called *taxonomists*.

taxonomy the science of classification according to the inferred (presumed) relationships among organisms

Biological classification systems have two main purposes: identifying organisms and providing a basis for recognizing natural groupings of living things. However, classification systems are artificial. They are developed by scientists to help deal with the diversity of life and to represent relationships among organisms.

Our present biological system of classification was developed from the system created by Swedish botanist Carl Linnaeus (1707–1778). His system was based on an organism's physical and structural features, and operated on the idea that the more features organisms have in common, the closer their relationship.

Linnaeus created rules for assigning names to plants and animals. He was the first to use **binomial nomenclature**, which assigns each organism a two-part scientific name using Latin words. Latin (and sometimes Greek) is still used today for naming organisms, and provides a common language for all scientists. A scientific name is often based on some characteristic such as colour or habitat; an example is *Castor canadensis* (*Castor* meaning "beaver," and *canadensis* meaning "from Canada"). The first part of any scientific name is called the **genus** (plural: genera). Its first letter is always capitalized and can be written alone; for example, the *Acer* genus refers to maple trees. The second part is called the **species** and is never used alone; for example, *Acer rubrum* refers to the red maple. Living organisms within a species can usually only breed with members of their own species to produce fertile offspring.

binomial nomenclature a method of naming organisms by using two names—the genus name and the species name. Scientific names are italicized.

genus the first part of a binomial name; a genus includes several species

species a group of organisms that look alike and can interbreed under natural conditions to produce fertile offspring

The two-name system provides an added advantage by indicating similarities in anatomy, embryology, and evolutionary ancestry. For example, binomial nomenclature suggests that the North American black bear (*Ursus americanus*) and the grizzly bear (*Ursus horribilis*) are closely related. Similar organisms are grouped into the same genus. The giant Alaskan brown bear (*Ursus arctos*) and the polar bear (*Ursus maritimus*) are other relatives belonging to the same genus. By contrast, the koala bear and the panda do not belong to the genus *Ursus* and are not considered true bears.

In our present classification system, there are seven main levels or **taxa** (singular: taxon), as shown in **Table 1**.

taxa categories used to classify organisms

Table 1 Levels of Classification

Levels of classification	Dandelion	Housefly	Human
kingdom	Plantae	Animalia	Animalia
phylum	Tracheophyta	Arthropoda	Chordata
class	Angiospermae	Insecta	Mammalia
order	Asterates	Diptera	Primates
family	Compositae	Muscidae	Hominidae
genus	*Taraxacum*	*Musca*	*Homo*
species	*officinale*	*domestica*	*sapiens*

Comparing Plants and Animals at the Cellular Level
Listen to a comparison of the structural and functional characteristics of plants and animals at the level of their cells.

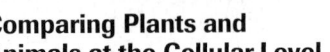

www.science.nelson.com 

Protista a kingdom originally proposed for all unicellular organisms such as the amoeba. More recently, multicellular algae have been added to the kingdom.

Monera in a five-kingdom system, a kingdom that includes organisms that lack a true nucleus

Archaebacteria in a six-kingdom system, a kingdom consisting of prokaryotic microorganisms distinct from eubacteria that possess a cell wall not containing peptidoglycan and that live in harsh environments such as salt lakes and thermal vents

Eubacteria in a six-kingdom system, a kingdom consisting of prokaryotic microorganisms that possess a peptidoglycan cell wall

Originally, the first level consisted of only two kingdoms: plants and animals. Later, single-celled organisms that displayed both plant and animal traits were discovered. To recognize this unique group, scientists created a third kingdom: **Protista**. However, shortly after the introduction of the protist kingdom, it was noted that certain microorganisms within this group shared an additional distinct feature. Bacteria and cyanobacteria, unlike protists, lack a true nucleus. This distinction resulted in the establishment of a fourth kingdom: **Monera**. The monerans are referred to as prokaryotes since the cells lack a true nucleus. All other groups of living organisms are known as eukaryotes. Later, taxonomists acknowledged that mushrooms and moulds are sufficiently different from plants and thus placed them in a separate kingdom called Fungi. This five-kingdom classification system, which includes Animalia, Plantae, Fungi, Protista, and Monera, was originally proposed by Robert Whittaker in 1969. It enjoyed wide acceptance until recently.

In the 1970s, microbiologist Carl Woese and other researchers at the University of Illinois conducted studies indicating that a group of prokaryotic microorganisms called **Archaebacteria** are sufficiently distinct from bacteria and other monerans that they constitute their own kingdom. Archaebacteria have been known for a long time. They thrive in harsh habitats such as salt lakes, hot springs, and the stomach chambers of cattle and other ruminants. Archaebacteria possess cell walls and ribosome components that are very different from those in **Eubacteria**. Eubacteria are prokaryotes that possess a rigid cell wall composed of peptidoglycan, a three-dimensional polymer containing carbohydrate and protein subunits. Thus, Woese and his colleagues proposed that the kingdom Monera be divided into two kingdoms, Archaebacteria and Eubacteria (true bacteria). The resulting six-kingdom system includes Animalia, Plantae, Fungi, Protista, Eubacteria, and Archaebacteria. **Table 2** on the next page summarizes a six-kingdom system of classification.

DNA sequencing studies conducted by Carol Bult and Carl Woese in 1996 revealed that some of the genes in archaebacteria are more closely related to the genes of humans and other eukaryotes than to those of eubacteria. Woese proposed that archaebacteria are so different from other prokaryotes that their name should not contain the term bacteria. He suggested the name *Archaea* for this group. While the six-kingdom system grows in popularity among biologists in general, many microbiologists feel that all traditional kingdom systems should be replaced with a system that better reflects the evolutionary history of life. This has led to a three-domain classification system (**Figure 7**). Scientists continue to update evolutionary history and classification schemes as more DNA evidence is collected and analyzed.

DID YOU KNOW?

Most Highly Evolved

Many scientists point out that humans may not be the most highly evolved creatures on the planet. The placement of humans at the top of the ladder is highly subjective.

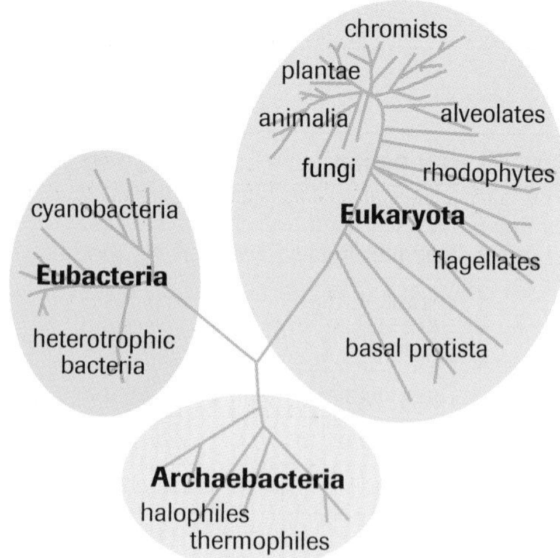

Figure 7
A three-domain system of classification

Table 2 A Six-Kingdom System of Classification

	Kingdom	General characteristics	Cell wall	Representative organisms
	1. Eubacteria	• simple organisms lacking nuclei (prokaryotic) • either heterotrophs or autotrophs • all can reproduce asexually • live nearly everywhere	often present (contains peptidoglycan)	bacteria, cyanobacteria
	2. Archaebacteria	• prokaryotic • heterotrophs • live in salt lakes, hot springs, animal guts	present (does not contain peptidoglycan)	methanogens, extreme thermophiles, extreme halophiles
	3. Protista	• most are single-celled; some are multicellular organisms; eukaryotic • some are autotrophs, some heterotrophs, some both • reproduce sexually and asexually • live in aquatic or moist habitats	absent	algae, protozoa
	4. Fungi	• most are multicellular • all are heterotrophs • reproduce sexually and asexually • most are terrestrial	present	mushrooms, yeasts, bread moulds
	5. Plantae	• all are multicellular • all are autotrophs • reproduce sexually and asexually • most are terrestrial	present	mosses, ferns, conifers, flowering plants
	6. Animalia	• all are multicellular • all are heterotrophs • most reproduce sexually • live in terrestrial and aquatic habitats	absent	sponges, worms, lobsters, starfish, fish, reptiles, birds, mammals

Practice

1. Describe a situation in which classification affects your life.
2. What is meant by the term *binomial nomenclature*?
3. Indicate the advantage of using a Latin name over a common (e.g., English) name. Provide at least one example.
4. List, in order, the major levels of classification, starting with kingdom.

phylogeny the history of the evolution of a species or a group of organisms

Today, most scientists believe that organisms have changed over time. The history of the evolution of organisms is called **phylogeny**. Relationships are often shown in a type of diagram called a phylogenetic tree, where the tree starts from the most ancestral form and includes branchings that lead to all of its descendants. **Figure 8** shows an overall picture of the relationships, but more specific diagrams are possible.

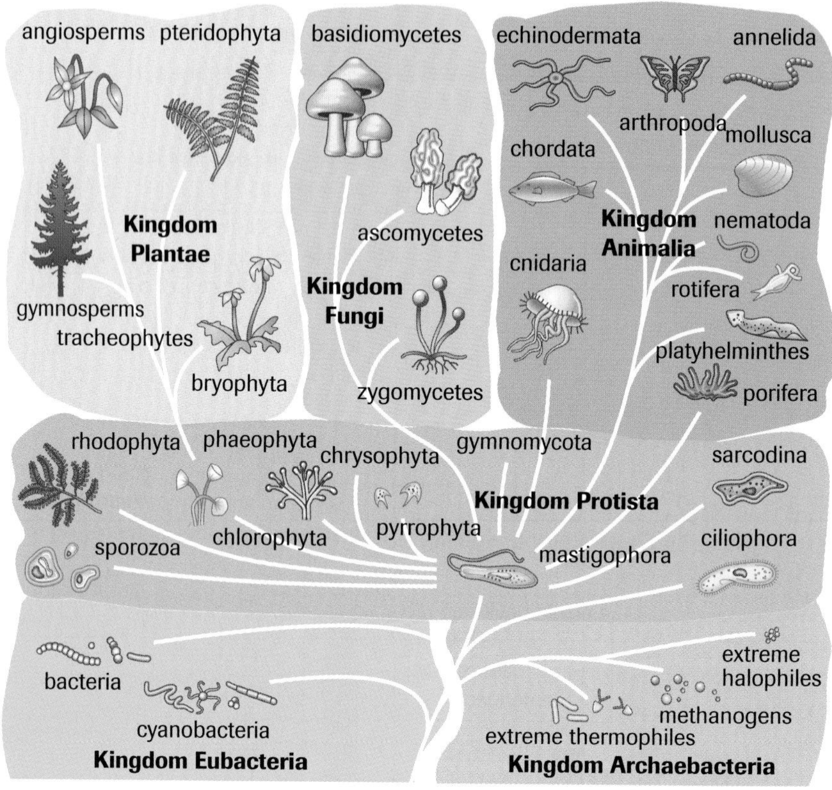

Figure 8
This phylogenetic tree shows relationships within the six kingdoms.

dichotomous key a two-part key used to identify living things. *Di* means "two."

Many scientists regularly use classification manuals to conduct their identification work. Usually it involves the use of a **dichotomous key**. The key is constructed so that a series of choices must be made, and each choice leads to a new branch of the key. If choices are made accurately, the end result is the name of the organism being identified.

INVESTIGATION 5.1 ***Introduction***

Using a Classification Key

Whale species are quite variable. For example, some whales are as small as 3.5 m in length, whereas others can reach 25 m or more. Nevertheless, whales can be classified into two general groups. In this investigation, you will use a classification key to group different whales into species.

Report Checklist

● Purpose	● Design	● Analysis
● Problem	○ Materials	○ Evaluation
○ Hypothesis	● Procedure	● Synthesis
● Prediction	● Evidence	

To perform this investigation, turn to page 162.

SUMMARY Classification of Organisms

- Taxonomy is used to help biologists identify organisms and recognize natural groupings of living things.
- Different organisms have different scientific names, which consist of a genus name and a species name.
- In taxonomy, there are seven main taxa arranged in order: kingdom, phylum, class, order, family, genus, and species. The taxa are used to group organisms by their similarities according to structure and/or evolutionary history.

Section 5.1 Questions

1. What is a phylogenetic tree?
2. Why is the classification of organisms important?
3. Discuss the importance of the use of scientific names in the study of biology.
4. Why is phylogeny sometimes called the foundation of taxonomy?
5. Which of the kingdoms is at the bottom of a phylogenetic tree? Why is it placed there?
6. The following is a list of some Latin (Lat.) and Greek (Gr.) words and their English definitions:
   - alopekos (Gr.): fox
   - felis (Lat.): cat
   - articus (Lat.): arctic
   - pous (Gr.): foot
   - canis (Lat.): dog
   - alpinous (Lat.): mountain
   - lagos (Lat.) or lepus (Gr.): rabbit
   - aquaticus (Lat.): found in water
   - mephitis (Lat.): bad odour
   - rufus (Lat.): reddish

   Match each scientific name with the correct common name.

   (a) *Felis concolor*
   (b) *Sorex arcticus*
   (c) *Canis rufus*
   (d) *Mephitis mephitis*
   (e) *Alopex lagopus*
   (f) *Eutamias alpinus*
   (g) *Sciurus arizonensis*
   (h) *Sylvilagus aquaticus*

   (i) arctic shrew
   (ii) swamp rabbit
   (iii) skunk
   (iv) red wolf
   (v) alpine chipmunk
   (vi) arctic fox
   (vii) mountain lion
   (viii) Arizona grey squirrel
7. Use the information in **Table 3** to answer the following questions.
   (a) Which of the species are the most closely related? Explain.
   (b) Is the river otter more closely related to the muskrat or the weasel? Why?
   (c) Is the groundhog more closely related to the chipmunk or the ferret? Why?
   (d) Which of the species is (are) the closest relative(s) of the squirrel? Explain.

Table 3 Names of Some Common Mammals

Common name	Scientific name	Family
red squirrel	*Tamiasciurus hudsonicus*	Sciuridae
shorttail weasel	*Mustela erminea*	Mustelidae
groundhog	*Marmota monax*	Sciuridae
mink	*Mustela vison*	Mustelidae
eastern chipmunk	*Tamias striatus*	Sciuridae
river otter	*Lutra canadensis*	Mustelidae
fisher	*Martes pennanti*	Mustelidae
muskrat	*Ondatra zibethica*	Cricetidae
black-footed ferret	*Mustela nigripes*	Mustelidae

5.2 Evidence of a Changing Earth

DID YOU KNOW ?

The Scientific Method
Francis Bacon (1561–1626) first proposed the scientific method, one way of finding out about the world around us. Bacon devised a method of testing a hypothesis using a controlled experiment. At about the same time, Galileo was using a telescope to provide compelling evidence that Earth was not the centre of the universe—a finding that contradicted the teachings of the church at the time.

As you saw earlier, the populations in an ecosystem change in response to changes in the environment. The introduction of a new species or a shift in the amount of nutrients can dramatically affect the equilibrium of the ecosystem. In fact, it is predicted that within your lifetime, changes to Earth's ecosystems will cause the extinction of many species. Have changes in the populations of organisms always occurred? How have these affected living species? Although it is impossible to directly observe what Earth was like millions of years ago, indirect evidence suggests that the types of organisms that lived in the past were very different from those of today. This evidence suggests that modern species evolved from ancestral ones.

Evidence for evolution comes from many lines of investigation. Some evidence comes from direct observation and experiment, while other evidence is more indirect. In the following sections, we examine scientific evidence gathered from the fossil record, the geographic distribution of species, comparative anatomy and embryology, behaviour, plant and animal breeding, and biochemistry and genetics.

paleontology the study of fossils

Evidence from Fossils

Strong evidence of a changing Earth can be seen from a careful examination of fossils. **Paleontology** (the study of fossils) has a central position in the study of evolution. Scientists have discovered approximately 250 000 fossil species, a number thought to represent only a fraction of the species that have lived on Earth. Burrows, footprints, and even chemical remains can fossilize. A complete set of fossils of all previous existing life forms will never be uncovered, since most organisms leave no evidence of their existence. However, fossilized remains, impressions, and traces of organisms from past geological ages provide scientists with direct physical evidence of past life. What patterns have been found in this album in rock?

EXTENSION

Fossil Formation
Fossils are commonly formed when the bodies of organisms become trapped in sediments. In this extension activity, you will find out how this process occurs.

www.science.nelson.com 

mini Investigation — Puzzling over Evidence

Biologists investigate the natural world through methodical observation and experimentation. As they accumulate evidence, they continually form and test tentative hypotheses toward the development of a theory. In this activity, you model this process by gathering and interpreting evidence, in order to develop and test hypotheses.

- Remove eight puzzle pieces at random from your group's "Evidence" envelope.
- Arrange the pieces on your desk. Discuss the evidence and make predictions about the missing puzzle pieces. Record the predictions in your notebook as your group's first tentative hypotheses.
- Remove two more puzzle pieces from the "Evidence" envelope.
- Add to and modify your original arrangement of puzzle pieces. Comment on the validity of your original hypotheses. Make and record a second set of hypotheses.
- Repeat the above process of obtaining new evidence and modifying your previous hypotheses. At some point you may wish to propose a theory–a tentative explanation that accounts for all the evidence.

(a) In what way do the puzzle pieces model evidence in science?

(b) What scientific processes were you modelling when you arranged your puzzle pieces?

(c) How did you test your hypotheses? How do scientists test hypotheses?

(d) Do you think it is possible to make valid predictions and develop valid theories even when you don't have all the evidence? Explain your reasoning.

(e) How does the "accumulation" of more and more evidence influence your ability to make predictions and/or formulate and test a theory?

1. Different species lived on Earth at various times in the past. Very few of today's species were alive even 1 million years ago, and almost all of the species that have lived are now extinct.
2. The complexity of living organisms generally increases from the most distant past to the present. When fossil deposits are arranged from most ancient to most recent, there is an obvious and systematic progression from only very simple organisms to species of ever-increasing complexity.
3. Living species and their most closely matching fossils are typically located in the same geographic region. For example, all fossils of ancient sloths are found in Central and South America, the only region in which modern, but smaller and very different, species of sloth live today (**Figure 1**).

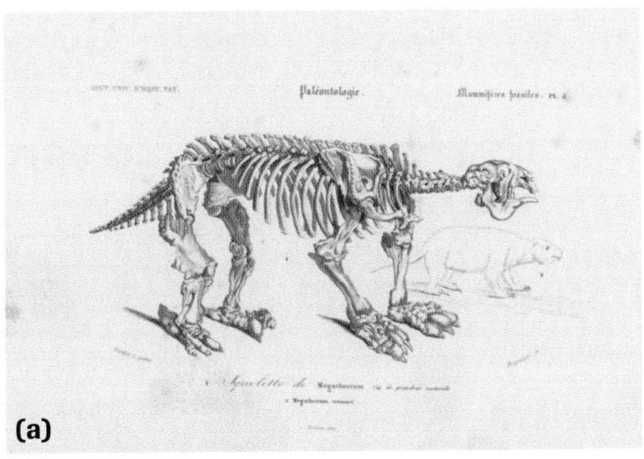

Figure 1
(a) sloth skeleton **(b)** living sloth

Dating the Past

By the early 1800s, evidence from geology strongly suggested that Earth might be hundreds of millions of years old, much older than the thousands of years assumed at the time. In his 1830 book, *Principles of Geology*, Sir Charles Lyell revolutionized geology with his argument that most geological change was slow and gradual and had been going on over vast expanses of time. Lyell based his theories on his observations of fossil deposits and of geological processes such as erosion and sedimentation.

However, Lyell's conclusions were not widely accepted and were severely attacked by Lord Kelvin, the most respected physicist of the day. Kelvin estimated that Earth was 15 to 20 million years old, based on rigorous mathematical and scientific calculations that assumed that Earth was gradually cooling down. Even though his estimate conflicted with the geological evidence, it agreed with the most widely held beliefs of the time.

In 1903, radioactivity was discovered, a source of heat energy. Kelvin's model had grossly underestimated the age of Earth because it had failed to account for the heat that is continuously generated within Earth by radioactive decay. Radioactive decay also provides a form of geologic clock, giving scientists a means to determine the absolute age of the Earth with great precision.

Radioactive decay changes a particular atom (parent isotope) into a daughter isotope of the same or a different element. For example, radioactive potassium 40 decays to become argon 40 or calcium 40, while uranium 238 decays into lead 206. Physicists measure these decay rates in units called half-lives, the amount of time it takes for half of a sample of the isotope to decay and become stable. They have determined that the

DID YOU KNOW ?

The Burgess Shale

Fossil beds in the Burgess Shale in British Columbia likely formed through a series of mudslides, which buried living organisms in moving sediment. The resulting fossils are superbly preserved (**Figure 2**). Many of the animals had unusual body forms not found in present-day animals. Discovered in 1909 by Charles D. Walcott of the Smithsonian Institute, it was immediately declared the most important geological find in the world. The Burgess Shale fossil beds became a UNESCO World Heritage Site in 1981.

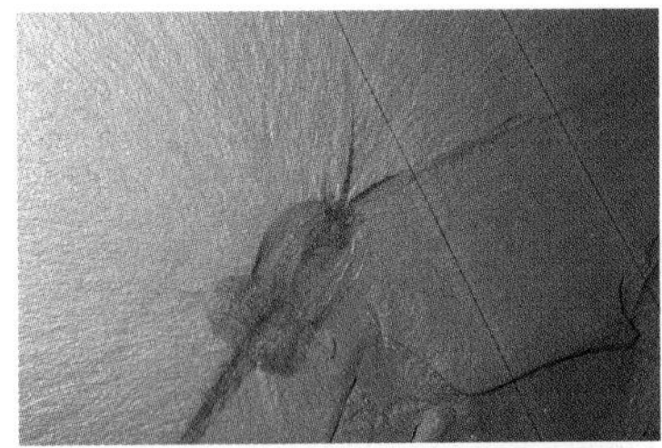

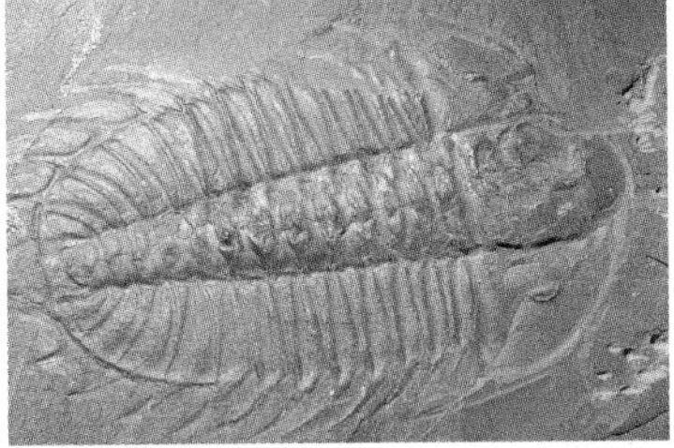

Figure 2

CAREER CONNECTION 

Paleontologist

Paleontologists work with fossils to explore the organisms found in various regions over Earth's history. Most paleontologists are college or university professors, but some also work for museums or for petroleum and mining companies. Find out what qualifications are needed for a career in paleontology.

www.science.nelson.com  

half-life for any particular isotope is a constant; it is not affected by temperature, moisture, or other environmental conditions. With constant half-lives, isotopes can be used as naturally occurring and extremely precise radiometric clocks.

radiometric dating a technique used to determine the age of a rock or fossil

By measuring the age of rock through these **radiometric dating** techniques, modern paleontologists can estimate accurate ages for fossils. Radiometric dating using a single isotope is not perfect, but when data from a variety of isotopes are combined, scientists can provide age estimates with a very small margin of error. The oldest fossils of living things discovered thus far date to approximately 3.8 billion years.

+ EXTENSION

Radiometric Dating

View this animation of dating a fossilized mollusc by radiometric dating.

www.science.nelson.com 

Practice

1. Offer an explanation for the observation that fossils of birds are rare, while fossils of clams are extremely common.
2. What is radiometric dating and of what value is it to paleontologists?

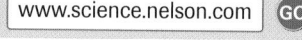

WEB Activity

Case Study—Finding Fossils and Famous Footprints

In 1976, some famous fossils dating from more than 3.6 million years ago were discovered in Tanzania (**Figure 3**). They represent some of the oldest fossil evidence for upright, bipedal, walking—a milestone in human evolution. Complete this online activity to find out more about these fossils and be introduced to Lucy!

www.science.nelson.com 

Figure 3

Evidence from Biogeography

biogeography the study of the geographic distribution of life on Earth

endemic a term used to describe a species that is found in one location only

Biogeography explores the variation and distribution of life over Earth's surface, both today and in the past. Patterns of geographic distribution provide important clues to the history of life on Earth.

Over long periods of time, Earth's landmasses have undergone dramatic changes by the process of continental drift. About 225 million years ago, Earth's continents were part of one landmass. The slow drift of Earth's tectonic plates eventually separated the ancient landmasses into the continents we see today. As a result, fossils of some species that date to 150 million years ago and older were once in the same geographic region, but are now distributed on different continents (**Figure 4**, next page). After the continents separated, most species younger than about 150 million years were restricted to separate continents. Most recent fossils of the same species are not found on these different continents. This strongly suggests they evolved *after* the breakup of the continents.

Islands that are far removed from landmasses are also of great interest to evolutionary biologists. Many of these islands are products of volcanic activity, and were barren ash and rock when they first were formed. Remote islands are homes to unique species, many of which are **endemic** (found nowhere else). This suggests that these species have evolved in isolation. Scientists hypothesize that the ancestors of endemic species came from other landmasses. But how? Any ancestors would have had to cross great distances of open ocean, and so most likely were animals capable of flight (birds and insects) and seeds carried by the wind or the sea. Other species may have travelled on rafts of vegetation or ice floes. Is there any evidence to support these conclusions?

DID YOU KNOW ?

The Royal Tyrrell Museum

The Royal Tyrrell Museum opened in 1985, commemorating Joseph Burr Tyrrell, the man credited with finding the first dinosaur fossils in the Drumheller Valley, Alberta, in 1884. You can view the museum's fabulous fossil collection or find out about its many active programs in person or online.

www.science.nelson.com 

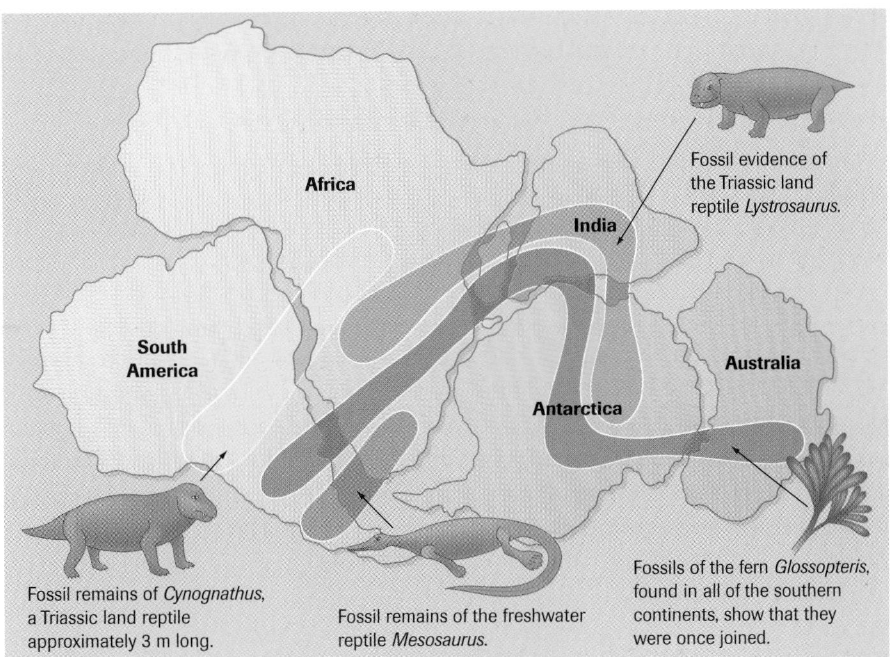

Figure 4
Fossil remains of species that lived more than 150 million years ago can be found on many continents. Fossils of more recent species (not shown) are found on separate continents.

DID YOU KNOW?

Flightless Birds
Virtually all of the world's large remote islands are home to unique species of flightless, ground-nesting birds. Even when very similar islands are separated by only short distances of open ocean, distinct species occur.

There is. The native species on remote islands are invariably and exclusively birds, insects, and other potentially mobile organisms. For example, the Hawaiian Islands are located in the Pacific Ocean, 3200 km from any continent. Species native to these islands include 0 native reptiles or amphibians, 2 native mammals—the monk seal and the hoary bat, 96 species of birds, and many, many insect species. Additionally, genetic testing of Hawaiian plants strongly suggests that the 1729 native species and varieties known today all descended from only 272 founding species.

SUMMARY Evidence of a Changing Earth

- Fossil evidence reveals that species living today are different from those living in the past.
- Fossils reveal a progression of different species on Earth over time, from simple forms in the most distant past to increasingly complex forms.
- Radiometric dating allows scientists to accurately determine the ages of rocks and fossils.
- Evidence from biogeography suggests that different species evolved independently in isolated parts of the world.

Section 5.2 Questions

1. Explain how the following patterns of fossils offer compelling evidence for evolution:
   (a) the relationship between the age of fossils and the kinds and complexity of fossils
   (b) the relationship between the geographical location of both fossils and living species
2. Would you expect to find more unique species on remote islands, such as Iceland, or islands that are close to a large landmass, such as the Queen Charlotte Islands? Give reasons for your answer.
3. Brainstorm a list of living plants and animals that you think might be able to reach the Hawaiian Islands from the coast of British Columbia. Be prepared to defend your choices.

Extension

4. Research carbon 14 (^{14}C) dating techniques, including why the percentage of ^{14}C begins to change after an organism dies. Report your findings to your class.

www.science.nelson.com 

5.3 Evidence of Evolution from Biology

homologous features features with similar structures but different functions

analogous features features that are similar in appearance and function, but do not appear to have the same evolutionary origin

A comparison of the physical anatomy and genetic makeup of organisms also provides evidence to support the theory that modern species evolved from ancestral species. Some of this evidence will be presented in this section.

Evidence from Anatomy

The forelimbs of a bird, whale, horse, and human all share very similar bone arrangements, even though they serve very different functions (**Figure 1**). These observations strongly suggest that an ancestral forelimb evolved modifications that better served new functions. Such features, with similar structure but different functions, are called **homologous features.** In contrast, **analogous features** are similar in appearance and in function, but do not appear to have the same evolutionary origin, such as a bird's wing and an insect's wing.

An evolutionary relationship among species is also evidenced in embryonic development (**Figure 2**). In the early weeks of development, human embryos possess a tail and gill slits, similar to those in chicken and fish embryos. The embryonic tail serves no function in humans and later forms a rudimentary tailbone. The gill slits become modified in both humans and birds to form various internal structures, including bones of the inner ear.

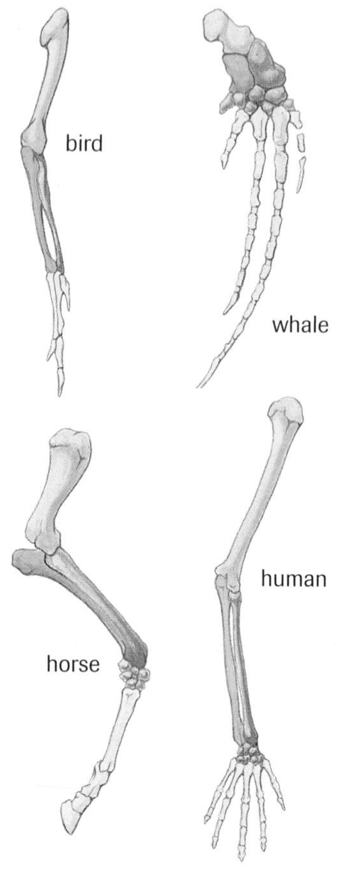

Figure 1
The forelimbs of each of these organisms are adapted to carry out very different functions, yet they all possess very similar bone structure.

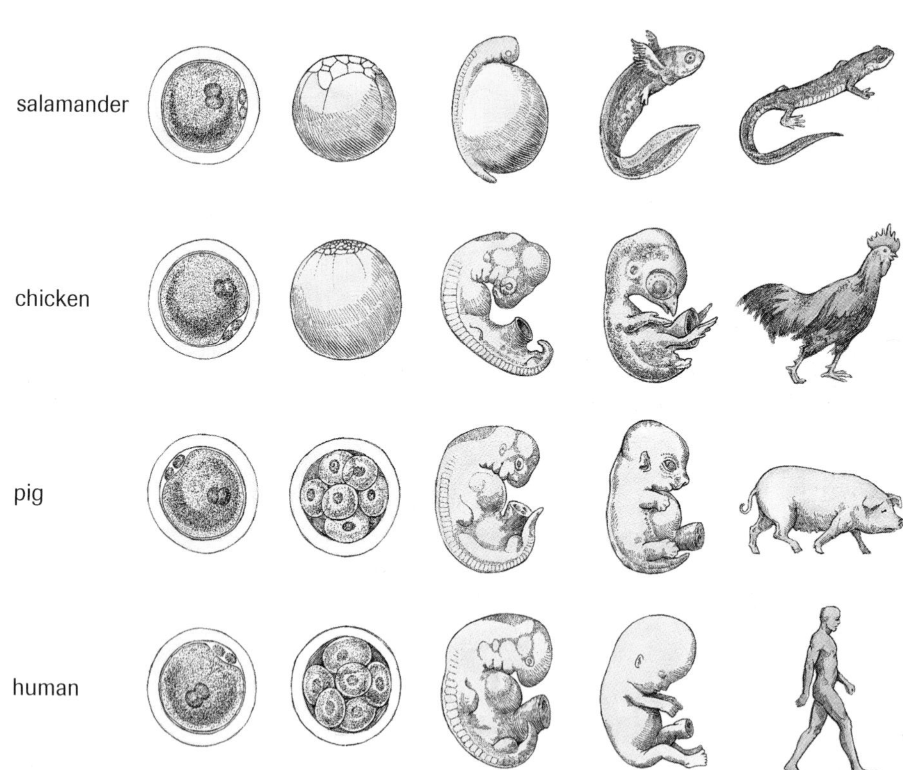

Figure 2
Homologous features such as tailbones are clearly evident in the embryos of these organisms.

Vestigial Features and Anatomical Oddities

Vestigial features are rudimentary structures that serve no useful function. Such features are present in virtually all species and provide perhaps the most compelling evidence for evolution. A reasonable explanation for vestigial features is that they once served some function in an ancient ancestor. Some modern species of whales and snakes have vestigial hip and leg bones—evidence that suggests they evolved from ancestors that walked on four limbs (**Figure 3**). Similarly, many mammals have vestigial toe bones elevated above the ground (**Figure 4**). Some beetles even have fully developed wings, trapped beneath fused covers. Blind cave salamanders have empty eye sockets, suggesting that they evolved from salamanders with fully functioning eyes.

vestigial features rudimentary structures with no useful function

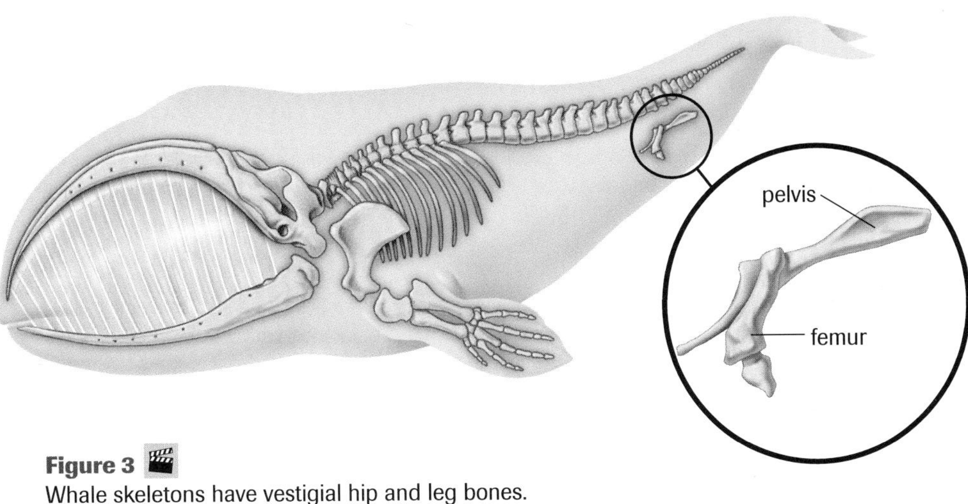

Figure 3
Whale skeletons have vestigial hip and leg bones.

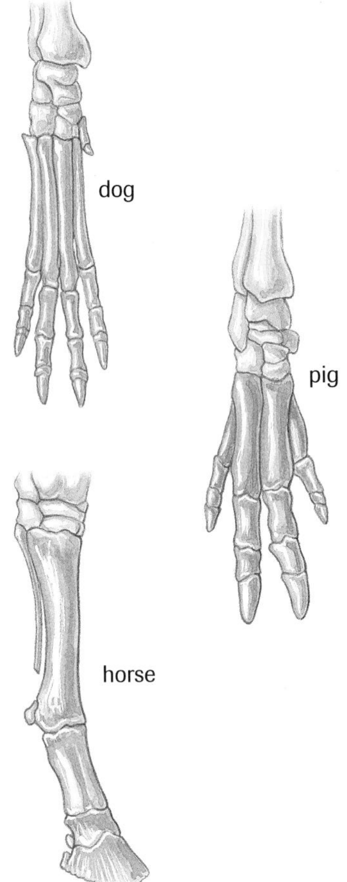

Figure 4
Dogs, pigs, and horses have at least one vestigial toe (blue). Although the bones remain, these digits no longer serve a purpose.

Practice

1. The shells of crabs and turtles serve a similar purpose. Are they homologous or analogous traits? What evidence did you use to reach your conclusion?
2. Would you consider human body hair to be a vestigial feature? Support your answer.

mini *Investigation* — *Variations on a Theme*

The forelimbs of different vertebrates are well adapted to serve specific functions. However, hypothesizing the potential adaptive advantage of such homologous features is not always easy. **Table 1** lists bird species with very different bills.

- Use print and Internet resources to explore the bill shapes of six of these species. Choose four species that are living (extant) and two that are extinct.

www.science.nelson.com 

(a) How does the shape of each bill contribute to the species' success?

(b) Write a hypothesis that explains the adaptive significance of each bill shape.

Table 1 Birds with Unique Bill Shapes

Extant	Extinct
pelican	dodo
nighthawk	diatryma
falcon	gastornis
bittern	
toucan	
hummingbird	
flamingo	
skimmer	
spoonbill	

Nucleotide Sequences and Amino Acids

This audio clip describes how the sequence of nucleotides found in the genes determines which amino acids make up each protein. If the DNA is changed through a mutation, this can change the final protein product.

www.science.nelson.com 

Evidence from Biochemistry

Evidence for evolution has also been found by comparing biochemical characteristics of different species. Proteins are molecules that make up many structures in organisms, such as muscle cells and skin cells. Proteins are made up of long chains of amino acids, and each type of protein has a unique number and sequence of amino acids. Many species possess similar proteins. Studies suggest that, over time, similar proteins in different species become increasingly different in terms of their amino acid sequences. For example, hemoglobin is an oxygen-carrying protein present in all vertebrates. When scientists determined the amino-acid sequence of hemoglobin from different species, they found that the sequence varied. The differences were greater between species that were less similar overall, such as a macaque and a lamprey (**Figure 5**). This is evidence that, over time, the hemoglobin molecules evolved to have different characteristics.

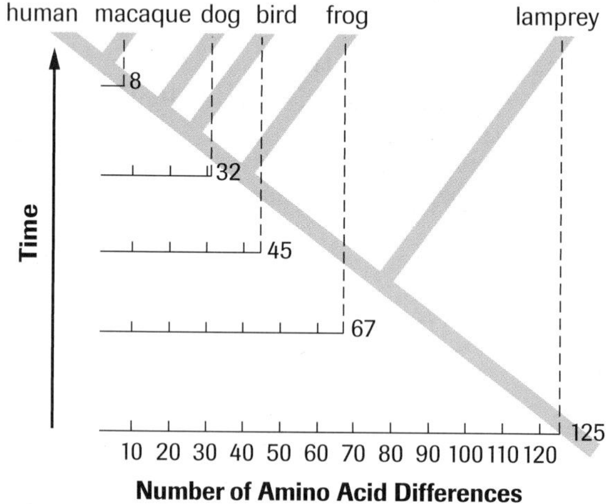

Figure 5
Differences in amino acid sequences in a portion of the hemoglobin protein reflect the degree of similarity among different species.

DNA the molecule that makes up genetic material

gene a segment of DNA that performs a specific function, such as coding for a particular protein

Scientists have also found evidence for evolution in DNA sequences. **DNA** (deoxyribose nucleic acid) is the hereditary material that determines which characteristics are passed on to the next generation. Every organism has a particular set of characteristics, or traits, that are inherited, such as eye colour in humans. Each DNA molecule contains many different **genes** that provide the instructions for these traits. Genes determine the particular traits of an individual, such as brown eye colour or green eye colour.

DNA is composed of four chemicals called nucleotide bases, or simply bases, arranged in different sequences (**Figure 6**). The four bases in DNA are adenine (A), thymine (T), cytosine (C), and guanine (G). DNA sequences from different species that code for the same protein vary in the number and order of the nucleotides.

cow AGTCCCCAAAGTGAAGGAGA CTATGGTTCCTAAGCACAAG GAAATGCCCTTCCCTAAATA

Figure 6
This is a segment of DNA from cows that codes for a milk protein.

Just as early biologists discovered homologous and vestigial *anatomical* features, geneticists have found large numbers of both homologous and vestigial *genes* in the DNA of virtually all species. For example, humans possess a set of defective genes that would allow us to make our own vitamin C. We have lost both the ability and the need to make vitamin C but still possess the useless genetic instructions to do so.

LAB EXERCISE 5.A

Report Checklist

○ Purpose	○ Design	● Analysis
○ Problem	○ Materials	○ Evaluation
○ Hypothesis	○ Procedure	○ Synthesis
○ Prediction	● Evidence	

Evidence from Genetics

DNA fingerprinting is now used widely in criminal investigations. With this technique, forensic scientists can determine the probability that a DNA sample is from a particular individual or a close relative, with an unprecedented degree of certainty. DNA samples obtained from closely related individuals have more of the same DNA sequences; samples from the same individual are identical. This same principle applies to the DNA sequences from different species. More closely related species are more likely to have more similarities in the sequence of their DNA. In this activity, you will compare sequences of DNA from different species to infer their phylogeny, or kinship.

The Closest of Kin

The sequences of real data in **Figure 7** represent a segment of DNA that codes for the same milk protein in six different species. Each letter represents one nucleotide base in the DNA segment. The letters have been vertically aligned and colour coded to highlight similarities and differences between the species. Use the following guidelines to assist you in analyzing this DNA information:

- Only a shared difference offers evidence of evolutionary kinship. It suggests species may have inherited the difference from a common ancestor.
- The more base differences species have in common, the more likely they are to be closely related.
- Base sequences common to all species offer no useful information about relationships.
- A difference exhibited by only one species offers no information about kinship.

Evidence

(a) Design and construct a data table or spreadsheet that can be used to tabulate the numbers of shared differences between each possible pair of species.

(b) Tabulate your data.

Analysis

(c) Which pair of species had the greatest number of shared differences in their bases?

(d) Based on this evidence, what species is most closely related to the

(i) deer (ii) peccary (iii) whale?

(e) What evidence suggests that whales may be more closely related to cows than they are to pigs?

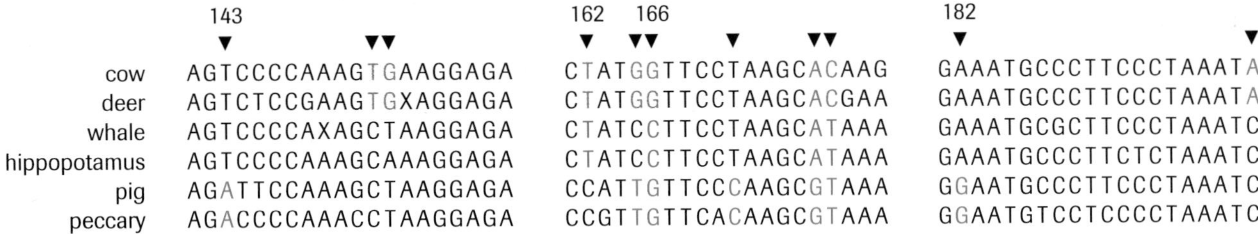

143
162 166
182
cow AGTCCCCAAAGTGAAGGAGA CTATGGTTCCTAAGCACAAG GAAATGCCCTTCCCTAAATA
deer AGTCTCCGAAGTGXAGGAGA CTATGGTTCCTAAGCACGAA GAAATGCCCTTCCCTAAATA
whale AGTCCCCAXAGCTAAGGAGA CTATCCTTCCTAAGCATAAA GAAATGCGCTTCCCTAAATC
hippopotamus AGTCCCCAAAGCAAAGGAGA CTATCCTTCCTAAGCATAAA GAAATGCCCTTCTCTAAATC
pig AGATTCCAAAGCTAAGGAGA CCATTGTTCCCAAGCGTAAA GGAATGCCCTTCCCTAAATC
peccary AGACCCCAAACCTAAGGAGA CCGTTGTTCACAAGCGTAAA GGAATGTCCTCCCCTAAATC

Figure 7
These base sequences include positions 141–200 of a portion of the DNA molecules encoding a milk protein in six mammal species. Coloured bases indicate genetic changes shared by more than one species. The "X" denotes a base for which the original DNA sequencing data were inconclusive.

Evidence from Artificial Selection

Since the beginning of agriculture, humans have used artificial selection to alter the appearance, behaviour, and even chemical makeup of plants and animals. They select the individuals with the desired traits, breed them, and then pick the best offspring to breed again. Today's domestic animals and crop plants have been artificially selected over many hundreds of generations. **Artificial selection** is another word for plant and animal breeding, in which people breed individuals with desired characteristics in order to get offspring with those same characteristics.

artificial selection the process of humans selecting and breeding individuals with the desired traits

As an example, did you know that cabbage, broccoli, cauliflower, and ornamental kale are all the same plant species? Over the centuries, farmers and plant breeders selected characteristics of a single plant species, the sea cabbage, to produce a range of edible and ornamental varieties (**Figure 8**). The fact that humans can use artificial selection to produce such dramatic changes in species over relatively short periods of time provides compelling evidence that similar and even more dramatic changes occur in nature over millions of years and countless generations.

CAREER CONNECTION

Breeder

Plant and animal breeders use artificial selection to modify crops and livestock to have traits that are useful for humans. Breeders may work at universities, colleges, corporations, or directly in agricultural production.

www.science.nelson.com 

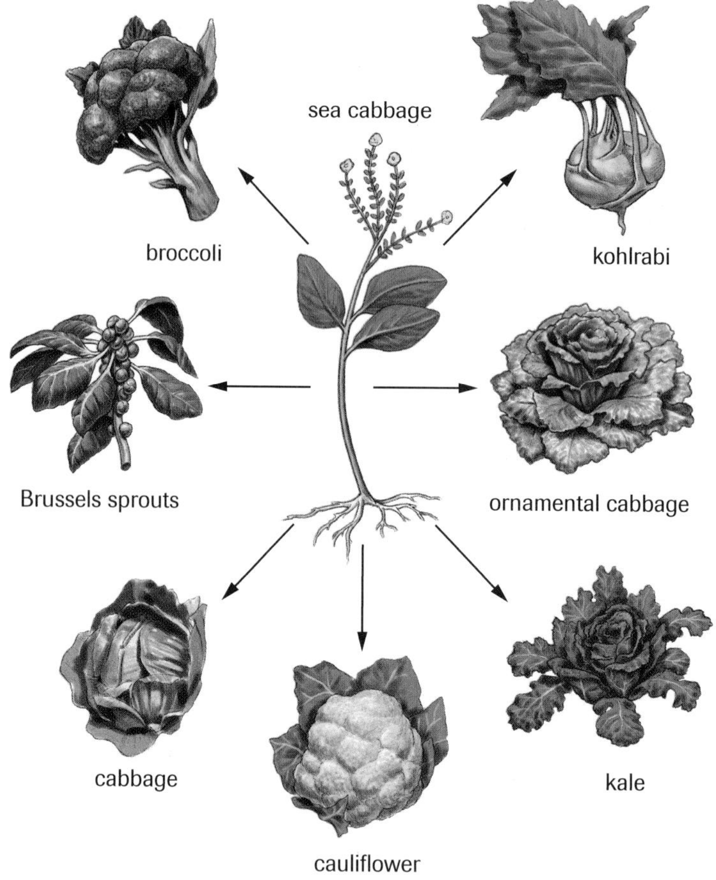

Figure 8
Artificial selection over many generations produced a range of useful varieties from sea cabbage.

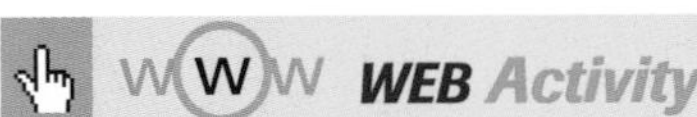

Case Study—Were Neanderthals Humans?

In the late 1990s, several samples of DNA were successfully extracted from the teeth of well-preserved Neanderthal fossils. The DNA was then copied and sequenced.

In this activity, you will go online to compare the actual DNA sequences of ancient Neanderthals, modern humans, and chimpanzees. Note that this research involved the analysis of mtDNA, DNA that is present within the mitochondria of all cells.

www.science.nelson.com GO

Evidence of Evolution from Biology

- Multiple lines of evidence suggest species have a shared ancestry.
- Homologous and vestigial features provide evidence of specific changes.
- DNA analysis can be used to reveal phylogenetic relationships between different species or groups.

Section 5.3 Questions

1. For each of the following vestigial features, write a hypothesis for its ancient function and indicate a change that may have led to the loss of this function. Show your answer in a graphic organizer.
   (a) pelvic (hip) bones in some whales
   (b) elevated toe on hind leg of deer
   (c) human "goosebumps"
   (d) human muscles for moving the outer ear
   (e) rudimentary wings in flightless insects, such as earwigs
2. Dolphin flippers contain a wrist and set of digit bones and associated muscles. Explain how this provides evidence that cats and dolphins share a common evolutionary origin.

Extension

3. Examine **Figure 9**. Each of these series of letters represents the partial sequence of amino acids for the same type of protein in each of six different species. Each letter represents a specific kind of amino acid. Highlighted letters show differences in the sequence as compared to that of the chicken. The order and type of each amino acid is coded by inherited genetic information. Therefore, based on evolutionary theory, we would expect more closely related species to have more similar sequences.

   Species: tuna, turtle, dog, screwworm fly, penguin.

chicken	GDIEKGKKIFVQGKCSQCH
________	GDVEKGKKIFVQGRCAQCH
________	GDIEKGKKIFVQGKCSOCH
________	GDVAKGKKTFVQGKCAQCH
________	GDVEKGKKIFVQGKCAQCH
________	GDVEKGKKIFVQGKCAQCH

   Figure 9

   Based on this evidence, compare each sequence to that of the chicken, and match each species with its most probable sequence.
4. New Zealand scientist David Lambert collected DNA samples from 7000-year-old nesting grounds of the Adélie penguin in Antarctica. He collected wonderfully preserved DNA samples from ancient frozen bones in layers of ice directly beneath the present-day nesting colonies. Use the Internet to learn his findings. What does Lambert's evidence suggest about the rate of evolutionary change in this species of penguin?

   www.science.nelson.com 

5.4 The Making of a Theory—Accounting for the Evidence

A scientific theory is a model that accounts for all of the known scientific evidence as completely as possible. It provides a plausible explanation of how things in nature are related and enables scientists to make testable predictions. As evidence accumulates, scientists alter or modify a theory to fit the new data.

Before the 18th century, it was widely believed that living things were "fixed" and that they retained the same form from when they first appeared on Earth. During the second half of the 18th century, a number of scholars began to speculate and speak out on the issue of evolution. Georges-Louis Leclerc de Buffon, a leading naturalist, proposed that species could change over time and that these changes could lead to new organisms. Similar views were put forth in 1760 by Carl Linnaeus, the founder of biological nomenclature, and in 1794 by Erasmus Darwin, the grandfather of Charles Darwin (**Figure 1**). Linnaeus proposed that the few species at creation had become hybrids, which had then formed many new species. Erasmus Darwin presented a strong case for the idea that all life had developed from a single source. Such ideas were not widely accepted.

Figure 1
Charles Darwin

spontaneous generation the belief that living things arose from non-living matter

inheritance of acquired characteristics the false concept of inheritance of features acquired during the life of an individual

Lamarck's Theory

In the early 1800s, a student of Buffon, Jean-Baptiste Pierre Antoine de Monet Chevalier de Lamarck, presented the first theory of evolution that included a *mechanism*. Lamarck believed that new, very simple species were continually being created by **spontaneous generation** (by arising spontaneously from non-living matter), and then gradually became more complex. He believed that organisms had a "force" or "desire" that led them to change for the better, and that organisms must be able to produce new parts to satisfy these needs and become better adapted to their environment. Lamarck reasoned that the use and disuse of certain structures could be passed on to the offspring. For example, Lamarck proposed that one generation of giraffe might have had to obtain food that was higher in trees. The continual stretching of the neck would lead to a slight elongation of the neck over a lifetime. Lamarck postulated that this acquired trait, a slightly longer neck, would be inherited by offspring. This pattern of inheritance over many generations eventually led to the very long necks now found in the giraffe (**Figure 2**). Today the term "Lamarckism" is used to describe the concept of **inheritance of acquired characteristics**. We now know that acquired traits cannot be inherited, but Lamarck did recognize that the environment played a role in driving evolutionary change.

Figure 2
Lamarck believed that the long neck of a giraffe came from generations spent reaching for food.

Practice

1. Make a two-column chart with the headings "Inherited traits" and "Acquired traits."
   (a) In each column, write examples of your own traits (these can be physical or behavioural).
   (b) Which, if any, of your inherited traits could be altered during your life? How?
   (c) Which, if any, of your acquired traits can be passed on to your offspring? How?

Darwin's Theory

In 1831, Charles Darwin set sail on HMS *Beagle* to travel around the world. He returned in 1836 filled with enthusiasm and questions about what he had seen and experienced. The following list highlights some of the now famous evidence Darwin gathered while on his voyage and the inferences he would later draw from them:

1. In South America, Darwin observed unusual fossil species that resembled giant variations of the sloths and armadillos living in the same region. He suspected that the living forms might have descended from the fossilized species.
2. He noted that species living in the South American tropics did not resemble those living in the African tropics. Instead, they were more like the species living in cooler parts of South America. He inferred that each such landmass might have acted like an isolated nursery, in which sets of species had evolved independently.
3. The harsh landscape of the Galapagos Islands was home to 13 very similar species of finches (**Figure 3**). Found nowhere else on Earth, these birds most closely resembled species living in a very different habitat on the coast of South America, 1000 km to the east. Darwin speculated that they had all evolved from a single species that had arrived in the Galapagos from South America.
4. Darwin observed fossil deposits of corals at an elevation of 3000 m in the Andes Mountains. After experiencing a severe earthquake that lifted portions of the coastline 3 m upward, Darwin became convinced that such geological forces, given vast expanses of time, could account for the location of the fossils and the mountains.

Long after his voyage, Darwin continued to gather evidence, performing thousands of experiments and bombarding experts in every field of biology with questions. He became keenly interested in artificial selection, soon recognizing that all species possessed inherited variations that could be selected to change the traits of a species in desirable ways. Darwin reasoned that if people could alter the appearance and behaviour of species through artificial selection, then the environment could have a similar selective effect on wild species.

Darwin found the final piece of his puzzle in a mathematics paper written in 1778 by Thomas Malthus, *Essay on the Principle of Population.* Malthus showed that all species produce far more offspring than are able to survive. Darwin realized that, since so many offspring were being born, there must be intense competition among them for suvival. Darwin then put together a workable theory of evolution by **natural selection**. By June of 1858, he had written a quarter of a million words toward a major treatise, when he received a letter from Alfred Russell Wallace, a brilliant naturalist working in Malaysia. Wallace had independently arrived at the same conclusions as Darwin and described his own theory in the letter. Learning of the situation, Darwin's colleagues convinced him to submit a paper along with Wallace's at a meeting on July 1, 1858. A year and a half later, Darwin published *On the Origin of Species by Means of Natural Selection or The Preservation of Favoured Races in the Struggle for Life.* It sold out on the first day. **Table 1** summarizes Darwin and Wallace's Theory of Evolution by Natural Selection.

grasping, probing beak eats insects

large crushing beak eats seeds

long pointed beak chisels through tree bark to find insects; uses a tool (a cactus spine or small twig) to probe for insects

parrotlike beak eats fruit

Figure 3 Some of the beak modifications that Darwin noted among the 13 similar species of finches on the Galapagos Islands

natural selection the result of differential reproductive success of individuals caused by variations in their inherited characteristics.

Table 1 The Theory of Evolution by Natural Selection

Observation 1	Individuals within any species exhibit many inherited variations.
Observation 2	Every generation produces far more offspring than can survive to reproduce.
Observation 3	Populations of species tend to remain stable in size.
Inference 1	Individuals of the same species are in a constant struggle for survival.
Inference 2	Individuals with more favourable variations are more likely to survive and pass these variations on. Survival is not random. *This* is natural selection.
Inference 3	Since individuals with more favourable variations contribute proportionately more offspring to succeeding generations, their favourable inherited variations will become more common. *This* is evolution.

Practice

2. After returning from his famous voyage, Darwin began to believe that species could change. What steps did he take to gather evidence to support this possibility?
3. Describe the impact that the principles in Malthus's essay had on Darwin's thinking.

Figure 4
Cheetahs rely on their speed to help them catch their prey.

Natural Selection

How does this process of natural selection operate in nature? Imagine an ancient population of cheetahs with different running speeds. The faster cheetahs probably caught prey more easily and stayed healthier. Such fit individuals might have been better able to compete for mates, provide better nourishment and protection for their young, and lead longer reproductive lives. Natural selection would favour the reproductive success of the faster individuals. Natural selection may therefore account for the running speed in modern-day cheetahs (**Figure 4**).

Darwin's theory is based on a very simple set of observations and logical reasoning. He observed that all species exhibited inherited variations. He reasoned that, because of those differences, some individuals are better adapted to survive and reproduce than others are. Over time, the inherited traits that provided the survival advantage would become more common in the population. The population would have evolved.

Even without evidence from chemistry and genetics, scientists had accumulated sufficient evidence for general agreement that Earth's populations had a history of change by the mid-1800s. This evidence from paleontology, geology, biogeography, anatomy, and artificial selection is consistent with this idea. However, it was not until the early 1900s that scientists formulated a reasonable explanation, or theory, that could explain *how* such change occurred—the *mechanism* of evolution. As you will read in the next section, this was not possible until scientists began to understand how traits are inherited from parent to offspring.

EXTENSION

The Peppered Moth
One example of natural selection at work is the changes in the peppered moth that occured during the Industrial Revolution. You can explore these changes by viewing an animation and then carrying out this extension activity.

www.science.nelson.com GO

SUMMARY The Making of a Theory—Accounting for the Evidence

- Buffon, Linnaeus, and Erasmus Darwin were among the first prominent scientists to suggest that species could change over time.
- Lamarck was the first to recognize that the environment played a central role in directing adaptation, and to develop a plausible theory of how evolution might occur—by the inheritance of acquired characteristics.
- Charles Darwin based his theory of evolution by natural selection on evidence from many sources, including his five-year voyage on the *Beagle*.
- Darwin and Wallace's theory of natural selection states that evolution occurs because those individuals best suited for survival contribute a greater proportion of offspring with similar traits to the next generation.

Section 5.4 Questions

1. In some wild deer populations, selection by humans favours the survival of smaller males, since large bucks are preferentially hunted.
   (a) What would you expect to happen to the genetic makeup of this population over time?
   (b) In these populations, will mutations for "small size" occur more often than for "large size"? Explain.
2. Create a table to compare and contrast Lamarck's and Darwin's explanations of the mechanism of evolution.
3. Sir Isaac Newton credited the work of Galileo and others for his own successes, declaring that: "If I have been able to see further, it was only because I stood on the shoulders of giants." Describe the contributions of four scientists on whose work Darwin relied for his achievement.

Sources of Inherited Variation 5.5

Recall that Darwin's theory of natural selection states that individuals that are better adapted to their environment will contribute more offspring to the next generation. These offspring have traits similar to their parents, and so will in turn be better adapted. Over time, natural selection leads to a change in the traits of the species as a whole—that is, to evolution. However, natural selection can only occur when there was variation in the traits of the individuals that make up a species. Where does this variation come from? When Darwin published *On the Origin of Species,* scientists were not able to answer this question. It took until the 1930s until biologists understood enough about genes and their role in inheritance to start to answer this question. Variability in a species may arise from two biological processes: mutations and sexual reproduction.

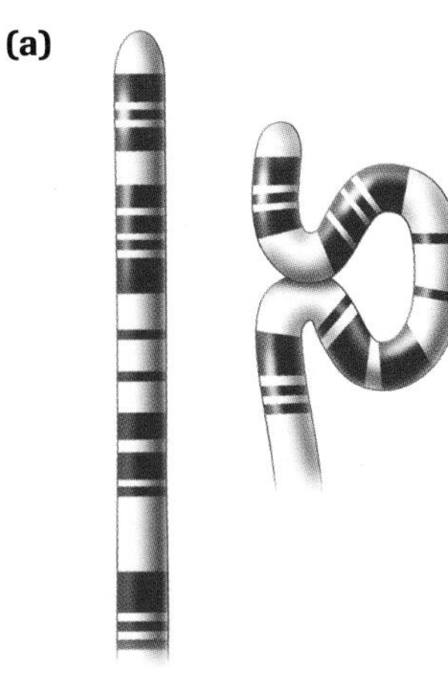

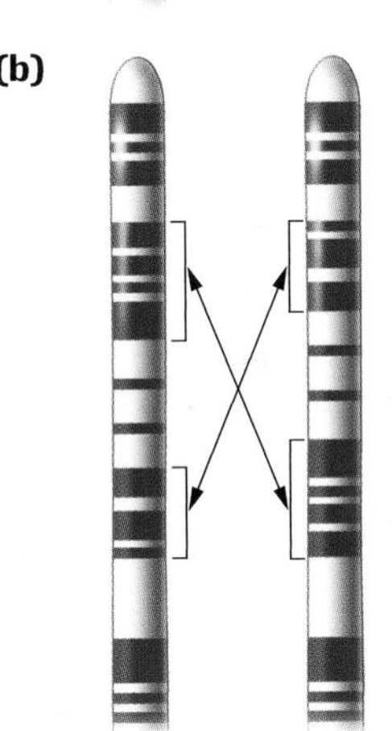

Figure 2
Some mutations result in the reversal of banding patterns along chromosomes. In **(a)**, the chromosome on the right undergoes a mutation in which the looped section breaks and re-attaches in the opposite "flipped" orientation **(b)**.

Mutations

DNA, the hereditary material, is found in the chromosomes of a cell (**Figure 1**). DNA is composed of long sequences of the four nucleotide bases—adenine (A), thymine (T), cytosine (C), and guanine (G). The sequence of these bases forms a code which, when translated by the cell, gives an organism specific inherited traits. Genes are segments of DNA that code for specific traits. Each gene has a specific DNA sequence. DNA is therefore like a blueprint for a particular individual organism.

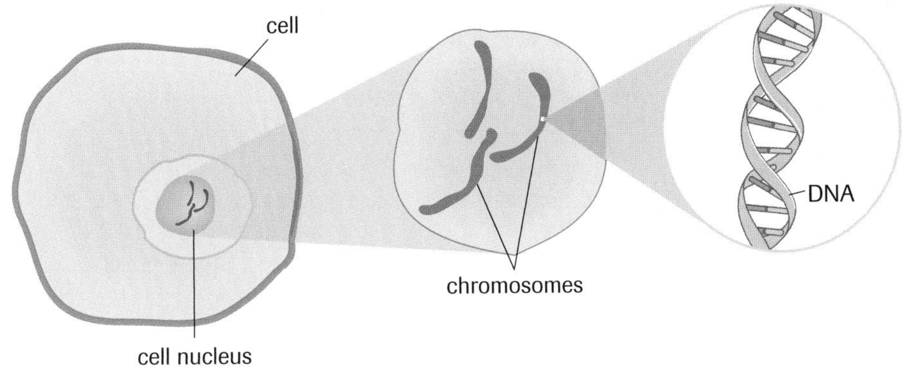

Figure 1
DNA, the genetic material, is packaged in chromosomes in the cell. The DNA molecule is composed of two strands of nucleotide bases.

In most cases, the DNA of an organism will remain the same throughout its life. Sometimes, however, DNA changes occur, and entirely new genetic information can arise. **Mutations** are random changes in the DNA itself, and they provide a continuous supply of new genetic information. Mutations can be caused by environmental factors such as chemicals or radiation, or from errors that arise when cells use or make copies of the DNA molecules. There are many types of mutations. Some involve the loss or duplication of entire sections of DNA, while others may be simple changes to the DNA sequence (**Figure 2**). Mutations are relatively rare in individuals—roughly about one new mutation per sex cell. In large populations reproducing over many generations, however, the number of mutations is substantial.

mutation a change in the DNA sequence in a chromosome

neutral mutation a mutation that has no effect on the organism

fitness an organism's reproductive success

harmful mutation a mutation that reduces an organism's fitness

beneficial mutation a mutation that enhances an organism's fitness

The effects of a mutation depend on what DNA sequence is altered and how it is affected. A **neutral mutation** has no immediate effect on an individual's **fitness**, or reproductive success. A **harmful mutation** reduces an individual's fitness. A **beneficial mutation** gives an individual a selective advantage. Most mutations are neutral or harmful in nature.

There are three common misconceptions about how mutations contribute to evolution. These misconceptions are given in **Table 1**, along with the accepted understanding based on observations.

Table 1 Mutation Misconceptions

Misconception	Accepted Understanding
Mutations occur when "needed," in response to environmental challenges.	Mutations occur at random, with harmful mutations being more common than beneficial mutations. There is no design to it.
Since harmful mutations are more common than beneficial mutations, they can accumulate and the species will steadily degrade.	Harmful mutations are *selected against* and therefore do not accumulate over the generations. The environment favours the fittest organisms. Harmful mutations can reduce or even eliminate the individual's chance of reproductive success.
Since mutations are random or chance events, then evolution is just pure chance.	Although beneficial mutations are rare, they are *selected for* and may accumulate over the generations. Beneficial mutations often give individuals improved survival and reproductive success.

+ EXTENSION 

Mutations and Changes in Proteins

Listen to a discussion of how mutations can cause proteins to change, which might then affect the survival of an organism.

www.science.nelson.com GO

Practice

1. In your own words, explain the role, if any, that neutral, harmful, and beneficial mutations each play in evolution.

asexual reproduction the production of offspring from a single parent; offspring inherit the genes of that parent only

siblings offspring from the same parent (in asexual reproduction) or parents (in sexual reproduction)

sexual reproduction the production of offspring by the union of sex cells from two different parents; the offspring inherit a combination of genes from both parents

Sexual Reproduction and Variability

In species that undergo **asexual reproduction**, such as bacteria, an individual reproduces without a mate. The offspring receives an identical copy of its parent's DNA. As a result, the offspring has identical traits to its parent and to any other offspring from that parent (**siblings**). The exception to this occurs if there is a mutation in the DNA. As you have read, mutations are relatively rare. As a result, there is very little inherited variability in asexually-reproducing species and very few traits that can be selected by natural selection.

In contrast, there is a great amount of inherited variability in species that undergo **sexual reproduction**. For example, think of the variation among just the people you know. Most plants and animals reproduce sexually. In sexual reproduction, the offspring are never identical to the parents or to other siblings (except for identical twins). Sexually reproducing species therefore have many traits on which natural selection can act.

Why are sexually-reproducing species so variable? There are three reasons.

1. Sexually-reproducing species have two copies of each gene. Each copy of the gene may be identical or different. In sexual reproduction, there are two parents. Both parents contribute one copy of each gene to the offspring. An offspring therefore inherits one copy of each gene from one parent and one copy from the other parent. The offspring therefore has a different combination of genes than either parent, and therefore will have its own unique set of traits.

2. The assortment of genes that an offspring inherits from either parent is determined randomly. Each sibling therefore has a unique combination of genes, and so siblings from sexual reproduction are not identical to each other. (Identical twins are an exception to this.) To illustrate, let's say that a large, black male dog is crossed with a small, brown female dog. A puppy from this cross might inherit any combination of these traits. For example, one puppy might be a large, brown female while another might be a small, black male. (There are other combinations as well.) The greater the number of genes a species has, the larger the number of combinations and the greater the genetic variability of the species as a whole.
3. Sexually reproducing species choose different mates. This process is not always random, but each combination of parents will give rise to different combinations of genes and traits in the next generation. In a small population of 1000 males and 1000 females, there are 1 million different possible mating pairs.

Table 2 connects genetics and Darwin's theory of natural selection.

DID YOU KNOW ?

Thomas Kuhn

A well-known philosophy of scientific thought put forward by Thomas Kuhn in a book published in 1962 proposes that scientific knowledge advances by gradual study and research, interspersed with abrupt jumps forward, known as "paradigm shifts." How might the theory of evolution help to back up Kuhn's philosophy?

Table 2 Genetic Mechanisms and Darwin's Theory

Darwinian evolution	Genetic mechanisms
inherited characteristics	Inherited characteristics are determined by genes. Organisms typically possess thousands of different genes.
population variability	Individuals of the same species differ from one another, in part because they possess different combinations of genes. The genetic makeup of all individuals within a population is called the population's **gene pool**.
source of new variations	New traits can arise when genes become mutated.
natural selection	Some genes determine traits that make the individual better suited for survival and reproductive success. Individuals with these traits will produce more offspring, some of which will inherit these advantageous genes.
evolutionary change	Over many generations, individuals carrying the genes that determine the most favourable traits for survival and reproductive success will become more common in the population. Evolution is this change in the population's gene pool.

gene pool all the genes in a certain population

mini *Investigation* Genetic Shuffle

In this activity, you will model the amount of possible variation for different numbers of traits in a sexually-reproducing species, using a deck of playing cards. Each card represents the gene for a particular trait. The suits represent the different forms of a gene. Since there are four suits in a deck of card, there are four possible forms for each gene in this model.

Materials: playing cards

- Obtain all four suits for any four different playing cards. Divide them into two sets to represent the genetic makeup of two parents. For example:

  Father: 3 of spades and 3 of clubs;
  8 of spades and 8 of clubs;
  Jack of spades and Jack of clubs;
  King of spades and King of clubs

  Mother: 3 of hearts and 3 of diamonds;
  8 of hearts and 8 of diamonds;
  Jack of hearts and Jack of diamonds;
  King of hearts and King of diamonds

- Using your cards, determine the number of all possible different genetic combinations from the two parents for one of the traits. Record your results in a table or spreadsheet.
- Repeat the procedure for two, three, and then four traits. You may wish to devise a method of organizing your different genetic combinations.

(a) What did you notice about the number of possible combinations as the number of traits increased?

(b) Humans possess genes for over 30 000 different genetic traits. With the exception of identical twins, is it surprising that no two siblings are alike? Explain.

INVESTIGATION 5.2 *Introduction*

Measuring Inherited Variation

In this investigation, you will design and conduct experiments to quantify inherited variations in living populations of a very successful species, *Homo sapiens.* You will then design and carry out your own investigation into the amount of variation in an inherited trait of a species of your choice.

To perform this investigation, turn to page 164.

Report Checklist

- ○ Purpose
- ○ Problem
- ● Hypothesis
- ● Prediction
- ● Design
- ● Materials
- ● Procedure
- ● Evidence
- ● Analysis
- ● Evaluation
- ● Synthesis

SUMMARY Sources of Inherited Variation

- Inherited variations are determined by differences in genes between individuals.
- The study of genetics redefined evolution as a change in the genetic makeup of a population over time.
- Since genes recombine during sexual reproduction, this process contributes to individual variability in populations.
- Mutations are the only source of new genetic material. Mutations may be neutral, harmful, or beneficial.
- Beneficial mutations may increase the fitness and reproductive success of an individual and therefore may become more common in a population. Harmful mutations decrease fitness and reproductive success and do not tend to accumulate.

Section 5.5 Questions

1. What key information regarding variation was missing in Darwin's explanation of the evolution of species?
2. Compare and contrast the contributions of sexual reproduction and mutation in producing variation within populations. Consider both short- and long-term influences.
3. Following their initial contact with non-indigenous people, many populations of indigenous peoples suffered devastating losses from previously unknown diseases. How might evolutionary biology account for their low resistance to these diseases?
4. Examine the collection of sea urchins in **Figure 3**. Prepare a design statement for an investigation to compare the inherited variation in these species.

Extension

5. Research Richard Dawkins's theory about "selfish genes." Prepare arguments and counter-arguments for a class debate on his theory.

www.science.nelson.com 

Figure 3
Sea urchin exoskeletons

Speciation and Evolution 5.6

Natural selection provides an explanation of how species become better adapted to their environment. Does it also account for the formation of new species (**speciation**) and, from there, entire new groups of living organisms? A species can be thought of as a population of individuals who are reproductively isolated—they are not capable of breeding with individuals of other species under natural conditions. Most new species are believed to arise by a three-step process called **allopatric speciation**.

speciation the formation of new species

allopatric speciation speciation by reproductive isolation

1. A physical barrier separates a single interbreeding population into two or more groups that are isolated from each other. Any mutations that occur in one of these isolated groups are not shared with the other population(s) (**Figure 1**).
2. Natural selection works on the separated groups independently, resulting in inherited differences in the two populations. In other words, the populations evolve independently. Differences in selective pressures will be greater if the populations experience pronounced differences in their environments.
3. In time, accumulated physical and/or behavioural differences between the populations become so pronounced that the groups, should they be reunited, would no longer be sexually compatible. At this point, they have formed two or more distinct species (**Figure 2**).

Physical barriers range in size from entire mountain ranges and oceans to river channels and canyons. On a smaller scale, human constructions such as dams and canals may produce insurmountable physical barriers to small organisms.

Speciation can also occur when a single population splits into distinct breeding populations when occupying a single geographic region (**Figure 3**). This process can be sudden. One form occurs when a mutation results in individuals with double or more the normal number of chromosomes. These individuals may be healthy and vigorous but reproductively isolated from the rest of the population. They are only able to mate with other similar polyploids. Many plant species are thought to have evolved by this mechanism.

Figure 1
Wood bison **(a)** and plains bison **(b)** are reproductively isolated. Wood bison live in northern wooded areas in Canada, while plains bison live on the Prairies in both Canada and the United States.

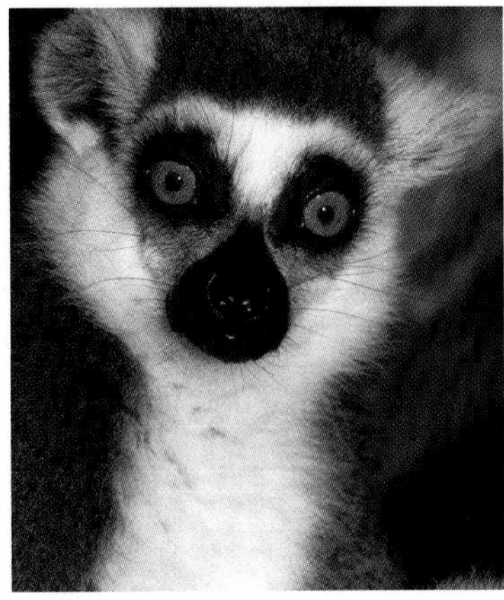

Figure 2
This black-and-white lemur of Madagascar island is an example of allopatric speciation. Separated from the continent of Africa for over 1 million years, Madagascar now hosts some 8000 plant species and 1200 animal species found nowhere else.

Figure 3
Genetic evidence strongly suggests that a number of different species of sticklebacks living in some lakes in British Columbia evolved as a result of mutations that produced sudden changes in chromosome numbers.

WWW **WEB Activity**

Case Study—Lactose Intolerance and Evolution

Lactose intolerance is the inability to digest lactose (milk sugar). Interestingly, certain groups of people, including First Nations people and those of African descent, are more likely to suffer from this condition. How does the theory of evolution account for these findings? Can we make and test predictions regarding the evolution of this condition? Working in a small group, investigate these questions by completing this Web Activity.

www.science.nelson.com GO

The Rate of Evolution

theory of gradualism the idea that speciation takes place slowly

theory of punctuated equilibrium the idea that species evolve rapidly, followed by a period of little or no change

Until the mid-20th century, most biologists thought that changes to species occurred at a slow, steady pace. By this **theory of gradualism**, we would expect to find many fossils that showed small changes in species over time. Instead, distinct species often appear abruptly in the fossil record, and then little further change is seen over very long periods of time. In 1972, Niles Eldridge of the American Museum of Natural History and Stephen Jay Gould of Harvard University proposed **the theory of punctuated equilibrium** to account for these patterns in the fossil record. This theory has three main assertions:

- many species evolve very rapidly in evolutionary time
- speciation usually occurs in small isolated populations, so intermediate fossils are very rare
- after an initial burst of evolution, species are well adapted to their environment and so do not change significantly over long periods of time

These contrasting theories about the rate of evolution are shown in **Figure 4**. To some extent, the differences between them are a matter of perspective. To paleontologists, a sudden or "rapid" change might mean the appearance of a new species in the fossil record within 100 000 years. In fact, both theories are needed to understand the fossil record while remaining compatible with many other forms of evidence.

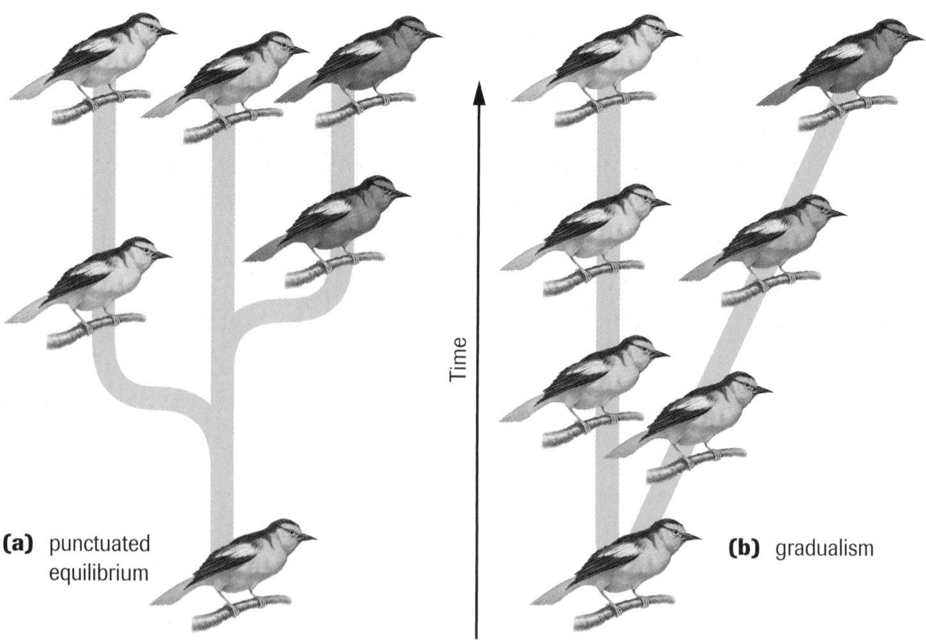

Figure 4
Two theories of the rate of evolution

Macroevolution: Diversification and Extinction

Figure 5, on the next page, shows the geological time scale and summarizes significant events in Earth's evolutionary history. Since life began, Earth has experienced an increase in diversity of living things. However, this trend has been interrupted by several major "extinction events," each identified by a thick red line in **Figure 5**. The Paleozoic era, for example, began with a rapid increase in the number of species, referred to as the Cambrian explosion, and ended 245 mya (million years ago) with the dramatic Permian extinction.

There is extensive fossil evidence for the Cambrian explosion. One of the most important fossil discoveries in the world, the Burgess Shale in Canada's Rocky Mountains, contains beautifully preserved 515-million-year-old fossils of marine life. The great diversity—more than 120 species—is evidence of **divergent evolution**, when species rapidly evolved into many different species during the early Cambrian period.

divergent evolution evolution into many different species

At the end of the Paleozoic era, between 240 and 225 mya, a series of cataclysmic events eradicated more than 90 % of the known marine species. The causes of this Permian extinction are unknown, but many scientists suspect tectonic movements. The Mesozoic era, well known for its dinosaurs, also came to a sudden end about 65 mya, when the remaining dinosaurs and many other species suddenly disappear from the fossil record. Considerable evidence supports the hypothesis that an asteroid impact caused this best-known mass extinction. The Chicxulub Crater, almost 10 km deep and 200 km in diameter at the edge of the Yucatán Peninsula (**Figure 6**), is thought to have been the impact site. The debris and energy released in the resulting fireball—equivalent to 100 million nuclear bombs—would have killed most of the plants and animals in North and South America within minutes. Tsunamis 120 m high would have devastated coastlines around the world, and atmospheric debris would have blocked out much of the sunlight for months or even years.

Figure 6
A computer-generated image of the moment of impact that created the 200-km-wide Chicxulub Crater, in the ocean floor at the edge of the Yucatán Peninsula.

While the mass extinctions that ended the Permian and the Mesozoic eras are dramatic, it is important to keep in mind that most extinctions of species result from the ongoing evolutionary forces of competition and environmental change. This "background" rate of extinction is slow—the average species exists for about a million years.

Putting the Theory of Evolution to Work: Predictions

All scientific theories are judged on their ability to (1) account for old and new evidence and (2) make testable predictions. How does the theory of evolution stand up to this judgement? As you have learned, the theory of evolution is clearly able to account for a wide range of evidence, but can it be used to make testable predictions?

Because evolution is usually a very slow process, it is difficult to witness evolutionary change directly, making it difficult to test predictions about the future evolution of a species. Predicting future *events*, however, provides an equally rigorous method of testing a theory. The following example illustrates such a test.

Prediction: Because they are not mobile, plants will have evolved toxic and bitter-tasting compounds to deter predators. These compounds are likely to be concentrated in their delicate leaves.

Evidence: Most plant tissues, and particularly leaf tissues, are far more toxic than animal tissues.

EXTENSION

Measuring Time
This video discusses evidence of changes in Earth's history resulting from the asteroid that hit the Yucatán Peninsula.

www.science.nelson.com 

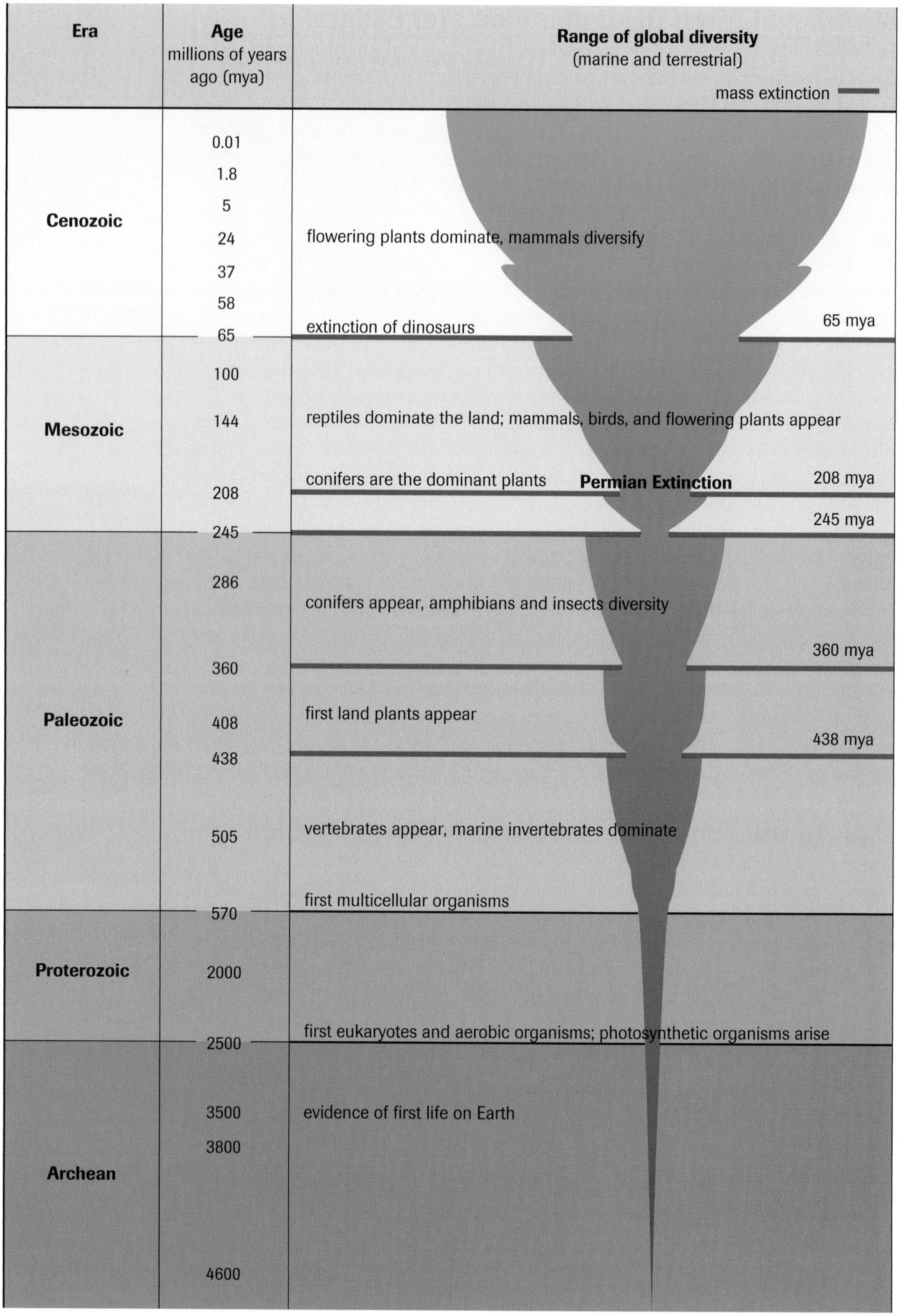

Era	Age millions of years ago (mya)	Range of global diversity (marine and terrestrial)	mass extinction
Cenozoic	0.01		
	1.8		
	5		
	24	flowering plants dominate, mammals diversify	
	37		
	58		
	65	extinction of dinosaurs	65 mya
Mesozoic	100		
	144	reptiles dominate the land; mammals, birds, and flowering plants appear	
	208	conifers are the dominant plants	208 mya
	245	Permian Extinction	245 mya
Paleozoic	286	conifers appear, amphibians and insects diversity	
	360		360 mya
	408	first land plants appear	
	438		438 mya
	505	vertebrates appear, marine invertebrates dominate	
	570	first multicellular organisms	
Proterozoic	2000		
	2500	first eukaryotes and aerobic organisms; photosynthetic organisms arise	
Archean	3500	evidence of first life on Earth	
	3800		
	4600		

Figure 5
Major events of life on Earth

Simulation—Natural Selection

The reproductive success of the peppered moth has been observed to be related to its colouring. In this online investigation, you will observe the effects of a change in the colour of environment on a population of virtual creatures of variable coloration. Will the simulation model the real-life observations with peppered moths?

www.science.nelson.com 

SUMMARY Speciation and Evolution

- New species have evolved when two or more populations become reproductively isolated from each other.
- Geographic isolation may be the most common cause of populations evolving into separate species (allopatry).
- The pace, or rate, of evolution is variable—the theories of gradualism and punctuated equilibrium account for various patterns seen in the fossil record.
- Earth has experienced periods of rapid diversification of living things—divergent evolution—as well as episodes of mass extinction.

Section 5.6 Questions

1. Outline the steps involved in allopatric speciation.
2. Living in the same region, the almost identical species of tree frog, *Hyla veriscolor* (**Figure 7 (a)**) and *Hyla chrysoscelis* (**Figure 7 (b)**) are distinguished only by their vocal calls and their DNA. *H. veriscolor* has exactly twice the number of chromosomes as *H. chrysoscelis.* How might *H. versicolor* have evolved?

(a)

(b)

Figure 7

3. Construction of a canal through Panama has affected marine and terrestrial species. Consult an atlas to see the extent of the canal.
   (a) Comment on effects on the evolution and speciation of Atlantic and Pacific marine organisms in the vicinity of the Panama Canal.
   (b) How might the construction of the Panama Canal have influenced the evolution of terrestrial species?
4. What aspect of the fossil record suggests that evolution may occur rapidly?
5. Compare and contrast the theories of punctuated equilibrium and gradualism.
6. Evolutionists have concluded that mammals evolved from a group of reptiles. Based on your understanding of fossil formation and evolution, make a testable prediction about the fossil records of mammals and reptiles. Conduct literature and Internet research to see if your prediction was valid.

www.science.nelson.com 

INVESTIGATION 5.1

Report Checklist		
● Purpose	● Design	● Analysis
● Problem	○ Materials	○ Evaluation
○ Hypothesis	● Procedure	● Synthesis
● Prediction	● Evidence	

Using a Classification Key

Whales are often grouped as either toothed or baleen whales. Baleen whales have a series of vertical plates that branch and crisscross at the opening of the mouth. Each plate acts as a filter, straining small marine life from the seawater.

Purpose

To identify various species of whales using a dichotomous key

Procedure

1. Use **Figure 1** to help you identify the whale's body structures referred to in the key.

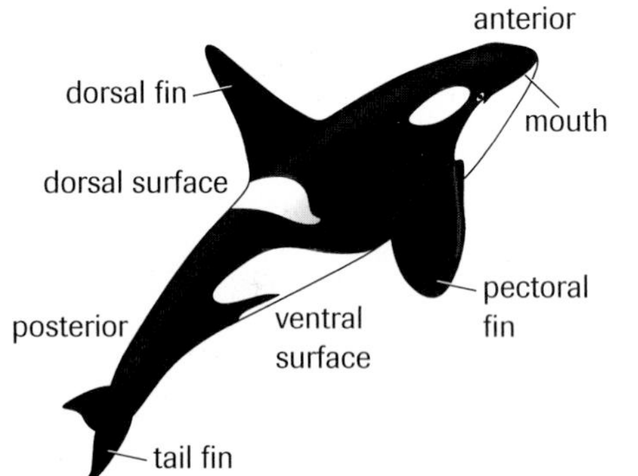

Figure 1

2. To identify each whale in **Figures 2** to **8**, start by reading part 1(a) and (b) of The Key (below). Then follow the "Go to" direction at the end of the appropriate sentence until the whale has been properly classified.

Analysis

(a) What are four characteristics used to classify whales?

(b) Why might biologists use a key?

(c) Provide an example of when a biologist might use a key to classify whales.

(d) Make a list of other characteristics that could be used to classify whales.

Evaluation and Synthesis

(e) Research to find out more about whales, for example, their distribution ranges and whether a species is threatened or endangered.

(f) Identify eight different trees or shrubs native to your locale and make a dichotomous key that allows others to identify them.

The Key	
1. (a) baleen plates (b) teeth	Go to 2. Go to 4.
2. (a) dorsal fin (b) no dorsal fin	Go to 3. bowhead whale (*Balaena mysticetus*)
3. (a) long pectoral fin (b) short pectoral fin	humpback whale (*Megaptera novaeangline*) blue whale (*Balaenoptera musculus*)
4. (a) no dorsal fin (b) large dorsal fin	Go to 5. killer whale (*Orincus orca*)
5. (a) small nose (b) large projection from nose	Go to 6. narwhal (*Mondon monoceros*)
6. (a) mouth on ventral surface (underside) of head (b) mouth at the front of head	sperm whale (*Physeter macrocephalus*) beluga (*Delphinapterus leucas*)

INVESTIGATION 5.1 *continued*

Figure 2
- teeth
- adult length: 6.0 m (females), 6.7 m (males)
- adult mass: 7.4 tonnes (t) (females), 10.5 t (males)

Figure 3
- baleen plates
- adult length: 13.7 m (females), 12.9 m (males)
- adult mass: 25 t–30 t

Figure 4
- teeth
- adult length: 3.5 m (females), 4.5 m (males)
- adult mass: 1.0 t (females), 1.2 t (males)

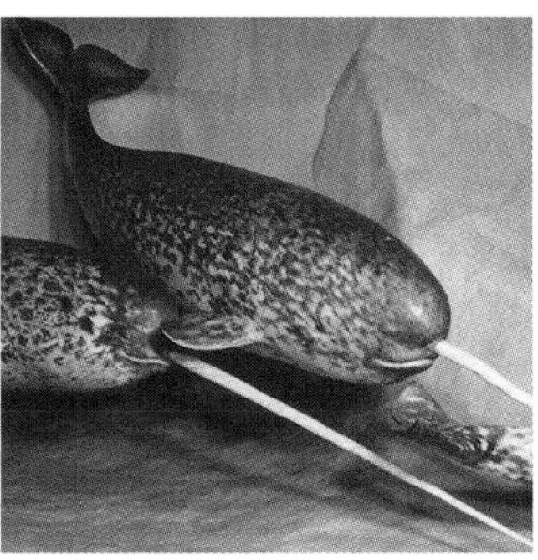

Figure 5
- teeth
- adult length: 4.2 m (females), 4.7 m (males)
- adult mass: 900 kg (females), 1.6 t (males)

Figure 6
- teeth
- adult length: 11 m (females), 15 m (males)
- adult mass: 20 t (females), 45 t (males)

Figure 7
- baleen plates
- adult length: 26.5 m (females), 25 m (males)
- adult mass: 200 t (females), 100 t (males)

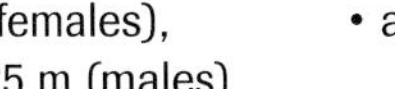

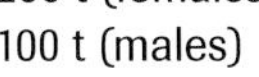

Figure 8
- baleen plates
- adult length: 14 m–15 m
- adult mass: 50 t–60 t

INVESTIGATION 5.2

Report Checklist

○ Purpose	● Design	● Analysis
○ Problem	● Materials	● Evaluation
● Hypothesis	● Procedure	● Synthesis
● Prediction	● Evidence	

Measuring Inherited Variation

If, as Darwin asserted, natural selection is occurring throughout the living world, then all species of organisms must possess inherited variations. In this investigation, you will design and conduct experiments to quantify inherited variations in living populations.

Part A: Human Variability

Humans are the only exclusively bipedal mammals—that is, we walk upright on two feet. This characteristic is clearly inherited. In this investigation, you will quantify variation in the length of the human foot and investigate whether such variation is inherited. Before beginning your investigation, generate one or more testable hypotheses regarding both variability and inheritability of human foot length.

Design Suggestions

1. Devise a method to accurately measure human foot length.
2. Consider using commercial shoe sizes for your data. How might this influence the accuracy and objectivity of the data? Would this be offset by the ability to obtain more data?
3. Gather and tabulate inheritance evidence as a set of ordered pairs. Each data set should include foot length of an offspring paired with the foot length of the biological parent of the same gender (boys with their father, girls with their mother).
4. Take into account the influence of student age in your investigation.
5. Use histograms to display sample variation and (x,y) coordinate graphs to display inheritability. **Figure 1** shows an example of each.

Analysis

(a) Comment on the degree of variation you observed in human foot length. Describe any patterns in the data.

(b) Did the range of male foot length differ from that in females?

(c) What was the mean foot length among the males and the females you studied?

(d) Were some foot lengths obviously more common? Were the more common foot length(s) closer to the mean of foot length or to one of the extremes?

(e) Describe any evidence you found that foot length is an inherited trait.

(a)

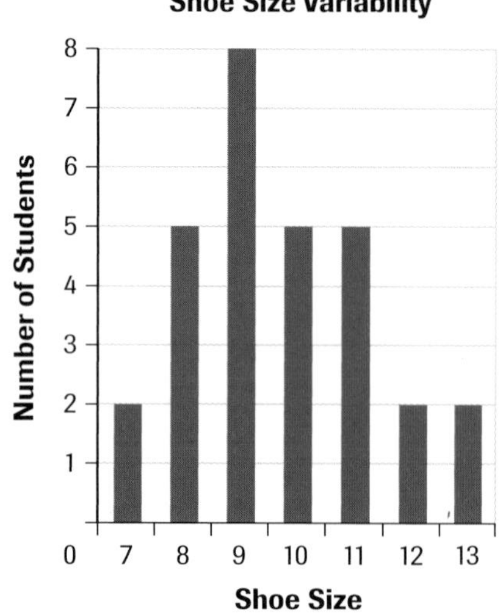

(b)

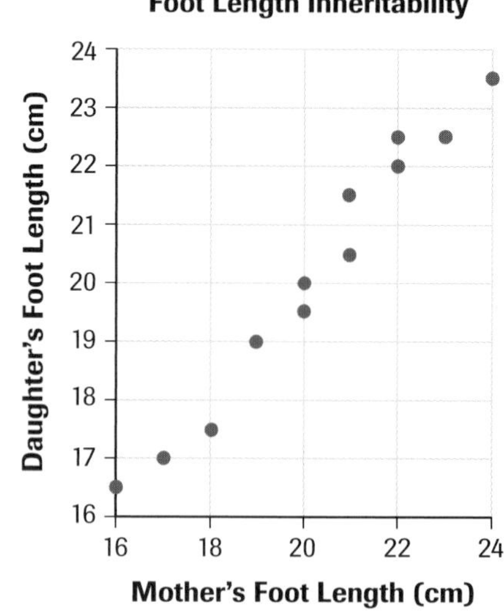

Figure 1
(a) histogram of number of male students versus shoe size
(b) daughter's foot length (cm) (y-axis) versus mother's foot length (cm) (x-axis)

INVESTIGATION 5.2 *continued*

(f) Does the evidence suggest that foot length is an inherited trait that remains unchanged between a child and the parent of the same gender? Explain.

Evaluation

(g) Do the sample data in **Figure 1** (**b**) appear realistic? Do you think they represent actual data? Explain.

(h) How might the age of the offspring have influenced the results of your investigation?

(i) Do you think the age of the parents influenced your results? Why?

(j) What could you do differently to eliminate or reduce the influence of offspring age?

(k) How could you modify the experimental design to determine whether both parents influence foot length?

Synthesis

(l) Foot length was chosen for this investigation because it was suspected of being an inherited trait, at least in part. What environmental factors could be partly responsible for human foot length?

(m) What physical human characteristics are variable but are not inherited?

(n) What role might sexual reproduction have played in influencing the variability and inheritability of foot length in this investigation?

Part B: Variations in Nature

Design and conduct an investigation similar to Part A, using a quantifiable characteristic of an animal or plant species. For example, you might investigate the number of seeds per fruit or seed germination time; or adult height of cats or dogs. Select a characteristic that you know or can assume is inherited. The evidence you collect must either support or refute the following hypothesis: All species exhibit variations in inherited traits.

Analysis

(o) Based on the findings of your investigation, as well as the investigations of your classmates, what general conclusions can you draw about the variability within species?

Evaluation

(p) What role does the variability of a trait have in influencing its evolution? Is variation necessary for evolution? Explain.

(q) How might the length or size of the following anatomical structures have proven advantageous for these animals?

(i) neck of a swan

(ii) an elephant's trunk

(iii) moose or elk antlers

(iv) long legs of herons

(v) rattlesnake fangs

Synthesis

(r) The results of a scientific study often lead to new questions which become the topic of future investigations. Generate three new questions that arise from your findings that could be the basis of additional investigations.

Chapter 5 SUMMARY

Outcomes

Knowledge

- explain the fundamental principles of taxonomy, i.e., domains, kingdoms, and binomial nomenclature (5.1)
- explain that variability in a species results from heritable mutations and that some mutations may have selective advantage(s), i.e., fossil record, Earth's history, embryology, biogeography, homologous and analogous structures, and biochemistry (5.5)
- discuss the significance of sexual reproduction to individual variation in populations and to the process of evolution (5.5)
- compare Lamarckian and Darwinian explanations of evolutionary change (5.4)
- summarize and describe lines of evidence to support the evolution of modern species from ancestral forms (5.2, 5.3, 5.6)
- explain speciation and the conditions required for this process (5.6)
- describe modern evolutionary theories, i.e., punctuated equilibrium versus gradualism (5.6)

STS

- explain that conventions of mathematics, nomenclature, and notation provide a basis for organizing and communicating scientific theory, relationships, and concepts (5.1)
- explain that scientific knowledge and theories develop through hypotheses, the collection of evidence, observation, and the ability to provide explanations (5.2, 5.3, 5.6)

Skills

- ask questions about observed relationships and plan investigations by designing an investigation to measure or describe an inherited variation in a plant or animal population (5.5); and hypothesizing the adaptive significance of the variations in a range of homologous structures in extant and extinct organisms (5.2, 5.3)
- conduct investigations and use a broad range of tools and techniques (all)
- analyze data and apply mathematical and conceptual models by: applying classification and binomial nomenclature systems in a field study (5.1), and analyzing data, actual or simulated, on plants and animals to demonstrate how morphology changes over time (5.3, 5.4, 5.5, 5.6)
- work as members of a team and apply the skills and conventions of science (all)

Key Terms

5.1

taxonomy
binomial nomenclature
genus
species
taxon (pl. taxa)
Protista
Monera
Archaebacteria
Eubacteria
phylogeny
dichotomous key

5.2

paleontology
radiometric dating
biogeography
endemic

5.3

homologous features
analogous features
vestigial features
DNA
gene
artificial selection

5.4

spontaneous generation
inheritance of acquired characteristics
natural selection

5.5

mutation
neutral mutation
fitness
harmful mutation
beneficial mutation
asexual reproduction
siblings
sexual reproduction
gene pool

5.6

speciation
allopatric speciation
theory of gradualism
theory of punctuated equilibrium
divergent evolution

MAKE a summary

1. Our current understanding of the evolution of life on Earth was gained using methods of scientific inquiry. We have used these methods to gather evidence and understand both the processes and the products of evolution. Design and construct a concept map that depicts these key elements. Your concept map should make creative use of information and communication technologies. You might construct a Web page concept map with hyperlinks to Web sites, information, or image files. Alternatively, you may want to make use of digital technology.
2. Revisit your answers to the Starting Points questions at the start of the chapter. Would you answer the questions differently now? Why?

Go To

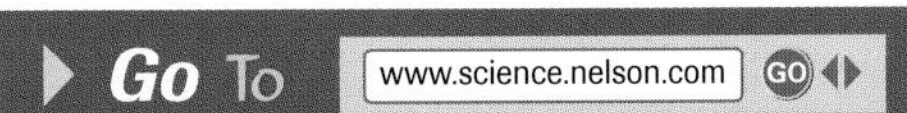

The following components are available on the Nelson Web site. Follow the links for *Nelson Biology Alberta 20–30.*

- an interactive Self Quiz for Chapter 5
- additional Diploma Exam-style Review Questions
- Illustrated Glossary
- additional IB-related material

There is more information on the Web site wherever you see the Go icon in the chapter.

EXTENSION

Little People of Flores

The remains of three-foot-tall humans are discovered on a remote Indonesian Island. How have scientists interpreted these skeletons?

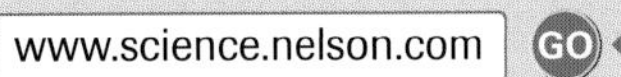
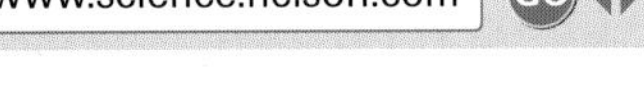

EXTENSION

Newts and Garter Snakes

Dr. Butch Brodie, (professor of biology at Indiana University) describes natural selection and the amazing predator-prey interactions of the toxic rough-skinned newt and the garter snake. A genetic mutation allows the snake to eat this highly poisonous prey. The newt's toxin is so strong it can quickly kill humans, yet the snake has managed to adapt to the toxin.

www.science.nelson.com

EXTENSION

T. rex

An astonishing adolescent growth spurt accounts for T. rex's enormous size. Scientists were able to make conclusions about the life span of this huge dinosaur by comparing fossilized bones to homologous bones in modern alligators.

www.science.nelson.com

UNIT 20 B PERFORMANCE TASK

The Sixth Extinction

In this Performance Task, you will use the knowledge and skills you have gained in this unit to compare past and current extinctions. Go to the Unit 20 B Performance Task link on the Nelson Web site and complete the task.

www.science.nelson.com

Chapter 5 REVIEW

Many of these questions are in the style of the Diploma Exam. You will find guidance for writing Diploma Exams in Appendix A5. Science Directing Words used in Diploma Exams are in bold type. Exam study tips and test-taking suggestions are on the Nelson Web site.

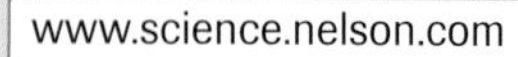

DO NOT WRITE IN THIS TEXTBOOK.

Part 1

1. Radiometric dating provided scientists with
   A. a method for determining the exact age of sedimentary deposits
   B. a method for determining the age of a fossil by measuring its radioactivity
   C. a method of dating that is not accurate for objects only a few thousand years old
   D. a method for accurately dating igneous rock and for estimating the age of Earth

2. The theory of evolution by acquired characteristics did not include which of the following ideas:
   A. strenuous activities can change organisms
   B. organisms can change during their own lifetime
   C. physical characteristics cannot be passed to offspring
   D. the environment plays a role in selecting favourable characteristics

3. Jean-Baptiste Lamarck is important to the study of evolution because he
   A. conducted genetic experiments with garden peas
   B. proposed a theory of evolution called adaptations
   C. proposed a theory of evolution called natural selection
   D. proposed that the environment could drive evolutionary change

Use the following information to answer questions 4 to 6.

Darwin's voyage allowed him to observe species with distinct inherited variations. Based on the work of Malthus, Darwin realized that all populations produce far more offspring than can survive long enough to reproduce. From this, Darwin developed the concept of natural selection.

4. Malthus's work was important to Darwin's theory of evolution because it led him to conclude that
   A. all species show inherited variation
   B. there is competition among individuals of the same species
   C. all populations can be expected to increase in size over time
   D. the individuals with the best traits will be more likely to survive and reproduce

5. Since he found inherited variations in all species, Darwin concluded that
   A. variations between individuals were random
   B. the environment did not influence the characteristics of individuals
   C. variation did not play a significant role in the mechanism of evolution
   D. some individuals might be better suited to the environment than others

6. According to Darwin's theory of natural selection, a struggle for survival is a result of
   A. the occurrence of mutations
   B. many species competing with one another
   C. the variation of traits among individuals of a species
   D. the large number of offspring born in each generation

7. A species of flying squirrel inhabited an island. Ten thousand years ago, ashes from a nearby volcano killed most of the vegetation, including all the trees. A few flying squirrels survived. Today, squirrels are abundant, living among the rocks and shrubs that now cover the island. In the present population, the "flight membranes" are mostly too small to be functional. The most probable explanation for this change is that
   A. all the squirrels that could fly left the island
   B. a new type of squirrel was introduced to the island
   C. natural selection no longer favoured those that could fly
   D. young squirrels were not taught to fly by their parents, so the membranes did not develop

8. NR Many poisonous frogs are brightly coloured (**Figure 1**). This adaptation is thought to protect the frog by warning off potential predators. Assume that each of the following steps occurred in the evolution of the warning coloration. Place them in chronological order from the earliest to the most recent. (Record all four digits of your answer.)
   1. Predators associated the foul-tasting frogs with their coloration and stopped feeding on them.
   2. Some frogs within the population had mutations that made them more brightly coloured.
   3. Some frogs within the population had mutations that made them toxic to some predators.
   4. These frogs were more likely to survive than others, and this trait became established among all the frogs of this species.

Figure 1

9. Examine and compare the following samples of DNA. Using this evidence, place species 1, 2, 3, and 4 in order from *most* closely related to *least* closely related to species X.

species X AATCCGAGGTATAGCTACCAGAATCCGGG

A. species 1 AATCGGAGGTATAGCTACCAGAATCCGGG
B. species 2 AATCCGAGCTATAGCCACCAGAATCCAGG
C. species 3 ATTTCTAGGTATAGGGACCAGCATCCTGG
D. species 4 AATCCGAGGTATAGCTACCAGAATCCCGG

10. NR Each of the following individuals had ideas about the evolution of life on Earth. Place their names in chronological order from the earliest to the most recent. (Record all four digits of your answer.)
    1. Buffon
    2. Darwin
    3. Wallace
    4. Lamarck

Part 2

11. When Europeans arrived in Hawaii, they introduced rats, cats, dogs, and other predators. As a direct consequence, 61 of Hawaii's 96 species of native birds have already gone extinct. **Relate** this set of events to the theory of evolution by describing how natural selection influenced Hawaii's bird species before and after the arrival of Europeans.

Use the following information to answer questions 12 to 16.

The computer simulation entitled "Methinks It Is Like a Weasel" uses the analogy of a monkey typing randomly at a keyboard to compare pure chance with natural selection. After reading the online introduction and background information, run the simulation several times, noting both the ongoing processes and the end results.

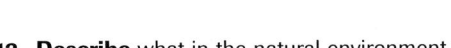

www.science.nelson.com GO

12. DE **Describe** what in the natural environment is being modelled by the phrase "Methinks it is like a weasel".

13. DE **Identify** the process that leads to changes in the alleles of both the monkey at the keyboard and cumulative selection.

14. DE **Why** don't the beneficial mutations that arise in the monkey at the keyboard accumulate?

15. DE **Describe** what happens to harmful changes in the cumulative selection simulation.

16. DE Could the monkey at the keyboard actually generate the phrase "Methinks it is like a weasel?" **Explain**.

17. It is thought that a billion prairie dogs once populated an area of over 100 million ha. Their current territory has been reduced and fragmented to less than 1 % of this original space. **Predict** the impacts from these changes in habitat on the prairie dog gene pool, as well as on the evolution and survival of the species.

Use the following information to answer questions 18 to 21.

A fascinating evolutionary relationship exists between the genetic disorder sickle cell anemia and the infectious disease malaria. View the online video that describes this relationship and answer the questions.

www.science.nelson.com GO

18. DE **Conclude** whether sickle cell anemia is a serious disorder.

19. DE **Conclude** whether malaria is a serious disorder.

20. DE **Conclude** whether it is always a disadvantage to have the sickle cell trait.

21. DE **Describe** how your geographic location influences whether the mutation that causes sickle cell anemia is harmful or beneficial.

Use the following information to answer questions 22 to 24.

Recent genetic analysis of purebred dogs, published in the journal *Science,* suggests that dog breeds can be distinguished with great accuracy by comparing their DNA. According to research scientist Elaine Ostrander, "At a DNA level, breeds are a very real concept. Every poodle is more closely related to a poodle than it is to a dog of any other breed."

22. DE **Describe** how this evidence supports the assertion that selection can lead to changes in the genetic makeup of a population.

23. DE **Describe** what this evidence suggests about the use of DNA analysis as a tool for evolutionary biologists.

24. DE **Describe** some possible advantages and disadvantages to comparing breeds or species based on their DNA as opposed to their physical or behavioural characteristics.

25. Some prions (infectious proteins) that cause diseases such as bovine spongiform encephalopathy (mad cow disease) and the inherited form of human spongiform encephalopathy (Creudtzfeldt-Jacob disease) result from single genetic mutations. Research the genetics of these diseases. **Explain** how they are transmitted and **why** they are not eliminated by natural selection.

www.science.nelson.com 

Many of these questions are in the style of the Diploma Exam. You will find guidance for writing Diploma Exams in Appendix A5. Science Directing Words used in Diploma Exams are in bold type. Exam study tips and test-taking suggestions are on the Nelson Web site.

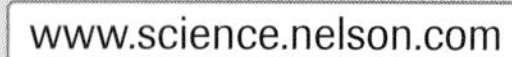

DO NOT WRITE IN THIS TEXTBOOK.

Part 1

1. All of the deer in a forest area of 100 km^2 can be described as a
   A. deer community
   B. deer population
   C. deer biome
   D. deer species

2. The cougar, African lion, and common house cat are all types of cats. They share all of the same taxonomic categories except
   A. family
   B. class
   C. genus
   D. order

3. In which taxonomic group do the members have the greatest number of similarities?
   A. kingdom
   B. family
   C. genus
   D. phylum

4. A niche is best described as
   A. biological components of an ecosystem
   B. abiotic factors of an ecosystem
   C. a population of a species of animals that occupies an area
   D. roles and interactions of a species within its community

5. A community includes
   A. the physical area where an organism lives
   B. all members of a certain species in a defined area
   C. the populations of all organisms that occupy a defined area
   D. all organisms in a population regardless of area

6. The addition of nutrients to a stream will immediately cause
   A. bacteria to increase, which will increase the level of dissolved oxygen in the stream
   B. bacteria to increase, which will decrease the level of dissolved oxygen in the stream
   C. bacteria to decrease, which will increase the level of dissolved oxygen in the stream
   D. bacteria to decrease, which will decrease the level of dissolved oxygen in the stream

7. Data were collected from three different sites along the North Saskatchewan River, and used to draw the graph in **Figure 1**. If a biologist took water samples from the river and measured the dissolved oxygen levels, she would find that dissolved oxygen is lowest at point
   A. W
   B. X
   C. Y
   D. Z

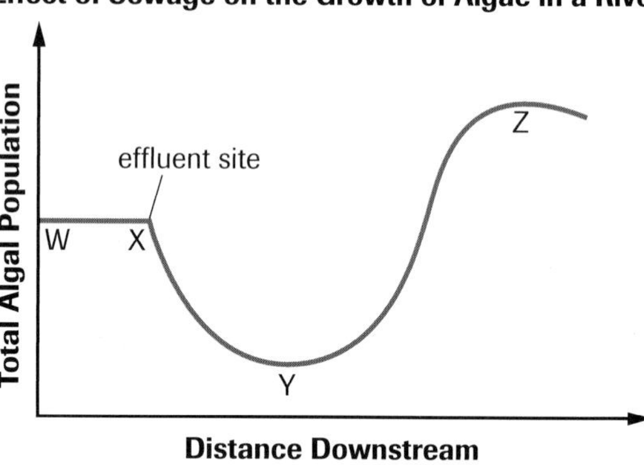

Figure 1

8. Which of the following statements is false?
   A. The littoral zone of a lake is farthest from the shore.
   B. The limnetic zone has more light than the profundal zone.
   C. The littoral zone is closer to the surface than the profundal zone.
   D. Aquatic plants do not usually grow in the profundal zone.

Use the following information to answer questions 9 to11.

Ecologists measured the amount of melted snow entering a river from April 1 to May 15. They also recorded the pH of the river. Their results are presented in **Figure 2**.

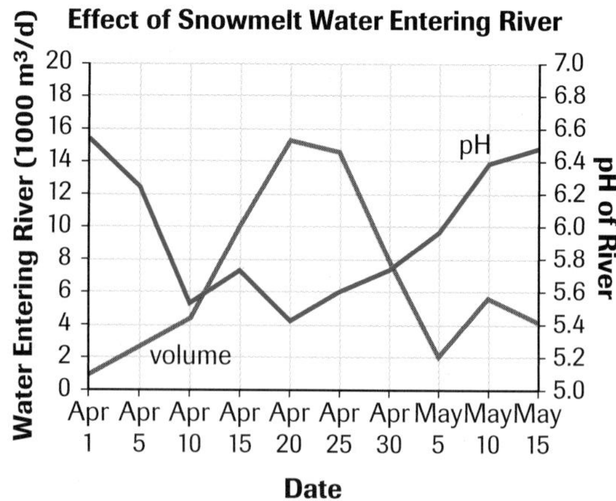

Figure 2

9. According to the data collected from the graph, as the snowmelt increases,
   A. the volume of water in the river increases and the pH becomes more acidic.
   B. the volume of water in the river decreases and the pH becomes more acidic.
   C. the volume of water in the river increases and the pH becomes more basic.
   D. the volume of water in the river decreases and the pH becomes more basic.

10. On which date was the water most acidic?
   A. April 1
   B. April 15
   C. April 20
   D. May 10

11. Which factor could account for the drop in pH during mid-April?
   A. increased photosynthesis during mid-April
   B. acid deposition enters the river with melting snow
   C. alkaline (basic) minerals in the soil are carried into the river with melting snow
   D. the increased volume of water entering the river dilutes the concentration of acids found in the river

---

12. Which of the following is not an acquired trait?
   A. the ability to read
   B. a suntan
   C. a tattoo
   D. sense of smell

13. NR Through natural selection, individuals with adaptations that increase their chances of survival will produce more offspring. As a result, those adaptations will become more common in the species over time and the species evolves. Sometimes, new adaptations in one species affect the evolution of an adaptation in another species. Consider the following pairs of adaptations. For each of the four pairs, record the number of the adaptation that is most likely to have evolved first. (Record all four digits of your answer from lowest-to-highest numerical order.)
   1. insect-pollinated flowers OR 2. sacks on the legs of honeybees that hold pollen
   3. the flying ability of insects OR 4. spider webs
   5. a brightly coloured butterfly species OR 6. the same species is poisonous
   7. certain mammals have forepaws that can grasp things OR 8. certain mammals begin living in trees

14. NR Place the following discoveries/theories in chronological order from earliest to most recent. (Record all four digits of your answer.)
   1. Wallace develops a theory of evolution by natural selection.
   2. First fossils are discovered.
   3. Darwin goes on a voyage on HMS *Beagle*.
   4. Lamarck hypothesizes the evolution of acquired characteristics.

Part 2

Use the following information to answer questions 15 to 18.

In an attempt to increase the local food supply for people, humans introduced 26 caribou (24 females and 2 males) to an island off the coast of Alaska in 1910. **Figure 3** shows how the reindeer population changed after the introduction.

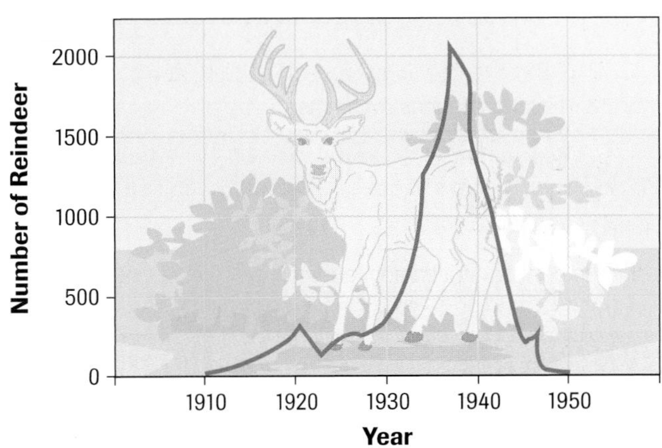

Figure 3

15. DE **Why** were more females introduced than male?

16. DE By 1937, the caribou population had soared to 2000. **Describe** the evidence that supports the hypothesis that the carrying capacity for reindeer had been exceeded.

17. DE Caribou feed on slow-growing lichens and moss. Would you expect to find more food for caribou on the island in 1931, 1935, or 1950? **Explain** your answer.

18. DE The introduction of a new species can cause major changes in an ecosystem. Should the caribou have been put on the island? **Explain** your position.

Use the following information to answer questions 19 to 25.

Scientists examined the aging of a lake over time. **Table 1** shows the data they collected from historical records. **Table 2**, on the next page, gives standard data on the change in solubility of carbon dioxide and oxygen with temperature. The scientists also collected historical data on fish populations in the lake over the same time period (**Table 3**).

Table 1 Recorded Lake Depth and Temperature

Year	Water depth (m)	Surface temp. (°C)	Bottom temp. (°C)
1885	25	25	10
1955	20	29	20
2000	14	30	25

Table 2 Solubility of Carbon Dioxide and Oxygen

Temp. (°C)	CO_2 solubility (ppm)	O_2 solubility (ppm)
0	1.00	14.6
5	0.83	12.7
10	0.70	11.3
15	0.59	10.1
20	0.51	9.1
25	0.43	8.3
30	0.38	7.5

Table 3 Fish Populations over Time

Year	Population of trout (per km^3)	Population of perch (per km^3)	Population of catfish (per km^3)
1885	12	22	14
1955	7	23	15
2000	1	12	16

19. **Describe** what happened to the lake as it aged, according to the data in **Table 1**. DE

20. **Outline** in a list factors that might explain why the lake became shallower as it aged. DE

21. **Graphically** represent the solubility of oxygen from the data in **Table 2**. DE

22. From the data from **Table 2**, **predict** the long-term consequences of prolonged warming. DE

23. **Explain** why the levels of carbon dioxide in many Canadian lakes increase during winter. DE

24. **Explain** the changes in fish populations over time shown by the data in **Table 3**. DE

25. **Identify** two human activities that may have accelerated the aging of the lake. For each of the activities, **describe** the negative environmental consequences and **explain** how those consequences can be minimized. DE

26. The removal of all trees from a forest is called clear-cutting. After cutting, different trees are separated and processed to make different products. Many of the products are sold to other countries, such as the United States. Write a unified response addressing the following aspects of clear-cutting. DE
    - **Why** is clear-cutting promoted by many businesses?
    - **Identify** some of the ecological problems associated with clear-cutting.
    - **Identify** and **explain** the roles of industry, government, and individuals to prevent the negative impact of uncontrolled clear-cutting of forests.

27. The Gaia Hypothesis proposes that Earth is alive. It suggests that our planet functions as a single organism that maintains conditions necessary for its survival. Although not accepted by all scientists, this theory provides many useful lessons about the interaction of physical, chemical, geological, and biological processes on Earth. Write a unified response that addresses the following aspects of the Gaia Hypothesis.
    - Based on your understanding of the biosphere, **outline** in a list, ways in which Earth is similar to an organism.
    - **Describe** one way that the Gaia Hypothesis might change the way scientists think about ecosystems.

Use the following information to answer questions 28 to 35.

Levels of nutrients, algae, and light penetration were measured throughout the year in the limnetic zone of a northern Alberta lake, producing the patterns shown in **Figure 4**.

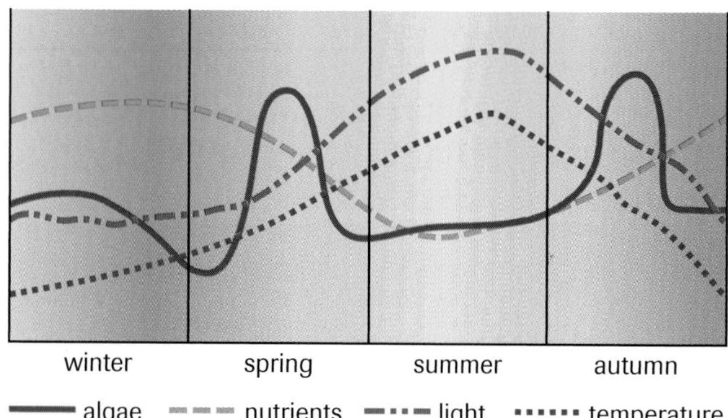

Figure 4

28. **Determine** from **Figure 4** at which times of the year the population of algae is highest. DE

29. **Explain** the changes in algae population. DE

30. **Explain** the changes in temperature. DE

31. **Why** do nutrient levels in the lake rise in winter but fall in summer? DE

32. **Explain** the fluctuations in light penetration. DE

33. Using **Figure 4** as a model, show **graphically** the changes you would expect to see in dissolved oxygen in the same lake. DE

34. Using **Figure 4** as a model, show **graphically** the changes you would expect to see in BOD in the same lake. DE

35. **Explain** how the patterns would change if sewage began to be dumped into the lake. DE

36. **Compare** (point out similarities and differences) how the theories of Lamarck and Darwin would explain each of the following:
   (a) **how** the giraffe evolved a long neck
   (b) **how** the cheetah became an extremely fast runner

37. Mutations are very rare events.
   (a) **Explain** if you agree with the above statement, if it were referring to an individual organism.
   (b) **How** would your answer differ if you were referring to mutation events in an entire population over long periods of time?
   (c) Would your answer to part (b) differ if you were referring to an elephant population? to a bacterial population? **Explain**.

38. **Describe** a testable hypothesis for Lamarck's theory of inheritable acquired traits. **Describe** an experimental design that would test your hypothesis.

39. **Relate** the variability of a species to its mode of reproduction (i.e., asexual or sexual).

40. DE Darwin recognized that natural selection by the environment could produce change in a way similar to the artificial selection used by plant and animal breeders. Write a unified response that addresses the following aspects of these two processes.
   - **Compare** the sources of new variation in each process. **Illustrate** your answer with an example.
   - **Describe** any role of selection for certain characteristics in each process. **Illustrate** your answer with an example.
   - **Describe** any role of selection against certain characteristics in each process. **Illustrate** your answer with an example.
   - **Compare** the length of time needed before noticeable differences can be seen. **Illustrate** your answer with an example.

41. DE As a result of human activity, extensive forests are becoming fragmented into small forest islands. Write a unified response that addresses the following aspects of forest fragmentation:
   - **How** might the increasing isolation of populations in these forests influence their success and evolution?
   - **How** might the effects differ for a large mammal species, such as the lynx, compared to an insect species, such as a beetle?

42. Evolutionary biologists have hypothesized that many epidemics—widespread diseases that usually kill their hosts, such as smallpox or plague—could only have evolved in large human populations. Further, they hypothesize that these diseases originated in mammals that were domesticated. Consider these hypotheses in relation to contact between European explorers and indigenous peoples, such as the Arawak, Aztec, Maya, Inca, Aboriginal peoples in North America, Aborigines in Australia, and Maori in New Zealand. Research the exchange of diseases between Europeans and any two of the indigenous peoples listed above. Look for evidence that supports one or both of these hypotheses. **Describe** your findings in a presentation to your class.

Use the following information to answer questions 43 to 47.

A study by Environment Canada showed variations in the number of prairie ponds in the 30 years from 1955 to 1984 (**Figure 5**). Graph A shows the number of ponds found in each year of the study. Graph B shows the total population of ducks each year. Scientists conducting the study suggest that the decline was caused by draining ponds to expand agricultural land.

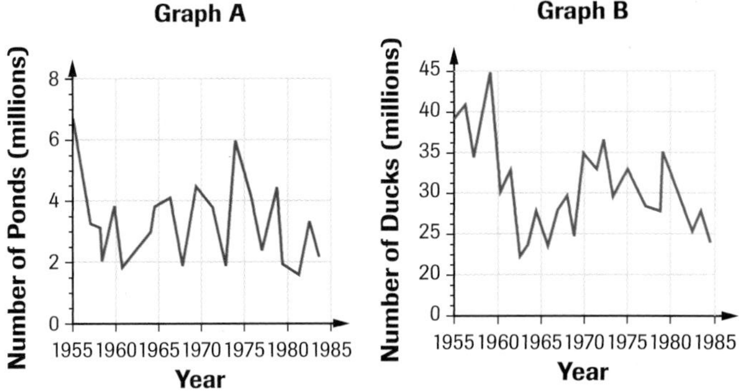

Figure 5

43. DE Farming is not the only cause of changes in the number of ponds. **Hypothesize** what abiotic factor might cause the number of ponds to fluctuate from year to year.

44. DE **Determine** the year in which the fewest number of ponds were found.

45. DE A hunters' group says that prairie ponds should be protected, to increase the number of ducks. Restate the hunters' position as a hypothesis, and **explain** whether the evidence in **Figure 5** support the hypothesis.

46. DE If the number of ducks declines, **predict** what other populations might be affected? **Explain** your answer.

47. DE Protecting ponds makes both aquatic and ecotone habitats available for wildlife but reduces the area of land on which a farmer can grow crops. Write a letter to a grain farmer, expressing your opinion about whether ponds on farmland should be protected or filled in. **Justify** your opinion.

---

48. Review the focusing questions on page 80. Using the knowledge you have gained from this unit, briefly **outline** a response to each of these questions.

unit

20 C

Photosynthesis and Cellular Respiration

For life to continue on Earth, two conditions must be met. First, matter must be continuously cycled. With few exceptions, the number of atoms on Earth is unchanging. Although the atoms may be rearranged into new molecules, matter is continuously exchanged between plants, animals, fungi, and microorganisms.

The second condition for life on Earth is a supply of energy. Solar energy supplies almost all life on Earth. Plants are the key to keeping the energy flowing. These photoautotrophs absorb carbon dioxide, water, and radiant energy from the environment and, through photosynthesis, transform these components into energy-rich sugars and oxygen gas. Then, through aerobic respiration, they convert the energy stored in these sugars and oxygen into the energy of ATP.

Heterotrophs, such as animals, fungi, and some protists, obtain nutrients from their environment by eating plants, animals, or both. Like plants, heterotrophs obtain energy in the form of ATP by cellular respiration in which large food molecules are broken down and carbon dioxide and water are returned to the environment. In this unit, you will investigate these transformations and exchanges of energy within our living world.

As you progress through the unit, think about these focusing questions:

- How does light energy from the environment enter living systems?
- How is the energy from light used to synthesize organic matter?
- How is the energy in organic matter released for use by living systems?
- How do humans in their applications of technologies impact photosynthesis and cellular respiration?

UNIT 20 C PERFORMANCE TASK

Student Aquarist

Ecosystems must maintain a delicate balance in order to remain healthy. How do factors such as temperature, light conditions, dissolved oxygen, and dissolved carbon dioxide affect the metabolic health of the organisms within an ecosystem? At the end of this unit, you may apply your skills and knowledge to complete this Performance Task.

www.science.nelson.com 

GENERAL OUTCOMES

In this unit, you will

- relate photosynthesis to storage of energy in compounds
- explain the role of cellular respiration in releasing potential energy from organic compounds

Unit 20 C ARE YOU READY?

Photosynthesis and Cellular Respiration

Prerequisites

Concepts

- organisms, cells, tissues, organ systems
- cellular structures and functions
- passive and active transport of matter

Skills

- use instruments effectively and accurately for collecting data

You can review prerequisite concepts and skills on the Nelson Web site and in the Appendices. 

A Unit Pre-Test is also available online.

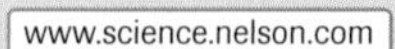

These questions will help you find out what you already know, and what you need to review, before you continue with this unit.

Knowledge

1. Match the following names and functions to the labelled components of the cells in **Figure 1** (one name and one function per label).

   Names: *cell membrane, nucleus, vacuole, mitochondrion, endoplasmic reticulum, Golgi apparatus, chloroplast, cell wall, flagellum*

   Functions: *energy conversion, protein storage, protection, material transport within the cell, overall control, food production, water and nutrient storage, controlled entry and exit from cell, locomotion*

(a)

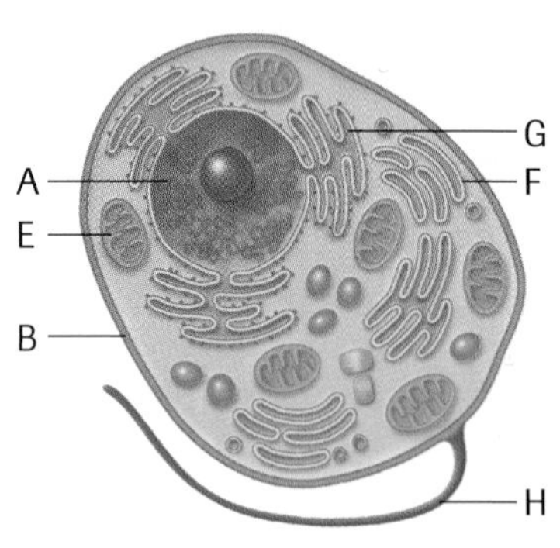

(b)

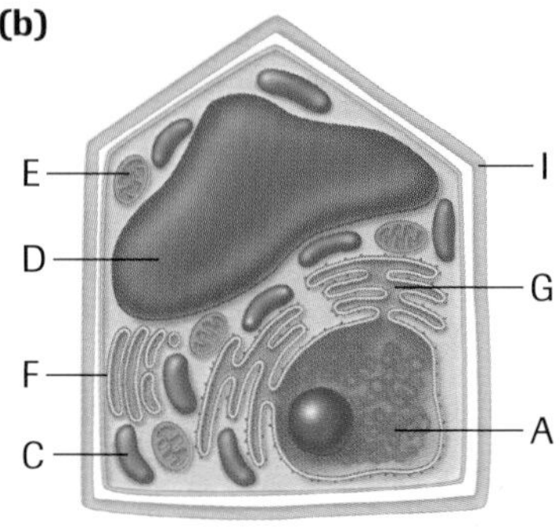

Figure 1
(a) A generalized animal cell; **(b)** A generalized plant cell

2. **Figures 2** and **3** show two processes that move materials into and out of cells.
   (a) What process is represented by **Figure 2**?
   (b) What process is represented by **Figure 3**?
   (c) Name the structure labelled "A" in **Figure 3**.
   (d) What is the substance that passes through structure A in **Figure 3**?

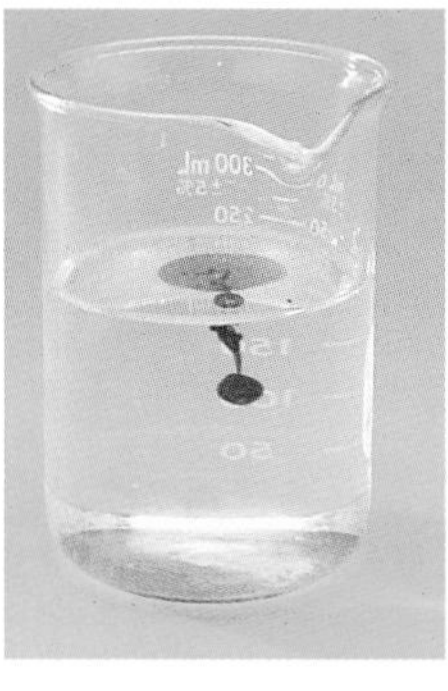

Figure 2

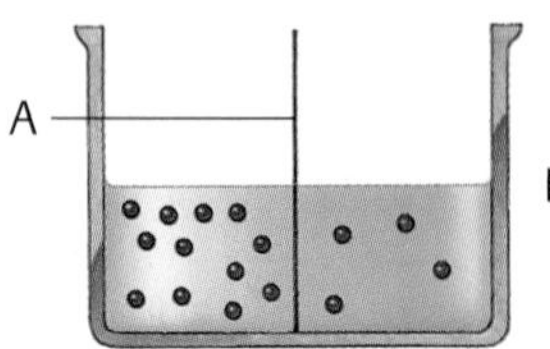

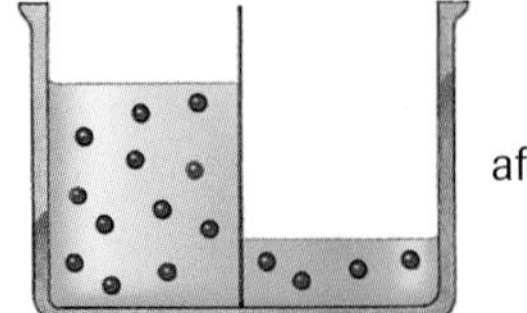

Figure 3

3. Compare passive transport by diffusion and osmosis with active transport in terms of (a) concentration gradients, (b) energy inputs, and (c) equilibrium and protein carrier molecules.

4. Match the following names to the labelled components of the leaf structure in **Figure 4** (one name per label).

   Names: *epidermis, guard cells, palisade tissue, spongy tissue, phloem, xylem, vascular tissue*

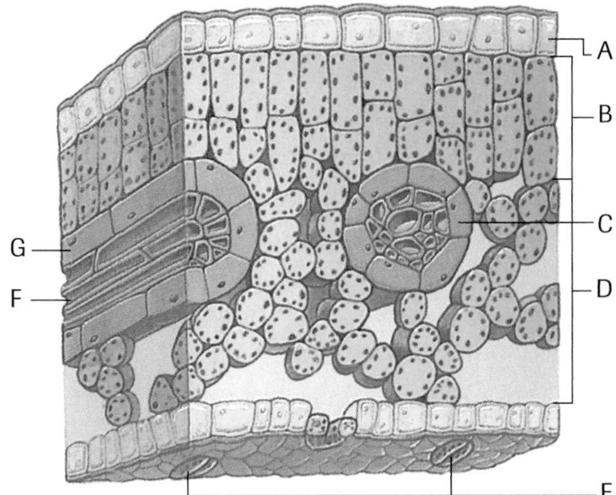

Figure 4
A typical leaf structure

5. **Figure 5** is a wet mount of onion cells viewed under medium power in a compound light microscope.
   (a) What might be the cause of the dark circles in **Figure 5**?
   (b) How could you avoid forming the circles?

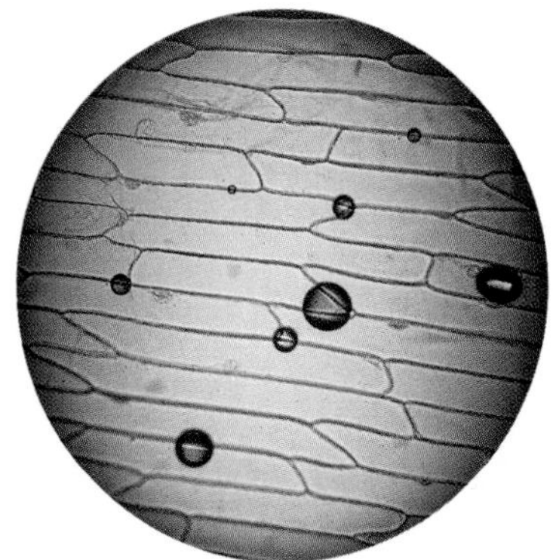

Figure 5
A wet mount of onion cells

Skills

6. Examine the following chemical equation:

CH_4	+	$2\ O_2$	$\rightarrow$	CO_2	+	H_2O
methane		oxygen		carbon dioxide		water

   Which of the reactants is a compound? Provide reasons for your answer.

7. Match the following parts of the compound light microscope to the labels in **Figure 6**.

   Microscope parts: *arm, ocular lens, coarse-adjustment knob, stage, fine-adjustment knob, base, condenser, objective lens, revolving nosepiece, stage clips, light source*

8. Place the following steps in the correct order for viewing a slide through a compound light microscope.
   (a) Rotate the nosepiece to the medium-power objective lens.
   (b) Use the fine-adjustment knob to bring the image into focus.
   (c) Place the slide on the stage and hold it in place with clips.
   (d) Use the coarse-adjustment knob to bring the low-power objective lens close to the slide.
   (e) Make sure the low-power objective lens is in place.

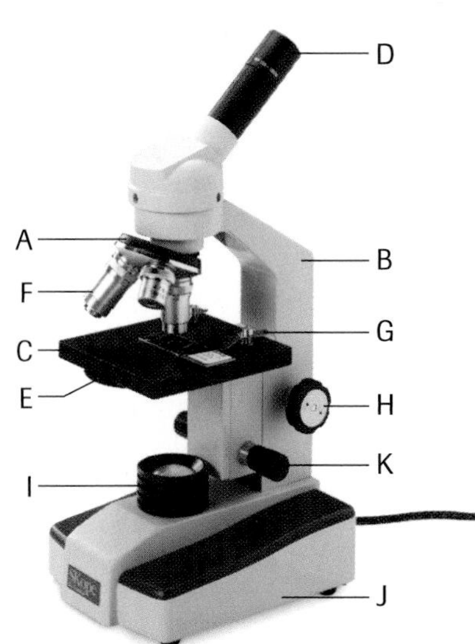

Figure 6
A compound light microscope

chapter

Photosynthesis

In this chapter

Photosynthesis is the process that converts energy from the Sun into chemical energy that is used by living cells. Photosynthesis occurs in a variety of organisms, but most notably in plants and certain groups of bacteria. The most obvious of these are the large land plants, but the world's oceans are also home to vast quantities of photosynthesizing microorganisms (**Figure 1** on the next page). All of these organisms convert carbon dioxide, $CO_2(g)$, into organic molecules using the light energy captured by chlorophyll.

From a human perspective, photosynthesis is the most important large-scale chemical process on Earth. We are completely dependent on photosynthesis for all the food we eat and the oxygen we breathe. In addition, all organic materials are constructed using the molecular building blocks and the energy supplied by photosynthesis. Therefore, we also rely on photosynthesis for things such as wood, paper, cotton, drugs, and fossil fuels.

As the human population grows and our rates of consumption grow, we become increasingly dependent on vast quantities of photosynthesis products. Recent estimates suggest that humans now consume, either directly or indirectly, close to 40 % of the net primary production of Earth's entire land surface. In other words, over one-third of the yearly production of all of Earth's terrestrial plants is used to meet human demands.

STARTING Points

Answer these questions as best you can with your current knowledge. Then, using the concepts and skills you have learned, you will revise your answers at the end of the chapter.

1. (a) Write the overall equation for photosynthesis.
   (b) Do the O_2 molecules produced in photosynthesis come from CO_2 or H_2O or both?
   (c) What is the purpose of water in photosynthesis?
2. Why are deciduous leaves green in the summer and yellow in the fall?
3. What does *carbon fixation* mean?
4. The process of photosynthesis requires energy in the form of ATP. How do plants obtain ATP for photosynthesis?
5. How are the processes of photosynthesis and cellular respiration dependent on each other?

Figure 1
Photosynthesizing organisms live in oceans, lakes, streams, and rivers, as well as on land.

Exploration Global Photosynthesis in Action

Earth is a dynamic planet of land and water. The seasons are accompanied by changing temperatures and levels of solar radiation—factors that dramatically influence the distribution and activity of photosynthesizing organisms.

Recent technological developments enable us to monitor such changes with great precision. In this Exploration, you will view an animation of biosphere data gathered over six years as part of the Sea-viewing Wide Field-of-view Sensor (SeaWiFS) Project. In the animation, areas of high plant life on land are shown in dark green, while areas of low plant life are shown in tan. In the oceans, areas of high active photosynthesis by phytoplankton are shown in red, and areas of lowest activity are shown in blue and purple (**Figure 2**).

(a) Generate a hypothesis to describe the overall pattern you expect to see on the land surface, and a hypothesis to describe what you expect to see in the oceans. Where and when do you think land plants and marine phytoplankton activity will peak?

(b) After recording your hypotheses, go to the Nelson Web site and follow the links to view the animation sequence.

www.science.nelson.com 

(c) Describe the patterns of changes you see over the six-year period.

(d) Note any surprises you observe. Was photosynthesis most active where you expected it to be?

(e) Suggest possible explanations to account for the patterns you witnessed on the land environment and in the marine environment.

Figure 2
SeaWiFS image of global photosynthesis activity

6.1 Chloroplasts and Photosynthetic Pigments

photon a packet of light

Light is a type of electromagnetic radiation (EMR). Many forms of electromagnetic radiation are familiar to us including X-rays, microwaves, and radio waves. All EMR occurs in the form of individual packets of energy called **photons**. Each photon corresponds to a small unit of energy of a particular wavelength (**Figure 1(a)**). Photons with short wavelengths have high energy and those with long wavelengths have low energy.

Light from the Sun is a mixture of different wavelengths. When passed through a transparent prism in an instrument called a spectroscope, the different wavelengths separate from one another according to their energies, forming the electromagnetic spectrum (**Figure 1(b)**). Most of the spectrum is invisible to humans, being either in the radio, infrared, or ultraviolet range, but a narrow band, from a wavelength of 380 nm (violet light) to 750 nm (red light), forms the visible part of the spectrum.

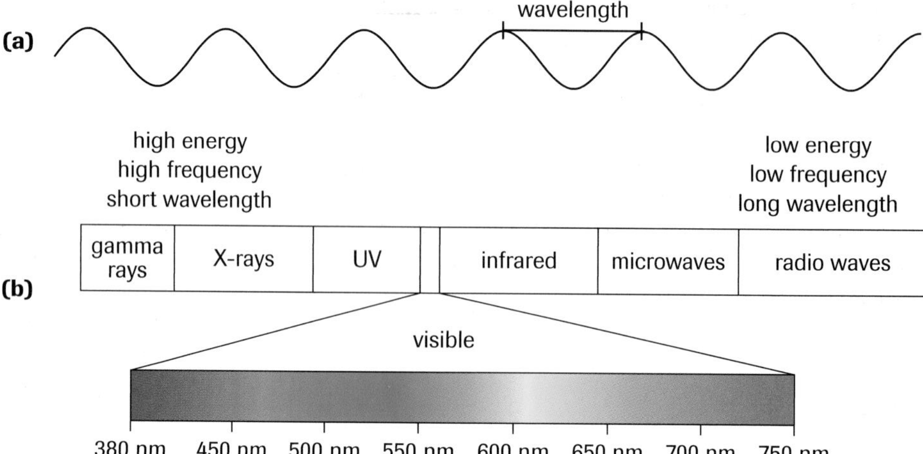

Figure 1
(a) Light is a form of electromagnetic radiation that travels as waves. One wavelength corresponds to a photon.
(b) Light is the visible portion of the electromagnetic radiation spectrum. Our eyes perceive photons of different wavelengths, or energies, as different colours.

CAREER CONNECTION

Nursery Operator

Nursery operators work with plants, growing and selling trees, shrubs, and other plants. They direct and supervise staff to plant, transplant, and feed trees and shrubs, and they also decide the appropriate environmental conditions required to grow particular plants.

Nursery operators often work outdoors on a regular basis, and their work is creative and rewarding. Find out more about this career by visiting the Nelson Web site.

www.science.nelson.com

Solar energy is the ultimate source of energy for most living things. As you saw in Chapter 2, organisms do not use this energy directly. Instead, photosynthetic organisms at the first trophic level in a food web (producers) capture solar energy and then store it as chemical energy in the bonds of glucose molecules. This energy is eventually passed to other organisms in the food web. All organisms, including those that carry out photosynthesis, release the energy in glucose molecules by cellular respiration to fuel cell activities.

Recall that the process of photosynthesis can be summarized by this equation:

$$\text{carbon dioxide} + \text{water} + \text{energy} \rightarrow \text{glucose} + \text{oxygen}$$
$$CO_2(g) + H_2O(l) + \text{energy} \rightarrow C_6H_{12}O_6(s) + O_2(g)$$

This equation includes only the compounds at the beginning and end of the process of photosynthesis. You will learn more about some of the important molecules involved in photosynthesis in the rest of this chapter.

Photosynthesis occurs only in green plants and some photosynthetic micro-organisms such as algae. Special pigments in these organisms capture photons from solar energy to begin the reactions that make up the photosynthesis process.

Practice

1. Name three large groups of organisms that carry out photosynthesis.
2. (a) Define *light*.
   (b) What is a photon?

mini Investigation Photosynthesis and Light

Green plants capture sunlight and transfer the energy to carbohydrates through the process of photosynthesis. When plants photosynthesize, they absorb carbon dioxide and produce oxygen. The oxygen produced is released into the environment. In this activity, you will observe the production of oxygen in photosynthesizing plant cells.

Materials: living green plants with leaves, baking soda, liquid soap or detergent, medicine dropper, water, drinking straw, 35 mm film canister with lid, 5 mL syringe, eye protection

- Add enough baking soda to barely cover the bottom of a film canister. Fill the canister with water (almost to the top), replace the lid, and shake to dissolve the baking soda.
- Remove the lid, add one small drop of liquid soap, replace the lid, and gently swirl the contents to dissolve the soap. Do not shake. The soap will help prevent static electricity.
- Use a new straw like a cookie-cutter to cut four leaf discs from a plant leaf. The leaf discs will accumulate inside the straw.

Never share straws with others. Always use a new straw. When finished using the straw, discard it in the garbage can.

- If the syringe you are using has a cap on the tip, remove the cap. Pull the plunger out of the syringe. Blow the leaf discs out of the straw and into the syringe. Replace the plunger.
- Draw 4 mL of baking-soda solution (prepared in the first two steps) into the syringe. Invert the syringe so that the tip end is pointing up. Gently push the plunger to remove the air near the tip.
- Put your finger over the syringe tip and pull the plunger. This will create a vacuum, which will pull air and oxygen from the leaf discs (**Figure 2**).

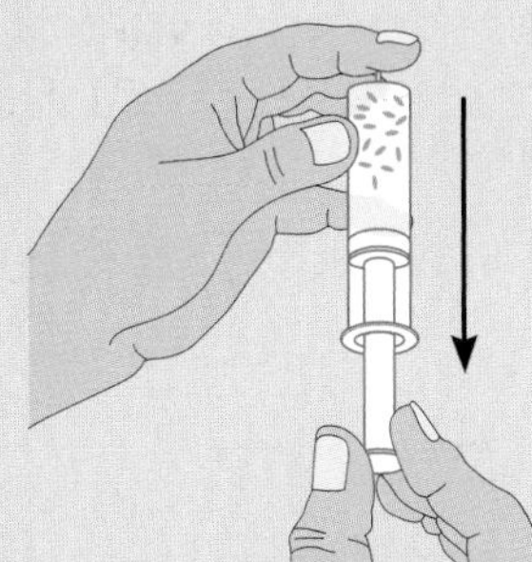

Figure 2

- Tip the end of the syringe down so that the leaf discs are in the solution. Release the plunger and remove your finger. Turn the syringe back up and tap the side repeatedly until all (or most) of the discs sink.
- Place the syringe, open end up, in bright sunlight.
- As the leaf discs photosynthesize, they will float to the top.

(a) (i) What causes the leaf discs to float to the top while they are in sunlight?
    (ii) Would the discs float to the top if the syringe was kept in the dark? Explain.
(b) Why is baking soda added to the solution in the syringe?
(c) Did the leaf discs all float to the top at the same time? Explain why or why not.
(d) How could this procedure be used to investigate whether or not different colours of light cause plants to photosynthesize equally well? Design a procedure for such an experiment (include a list of materials).

Chlorophyll

Photosynthesis is carried out by a number of different organisms, including plants, algae, some protists, and cyanobacteria. These organisms all contain the green-coloured pigment called **chlorophyll**. Chlorophyll absorbs photons from solar energy and begins the process of photosynthesis. Several types of chlorophyll are found in photosynthetic organisms; chlorophyll *a* (blue-green) and chlorophyll *b* (yellow-green) are two common forms. All photosynthetic organisms use chlorophyll *a* as the primary light-absorbing pigment.

chlorophyll the light-absorbing green-coloured pigment that begins the process of photosynthesis

Chlorophylls *a* and *b* absorb photons with energies in the blue-violet and red regions of the spectrum and reflect or transmit those with wavelengths between about 500 nm and 600 nm, which our eyes see as green light. This is why most photosynthesizing organisms look green in white light. Using a sophisticated instrument called a

+ EXTENSION

The Action Spectrum, the Absorption Spectrum and Photosynthesis

Listen to this audio clip, which explores absorption and action spectra for the primary photosynthetic pigments chlorophyll *a* and *b*.

spectrophotometer, the absorption spectrum of pigments, such as chlorophyll *a* and chlorophyll *b*, can be determined with accuracy, as **Figure 3** shows.

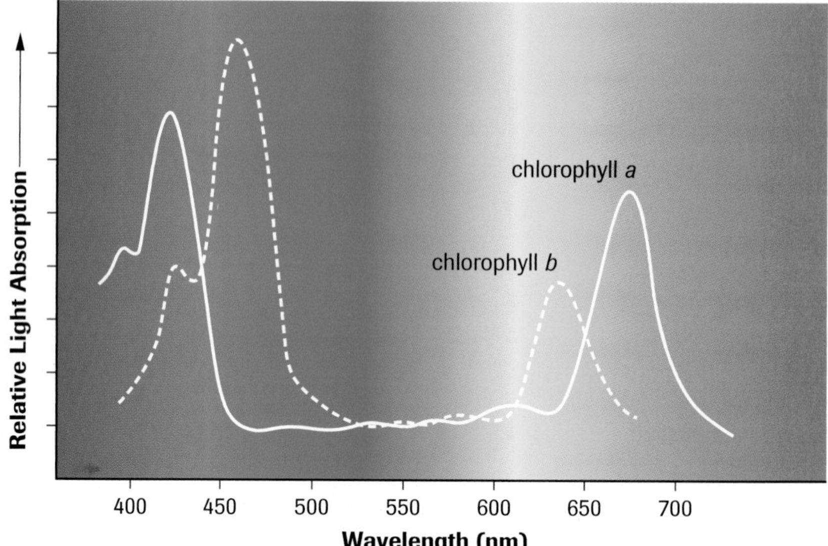

Figure 3
The absorption spectrum of chlorophyll *a* and chlorophyll *b*.

Chlorophyll *a* is the only pigment that can transfer the energy from sunlight to the reactions of photosynthesis. Chlorophyll *b* acts as an accessory pigment, absorbing photons that chlorophyll *a* absorbs poorly, or not at all. Other compounds, called carotenoids, also act as accessory pigments. These and other accessory pigments usually transfer the energy they absorb back to a molecule of chlorophyll *a*.

In spring and summer, most leaves appear green because of the high concentration of chlorophyll in the chloroplasts of leaf cells. Although the accessory pigments are also present, their colours are overwhelmed by the green light reflected by chlorophyll. With the onset of cooler autumn temperatures, plants stop producing chlorophyll molecules and disassemble those already in the leaves. This causes the yellow, red, and brown colours of autumn leaves to become visible, as **Figure 4** shows.

Figure 4
Autumn leaves contain less chlorophyll, so the colours of the accessory and other pigments can be seen.

Practice

3. What is the primary light absorbing pigment in all photosynthetic organisms?
4. What colour(s) of the spectrum is absorbed by chlorophyll *a* and chlorophyll *b*? What colour(s) is transmitted by these pigments?

INVESTIGATION 6.1 *Introduction*

Separating Plant Pigments from Leaves

Look at **Figure 5** with unaided eyes and determine its colour. Now look at the figure with a magnifying glass. What colours do you see? The spring and summer leaves of deciduous trees appear green in colour. Do green leaves contain only green pigments, or is there a mixture of pigments with the green variety predominating? Investigation 6.1 will help you decide.

To perform this investigation, turn to page 195. 

Report Checklist

● Purpose	○ Design	● Analysis
● Problem	○ Materials	● Evaluation
○ Hypothesis	○ Procedure	○ Synthesis
● Prediction	● Evidence	

Figure 5
A colour made up of other colours.

Chloroplasts

Leaves are the primary photosynthetic organs of most plants. To undergo photosynthesis, a plant cell must contain chlorophyll, and it must be able to obtain carbon dioxide and water, and capture solar energy from its environment. Plant cells contain chloropyll within the photosynthetic membranes of discrete organelles called **chloroplasts.** Because they contain chlorophyll, chloroplasts give leaves, stems, and unripened fruit their characteristic green colour. Since chloroplasts are found only in these parts, no other structures in a plant are able to photosynthesize.

A typical plant cell chloroplast is approximately 3 μm to 8 μm in length and 2 μm to 3 μm in diameter. Chloroplasts have two limiting membranes, an outer membrane and an inner membrane (**Figure 6**). These membranes enclose an interior space filled with a protein-rich semiliquid material called **stroma**. Within the stroma, a system of membrane-bound sacs called **thylakoids** stack on top of one another to form characteristic columns called **grana**. A typical chloroplast has approximately 60 grana, each consisting of 30 to 50 thylakoids. Adjacent grana are connected to one another by unstacked thylakoids called **lamellae**. Photosynthesis occurs partly within the stroma and partly within the **thylakoid membrane**, which contains light-gathering pigment molecules and other molecules and complexes that are essential to the process. Thylakoid membranes enclose an interior (water-filled) thylakoid space called the **thylakoid lumen**. The structure of the thylakoid system within the chloroplast greatly increases the surface area of the thylakoid membrane and, therefore, also significantly increases the efficiency of photosynthesis. Chloroplasts are able to replicate, by division, independently of the cell. Starch grains and lipid droplets may also be found in chloroplasts.

chloroplast a membrane-bound organelle in green plant and algal cells that carries out photosynthesis

stroma the protein-rich semiliquid material in the interior of a chloroplast

thylakoid a system of interconnected flattened membrane sacs forming a separate compartment within the stroma of a chloroplast

grana (singular: *granum*) stacks of thylakoids

lamellae (singular: *lamella*) groups of unstacked thylakoids between grana

thylakoid membrane the photosynthetic membrane within a chloroplast that contains light-gathering pigment molecules and electron transport chains

thylakoid lumen the fluid-filled space inside a thylakoid

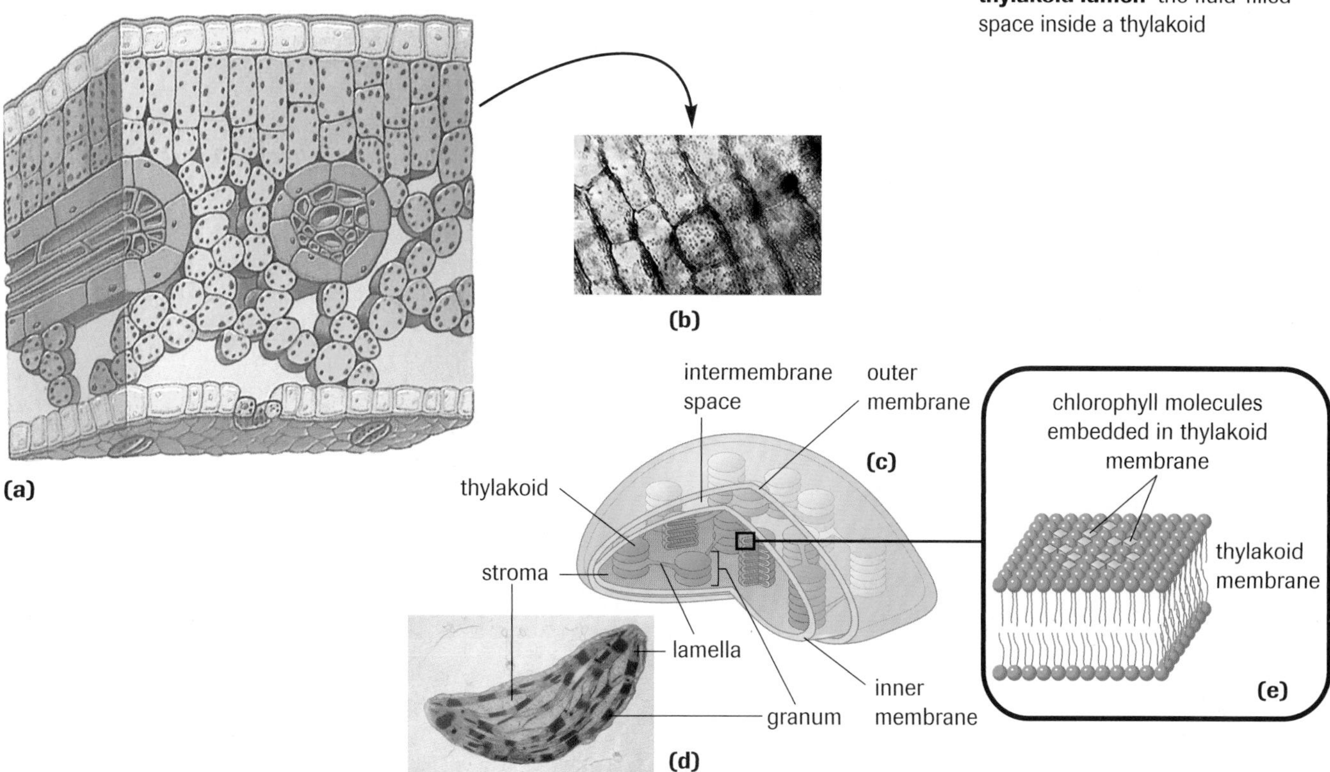

Figure 6
(a) Leaf cross section with mesophyll cells containing chloroplasts
(b) Chloroplasts within plant cells
(c) An artist's representation of a chloroplast, showing key components
(d) An electron micrograph of a chloroplast
(e) Chlorophyll molecules in the thylakoid membrane

Case Study

Using Satellite and Airborne Technology to Monitor Photosynthesis and Productivity

Healthy crop plants generally have a high chlorophyll content and a normal leaf structure. The leaves reflect green and infrared light and a small amount of red light—the red light is readily absorbed by higher concentrations of chlorophyll. In contrast, stressed or damaged plants have a lower chlorophyll content and an altered leaf structure. These changes reduce the amount of green and infrared light that is reflected. The ratio of reflected infrared light to reflected red light is an excellent indicator of plant health, and changes in this ratio are an early indication of stress conditions. These ratios form the basis of some standards, or health indexes, such as the normalized differential vegetation index (NDVI).

Farmers can assess stresses within fields using this same technology. The airborne image of fields near Altona, Manitoba (**Figure 7**) can be used in a variety of ways. The more deeply coloured red (wheat) and pink (canola) regions are healthy while the darker and duller regions have thin or missing vegetation. This image was obtained using a compact airborne spectrographic imager (CASI) instrument.

Deforestation is a global problem, with many serious consequences. In tropical countries, valuable rain forest is being destroyed to clear potentially valuable agricultural and pasture land. The loss of forests increases soil erosion, damages or destroys fisheries and wildlife habitat, and threatens water supplies. In some countries, such as Haiti, the results have been devastating, with most of the land base now completely devoid of crops or forests. Forestry is one of Canada's biggest industries and proper forest management is essential for a healthy, strong, sustainable economy. Remote sensing technology provides the best way to monitor the overall extent and health of our forest resources.

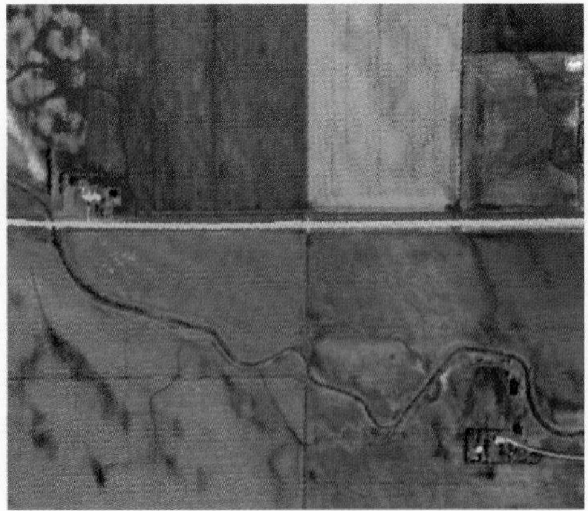

Figure 7
Remote sensing technology can provide valuable information to assess field crop health. The dark patches in the lower-left corner reveal poorly drained soil.

Clear cutting has been practised for decades in Whitecourt, Alberta. Recently however, an increasing demand for wood has accelerated this cutting and placed added stress on the land base (**Figure 8**). In addition to harvesting for the forestry industry, cuts have been made in the area for running seismic lines for oil and gas exploration.

Figure 8
This image of clear cutting near Whitecourt, Alberta reveals a highly dissected forest.

Case Study Questions

1. What symptoms of plant stress can be used to advantage by remote sensing technologies?
2. Suggest a reason why healthy plants reflect less light from the red end of the spectrum than plants under stress.
3. What ratio is used in the NDVI?
4. List some of the potentially negative consequences of excessive clear cutting. Why might Canadians be particularly concerned about the health of our forest ecosystems?
5. What advantages might the use of remote monitoring of forest management practices have over on-the-ground inspections?
6. Why are different sensor technologies often used to monitor clear cutting in tropical rain forests and temperate forests?
7. How have Aboriginal people living on First Nations and Métis Settlement lands in Alberta benefited from their forest reserves?
8. Investigate clear-cutting activities on First Nations lands such as the Morley First Nation in southern Alberta during the 90s. Report on your findings by creating a pamphlet.

www.science.nelson.com 

SUMMARY Chloroplasts and Photosynthetic Pigments

- Light is a form of energy that travels in the form of photons.
- Chlorophyll *a* is the only pigment that can transfer the energy of light to the carbon fixation reactions of photosynthesis. Chlorophyll *b* and the carotenoids act as accessory pigments, transferring their energy to chlorophyll *a*.
- Chloroplasts have an outer membrane and an inner membrane. The interior space contains a semiliquid material called stroma with a system of membrane-bound sacs called thylakoids, some of which are stacked on top of one another to form grana. Thylakoid membranes contain chlorophyll molecules and electron transport chains.

+ EXTENSION

Action Spectrum

In this Virtual Biology Lab, you will measure which wavelengths of light are most effective for photosynthesis.

www.science.nelson.com GO

Section 6.1 Questions

1. (a) How are the wavelength and energy of a photon related?
   (b) Which possesses a higher energy value: red light or green light? Explain.
   (c) How is the colour of light related to its energy? Provide examples.
2. (a) What pigments are present in green leaves?
   (b) Explain why yellow-coloured pigments are visible in autumn leaves but not in summer leaves.
3. What do all photosynthetic organisms have in common?
4. Label parts A, B, C, and D of the chloroplast in **Figure 9**.

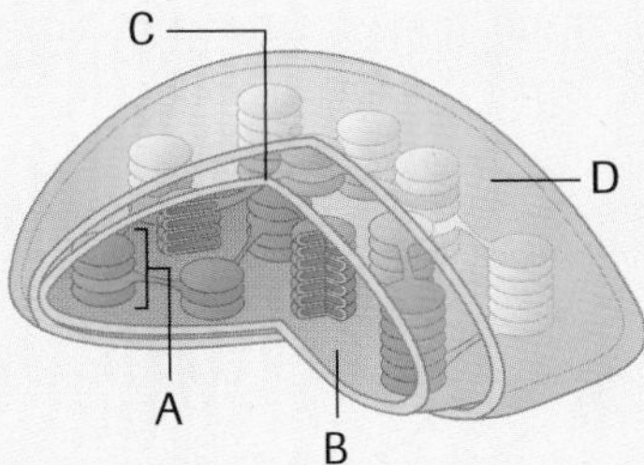

Figure 9
A chloroplast

5. Many lightbulb manufacturers produce fluorescent tubes labelled as "growlights" that they claim emit "full-spectrum light that imitates sunlight." Conduct research to determine whether fluorescent tubes labelled as "growlights" are more effective sources of artificial light for growing plants indoors than tubes without this label.

www.science.nelson.com 

6. Several biotechnology companies are experimenting with the possibility of producing a "green" (environmentally friendly) plastic from plants. One procedure converts sugar from corn to polylactide, a plastic similar to the plastic polyethylene terephthalate, which is used to make pop bottles and a variety of synthetic fabrics. Conduct research to complete the following tasks:
   (a) Describe one or two other "green" plastics and their potential uses.
   (b) Describe some of the costs and benefits of producing "green" products on a large scale.

www.science.nelson.com 

7. Recent advances in remote sensing have made detection of plant health possible on a large scale. Using satellite images, spectral analysis, and other sensing technologies, farmers may now detect problems in large fields of crops before they are identified at ground level. Conduct library and/or Internet research about spectral remote sensing as applied to plants to answer the following questions:
   (a) What characteristic(s) of plants do remote sensing systems detect to provide information regarding a crop's overall health?
   (b) Why would a farmer spend money to have crops tested by these methods? What advantages are gained by the procedure?
   (c) Describe the strategy or strategies you used to conduct your Internet search. List the advantages and disadvantages of each strategy.

www.science.nelson.com 

6.2 The Reactions of Photosynthesis

A Brief History of Photosynthesis Research

Our current understanding of photosynthesis is constructed from the work of many scientists from the 1600s onward, and the work continues today. Read about some of the classic experiments in photosynthesis research and complete the questions to assess your understanding.

www.science.nelson.com 

As you have learned, chlorophyll and other pigments located within the chloroplasts of green plants capture packages of energy called photons from sunlight. During photosynthesis, this captured energy is converted into chemical energy in the bonds of glucose molecules. Each molecule of glucose is synthesized from six molecules of carbon dioxide and six molecules of water.

Photosynthesis is a process made up of a series of complex chemical reactions that form a variety of intermediate and final energy-rich molecules. These molecules serve a number of different energy-related functions within cells (**Table 1**).

Table 1 Energy-Containing Molecules Formed during Photosynthesis

Molecule	Function
ATP	• principal energy-supply molecule for cellular functions of all living cells • provides an immediate source of energy for cellular processes, such as growth and movement
NADPH	• electron donor (NADPH) involved in energy transfers
glucose	• transport molecule ("blood sugar") • medium-term energy storage in most cells

ATP a molecule containing three high-energy phosphate bonds that acts as the primary energy-transferring molecule in living organisms

ADP a molecule containing two high-energy phosphate bonds that may be formed by breaking one of the phosphate bonds in ATP

Glucose is used to store energy for later use by cells. However, of all the energy-rich molecules in living cells, none is more significant than **ATP** (adenosine triphosphate). ATP is used by all living cells, both plant and animal, to provide immediate energy for cellular functions, such as synthesis of needed chemicals and transport of materials across cell membranes. ATP is formed by the addition of an inorganic phosphate group (P_i) to a molecule of lower-energy **ADP** (adenosine diphosphate). Later, this same energy can be released to the cell by a chemical reaction that splits ATP back into ADP and P_i (**Figure 1**).

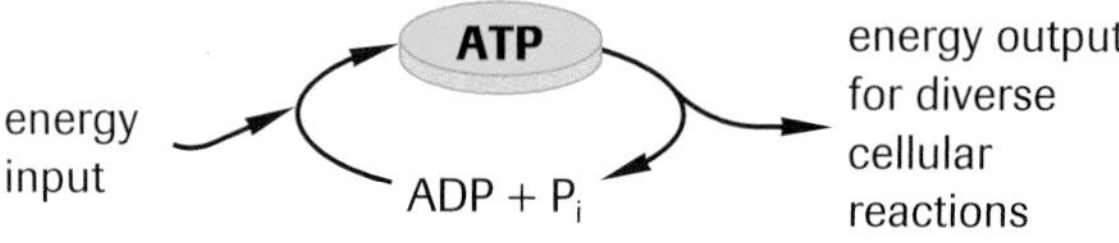

Figure 1
Energy is stored when ATP is formed from a phosphate group and ADP. This energy can be released when needed by the reversal of this reaction.

NADP$^+$ a compound that accepts one hydrogen atom and two electrons, forming NADPH; is an electron acceptor

NADPH a compound that donates one hydrogen atom and two electrons to another molecule, to reform NADP$^+$; is an electron donor

The compound **NADP$^+$** (nicotinamide dinucleotide phosphate) may also participate in many cellular reactions. At several places during photosynthesis, NADP$^+$ accepts one hydrogen atom and two electrons to form **NADPH**. NADPH may then donate electrons to other molecules in the cell, and so becomes NADP$^+$ again. In the rest of this section, you will find out how the gain and loss of electrons from NADP$^+$ and NADPH contributes to the process of photosynthesis.

An Overview of Photosynthesis

As you have learned, chlorophyll molecules and other pigments located within chloroplasts are able to absorb solar energy. To be useful to the plant, this solar energy must be converted to chemical energy. Once the energy is in a chemical form, it can be transported throughout the cell and to other parts of the plant, and it can also be stored.

The pigments and chemicals involved in these pathways are arranged within the chloroplast to make these tasks operate efficiently. While these physical arrangements and chemical pathways are complex and involve many intermediate steps, the overall process is relatively straightforward and can be broken down into the following three distinct, but connected, stages.

Stage 1: *capturing solar energy and transferring it to electrons*

Stage 2: *using captured solar energy to make ATP and to transfer high-energy electrons to $NADP^+$; yields NADPH, which is then used as a high-energy electron carrier molecule*

Stage 3: *using energy stored in ATP and high-energy electrons carried by NADPH to form energy-rich organic molecules, such as glucose, from CO_2*

The first two stages involve a series of reactions that are directly energized by light, called the **light-dependent reactions**. These reactions require chlorophyll and occur on the thylakoid membranes in chloroplasts. Chlorophyll absorbs the light energy that is eventually transferred to carbohydrate molecules in the last stage of the process. The reactions of the third stage result in **carbon fixation**—the incorporation of the carbon of $CO_2(g)$ into organic compounds, such as glucose. These reactions take place in the stroma of the chloroplast and utilize the energy of ATP and high energy electrons carried by NADPH. Carbon fixation takes place in the stroma by means of a cyclic sequence of enzyme-catalyzed reactions called the **Calvin cycle** (**Figure 2**). The reactions of the Calvin cycle are **light-independent reactions**.

light-dependent reactions the first set of reactions of photosynthesis in which light energy excites electrons in chlorophyll molecules, powers chemiosmotic ATP synthesis, and results in the reduction of $NADP^+$ to NADPH

carbon fixation the process of incorporating CO_2 into carbohydrate molecules

Calvin cycle a cyclic set of reactions occurring in the stroma of chloroplasts that fixes the carbon of CO_2 into carbohydrate molecules and recycles coenzymes

light-independent reactions the second set of reactions in photosynthesis (the Calvin cycle); these reactions do not require solar energy

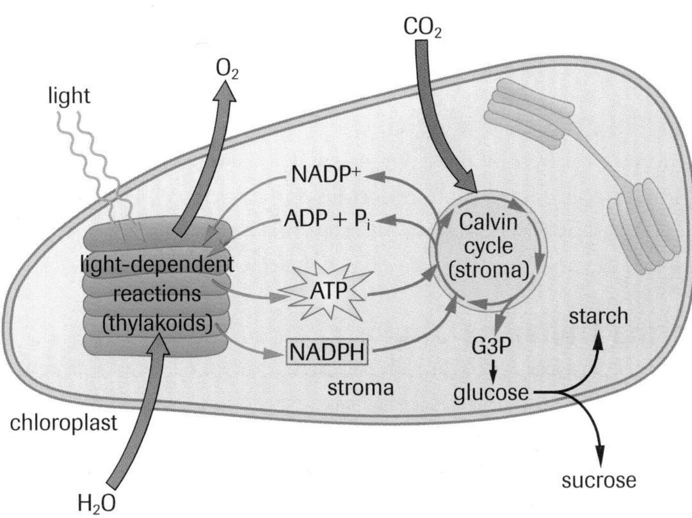

Figure 2
An overview of photosynthesis. The light-dependent reactions of photosynthesis occur in the thylakoid membranes of chloroplasts and transfer the energy of light to ATP and NADPH. The Calvin cycle takes place in the stroma and uses NADPH to reduce CO_2 to organic compounds, such as glucose and other carbohydrates.

Practice

1. Name three energy-containing molecules that are formed during photosynthesis.
2. Where do the light-dependent reactions of photosynthesis take place?
3. Where does carbon fixation take place?

Stage 1: Capturing Solar Energy

Within the chloroplasts, chlorophyll and other pigment molecules are found in clusters embedded in the thylakoid membranes. These molecule arrangements are called **photosystems.** As you will soon see, the light-dependent reactions rely on two distinct but interconnected photosystems—photosystems I and II—numbered in order of their discovery. These molecules are responsible for the actual capturing of light energy.

photosystem a cluster of photosynthetic pigments embedded in a thylakoid membrane of a chloroplast that absorbs light energy

Solar energy is captured when an electron in a chlorophyll molecule (or in another pigment molecule) absorbs a photon. Electrons are high-energy particles present in all atoms. Before a photon of light strikes, the electron has a relatively low amount of energy. After the photon is absorbed, the electron has a relatively high amount of energy, and is said to be excited. The photon has now been converted to chemical energy!

Still in the thylakoid membrane, the excited electron is then removed from the photosystem and passed from one molecular complex to another in a long series of steps often referred to as an **electron transport chain.**

electron transport chain a series of progressively stronger electron acceptors; each time an electron is transferred, energy is released

The electrons that are being removed from each photosystem to enter the electron transport chain must be replaced. These replacement electrons come from water molecules, in a process call photolysis. In **photolysis,** the solar energy absorbed by the chlorophyll is used to split water into hydrogen ions (H^+) and oxygen gas. Photolysis occurs in the thylakoid lumen.

photolysis a chemical reaction in which a compound is broken down by light; in photosynthesis, water molecules are split by photolysis

Two water molecules are consumed for every four electrons transferred to a photosystem.

$$2\ H_2O(l) + \text{energy} \rightarrow 4\ H^+ + 4\ e^- + O_2(g)$$

EXTENSION

Is Light Necessary for Photosynthesis?

Plants seem to need light to stay alive. In this activity, you will analyze leaves exposed to sunlight and leaves "starved" of sunlight to determine whether leaves need light to produce starch, a molecule made from glucose.

www.science.nelson.com 

Practice

4. Where are photosystems I and II located?
5. What happens when chlorophyll absorbs a photon?
6. How are the electrons that are passed on to the electron transport chain replaced?

Stage 2: Electron Transfer and ATP Synthesis

The solar energy captured by the pigments within photosystems must now be used to form additional stable energy-rich molecules and to make ATP from ADP and P_i. These tasks are performed by two distinctly different mechanisms—one involving the buildup of charged particles and the other involving the direct transfer of electrons.

The Electron Transport Chain

Both of these mechanisms depend on the electron transport chain. In many ways, the electron transport chain is similar to the set of stairs shown in **Figure 3** on the next page. Solar energy is used to excite electrons that have been removed from a water molecule. This added energy lifts them up in a single leap to the top of the energy stairway (the electron transport chain). This potential energy is then gradually released as the electrons travel down the stairs to their original lower energy level. Some of this released energy is captured to make ATP. The electrons eventually rejoin H^+ ions in the formation of new compounds.

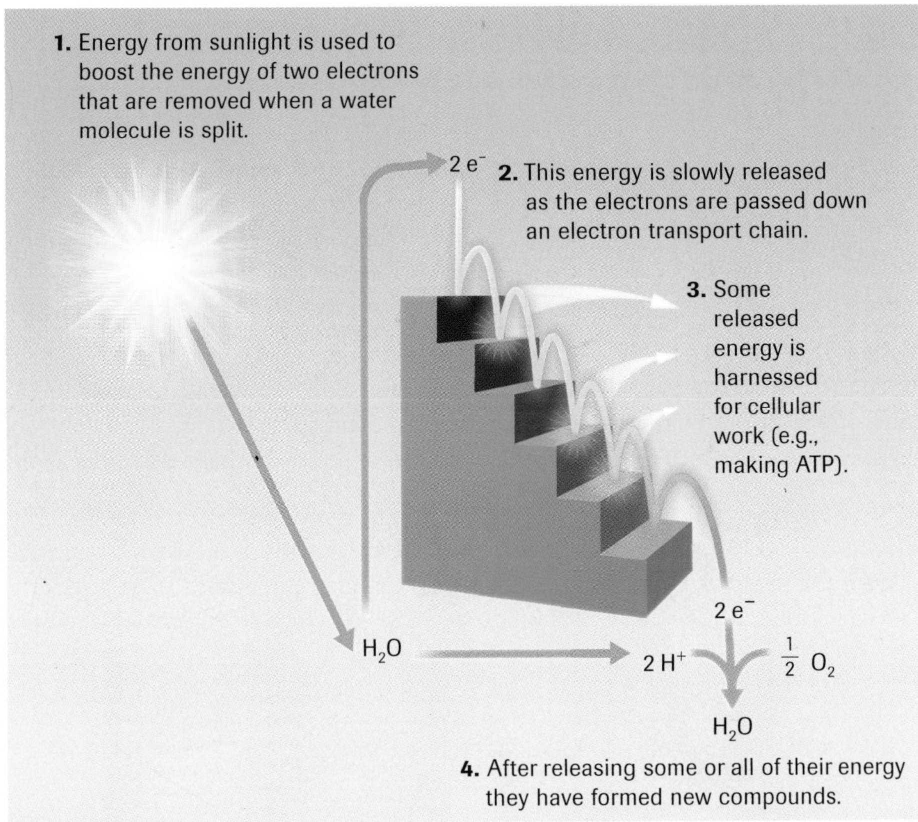

1. Energy from sunlight is used to boost the energy of two electrons that are removed when a water molecule is split.
2 e⁻
2. This energy is slowly released as the electrons are passed down an electron transport chain.
3. Some released energy is harnessed for cellular work (e.g., making ATP).
2 e⁻
H₂O
2 H⁺
½ O₂
H₂O
4. After releasing some or all of their energy they have formed new compounds.

Figure 3
The step-by-step release of energy by electron transport chains enables cells to release energy in smaller, usable amounts.

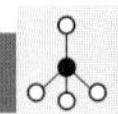

CHEMISTRY CONNECTION

Energy

There are two classes of energy: potential energy and kinetic energy. In simple terms, potential energy is stored energy and kinetic energy is the energy of motion. The energy captured in photosynthesis is potential energy. Your chemistry textbook contains more information on the types of energy.

www.science.nelson.com 

Oxidation–Reduction Reactions

How does the transfer of electrons release energy? At each step in the electron transport chain, a higher-energy electron donor passes an electron to a lower-energy electron acceptor. Such reactions are called oxidation–reduction or redox reactions. An **oxidation** is a reaction in which an atom or molecule loses electrons. A **reduction** is a reaction in which an atom or molecule gains electrons. An electron transfer between two substances always involves both an oxidation and a reduction.

oxidation a reaction in which an atom or molecule loses electrons

reduction a reaction in which an atom or molecule gains electrons

Electron donors, such as NADPH (an electron carrier in the electron transport chain in chloroplasts), tend to lose electrons. Electron acceptors, such as $NADP^+$, tend to gain electrons. When NADPH is oxidized, it loses a hydrogen nucleus (H^+) and its two electrons ($2\ e^-$), and is converted to $NADP^+$. When $NADP^+$ is reduced, it gains a hydrogen nucleus and its two electrons, and is converted to NADPH. When an element or molecule gains electrons (is reduced), it releases energy and becomes more stable. Therefore, whenever $NADP^+$ is converted to NADPH, energy is released. NADPH then donates electrons to other molecules for other processes in the cell, such as in the dark reactions of photosynthesis (Stage 3).

Learning Tip

Remember: LEO goes GER.
Loss of Electrons is Oxidation;
Gain of Electrons is Reduction

Practice

7. What happens to the electrons that are released during photolysis?
8. What is the role of electron donors and electron acceptors in the steps of the electron transport chain?
9. What is an oxidation? What is a reduction?
10. What is the role of oxidations and reductions in the electron transport chain?

+ EXTENSION 

Electron Transport in the Thylakoid Membrane

Listen to this audio clip for information on how changes in the energy levels of electrons allow plants to capture and transform light energy into chemical energy through the process of photosynthesis.

Let's now follow the pathway of other electrons that were first excited by light in photosystem II (**Figure 4**). As the electrons are passed along an electron transport chain from one chemical complex to another, they are also carried across the thylakoid membrane—from the outer surface—toward the thylakoid lumen, as seen in (**A**). In doing so, they release energy, which is used to "pull" a number of positively charged hydrogen ions

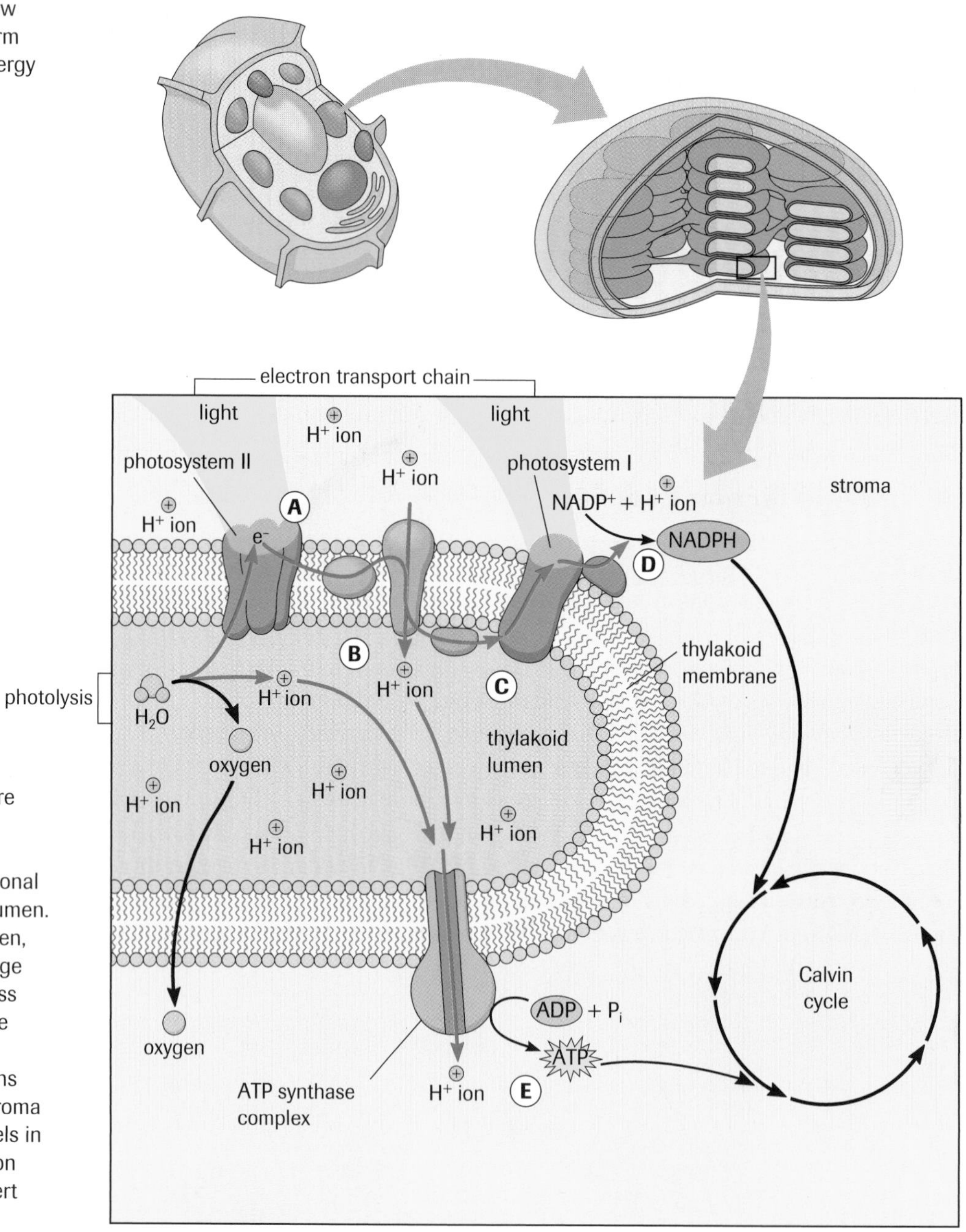

Figure 4
H^+ ions are released into the thylakoid lumen as electrons are removed from water. As these electrons are passed along an electron transport chain, additional H^+ ions are pumped into the lumen. H^+ ions accumulate in the lumen, increasing the gradient of charge and H^+ ion concentration across the thylakoid membrane. As the concentration and electrical gradients begin to build, H^+ ions move from the lumen to the stroma through special protein channels in the thylakoid membrane. The ion flow drives enzymes that convert ADP and P_i into ATP.

(H^+) across the membrane into the lumen (**B**). The electrons have now lost much of the energy that they received from light in photosystem II. However, their journey is not over. As H^+ ions are continuously pulled across the thylakoid membrane, their concentration increases inside the lumen and a positive charge begins to build up.

After moving to the inside of the thylakoid membrane, the electrons are transferred to a second photosystem—photosystem I (**C**). Here, they replace electrons that are energized by light. The electrons that are energized in photosystem I, unlike those in photosystem II, are not passed across the thylakoid membrane. Instead, they are transferred via a series of chemical complexes to $NADP^+$ (**D**). Each $NADP^+$ is able to accept two high-energy electrons and an H^+ ion from the surroundings as it changes to NADPH. The NADPH molecules formed in this process are used to transfer high-energy electrons to the Calvin cycle in Stage 3.

Key steps in electron transfer during the light-dependent reactions of photosynthesis are:

1. Electrons from photosystem II are transferred along an electron transport chain and across the thylakoid membrane to the inner surface.
2. Some of their energy is used to pull H^+ ions across the membrane, resulting in a buildup of positive charge within the lumen.
3. The electrons, having lost much of their original energy, are then transferred to chlorophyll molecules in the photosystem I complex, where they again absorb solar energy and reach an excited state.
4. High-energy electrons from photosystem I are transferred to $NADP^+$ to form NADPH.

DID YOU KNOW ?

The Cost of Chlorophyll

Leaves from shade-tolerant plants have more chlorophyll per photosystem than leaves from light-loving plants. This added cost is necessary to ensure enough light is captured for photosynthesis.

Chemiosmosis

Recall the H^+ ions that were pulled across the thylakoid membrane by the first electron transport chain at position (**B**). This process results in increasing concentration and electrical gradients across the thylakoid membrane. These gradients can now be put to good use. The H^+ ions are unable to escape from the lumen except through specialized protein complexes embedded in the membrane, named **ATP synthase complexes**. As the H^+ ions rush through these complexes, they release energy. The complexes are able to use some of the energy released by H^+ ions to combine ADP with P_i. The process of making ATP using the energy from an H^+ ion gradient is called **chemiosmosis**. Note that the energy stored in the H^+ ion gradient is derived from the energy of the electrons energized by photosystem II. As a result, it can be stated that the energy used by the plant to make ATP originally comes from sunlight.

Overall, the light-dependent reactions consume water and result in the formation of ATP, NADPH, and oxygen. ATP and NADPH play a critical role in the next phase of photosynthesis: carbon fixation.

ATP synthase complex a specialized protein complex embedded in the thylakoid membrane that allows H^+ ions to escape from the lumen and uses the resulting energy to generate ATP

chemiosmosis a process for synthesizing ATP using the energy of an electrochemical gradient and the ATP synthase enzyme

Practice

11. Where does the energy used to pull H^+ into the thylakoid lumen come from?
12. What are the H^+ ions that are pulled inside the thylakoid membranes used for?
13. Why is the production of NADPH important?
14. What is chemiosmosis?

Figure 5
Dr. Rudolph Arthur Marcus

 WEB Activity

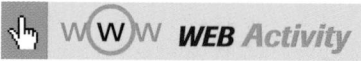

Canadian Achievers—Dr. Rudolph Arthur Marcus

The formation of ATP during photosynthesis depends on the transfer of electrons. Dr. Marcus (**Figure 5**), born and educated in Montreal, Quebec, was a main contributor to the development of this idea. From 1956 to 1964, he published a number of papers on what is now called the Marcus theory of electron transfer reactions. The Marcus theory also explained other phenomena that are very different from photosynthesis. Find out more about the life and work of Marcus, and then explain how his work contributed to our understanding of photosynthesis.

www.science.nelson.com GO

EXPLORE an issue

Harnessing Light Energy

Issue Checklist

- ● Issue
- ● Resolution
- ○ Design
- ● Evidence
- ● Analysis
- ● Evaluation

By utilizing sunlight, plants produce food through photosynthesis. When we use plants for food, we are using photosynthesis to meet our basic biological energy demands. Photosynthesis also supplies the wood we use as fuel, and was even responsible for producing the fossil fuels we use today. However, with an ever-increasing demand for abundant, environmentally friendly energy supplies, scientists are researching and refining artificial technologies for capturing and utilizing light energy.

Photosynthesis converts light energy directly into chemical energy. However, the most widely used solar technologies to date convert solar energy into heat (solar collectors such as rooftop solar hot-water heaters) or electrical energy (solar (photovoltaic) cells).

Recently, scientists have started to investigate mimicking photosynthesis by using chemical processes to create artificial photosynthetic systems. Some researchers believe that such artificial photosynthetic technology holds great promise. Some scientists are researching how to directly harness solar energy in the form of ATP, while others are attempting to mimic the carbon fixation reactions in the Calvin cycle. One research team is designing and using artificial catalysts that are able to use solar energy to convert CO_2 to CO—the first stage in the fixation of carbon. This could lead to the production of inexpensive fuels such as methanol and raw materials for the chemical industry.

How do these three technological approaches: converting solar energy into heat energy, electrical energy, and chemical energy compare to the efficiency of plant photosynthesis? What are the advantages and disadvantages of each method as a source of clean energy?

1. Conduct library and/or Internet research to investigate current efforts in the field of solar energy technologies.

   www.science.nelson.com 

   (a) How efficient are plants at converting solar energy into useable biomass energy?
   (b) How efficient are solar collectors? What are the advantages and disadvantages of such systems?
   (c) How efficient are photovoltaic cells? What are the advantages and disadvantages of such systems?
   (d) Why is it important to factor in life expectancy and cost when judging the value of a new technological innovation?
   (e) Has artificial photosynthesis been achieved?
   (f) What are the possible applications of artificial photosynthetic systems? Outline the advantages they might have over non-photosynthesis-based methods.

2. As a scientific researcher, you are attending an upcoming environmental conference to discuss artificial photosynthesis. Prepare a brochure or slide presentation highlighting the possible applications of this new technology.

Stage 3: The Calvin Cycle and Carbon Fixation

The final stage of photosynthesis is carbon fixation, which is the formation of high-energy organic molecules from CO_2. This process is referred to as the Calvin cycle, in honour of Melvin Calvin, who won the 1961 Nobel Prize in Chemistry for his work in discovering this pathway. The cycle involves a large number of light-independent reactions and is presented in a simplified form in **Figure 6** on the next page.

The Calvin cycle utilizes both ATP molecules and high-energy electrons carried by NADPH from the light-dependent reactions (Stages 1 and 2) to make G3P, a sugar that is

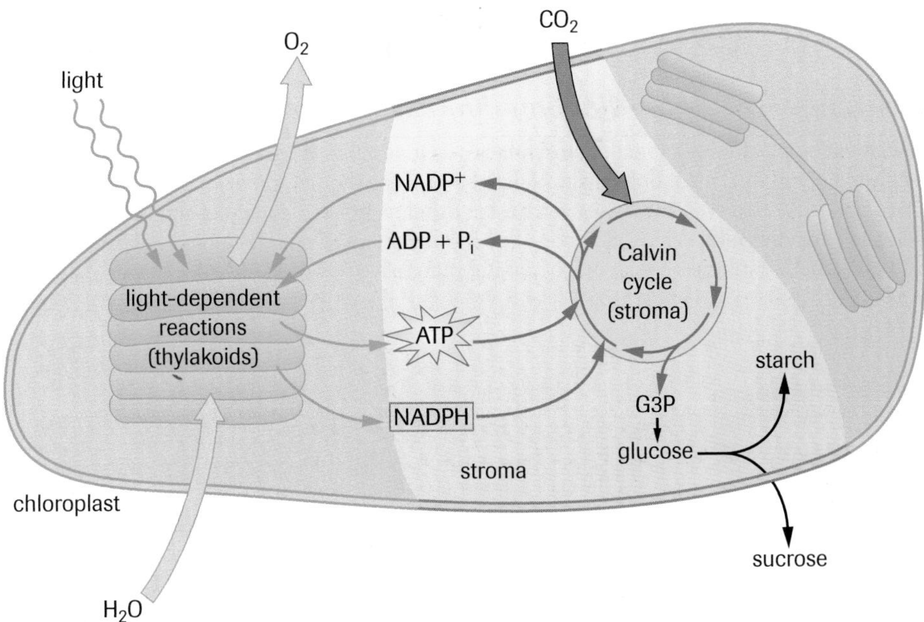

Figure 6
The Calvin cycle is the final stage of photosynthesis and takes place in the stroma. It uses NADPH and ATP to reduce CO_2 to G3P, a sugar that is used to make glucose and other carbohydrates, such as sucrose, cellulose, and starch.

used to create glucose. In these carbohydrates, the carbon and oxygen atoms are supplied by the CO_2 while the hydrogen atoms are supplied by the light-dependent reactions. Three ATPs and two NADPHs are consumed for every CO_2 that enters the cycle. Therefore, the building of even one simple sugar molecule such as glucose ($C_6H_{12}O_6$) requires the energy from 18 ATP molecules and the electrons and protons carried by 12 NADPH molecules.

Note that the amount of water produced during the Calvin cycle is less than that consumed during the light-dependent reactions. In total, there is a net consumption of six water molecules for every one glucose molecule formed.

In order for the Calvin cycle to operate within the stroma of the chloroplast, CO_2 must be readily available. In most plants CO_2 diffuses directly into the photosynthesizing plant leaf cells and chloroplasts from air spaces within the leaves. These air spaces are connected to the outside environment via tiny openings in the surface of the leaves.

DID YOU KNOW ?

Benson and Bassham

Melvin Calvin did not explain carbon fixation on his own. Andrew Benson and James Bassham also made significant contributions. The Calvin cycle is therefore also called the Calvin-Benson cycle or the Calvin-Benson-Bassham (CBB) cycle.

Practice

15. Where in the chloroplast does the Calvin cycle occur?

16. Name the final product of the Calvin cycle. What happens to this compound?

INVESTIGATION 6.2 *Introduction*

How Does Carbon Dioxide Concentration Affect the Rate of Photosynthesis?

Photosynthesis involves light-dependent reactions and biochemical reactions that do not directly require solar energy. Plants live in a variety of environments on Earth. Do changes in environmental conditions affect the rate of photosynthesis? In Investigation 6.2. you will design experiments to measure the rate of photosynthesis in various conditions of light intensity, temperature, CO_2 concentration, and other factors.

Report Checklist

○ Purpose	● Design	● Analysis
○ Problem	○ Materials	● Evaluation
○ Hypothesis	● Procedure	● Synthesis
● Prediction	● Evidence	

To perform this investigation, turn to page 197. 

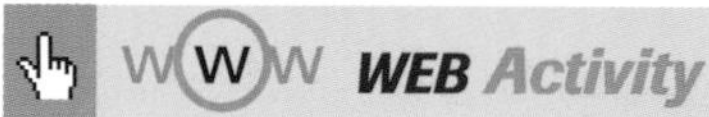

Web Quest—Factors Affecting Photosynthesis

How do different variables affect photosynthesis? Is it possible to speed it up or slow it down, just by changing the colour or intensity of light? How does the CO_2 present affect photosynthesis? This Web Quest lets you design experiments in a computer simulation to find the answers to these questions and more. See if you can figure out the optimal levels of different variables for the optimal rate of photosynthesis!

www.science.nelson.com 

SUMMARY The Reactions of Photosynthesis

- The light-dependent reactions of photosynthesis take place within chloroplasts in two stages:
  - Stage 1: Both photosystems I and II capture light energy and transfer it to electrons.
  - Stage 2: The energy transferred to the electrons is used to produce a buildup of H^+ ions inside the thylakoid space, and to produce high-energy NADPH molecules.
- The light-dependent reactions consume water and form ATP, NADPH, and oxygen.
- The following events occur in chemiosmosis during Stage 2:
  - H^+ ions are pulled across the thylakoid membrane by the electron transport chain, creating an H^+ ion gradient and a buildup of positive charge within the lumen.
  - The H^+ ions leave the lumen, passing through ATP synthase complexes embedded in the thylakoid membrane.
  - The concentrated H^+ ions release energy as they escape from the thylakoid space and this energy is used to form high-energy ATP molecules.
- The Calvin cycle is Stage 3 of photosynthesis and takes place in the stroma. It uses NADPH and ATP to reduce CO_2 to G3P, which is then used to make glucose. Glucose is then made into other carbohydrates.
- Building one simple sugar molecule such as glucose ($C_6H_{12}O_6$) requires the energy from 18 ATP molecules and the electrons and protons carried by 12 NADPH molecules.

Section 6.2 Questions

1. What is ATP?
2. Write an equation to represent the overall reaction of photosynthesis.
3. (a) What is the primary function of photosynthesis?
   (b) Where in the chloroplast do the light-dependent reactions occur?
   (c) What are the products of the light-dependent reactions?
   (d) In what phase of photosynthesis are the products of the light-dependent reactions used?
4. (a) Name the gas released as a byproduct of the light-dependent reactions of photosynthesis.
   (b) Name the molecule that is the source of this gas.
5. In an experiment, a bean plant is illuminated with green light and another bean plant of similar size is illuminated with equally intense blue light. If all other conditions are controlled, how will the photosynthetic rates of the two plants most probably compare?
6. (a) How many molecules of CO_2 must enter the Calvin cycle for a plant to ultimately produce a sugar, such as sucrose, that contains 12 carbon atoms?
   (b) How many ATP molecules will be used?
   (c) How many NADPH molecules will be used?
7. On a sheet of blank paper, draw a labelled diagram with a single caption to teach the process of photosynthesis to a grade 4 student who has never heard of the process.

INVESTIGATION 6.1

Separating Plant Pigments from Leaves

Report Checklist

- ● Purpose
- ● Problem
- ○ Hypothesis
- ● Prediction
- ○ Design
- ○ Materials
- ○ Procedure
- ● Evidence
- ● Analysis
- ● Evaluation
- ○ Synthesis

Plants produce thousands of different chemical compounds, many of which have been found to be useful in medicine, as foods, and in industry. The first step to finding useful plant compounds is to separate the components of a plant tissue. The properties of each separate component may then be tested and the compound identified. Chromatography is a technique that separates different chemicals in a mixture based on their solubility in a particular solvent solution. In this activity, you will use paper chromatography to separate some of the different pigments found in a plant leaf.

Materials

safety goggles
laboratory apron
spinach leaf
chromatography solvent (acetone)
filter paper, 12 cm long
dime
test tube rack
scissors
pencil
chromatography tube with cork stopper
cork stopper with a paper-clip hook

The chromatography solvent is volatile and flammable.

Use the solvent only under a fume hood.

Do not use the solvent in a room with an open flame.

Chemicals should be dispensed only by the teacher.

Wear eye protection and a laboratory apron at all times.

Procedure

1. Obtain a piece of filter paper that is long enough so the tip of the strip reaches the solvent when the strip is suspended in the test tube. Handle the paper by the edges only, to avoid transferring oil from your skin.
2. With the scissors, trim the filter paper to a point at one end. At 3 cm above the point, draw a light line in pencil across the width of the filter paper.
3. Obtain a fresh spinach leaf and place it over the pencil line on the filter paper.
4. Roll the edge of a dime across the leaf, so that the dime edge crushes the leaf tissue onto the filter paper along the pencil line.
5. Repeat step 4 several times until the pencil line has been soaked with a thin, dark band of spinach leaf extract.
6. Obtain the cork stopper with a hook formed from a paper clip. Insert the hook into the upper (straight) edge of the chromatography paper strip.
7. Obtain a chromatography tube containing 3 mL of chromatography solvent from your teacher. Keep the tube tightly stoppered and standing upright in the test tube rack.
8. Under the fume hood, remove the cork stopper that is in the chromatography tube. Replace it with the stopper to which you attached the paper strip in step 6, as shown in **Figure 1**. The tip of the paper must just touch the solvent, and the line of leaf extract must stay above the surface of the solvent. Ensure that the chromatography paper is not touching the sides of the chromatography tube. Tightly stopper the chromatography tube and carefully stand the tube upright in the test tube rack.

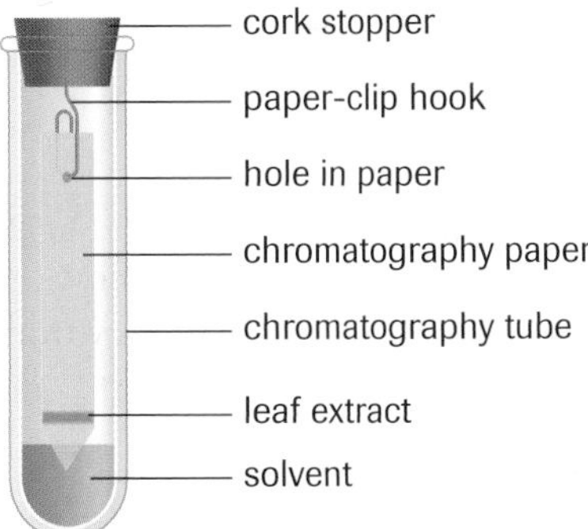

Figure 1
A chromatography setup

9. Observe the movement of solvent and extract for 15 min to 30 min. Remove the paper strip before the solvent reaches the top of the paper, and replace the stopper in the tube.
10. Still working under the fume hood, draw a pencil line across the paper strip at the uppermost point reached by the solvent before it dries and becomes invisible. Also mark each pigment band and record its colour before it fades. Keep the paper strip under the fume hood until it is completely dry.

INVESTIGATION 6.1 *continued*

(a) At your desk, measure and record the distance from the original pencil line to the middle of each pigment band. Also measure and record the distance the solvent travelled from the pencil line.

Analysis

(b) After chromatography, compounds may be identified from their R_f values. These values compare the distance travelled by a compound with the distance travelled by the solvent. Calculate the R_f values for each compound on your filter paper according to the following equation:

$$R_f = \frac{\text{distance travelled by compound}}{\text{distance travelled by solvent}}$$

(c) How many compounds were you able to separate using chromatography?

(d) Draw a life-sized diagram of your chromatography strip, showing the precise locations of the pigments and solvent solution.

Evaluation

(e) The more soluble a compound is in a solvent, the farther it will travel during chromatography. **Table 1** gives some properties of pigments commonly found in plant leaves. Which pigments were in your leaf extract? Explain your answer.

Table 1 Common Leaf Pigments

Pigment	Colour	Relative solubility in acetone
chlorophyll *a*	bright green to blue-green	medium
chlorophyll *b*	yellow-green to olive green	medium-low
carotenes	dull yellow-orange	high
xanthophylls	bright yellow to orange	medium-high

(f) List the R_f values for the pigments you identified in the preceding question. Describe the relationship between R_f value and solubility.

(g) Compare your R_f values to those recorded by the other groups in your class. Were the R_f values for each pigment always the same? How might this affect the use of R_f values to identify chemical compounds?

(h) Suggest a step that could be added to the procedure to isolate a specific compound for chemical testing.

Extension

(i) Obtain a black water-soluble marker. Repeat steps 1 to 3, but replace the solvent with water and use the marker to draw a line across a piece of filter paper in step 3. Allow the ink to dry and then draw another line on top of the first. Repeat this several times until you have a very dark ink line across the paper. Perform a chromatography as in this activity. Report your findings to the class.

(j) The colourful Haida mask in **Figure 2** may have been dyed using pigments obtained from local plants. Brainstorm methods the Haida people might use to extract these pigments from leaves, roots, and stems.

Figure 2
Haida mask

+ EXTENSION

Chromatography
In this Virtual Biology Lab, you can use TLC (thin-layer chromatography) to separate and analyze the pigments in a spinach leaf extract.

www.science.nelson.com 

INVESTIGATION 6.2

Report Checklist

- ○ Purpose
- ○ Problem
- ○ Hypothesis
- ● Prediction
- ● Design
- ○ Materials
- ● Procedure
- ● Evidence
- ● Analysis
- ● Evaluation
- ● Synthesis

How Does Carbon Dioxide Concentration Affect the Rate of Photosynthesis?

Photosynthesis involves light-dependent reactions and biochemical reactions that do not directly require light. Plants live in a variety of environments on Earth. Do changes in environmental conditions affect the rate of photosynthesis? In this investigation, you will measure the rate of photosynthesis in various conditions by quantifying the amount of oxygen being released from a photosynthesizing solution.

Problems

1. How do changes in light intensity, temperature, and CO_2 concentration affect the rate of photosynthesis?
2. Develop your own question regarding the effect of an environmental condition of your choice on the rate of photosynthesis.

Predictions

(a) Predict the effect that changes in each of the following environmental conditions will have on the rate of photosynthesis:
  (i) light intensity
  (ii) temperature
  (iii) CO_2 concentration
  (iv) another environmental condition of your choice

Design

The procedure outlined in this investigation provides a method for measuring the rate of photosynthesis of plants submersed in an aqueous sodium bicarbonate buffer (pH 7). Sodium bicarbonate is used as a source of $CO_2(aq)$. You will use this procedure to measure the rate of photosynthesis in four experiments that you will design and perform. In each case, you must conduct controlled experiments that allow you to make reasonable comparisons.

(b) Design three experimental procedures to determine
  (i) the effect of varying light intensity on the rate of photosynthesis
  (ii) the effect of varying temperature on the rate of photosynthesis
  (iii) the effect of varying concentration of dissolved carbon dioxide on the rate of photosynthesis

Have your teacher approve each experimental procedure, then carry out the experiments. Use the procedure outlined in this investigation to measure the rate of photosynthesis in each case. Record all observations and measurements in a suitable table format.

(c) Design an experimental procedure to test the prediction you made in (a) (iv). Obtain teacher approval, then carry out the experiment. Record all observations and measurements in suitable table format.

Materials

safety goggles
laboratory apron
500 mL conical flask or large test tube
plants (terrestrial plants or water plants)
sodium bicarbonate buffer, pH 7
rubber stopper with glass tubing
rubber tubing
50 mL burette
distilled water
500 mL beaker
utility stand and clamp
rubber bulb
ice
sodium bicarbonate
thermometer
light intensity meter
other materials and equipment as necessary
200 W light bulb

Procedure

1. Put on your safety goggles and lab apron.
2. Fill the 500 mL conical flask with plant material.
3. Add enough sodium bicarbonate buffer to submerse the plant material.
4. Put the stopper with glass tubing onto the mouth of the conical flask. Make sure that the glass tubing does not touch the contents of the flask.
5. Place 400 mL of water into a 500 mL beaker. Fill the burette with water to the top, then invert it in the beaker and secure it with a clamp to the utility stand (**Figure 1**, next page).
6. Use rubber tubing to connect the open end of the glass top in the stopper of the flask to the bottom of the burette. The rubber tubing needs to be air tight within the glass tubing, but should fit loosely in the bottom of the burette. Be sure there is space for the water to escape when the gas bubbles up the burette.

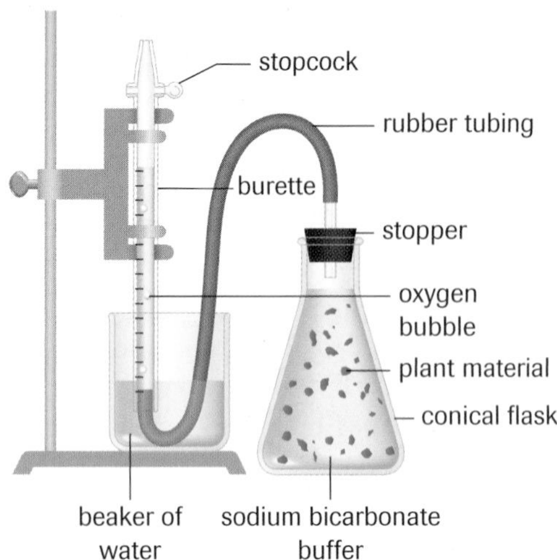

Figure 1
Gas collection apparatus setup

7. Open the burette stopcock carefully and allow the water level to drop to the 50 mL level on the burette.
8. Subject the system to conditions according to your design. Allow several minutes for the system to stabilize.
9. Follow the rate of photosynthesis by either counting the number of bubbles over 1 min spans or measuring the amount of water displaced over 5 min spans. Measure for a total of 10 min for each condition. If you get no bubbles, check if the meniscus in the tubing is moving. If it is, then your burette valve is leaking. Your teacher will help you correct this problem.

Analysis

(d) In tables, summarize the results for the variables you tested. Draw suitable graphs using your data.

(e) Analyze your results for trends and patterns. Answer the Questions.

(f) Compare your results with those of the rest of the class.

Evaluation

(g) In your report, evaluate your predictions, taking into account possible sources of error. Draw reasonable conclusions.

(h) Describe how you could improve your experimental methods and the assay technique.

(i) Suggest other experiments you could perform to extend your knowledge of photosynthetic activity.

(j) The experiments you conducted in this investigation were carried out with plants submerged in water. Design a procedure for carrying out the same types of experiments in air instead of water. Draw a labelled diagram, like **Figure 1**, to illustrate your experimental design.

(k) What environmental conditions affecting the rate of photosynthesis can be tested in an air environment that could not be tested in a water environment?

Synthesis

(l) Suggest a procedure you might use to identify the type of gas produced by the plant material in these experiments.

EXTENSION

Carbon Dioxide Fixation

You can confirm the results of the experiment you designed or carry out additional experiments on factors that affect the rate of photosynthesis in the Virtual Biology Lab.

www.science.nelson.com 

Chapter 6 SUMMARY

Outcomes

Knowledge

- explain, in general terms, how pigments absorb light and transfer that energy as reducing power in $NADP^+$, NADPH, and finally into chemical potential in ATP by chemiosmosis, describing where those processes occur in the chloroplast (6.1, 6.2)
- explain, in general terms, how the products of the light-dependent reactions, NADPH and ATP, are used to reduce carbon in the light-independent reactions for the production of glucose, describing where the process occurs in the chloroplast (6.2)

STS

- explain how scientific knowledge may lead to the development of new technologies and new technologies may lead to scientific discovery (6.2)
- explain that the appropriateness, risks, and benefits of technologies need to be assessed for each potential application from a variety of perspectives, including sustainability (6.2)

Skills

- ask questions and plan investigations (6.1, 6.2)
- conduct investigations and gather and record data and information (6.1, 6.2)
- analyze data and apply mathematical and conceptual models by: collecting and interpreting data and calculating R_f (reference flow) values from chromatography experiments (6.1); and drawing analogies between the storage of energy by photosynthesis and the storage of energy by active solar generating systems (6.2)
- work as members of a team and apply the skills and conventions of science (all)

Key Terms

6.1

photon
chlorophyll
chloroplast
stroma
thylakoid
grana
lamellae
thylakoid membrane
thylakoid lumen

6.2

ATP
ADP
$NADP^+$
NADPH
light-dependent reactions
carbon fixation
Calvin cycle
light-independent reactions
photosystem
electron transport chain
photolysis
oxidation
reduction
ATP synthase complex
chemiosmosis

MAKE a summary

1. Using a large piece of paper, draw a poster summarizing the three stages of photosynthesis. The paper represents the cytoplasm of a plant cell. Draw a chloroplast covering at least half ot the paper. Place different drawings representing each stage of the process in the appropriate locations.
2. Revisit your answers to the Starting Points questions at the start of the chapter. Would you answer the questions differently now? Why?

Go To

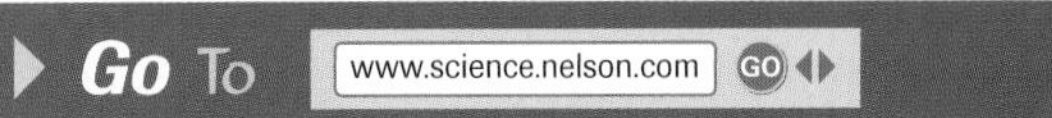

The following components are available on the Nelson Web site. Follow the links for *Nelson Biology Alberta 20–30.*

- an interactive Self Quiz for Chapter 6
- additional Diploma Exam-style Review Questions
- Illustrated Glossary
- additional IB-related material

There is more information on the Web site wherever you see the Go icon in the chapter.

EXTENSION

Low Light Life

Dr. Tom Beatty, (a microbiologist from the University of British Columbia) and his team have discovered photosynthetic bacteria in the deep-sea oases formed around hydrothermal vents. This bacteria uses the light generated by infrared energy from the hot environment and stray photons produced by chemical reactions.

www.science.nelson.com GO

Many of these questions are in the style of the Diploma Exam. You will find guidance for writing Diploma Exams in Appendix A5. Science Directing Words used in Diploma Exams are in bold type. Exam study tips and test-taking suggestions are on the Nelson Web site.

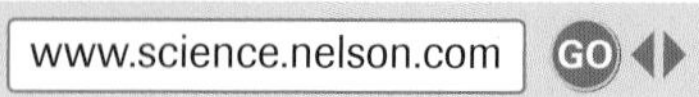

DO NOT WRITE IN THIS TEXTBOOK.

Part 1

1. The raw materials for photosynthesis are
   A. oxygen and water
   B. carbon dioxide and water
   C. glucose and oxygen
   D. oxygen and carbon dioxide

2. The word equation that summarizes photosynthesis is
   A. water + starch → glucose + glucose + glucose
   B. water + carbon dioxide → oxygen + glucose
   C. glucose + oxygen → water + carbon dioxide
   D. carbon dioxide + glucose → water + oxygen

Use the following information to answer questions 3 and 4.

Figure 1 shows events taking place inside the chloroplast during photosynthesis. The tan region is the stoma and the green region is the thylakoid lumen. These regions are separated by the thylakoid membrane.

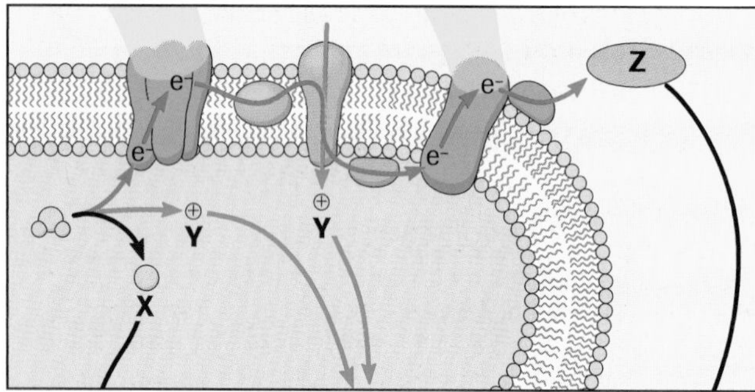

Figure 1

3. The letters X, Y, and Z represent
   A. water (X), NADPH (Y), H^+ (Z)
   B. chlorophyll (X), oxygen (Y), ATP (Z)
   C. NADPH (X), H^+ (Y), water (Z)
   D. oxygen (X), H^+ (Y), NADPH (Z)

4. The function of the electron transport chain in this pathway is to
   A. energize electrons for the reduction of $NADP^+$
   B. pump H^+ ions out of the lumen to generate ATP
   C. move electrons from photosystem I to photosystem II
   D. produce oxygen

5. The process of splitting water to release hydrogen ions, electrons, and oxygen occurs
   A. during the light-dependent reactions
   B. during the Calvin cycle
   C. during photorespiration
   D. during carbon fixation

6. The process of incorporating the carbon of carbon dioxide into carbohydrates occurs
   A. during the light-dependent reactions
   B. during the Calvin cycle
   C. during carbon fixation
   D. during B and C

Use the following information to answer questions 7 and 8.

The herbicide 3-(3,4-dichlorophenyl)-1,1 -dimethylurea (DSMU) blocks the transfer of electrons from photosystem II into the electron transport chain.

7. This herbicide would effect ATP and glucose production in the following ways:
   A. increase ATP production; decrease glucose production
   B. decrease ATP production; increase glucose production
   C. stop ATP production; stop glucose production
   D. decrease ATP production; stop glucose production

8. The herbicide will kill the plant because it will
   A. stop the production of glucose and other carbohydrates
   B. stop the production of ATP
   C. stop the production of oxygen gas
   D. stop the pumping of H^+ ions across the thylakoid membrane

9. NR The following data were collected from several different chromatography experiments using the same solvent. **Calculate** the R_f values for each of the pigments and then place these values in order from most soluble to least soluble. (Record all four digits of your answer, rounded to two decimal places.)

Pigment	A	B	C	D
Solvent distance travelled	12.1 mm	6.0 mm	8.4 mm	9.5 mm
Pigment distance travelled	5.8 mm	2.2 mm	8.1 mm	1.4 mm

10. NR Place the following molecules in the order that they first appear directly in the chemical pathways of photosynthesis. (Record all four digits of your answer.)
    1. CO_2
    2. glucose
    3. oxygen
    4. water

Part 2

11. (a) **Determine** which has more energy: short wavelengths or long wavelengths of electromagnetic radiation.
    (b) **Identify** the range of wavelengths plants use in photosynthesis.

12. Some old biology textbooks called the carbon fixation reactions of photosynthesis the "dark reactions."
    (a) **Why** did they use this term?
    (b) **Why** is this misleading?

Use the following information to answer questions 13 to 18.

The data in **Table 1** were obtained by extracting the pigments from spinach leaves and placing them in an instrument called a spectrophotometer that measures the amount of light (of different wavelengths) absorbed by pigments.

Table 1 Absorption Spectrum of Spinach Leaf Pigments

Wavelength (nm)	Absorbance (%)	Wavelength (nm)	Absorbance (%)
400	0.42	560	0.12
420	0.68	580	0.15
440	0.60	600	0.17
460	0.58	620	0.25
480	0.83	640	0.40
500	0.23	660	0.32
520	0.11	670	0.56
540	0.12	680	0.24

13. **Sketch** a line graph of the data with percent absorbance along the vertical axis and wavelength along the horizontal axis. Indicate the colours of the visible spectrum corresponding to the wavelengths along the horizontal axis. DE

14. **Identify** the colours of an intact spinach leaf that would be least visible. Explain. DE

15. **Identify** the colour that is least absorbed by the pigment extract. Explain. DE

16. **Compare** this graph to the absorption spectrum in **Figure 3** on page 182. Identify the pigment most likely responsible for the peak at 670 nm. DE

17. **Why** are there no peaks in the range of 500 nm to 620 nm? DE

18. **Identify** the pigments primarily responsible for absorption in the range of 400 nm to 480 nm. DE

Use the following information to answer questions 19 to 21.

A research scientist is able to remove and isolate chloroplasts from plant cells. She places them in an acidic solution of pH 4 (having a very high H^+ concentration) and waits until both the stroma and inner thylakoid space reach this same pH level. She then removes the chloroplasts and places them in a solution of pH 8 in the dark. She notices that the chloroplasts begin synthesizing ATP.

19. **Explain** the scientist's observations. DE

20. **Why** did she choose to perform the experiment in the dark rather than the light? DE

21. **Describe** the expected result if she had tested for the presence of products from the Calvin cycle? Explain. DE

Use the following information to answer questions 22 to 24.

Supplies of fossil fuels are limited, and concerns over increasing atmospheric CO_2 levels are providing an incentive to make better use of solar energy. In the future, photosynthetic organisms may be used to harness solar energy to produce clean-burning fuels, such as ethanol or hydrogen gas. Researchers have already had some success getting certain algae to produce hydrogen gas from water using photosystem II, while others are attempting to harness photosynthesis processes to produce methane gas (CH_4).

22. **Describe** the advantages of hydrogen gas as a fuel compared to methane. DE

23. Considering all of the products of photosynthesis, **describe** a safety problem that might arise if either of these fuels were being produced in large quantities by photosynthetic processes. DE

24. If photosynthesis were used as a source of methane gas, **conclude** whether burning methane as a fuel would have any influence on atmospheric CO_2 levels. **Explain** your conclusion. DE

25. Biomass is plant matter such as trees, grasses, and agricultural crops. Conduct research on using biomass as a fuel source (biofuel). Then, write a unified response addressing the following aspects of using biofuel.
    - **Describe** how electricity is generated from biofuel.
    - **Determine** what proportion of electric power production in Canada comes from biomass energy. **Summarize** the potential for increasing the amount of electricity produced by biomass.
    - **Compare** the costs and benefits of producing automobile fuel from biomass with those of producing fuel from petroleum.

www.science.nelson.com 

chapter 7

Cellular Respiration

In this chapter

- Exploration: Clothespins and Muscle Fatigue
- Web Activity: ATP in Action
- Chemistry Connection: Combustion of Glucose
- Web Activity: Respiration in Motion
- Investigation 7.1: Measuring Oxygen Consumption in Germinating Seeds
- Mini Investigation: Facultative Microbes
- Explore an Issue: Aerobic versus Anaerobic Waste Treatment
- Mini Investigation: Metabolic Poisons

As she skated into the final stretch, speed skater Cindy Klassen dug deep and poured on a final surge of energy to win the women's 1500-m event at the 2006 Winter Olympic Games in Turin. Her winning time of 1 min, 55.27 sec. didn't beat her own world-record time of 1 min, 51.79 sec., which she had set a few months earlier. Klassen won five medals at the games, tying the record for most medals won at an Olympics by a speed skater and breaking the record for most medals won by a Canadian at a single Olympic games.

Klassen's exceptional athletic ability was honed to the elite level through extensive training at Calgary's Olympic Oval. Coaches and exercise physiologists looked at every aspect of Klassen's physical performance and technique, trying to shave seconds off her times. To do this, they had to understand the body's energy demands at the cellular level. Cellular respiration is the process cells use to release energy needed for all kinds of work, including muscle contraction. There are two types of cellular respiration: aerobic respiration and anaerobic respiration. During a race, a speed skater's cells are likely to use both types. In this chapter, you will learn the biochemical steps involved in these processes and how these processes are essential for normal people doing everyday activities, not just for Olympic athletes.

STARTING Points

Answer these questions as best you can with your current knowledge. Then, using the concepts and skills you have learned, you will revise your answers at the end of the chapter.

1. (a) What do organisms do with the oxygen they absorb from the air?
   (b) What is the source of carbon in the carbon dioxide excreted by these organisms?
   (c) Why is carbon dioxide excreted?
2. (a) Why do bakers add yeast to flour and water when making bread?
   (b) When yeast is added to grape juice at room temperature, vigorous bubbling occurs. What gas produces the bubbles?
   (c) After a while, the bubbling stops. Why does it stop?
   (d) What type of beverage is produced by this process?
   (e) What is the name of this process?
3. (a) After a long, hard run, your muscles feel sore and stiff. What is the cause of these symptoms?
   (b) Why do you pant at the end of the run?

Career Connections:
Food Scientist; Kinesiologist

Figure 1
Cindy Klassen started out as a hockey player before taking up speed skating. Both of these activities place great energy demands on the body.

Exploration — Clothespins and Muscle Fatigue

Automobiles and machines must be supplied with gasoline or electricity as a source of energy before they can move. Your muscles require energy in the form of ATP to contract. Muscles can produce ATP by using oxygen (aerobic respiration) or not using it (anaerobic respiration). Anaerobic respiration in muscle cells produces lactic acid. When muscles do a lot of work quickly, lactic acid buildup reduces their ability to contract until exhaustion eventually sets in and contraction stops altogether. This is called muscle fatigue.

Materials: clothespin, timer

- Hold a clothespin in the thumb and index finger of your dominant hand.
- Count the number of times you can open and close the clothespin in a 20 s period while holding your other fingers straight out. Make sure to squeeze quickly and completely to get the maximum number of squeezes for each trial.
- Repeat this process for nine more 20 s periods, recording the result for each trial in a suitable table. Do not rest your fingers between trials.
- Repeat the procedure for the nondominant hand.

(a) Prepare a suitable graph of the data you collected.
(b) What happened to your strength as you progressed through each trial?
(c) Describe how your hand and fingers felt during the end of your trials.
(d) What factors might cause you to get more squeezes (to have less fatigue)?
(e) Were your results different for the dominant and the nondominant hand? Explain why they would be different.
(f) Your muscles would probably recover after 10 min of rest to operate at the original squeeze rate. Explain why.

7.1 The Importance of Cellular Respiration

As you have learned, photosynthesis converts light energy into chemical energy via a series of complex chemical reactions that form a variety of intermediate and final energy-rich molecules. These molecules serve a variety of different energy-related functions within cells.

The primary function of photosynthesis is to convert solar energy into glucose molecules. The glucose molecules may be used immediately. Glucose may then be used immediately, transported to other cells, stored for a medium-term, or used to synthesize molecules that can store energy long-term. Plant cells synthesize starch for long-term storage, by joining many glucose molecules together. Animal and fungal cells link together glucose molecules obtained from their food to form the storage compound glycogen.

When cells require energy for a particular process, it must be supplied in the more directly usable form of ATP. This is the role of cellular respiration. The cells of both animals and plants release the energy stored in the bonds of glucose molecules through the process of cellular respiration. Recall that the process of cellular respiration can be summarized by this equation:

$$\text{glucose} + \text{oxygen} \rightarrow \text{carbon dioxide} + \text{water} + \text{energy}$$
$$C_6H_{12}O_6(s) + O_2(g) \rightarrow CO_2(g) + H_2O(l) + \text{energy}$$

As we saw with photosynthesis, this equation includes only the compounds at the beginning and end of the process. It is the intermediate products that are used by the cells. In cellular respiration, the intermediate products include NADH, $FADH_2$, and ATP.

NADH an electron carrier, donates electrons in cellular processes

NAD^+ an electron carrier, accepts electrons in cellular processes

$FADH_2$ an electron carrier, donates electrons in cellular processes

FAD^+ an electron carrier, accepts electrons in cellular processes

NADH is the reduced form of **NAD^+** (nicotinamide adenine dinucleotide). **$FADH_2$** is the reduced form of **FAD^+** (flavin adenine dinucleotide). Like NADPH and $NADP^+$ in photosynthesis, these compounds serve as electron carriers. Their role is to transfer electrons through oxidation–reduction reactions. Recall that in an oxidization reaction, electrons are lost and in a reduction reaction, electrons are gained. The transfer of electrons releases energy that can be used in cellular respiration and other cellular processes.

The transfer of electrons from one reactive atom to another produces more stable ions or compounds. The fact that the products have less energy than the reactants indicates that energy is released during the oxidation reaction. This energy can be used to make ATP. **Figure 1** on the next page shows how the energy from an oxidation–reduction reaction is used to attach phosphates to ADP. The product, ATP, is a high-energy compound.

Each time electrons are transferred in oxidation–reduction reactions, energy is made available for the cell to make ATP. Electron transport chains shuttle electrons from one molecule to another. For example, the oxidizing agent NAD^+, along with H^+ remove high-energy electrons from organic molecules and form NADH. It then transfers these electrons to energy releasing chemical pathways. The energy released in these pathways is transferred to ADP and P_i to form ATP.

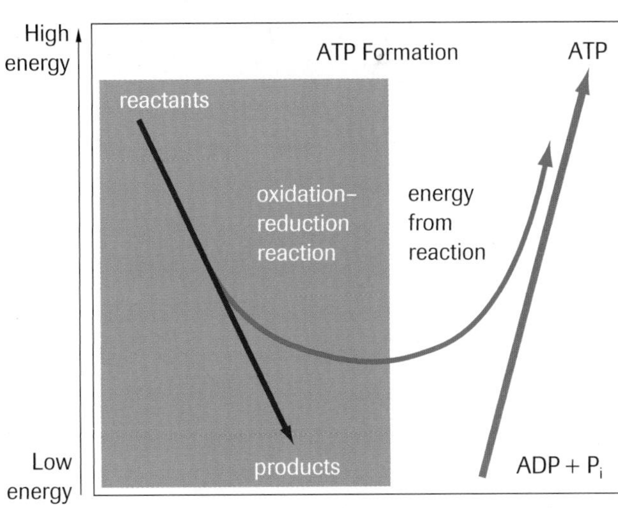

Figure 1
The energy released from the oxidation–reduction reaction is used to attach a free phosphate to ADP to make ATP. Note that ATP is a high-energy compound. The oxidation–reduction reaction could be the transfer of electrons from high-energy compounds such as when NADH is oxidized to form NAD^+ and H^+.

Practice

1. What is the primary function of cellular respiration?
2. How do the oxidation and reduction reactions in electron transfer help to form ATP?

Energy, Cells, and ATP

The energy demands for most cellular processes are supplied by the energy stored in ATP. These energy demands are very diverse. Some, such as chromosome movement in cell division, occur in virtually all living cells, and others, such as bioluminescence (the production of light) occur only in highly specialized cells in a few organisms. These energy demands are not trivial. It is estimated that a typical human cell contains approximately one billion molecules of ATP. These are continuously broken down into ADP and P_i as they release energy to do work, and are then reformed only to be used again.

Active transport (**Figure 2**) can be used to move substances either into or out of the cell. The carrier proteins are often referred to as "pumps." Various types of active transport pumps are found in the membranes of different cells. Potassium and sodium ions are moved into and out of cells by a pump known as the **sodium–potassium pump** (**Figure 3**, next page). Without this pump, nerve cells and muscle cells could not function properly. Other substances, such as vitamins, amino acids, and hydrogen ions are also actively transported across membranes by specialized carrier proteins. All of these pumps require energy from ATP to operate.

active transport the movement of substances through a membrane against a concentration gradient using membrane-bound carrier proteins and energy from ATP

sodium–potassium pump an active-transport mechanism that pumps sodium and potassium ions into and out of a cell

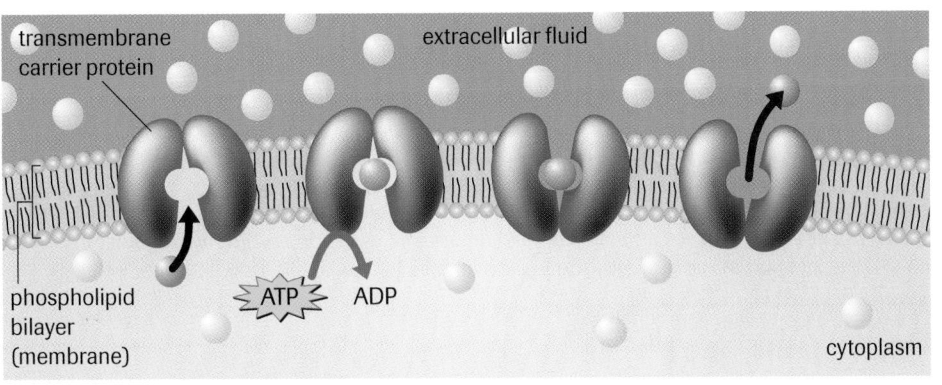

Figure 2
Active transport. The molecule to be transported attaches to an open binding site on one side of the carrier protein. ATP is converted to ADP on the carrier protein and releases energy. The energy causes a change in the shape of the protein that carries the solute to the other side of the membrane.

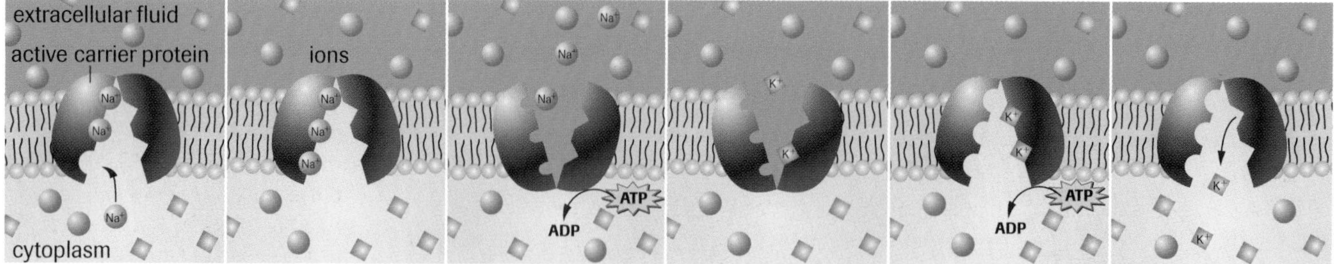

Figure 3
The energy of ATP is used to actively transport three sodium ions out of a cell for every two potassium ions that are transported into the cell.

Another critical use of ATP is that of large-scale motion. In order for you to move, your muscles must contract. The process of muscle contraction involves two different protein molecules sliding past each other. The energy from ATP is used to change the shape of one of the molecules resulting on it pulling on the other. This general process is responsible for all the movements of contractile fibres. (Muscle physiology is covered in detail in Chapter 9.)

Most processes that require ATP energy can be placed in one of categories in **Table 1**.

Table 1 Uses of ATP Energy

Functions requiring ATP	Role of ATP	Examples
motion	• causes various specialized fibres within cells to contract causing movement of the cell or movements within the cell	• chromosome movements during cell division • movement of organelles such as contractile vacuoles emptying • cytoplasmic streaming • formation of pseudopods in lymphocytes or in amoebas • beating of cilia and flagella such as in sperm cells or in certain single-celled organisms
	• causes muscle fibres to contract	• contraction of skeletal, smooth, and cardiac muscles
transport of ions and molecules	• powers active transport of molecules against a concentration gradient across a membrane	• sodium–potassium pump • hydrogen ion pump
building molecules	• provides the energy needed to build many large molecules	• joining amino acids in protein synthesis • Building new strands of DNA during DNA replication
switching reactions on or off	• alters the shape of a molecule, which alters the function of the molecule	• switches certain enzymes on or off
bioluminescence	• reacts with a molecule called luciferin and oxygen	• produces light in some light-generating species such as glow-worms and fireflies

WWW **WEB Activity**

Simulation—ATP in Action

Follow the Nelson links to view animations of various cellular processes requiring ATP energy. Briefly explain each process and indicate the importance of the process to the organism, and how ATP is involved in the process. You may wish to include a labelled sketch of the process.

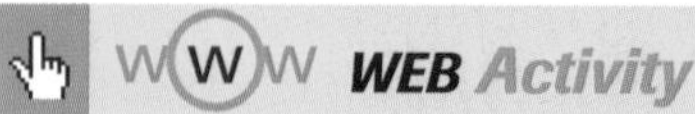

Glucose and ATP

All cells use energy from ATP molecules to meet their metabolic energy needs. However, ATP molecules are not abundant in food and provide a relatively small amount of energy per molecule. Molecules with a higher energy content are therefore useful for both long-term storage of chemical energy and for bulk transporting of chemical energy within cells and multicellular organisms. Carbohydrates, most notably in the form of glucose, are the most usable source of energy. Glucose, along with oxygen, is one of the substrates of cellular respiration. During cellular respiration, some of the energy in glucose is converted to ATP.

A useful analogy for the relationship between ATP, glucose, and other energy-rich molecules is that of money. In our analogy, a cell is like a large factory in which all operations are performed by vending machines that only accept one-dollar coins. In order to perform any task (any cellular action) within the factory, one must insert one or more one-dollar coins into a vending machine. In real cells, the one-dollar coins are analogous to ATP molecules. Virtually all processes conducted by cells use ATP molecules, and only ATP molecules, as their immediate energy source.

In contrast, a glucose molecule contains approximately 100 times as much energy as an individual ATP molecule, but this energy cannot be directly used by the cell. It is like a $100 bill in our cell factory. It is certainly valuable, but must be exchanged for coins before it can be used to operate the vending machines. Similarly, in real cells, the energy content of glucose and other energy-rich molecules can be exchanged or converted into the energy of numerous ATP molecules for the running of cellular activities.

Glucose (**Figure 4**), a simple sugar or monosaccharide, is well suited to its role as a convenient energy supply molecule. Glucose is our "blood sugar." It has a high energy content and is relatively small and highly soluble. These latter two properties make glucose ideal for transportation within and between cells, and throughout the body.

CAREER CONNECTION 

Food Scientist

Food scientists research and develop new and improved methods of food processing, preserving, and packaging. Healthy and safe food products must be continually tested for nutritional value and high quality, so food scientists are essential in food inspection and monitoring programs.

Find out how you might become a food scientist.

www.science.nelson.com 

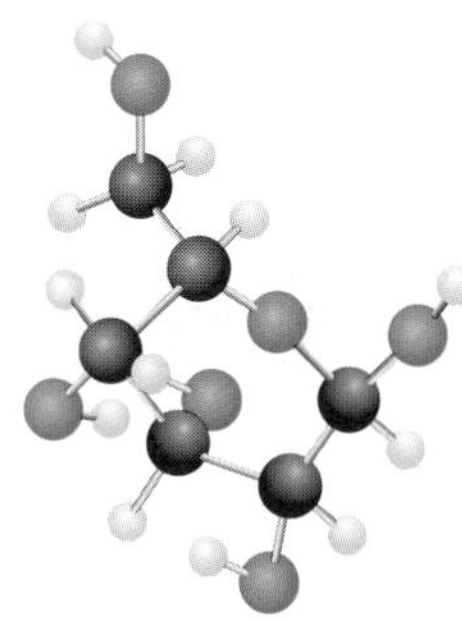

Figure 4
A glucose molecule

Practice

3. Active transport involves carrier proteins imbedded in the membranes of cells. How do these carrier proteins use ATP to transport molecules across the membrane?
4. How is ATP used in muscle contraction?
5. One glucose molecule has 100 times more stored energy than one ATP molecule. Explain why can't cells use glucose to run their processes.

Releasing Energy

During respiration, the chemical bonds of reactant food molecules are broken and new bonds are formed in the resulting chemical products. It always takes energy to break chemical bonds, and energy is always released when new bonds form. In simple terms, respiration is an energy-releasing process because more energy is released during the formation of product molecules than is consumed to break apart the reactant molecules (**Figure 5** on page 208).

The energy released by cellular respiration is used to synthesize ATP molecules to be used as the energy currency within the cell. The fundamental role of cellular respiration is to transfer the energy content of food molecules into the energy content of ATP.

Because food molecules such as glucose have a relatively large energy content, a single molecule can be used to form many lower-energy molecules. In our analogy, this is like exchanging the high-energy content of a $100 bill for the energy content of many one-dollar coins. Unlike a simple banking machine, however, the process of cellular respiration is not 100 % efficient. In fact, it is estimated that, at best, only 36 % of the

DID YOU KNOW ?

Breaking Chemical Bonds

Energy is only released when new chemical bonds form. Similarly, energy is always required (used) when bonds are broken. In the case of ATP, energy is released when the phosphate group is removed because new bonds form between the phosphate group and other chemicals involved in the reaction. This is the important source of energy available to the cell.

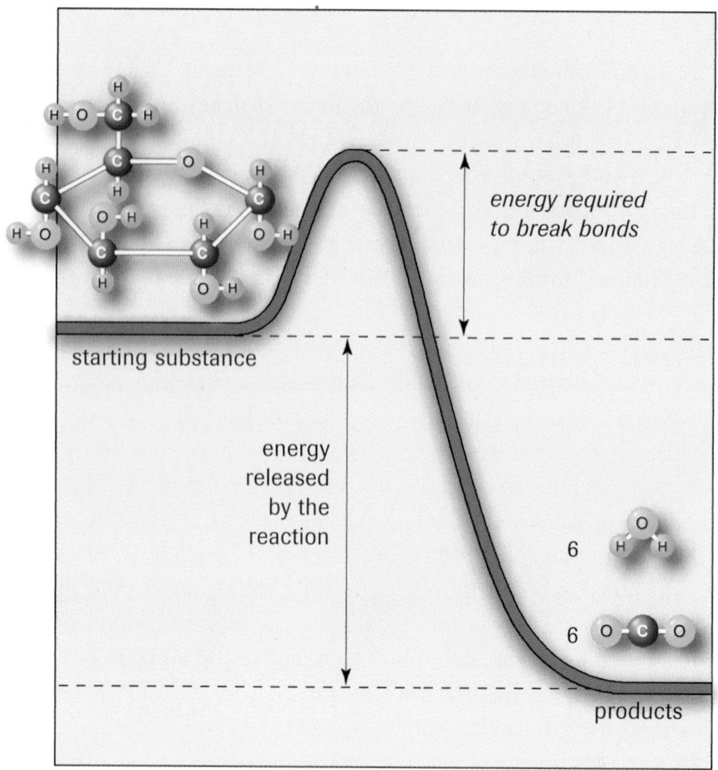

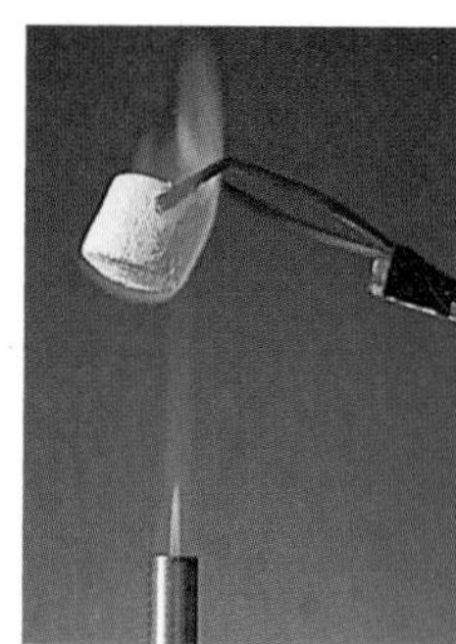

Figure 5
Energy is needed to break the bonds. The energy that is released is the energy from bond formation. The photo shows glucose burning. The high-energy compound, glucose, is converted to low-energy compounds, carbon dioxide, and water.

energy content of a single glucose molecule is converted into the energy of ATP; the remaining 64 % is released as heat. This is analogous to receiving $36 in one-dollar coins in exchange for a $100 bill.

An efficiency of 36 % may not seem very impressive, but keep in mind that cellular respiration involves many complex chemical pathways within cells. For comparison, high-performance racecar engines are slightly less efficient. In these engines only 30 % to 34 % of the energy from fuel combustion is converted to forward motion. The remaining 66 % to 70 % is lost as waste thermal energy. Typical automobiles driven by the public achieve efficiencies of only 25 % to 30 %.

The thermal energy is not waste for all organisms. While the vast majority of living species do not use this thermal energy, two small but significant groups of organisms use it to maintain a constant body temperature. These are warm-blooded organisms (birds and mammals) a group to which we belong. Your body's warmth is a direct product of the inefficient conversion of food energy to ATP energy.

Two Types of Cellular Respiration

While the goal of respiration is a simple one—the conversion of stored food energy into the usable energy of ATP—the process is not. Like photosynthesis, the chemical pathways of respiration are complex and involve many intermediate stages and molecules. A major variable that influences and limits the available chemical pathways of cellular respiration is the presence or absence of oxygen gas.

aerobic cellular respiration the set of reactions that takes place in the cell in the presence of oxygen and releases energy stored in glucose

Aerobic cellular respiration takes place in the presence of oxygen and involves the complete oxidation of glucose. The end products of aerobic cellular respiration are carbon dioxide gas, water, and 36 ATP molecules. Aerobic cellular respiration involves four stages.

Stage 1: glycolysis
Stage 2: pyruvate oxidation
Stage 3: the Krebs cycle
Stage 4: the electron transport chain and chemiosmosis

This equation summarizes aerobic respiration:

$$C_6H_{12}O_6 + 6\,O_2 + 36\,ADP + 36\,P_i \rightarrow 6\,CO_2 + 6\,H_2O + 36\,ATP$$

glucose + oxygen + ADP + inorganic phosphate → carbon dioxide + water + ATP

Anaerobic cellular respiration takes place in the absence of oxygen, and glucose is not completely oxidized. There are two main types of anaerobic cellular respiration, which have different end-products. Both types of cellular respiration occur in two stages that take place in the cytoplasm of the cell.

anaerobic cellular respiration the set of reactions that takes place in the cell in the absence of oxygen and releases energy stored in glucose

Stage 1: glycolysis
Stage 2: fermentation

The equations below summarize the two types of anaerobic cellular respiration that occur in eukaryotes:

$$C_6H_{12}O_6 + 2\,ADP + 2\,P_i \rightarrow 2\,C_2H_5OH + 2\,CO_2 + 2\,ATP$$

glucose + ADP + inorganic phosphate → ethanol + carbon dioxide + ATP

$$C_6H_{12}O_6 + 2\,ADP + 2\,P_i \rightarrow 2\,C_3H_6O_3 + 2\,ATP$$

glucose + ADP + inorganic phosphate → lactic acid + ATP

Notice that the first stage for both aerobic and anaerobic respiration is glycolysis! Also, from the three summary equations, you can see that aerobic respiration produces many more ATP molecules than do either type of anaerobic respiration. You will find out more about these processes in the rest of the chapter.

+ EXTENSION

Where Pathways Start and Finish
View this brief animation comparing anaerobic and aerobic respiration. Where does each process occur in the cell, and how much ATP does each process produce?

www.science.nelson.com 

SUMMARY The Importance of Cellular Respiration

- Cells cannot use high-energy molecules, such as glucose, directly. Cellular respiration converts glucose into energy-containing molecules the cells can use directly, such as ATP.
- Cells use ATP for their immediate energy needs.
- Aerobic cellular respiration takes place in the presence of oxygen and produces 36 ATP molecules per glucose molecule.
- Anaerobic respiration takes place in the absence of oxygen and produces 2 ATP molecules per glucose molecule.

Section 7.1 Questions

1. What are the characteristics of glucose that make it well suited as an energy supply molecule within our bodies?
2. The conversion of glucose energy to ATP energy is less than 50 % efficient. In what way do birds and mammals take advantage of this inefficiency?
3. Briefly describe one cellular process that involves the use of active transport. How is ATP involved in this process?
4. Why is cellular respiration necessary?
5. What are the four stages of aerobic respiration?

7.2 Glycolysis

In the previous section, you found out that cells may undergo two types of cellular respiration, depending on whether oxygen is available. Aerobic cellular respiration takes place in the presence of oxygen, and anaerobic cellular respiration takes place in the absence of oxygen. However, both types of cellular respiration begin with exactly the same process, called **glycolysis**.

glycolysis a process for harnessing energy in which a glucose molecule is broken into two pyruvate molecules in the cytoplasm of a cell

Recall that glucose is a high-energy molecule that cannot be used directly by the cell. Glycolysis is Greek for "sugar splitting," and this accurately describes what happens to glucose during this first stage of cellular respiration. The carbon backbone of glucose is essentially split in half. As you can see in **Figure 1**, glucose is a six-carbon sugar. At the end of glycolysis, glucose has been converted to a three-carbon sugar called pyruvate.

Although it occurs in both types of cellular respiration, glycolysis itself is an anaerobic process: it does not require oxygen. Glycolysis takes place in the cytoplasm of the cell. There are ten reactions in glycolysis, each of which is catalyzed by a specific enzyme in the cytoplasm. During these reactions, two ATP molecules are used and four ATP molecules are produced. Glycolysis therefore produces a net total of two ATP molecules. Glycolysis also produces two $NADH^+$ ions.

Glycolysis

In this animation, you can see all the intermediate molecules that form as glycolysis converts one glucose molecule to two pyruvate molecules, and how ATP and $NADH^+$ are formed.

www.science.nelson.com

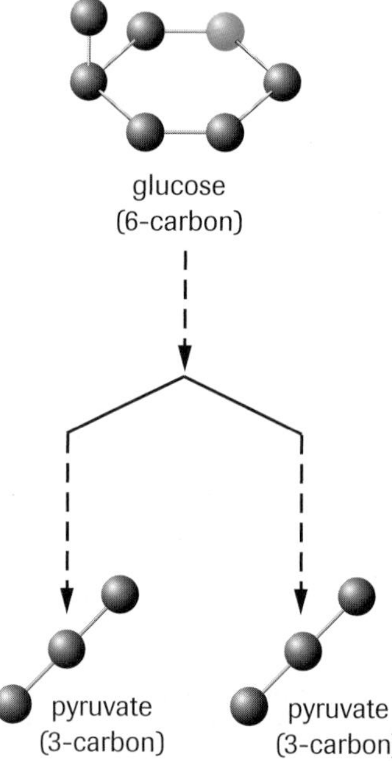

Figure 1
In a series of reactions called glycolysis, a 6-carbon glucose molecule is split into two 3-carbon pyruvate molecules. (For simplicity, the side-group oxygen and hydrogen atoms are not illustrated here.)

Figure 2 on the next page summarizes the reactions of the glycolytic pathway. The long arrow represents the entire pathway of chemical steps that occur during glycolysis. The emphasis is on the key features of this process; the numerous intermediate chemical compounds and reactions are not shown in detail.

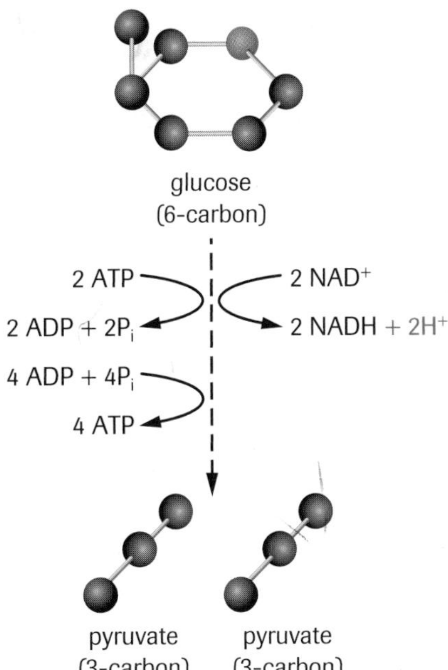

Figure 2
Summary of the glycolytic pathway. Glycolysis is a series of ten chemical reactions, the details of which are not shown.

As you study **Figure 2**, note the following key events:

- Two ATP molecules are used in the first stages of glycolysis. This represents an "investment of energy."
- During glycolysis, oxidation–reduction reactions occur in which two positively charged NAD^+ ions remove hydrogen atoms from the pathway to form two NADH molecules and release two H^+ ions into the cytoplasm.
- In the later stages of glycolysis, enough energy is released to join four ADP molecules with four P_i molecules to form four ATP molecules.
- When glycolysis is complete, the cell has consumed a single glucose molecule and produced two ATP molecules, two NADH molecules, and two pyruvate molecules.
- These ATP molecules are available to supply energy for cellular functions.

Note that the original glucose molecule contained 24 atoms (six C, twelve H, and six O). Of these, six carbon, eight hydrogen, and six oxygen atoms are now held in the two pyruvate molecules ($C_3H_4O_3$). The remaining four high-energy hydrogen atoms are in the form of two NADH molecules and two H^+ ions. **Table 1** lists the reactants and products of glycolysis.

Table 1 The Reactants and Products of Glycolysis

Reactants	Products
glucose	2 pyruvate
2 NAD^+	2 NADH
2 ATP	2 ADP
4 ADP	4 ATP

The net equation for glycolysis is

$$1 \text{ glucose} + 2 \text{ ADP} + 2 \text{ P}_i + 2 \text{ NAD}^+ \rightarrow 2 \text{ pyruvate} + 2 \text{ ATP} + 2 \text{ NADH} + 2\text{H}^+$$

EXTENSION 

ATP and Glycolysis

Listen to this audio clip to find out why ATP must be a reactant in glycolysis, even though the role of this process is to produce energy for a cell.

By itself, glycolysis is not a highly efficient energy-harnessing mechanism. One glucose molecule contains over 90 times as much available energy as a cell obtains when it uses a single ATP. This means that the process of glycolysis transfers only about 2.2 % of the free energy available in glucose to ATP. Some of the energy is released as thermal energy during the process, but the vast majority is still trapped in the two pyruvate and two NADH molecules. The 2.2 % conversion efficiency value applies to glycolysis only; it does not take into consideration the possibility of obtaining additional ATP by further processing pyruvate and NADH in the remaining stages of aerobic respiration.

Some simple single-celled microorganisms can use glycolysis for all their energy needs. However, glycolysis yields only two ATP molecules from each glucose molecule processed. This is not enough to satisfy the energy needs of most multicellular organisms. Nevertheless, all organisms, large and small, multicellular or not, carry out glycolysis either as their only source of ATP or as the first part of a more productive energy-yielding process, such as aerobic respiration.

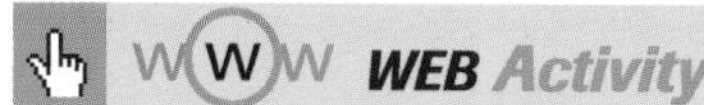

Simulation—Respiration in Motion

Respiration involves many reactions and processes that can be difficult to visualize. In this activity, you will explore some animations and act out a specific step for the rest of the class. In groups, follow the Nelson Web links and view various animations of respiration pathways. Your group will then be assigned a specific step or process and will create a short skit. As each group acts out a skit for the class, students will guess which step of respiration is being modelled. Your teacher will provide you with suggestions and rules.

www.science.nelson.com 

SUMMARY Glycolysis

- Glycolysis occurs in the cytoplasm. It produces two 3-carbon pyruvate molecules from a 6-carbon glucose molecule. Glycolysis produces two ATP (net) and two NADH.
- The efficiency of glycolysis is only 2.2 % with most of the original energy of the glucose remaining in the pyruvate and NADH molecules.
- The net equation for glycolysis is

  $1 \text{ glucose} + 2\text{ ADP} + 2\text{ P}_i + 2\text{ NAD}^+ \rightarrow 2\text{ pyruvate} + 2\text{ ATP} + 2\text{ NADH} + 2\text{H}^+$

Section 7.2 Questions

1. Write an overall chemical equation for glycolysis.
2. (a) What does *glycolysis* mean?
   (b) List the final products of glycolysis.
3. As a result of glycolysis, only a small portion of the energy of glucose has been converted to ATP. In what form is the rest of the usable energy found at this stage of the process?

Aerobic Cellular Respiration 7.3

Under aerobic conditions (oxygen gas is available), cells will undergo aerobic cellular respiration. The end products of aerobic cellular respiration are carbon dioxide gas, water, and relatively large numbers of ATP molecules. Recall that aerobic cellular respiration has four stages. These are:

Stage 1: glycolysis—a ten-step process occurring in the cytoplasm

Stage 2: pyruvate oxidation—a one-step process occurring in mitochondria

Stage 3: the Krebs cycle—an eight-step cyclical process occurring in mitochondria

Stage 4: the electron transport chain and chemiosmosis (oxidative phosphorylation)—a multi-step process occurring in the inner mitochondrial membrane

In the previous section, you looked at Stage 1, glycolysis, which takes place in the cytoplasm. In this section, you will learn about the last three stages, which all take place within mitochondria.

CHEMISTRY CONNECTION

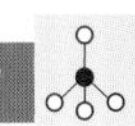

Combustion of Glucose

Aerobic respiration can be thought of as complete combustion, since the products are carbon dioxide, water, and energy. Your chemistry textbook has more information on combustion reactions.

www.science.nelson.com

INVESTIGATION 7.1 *Introduction*

Measuring Oxygen Consumption in Germinating Seeds

Plant seeds contain living embryos that require energy to carry out the functions of life. When they germinate, they experience high rates of growth and cell division. What happens to a plant seed's rate of energy metabolism when it germinates and starts to grow? Do germinating seeds absorb or release thermal energy?

Report Checklist

- ○ Purpose
- ○ Problem
- ○ Hypothesis
- ● Prediction
- ○ Design
- ○ Materials
- ○ Procedure
- ● Evidence
- ● Analysis
- ● Evaluation
- ● Synthesis

Investigation 7.1 provides you with an opportunity to conduct controlled experiments on the relationship between growth and the rate of metabolic activity.

To perform this investigation, turn to page 229.

Mitochondria

Mitochondria (singular: mitochondrion) are round or sausage-shaped organelles that are usually scattered throughout a cell's cytoplasm. These vital organelles specialize in the production of large quantities of ATP, the main energy-carrying molecule in living cells. The processes that produce ATP in mitochondria cannot proceed without free oxygen.

mitochondrion a eukaryotic cell organelle in which aerobic cellular respiration occurs

Mitochondria possess a double membrane composed of a smooth outer membrane and a highly folded inner membrane (**Figure 1**, next page). The outer membrane plays a role similar to that of the cell membrane, but the inner membrane performs many functions associated with cellular respiration. The inner membrane also creates two compartments within the mitochondrion. The **mitochondrial matrix** is a protein-rich liquid that fills the innermost space of a mitochondrion, and a fluid-filled **intermembrane space** lies between the inner and outer membrane. Each of these compartments play a critical role in aerobic respiration.

mitochondrial matrix the fluid that fills the interior space of the mitochondrion

intermembrane space the fluid-filled space between the inner and outer mitochondrial membranes

Figure 2 on the next page illustrates the four stages of respiration and indicates their locations within the cell.

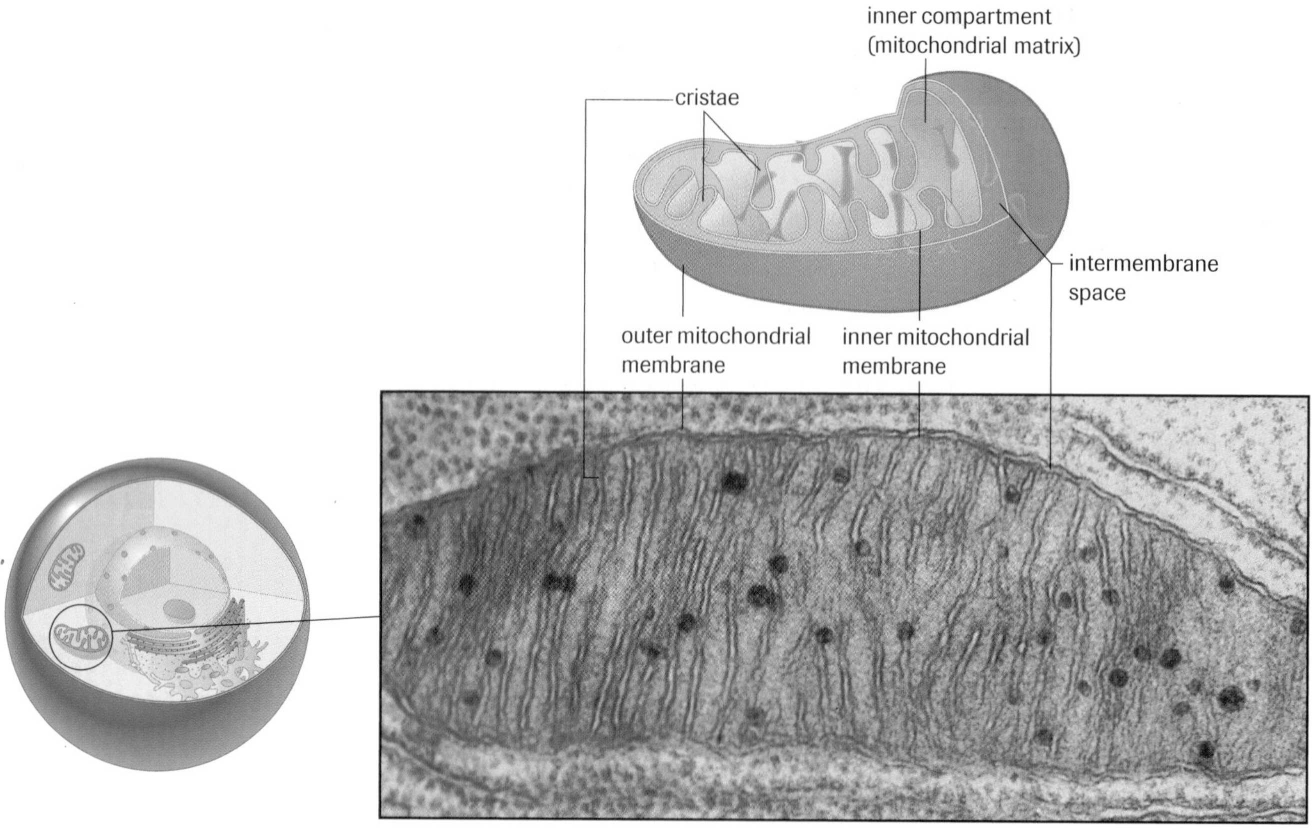

Figure 1
Diagram and transmission electron micrograph of a typical mitochondrion

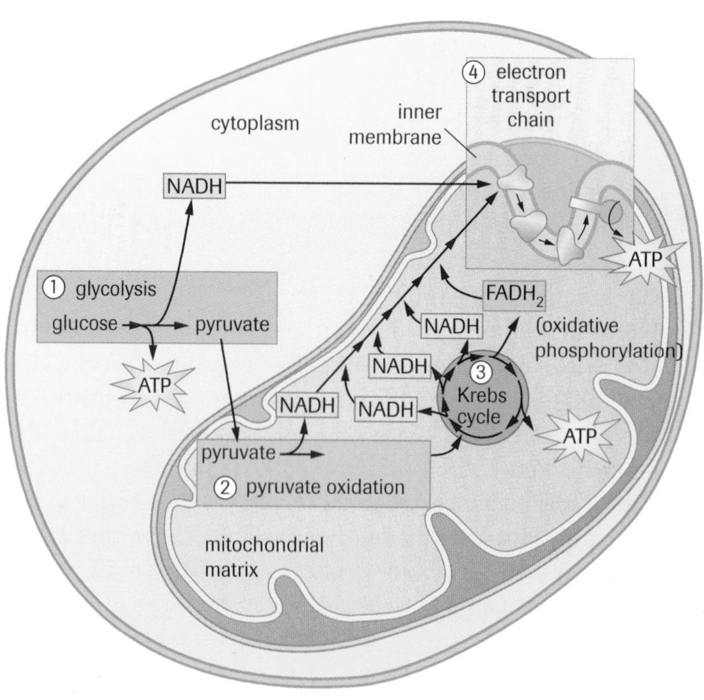

Figure 2
In eukaryotic cells, glycolysis (1) occurs in the cytoplasm (pink). Pyruvate oxidation (2) and the Krebs cycle (3) occur in the mitochondrial matrix (blue and purple respectively). The electron transport chain (4) is embedded in the inner mitochondrial membrane (green).

Stage 2: Pyruvate Oxidation

Recall that by the end of Stage 1, glycolysis, the cell had formed two ATPs, two NADHs and two pyruvate molecules—all in the cytoplasm. Pyruvate oxidation is a chemical pathway that connects glycolysis in the cytoplasm with the Krebs cycle in the mitochondrial matrix (**Figure 2**, previous page). Stage 2 begins when the two pyruvate molecules formed in glycolysis are transported through the two mitochondrial membranes into the matrix. There, the following three changes occur (**Figure 3**):

1. A CO_2 is removed from each pyruvate and released as a waste product. This step is the source of one-third of the carbon dioxide that you breathe out.
2. The remaining 2-carbon portions are oxidized by NAD^+. Each NAD^+ molecule gains two hydrogen ions (two protons and two electrons) from pyruvate, and the remaining 2-carbon compound becomes an acetic acid (acetyl) group. This converts pyruvate to an acetic acid group and transfers high-energy hydrogens to NAD^+.
3. A compound called coenzyme A (CoA) becomes attached to the acetic acid group, forming acetyl-CoA. The acetyl-CoA then enters the next stage of aerobic cellular respiration, the Krebs cycle.

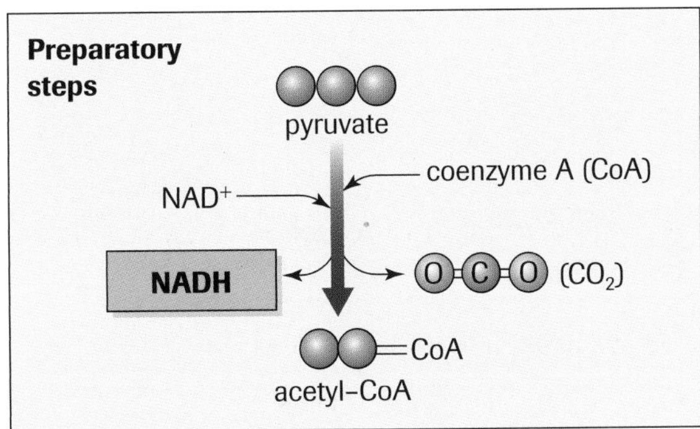

Figure 3
Pyruvate oxidation results in three changes to pyruvate:
1. A CO_2 portion is removed.
2. NAD^+ is reduced by two H atoms.
3. Coenzyme A is attached to the remaining 2-carbon portion (acetyl group).

The two molecules of acetyl-CoA enter the Krebs cycle, while the two molecules of NADH proceed to Stage 4 (electron transport and chemiosmosis). The two CO_2 molecules produced during pyruvate oxidation diffuse out of the mitochondrion and then out of the cell as a low-energy waste product.

Practice

1. What stages of aerobic cellular respiration take place in the mitochondria?
2. What happens to NAD^+ in Stage 2 of aerobic cellular respiration?
3. What is the role of coenzyme A?

Stage 3: The Krebs Cycle

In 1937, Sir Hans Krebs (1900–81), a biochemist working at the University of Sheffield in England, discovered the series of metabolic reactions that became known as the Krebs cycle. He received the 1953 Nobel Prize in Physiology or Medicine for this important discovery. Fritz Albert Lipmann (1899–1986) shared the Nobel Prize with Krebs for his discovery of coenzyme A and the key role it plays in metabolism.

The **Krebs cycle** is an eight-step process, each step catalyzed by a specific enzyme. It is a cyclic process because one of the products of Step 8, is a reactant in Step 1 (**Figure 4**, next page). Key features of the Krebs cycle are outlined in **Table 1**, on the next page.

Krebs cycle a cyclic series of reactions that transfers energy from organic molecules to ATP, NADH, and $FADH_2$, and removes carbon atoms as CO_2

The Krebs Cycle—Details

In this animation, view the details of the intermediate stages of pyruvate oxidation and the Krebs Cycle. These reactions all take place in the inner compartment of mitochondria.

www.science.nelson.com 

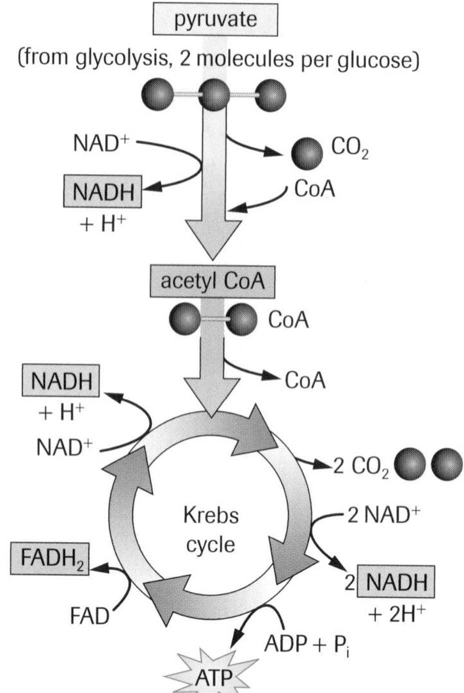

Figure 4

The Krebs cycle begins when acetyl-CoA condenses with oxaloacetate to form citrate. In one turn of the cycle, the two carbon atoms that were originally in a glucose molecule are removed as CO_2, and free energy is transferred to ATP, NADH, and $FADH_2$.

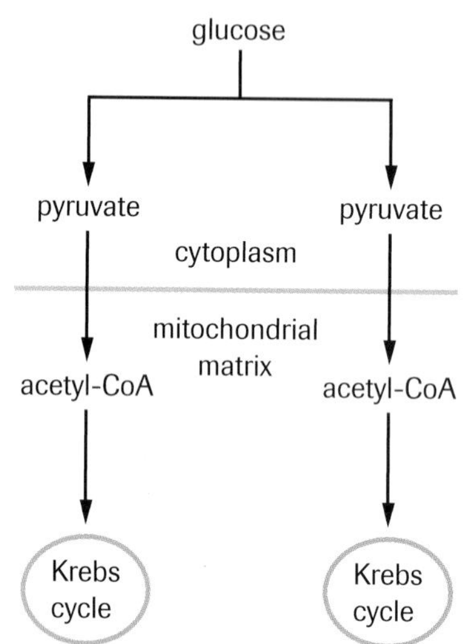

Figure 5

Table 1 Key Features of the Krebs Cycle

• Since two molecules of acetyl-CoA are formed from one molecule of glucose, the Krebs cycle occurs twice for each molecule of glucose processed (**Figure 5**).
• As acetyl-CoA enters the cycle the CoA is released and can be used for the next pyruvate.
• During one complete cycle a total of three NAD^+s and one FAD are reduced to form three NADHs and one $FADH_2$.
• During one complete cycle an ADP and a P_i are combined to form one ATP.
• During one complete cycle two CO_2 molecules are produced. These are released as waste.

Notice that by the end of the Krebs cycle, all six carbon atoms of glucose have been oxidized to CO_2 and released from the cell as metabolic waste. All that is left of the original glucose molecule is some of its free energy in the form of ATP and high-energy NADH and $FADH_2$. NADH and $FADH_2$ now go on to Stage 4 of the process, electron transport and chemiosmosis, where much of their energy will be transferred to ATP.

Stage 4: Electron Transport and Chemiosmosis

NADH and $FADH_2$ eventually transfer the hydrogen atom electrons they carry to a series of compounds, mainly proteins, which are associated with the inner mitochondrial membrane called the electron transport chain (ETC). **Figure 6** on the next page illustrates this process beginning with a single NADH molecule. The NADH gives up two high-energy electrons at the beginning of the ETC. At the same time, it releases an additional

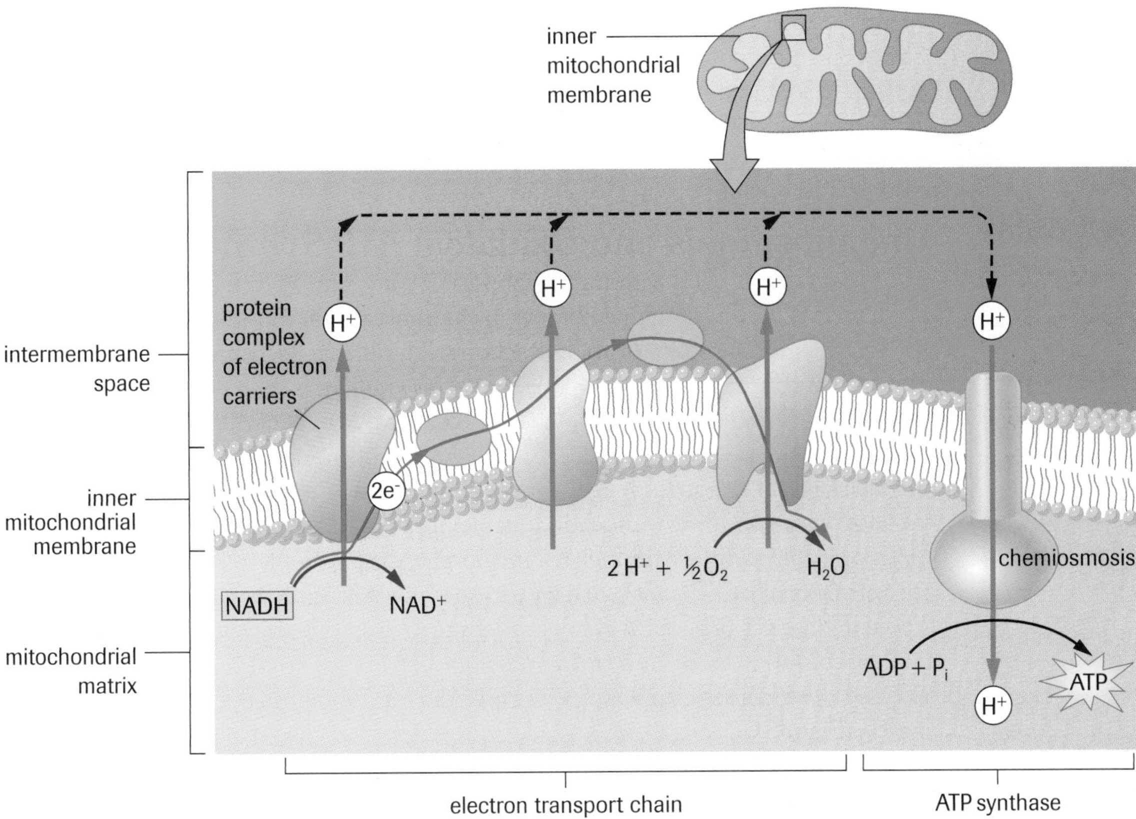

Figure 6
The NADH carries the electrons gained from food to the electron transport chain. As these electrons are passed along carrier molecules, the energy released is used to pump hydrogen ions across the membrane. The electrons are finally accepted by oxygen molecules. Water is the byproduct of the electron transport chain.

H^+ ion into the matrix. The electrons shuttle through the ETC like a baton handed from runner to runner in a relay race. As the electrons move from carrier molecule to carrier molecule in the ETC, they release energy. This energy is used to force a number of H^+ ions from within the mitochondrial matrix across the inner membrane. Each of these ions gains potential energy as they move through proton pumps into the intermembrane space. By the time the two electrons reach the last component of the ETC, they are in a low energy state, having transferred much of their initial energy to the H^+ ions that have been pumped across the inner mitochondrial membrane at three different locations. Oxygen strips the two electrons from the final carrier in the chain and, together with two H^+ ions from the matrix, forms water. As such, oxygen acts as the final electron acceptor in the electron transport process. This final step in the ETC is the reason all aerobic organisms, like humans, must obtain oxygen gas from their environment on a continuous basis.

Note that the ETC is an ongoing process with countless NADHs delivering their electrons to the chain in a continuous flow. $FADH_2$ behaves in a very similar fashion to NADH, delivering its electrons to the ETC. A significant difference however, is that the electrons removed from the $FADH_2$ have a lower energy content and enter the ETC at a different location. The result is that the energy they release is not able to pump as many H^+ ions across the inner mitochondrial membrane.

The electron transport process releases a relatively large quantity of energy. As mentioned earlier, the energy lost by the electron pair during electron transport is used to pump H^+ ions into the intermembrane space. This mechanism converts one form of energy into another—the chemical energy of the electrons is converted to electrochemical potential

DID YOU KNOW ?

Cyanide Blocks the Electron Transport Chain

Cyanide prevents oxygen from acting as the final electron acceptor in the electron transport chain. This disruption virtually shuts down ATP production, resulting in coma and death. That is why cyanide is a poison. However, it is not poisonous to all organisms. Some anaerobic bacteria actually live on cyanide—they use it in the same way aerobes use oxygen!

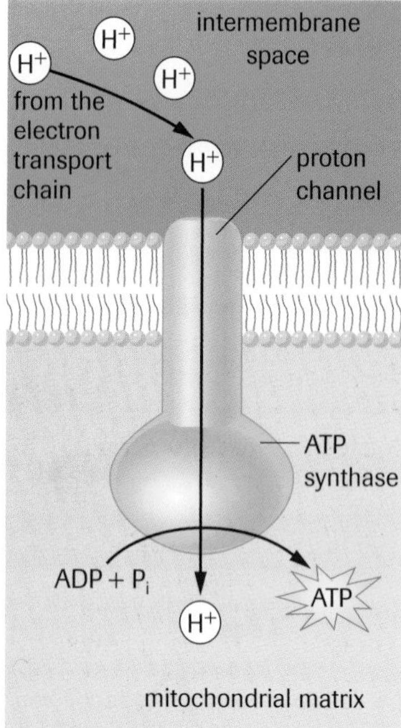

Figure 7
One molecule of ATP is synthesized from ADP and P_i as an H^+ ion passes through the ATPase complex into the mitochondrial matrix from the H^+ reservoir in the intermembrane space.

energy of an H^+ ion gradient that forms across the inner mitochondrial membrane. Electrochemical potential energy is the type of stored energy possessed by a charged battery. It is caused by an accumulation of charged objects (ions, protons, electrons, etc.) on one side of an insulator. As you are about to learn, this energy is used by cells in a process called chemiosmosis to generate large numbers of ATP!

Chemiosmosis and Oxidative ATP Synthesis

The production of ATP within mitochondria is very similar to the ATP synthesis that occurs across the thylakoid membranes in chloroplasts. The H^+ ions that accumulate in the intermembrane space of the mitochondrion during electron transport create an electrochemical gradient that stores energy. This gradient is caused by a higher positive charge in the intermembrane space than in the matrix. The intermembrane space essentially becomes an H^+ reservoir because the inner mitochondrial membrane is virtually impermeable to H^+ ions. The electrochemical gradient creates a potential difference (voltage) across the inner mitochondrial membrane similar to that in a chemical cell or battery. Unable to diffuse through the membrane, the protons are forced to pass through special proton channels associated with the enzyme ATP synthase (ATPase). The energy stored in the electrochemical gradient produces a force that moves H^+ ions through an ATPase complex. As H^+ ions move through the ATPase complex, the energy that is released drives the synthesis of ATP from ADP and inorganic phosphate (P_i) in the matrix (**Figure 7**).

Thus, some of the energy in the pumping of H^+ ions across the membrane is harvested as chemical potential energy in ATP. The electrons removed from a single NADH pump enough H^+ ions across the inner membrane to generate three ATPs, while the electrons from a single $FADH_2$ pump enough H^+ ions across the membrane to yield two ATPs.

Electron transport followed by chemiosmosis is the last stage of the oxidative phosphorylation process that began with the reduction of NAD^+ and FAD with hydrogen atoms from the original glucose molecule. The continual production of ATP by this method is dependent on the establishment and maintenance of an H^+ reservoir. This condition requires the continual movement of electrons through the ETC, which, in turn, is dependent on the availability of oxygen to act as the final electron acceptor. Oxygen is needed to keep the electrons flowing through the ETC. Electrons are "pulled down" the chain in an energy-yielding "fall," similar to gravity pulling a skydiver down toward Earth's surface. The energy released in the fall keeps H^+ ions moving into the H^+ reservoir so that they can "fall back" into the matrix and drive the synthesis of ATP. Since the energy released in the ETC results from a series of oxidation reactions, the end result—the production of ATP—is often referred to as **oxidative ATP synthesis**.

After ATP molecules are formed by chemiosmosis, they are transported through both mitochondrial membranes into the cytoplasm, where they are used to drive processes requiring energy such as movement, active transport, and synthesis reactions throughout the cell.

As you can see, the three stages of aerobic respiration (pyruvate oxidation, the Krebs cycle, and electron transport and chemiosmosis) are all linked to one another and are all dependent on glycolysis for the production of pyruvate. Note that the last stage of the energy transferring processes—chemiosmosis and electron transport—are dependent on the availability of electrons (from food such as glucose) and oxygen (for its ability to act as a final electron acceptor).

DID YOU KNOW ?

Chemiosmosis

Chemiosmosis was first worked out by Peter Mitchell in 1961. He received the 1978 Nobel Prize in Chemistry for "his contribution to the understanding of biological energy transfer through the formulation of the chemiosmotic theory." Mitchell called the process chemiosmosis because the energy that drives the synthesis of ATP comes from the "osmosis" of protons through a membrane from one compartment into another.

oxidative ATP synthesis the production of ATP from a series of oxidation reactions

Practice

4. Describe the function of NAD^+ and FAD in aerobic cellular respiration.
5. What are the final products of aerobic cellular respiration?
6. As a result of glycolysis, pyruvate oxidation, and the Krebs cycle, only a small portion of the energy of glucose has been converted to ATP. In what form is the rest of the usable energy found at this stage of the process?

The Aerobic Respiration Energy Balance Sheet

How much energy was transferred from glucose to ATP in the entire aerobic respiration process? We may calculate two values in answer to this question: a theoretical value and an actual value. Although the actual value gives a more realistic total, it too varies according to the type of cell and various environmental conditions. **Figure 8** summarizes the theoretical yield of 36 ATP and its sources. Note that the NADHs produced during glycolysis are not able to generate three ATP each. Instead they transfer their electrons to FADs which are then used in the ETC to produce two ATPs each.

Numerous experiments have demonstrated that under normal conditions cells are not able to achieve this theoretical maximum yield of 36 ATP per glucose. Instead, cells have an actual yield of approximately 30 ATP per glucose molecule. Recall that glycolysis was only 2.2 % efficient. By comparison, even at this reduced level, aerobic respiration is over 32 % efficient! A dramatic improvement and a compelling reason that so many organisms utilize oxygen gas to release energy from their food.

+ EXTENSION 

Effect of Hypothermia (Reduced Body Temperature) on the Respiration Rate of a Ground Squirrel

Many animals have very low metabolic rates during winter months. In this Virtual Biology Lab, you will manipulate the body temperature of a ground squirrel to test how this affects its rate of aerobic cellular respiration.

www.science.nelson.com GO

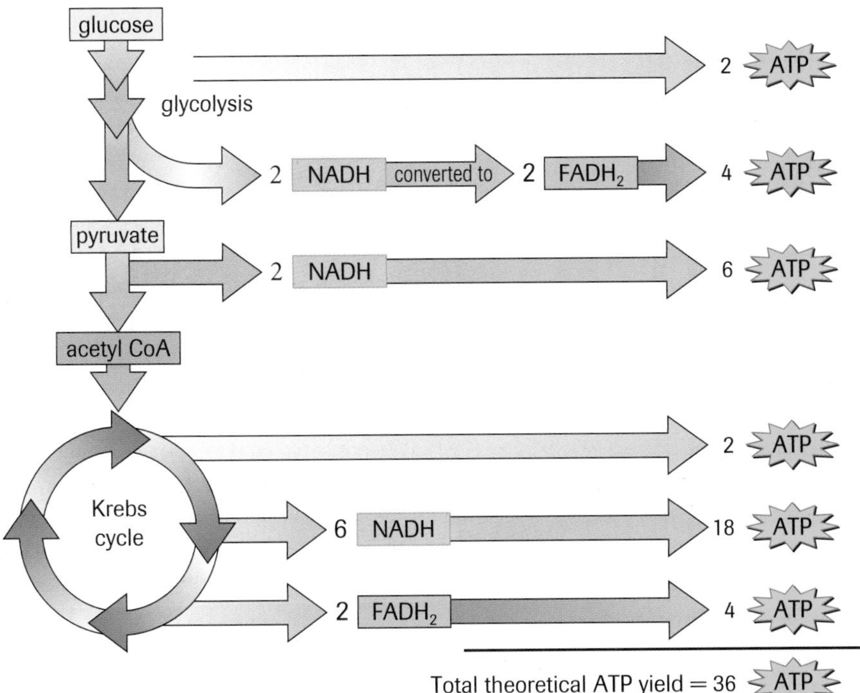

Figure 8 
Theoretical ATP yield from the aerobic respiration of one glucose molecule

SUMMARY Aerobic Cellular Respiration

- Aerobic cellular respiration involves four stages: glycolysis, pyruvate oxidation, the Krebs cycle, and electron transport and chemiosmosis.
- Pyruvate oxidation occurs in the mitochondria. In the process, a CO_2 portion is cleaved from pyruvate and removed from the cell as waste. The remaining 2-carbon acetyl group attaches to coenzyme A to produce acetyl-CoA. In this reaction, two NADH and two CO_2 are formed (one for each of the two pyruvate molecules).
- The Krebs cycle occurs in the mitochondrial matrix. The two carbon atoms introduced by acetyl-CoA are removed as two CO_2. One ATP, one $FADH_2$ and three NADH are produced.
- The electron transport chain, associated with the inner mitochondrial membrane, transports electrons through a series of reactions that transfers energy to H^+ ions as they are pumped into the mitochondrial intermembrane space. This creates an electrochemical gradient.
- In chemiosmosis, protons move through ATPase complexes embedded in the inner mitochondrial membrane, releasing free energy that drives the synthesis of ATP.
- Oxygen is the final acceptor of electrons that pass through the electron transport chain. If oxygen is not available, the Krebs cycle, electron transport, and chemiosmosis come to a halt.
- The overall equation for aerobic respiration is:

$$\text{glucose } (C_6H_{12}O_6) + 6\ O_2 + 36\ \text{ADP} + 36\ P_i \rightarrow 6\ CO_2 + 6\ H_2O + 36\ \text{ATP}$$

Section 7.3 Questions

1. Arrange the following types of cells in order of increasing number of mitochondria in the cytoplasm: nerve cell, skin cell, fat cell, heart muscle cell. Provide a rationale for your sequence.
2. (a) In eukaryotic cells, where does glycolysis occur?
   (b) What two products of glycolysis may be transported into mitochondria for further processing?
3. Describe two functions that mitochondrial membranes serve in energy metabolism.
4. Why is aerobic cellular respiration a more efficient energy-extracting process than glycolysis alone?
5. (a) What part of a glucose molecule provides electrons in cellular respiration?
   (b) Describe how electron transport complexes set up a proton gradient in response to electron flow.
   (c) How is the energy used to drive the synthesis of ATP?
   (d) What is the name of this process?
   (e) Who discovered this mechanism?
6. (a) Distinguish between an electron carrier and a terminal electron acceptor.
   (b) What is the final electron acceptor in aerobic respiration?
7. Explain how the following overall equation for cellular respiration is misleading:

   $$C_6H_{12}O_6 + 6\ O_2 \longrightarrow 6\ CO_2 + 6\ H_2O$$

8. Explain why CO_2 does not serve as a source of free energy in living systems.
9. (a) Explain the role of $FADH_2$ in the electron transport chain.
   (b) Explain why $FADH_2$ does not generate as many ATP molecules as NADH does.
10. Aerobic cellular respiration stops if no oxygen is present. Explain why.

Anaerobic Cellular Respiration 7.4

Glycolysis allows organisms to obtain energy from nutrients in the absence of oxygen. As you will recall, during glycolysis NAD^+ is converted to NADH. Glycolysis cannot occur without this reaction. Cells possess a limited supply of NAD^+ and, without a mechanism to convert NADH into NAD^+, glycolysis will come to a halt. If glycolysis stops, ATP can no longer be formed and cell death soon follows.

In aerobic organisms, all NADH is converted into NAD^+ in the ETC—a process that requires oxygen. Without oxygen, the ETC cannot operate and, as a result, anaerobic organisms have evolved several ways of recycling NAD^+ and allowing glycolysis to continue. One method involves transferring the hydrogen atoms of NADH to certain organic molecules instead of to the electron transport chain. This process is called fermentation. Bacteria have evolved dozens of different forms of fermentation, but eukaryotes (organisms whose cells contain nuclei, such as humans) primarily use two methods: **alcohol fermentation** and **lactic acid fermentation.**

Both types of fermentation processes occur in only two stages, all within the cytoplasm of the cell. All fermenting organisms perform the same first stage—glycolysis. It is the second stage that is variable, with different organisms using different pathways.

Stage 1: glycolysis—the identical 10-step process used in aerobic respiration

Stage 2: fermentation—recycles some of the products of glycolysis in two different pathways where either carbon dioxide and ethanol (alcohol fermentation) or lactic acid (lactic acid fermentation) are the final waste products

+ EXTENSION 

Effect of Physical Activity on Scorpion Respiration Rate

In this Virtual Biology Lab, you will modify the amount of muscle activity in a scorpion and observe the effect on respiration rate. Will the animal move from aerobic respiration to anaerobic respiration? How would you be able to tell?

www.science.nelson.com 

alcohol fermentation a form of fermentation occurring in yeast in which NADH passes its hydrogen atoms to acetaldehyde, generating carbon dioxide, ethanol, and NAD^+

lactic acid fermentation a form of fermentation occurring in animal cells in which NADH transfers its hydrogen atoms to pyruvate, regenerating NAD^+ and lactic acid

Alcohol Fermentation

In alcohol fermentation, NADHs molecules produced during glycolysis pass their hydrogen atoms to acetaldehyde, a compound formed when a carbon dioxide molecule is removed from pyruvate by the enzyme pyruvate decarboxylase, as shown in **Figure 1**.

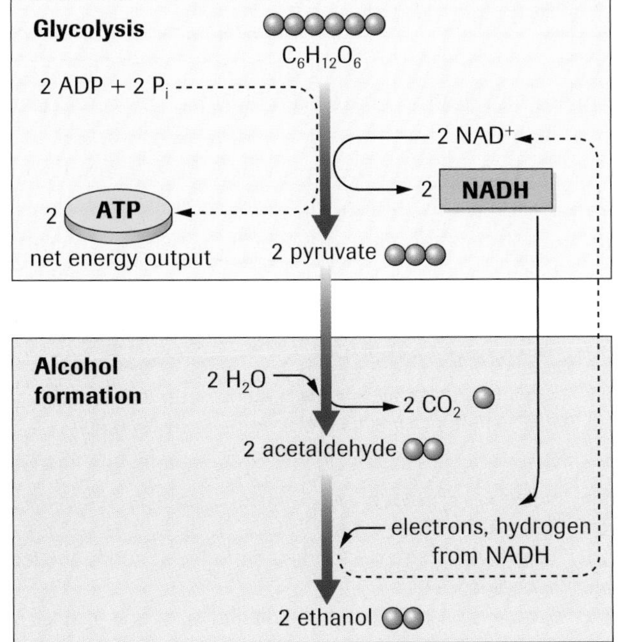

Figure 1
Alcohol fermentation creates ethanol and carbon dioxide from glucose. In the process, NADH is oxidized to NAD^+, allowing glycolysis to continue.

Figure 2
Alcohol fermentation is used in the production of baked goods and products such as wine, beer, and soy sauce.

This forms ethanol, the type of alcohol used in alcoholic beverages. This process recycles NAD^+ and so allows glycolysis to continue. The two ATP molecules produced during glycolysis satisfy the organism's energy needs, and the ethanol and carbon dioxide are released as waste products. The overall equation for alcohol fermentation is

$$\text{glucose } (C_6H_{12}O_6) + 2 \text{ ADP} + 2 \text{ P}_i \rightarrow 2 \text{ ethanol } (C_2H_5OH) + 2 \text{ CO}_2 + 2 \text{ ATP}$$

Applications of Alcohol Fermentation

Humans have learned ways of making use of these products of fermentation. Alcohol fermentation carried out by yeast (a variety of single-celled fungi) is of great historical, economic, and cultural importance. Breads and pastries, wine, beer, liquor, and soy sauce are all produced using fermentation (**Figure 2**).

Bread is leavened by mixing live yeast cells with starches (in flour) and water. The yeast cells ferment the glucose from the starch and release carbon dioxide and ethanol. Small bubbles of carbon dioxide gas cause the bread to rise (or leaven), and the ethanol evaporates away when the bread is baked. In beer making and winemaking, yeast cells ferment the sugars found in carbohydrate-rich fruit juices, such as grape juice. The mixture bubbles as the yeast cells release carbon dioxide gas and ethanol during fermentation. In winemaking, fermentation ends when the concentration of ethanol reaches approximately 12 %. At this point, the yeast cells die as a result of alcohol accumulation and the product is ready to be consumed as a beverage.

Microbial fermentation is used to make many different food products. **Table 1** lists a few of these foods and the raw materials from which they are made.

Table 1 Sample Food Products Dependent on Microbial Fermentation

Food	Raw material
bread	flour
soy sauce	soya bean
vinegar	alcohol (from fruit or grain fermentation)
chocolate	cacao bean
sauerkraut	cabbage
wine and beer	grapes and barley

Figure 3
Although Louis Pasteur (1822–95) is best known for introducing the process of pasteurization, he also pioneered the vaccines against rabies and anthrax.

While such fermentation products have been produced for centuries, it was not until 1803 that scientists discovered that the yeasts being used in many of these processes were alive. Later, Louis Pasteur (**Figure 3**) provided experimental evidence that yeast was responsible for alcohol fermentation. His work on these processes helped lead him to the monumental discovery that many diseases are caused by microbes.

Practice

1. What is the key advantage of anaerobic respiration? Suggest some specific situations in which this would benefit organisms in the natural environment.
2. Name a nonalcoholic final product of alcohol fermentation, other than ATP.
3. (a) How many molecules of ethanol are produced by the fermentation of one molecule of glucose?
   (b) How many molecules of carbon dioxide are produced during the fermentation of one molecule of glucose?
   (c) How much oxygen is used during the fermentation of one glucose molecule?

mini *Investigation* — *Facultative Microbes*

Facultative organisms are those organisms that are able to use either aerobic or anaerobic respiration depending on the environmental conditions in which they are living. Yeast is a good example of this type of organism. In the presence of oxygen, they use aerobic respiration to generate their ATP supplies, in the absence of oxygen they use glycolysis and alcohol fermentation. In this mini investigation you will examine the changes in net gas production associated with a switch from aerobic to anaerobic respiration.

Materials: 3 g Brewers yeast, 50 mL grape juice or apple cider (with no preservatives), 125 mL Erlenmeyer flask, large balloon

- Place 3 g of yeast in the Erlenmeyer flask.
- Add 50 mL of grape juice or apple cider to the flask.
- Allow the yeast to sit for several minutes and then gently stir the mixture to disperse the yeast.
- Cover the flask tightly with the balloon
- Make regular observations over a period of several days documenting changes in the apparent gas volume in the balloon.
- At the end of your experiment, remove the balloon and smell the contents of the flask. Record your observations.
- Display your results using a graphical format.

(a) Were the initial conditions aerobic or anaerobic?

(b) The presence of oxygen gas does not prevent or interfere with the chemical reactions in anaerobic respiration and fermentation pathways. Why then does yeast not continue to follow these pathways when oxygen is present?

(c) During aerobic respiration what gas(es) is produced and consumed? How might this influence the volume of gas in the balloon?

(d) During anaerobic respiration what gas(es) is produced and consumed? How might this influence the volume of gas in the balloon?

(e) Was there evidence of a switch from anaerobic to aerobic or aerobic to anaerobic respiration? Account for these results.

(f) What distinctive odour provided evidence of anaerobic respiration or fermentation?

(g) Suggest modifications to the experimental design that could be used to maintain aerobic conditions over an extended period of time.

EXPLORE an issue

Issue Checklist

- ● Issue
- ● Resolution
- ○ Design
- ● Evidence
- ● Analysis
- ● Evaluation

Aerobic versus Anaerobic Waste Treatment

Human activities produce large amounts of organic wastes. Solid, liquid, and gaseous wastes must be treated to prevent contamination of soil, water, and air. Cities generate enormous volumes of human sewage and household waste (**Figure 4**). Industry and agriculture also produce large volumes of organic waste. Many microbes can use a wide range of organic material as food so they are often used to process waste into less harmful or even valuable compounds. Choosing whether to use an anaerobic or an aerobic microbe to process waste is influenced by many factors.

Understanding the Issue

In a group, use print and Internet resources to research the factors influencing the choice of aerobic and anaerobic systems for a number of the following waste/biomass processing systems:

www.science.nelson.com 

- biogas generation
- municipal sewage treatment plant
- household/cottage septic systems
- landfill gas production
- biomass ethanol production

For each system investigate and report on the following:

Raw material(s) – Give a general description of their chemical and physical makeup.

Figure 4
Garbage collection is a familiar activity in most municipalities.

Source of raw materials – Where and why is this material produced in large quantities?

Microbial respiration system(s) – Does the processing of this material involve anaerobic, aerobic, or both forms of respiration/fermentation?

Products – What respiration/fermentation products are produced in this process? Of what value are these products?

Evaluation – Based on your research, is the system an effective way to process waste/biomass? What recommendations would you make to improve or enhance efficient use of this system?

Questions

1. How is oxygen provided in waste treatment systems?
2. How does the presence or absence of oxygen influence the rate of sewage waste processing?
3. Compare, in general terms, the energy content of the final products of aerobic versus anaerobic systems. How can this difference influence the choice of systems and the benefits and uses of such systems?
4. Ethanol is now being used widely as a gasoline fuel additive. What is the main source of this ethanol? What are the benefits of adding ethanol to gasoline?

Lactic Acid Fermentation

Under normal conditions, animals such as humans obtain energy from glucose by aerobic respiration. However, during strenuous exercise, muscle cells demand more ATP energy than can be supplied by aerobic respiration alone. Under such conditions additional ATPs are supplied by lactic acid fermentation, shown in **Figure 5**.

The Impacts of Lactic Acid Production

Listen to this audio clip for an explanation about lactic acid production during a workout and how this lactic acid has both positive and negative impacts on the body.

www.science.nelson.com 

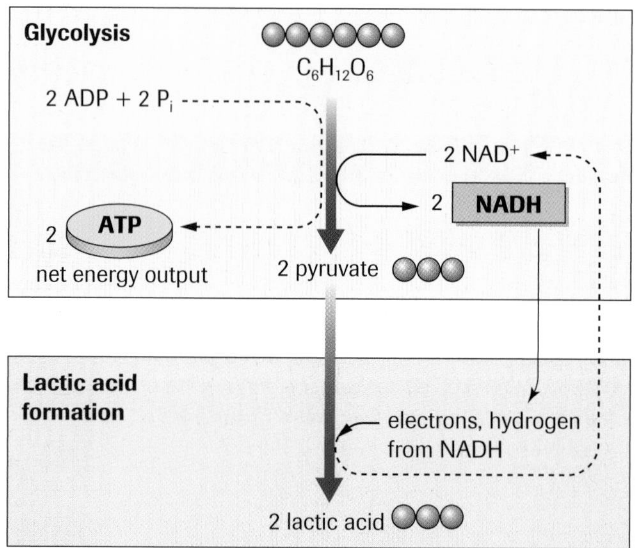

Figure 5
Lactic acid fermentation produces lactic acid from glucose. In the process, NADH is oxidized to NAD^+, allowing glycolysis to continue.

In lactic acid fermentation, NADH produced in glycolysis transfers its hydrogen atoms to pyruvate in the cytoplasm of the cell, regenerating NAD^+ and allowing glycolysis to continue. This results in a change of pyruvate into lactic acid. The overall equation for lactic acid fermentation is

$$\text{glucose } (C_6H_{12}O_6) + 2\text{ ADP} + 2\text{ P}_i \rightarrow 2\text{ lactic acid } (C_3H_6O_3) + 2\text{ ATP}$$

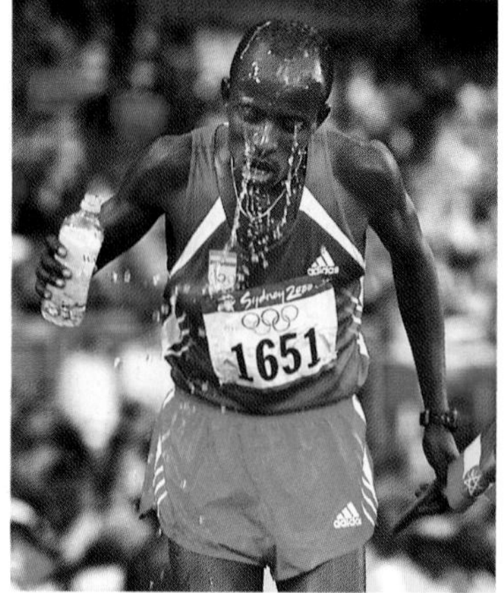

Figure 6
Marathon runners are fatigued after a race because of the accumulation of lactic acid in their muscles. Panting provides the oxygen needed to metabolize the excess lactic acid.

Accumulation of lactic acid molecules in muscle tissue causes stiffness, soreness, and fatigue. Lactic acid is transported through the bloodstream from the muscles to the liver. When vigorous exercise ceases, lactic acid is converted back to pyruvate, which then goes through the remaining stages of aerobic respiration. The extra oxygen required to chemically process this lactic acid (through the aerobic pathway) is referred to as oxygen debt. Panting after bouts of strenuous exercise is the body's way of "paying" the oxygen debt (**Figure 6**, previous page).

Exercise Physiology: VO_2 max and the Lactic Acid Threshold

Exercise physiology is a branch of biology that deals with the body's biological responses to exercise. Scientists in this field try to answer such questions as "Why do muscles become sore and fatigued after a bout of strenuous exercise? How can athletes train to control fatigue and maximize the amount of oxygen that enters their bloodstream? Why does exercise deplete the body of its water reserves and how can athletes avoid dehydration?" Exercise physiologists search for solutions to practical problems faced by individuals who engage in sports and athletic activities. The most common problem faced by athletes is a shortage of energy. Therefore, particular emphasis is placed on the study of aerobic and anaerobic metabolism and its relationship to cardiopulmonary fitness, also known as aerobic fitness. Aerobic fitness is a measure of the ability of the heart, lungs, and bloodstream to supply oxygen to the cells of the body (especially the muscle cells) during physical activity. Aerobic fitness is one of the factors used by physiologists to judge a person's overall physical fitness. Other factors include muscular strength, muscular endurance, flexibility, and body composition (the ratio of fat to bone to muscle).

Since muscle cells need energy from ATP to contract, it is assumed that ATP production (by aerobic respiration) will be increased if more oxygen is absorbed and used by the cells of the body (especially muscle cells) in a given period of time. Exercise physiologists measure a value called the **maximum oxygen consumption (VO_2 max)**, as a measure of a body's capacity to generate the energy required for physical activity. VO_2 max measures the maximum volume of oxygen, in millilitres, that the cells of the body can remove from the bloodstream in one minute per kilogram of body mass while the body experiences maximal exertion. VO_2 max values are typically expressed in mL/kg/min, and are measured directly by a maximal exercise test, also known as a treadmill exercise test. During the test, the person or animal is forced to move faster and faster on a treadmill while expired air is collected and measured by a computer (**Figure 7**). The entire test usually lasts between 10 min and 15 min. Needless to say, the test is not pleasant since one must achieve a rather painful state of maximal exertion. Indirect methods of estimating the value of VO_2 max have been developed that require much less physical strain.

In general, individuals with higher VO_2 max values may be considered more aerobically fit than individuals with lower values.

VO_2 max values vary between 20 mL/kg/min and 90 mL/kg/min. The average value for a typical North American is about 35 mL/kg/min, while elite endurance athletes reach values of 70 mL/kg/min. **Figure 8**, on the next page, shows average VO_2 max values for the athletes of various sports. VO_2 max values may be increased with exercise and training, but genetic variation helps to explain why everyone cannot train to be an elite athlete. Exercising harder, more frequently, and for longer durations will increase VO_2 max values to a degree. However, VO_2 max values also decrease with age. In any case, there is not always a direct correlation between VO_2 max values and overall athletic performance. Although it is true that elite athletes have VO_2 max values that are higher than the population mean, factors such as mental attitude, running efficiency, and the amount of lactic acid produced during exercise greatly influence overall performance.

Since oxygen cannot reach all the body's mitochondria all the time, lactic acid fermentation occurs continuously as you exercise. However, as exercise intensity increases, lactic acid production increases. The lactic acid threshold is the value of exercise intensity at which blood lactic acid concentration begins to increase sharply (**Figure 9**, next page). Exercising at or below this intensity may be sustainable for hours, but exercising

+ EXTENSION

Estimating VO_2 max
In this activity, you will carry out the Rockport Fitness Walking Test. This is a standard test used to estimate the value of VO_2 max. You will walk a distance of 1.6 km on level ground as quickly as possible, without running. You will record how long it took you complete the walk, and measure your heart rate after the walk. You will then substitute these measurements, your age, gender, and mass, into an equation to calculate your VO_2 max.

www.science.nelson.com 

maximum oxygen consumption, VO_2 max the maximum volume of oxygen, in millilitres, that the cells of the body can remove from the bloodstream in one minute per kilogram of body mass while the body experiences maximal exertion

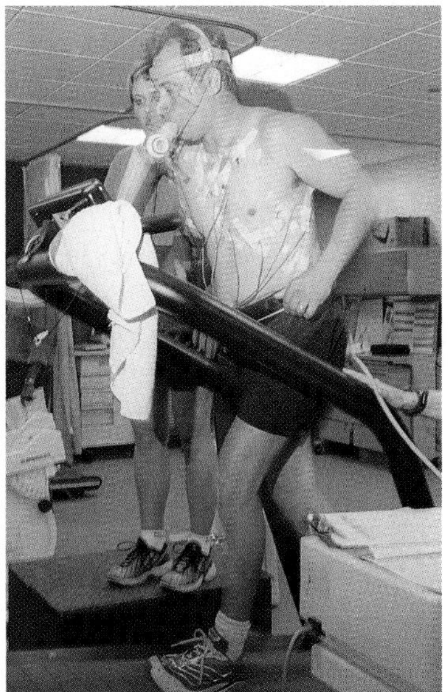

Figure 7
A maximal exertion test being conducted in a human performance lab. The apparatus is used to make precise measurements of VO_2 max.

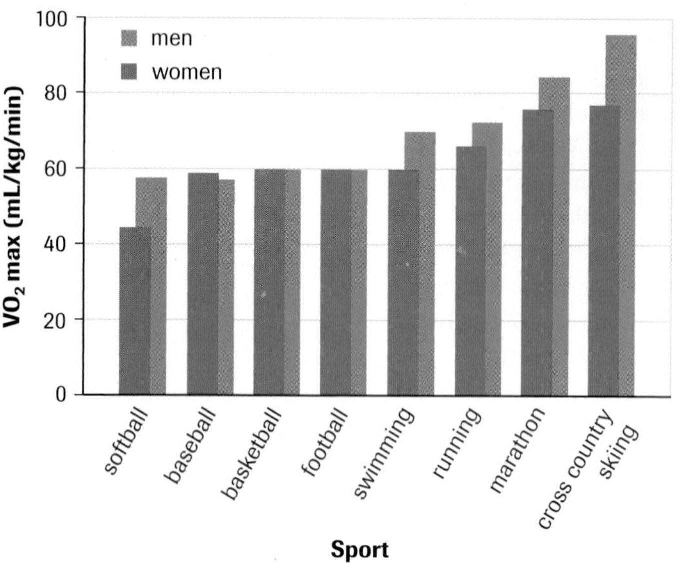

Figure 8
VO_2 max values for athletes in popular sports

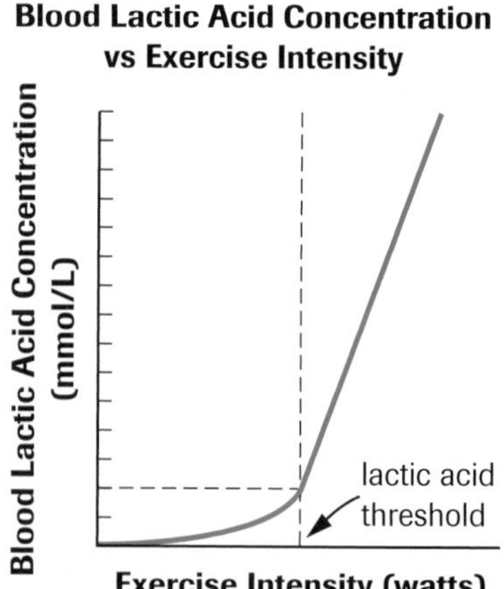

Figure 9
The lactic acid threshold

beyond the lactic acid threshold may limit the duration of the exercise because of increased pain, muscle stiffness, and fatigue.

In general, athletic training improves blood circulation and increases the efficiency of oxygen delivery to the cells of the body. The result is a decrease in lactic acid production at any given exercise intensity level and an increase in the lactic acid threshold. With a higher **lactic acid threshold**, the person will be able to sustain greater exercise intensities and improved athletic performance. One measure of performance is the percentage of VO_2 max at which the lactic acid threshold is reached. Untrained individuals usually reach the lactic acid threshold at about 60 % of VO_2 max. Elite endurance athletes typically reach their lactic acid thresholds at or above 80 % of VO_2 max.

lactic acid threshold the value of exercise intensity at which lactic acid production increases

CAREER CONNECTION

Kinesiologist

Kinesiologists work in the field of human movement, helping people rehabilitate from physical injuries. To be accepted into a kinesiology program, candidates must possess high marks in biology, chemistry, math, and physics. Kinesiologists work in a variety of settings, including hospitals, clinics, and fitness centres. Some large corporations, such as General Motors, hire kinesiologists to advise on ways to improve workers' safety and efficiency on assembly lines—known as ergonomics. Research other career opportunities in the specialized field of ergonomics.

www.science.nelson.com 

Practice

4. In addition to ATP, name the other final products of both types of fermentation.
5. How does a human feel the presence of lactic acid in the tissues of the body?
6. Why are VO_2 max values not perfectly correlated with overall athletic performance?

Supplements and Toxins

In addition to our own physical condition and health, environmental factors can have an impact on cellular respiration. Chemicals we ingest or inhale can directly affect cellular respiration pathways in a variety of ways. Some compounds may act as buffers—countering the acidic effects of lactic acid fermentation and potentially enhancing short-term athletic performance. Other chemicals may act as metabolic poisons—inhibiting cellular respiration by interfering with a critical step in a chemical pathway.

Creatine phosphate occurs naturally in the body and in foods. More recently, some high-performance athletes have consumed it as a dietary supplement. Creatine phosphate may serve as a source of energy by donating its phosphate to ADP, thus creating ATP. Some have also hypothesized that increasing the amount of creatine in the diet might increase the concentration of creatine phosphate in muscles. This might increase the availability of high-energy phosphate for ATP and energy production during muscle contraction. Creatine also has the potential to act as a buffer in muscle cells and potentially counter or delay the onset of some of the symptoms associated with lactic acid fermentation.

Many claims have been made regarding the value of creatine supplements. It is said to enhance athletic performance by increasing muscle strength and mass, by providing an instant energy source, and by delaying fatigue. The ultimate benefits and risks associated with its use are not conclusive, however, and potential harmful side-effects are possible. Many medical researchers urge caution and do not recommend its use.

While some chemicals, like creatine phosphate, may enhance respiration under certain conditions, other chemicals have the potential to do quite the opposite. Chemical toxicity can result from a wide range of mechanisms. As you may know, carbon monoxide poisoning is due to this gas's ability to bind to the hemoglobin proteins in your red blood cells. These proteins are responsible for carrying oxygen gas throughout your body. Carbon monoxide competes aggressively for the same binding sites on the hemoglobin molecules. The result is a severe drop in your blood's oxygen-carrying capacity and possible death by asphyxiation. Oxygen is the final electron acceptor that drives the electron transport chain. Without oxygen there is an immediate halt to electron transport and the pumping of hydrogen ions across the inner mitochondrial membrane. Without this activity, H^+ ions are no longer available to drive the formation of ATP—the cell's vital energy source. Cell death follows shortly thereafter.

Rather than limiting the body's access to one of the reactants in cellular respiration, some toxic compounds such as cyanide and hydrogen sulfide directly act on a specific reaction within a respiration pathway.

DID YOU KNOW?

Death and Rigor Mortis

There are two things that happen soon after death: one is a gradual drop in body temperature, and the other is stiffening of the muscles, known as rigor mortis. Rigor mortis is caused not by the drop in body temperature, but by the fermentation of glucose in muscle cells, leading to high levels of lactic acid. The lactic acid causes muscle tissue to become rigid. Rigor mortis sets in much sooner if death occurs immediately following strenuous activity, such as running.

mini *Investigation* Metabolic Poisons

Cyanide and hydrogen sulfide are metabolic poisons that enter the environment both from natural sources and as a direct result of human activities. In this mini investigation you will research and document various aspects of the toxicity, sources, and environmental and human health implications of these compounds. Imagine that you are one member of a research team that is preparing a resource binder on environmental toxins.

Using Internet and print resources provide answers and explanations for each of the following and then present them in the form of a two page Fact Sheet that would be suitable for inclusion in the binder.

(a) What stage(s) in cellular respiration are affected by cyanide and hydrogen sulfide?

(b) With what specific compounds do these poisons interfere?

(c) Do these compounds have any commercial value as toxins? Give examples of their use.

(d) Do these compounds occur naturally? If so, where are they found?

(e) What human activities produce these toxins as an industrial pollutant?

(f) How do these toxins impact the health of the environment in the locations in which they occur?

(g) What methods, if any, are used to reduce cyanide and/or hydrogen sulfide pollution?

SUMMARY Anaerobic Cellular Respiration

- When oxygen is not available, eukaryotes still carry out glycolysis. They recycle the NAD^+ needed for glycolysis by transferring the hydrogen atoms in NADH to pyruvate or acetaldehyde.
- In alcohol fermentation, a molecule of CO_2 is removed from pyruvate, forming a molecule of acetaldehyde. The acetaldehyde is converted to ethanol by attaching hydrogen from NADH.

- In lactic acid fermentation, pyruvate molecules accept the hydrogens from NADHs and form molecules of lactic acid.
- Alcohol fermentation occurs in yeast cells and is used in wine, beer, and bread making.
- Lactic acid fermentation occurs in animal muscle cells during strenuous exercise.
- The maximum oxygen uptake, or VO_2 max, is the maximum volume of oxygen that the cells of the body can remove from the bloodstream in one minute per kilogram of body mass while the body experiences maximal exertion. The lactic acid threshold is the value of exercise intensity at which blood lactic acid concentration begins to increase sharply.
- Chemical toxins, such as carbon monoxide, cyanide, and hydrogen sulfide, can hinder cellular respiration.

Section 7.4 Questions

1. List two differences between aerobic respiration and fermentation.
2. A student regularly runs 3 km each afternoon at a slow, leisurely pace. One day, she runs 1 km as fast as she can. Afterward, she is winded and feels pain in her chest and leg muscles. What is responsible for her symptoms?
3. What role does alcohol fermentation play in the food industry?
4. Compare and contrast the use of anaerobic and aerobic microbes in waste treatment.
5. Define *maximum oxygen consumption, VO_2max.*
6. (a) Determine the value of the lactic acid threshold from **Figure 10**.
   (b) What does this value mean?
7. When Henry Ford built the first Model T in 1908, he expected it to run on pure ethanol produced by fermenting corn. From 1920 to 1924, the Standard Oil Company in Baltimore produced and sold a mixture of ethanol and gasoline called gasohol. However, high corn prices and transportation difficulties terminated the project.
   (a) Research gasohol on the Internet or at the library. List three advantages and three disadvantages of gasohol production in Canada.
   (b) Comment on the viability of a gasohol industry in Canada.

   www.science.nelson.com GO

8. Alcoholic beverages, such as wine and beer, have been produced by humans since the earliest days of agriculture. How do you suppose the process of fermentation was first discovered?

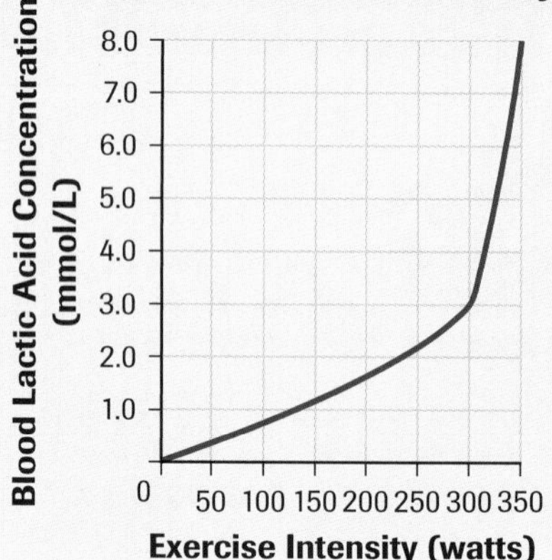

Figure 10

9. Lactic acid fermentation is used in the food industry. Use Internet and print sources to answer the following questions.
   (a) What foods depend on lactic acid fermentation?
   (b) What microbes are used in each food in (a).

   www.science.nelson.com GO

10. Conduct library and/or Internet research to answer the following questions.
    (a) How do long-distance runners make use of the lactic acid threshold in their training?
    (b) What is blood doping? What are the perceived metabolic benefits of this practice? What are some of the dangers associated with blood doping?

    www.science.nelson.com GO

11. Investigate the claim that, historically, Aboriginal athletes were some of the world's greatest long-distance runners.

    www.science.nelson.com GO

INVESTIGATION 7.1

Measuring Oxygen Consumption in Germinating Seeds

When seeds are dormant, they are not actively growing. When the right conditions are met, a dormant seed germinates and begins to grow into a seedling. As growth occurs, cells release the energy stored in cellular compounds such as starch and glucose by breaking them down. The cells then use this energy to fuel their growth. When oxygen is present, energy is released through the process of cellular respiration. The following equation summarizes this process:

$$C_6H_{12}O_6(s) + 6\ O_2(g) \rightarrow 6\ CO_2(g) + 6\ H_2O(l) + \text{energy}$$

glucose + oxygen → carbon dioxide + water + energy

The higher its energy demands, the more quickly a cell will consume both glucose and oxygen. In this investigation, you will compare the energy demands of dormant (dry) seeds and germinating (pre-soaked) seeds by measuring the rates of oxygen consumption using an apparatus called a respirometer.

The respirometer you will use consists of a test tube with a three-hole stopper that holds a thermometer and a straight and a bent piece of glass tubing. When assembly is complete, the respirometer is sealed off from the outside air. The sealed respirometer also contains solid potassium hydroxide (KOH) pellets. KOH reacts with carbon dioxide gas according to the following chemical equation:

$$CO_2(g) + 2\ KOH(s) \rightarrow K_2CO_3(s) + H_2O(l)$$

carbon dioxide + potassium hydroxide → potassium carbonate + water

This reaction with carbon dioxide gas produces a solid (K_2CO_3) and a liquid (H_2O). Therefore, any carbon dioxide gas produced during respiration will not contribute to the volume of gas in the respirometer.

Any change in the volume of gas inside the respirometer will cause the food colouring to move within the bent glass tubing. If gases are consumed, the food colouring will move toward the test tube. The rate of oxygen consumption can be determined by measuring the distance the food colouring moves over time.

The thermometer can be used to determine whether or not actively germinating seeds absorb or release thermal energy.

Report Checklist

○ Purpose	○ Design	● Analysis
○ Problem	○ Materials	● Evaluation
○ Hypothesis	○ Procedure	● Synthesis
● Prediction	● Evidence	

Problems

How does the rate of oxygen consumption by germinating and nongerminating pea seeds vary? Do the activities of germinating seeds absorb or release thermal energy?

Predictions

(a) Predict whether germinating or non-germinating pea seeds will consume more oxygen in 15 min.

(b) Predict whether germination or non-germinating pea seeds will absorb or release thermal energy

Materials

- pea seeds (dry and pre-soaked)
- water
- paper towels
- nonabsorbent cotton
- laboratory scoop or forceps
- potassium hydroxide pellets (KOH)
- petroleum jelly
- liquid food colouring
- tape
- safety goggles
- laboratory apron
- 2 thermometers
- 2 straight glass tubes
- 2 bent glass tubes
- 2 three-hole test-tube stoppers
- 2 large test tubes
- 2 millimetre rulers
- 2 pinch clamps
- 2 pieces of rubber tubing
- 2 test-tube clamps
- 2 retort stands
- medicine dropper

KOH is highly corrosive.

Avoid any contact with your skin. Wash under cold, running water for 5 min if you get KOH on your skin.

KOH could cause blindness. If KOH comes in contact with your eyes, wash with water for 15 min and seek medical help immediately.

Wear eye protection and a laboratory apron at all times.

Procedure

1. Place 30 dry pea seeds in a large test tube and place a layer of cotton on top of the seeds. Using forceps or a scoop, add approximately 30 KOH pellets on top of the cotton.

INVESTIGATION 7.1 *continued*

2. Assemble the respirometer as shown in **Figure 1**. Attach a millimetre ruler to the end of the bent glass tubing, using tape. Seal all stopper openings with petroleum jelly. Do not add the food colouring or the pinch clamp at this time.

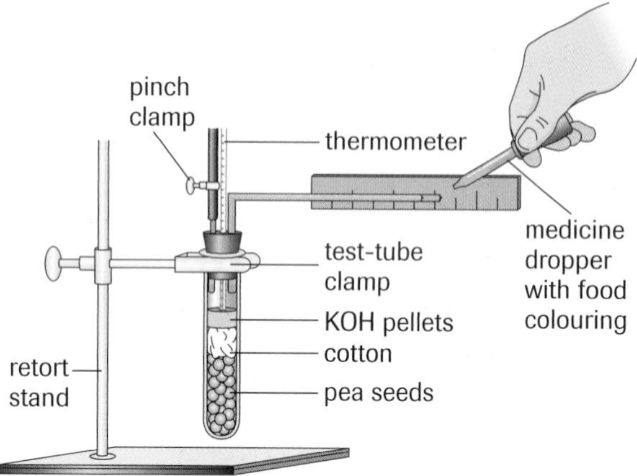

Figure 1
A respirometer

3. Repeat steps 1 and 2 with 30 pre-soaked, germinating pea seeds.
4. Allow both respirometers to stand undisturbed for 5 min.
5. With the medicine dropper, add a few drops of food colouring to the ends of the bent glass tubing.
6. Attach and close a pinch clamp to the rubber tubing on each respirometer.

(c) Record the time at which the pinch clamps were closed. Note the position of the food colouring.

(d) Measure and record the initial temperature in both respirometers.

(e) Record the position of the food colouring and the temperature inside the respirometers every minute for 15 minutes.

Analysis

(f) Graph your data by plotting the distance the food colouring moved on the *y*-axis and the time on the *x*-axis. Plot the data set for both the dry and the pre-soaked peas on the same graph.

(g) Determine the oxygen consumption rates for dry and germinating seeds using the following formula:

$$\text{average } O_2 \text{ consumption rate} = \frac{\text{total distance travelled}}{\text{total time}}$$

(h) Create a graph of temperature versus time. Plot the data for the dry and pre-soaked pea seeds on the same graph.

Evaluation

(i) Evaluate your prediction based on your analysis.

(j) Write a hypothesis that explains your findings, referring to the chemical reaction for respiration.

(k) In which direction does the food colouring first move?

(l) What is the purpose of the ruler?

(m) Why was the cotton used?

(n) Explain how the respirometer works.

(o) Why were the openings in the test-tube stopper sealed with petroleum jelly?

(p) What process in the peas caused the food colouring to move into the glass tubing?

(q) How would the results of this experiment differ if KOH had not been added to the test tubes?

(r) What plant process produces oxygen gas? Explain why this process does not affect the results of this experiment.

(s) During respiration, glucose ($C_6H_{12}O_6$) is consumed. What was the source of glucose in the germinating seeds?

(t) Do actively respiring seeds absorb or release thermal energy? Account for this observation based on your understanding of the chemical reactions that occur *during* respiration.

Synthesis

(u) Seeds will not germinate if they are too wet. Why?

(v) Design and conduct an experiment to investigate the effect of temperature on the respiration rate in germinating peas. Be sure to control for the effects of temperature on the volume of gases.

Chapter 7 SUMMARY

Outcomes

Knowledge

- explain, in general terms, how carbohydrates are oxidized by glycolysis and the Krebs cycle to produce reducing power in NADH and $FADH_2$, and chemical potential in ATP, describing where in the cell those processes occur (7.2, 7.3)
- explain, in general terms, how chemiosmosis converts the reducing power of NADH and $FADH_2$ to the chemical potential of ATP, describing where in the mitochondria the process occurs (7.3)
- distinguish, in general terms, among aerobic respiration, anaerobic respiration, and fermentation (7.3, 7.4)
- summarize and explain the role of ATP in cell metabolism (7.1, 7.2, 7.3, 7.4)

STS

- explain that science and technology are developed to meet societal needs and expand human capability (7.4)
- explain that science and technology have consequences for humans and the environment (7.4)

Skills

- ask questions and plan investigations (7.3, 7.4)
- conduct investigations and gather and record data and information by: using experimental methods to demonstrate, quantitatively, the oxygen consumption of germinating seeds (7.3); measuring temperature change over time of germinating and non-germinating seeds (7.3); investigating and integrating, from print and electronic sources, information on the action of metabolic toxins, such as hydrogen sulfide and cyanide, on cellular respiration (7.4)
- analyze data and apply mathematical and conceptual models (7.3, 7.4)
- work as members of a team and apply the skills and conventions of science (all)

Key Terms

7.1

NADH
NAD^+
$FADH_2$
FAD^+
active transport
sodium–potassium pump
aerobic cellular respiration
anaerobic cellular respiration

7.2

glycolysis

7.3

mitochondrion
mitochondrial matrix
intermembrane space
Krebs cycle
oxidative ATP synthesis

7.4

alcohol fermentation
lactic acid fermentation
maximum oxygen consumption, VO_2 max
lactic acid threshold

MAKE a summary

1. Draw a large, well labelled poster summarizing the four stages of cellular respiration. Have the area of the sheet represent the cytoplasm of an animal cell. Draw a very large mitochondrion covering at least one half of the area. Add coloured cartoons representing each stage of the process and place them in their respective locations. Use arrows to indicate the movement of intermediate molecules. Show the ATP yield from each stage and the overall ATP yield from the entire process.
2. Revisit your answers to the Starting Points questions at the start of the chapter. Would you answer the questions differently now? Why?

Go To

The following components are available on the Nelson Web site. Follow the links for *Nelson Biology Alberta 20–30.*

- an interactive Self Quiz for Chapter 7
- additional Diploma Exam-style Review Questions
- Illustrated Glossary
- additional IB-related material

There is more information on the Web site wherever you see the Go icon in the chapter.

UNIT 20 C PERFORMANCE TASK

Student Aquarist

In this Performance Task, you will create an aquatic ecosystem and manipulate its biotic and abiotic factors and monitor the effects these changes have on the metabolic health of the ecosystem's plants and animals. Go to the Unit 20 C Performance Task link on the Nelson Web site to complete this task.

www.science.nelson.com 

Chapter 7 REVIEW

Many of these questions are in the style of the Diploma Exam. You will find guidance for writing Diploma Exams in Appendix A5. Science Directing Words used in Diploma Exams are in bold type. Exam study tips and test-taking suggestions are on the Nelson Web site.

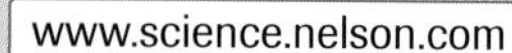

DO NOT WRITE IN THIS TEXTBOOK.

Part 1

Use the following information to answer questions 1 to 3.

Figure 1 is a cut-away diagram of a mitochondrian.

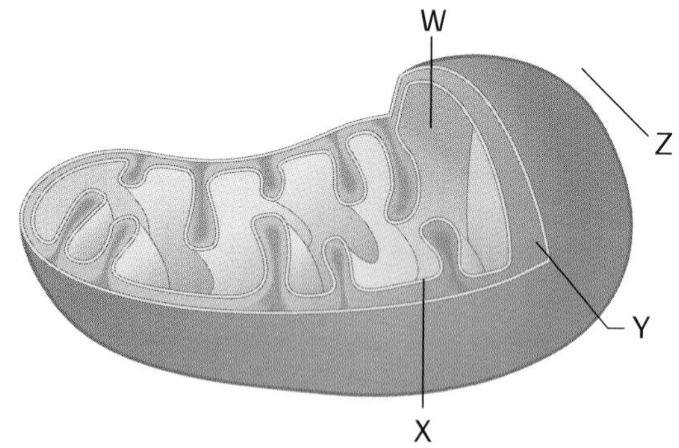

Figure 1

1. The following processes occur in the locations indicated.
   A. glycolysis (W), Krebs cycle (X), electron transport Y)
   B. glycolysis (Y), Krebs cycle (Z), electron transport (X)
   C. glycolysis (Z), Krebs cycle (W), electron transport (X)
   D. glycolysis (Z), Krebs cycle (Y), electron transport (X)

2. In an active mitochondrion the concentration of H^+ ions is greatest at
   A. W
   B. X
   C. Y
   D. Z

3. Imagine that you are able to design an experiment to measure the movement of ATP and ADP molecules within a cell. Which pattern would you expect your results to show?
   A. ATP moves from W to Y; ADP moves from Y to W
   B. ATP moves from W to Z; ADP moves from Z to W
   C. ATP moves from Y to Z; ADP moves from Z to Y
   D. ATP moves from Z to W; ADP moves from W to Z

---

4. Which of the following processes does NOT use ATP as the primary energy source?
   A. active transport
   B. muscle contraction
   C. protein synthesis
   D. osmosis

5. In glycolysis, glucose must first be activated. The activation of glucose requires
   A. two molecules of O_2
   B. two molecules of H_2O
   C. two molecules of ATP
   D. two molecules of NAD

6. Which of the following is involved in the lactic acid fermentation pathway after glycolysis?
   A. production of carbon dioxide
   B. oxidation of NADH
   C. production of ATP
   D. consumption of lactic acid

7. An increased level of aerobic fitness is associated with
   A. a low VO_2 max
   B. a high VO_2 max
   C. a low lactic acid threshold
   D. a high VO_2 max and a low lactic acid threshold

8. NR Each of the following compounds can be used by a cell to produce ATPs. Choose the four compounds that could yield the greatest number of ATPs and place them in order from greatest to least energy. (Record all four digits of your answer.)
1. pyruvate
2. NAD^+
3. $FADH_2$
4. glucose
5. NADH
6. acetyl-CoA
7. FAD
8. ADP + P_i

9. NR The complete oxidation of glucose to carbon dioxide and water releases 2870 kJ of energy per mole. Aerobic respiration only captures about 930 kJ of this available energy. Calculate the approximate efficiency of aerobic respiration as a percentage to one decimal place. (Record all four digits of your answer.)

Part 2

10. Explain what happens to the rest of the energy in question 9.

11. (a) **Determine** the net gain in ATP when one glucose molecule undergoes aerobic cellular respiration.
   (b) **Determine** the net gain in ATP when one glucose molecule undergoes alcohol fermentation.

12. Name the four stages of aerobic cellular respiration and **describe** where in a cell each stage occurs.

13. Oxygen is the final electron acceptor in the electron transport chain. If it is only needed in the last reaction of this pathway, **explain** how a lack of oxygen causes both the electron transport chain and the Krebs cycle to come to a complete stop.

14. Oxygen is toxic or unavailable to some cells such as yeast. **Summarize** how yeast cells produce ATP from glucose.

Use the following information to answer questions 15 and 16.

Marathon runners have learned that taking walking breaks during a race may get them to the finish line faster than running all the way.

15. **Identify** the compound that is more likely to accumulate if the runner does not take any breaks. DE

16. **How** would the walking breaks influence the accumulation of this substance? DE

---

17. **Explain** why it is essential that muscle cells convert pyruvate into lactic acid during strenuous exercise, even though the cell obtains very little energy in this process and lactic acid accumulation causes muscle fatigue and pain.

Use the following information to answer questions 18 and 19.

A geneticist gives you two test tubes containing two types of yeast cells that are the same in every way except that one can carry out only aerobic respiration and the other can carry out only anaerobic respiration. The tubes are labelled A and B and they look the same. Yeast from tube A grows rapidly whereas yeast from tube B grows slowly.

18. **Identify** the tube that contains the cells that only perform aerobic respiration. **Explain** how you made your choice. DE

19. **Design** two different experiments that could be used to verify your results. DE

---

20. There is growing interest in the industrial production of ethanol. Sometimes referred to as "green gasoline," ethanol is used as a fuel additive for automobiles. Ethanol use is being encouraged both to reduce dependence on fossil fuels and as a way to reduce greenhouse-gas emissions. While ethanol fuel has promise, many feel that its potential is being over-stated. Use the Internet and other resources to find out more about ethanol fuel. Based on your research, write a unified response addressing the following aspects of the use of ethanol as "green gasoline." DE
    - **Outline** the basic steps in commercial ethanol production. What sources of biomass are available to produce the ethanol and how are these materials processed to produce ethanol?
    - **Explain** the potential advantages of replacing petroleum-based fuels with ethanol.
    - **Summarize** the energy inputs involved in growing, transporting, and processing these biomass sources. **Explain** how these inputs influence your answer to the previous question.
    - **Describe** how scientists are using genetic engineering to improve the efficiency of ethanol production.
    - Brazil produces enough ethanol to meet 40 % of its primary energy needs. Does Canada have the same potential for ethanol production? Provide data to **justify** your answer.

www.science.nelson.com  

Extension

Use the following information to answer questions 21 to 25.

A 30-year-old, 75 kg male runner completes a marathon in 2 h and 35 min. His oxygen consumption at 15 min intervals is shown in **Table 1**. Oxygen consumption is given by the equation

$$\text{oxygen consumption (mL/min)} = VO_2 \text{ max (mL/kg/min)} \times \text{mass (kg)}$$

Table 1 VO_2 Max Data for Male Runner

Time (min)	VO_2 max (mL/kg/min)	Time (min)	VO_2 max (mL/kg/min)
0	15	150	65
15	40	165	50
30	70	180	45
45	90	195	40
60	90	210	35
75	75	225	30
90	70	240	25
105	65	255	20
120	65	270	15
135	65	290	15

21. **Sketch** a graph to display the data in **Table 1**. DE

22. **Identify** the runner's resting VO_2 max. DE

23. **Determine** his oxygen consumption while resting and during his highest VO_2 max. DE

24. **Explain** what is happening during each phase of the graph. DE

25. Use your knowledge of oxygen consumption during exercise to **explain** the oxygen consumption after the race is finished. DE

Many of these questions are in the style of the Diploma Exam. You will find guidance for writing Diploma Exams in Appendix A5. Science Directing Words used in Diploma Exams are in bold type. Exam study tips and test-taking suggestions are on the Nelson Web site.

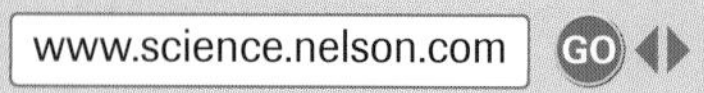

DO NOT WRITE IN THIS TEXTBOOK.

Part 1

Use the following information to answer questions 1 to 3.

The three graphs in **Figure 1** represent energy profiles of chemical processes that occur within cells.

Graph X

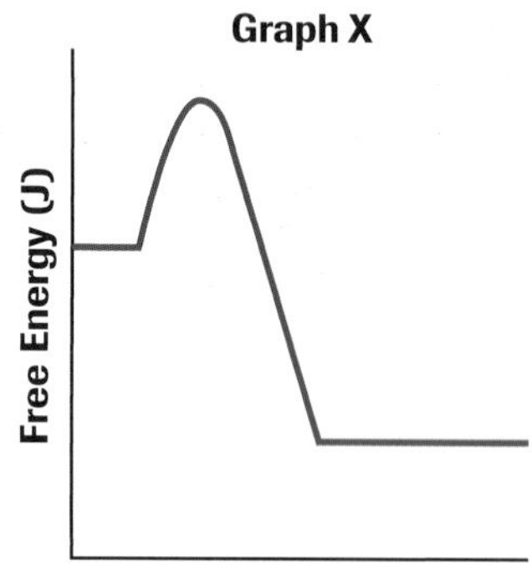

Graph Y

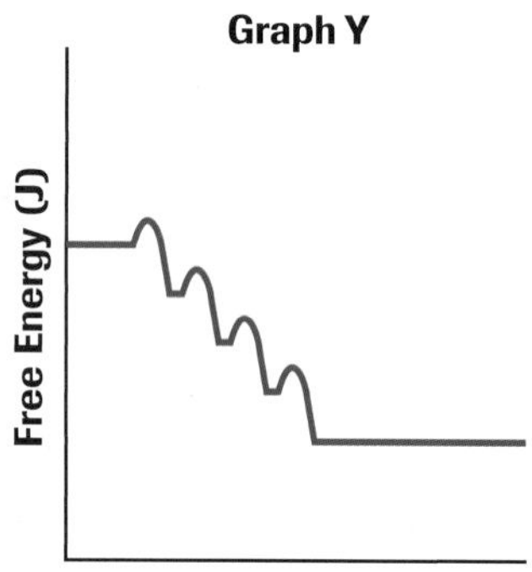

Graph Z

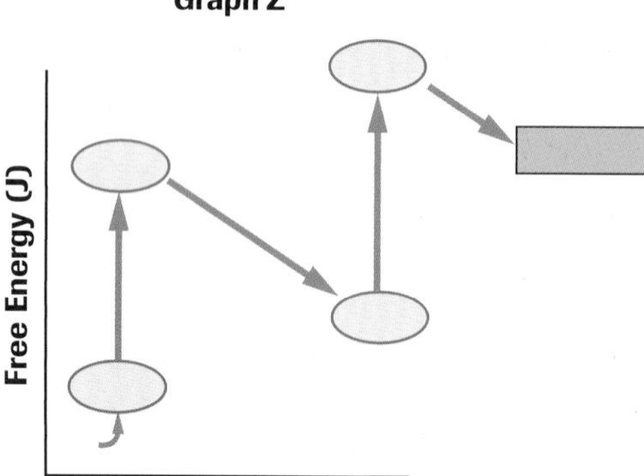

Figure 1

1. The three energy profiles could represent the following processes:
   A. a single reaction (X); the light-dependent reactions (Y); the Krebs cycle (Z)
   B. the electron transport chain (X); glycolysis (Y); the light-dependent reactions (Z)
   C. the Krebs cycle (X); the electron transport chain (Y); glycolysis (Z)
   D. a single reaction (X); the electron transport chain (Y); the light-dependent reactions (Z)

2. The jumps in the energy profile in Graph Z represent
   A. the addition of ATP energy
   B. redox reactions
   C. the absorption of light energy
   D. the action of enzymes

3. In Graph X, the initial increase in energy represents
   A. the energy needed to break bonds
   B. the energy released as bonds form
   C. the energy provided by ATP
   D. an energy increase due to the addition of an enzyme

---

4. The range of wavelengths of light that is visible to humans is
   A. 380 nm – 550 nm
   B. 400 nm – 600 nm
   C. 380 nm – 750 nm
   D. 200 nm – 900 nm

Use the following information to answer questions 5 and 6.

Figure 2 shows major steps in photosynthesis and cellular respiration, and the molecules that link these two processes.

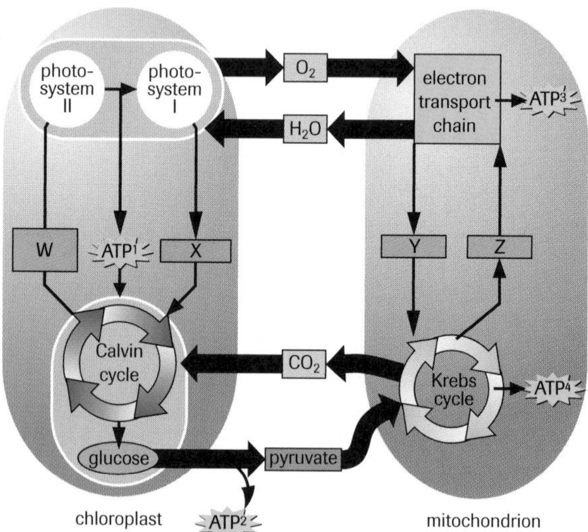

Figure 2

5. Labels W, X, Y, and Z correspond to
   A. H_2O (W); O_2 (X); pyruvate (Y); CO_2 (Z)
   B. O_2 (W); H_2O (X); CO_2 (Y); pyruvate (Z)
   C. O_2 (W); H_2O (X); pyruvate (Y); CO_2 (Z)
   D. CO_2 (W); pyruvate (X); O_2 (Y); H_2O (Z)

6. The ATPs that are of value to the cell for performing cellular functions such as active transport and movement are
   A. all the ATPs
   B. ATP 1 and 2 only
   C. ATP 3 and 4 only
   D. ATP 2, 3, and 4 only

7. NR Choose the steps from the following list that occur in photosynthesis and place them in the order in which they occur in the cell. (Record all four digits of your answer.)
   1. NAD^+ is reduced
   2. H_2O is split
   3. acetyl-CoA forms
   4. CO_2 is produced
   5. CO_2 is fixed
   6. NADPH is oxidized
   7. $FADH_2$ is oxidized
   8. ATP is used

8. NR Using the following formula, calculate the VO_2 max for a 29 year old male with a mass of 80 kg who is able to walk 1.6 km in 8.5 minutes with a final heart rate of 78 beats per minute. (Record your answer to one decimal place.)

VO_2 max (mL/kg/min) =
$132.853 - 0.1696m - 0.3877a + 6.3150g - 3.2649t - 0.1565r$

Part 2

9. **Summarize** what happens during the light-dependent reactions of photosynthesis.

10. **Compare** the general equations of photosynthesis and aerobic respiration. **Outline** the similarities and differences in a table.

Use the following information to answer questions 11 to 13.

Hibernating animals rely on a special kind of tissue called brown fat. This tissue is located around vital internal organs, such as the heart, liver, and kidneys, and releases an unusually large amount of thermal energy when it is metabolically active. This occurs when the animal is "waking up" from hibernation. Researchers have discovered that the mitochondria in this tissue produce a chemical that disrupts the functioning of the electron transport chain, by making the inner membrane permeable to H^+ ions. A drug, dinitrophenol, has the same effect on mitochondria in normal tissues. The drug was prescribed in low doses the 1940s to help obese patients lose weight but its use was discontinued after several patients died.

11. DE **Explain** whether the mitochondria in brown tissue would be able to generate more ATP than the mitochondria in normal tissue.

12. DE **How** would the permeability of the inner membrane to H^+ ions result in additional thermal energy production?

13. DE **Hypothesize** how using dinitrophenol could have caused the deaths.

14. (a) In active muscle tissue, **explain** what happens when the supply of oxygen is not adequate for the demands of oxidative phosphorylation.
    (b) **Why** does deep breathing continue even after strenuous exercise (e.g., running) has stopped?

15. Chemical bonds are forces of attraction that exist between atoms. These forces of attraction vary in their strength. When a chemical reaction occurs, old bonds break and new bonds form as atoms become rearranged. Use this information to **explain** how some reactions require energy while others release energy.

Use the following information to answer questions 16 to 22.

Many people are aware that plants produce oxygen gas—a gas that we need to breathe. This understanding has led to the widespread belief that entire ecosystems such as forested areas are net producers of oxygen. This belief, however, is somewhat misleading. In order for there to be a net production of oxygen gas, photosynthesis must be occurring faster than cellular respiration. The following equations summarize the overall reactions of photosynthesis and respiration:

$6\ CO_2 + 12\ H_2O + \text{solar energy} \rightarrow C_6H_{12}O_6 + 6\ H_2O + 6\ O_2$

$C_6H_{12}O_6 + 6\ O_2 + 36\ ADP + 36\ P_i \rightarrow 6\ CO_2 + 6\ H_2O + 36\ ATP$

16. DE **Identify** the chemical process that produces oxygen gas.

17. DE **Identify** the chemical process that consumes oxygen gas.

18. DE If there were a net production of oxygen gas in an ecosystem, **identify** the chemical that must be accumulating. **Identify** the atmospheric chemical that must be decreasing in concentration.

19. DE **How** would this affect the total biomass of the ecosystem over time?

20. DE **Explain** whether it is possible for such a situation to continue over a very long period of time.

21. DE **Outline** some natural processes that keep biomass from accumulating over time.

22. DE **How** might our understanding of these relationships influence strategies to combat climate change?

23. Review the focusing questions on page 174. Using the knowledge you have gained from this unit, briefly **outline** a response to each of these questions.

unit

20 D

Human Systems

The human body is organized into a number of different organ systems. Each of these organ systems has a critical role in maintaining your health. For example, your cardiovascular system transports nutrients and oxygen to your cells, and wastes and carbon dioxide from your cells. Elite athletes, such as the Olympic gold-medal winner Chandra Crawford, must have a healthy cardiovascular system. Unfortunately, cardiovascular disease is the leading cause of death in North America. About 44 000 Canadians, 40 % of them younger than 65, die each year from cardiovascular disease. Over 4000 patients in Canada and the United States are on the waiting list for a new heart.

Dr. Michael Sefton, director of the Institute of Biomaterials and Biomedical Engineering at the University of Toronto, is developing a possible way to provide an almost unlimited number of hearts for transplant. Sefton's "heart in a box" is a transplantable heart that can be grown in the laboratory. First, researchers create scaffolding—a supporting framework—of biodegradable plastic around which the cells will grow. Next, they seed the scaffolding with living cells and place it in an incubator that maintains constant temperature and provides nutrients and oxygen. Although researchers have not yet been able to grow a complete living heart, they have successfully grown components of the heart.

As you progress through the unit, think about these focusing questions:

- How do specialized structures function in the overall biochemical balance of the living system?
- What conditions result if these structures do not function normally?

UNIT 20 D PERFORMANCE TASK

Determining Fitness Level

Despite the increase in performance of elite athletes, the fitness level of the general public has been decreasing. The ability to perform physical activity depends on your body's ability to deliver oxygen to your cells. How can you design a fitness test to determine the amount of oxygen being delivered to your tissues? At the end of this unit, you may apply your skills and knowledge to complete this Performance Task.

www.science.nelson.com 

GENERAL OUTCOMES

In this unit, you will

- explain how the human digestive and respiratory systems exchange energy and matter with the environment
- explain the role of the circulatory and defence systems in maintaining an internal equilibrium
- explain the role of the excretory system in maintaining an internal equilibrium in humans through the exchange of energy and matter with the environment
- explain the role of the motor system in the function of other body systems

▸ Unit 20 D Human Systems

ARE YOU READY?

These questions will help you find out what you already know, and what you need to review, before you continue with this unit.

▸ Prerequisites

Concepts

- cells, organs, tissues, systems
- structure and function
- response to stimuli
- active and passive transport

Skills

- state a prediction and a hypothesis
- identify major variables
- organize data in appropriate formats
- interpret patterns and trends in data
- state a conclusion based on experimental data

You can review prerequisite concepts and skills on the Nelson Web site and in the Appendices.

A Unit Pre-Test is also available online.

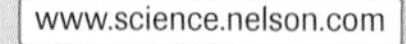

Knowledge

1. Examine **Figure 1** and explain the function of each of the labelled tissues.

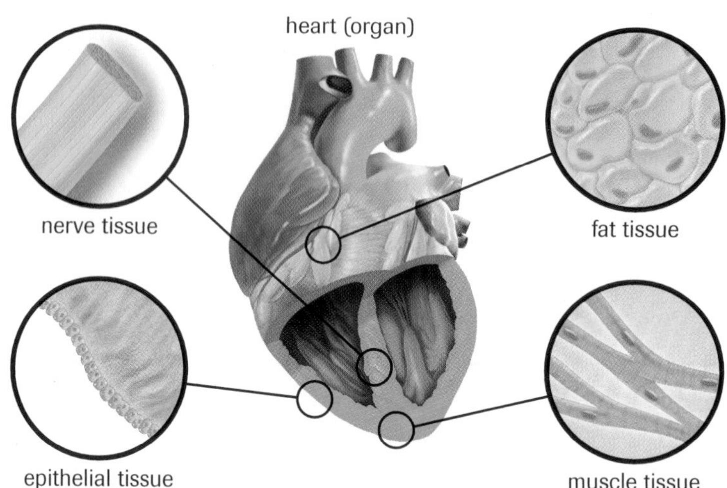

Figure 1
Tissues of the human heart

2. Explain what happens to an animal cell placed in
   (a) a hypertonic solution;
   (b) a hypotonic solution.

3. Copy **Table 1** into your notebook and fill in the blank spaces.

Table 1 Cellular Organization of Some Organ Systems

Level of cellular organization		Excretory system	
organ	ovary		
tissue		epithelial, blood, nerve, fat (adipose), and connective	
cell	egg		white blood cell (leukocyte)

4. In **Table 2**, match the organ(s) with the corresponding regulatory function. (*Note:* An organ can have more than one function, and a function can be linked to more than one organ.)

Table 2 Regulatory Functions of Some Organs

Organ(s)	Regulatory function
(a) skin	(i) disease prevention
(b) lymph vessels and lymph nodes	(ii) thermoregulation (regulation of body temperature)
(c) pancreas	(iii) maintaining blood sugar
(d) heart	(iv) maintaining blood pressure
(e) kidneys	(v) maintaining blood pH

Skills and STS Connections

5. A group of students conducts an experiment to determine how the body responds to stress. An ice cube is placed on the back of a subject's neck while another group member monitors changes in the subject's pulse.
   (a) Why is pulse used to monitor stress?
   (b) Create a hypothesis for the experiment.
   (c) Identify the manipulated and responding variables in the experiment.
   (d) What variables must be controlled to obtain reliable data?
   (e) Design a data table for the experiment.
   (f) Would you expect identical data from different subjects? Explain your answer.
   (g) Through the course of the experiment, when would you take the pulse? Give your reasons.
   (h) What practical information might the experiment provide?

6. **Figure 2** shows a white blood cell at two consecutive times.

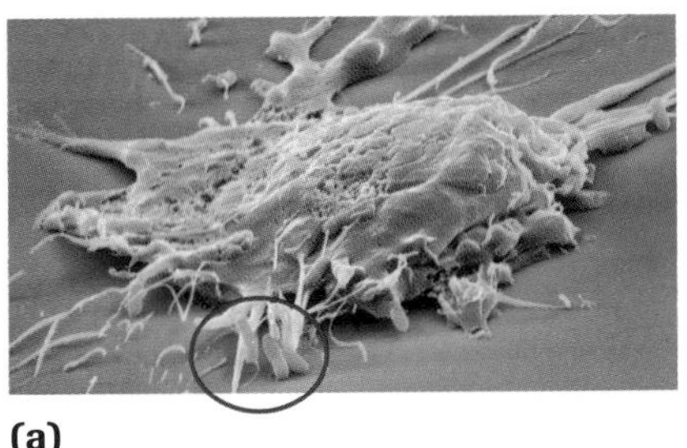

(a)

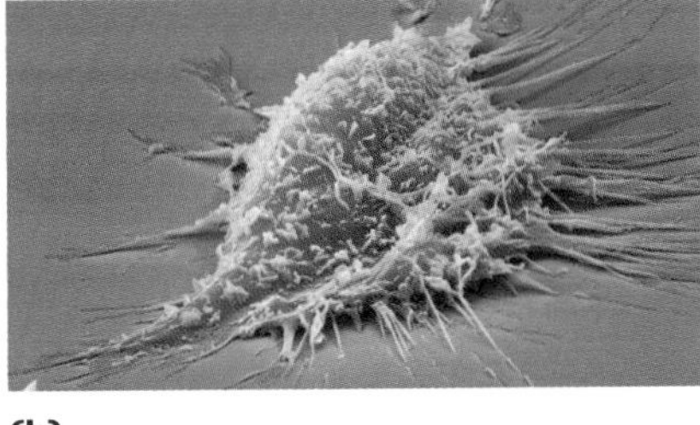

(b)

Figure 2
(a) At the first time point, bacteria cells (shown in the circle) are on the surface of the white blood cell.
(b) At the second time point, the bacteria cells are no longer visible.

   (a) Describe what is happening in **Figure 2**. Draw a conclusion from the photos.
   (b) Explain how this process helps to maintain a balanced internal environment.

7. Scientists monitored six types of ions in the cells of *Sargassum* (a brown alga often called seaweed) when maintained in brackish water (a mixture of salt and fresh water) and in marine water (seawater). The scientists noted that the concentration of ions did not change. The results are shown in **Table 3**.

Table 3 Ion Concentrations of *Sargassum* Cells

	Ion concentration*		
Ion	**Cell**	**Marine water**	**Brackish water**
calcium	1.7	12	1.7
magnesium	0.005	57	6.5
sulfate	0.01	36	2.8
sodium	90	500	60
potassium	490	12	1.4
chloride	520	520	74

*All concentrations are measured in mmol/L.

Assume that the cell membrane is permeable to all of the ions.
   (a) Which ion must be actively transported inside the cell in both brackish water and marine water? Explain your answer.
   (b) Which ion enters the cell by diffusion from marine water, but must be actively transported inside the cell from brackish water? Explain.
   (c) Explain how a cell could maintain its sodium ion concentration despite living in marine or brackish water environments.

chapter

Nutrients, Enzymes, and the Digestive System

In this chapter

- Exploration: Canada's Food Guide to Healthy Eating
- Chemistry Connection: Polymers
- Investigation 8.1: Identifying Carbohydrates
- Case Study: Fats and Health
- Investigation 8.2: Identifying Lipids and Proteins
- Explore an Issue: Irradiation Technology
- Investigation 8.3: Factors That Affect the Catalase Enzyme Reaction
- Explore an Issue: Fad Diets
- Web Activity: What Are You Eating?
- Investigation 8.4: Effect of pH and Temperature on Starch Digestion
- Mini Investigation: Emulsification of Fats

Canada has a multicultural society, which includes a wide variety of foods and styles of cooking. The foods of various cultures differ not only in flavour, but also in the types of ingredients used (**Figure 1**, next page).

Different diets may result in unique health problems. The high rate of heart disease in North America is due in part to the large amounts of fat consumed. Some people have decided that a vegetarian diet is healthier. Recently, high-protein, low-carbohydrate diets have become popular. However, diets high in animal protein also have higher amounts of cholesterol and saturated fats, which have been linked with cardiovascular disease.

The digestive system is responsible for converting the components of our diets into the molecules that are taken up and used by the cells of the body. Once inside the cells, these molecules supply the body with energy and the raw materials for the synthesis of essential chemical compounds used for growth, maintenance, and tissue repair.

STARTING points

Answer these questions as best you can with your current knowledge. Then, using the concepts and skills you have learned, you will revise your answers at the end of the chapter.

1. Make a list of the essential nutrients that must be included in every diet.
2. Copy and complete the chart below in your notebook.

Nutrient	Undergoes digestion? yes	no	Components after digested	Use by the body
protein				build structure
vitamins				coenzymes: assist enzymes, bind to substrate molecules
fats			fatty acid + glycerol	
polysaccharides				
water				

3. Make a list of the digestive system organs that you already know.

Career Connections:
Registered Dietician; X-ray Technician; Health Service Administrator

Figure 1
Typical cuisine from **(a)** North America, **(b)** Japan, **(c)** China, **(d)** South America

Exploration — *Canada's Food Guide to Healthy Eating*

- Go to the Nelson Web site and find the link to Health Canada's Food Guide to Healthy Eating.

www.science.nelson.com 

(a) What recommendations does the food guide give? Why do you think it is recommended to eat large amounts of some foods and smaller amounts of others?

(b) According to the guide, which foods should be eaten in larger quantities? Which foods should be eaten in smaller quantities?

(c) Write down everything you might eat on a typical day. Score yourself using the Healthy Eating Scorecard.

(d) Research the typical daily diet of a person from a different culture in a country outside of North America. Compare your diet to it.

8.1 Essential Nutrients

Living things are composed of nonliving chemicals (**Figure 1**). Proteins, carbohydrates, lipids (fats), vitamins and minerals, and nucleic acids are often categorized as the chemicals of living things despite the fact that none of them are capable of life by themselves.

Scientific investigations have shown that the same principles of chemistry apply in both the physical world and the living world. An understanding of life comes from an understanding of how chemical reactions are regulated within cells.

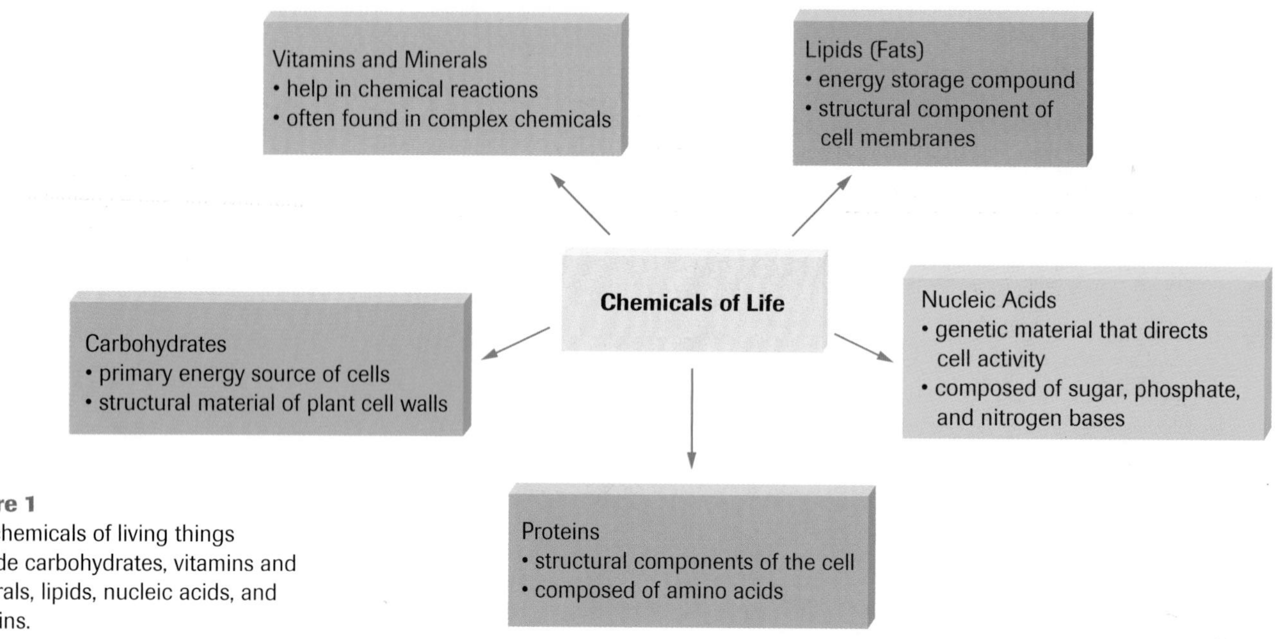

Figure 1
The chemicals of living things include carbohydrates, vitamins and minerals, lipids, nucleic acids, and proteins.

The foods you eat can be classified into three major groups of nutrients: carbohydrates, proteins, and lipids. These nutrients make up the bulk of what you eat. Vitamins and minerals are also required, but in much smaller amounts. Water is also essential for life, although it is not considered a nutrient. Most of the food you eat is a combination of nutrients. For example, the cereal you eat for breakfast or the bowl of vegetable soup you have for lunch is a combination of carbohydrates, proteins, and lipids, as well as some vitamins and minerals.

Carbohydrates

carbohydrate a molecule composed of sugar subunits that contain carbon, hydrogen, and oxygen in a 1:2:1 ratio

Carbohydrates are often described as energy nutrients. They provide a fast source of energy and make up the largest component in most diets. Potatoes, bread, corn, rice, and fruit contain large amounts of carbohydrates. Marathon runners often consume large quantities of carbohydrates a few days before a race to make sure that they have maximum energy reserves. However, under normal circumstances, it is not a good idea to eat excess quantities of carbohydrates because they will be stored as fat.

The human body is not able to make carbohydrates. You rely on plants as your source of carbohydrates. Using energy from the Sun, plants combine carbon dioxide and water to synthesize carbohydrates through the process of photosynthesis.

Carbohydrate Chemistry

Carbohydrates are either single sugar units or **polymers** of many sugar units. Single sugar units usually contain carbon, hydrogen, and oxygen in a 1:2:1 ratio. For example, triose sugars have the molecular formula $C_3H_6O_3$, and hexose sugars have the molecular formula $C_6H_{12}O_6$. The word *triose* refers to the fact that the sugars have a three-carbon chain (the prefix *tri-* means three). Hexose sugars contain six-carbon chain sugars (the prefix *hex-* means six). Many of the most important sugars contain either three-, five-, or six-chain sugars. Those that contain more than five carbons are often in a ring form.

polymer a molecule composed of three or more subunits

Common sugars like glucose, found in human blood; fructose, a plant sugar commonly found in fruits; and deoxyribose, a sugar component of the DNA molecule, can be identified as sugars by the *-ose* suffix. Even the large molecule cellulose, which makes up plant cell walls, is a carbohydrate.

Carbohydrates can also be classified according to the number of sugar units they contain. **Monosaccharides** are the simplest sugars, containing a single sugar unit. Glucose, galactose, and fructose are three common monosaccharides. **Figure 2** shows that they are **isomers**—that is, all three molecules have the same molecular formula, $C_6H_{12}O_6$, but different structural arrangements. The different chemical properties of these monosaccharides can be explained by their different structural arrangements. For example, fructose is much sweeter than glucose and is often used by food manufacturers to sweeten their products. The three sugars rotate between the straight-chain form and the ring structure, shown in **Figure 2**.

monosaccharide a single sugar unit

isomer one of a group of chemicals that have the same chemical formula but different arrangements of the atoms

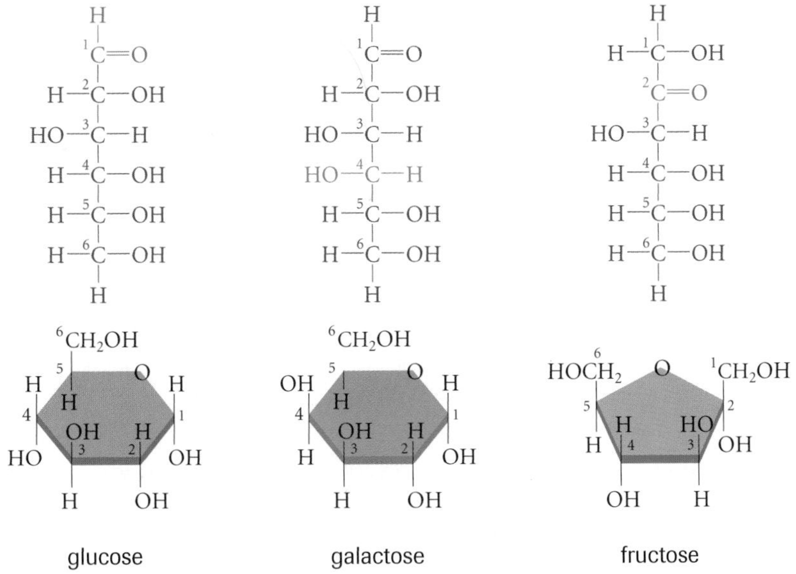

glucose

galactose

fructose

Figure 2
Glucose, galactose, and fructose are isomers.

disaccharide a sugar formed by the joining of two monosaccharide subunits

dehydration synthesis the process by which larger molecules are formed by the removal of water from two smaller molecules

hydrolysis the process by which larger molecules are split into smaller molecules by the addition of water

The combination of two monosaccharides forms a **disaccharide**. Sucrose (white table sugar) is a disaccharide formed from glucose and fructose. Sucrose is extracted from plants such as sugar cane and sugar beet. Maltose (malt sugar) is a disaccharide formed from two glucose units. Maltose is commonly found in the seeds of germinating plants. Lactose (milk sugar) is composed of glucose and galactose units. All disaccharides are formed by a process called **dehydration synthesis** (or dehydrolysis), in which a water molecule is formed from the two monosaccharide molecules (**Figure 3**, next page). The opposite reaction is **hydrolysis**, in which a water molecule is used to break the bond of the disaccharide.

Condensation and Hydrolysis

View this animation of condensation (dehydration synthesis) and hydrolysis.

www.science.nelson.com

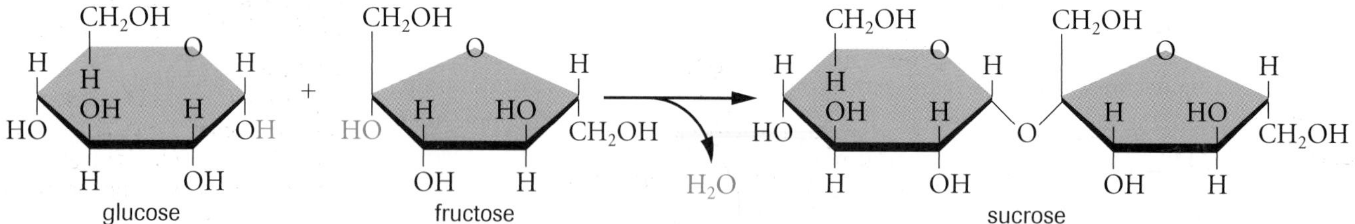

Figure 3
The formation of a disaccharide by dehydration synthesis. Note: Sucrose can only exist in the ring form.

polysaccharide a carbohydrate composed of many single sugar subunits

starch a plant carbohydrate used to store energy

Polysaccharides are carbohydrates formed by the union of many monosaccharide subunits. **Starch**, for example, is a plant polysaccharide that is composed of multiple subunits of glucose. Plants store energy in the chemical bonds of the starch molecule. Starches can exist in two different forms: amylose and amylopectin. Both molecules tend to bend in the shape of a helix, or coil (**Figure 4**). The amylose molecules contain up to 1000 or more glucose units with the first carbon of a glucose molecule linked to the fourth carbon in the next molecule (**Figure 4 (a)**). The amylopectins contain between 1000 and 6000 glucose subunits and have short branching chains of between 24 and 36 glucose units extending from the main branch (**Figure 4 (b)**).

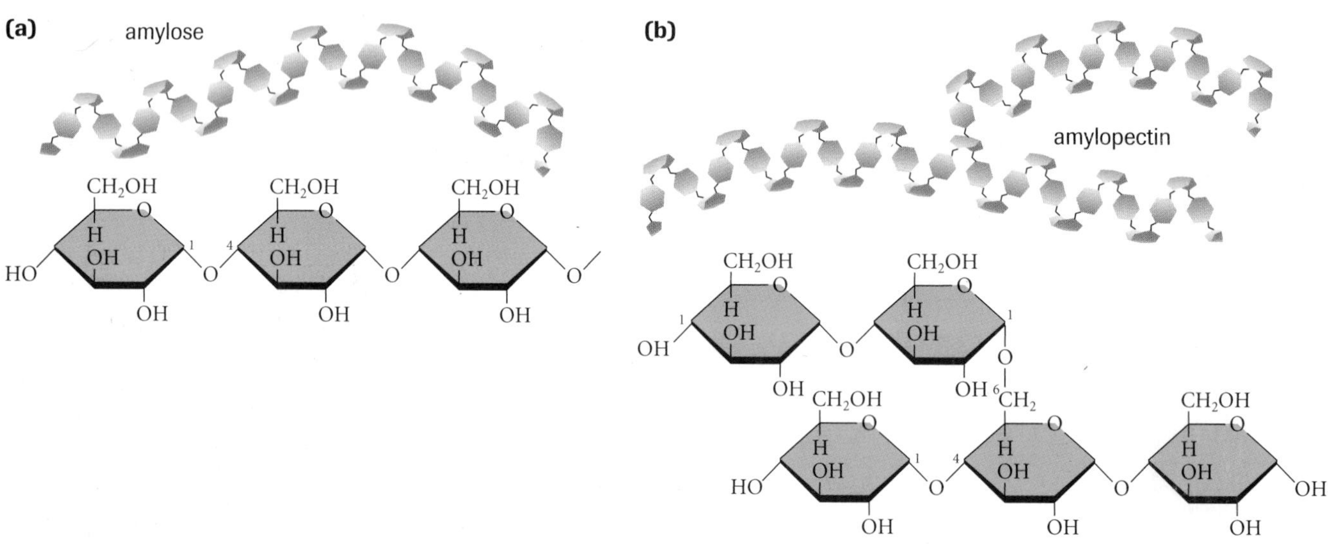

Figure 4
(a) Amylose is an unbranched polymer of glucose.
(b) Amylopectin is a branched polymer of glucose.

glycogen the form of carbohydrate storage in animals

cellulose a plant polysaccharide that makes up plant cell walls

DID YOU KNOW ?

Carbohydrates for Energy

Athletes often eat starches. Since these complex carbohydrates are broken down slowly, they provide a prolonged source of energy without dramatically changing blood sugar levels.

Animals store carbohydrates in the form of a polysaccharide called **glycogen**. The structure of glycogen resembles that of the amylopectin starch molecule, except that its branching structures contain only 16 to 24 glucose units.

Plant cell walls are made up of the polysaccharide **cellulose**. Over 50 % of all organic carbon in the biosphere is tied up as cellulose. Cellulose molecules, like starch and glycogen, are composed of many glucose subunits. However, the bonding of the linking oxygen atoms differs between starch and cellulose; cellulose tends not to form coiled structures. The many layers of cellulose are attracted to one another by hydrogen bonds between the –OH groups (**Figure 5**, next page).

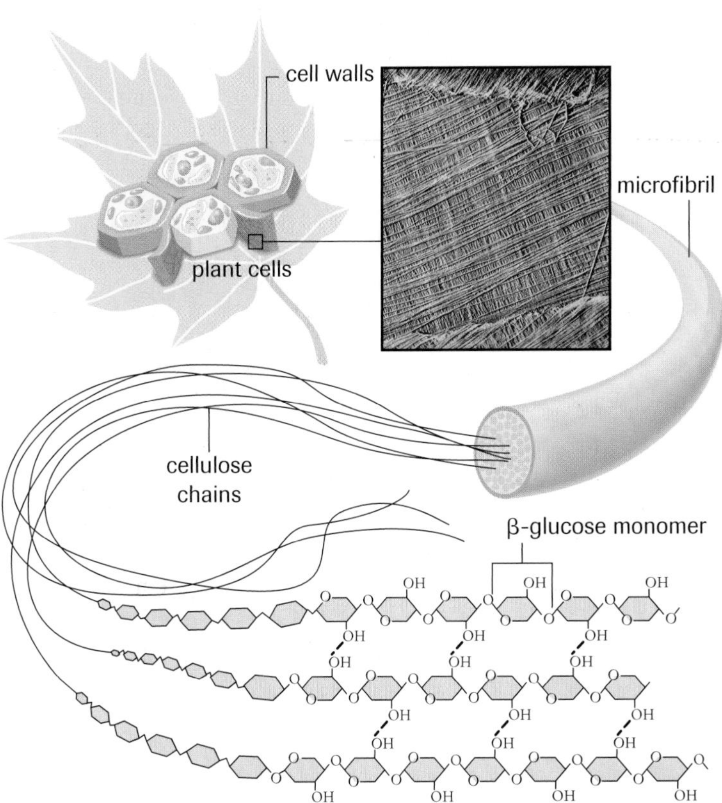

Figure 5

Cellulose fibres are composed of microfibrils, which are composed of many cellulose molecules held together by hydrogen bonds.

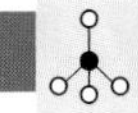

CHEMISTRY CONNECTION

Polymers

Glycogen, starch, and cellulose are three examples of naturally occurring polymers. Synthetic polymers, such as nylon, polyvinyl chloride, or polyesters, are commonly used in many consumer products. You can find out more information about polymers in your chemistry course.

www.science.nelson.com 

Practice

1. What is the primary function of carbohydrates?
2. Name three single sugars and indicate where you would expect to find these sugars.
3. Copy and complete the following table.

Table 1 Common Sugars

Sugar	Composed of	Source	
maltose			
sucrose			
lactose			

4. What happens to carbohydrates that are not immediately used by your body? Why might you want to limit your carbohydrate intake?
5. How can you recognize ingredients on food labels that are sugars?
6. How are starch and cellulose alike? How do they differ?

EXTENSION

Hydrolysis and Dehydrolysis

Listen to this audio clip for an analysis of the important elements associated with the synthesis and digestion of organic molecules in living organisms.

www.science.nelson.com 

INVESTIGATION 8.1 *Introduction*

Identifying Carbohydrates

Different classes of carbohydrates react differently to the chemical reagent Benedict's solution. In this investigation, you will use Benedict's solution to determine which of three unknowns is a specific type of carbohydrate.

Report Checklist

- ○ Purpose
- ● Problem
- ● Hypothesis
- ● Prediction
- ● Design
- ○ Materials
- ○ Procedure
- ● Evidence
- ● Analysis
- ● Evaluation
- ○ Synthesis

To perform this investigation, turn to page 271.

Lipids

You may have noticed while doing dishes how fat floats on the surface of water. This is because lipids are nonpolar. They are insoluble in polar solvents such as water. Many lipids are composed of two structural units: glycerol and fatty acids. Like complex carbohydrates, glycerol and fatty acids can be combined by dehydration synthesis (**Figure 6**).

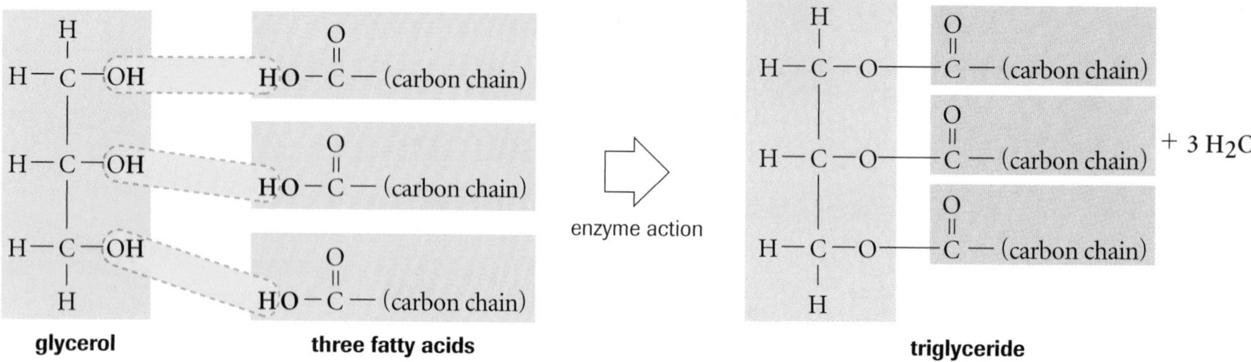

Figure 6
Triglycerides are formed by the union of glycerol and three fatty acids. Note the removal of water in the synthesis. The terms monoglyceride and diglyceride are used to describe the joining of glycerol with one or two fatty acids, respectively.

An important function of lipids is the storage of energy. Glycogen supplies are limited in most animals. Once glycogen stores have been built up, excess carbohydrates are converted into fat. This helps explain why eating carbohydrates can cause an increase in fat storage. Other lipids serve as key components in cell membranes, act as cushions for delicate organs of the body, serve as carriers for vitamins A, D, E, and K, and are the raw materials for the synthesis of hormones and other important chemicals. A layer of lipids at the base of the skin insulates you against the cold. The thicker the layer of fat, the better the insulation. Taking their cue from marine mammals, marathon swimmers often coat their bodies with a layer of fat before entering cold water.

triglyceride a lipid composed of glycerol and three fatty acids

fat a lipid composed of glycerol and saturated fatty acids; solid at room temperature

oil a lipid composed of glycerol and unsaturated fatty acids; liquid at room temperature

Triglycerides are formed by the union of glycerol and three fatty acids (**Figure 6**). Triglycerides that are solid at room temperature are called **fats.** Most of the fatty acids in animal fats are *saturated* (**Figure 7**). This means that only single bonds exist between the carbon atoms. Because the single covalent bonds tend to be stable, animal fats are difficult to break down. Triglycerides that are liquid at room temperature are called **oils.** The fatty acids of most plants are unsaturated. This means that they contain double bonds

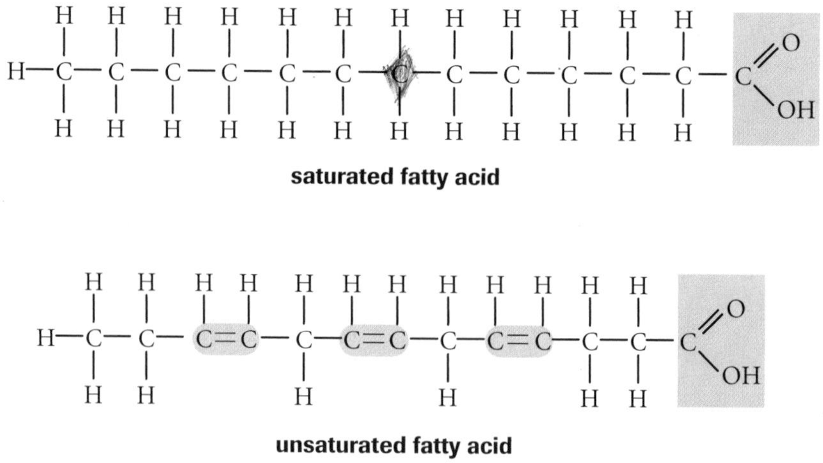

saturated fatty acid

unsaturated fatty acid

Figure 7
Saturated fats do not have double bonds between carbon atoms; unsaturated fats do.

between the carbon atoms. If the fatty acid contains only one double bond, it is monounsaturated; if it contains two or more double bonds, it is polyunsaturated. The unsaturated double bonds are somewhat reactive, and, therefore, plant oils are more easily broken down than animal fats.

A second group of lipids, called **phospholipids**, have a phosphate group bonded to the glycerol backbone of the molecule (**Figure 8**). The negatively charged phosphate replaces one of the fatty acids, providing a polar end to the lipid. The polar end of phospholipids is soluble in water, while the nonpolar end is insoluble. These special properties make phospholipids well suited for cell membranes.

phospholipid a lipid with a phosphate molecule attached to the glycerol backbone, making the molecule polar; the major components of cell membranes

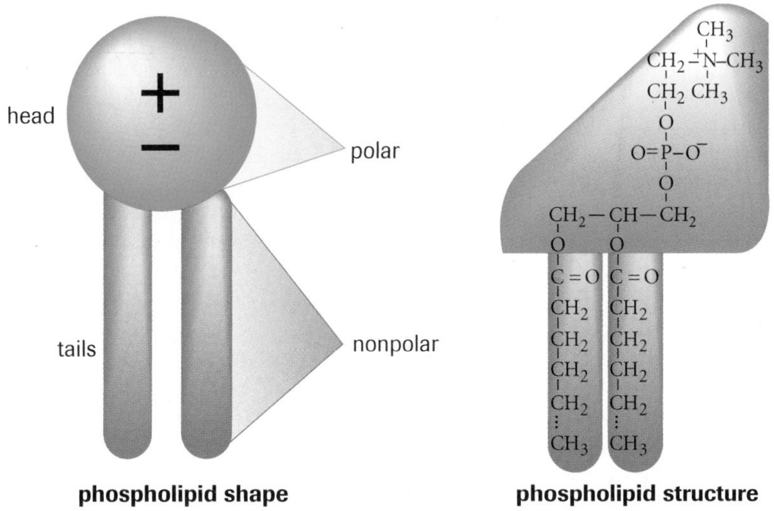

head
polar
tails
nonpolar

CH_3
$CH_2-\overset{+}{N}-CH_3$
CH_2 CH_3
O
$O=P-O^-$
O
$CH_2-CH-CH_2$
O O
C=O C=O
CH_2 CH_2
CH_2 CH_2
CH_2 CH_2
CH_2 CH_2
CH_3 CH_3

phospholipid shape **phospholipid structure**

Figure 8
Phospholipid shape and structure. The phosphate group makes these lipids soluble in water as well as in lipids.

Waxes make up a third group of lipids. In waxes, long-chain fatty acids are joined to long-chain alcohols or to carbon rings. These long, stable molecules are insoluble in water, making them well suited as a waterproof coating for plant leaves or animal feathers and fur.

wax a long-chain lipid that is insoluble in water

Practice

7. What are fats?
8. What are the two structural components of fats?
9. How do saturated fats differ from unsaturated fats?
10. Are fats essential to your diet? Explain your answer.

Liposome Technology for Drug Delivery

Lipids can assemble themselves into double-layered spheres approximately the size of a cell. The spheres are known as liposomes. They function like cell membranes because they can fuse with a cell and deliver their contents to the cell's interior. Liposomes are used with cancer-fighting drugs to help the drugs target tumours. This helps to reduce unwanted side effects from drug interactions with healthy tissues and also enables patients to accept higher doses of anti-cancer drugs. One of these liposomal drugs was discovered by Dr. Theresa Allen and her research group at the University of Alberta.

Liposomes are also showing promise as a means of increasing the efficiency of gene therapy. Gene therapy is the process of introducing new genes into the DNA of a person's cells to correct a genetic disease. In a process similar to endocytosis, researchers have successfully inserted DNA into liposomes that have fused with target cells.

Case Study

Fats and Health

Although fats are a required part of your diet, problems arise when you consume too much. Doctors recommend that no more than 30 % of total energy intake be in the form of fats. Fats are concentrated energy sources containing more than twice as much energy as an equivalent mass of carbohydrate or protein. By eating 100 g of fat, you take in about 3780 kJ of energy. (The kilojoule, kJ, is a unit used to measure food energy.) By comparison, 100 g of carbohydrates or protein yield 1680 kJ of energy. When energy input or consumption exceeds energy output, the result is weight gain.

Heart disease has been associated with diets high in saturated fats. Recall that the single bonds between the carbon molecules make the fats stable. The stable fats tend to remain intact inside the cells of the body much longer than more reactive macromolecules. High-fat diets and obesity have also been linked to certain types of cancer, such as breast, colon, and prostate. Obesity has also been linked to high blood pressure and adult-onset diabetes. According to one report, over 80 % of people with adult-onset diabetes are overweight.

The Cholesterol Controversy

Heart disease, the number-one killer of North Americans, can be caused by the accumulation of cholesterol in the blood vessels. Scientific research on cholesterol has changed direction in recent years. Lipid-rich foods, such as fish and olive oil, were once thought to raise blood cholesterol levels. Currently, most scientists believe that these foods may actually reduce blood cholesterol levels. Similarly, alcohol in moderate consumption may contribute to a decrease in blood cholesterol levels. Added to this confusion is the fact that genes play a major role in determining cholesterol levels. Research indicates that people with a certain genetic makeup are predisposed to atherosclerosis, which is a buildup of cholesterol in the walls of blood vessels that causes narrowing of the vessels (**Figure 9**).

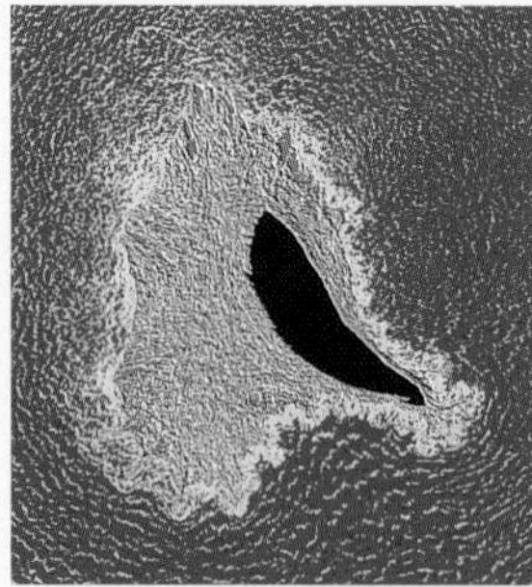

Figure 9
Atherosclerosis (tan area) causes restricted blood flow in blood vessels and can lead to a blockage, possibly causing a heart attack or stroke.

Not all cholesterol is bad. Cholesterol is found naturally in cell membranes and acts as the raw material for the synthesis of certain hormones—sex hormones are made from it.

The cells of the body package cholesterol in water-soluble protein in order to transport it in the blood. Two important types are low-density lipoprotein and high-density lipoprotein.

Low-Density Lipoprotein (LDL)

LDL is considered to be "bad" cholesterol. About 70 % of cholesterol intake is in the form of LDL. High levels of LDL have been associated with the clogging of arteries. LDL particles bind to receptor sites on cell membranes and are removed from the blood (principally by the liver). However, as the level of LDL increases and exceeds the number of receptor sites, excess LDL-cholesterol begins to form deposits in the walls of arteries. The accumulation of cholesterol and other substances in the artery walls is known as plaque. Unfortunately, plaque restricts blood flow and can lead to a heart attack or stroke.

High-Density Lipoprotein (HDL)

HDL is often called "good" cholesterol. HDL carries bad cholesterol back to the liver, which begins breaking it down. HDL lowers blood cholesterol. Most researchers now believe that the balance between LDL and HDL is critical in assessing the risks of cardiovascular disease. Some researchers believe that exercise increases the level of HDL. Strong evidence also supports the theory that fibre, or cellulose, in the diet helps reduce cholesterol. It is believed that fibre binds to cholesterol in the gastrointestinal tract. However, it should be pointed out that fibre does not affect everyone the same way.

Trans Fats

By adding hydrogen molecules to unsaturated fats, such as vegetable oils, manufacturers are able to convert them into more stable saturated fats. This process, known as hydrogenation, is used to convert vegetable oil into margarine or shortening. The word *trans* comes from the transformation of unsaturated fats, with reactive double bonds between carbon atoms, into the more stable, less reactive saturated fats. The process increases the shelf-life of foods.

By increasing the shelf-life of trans fats, manufacturers also make them more difficult for you to break down. Rather than becoming a source of energy, these fats are stored in the body. Trans fats lead to obesity. Scientific evidence shows that the consumption of trans fats and dietary cholesterol raises LDL levels while lowering HDL levels, which increases the risk of heart disease. Many physicians indicate that trans fats are far worse than naturally occurring saturated fats. On November 23, 2004, the House of Commons passed a motion calling for a task force to create a regulation that would limit the trans fat content in all food products. Although no maximum daily intake has been established in Canada, most experts advocate between 1 g and 2 g of trans fats at most. Many North Americans consume as much as 20 g of trans fats per day. It's easy to see how when you look at the following examples:

- Five small chicken nuggets from a fast-food outlet contained nearly 4 g of trans fats.
- An apple danish from a donut shop contained about 2.7 g of trans fats.
- One large serving of French fries contained as much as 6 g of trans fats.

Case Study Questions

1. Doctors recommend that no more than 30 % of your dietary intake be fat. Why should fat consumption be limited?
2. Differentiate between "good" and "bad" cholesterol.
3. The level of LDL in your blood does not solely determine your risk for heart attack.
   (a) What influence do genes have?
   (b) What influence do HDL levels have?
4. What are trans fats? Why are they a reason for concern?
5. Should legislation be introduced to limit trans fats in foods?

Proteins

Unlike carbohydrates and fats, proteins are not primarily energy compounds. **Proteins** are used to form the structural parts of a cell. Whenever cells are damaged and require repair, proteins are manufactured. Your cells also make proteins to build structures for new cells. Proteins are composed of building blocks called **amino acids**. **Figure 10** shows the general structure of an amino acid. The NH_2 group is the amino group, and the COOH group is the carboxyl group. The R group can represent a number of different structures and differentiates one amino acid from another.

protein a chain of amino acids that form the structural parts of cells or act as antibodies or enzymes

amino acid a chemical that contains nitrogen; can be linked together to form proteins

Cytoplasmic organelles like the mitochondria and ribosomes are composed largely of protein. The predominant part of muscles, nerves, skin, and hair is protein. Antibodies are specialized proteins that help the body defend itself against disease; enzymes are proteins that speed chemical reactions. Like lipids and carbohydrates, proteins are composed of carbon, hydrogen, and oxygen. However, proteins contain nitrogen and, often, sulfur atoms as well. Like sugars and lipids, proteins can supply energy for the tissues, although energy production is not their main function.

The diversity among people and among different species can, in part, be explained by proteins. A limited number of carbohydrates and lipids are found in all living things, but the array of proteins is almost infinite. Proteins are composed of 20 different amino acids. With a change in position of a single amino acid, the structure of a protein can be altered. The structure of six amino acids is shown in **Figure 11**. A small protein may contain only a few amino acids, while a large one may have more than 250 000 amino acids.

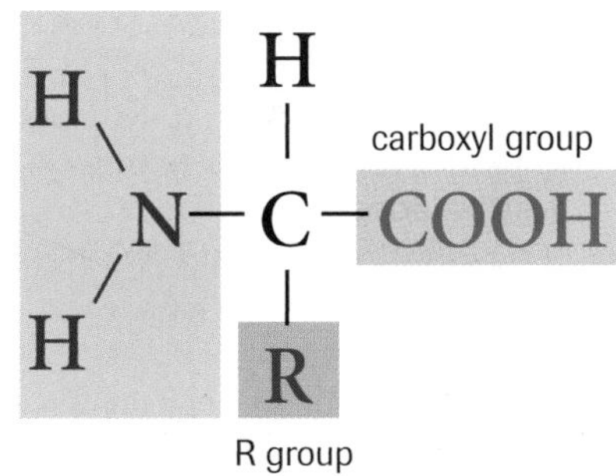

Figure 10
Amino acid structure

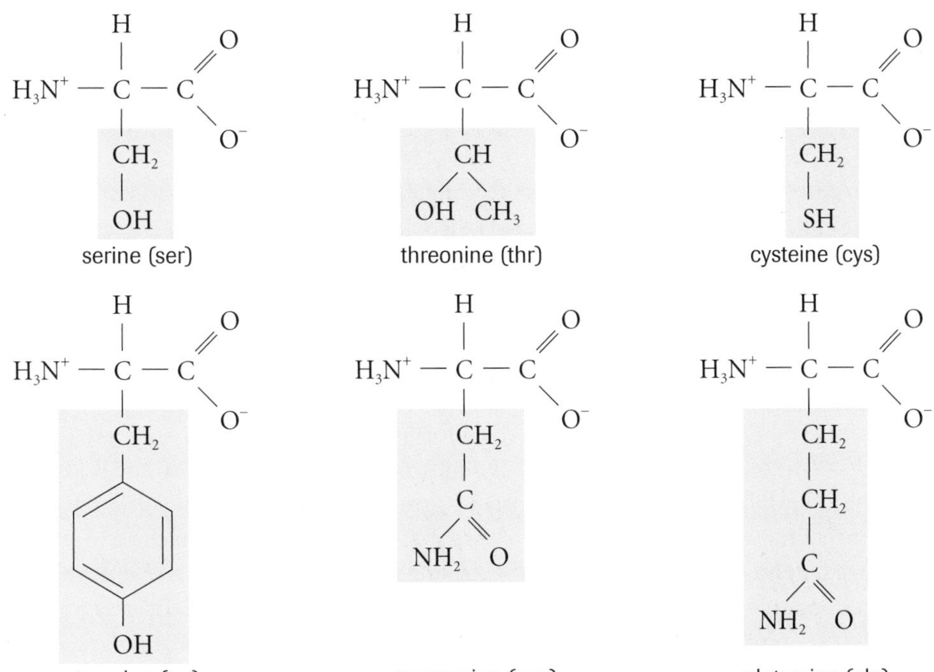

Figure 11
Each amino acid contains an amino and a carboxyl group, which are shown in their ionized form as they would be inside a cell.

The order and number of amino acids determine the type of protein. Fish protein is distinctively different from cow protein and human protein. The protein you eat is digested and absorbed, and the individual amino acids are carried in the blood to the cells of your body. Your cells reassemble the amino acids in sequences that are determined by your genes. **Figure 12** shows how amino acids are joined. As in carbohydrate and lipid synthesis, a water molecule is removed during the synthesis of protein. The covalent bond that forms between the carboxyl group of one amino acid and the amino group of the adjoining amino acid is called a **peptide bond**. For this reason, chains of amino acids are referred to as **polypeptides**.

peptide bond the bond that joins amino acids

polypeptide a chain of three or more amino acids

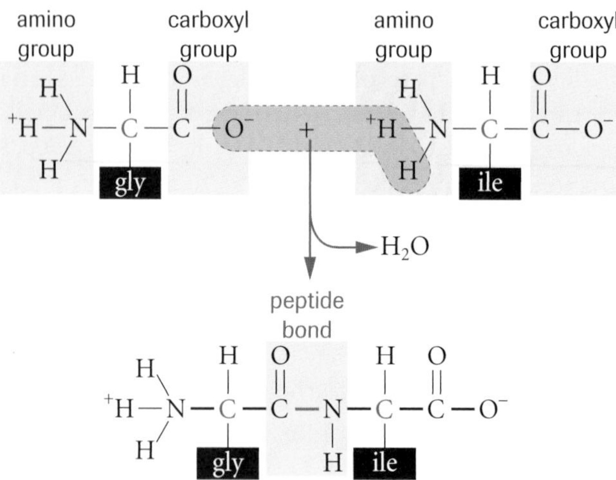

Figure 12 Dehydration synthesis of amino acids to form a polypeptide

The importance of proteins in the diet cannot be overestimated. Although the body is capable of making many of the amino acids, there are eight amino acids that the body cannot synthesize. These are called **essential amino acids** and must be obtained from your food. The lack of any one of the essential amino acids will lead to specific protein deficiencies and disease.

essential amino acid an amino acid that must be obtained from the diet

Structure of Proteins

Proteins are polypeptides that are folded into specific three-dimensional shapes. Some proteins contain more than one polypeptide. A protein's shape, or structure, determines its function. The structure of a protein is determined by its sequence of amino acids. Changing just a single amino acid can alter the structure of a protein. There are four levels of protein structure: primary, secondary, tertiary, and quaternary.

The primary structure of a protein is the unique sequence of amino acids in the chain (**Figure 13 (a)**, next page). British chemist Frederick Sanger was the first to determine the primary structure of a protein. He identified the amino acid sequence of cow insulin. The primary structure of a protein determines its secondary structure. Depending on the amino acids in the polypeptide chain, folds and coils can occur along the length of the chain. These make up the secondary structure. Hydrogen bonding between amino acids pulls the chain into helical coils and pleated sheets (**Figure 13 (b)**, next page).

Additional folding of the polypeptide chain forms the tertiary structure (**Figure 13 (c)**, next page). The tertiary structure occurs because of interactions between the R groups of different amino acids. An example of an R-group interaction is a disulfide bridge. When the sulfur-containing R groups of two cysteine amino acids are close together, they form a bond called a disulfide bridge. A single polypeptide chain of hemoglobin, the iron-containing pigment found in red blood cells, is a tertiary protein structure.

Quaternary proteins are large globular proteins formed from two or more polypeptides (**Figure 13 (d)**, next page). Hemoglobin is a quaternary protein. It contains four individual polypeptide chains that combine to form the functional hemoglobin molecule.

Registered Dietician

As many Canadians rely more on fast food, concern has been raised about how diet affects health. Dieticians provide information on how many calories should be consumed and the types of foods needed to maintain health. Investigate career possibilities for registered dieticians.

www.science.nelson.com 

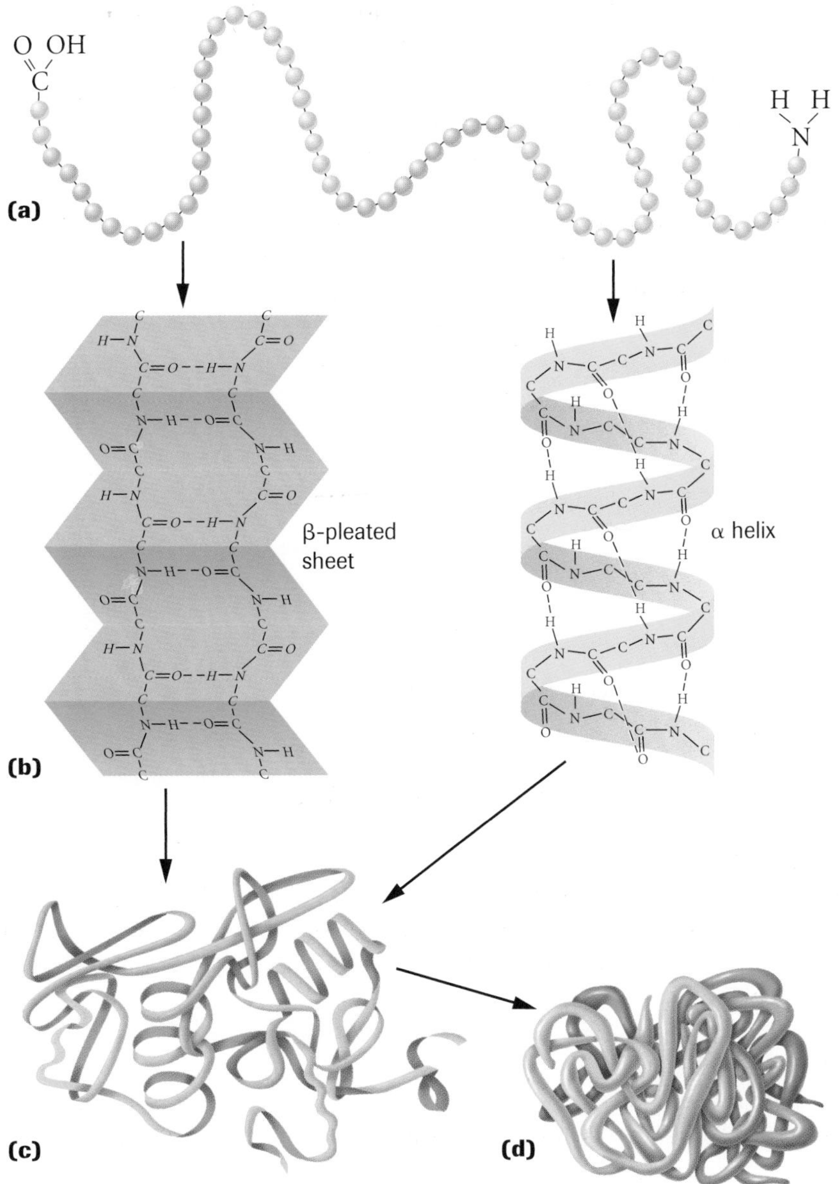

Figure 13
(a) The primary structure of a protein is the sequence of amino acids in the polypeptide strand.
(b) Hydrogen bonds that form with nearby amino acids coil and fold the polypeptide into α helices and β-pleated sheets; these constitute the polypeptide's secondary structure.
(c) The polypeptide folds further to form its tertiary structure. These fold are stabilized by R group interactions.
(d) The clustering of two or more polypeptides in tertiary structure generates the quaternary structure of a protein.

Denaturation and Coagulation

Exposing a protein to excess heat, radiation, or a change in pH will alter its shape. Physical or chemical factors that disrupt bonds cause changes in the configuration of the protein, a process called **denaturation**. The protein may uncoil or assume a new shape. The result is a change in the protein's physical properties as well as its biological activity. Once the physical or chemical factor is removed, the protein may assume its original shape.

A permanent change in protein shape is referred to as **coagulation**. The boiling of an egg, for example, causes the shape of proteins to be altered. The proteins in the egg are said to have coagulated because no matter how much cooling takes place, they will never assume their original shape.

denaturation the process that occurs when the bonds of a protein molecule are disrupted, causing a temporary change in shape

coagulation the process that occurs when the bonds of a protein molecule are disrupted, causing a permanent change in shape

INVESTIGATION 8.2 *Introduction*

Identifying Lipids and Proteins

Lipids and proteins have different chemical compositions, and therefore can be distinguished based on their reaction with certain chemicals. In this investigation, you will use chemical reagents to conduct tests on some common foods and on unknown samples to determine if they contain lipids or proteins.

Report Checklist

- ● Purpose
- ○ Problem
- ○ Hypothesis
- ● Prediction
- ○ Design
- ○ Materials
- ○ Procedure
- ● Evidence
- ● Analysis
- ● Evaluation
- ● Synthesis

To perform this investigation, turn to page 272.

EXPLORE an issue

Irradiation Technology

Issue Checklist

- ○ Issue
- ● Resolution
- ○ Design
- ● Evidence
- ● Analysis
- ● Evaluation

Food irradiation is a process in which foods are exposed to high levels of radiation to disrupt the DNA of bacteria and other harmful agents growing on the food (**Figure 14**) that could otherwise cause food-borne diseases. This technology is so effective that the food eaten by astronauts is sterilized by irradiation so they do not ingest any microbes that could make them sick while in space.

Irradiation extends the shelf-life of food since food spoilage is caused by bacteria and other microbes. With an extended shelf-life, foods can be transported over greater distances and, consequently, a greater variety of foods are available to consumers at a lower price.

The food does not become radioactive, and the nutritional value that is lost is approximately the same as that lost in cooking. However, it should be noted that the radiation can alter the molecular chemistry of the food, creating radiolytic products. In some studies, benzene and formaldehyde have been identified.

The ionizing energy does create a large number of short-lived free radicals that would be potentially harmful if they persisted, but many experts say they do not. These short-lived free radicals kill microorganisms such as *Salmonella* and inhibit sprouting and ripening in fruits and vegetables. The irradiation of cereal grains kills invading insects that also lead to food contamination and spoilage.

Opponents of radiation technology indicate that some of the new chemical bonds formed in irradiated foods can be harmful, and it is for this reason that they claim the technology should be severely restricted or eliminated completely. In addition, beneficial chemicals, such as vitamins, are often destroyed by the process. Opponents also point out that animals fed irradiated foods have demonstrated various health problems, including premature births, mutations, organ damage, and immune system dysfunction.

Proponents of irradiation technology say that this technology, like traditional methods of preservation, such as salting, canning, and freezing, changes the food only slightly while significantly reducing the spoilage by bacteria.

Despite the many benefits, irradiation is not for all foods. Foods high in fats, such as dairy products and fatty fish, can develop bad odours and tastes because of the breakdown of fat to fatty acids. The technology is much more accepted in North America and Asia, and European governments are more reluctant to use it. At this time, there are no standards for labelling irradiated food.

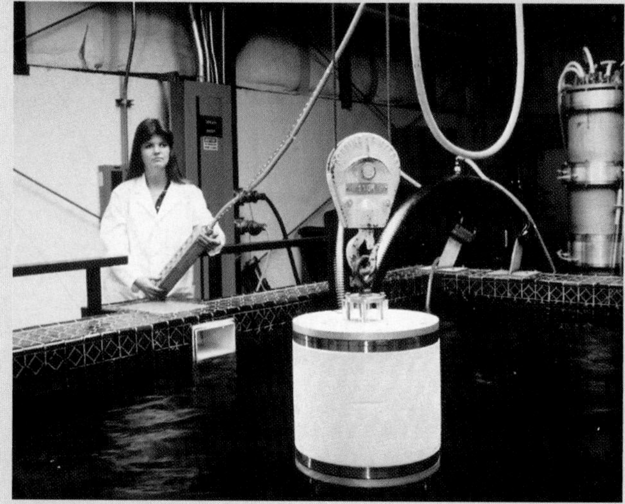

Figure 14
A technician moves a container of fruit above a pool that is used to study food irradiation. The pool contains an accelerator that produces X-rays.

Statement
Irradiated foods should be allowed.

1. Form a group and research the issue.

www.science.nelson.com 

2. Discuss the issue with class members and others in preparation for a debate.
3. Write a list of points and counterpoints that your group has considered.
4. Take a stand. Decide if you agree or disagree with the statement.
5. Defend your position in the debate.
6. What responsibilities do governments have in regulating irradiation technology?

SUMMARY Essential Nutrients

- Carbohydrates are molecules that contain hydrogen, carbon, and oxygen. Carbohydrates are the preferred source of energy for cells.
- Lipids are compounds formed from glycerol and fatty acids. Lipids are energy-storage compounds.
- Proteins are molecules constructed of amino acids. Proteins are the structural components of cells.

Table 2 Nutrients: An Overview

Nutrient	Sources	Function in humans
carbohydrates	• plants	• energy source
lipids	• plant oils (unsaturated fats) • animal fats (saturated fats)	• energy storage • insulation of skin and cushioning of organs • synthesis of hormones (steroids)
proteins	• plants and animals	• structural components of the cell • enzymes • antibodies

Section 8.1 Questions

1. Provide an example of dehydration synthesis by showing how two monosaccharides form a disaccharide. Show the reactants and end products of the reaction.
2. Explain why marathon runners consume large quantities of carbohydrates a few days prior to a big race.
3. Why is cellulose, or fibre, considered to be an important part of the diet?
4. The following information was gathered by analyzing amino acid sequences of a protein. **Table 3** shows the number of amino acids that are different between two organisms.

Table 3 Amino Acid Differences between Some Organisms

Organism	dog	horse	donkey	pig	duck
dog	-	10	8	4	12
horse		-	1	5	16
donkey			-	4	15
pig				-	13
duck					-

   a) From the information in the table, which two organisms do you think are most closely related? Why?
   b) How similar do you think the amino acids would be between a dog and a fish? Would you expect the amino acids to be more or less similar than those of a dog and a duck? Give your reasons.

5. Using **Figure 15**, identify advantages or disadvantages associated with each of the foods listed.

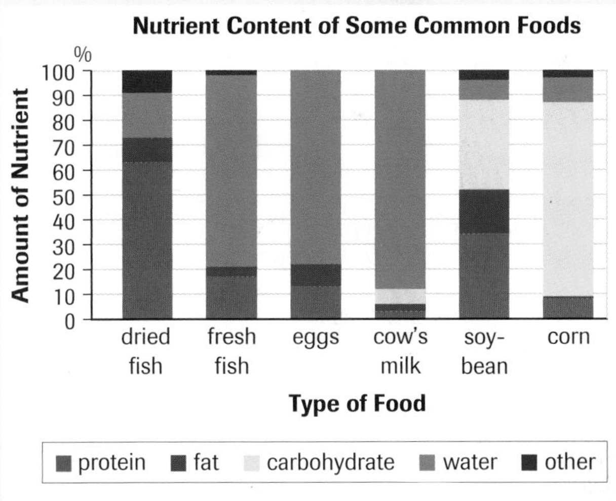

Figure 15

6. A student believes that the sugar inside a diet chocolate bar is sucrose because a test with Benedict's solution yields negative results. How would you go about testing whether or not the sugar present is a nonreducing sugar?

8.2 Enzymes

catalyst a chemical that increases the rate of chemical reactions without altering the products or being altered itself

enzyme a protein catalyst that permits chemical reactions to proceed at low temperatures

substrate a molecule on which an enzyme works

Molecules are in constant motion. Even molecules in solids vibrate in fixed positions. Although chemical reactions sometimes occur when molecules collide, most reactions do not occur spontaneously. Adding thermal energy to a system increases the system's kinetic energy. This means that the molecules move faster, increasing the number of collisions and the probability of a reaction taking place. However, heating cells is dangerous—too much thermal energy could destroy the cell.

Chemical reactions must proceed at relatively low temperatures within cells. **Catalysts** are chemicals that speed up chemical reactions at low temperatures without altering the products formed by the reaction. The catalyst remains unchanged after the chemical reaction, and so can be used again and again. Reactions that occur within living organisms are regulated by protein catalysts called **enzymes**. Enzymes permit low-temperature reactions by reducing the reaction's activation energy. **Figure 1** compares two energy-releasing reactions—one with an enzyme, and one without.

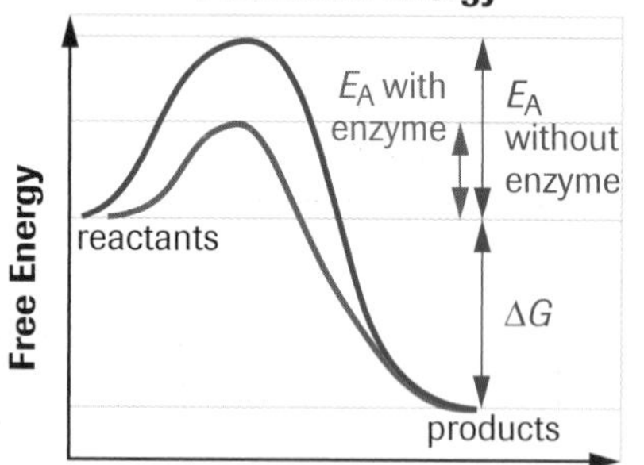

Figure 1
An enzyme decreases the activation energy needed for a reaction to occur.

The molecules on which the enzyme works are called the **substrates**. Each substrate molecule combines with a specific enzyme. The substrate molecules are changed during the reaction, and a product is formed. It has been estimated that about 200 000 different chemical reactions occur within the cells of your body. Each reaction uses a specific enzyme to catalyze it.

Enzymes are identified by the suffix *-ase*, which is added to the name of the substrate that the enzyme combines with. Carbohydrases break down carbohydrates; for example, the enzyme that controls the hydrolysis of sucrose into its two component parts—glucose and fructose—is called sucrase. Proteases break down proteins, while lipases act on lipids.

Enzymes increase the probability of reactions occurring by bringing substrate molecules together. Enzymes have folded surfaces that trap particular substrate molecules, aligning them to cause the chemical reaction. Having large molecules collide is not enough—the molecules must collide at the appropriate binding sites if the reaction is to proceed.

active site the area of an enzyme that combines with the substrate

The **active site** of the enzyme is the area that joins with the substrate molecules. Each enzyme has a specially shaped active site that provides a "dock" for specific substrate molecules. This long-standing model, called the "lock-and-key model," was first proposed by Emil Fischer in 1890. The temporary joining of the enzyme with the substrate forms the enzyme-substrate complex (**Figure 2**).

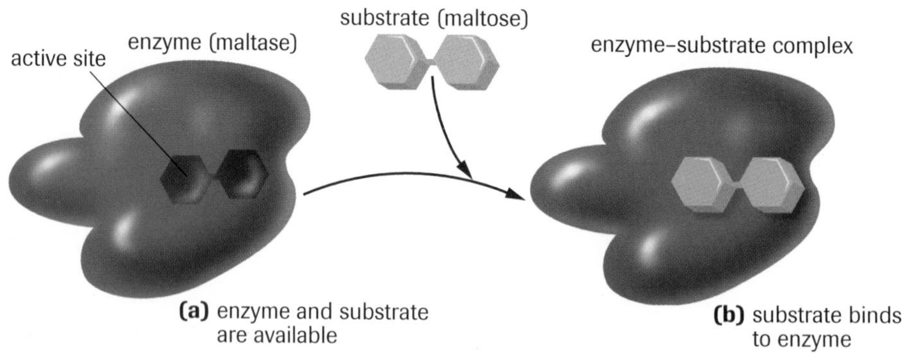

Figure 2
The enzyme maltase binds to maltose, its substrate.

cofactor an inorganic ion that helps an enzyme combine with a substrate molecule

coenzyme an organic molecule synthesized from a vitamin that helps an enzyme to combine with a substrate molecule

A modified theory, called the "induced-fit model," replaced the lock-and-key model in 1973. The induced-fit model suggests that the actual shape of the active site is altered slightly when the substrate molecules are trapped, making the fit between enzyme and substrate even tighter during the formation of the enzyme-substrate complex (**Figure 2** , previous page).

Some enzymes require **cofactors** or **coenzymes** to help them bind to substrate molecules. Cofactors are inorganic ions such as iron, zinc, and potassium, as well as copper-containing compounds. Coenzymes are organic molecules that are synthesized from vitamins. Coenzymes and some cofactors may work with more than one enzyme.

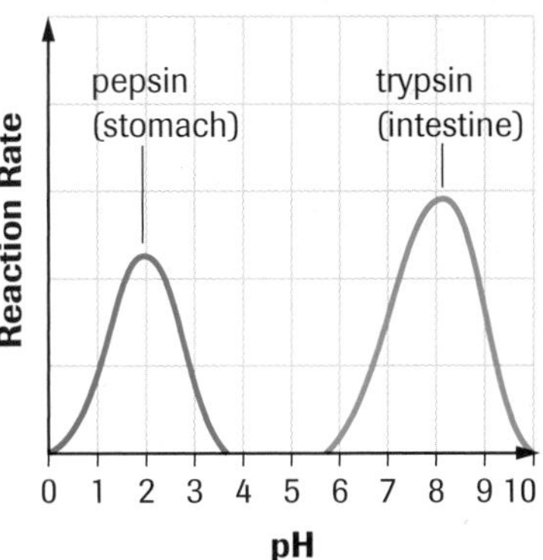

Figure 3
Different enzymes function within different pH ranges.

Factors Affecting Enzyme Reactions

It has been estimated that a single enzyme can catalyze between 100 reactions and 30 million reactions every minute. Why do some reactions occur much faster than others? To compare reaction rates, you must examine the different factors that affect enzymes.

pH

The graph in **Figure 3** indicates that enzymes function best within certain pH ranges. The enzyme pepsin, shown in green, operates best in an acidic condition. Not surprisingly, this enzyme is found in the stomach, an area of low pH. The second enzyme, trypsin, shown in blue, is most effective in a basic medium. Not surprisingly, trypsin is found in the small intestine, an area that is generally about pH 9.

To understand why pH affects enzyme activity, you must look at the molecular structure of the protein molecule. Remember that the folds in the protein molecule are created by hydrogen bonds between negatively charged acid groups and positively charged amino groups. The addition of positively charged H^+ ions, characteristic of an acidic solution, or the introduction of negatively charged OH^- ions, characteristic of a basic solution, will affect the hydrogen bonds. Thus, the three-dimensional shape of an enzyme is altered by a change in pH. When the folds in the protein are changed, the active site of the enzyme is transformed, altering the reaction.

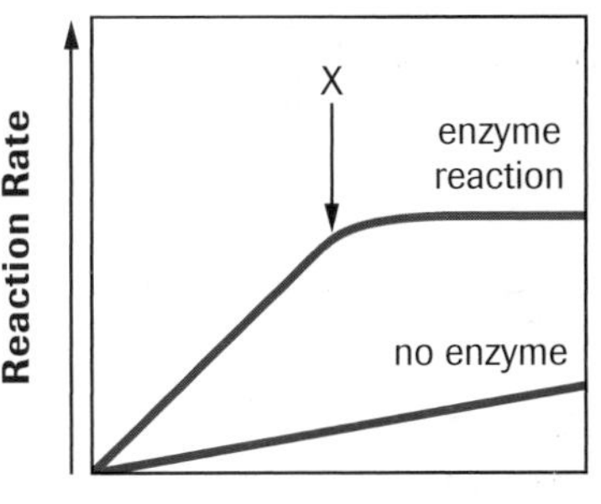

Figure 4
A higher concentration of substrate molecules increases the reaction rate.

Substrate Molecule Concentration

Enzyme activity can also be affected by the concentration of substrate molecules. For chemical reactions, the greater the number of substrate molecules, the greater the number of collisions, and the greater the rate of the reaction. Up to a point, enzyme-catalyzed reactions behave in the same manner. The reaction rate shown in **Figure 4** begins to level off at point X because there is a limit to the amount of enzyme available. Substrate molecules cannot join with the active site of an enzyme until it is free. Once the number of substrate molecules exceeds the number of enzyme molecules, the excess substrate molecules will not gain access to the active site of an enzyme. Therefore, the reaction rate begins to level off.

Temperature

The graph in **Figure 5** indicates how temperature affects enzyme-catalyzed reactions. The fact that reaction rates increase as the temperature increases should not be surprising. As energy is added, the molecules begin to move faster. The faster the molecules move, the greater the number of collisions. Subsequently, more collisions cause a greater number of products to be formed. But why do reaction rates in our cells peak at about 37 °C and then drop, even though the molecules are moving faster and colliding more often?

To answer this question, recall some important facts about enzymes. The fact that enzymes are proteins is particularly significant because at high temperatures, proteins change shape or are denatured. Any change in enzyme shape will have an effect on the formation of the

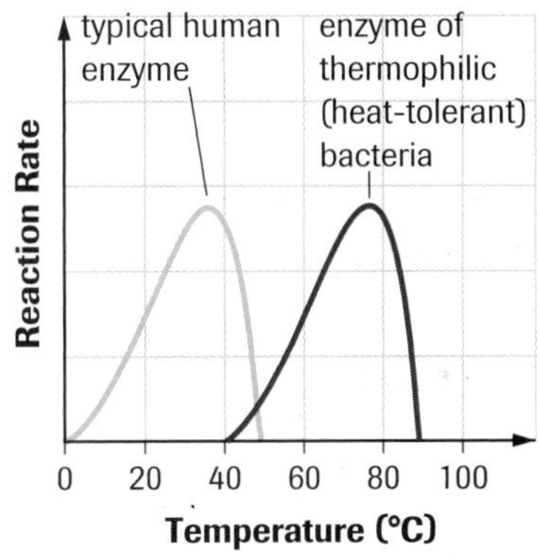

Figure 5
Different enzymes function within different temperature ranges.

enzyme-substrate complex. The greater the change to the active site of the enzyme, the less effective the enzyme. Once the enzyme is denatured, the active site is so severely altered that the substrate can no longer bind with the enzyme. The reaction is no longer catalyzed by the enzyme and, therefore, proceeds at a much slower rate.

The effect of temperature on enzymes helps explain why high fevers can be so dangerous. The relationship between temperature and enzyme-catalyzed reactions also indicates some of the advantages of being a homeotherm, an animal that maintains a constant body temperature. Mammals, birds, and other homeotherms keep their bodies at optimal temperatures for reactions.

Competitive Inhibition

competitive inhibitor a molecule with a shape complementary to a specific enzyme that competes with the substrate for access to the active site of the enzyme and blocks chemical reactions

Inhibitor molecules can affect enzyme reactions. Often referred to as **competitive inhibitors**, these molecules have shapes very similar to that of the substrate. The inhibitors actually compete with the substrate molecules for the active sites of the enzymes (**Figure 6**). As long as the inhibitors remain joined to the enzyme, the substrate cannot bind, and the enzyme cannot function properly.

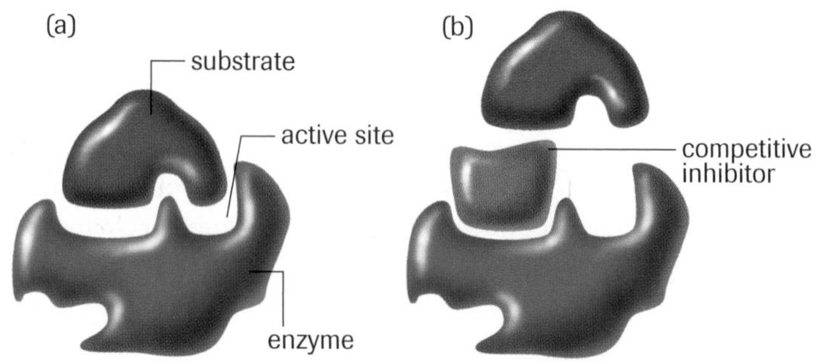

Figure 6
(a) The substrate normally binds to the active site.
(b) A competitive inhibitor competes with the substrate for the active site.

INVESTIGATION 8.3 *Introduction*

Factors That Affect the Catalase Enzyme Reaction

Catalase is an enzyme found in many species that live in oxygen-rich environments. Catalase breaks down hydrogen peroxide (H_2O_2), a toxin. What factors affect the rate of catalase activity?

Report Checklist

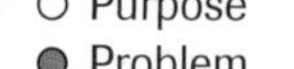

○ Purpose	● Design	● Analysis
● Problem	○ Materials	● Evaluation
● Hypothesis	○ Procedure	○ Synthesis
● Prediction	● Evidence	

To perform this investigation, turn to page 274.

Regulation of Enzyme Activity

Metabolic pathways are orderly sequences of chemical reactions, with enzymes regulating each step of the reaction. Consider the following example of a metabolic pathway. Testosterone is a male sex hormone synthesized from cholesterol or other steroids. The hormone, which is produced in larger quantities from puberty onward, is responsible for the development of secondary male sex characteristics.

Can you imagine what would happen if all of the steroids in the body were converted into testosterone? The regulation of chemicals produced by metabolic pathways is essential. The production of chemicals within a cell is regulated by the need for those chemicals. As the product from a series of chemical reactions begins to accumulate within a cell, the product interferes with one of the enzymes in a process known as **feedback inhibition**. The interference slows the reaction rate, preventing the accumulation of final products. The final product of the metabolic pathway interferes with the enzyme by combining with its regulatory site. The binding

feedback inhibition the inhibition of an enzyme in a metabolic pathway by the final product of that pathway

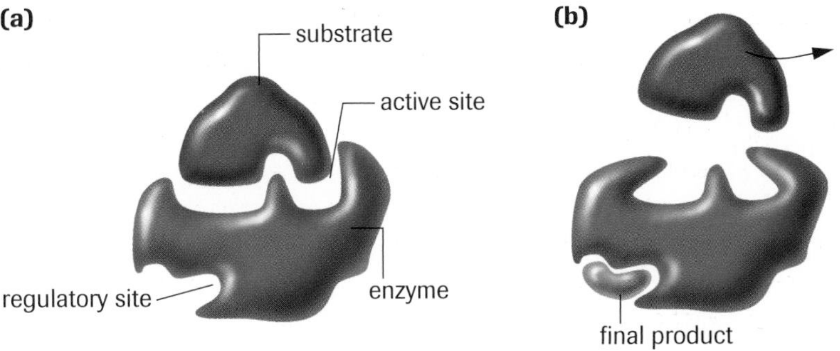

Figure 7
(a) The substrate can bind to the active site.
(b) The final product attaches to the regulatory site and changes the shape of the enzyme so that the substrate can no longer bind.

of the final product with the regulatory site of the enzyme alters the active site, and thus prevents the union of the enzyme and substrate (**Figure 7**).

Regulatory sites are not just used to turn off metabolic pathways. A buildup of the initial substrate can turn on enzyme activity. If the substrate molecule combines at the regulatory site of one of the enzymes, **precursor activity** occurs. During precursor activity, the combination of the substrate and enzyme actually improves the fit of the enzyme-substrate complex. This speeds up the formation of final products. Both feedback inhibition and precursor activity involve the binding of a molecule with the regulatory site of the enzyme. Both processes are called **allosteric activity**. The binding of the final product with the regulatory site of the enzyme will change the enzyme's active site, thereby inhibiting subsequent reactions. The binding of one of the initial reactants with the regulatory site will help mould the active site of the enzyme, improving the fit between substrate and enzyme. **Figure 8** summarizes these processes.

precursor activity the activation of the last enzyme in a metabolic pathway by the initial substrate

allosteric activity a change in an enzyme caused by the binding of a molecule

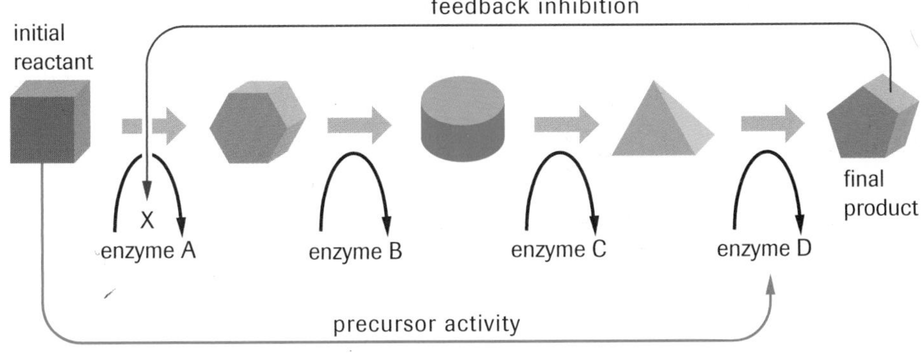

Figure 8
Allosteric activity involves both precursor activity and feedback inhibition. Precursor activities turn metabolic pathways "on," while feedback inhibition activities turn metabolic pathways "off."

SUMMARY *Enzymes*

- Chemical reactions within cells are regulated by enzymes. Enzymes are protein catalysts that lower activation energy and permit chemical reactions to proceed at body temperature.
- Cofactors are inorganic ions that help enzymes combine with substrate molecules. Coenzymes are organic molecules that help enzymes combine with substrate molecules.
- A competitive inhibitor has a shape complementary to a specific enzyme, thereby permitting it access to the active site of the enzyme. Inhibitors block chemical reactions.

- Feedback inhibition is the inhibition of the first enzyme in a metabolic pathway by the final product of that pathway.
- Precursor activity is the activation of the last enzyme in a metabolic pathway by the initial substrate.

Section 8.2 Questions

1. Explain the importance of enzymes in metabolic reactions.
2. How do enzymes increase the rate of reactions?
3. List and explain four factors that affect the rate of chemical reactions.
4. How do cofactors and coenzymes work?
5. What are competitive inhibitors?
6. What is allosteric activity?
7. How are metabolic pathways regulated by the accumulation of the final products of the reaction?
8. Explain how scientists have used chemical mimicry to combat disease.
9. Explain how enzymes work in the lock-and-key model. How has the induced-fit model changed the way in which biochemists describe enzyme activities?
10. Use the metabolic pathway in **Figure 9** to explain feedback inhibition.
11. Use **Figure 10** to answer the following questions.
    (a) Match labels A, B, and C in the diagram to the following: reactants, products, and activation energy.
    (b) How will decreasing the number of substrate molecules affect the rate of reaction? Explain your answer.
    (c) If an enzyme is introduced into this chemical reaction, explain how the reaction curve would change.
12. The reaction shown in **Figure 11** is catalyzed by an enzyme.
    (a) Complete the graph by showing what would happen if a competitive inhibitor was added at "T."
    (b) Explain why the inhibitor would affect the rate of the chemical reaction.
13. Using the information that you have gained about enzymes, explain why high fevers can be dangerous.

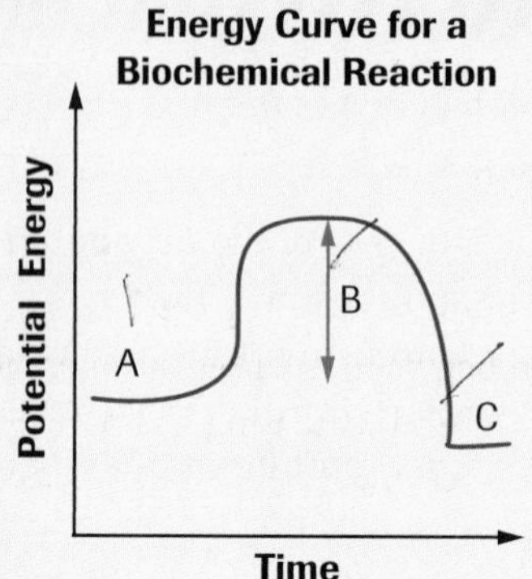

Figure 10

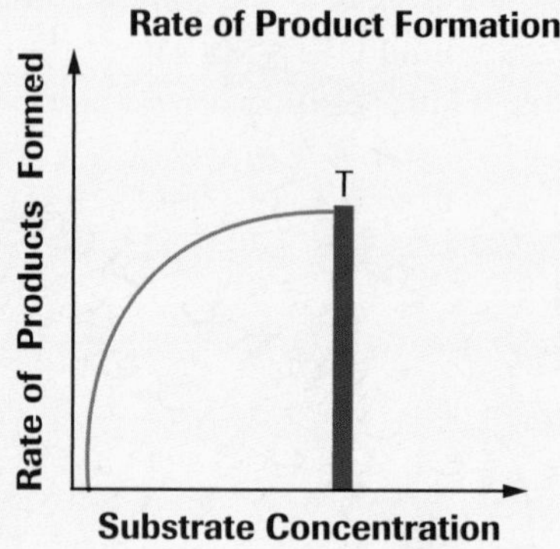

Figure 11

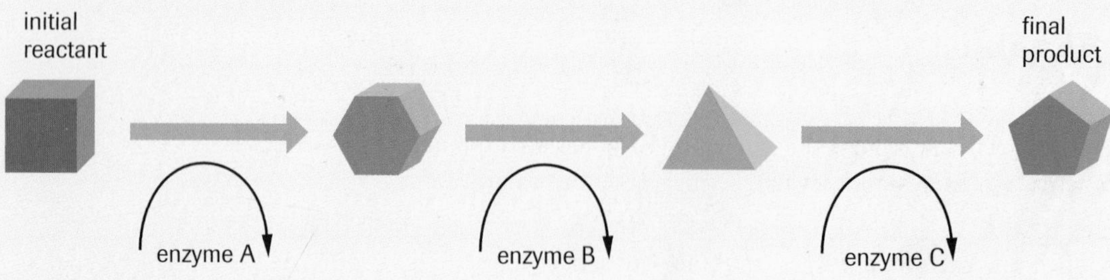

Figure 9

Ingestion 8.3

There are four components of the digestive process:

1. ingestion—the taking in of nutrients
2. digestion—the breakdown of complex organic molecules into smaller components by enzymes
3. absorption—the transport of digested nutrients to the cells of the body
4. egestion—the removal of food waste from the body

The digestive tract of adult humans, normally 6.5 m to 9 m long, stores and breaks down organic molecules into simpler components. **Figure 1** shows the entire digestive system. Physical (mechanical) digestion begins in the mouth, where food is chewed and formed into a bolus (the Greek word for ball) by the tongue. Physical digestion breaks food into smaller pieces, increasing the surface area for chemical digestion.

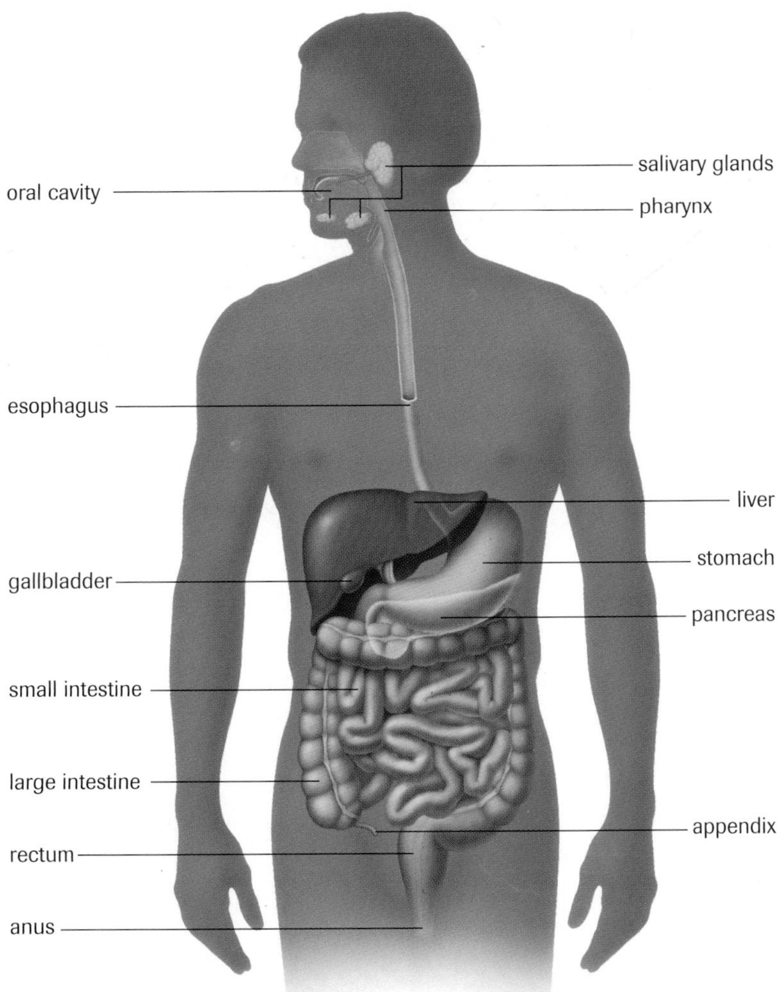

Figure 1
The human digestive system and accessory organs

CAREER CONNECTION 

X-ray Technician

X-ray technicians perform various functions, such as advising patients how to prepare for X rays and ensuring that the X ray is taken safely. X-ray technicians need to know the fundamentals of anatomy, disease, and how trauma affects various organ systems. Research the programs available for certification as an X-ray technician.

www.science.nelson.com  

amylase an enzyme that breaks down complex carbohydrates

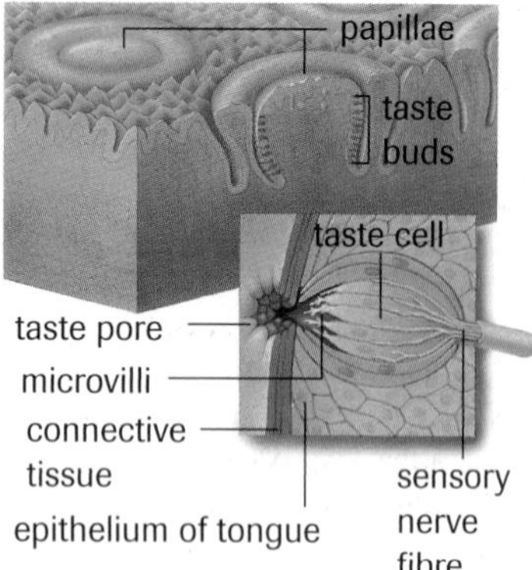

Figure 2
Taste buds are located along the tongue.

Salivary Glands

Saliva, the watery fluid produced by the salivary glands, contains **amylase** enzymes, which break down starches (complex carbohydrates) to simpler carbohydrates. Saliva dissolves food particles and makes it possible to taste what is being eaten. It also lubricates the food so that it can be swallowed.

We detect the flavour when food particles dissolved in saliva penetrate the cells of the taste buds located on the tongue and cheeks. (Our sense of smell is also involved in tasting food.) Different types of receptors respond to specific flavours. For example, the taste buds are equipped with receptors (**Figure 2**) that have a specific geometry that permits the identification of sweet tastes from carbohydrates. Nerve cells for taste are stimulated when receptor sites are bound by chemical compounds with a complementary shape. Try dissolving foods in saliva by drying your tongue and then placing a few grains of salt on it. You will not detect any flavour until the crystals dissolve in your saliva.

Teeth

The teeth are important structures for physical digestion (**Figure 3**). Eight chisel-shaped teeth at the front of your mouth, called incisors, are specialized for cutting. The incisors are bordered by sharp, dagger-shaped canine teeth that are specialized for tearing. Next to the canine teeth are the premolars. These broad, flattened teeth are specialized for grinding. The molars are next. These teeth tend to be even broader and have cusps that are even more flattened. They are designed for crushing food. The last set of molars are the wisdom teeth, so called because they usually do not emerge until we reach about 16 to 20 years of age. Each tooth is covered with enamel, which is the hardest substance in the human body.

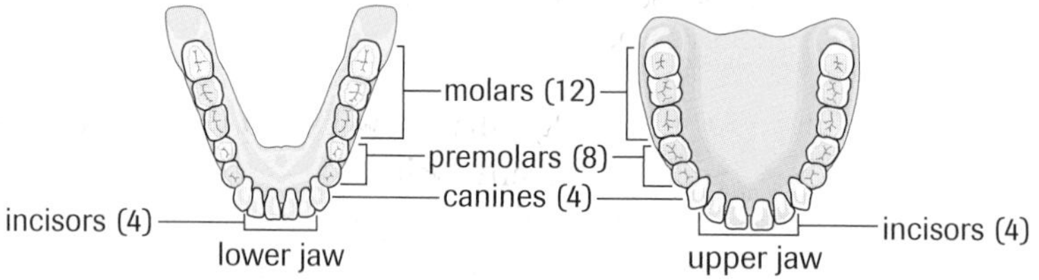

Figure 3
Human adult teeth

peristalsis rhythmic, wavelike contractions of muscle that move food along the gastrointestinal tract

Esophagus

Once swallowed, food travels from the mouth to the stomach by way of the esophagus. The bolus of food stretches the walls of the esophagus, activating muscles that set up waves of rhythmic contractions called **peristalsis**. Peristaltic contractions, which are involuntary, move food along the gastrointestinal tract (**Figure 4**). The only points at which food is moved voluntarily along the tract is during swallowing and during the last phase, egestion. Peristaltic action will move food or fluid from the esophagus to the stomach even if you stand on your head.

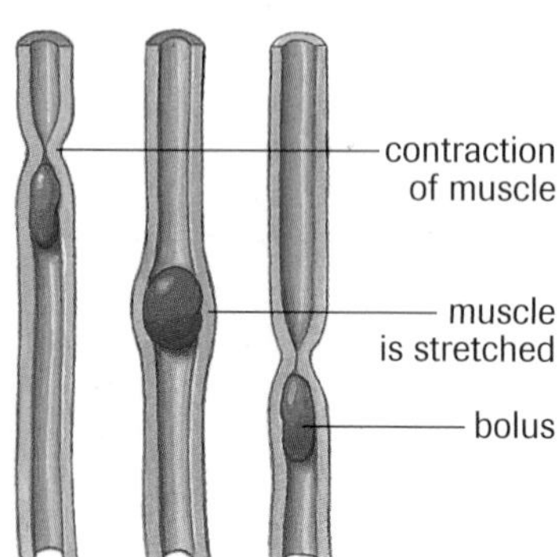

Figure 4
Rhythmic contractions of muscle move food along the digestive tract.

Practice

1. What are the functions of saliva?
2. How does chewing assist in the digestion of food?
3. What are amylase enzymes and why are they necessary?
4. How is food moved along the esophagus?

Stomach

The stomach is the site of food storage and initial protein digestion. The stomach contains three layers of muscle, which run in different directions so that the muscle contractions can churn the food (**Figure 5 (a)**).The movement of food to and from the stomach is regulated by circular muscles called **sphincters**. Sphincters act like the drawstrings on a bag. Contraction of the lower esophageal sphincter (LES) closes the opening to the stomach, while its relaxation allows food to enter. The LES prevents food and acid from being regurgitated up into the esophagus. A second sphincter, the pyloric sphincter, regulates the movement of food and stomach acids into the small intestine (**Figure 5 (b)**).

sphincter a constrictor muscle that regulates the opening and closing of a tubelike structure

Activation of Digestive Zymogens

What are digestive zymogens? This audio clip will give you information on a number of protein-digesting enzymes that are secreted into the stomach and duodenum, and unravel the mechanism of how they are activated from a zymogen state.

www.science.nelson.com 

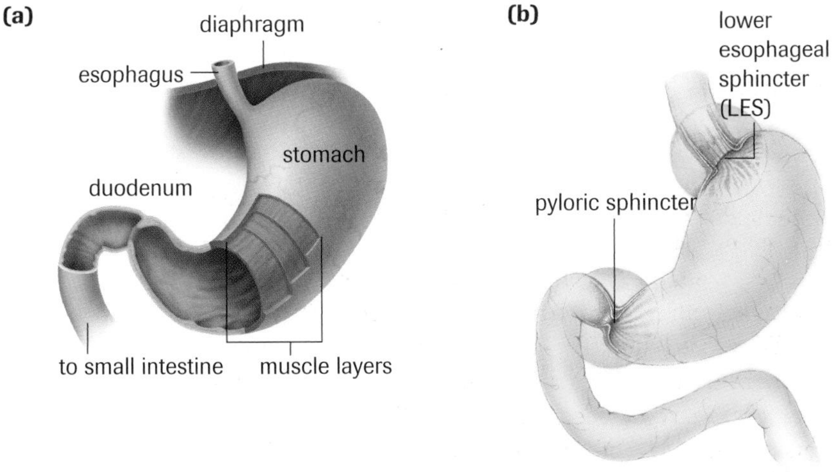

Figure 5
(a) Muscle is responsible for the contractions of the stomach.
(b) Sphincters regulate the movement of food.

The J-shaped stomach has numerous ridges that allow it to expand so that it can store about 1.5 L of food. Millions of cells line the inner wall of the stomach. These cells secrete the various stomach fluids, called gastric fluids or gastric juice, that aid digestion. Contractions of the stomach mix the food with the gastric fluids. Therefore, the stomach is involved in both physical and chemical digestion. Approximately 500 mL of these fluids are produced following a large meal. Gastric fluid includes **mucus**, hydrochloric acid (HCl), pepsinogens, and other substances. Hydrochloric acid kills many harmful substances that are ingested with food. It also converts pepsinogen into its active form, **pepsin**, which is a protein-digesting enzyme. Pepsin breaks the long amino acid chains in proteins into shorter chains, called polypeptides.

mucus a protective lubricating substance composed mostly of protein

pepsin a protein-digesting enzyme produced in the stomach

The pH inside the stomach normally ranges between 2.0 and 3.0, but may approach pH 1.0. Acids with a pH of 2.0 can dissolve fibres in a rug! It is the high acidity of hydrochloric acid that makes it effective at killing pathogens and allows pepsin to do its work. How does the stomach safely store these strong chemicals, both of which dissolve the proteins that make up cells? A layer of alkaline mucus protects the stomach lining from being digested. Pepsinogen moves through the cell membrane and mucous lining, is activated by HCl, and becomes pepsin. The pepsin breaks down the proteins in the food, but not the proteins of the stomach's cells because these proteins are protected by the mucous layer. The esophagus does not have a protective mucous layer, so if the LES is weak, stomach acid may enter the esophagus and damage its lining. This causes the pain known as heartburn.

DID YOU KNOW ?

How Big Is Your Stomach?

The stomach capacity of a newborn human baby can be as little as 60 mL. An adult stomach has a maximum capacity of about 1.5 L, while the stomach of a cow is divided into four compartments and may hold up to 300 L.

ulcer a lesion on the surface of an organ

Peptic Ulcers

When the protective mucous lining of the stomach breaks down, the cell membrane is exposed to the HCl and pepsin. The destruction of the cell membrane leads to a peptic **ulcer**. Beneath the thin layer of cells is a rich network of blood vessels. As the acids irritate the cells of the stomach lining, there is an increase in blood flow and acid secretions. With this increased blood flow and acid secretion, more tissue is burned, and the cycle continues. Eventually the blood vessels begin to break down.

Most ulcers are the result of an infection by a bacterium called *Helicobacter pylori (H. pylori)*. Dr. Barry Marshall, an Australian physician, first made this connection in the early 1980s. Scientists were initially skeptical of Dr. Marshall's findings, since it was believed that bacteria would be unable to survive the highly acidic conditions of the stomach. In 2005, Dr. Marshall received a Nobel Prize in Physiology or Medicine for his work with *H. pylori* and ulcers. A simple breath test for the presence of *H. pylori* is now widely available. Dr. Marshall is currently working in the United States, where he is investigating a possible link between the microbe and some forms of stomach cancer.

If an *H. pylori* infection is found early enough, treatment with an antibiotic can cure the ulcer. In some cases, the amount of damage is severe enough to also require surgery. A device called an endoscope can be fitted with a light-emitting glass fibre and then positioned inside a patient's body (**Figure 6**). Physicians then use the endoscope to view the damage. Tiny forceps fitted in the endoscope may be used to extract small pieces of tissue for a biopsy. Special lasers designed for surgical applications may be used to remove any damaged tissue. The laser beam is thinner than most scalpels and provides the added advantage of sealing small blood vessels.

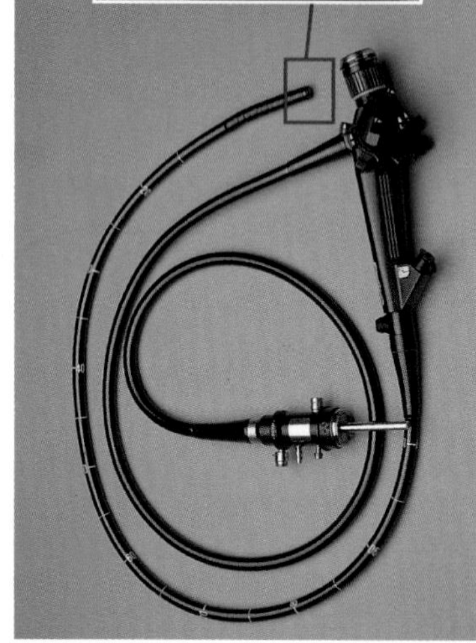

Figure 6
The endoscope can be used to look inside the body.

EXPLORE an issue

Issue Checklist

○ Issue ● Resolution ○ Design ● Evidence ● Analysis ● Evaluation

Fad Diets

Dieting is big business. An array of low-calorie food products and specialized diet plans are competing in an ever-expanding market. Diet plans like the Atkins Diet are high in protein and low in carbohydrates, while the Beverly Hills Diet recommends low protein and high carbohydrate consumption. Some weight-loss plans include appetite suppressants such as amphetamines, as well as laxatives.

People who are overweight are more prone to certain diseases such as atherosclerosis and diabetes; however, being underweight can also cause problems, such as fatigue and increased risk of illness and injury.

Statement
Specialized diet plans may actually contribute to malnutrition in people who use them consistently.

Point
Some diets emphasize high-calorie fatty foods such as steaks, cheese, and milk, which can increase cholesterol levels. Liquid protein diets provide only about 400 calories per day, whereas most people need about 1200 calories per day.

Counterpoint
Low-calorie, nonfattening foods are carefully monitored by nutritionists. Prepared products are not the only answer to good eating. People must take responsibility for maintaining a healthy balance in their food intake. Dieting alone cannot be expected to perform miracles.

1. Research the issue.

www.science.nelson.com 

2. Reflect on your findings. Discuss the various viewpoints with others.
3. Prepare for the class debate.

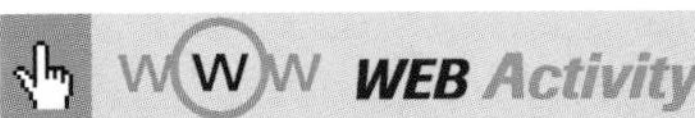

Web Quest—What Are You Eating?

Have you ever explored the intake and output of energy in your own body? This Web Quest guides you through collecting data on your own food intake and physical activity. Using this information, you can then analyze the data and find out exactly what is happening with calories coming in and going out of your own body!

www.science.nelson.com 

SUMMARY Ingestion

- Saliva contains amylase enzymes that initiate carbohydrate breakdown, and it dissolves food particles, activates the taste buds, and lubricates the food.
- Teeth bite, tear, grind, and crush food into smaller particles.
- After food is swallowed, movement through the esophagus is regulated by peristalsis, contractions of muscle.
- Sphincter muscles regulate the movement of food into and out of the stomach.
- Digestive fluids in the stomach include hydrochloric acid (HCl), pepsinogens, and mucus. HCl kills pathogens and helps convert pepsinogen into pepsin. Pepsin digests proteins. Mucus protects the stomach from the above two fluids.

EXTENSION

Dying To Be Thin

For some young people, the conflict between real and fashionable images of the body can lead to an eating disorder. In severe cases, eating disorders such as anorexia can cause low blood pressure, bone loss, damage to the kidneys, liver and heart, and even death.

www.science.nelson.com 

Section 8.3 Questions

1. How are the digestive system and other organ systems interdependent?
2. Differentiate between physical and chemical digestion. Provide examples of each.
3. Is the movement of food through your digestive system voluntary or involuntary? What mechanisms are responsible for moving food along the gastrointestinal tract?
4. The type of teeth that a mammal has is matched to diet. Keeping in mind the function of different types of teeth, name an animal that would have well-developed (a) canines, and (b) molars and premolars.
5. How is movement of food into and out of the stomach regulated?
6. What substances make up gastric fluid?
7. What is the function of the mucous layer that lines the stomach?
8. What is an endoscope and why is it useful?
9. List and discuss two factors that affect enzyme activity. Provide two examples.
10. State the functions of the enzymes amylase and pepsin.
11. What are two factors that contribute to stomach ulcers?
12. In stomach cells, protein-digesting enzymes are stored in the inactive form. Once the enzymes leave the stomach, an acid in the stomach changes the shape of the inactive enzyme, making it active. The active enzyme begins to digest proteins. Why must protein-digesting enzymes be stored in the inactive form?
13. Where would you expect to find digestive enzymes that function best at a pH of 2.0? at a pH of about 7.0?
14. Why does the low pH of the stomach stop the starch digestion that begins in the mouth? What is the advantage to the body of this delay?
15. Would a mouth with a pH of 5.0 have more or less tooth decay than a mouth with a pH of 7.0? Why?
16. Find out about the different kinds of ulcers. Learn about the risk factors, symptoms, and treatments.

    www.science.nelson.com 

17. Heartburn, or acid indigestion, occurs when stomach acids back up into the esophagus, burning its lining. Antacids can be taken to reduce the burning sensation. How might using antacids to mask the pain of heartburn inadvertently lead to more serious problems?

8.4 Digestion

CAREER CONNECTION

Health Service Administrator

These health professionals direct and evaluate health programs and plans. Health service administrators have opportunities to work in a wide range of fields, including medicine, pharmacy, accounting, and management. If you are interested in medical service and administration, explore this career further.

www.science.nelson.com 

Most chemical digestion takes place in the small intestine, so named because of its narrow diameter. In humans, the small intestine is up to 7 m in length, but only 2.5 cm in diameter (**Figure 1**). The large intestine, by comparison, is only 1.5 m in length, but 7.6 cm in diameter. In mammals, the length of the small intestine is related to diet. Meats are relatively easy to digest, while plant materials are more difficult to digest. Accordingly, carnivores, such as wolves and lions, have short small intestines while herbivores, such as rabbits, have long small intestines. Omnivores, such as raccoons, pigs, bears, and humans, have small intestines that are of intermediate length, allowing them to digest both types of food.

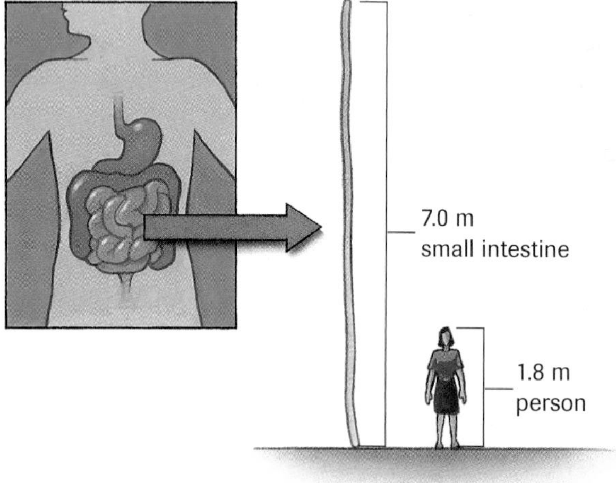

Figure 1
A comparison of the length of the small intestine to the height of a person

Small Intestine

The majority of digestion occurs in the first 25 cm to 30 cm of the small intestine, an area known as the **duodenum**. The second and third components of the small intestine are called the jejunum and the ileum. The small intestine secretes digestive enzymes and moves its contents along by peristalsis.

duodenum the first segment of the small intestine

The stomach absorbs some water, specific vitamins, some medicines, and alcohol, but most absorption takes place within the small intestine. Long fingerlike projections called **villi** (singular: villus) greatly increase the surface area of the small intestine (**Figure 2 (a)**). One estimate suggests that villi account for a tenfold increase in surface area for absorption. The cells that make up the lining of each villus have **microvilli**, which are fine, threadlike extensions of the membrane that further increase the surface for absorption (**Figure 2 (b)**).

villi small, fingerlike projections that extend into the small intestine to increase surface area for absorption

microvilli microscopic, fingerlike projections of the cell membrane

(a)

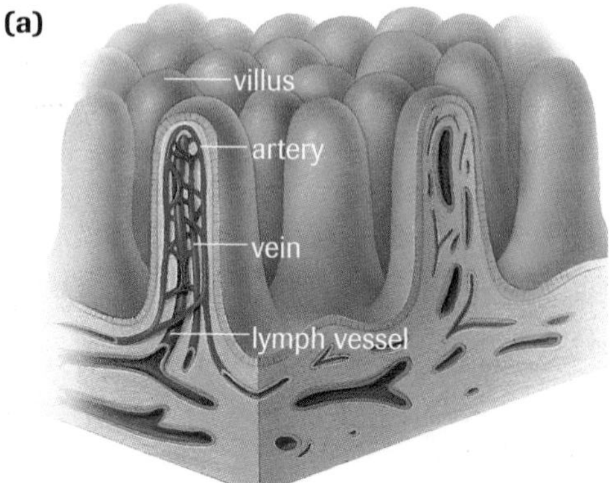

(b)

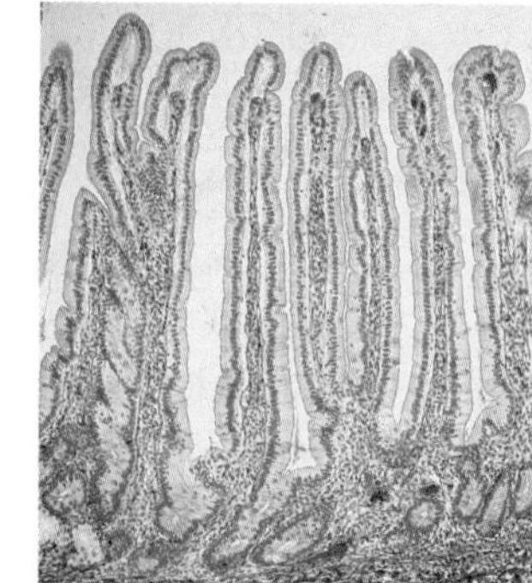

Figure 2
(a) Blood and lymph vessels of a villus
(b) Microvilli

Each villus is supplied with a **capillary** network that intertwines with lymph vessels called **lacteals** that transport materials. Some nutrients are absorbed by diffusion, but some nutrients are actively transported from the digestive tract. Monosaccharides and amino acids are absorbed into the capillary networks; fats are absorbed into the lacteals.

capillary a blood vessel that connects arteries and veins; the site of fluid and gas exchange

lacteal a small vessel that transports the products of fat digestion to the circulatory system

Pancreas

As you already know, food moves from the stomach to the small intestine. Partially digested food reaches the small intestine already soaked in HCl and pepsin. How are the cells of the small intestine protected? To answer this question, you must look beyond the small intestine to the pancreas.

When acids enter the small intestine, a chemical called prosecretin is converted into **secretin**. Secretin is absorbed into the bloodstream and carried to the pancreas, where it signals the release of a solution containing bicarbonate ions. Bicarbonate ions (HCO_3^-) are released from the pancreas and carried to the small intestine, where they buffer the HCl in gastric fluid and raise the pH from about 2.5 to 9.0. The basic pH inactivates pepsin. Thus, the small intestine is protected from stomach acids by the release of secretin. These steps are summarized in **Figure 3**.

secretin a hormone released from the duodenum that stimulates pancreatic and bile secretions

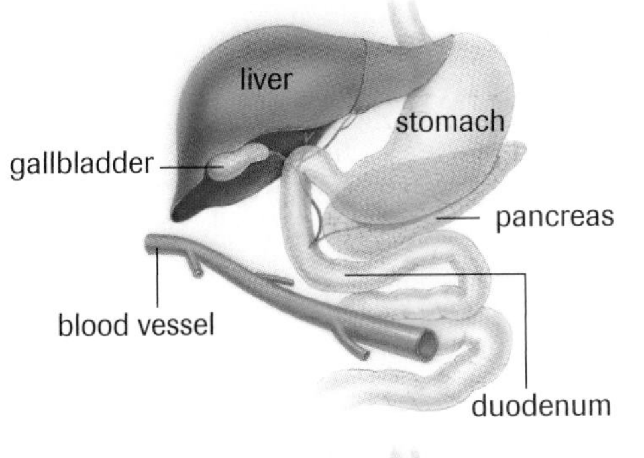

- HCl enters the duodenum from the stomach.
- HCl stimulates the conversion of prosecretin into secretin.

prosecretin (inactive form) —HCl→ **secretin (active form)**

- Secretin is aborbed into the blood vessels.

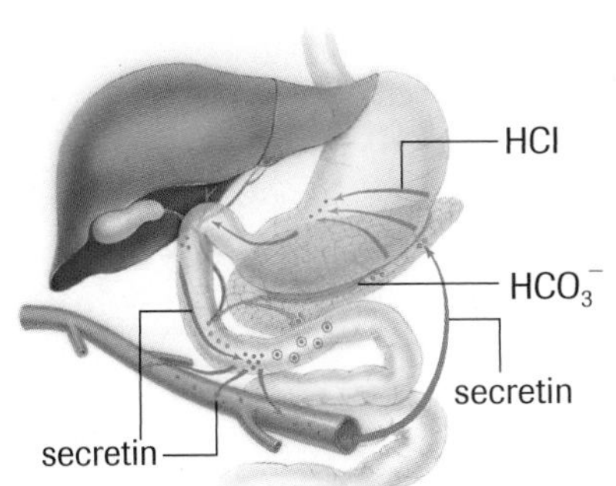

- Secretin is carried by the circulatory system to the pancreas.
- Here secretin acts as a chemical messenger, stimulating the release of pancreatic fluids.
- The HCO_3^- ions, released by the pancreas, neutralize the HCl from the stomach. The neutralization of acid protects the lining of the duodenum.

Figure 3
The function of secretin

The pancreatic secretions also contain enzymes that promote the breakdown of the three major components of food: proteins, carbohydrates, and lipids. A protein-digesting enzyme, called trypsinogen, is released from the pancreas. Once trypsinogen reaches the small intestine, an enzyme called **enterokinase** converts the inactive trypsinogen into **trypsin**, which acts on the partially digested proteins. Trypsin breaks down long-chain polypeptides into shorter-chain peptides.

enterokinase an enzyme of the small intestine that converts trypsinogen to trypsin

trypsin a protein-digesting enzyme

A second group of enzymes, the **erepsins**, are released from the pancreas and small intestine. They complete protein digestion by breaking the bonds between short-chain peptides, releasing individual amino acids (**Figure 4**, next page).

erepsin an enzyme that completes protein digestion by converting short-chain peptides to amino acids

The pancreas also releases amylase enzymes, which continue the digestion of carbohydrates begun in the mouth by salivary amylase. The intermediate-size chains are broken down into disaccharides. The small intestine releases disaccharide enzymes, called disaccharidases, which complete the digestion of carbohydrates.

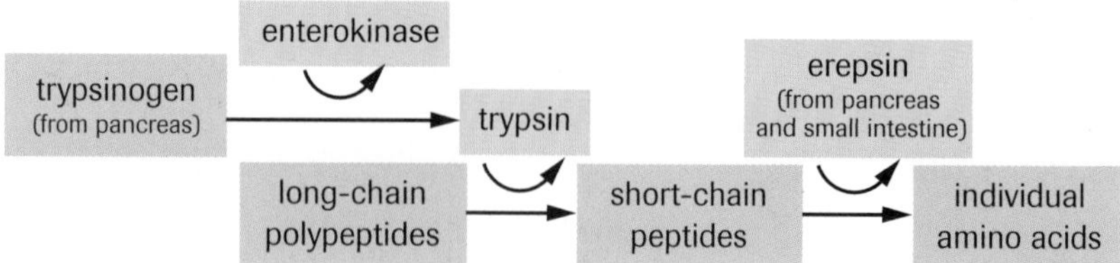

Figure 4
Breakdown of proteins in the small intestine

lipase a lipid-digesting enzyme

Lipases are enzymes released from the pancreas that break down lipids (fats). There are two different types of lipid-digesting enzymes. Pancreatic lipase, the most common, breaks down fats into fatty acids and glycerol. Phospholipase acts on phospholipids.

For a summary of the enzymes found in the small intestine, where they are produced, and the reactions that take place, see **Table 1**.

Table 1 Digestion in the Small Intestine

Enzyme	Produced by	Reaction
lipase	pancreas	fat droplets + $H_2O \rightarrow$ glycerol + fatty acids
trypsin	pancreas	protein + $H_2O \rightarrow$ peptides
erepsin	pancreas, small intestine	peptides + $H_2O \rightarrow$ amino acids
pancreatic amylases	pancreas	starch + $H_2O \rightarrow$ maltose
maltase	small intestine	maltose + $H_2O \rightarrow$ glucose

INVESTIGATION 8.4 ***Introduction***

Effect of pH and Temperature on Starch Digestion

The digestion of many components of food is not accomplished in the stomach, but in the small intestine. For example, starch digestion occurs mainly in the small intestine. What happens to these components when they are in the stomach?

To perform this investigation, turn to page 275.

Report Checklist

- ○ Purpose
- ● Problem
- ● Hypothesis
- ● Prediction
- ○ Design
- ○ Materials
- ○ Procedure
- ● Evidence
- ● Analysis
- ● Evaluation
- ● Synthesis

DID YOU KNOW?

Are You Lactose Intolerant?

Many people are unable to digest lactose (milk sugar) because their bodies do not produce sufficient quantities of the enzyme lactase. Normally, the disaccharide lactose is broken down into two monosaccharides, which are then absorbed into the blood. Lactose-intolerant people are unable to break down lactose in the small intestine, so when it moves to the large intestine, water is drawn in by osmosis, causing diarrhea.

Practice

1. How are the cells of the small intestine protected from stomach acid? Explain the mechanism and the chemicals involved.
2. What enzymes secreted by the pancreas promote digestion?
3. Explain the chemicals and processes involved in protein digestion and carbohydrate digestion. Why are carbohydrates not digested in the stomach?
4. List the lipid-digesting enzymes secreted from the pancreas. Do these enzymes allow for complete breakdown of lipids?
5. How is the duodenum protected against stomach acid? Why does pepsin not remain active in the duodenum?
6. In cases of extreme obesity, a section of the small intestine may be removed. What effect do you think this procedure has on the patient?
7. Describe what the inside of the small intestine looks like and how this organ increases the efficiency of its operation.

Liver and Gallbladder

The liver continually produces a fluid called bile. Bile contains **bile salts**, which aid fat digestion. When the stomach is empty, bile is stored and concentrated in the gallbladder.

bile salt a component of bile that breaks down large fat globules

When there are fats in the small intestine, the hormone **cholecystokinin** (CCK) is released. CCK is carried in the blood to the gallbladder (**Figure 5**) and triggers the gallbladder to release bile salts. Once inside the small intestine, the bile salts emulsify, or break down, large fat globules. The breakdown of fat globules into smaller droplets is physical digestion, not chemical digestion, since chemical bonds are not broken. The physical digestion prepares the fat for chemical digestion by increasing the exposed surface area on which fat-digesting enzymes, such as pancreatic lipase, can work.

cholecystokinin a hormone secreted by the small intestine that stimulates the release of bile salts

- Fats enter the duodenum and stimulate the release of the hormone CCK.
- CCK is carried by the bloodstream to the gallbladder.
- CCK stimulates the release of bile salts from the gallbladder.
- Bile emulsifies fats.

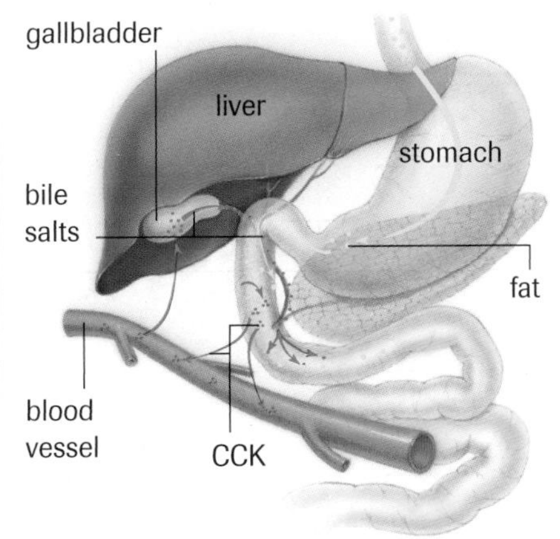

Figure 5
The function of cholecystokinin

Bile also contains pigments. The liver breaks down hemoglobin from red blood cells and stores the products in the gallbladder for removal. The characteristic brown colour of feces results from hemoglobin breakdown.

The liver also stores glycogen and vitamins A, B_{12}, and D. In addition, the liver is able to **detoxify** many substances in the body. Harmful chemicals are made soluble and can be dissolved in the blood and eliminated in the urine. One of the more common poisons is alcohol.

detoxify to remove the effects of a poison

Table 2 outlines the various functions of the liver.

Table 2 Liver Functions

Function	Examples
synthesis	• produces bile salts, which are stored in the gallbladder and which emulsify fats • manufactures blood proteins
breakdown/conversion	• removes the highly toxic nitrogen group from amino acids, forming urea (the main component of urine) • converts the toxic component of hemoglobin, allowing it to be excreted with bile salts • converts glucose into glycogen and glycogen into glucose to maintain a constant blood sugar level
storage	• stores glycogen • stores vitamins A, B_{12}, and D
detoxification	• converts harmful compounds, such as alcohol, to less harmful products

DID YOU KNOW ?

Lily-Livered

The liver was once considered to be the centre of emotions. The term lily-livered, meaning cowardly, implies inadequate blood flow to the liver.

Liver and Gallbladder Problems

gallstone crystals of bile salts that form in the gallbladder

jaundice the yellowish discoloration of the skin and other tissues brought about by the collection of bile pigments in the blood

cirrhosis chronic inflammation of the liver tissue characterized by the growth of nonfunctioning fibrous tissue

The production and concentration of bile can result in certain problems. Cholesterol, an insoluble component of bile, acts as a binding agent for the salt crystals found in bile. The crystals precipitate and form larger crystals called **gallstones**. Gallstones can block the bile duct, impairing fat digestion and causing considerable pain. Any obstruction of the bile duct or accelerated destruction of red blood cells can cause **jaundice**, turning skin and other tissues yellow.

Alcohol, like many other harmful agents, can destroy liver tissue if consumed in large quantities. Damaged liver cells are replaced by fibrous connective tissue and nodules, which are not able to carry out normal liver functions. This condition, which can also result from nutritional deprivation or infection, is referred to as **cirrhosis** of the liver.

mini *Investigation* — *Emulsification of Fats*

Materials: eyedropper, test tube, vegetable oil, bile salts or liquid soap, hand lens (magnifying glass), test tube stopper

- Fill a test tube one-quarter full of water.
- Add 10 drops of vegetable oil. Record the location and appearance of the oil in the test tube.
- Shake the test tube (with stopper) and immediately examine its contents with the hand lens. Record your observations.
- Let the test tube stand for 2 min to 3 min. Observe any changes.
- Add about 5 drops of liquid soap or a pinch of bile salts to the test tube.
- Shake the test tube (with stopper). Immediately examine the contents with the hand lens and record your observations.

(a) What effect did the liquid soap or bile salts have on the oil?

Large Intestine

colon the largest segment of the large intestine, where water reabsorption occurs

Chemical digestion is complete by the time food reaches the large intestine. The **colon**, the largest part of the large intestine, must store waste long enough to reabsorb water from it. Some inorganic salts, minerals, and vitamins are also absorbed with the water.

The large intestine houses bacteria, such as *Escherichia coli (E. coli)*, which are essential to life and use waste materials to synthesize vitamins B and K. Cellulose, the long-chain carbohydrate characteristic of plant cell walls, reaches the large intestine undigested. Although cellulose cannot be broken down by humans, it serves an important function: cellulose provides bulk. As wastes build up in the large intestine, receptors in the wall of the intestine provide information to the central nervous system, which, in turn, prompts a bowel movement. The bowel movement ensures the removal of potentially toxic wastes from the body. Individuals who do not eat sufficient amounts of cellulose (roughage or fibre) have fewer bowel movements. This means that wastes and toxins remain in their bodies for longer periods of time. Scientists have determined that cancer of the colon can be related to diet. Individuals who eat mostly processed, highly refined foods are more likely to develop cancer of the colon.

The Negative Impacts of Gallstones
Listen to this audio clip to identify the components of bile and investigate the negative effects associated with gallstones and gallbladder dysfunction.

www.science.nelson.com 

Practice

8. What are the components of bile? Where is bile produced and where is it stored?
9. Explain the importance of bile salts in digestion.
10. Why doesn't fat dissolve in water?
11. Why is the liver important in processing toxins in the body? What happens if the level of toxins is very high?
12. What is the function of the colon in the digestive system?
13. Why is cellulose considered to be an important part of your diet?

Control of Digestion

The control of digestion is exerted by the nervous and hormonal systems. Seeing, smelling, or tasting food will produce gastric secretions even before there is any food in the stomach. Swallowing motions also stimulate production of gastric juices, regardless of whether food is actually swallowed.

Hormones play a large role in the control mechanism. For example, secretin is released when acid from the stomach moves into the small intestine along with food. Secretin is absorbed into the blood and travels to the pancreas where it initiates the release of substances that raise the pH of the small intestine. Another hormone, called **gastrin**, is produced when the walls of the stomach are distended by the presence of food. Partially digested protein in the stomach also stimulates the release of gastrin. Gastrin travels in the blood to the parietal cells of the stomach and signals them to release HCl (**Figure 6 (a)**).

gastrin a hormone secreted by the stomach that stimulates the release of HCl

The speed at which the digestive system processes food can also be controllled. When food enters the stomach, nerves in the stomach wall cause the muscles to contract and gastric fluids to be secreted. A large meal will activate more receptors, causing more forceful stomach contractions and faster emptying. If the meal is fatty, the small intestine secretes **enterogastrone**, which slows peristaltic movements, allowing time for fat digestion and absorption (**Figure 6 (b)**).

enterogastrone a hormone secreted by the small intestine that decreases gastric secretions and motility

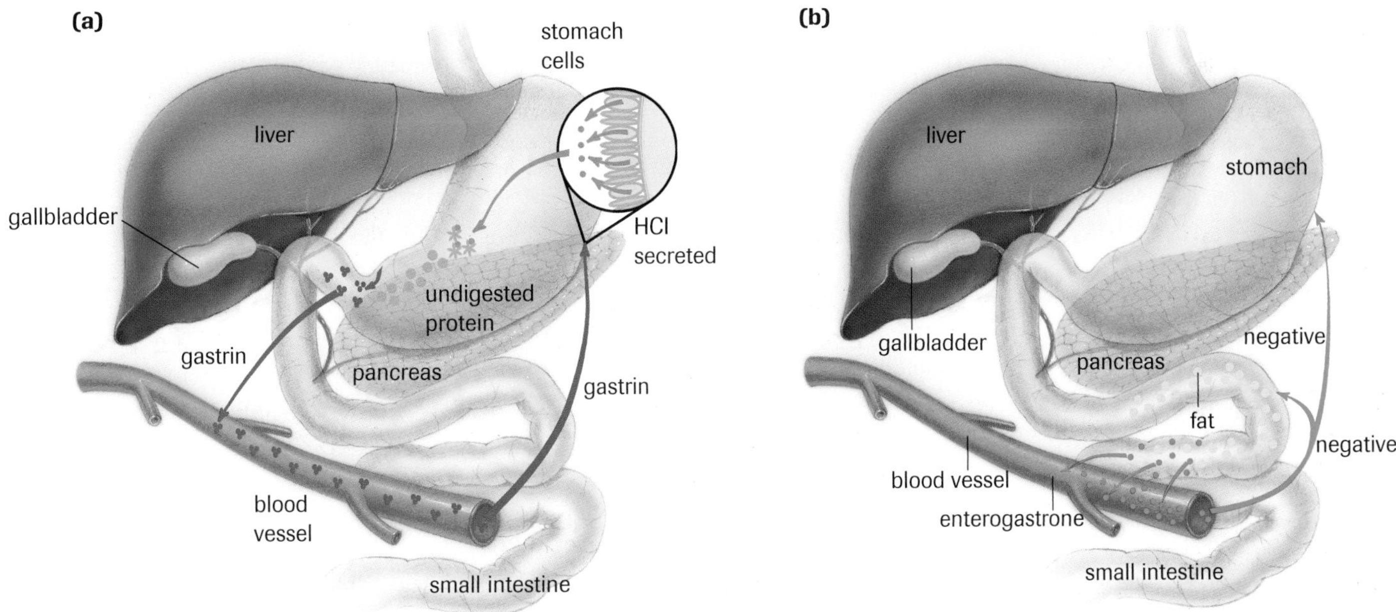

Figure 6
The function of **(a)** gastrin and **(b)** enterogastrone

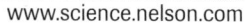

Digestion

Table 3 Digestive Organs and Their Functions

Organ	Function
mouth	chewing of food and digestion of starch
stomach	storage of food and initial digestion of proteins
small intestine	digestion of carbohydrates, proteins, lipids; the absorption of nutrients
pancreas	production of digestive enzymes that act on food in the small intestine; storage of bicarbonate ions that neutralize stomach acid in the small intestine
large intestine	absorption of water and storage of undigested food

EXTENSION

Tummy Bugs

Dr. Lora Hooper (Washington University in St. Louis, Missouri) is part of a team that recently discovered some stomach bugs responsible for turning on our genes to aid in digestion. These bacteria also produce a chemical that strengthens the stomach lining.

www.science.nelson.com 

Table 4 Organs and Substances Involved in Digestion

Organ of secretion	Secretion	Function
salivary glands	salivary amylase	initiates the breakdown of polysaccharides to simpler carbohydrates
stomach	hydrochloric acid	converts pepsinogen to pepsin; kills microbes
	pepsinogen	when converted to pepsin, initiates the digestion of proteins
	mucus	protects the stomach from pepsin and HCl
pancreas	pancreatic amylase	continues the breakdown of carbohydrates into disaccharides
	bicarbonate ions	neutalize HCl from the stomach
	trypsinogen	when activated to trypsin, converts long-chain peptides into short-chain peptides
	lipase	breaks down fats to glycerol and fatty acids
small intestine	erepsin	completes the breakdown of proteins
	disaccharidases (e.g., maltase)	break down disaccharides (e.g., maltose) into monosaccharides
liver	bile	emulsifies fat
gallbladder	bile	stores and secretes concentrated bile from the liver
large intestine	mucus	helps movement of food waste

Section 8.4 Questions

1. What important physical change must fats undergo before chemical change can take place? Where and how does this physical change occur?
2. Explain the mechanism that triggers the release of bile salts.
3. Are nutrients absorbed passively or actively in the digestive tract? Where are carbohydrates, amino acids, and fats absorbed?
4. Sketch the two ways in which absorbed nutrients leave the intestine and get to body cells.
5. What are some signals that trigger the secretion of digestive fluids even in the absence of food in the stomach?
6. How do hormones help regulate digestion?
7. What are gallstones and what causes them?
8. What is jaundice? Why does this condition produce a yellowing of the skin?
9. What kind of dietary changes would a person without a gallbladder need to make? Why?
10. Research the latest techniques used in the removal of gallstones.

www.science.nelson.com 

INVESTIGATION 8.1

Identifying Carbohydrates

Report Checklist

○ Purpose	● Design	● Analysis
● Problem	○ Materials	● Evaluation
● Hypothesis	○ Procedure	○ Synthesis
● Prediction	● Evidence	

Benedict's solution identifies reducing sugars, and iodine solution identifies starches. Iodine turns blue-black in the presence of starches. The Cu^{2+} ions in the Benedict's solution are converted to Cu^{+} ions in the presence of a reducing sugar. Not all sugars are reducing sugars. All monosaccharides are reducing sugars, but some disaccharides will not react with Benedict's solution.

Table 1 summarizes the quantitative results obtained when a reducing sugar reacts with Benedict's solution.

Table 1 Reducing Sugar and Benedict's Solution Reactions

Colour of Benedict's solution	Approximate % of sugar
blue	negative
light green	0.5–1.0
green to yellow	1.0–1.5
orange	1.5–2.0
red to red brown	> 2.0

Purpose

To identify reducing sugars qualitatively and quantitatively

Materials

- safety goggles
- lab apron
- test-tube brushes
- detergent
- 400 mL beaker
- hot plate
- thermometer or temperature probe
- 10 mL graduated cylinder
- distilled H_2O
- 5 % fructose solution
- 5 % glucose (dextrose) solution
- 5 % sucrose solution
- 5 % maltose solution
- 5 % starch solution
- 9 test tubes
- test-tube rack
- Benedict's solution
- wax pencil
- test-tube clamp
- 5 medicine droppers
- depression plates
- iodine solution
- solutions X, Y, and Z

Caution: The chemicals used are toxic and are irritants. Avoid skin and eye contact. Wash all splashes off your skin and clothing thoroughly. If you get any chemical in your eyes, rinse for at least 15 min and inform your teacher.

Procedure

Before you begin:

- Make sure that all the glassware is clean and well rinsed.
- Note the location of the eyewash station.

Part I: Reducing Sugars

Caution: Handle hot objects and their contents carefully to avoid burns.

1. Prepare a water bath by heating 300 mL of tap water in a 400 mL beaker until it reaches approximately 80 °C (**Figure 1**).

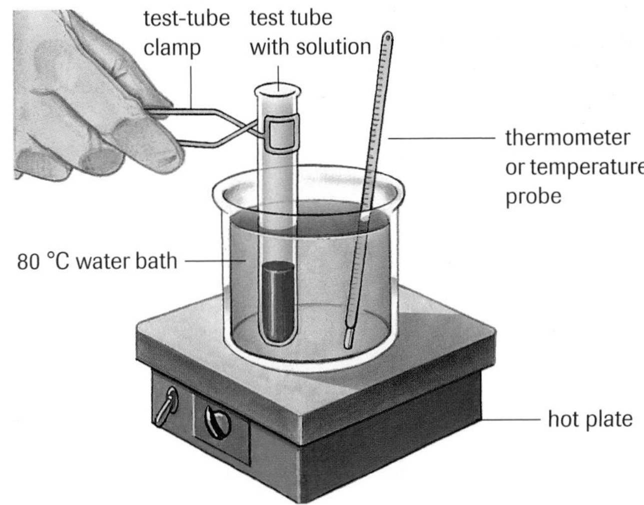

Figure 1
Heating a test tube in a hot water bath

2. Label the test tubes 1 to 6. Using a 10 mL graduated cylinder, measure 3 mL each of distilled water, fructose, glucose, maltose, sucrose, and starch solutions. Record which tube contains each solution. Pour each solution into a separate test tube. Clean and rinse the graduated cylinder after each solution. Add 1 mL of Benedict's solution to each of the test tubes.
3. Using a test-tube clamp, place each of the test tubes in the hot water bath (**Figure 1**). Observe for 6 min.

(a) Record any colour changes.

Part II: Iodine Test

4. Using a medicine dropper, place a drop of water on a depression plate and add a drop of iodine.

(b) Record the colour of the solution.

5. Repeat the procedure, this time using drops of starch, glucose, maltose, and sucrose instead of water.

(c) Record the colour of the solutions. Which solutions indicated a positive test?

INVESTIGATION 8.1 *continued*

Part III: Checking Unknown Solutions

6. Test the three unknown solutions for reducing sugars and starches. Design your own table, showing both qualitative and quantitative data.

(d) Record your data.

Analysis and Evaluation

(e) Why should the graduated cylinder be cleaned and rinsed after the measurement of each solution?

(f) Which test tube served as a control in the test for reducing sugars and starches?

(g) What laboratory data suggest that not all sugars are reducing sugars?

(h) A student decides to sabotage the laboratory results of his classmates and places a sugar cube into solution Z. Explain the effect of dissolving a sugar cube in the solution.

(i) A drop of iodine accidently falls on a piece of paper. Predict the colour change, if any, and provide an explanation for your prediction.

INVESTIGATION 8.2

Identifying Lipids and Proteins

In this investigation, you will use laboratory tests to identify lipids and proteins. You will then use these tests to establish which of these nutrients are present in an unknown sample. Read the investigation, then predict whether lipid, protein, or neither will be present in the unknown sample. Record your evidence, then complete the analysis and evaluation of the evidence.

Report Checklist

○ Purpose	○ Design	● Analysis
● Problem	○ Materials	● Evaluation
● Hypothesis	○ Procedure	● Synthesis
● Prediction	● Evidence	

Problem

Does the unknown sample contain lipids or proteins?

Materials

goggles
lab apron
5–10 test tubes
test-tube rack
test-tube brush
10 mL graduated cylinder
distilled water
waterproof marker
medicine droppers
rubber stoppers
detergent solution

For lipid tests:
Sudan IV indicator
unglazed brown paper (2 letter-sized sheets)
unknown solution
vegetable oil
skim milk
whipping cream

For protein test:
Biuret reagent
gelatin
egg albumin
skim milk
unknown solution

Sudan IV indicator is flammable, and both Sudan IV and Biuret reagent are toxic and can cause an itchy rash. Avoid skin and eye contact. Wash all splashes off your skin and clothing thoroughly. If you get any chemical in your eyes, rinse for at least 15 min and inform your teacher.

Procedure

Before you begin

- make sure that all the glassware is clean and well rinsed;
- note the location of the eyewash station; and
- put on your apron and goggles.

Part I: Sudan IV Lipid Test

Sudan IV solution is an indicator of lipids, which are soluble in certain solvents. Lipids turn from a pink to a red colour. Polar compounds will not assume the pink colour of the Sudan IV indicator.

1. Using a 10 mL graduated cylinder, measure 3 mL each of distilled water, vegetable oil, skim milk, whipping cream, and the unknown solution.
2. Pour each solution into a separate labelled test tube. Clean and rinse the graduated cylinder after each solution.
3. Add 6 drops of Sudan IV indicator to each test tube.
4. Place stoppers on the test tubes and shake them vigorously for 2 min. Record the colour of the mixtures in a chart.

Part II: Translucence Lipid Test

Lipids can be detected using unglazed brown paper. Because lipids allow the transmission of light through the brown paper, the test is often called the translucence test.

5. Draw one circle (10 cm diameter) on a piece of unglazed brown paper.
6. Place 1 drop of water in the circle and label the circle accordingly.
7. Using more sheets, draw a total of 7 more circles (10 cm diameter).
8. Place 1 drop of vegetable oil, skim milk, whipping cream, and unknown solution, each inside its own circle, labelling the circles as you do.
9. When the water has evaporated, hold both papers to the light and observe. In a chart, record whether or not the papers appear translucent.

Part III: Protein Test

Proteins can be detected by means of the Biuret reagent test. Biuret reagent reacts with the peptide bonds that join amino acids together, producing colour changes from blue, indicating no protein, to pink (+), violet (++), and purple (+++). The + sign indicates the relative amounts of peptide bonds.

10. Measure 2 mL of water, gelatin, albumin, skim milk, and the unknown solution into separate labelled test tubes.
11. Add 2 mL of Biuret reagent to each of the test tubes, then tap the test tubes with your fingers to mix the contents. Record any colour changes in a chart.

Analysis

(a) Explain the advantage of using two separate tests for lipids.

(b) Which test tube served as a control in the test for lipids, and proteins?

(c) Summarize your group's findings about the nutrients present in your unknown solution. Be sure to include the identifying code.

Evaluation

(d) Why should the graduated cylinder be cleaned and rinsed after measuring out each solution?

(e) List possible sources of error, and indicate how you could improve your method.

Synthesis

(f) A student heats a test tube containing a large amount of protein and Biuret reagent. She notices a colour change from violet to blue. Explain why.

(g) Predict the results of a lipid test on samples of butter and margarine.

INVESTIGATION 8.3

Factors That Affect the Catalase Enzyme Reaction

Report Checklist

○ Purpose	● Design	● Analysis
● Problem	○ Materials	● Evaluation
● Hypothesis	○ Procedure	○ Synthesis
● Prediction	● Evidence	

Organisms that live in oxygen-rich environments need the catalase enzyme. The catalase enzyme breaks down hydrogen peroxide (H_2O_2), a toxin that forms readily from H_2O and O_2. The reaction below describes the effect of the catalase enzyme.

The formation of hydrogen peroxide:

$$2\,H_2O + O_2 \rightarrow 2\,H_2O_2 \text{ (hydrogen peroxide)}$$

The effect of catalase:

$$2\,H_2O_2 \xrightarrow{\text{catalase}} 2\,H_2O + O_2$$

Purpose

To identify factors that affect the rate of enzyme-catalyzed reactions

Materials

safety goggles	fine sand
lab apron	scalpel
6 test tubes	potato
waterproof marker	chicken liver (fresh)
3 % hydrogen peroxide	stirring rod
tweezers or forceps	mortar and pestle
10 mL graduated cylinder	

Caution: Hydrogen peroxide is a strong irritant. Avoid skin and eye contact. Wash all splashes off your skin and clothing thoroughly. If you get any chemical in your eyes, rinse for at least 15 min and inform your teacher.

Procedure

Part I: Identifying the Enzyme

1. Label three clean test tubes 1, 2, and 3.
2. Using a 10 mL graduated cylinder, measure 2 mL of hydrogen peroxide and add it to test tube 1. Add a sprinkle of sand to the test tube and observe.
3. Add 2 mL of H_2O_2 to test tubes 2 and 3. Using the scalpel, remove a piece of potato approximately the size of a raisin and add it to test tube 2. Observe the reaction. Repeat the procedure once again, but this time add a piece of liver the size of a raisin to test tube 3. Observe the reaction.
4. Compare the reaction rates of the three test tubes. Use 0 to indicate little or no reaction, 1 to indicate slow, 2 to indicate moderate, 3 for fast, and 4 for very fast.

(a) Record your results.

Part II: Factors That Affect Reaction Rates

5. Divide the hydrogen peroxide used in test tube 3 into two clean test tubes. Label one of the test tubes 4 and the other 5. Using tweezers or forceps, remove the liver from test tube 3 and divide it equally into test tubes 4 and 5. Add a second piece of liver to test tube 4 and observe. Add 1 mL of fresh hydrogen peroxide to test tube 5 and observe.

(b) Record your results.

6. Using a scalpel, cut another section of liver the size of a raisin. Add sand to a mortar and grind the liver into smaller pieces with the pestle. Remove the liver and place it in a clean test tube labelled 6. Add 2 mL of H_2O_2 and compare the reaction rate of the liver in test tube 6 with that of the uncrushed liver in test tube 3.

(c) Record your results.

Analysis and Evaluation

(d) In Part I, which test tube served as the control?

(e) Account for the different reaction rates between the liver and potato.

(f) Explain the different reaction rates in test tubes 4 and 5.

(g) Why did the crushed liver in test tube 6 react differently from the uncrushed liver in test tube 3?

(h) Predict what would happen if the liver in test tube 3 were boiled before adding the H_2O_2. Give reasons for your prediction.

+ *EXTENSION*

Catalase and the Breakdown of Hydrogen Peroxide

Catalase plays an essential role in preventing hydrogen peroxide from reaching toxic levels. This audio clip explores hydrogen peroxide production in living organisms and how catalase is involved.

www.science.nelson.com

INVESTIGATION 8.4

Effect of pH and Temperature on Starch Digestion

Report Checklist

- ○ Purpose
- ● Problem
- ● Hypothesis
- ● Prediction
- ○ Design
- ○ Materials
- ○ Procedure
- ● Evidence
- ● Analysis
- ● Evaluation
- ● Synthesis

Very little starch is broken down in the mouth. The low pH of the digestive fluids in the stomach halts digestion of carbohydrates such as starch until the carbohydrates leave the stomach and enter the small intestine.

Purpose

To determine the pH and temperature at which amylase digests starch most quickly

Design

A cornstarch suspension will be mixed with an enzyme solution at different pH levels and at different temperatures to see which acidity level and which temperature result in the most complete breakdown of starch. The efficiency can be measured by how much sugar is produced. Benedict's reagent is used to indicate the presence of maltose, a disaccharide.

Benedict's reagent is toxic and can cause a rash. Avoid skin and eye contact. Wash all splashes off your skin and clothing thoroughly. If you get any chemical in your eyes, rinse for at least 15 min and inform your teacher.

Materials

- apron
- goggles
- 10 test tubes
- 1 % cornstarch suspension
- Benedict's reagent
- ice cubes
- two 250 mL beakers
- ring clamp
- 25 mL graduated cylinder
- eyedropper
- rubber stoppers for test tubes
- test-tube rack
- 5 % amylase solutions at pH 2.0, 7.0, and 12.0
- hot plate
- thermometers
- utility stand
- tap water
- labelling materials
- timer or watch
- glass stirring rod

Procedure

Part I: The Effect of pH on Starch Digestion

1. Create a table in your notebook or a spreadsheet and complete it as you perform each step in the activity.
2. Put on your apron and goggles.
3. Label 4 test tubes from 1 to 4. Set up a water bath as shown in **Figure 1**.

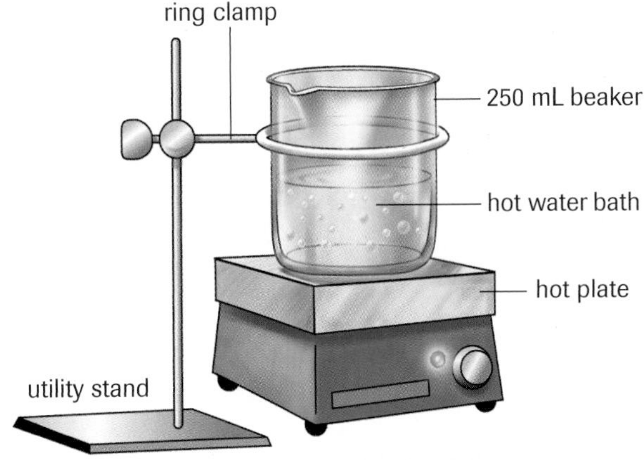

Figure 1
Water bath setup

4. Place 15 mL of the 1 % cornstarch suspension into each of the 4 test tubes.
5. Add 5 drops of the pH 2.0 amylase solution to test tube 2. Add 5 drops of the pH 7.0 amylase solution to test tube 3. Add 5 drops of the pH 12.0 amylase solution to test tube 4. Put a rubber stopper in each test tube and shake (**Figure 2**).

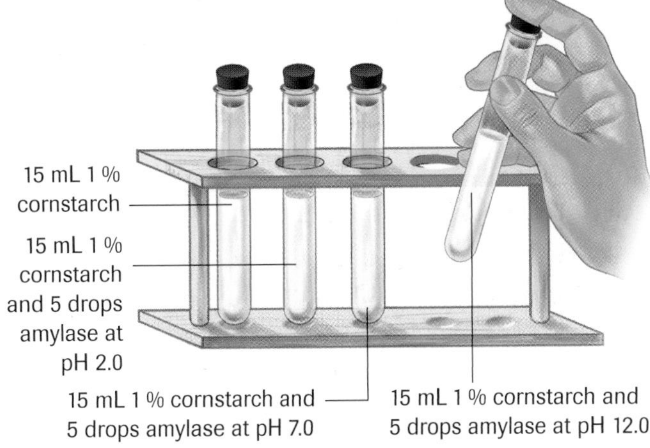

Figure 2
Test-tube setup

6. Let the test tubes sit for 20 min. Record your observations of each test tube. A colour change from blue to yellow to orange indicates maltose.

7. Add 5 mL of Benedict's reagent to each of the 4 test tubes and place them in the hot water bath at 100 °C. If you use the same cylinder as in Step 4, make sure to rinse and dry it first. Record your observations after 5 min. Do not let the test tubes sit in the hot water bath for more than 5 min.

Analysis

(a) In which test tube did starch digestion occur? How could you tell?

(b) What is the function of test tube 1?

(c) At what pH does amylase work best to digest starch?

Part II: The Effect of Temperature on Starch Digestion

8. Create a table to record your data as you perform each step in the activity.
9. Label 6 test tubes from 1 to 6.
10. Place 15 mL of cornstarch suspension in each test tube.
11. Add 5 drops of amylase solution at pH 7.0 to test tubes 1, 3, and 5.
12. Place test tubes 1 and 2 in the hot water bath and heat until the cornstarch suspension reaches 50 °C. Do not heat the contents of the test tubes above 50 °C (**Figure 3**).

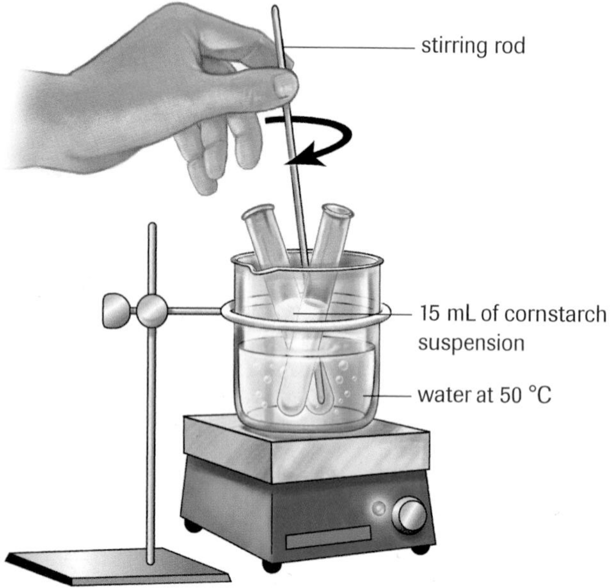

Figure 3
Heating the test tubes

13. Place test tubes 3 and 4 in a beaker of ice water. Let the cornstarch suspensions chill to a temperature between 0 °C and 5 °C. Stirring the water with a stirring rod may speed the cooling process.
14. Keep test tubes 5 and 6 at room temperature. Record the temperature of the cornstarch suspension.
15. Let all test tubes stand for 20 min. Maintain temperature conditions for the test tubes. Record your observations of each test tube.
16. Add 5 mL of Benedict's reagent to each test tube and place them in a hot water bath at 100 °C for 5 min. Record your observations in the table.

Analysis

(d) What would overheating have done to the contents of test tubes 1 and 2? What happens to the ability of the enzyme to convert starch to sugar at the tested temperatures?

(e) What was the function of test tubes 2, 4, and 6?

(f) At what temperature did amylase work best to convert starch to sugar?

Evaluation

(g) Identify possible sources of error, and indicate how you could improve the procedure.

Synthesis

(h) How are the conditions in the experiment similar to the conditions in the digestive system? How are they different?

Chapter 8 SUMMARY

Outcomes

Knowledge

- describe the chemical nature of carbohydrates, fats, and proteins and their enzymes, i.e., carbohydrases, proteases, and lipases (8.1)
- explain enzyme action and factors influencing that action, i.e., temperature, pH, substrate concentration, feedback inhibition, competitive inhibition (8.2)
- identify the principal structures of the digestive system, i.e., mouth, esophagus, stomach, sphincters, small and large intestines, liver, pancreas, gallbladder (8.3)
- describe the chemical and physical processing of matter through the digestive system into the bloodstream (8.4)

STS

- explain that the goal of technology is to provide solutions to practical problems by discussing and evaluating the role of food treatment to solve problems of food spoilage (8.1)
- explain that the products of technology are devices, systems, and processes that meet given needs; however, these products cannot solve all problems (8.1)

Skills

- ask questions and plan investigations (8.1, 8.2, 8.4)
- conduct investigations and gather and record data and information: by performing experiments to detect the presence of carbohydrates, proteins, and lipids (8.1) and; performing an experiment to investigate the influence of enzyme concentration, temperature, or pH on activity of enzymes (8.2, 8.4)
- analyze data and apply mathematical and conceptual models (8.2, 8.4)
- work as members of a team and apply the skills and conventions of science (all)

Key Terms

8.1

carbohydrate
polymer
monosaccharide
isomer
disaccharide
dehydration synthesis
hydrolysis
polysaccharide
starch
glycogen
cellulose
triglyceride
fat
oil
phospholipid
wax
protein
amino acid
peptide bond
polypeptide
essential amino acid
denaturation
coagulation

8.2

catalyst
enzyme
substrate
active site
cofactor
coenzyme
competitive inhibitor
feedback inhibition
precursor activity
allosteric activity

8.3

amylase
peristalsis
sphincter
mucus
pepsin
ulcer

8.4

duodenum
villi
microvilli
capillary
lacteal
secretin
enterokinase
trypsin
erepsin
lipase
bile salt
cholecystokinin
detoxify
gallstone
jaundice
cirrhosis
colon
gastrin
enterogastrone

MAKE a summary

1. In this chapter, you studied the importance of digestion in providing substances needed for energy and growth. Create a concept map that shows how the digestive system exchanges matter and energy with the environment. Check other concept maps to help you make your sketch clear.
2. Revisit your answers to the Starting Points questions at the start of the chapter. Would you answer the questions differently now? Why?

Go To

The following components are available on the Nelson Web site. Follow the links for *Nelson Biology Alberta 20–30*.

- an interactive Self Quiz for Chapter 8
- additional Diploma Exam-style Review Questions
- Illustrated Glossary
- additional IB-related material

There is more information on the Web site wherever you see the Go icon in the chapter.

Many of these questions are in the style of the Diploma Exam. You will find guidance for writing Diploma Exams in Appendix A5. Science Directing Words used in Diploma Exams are in bold type. Exam study tips and test-taking suggestions are on the Nelson Web site.

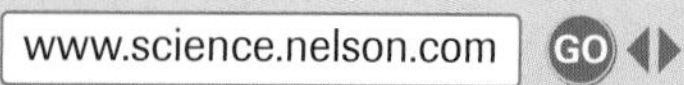

DO NOT WRITE IN THIS TEXTBOOK.

Part 1

Use the following information to answer questions 1 and 2.

Figure 1 shows the substrates and product of an enzyme-catalyzed reaction.

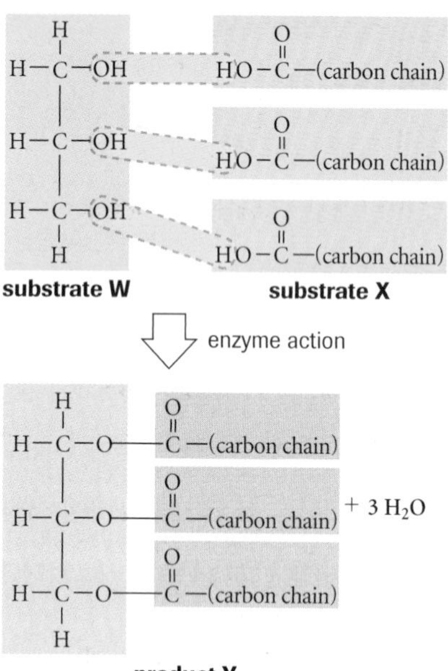

Figure 1

1. **Identify** the process and final product shown in the reaction.
   A. process is dehydration synthesis; final product (Y) is a triglyceride
   B. process is dehydration synthesis; final product (Y) is a polypeptide
   C. process is hydrolysis; final product (Y) is a triglyceride
   D. process is hydrolysis; final product (Y) is a polypeptide

2. **Identify** the initial substrates shown in the reaction.
   A. substrate W is glycerol; substrate X is a fatty acid
   B. substrate W is an amino acid; substrate X is a monosaccharide
   C. substrate W is a disaccharide; substrate X is a triglyceride
   D. substrate W is an amino acid; substrate X is glycerol

3. In chemical reactions, enzymes
   A. prevent energy loss
   B. lower the amount of energy required to initiate a chemical reaction
   C. increase the energy of the reactants
   D. decrease the energy of the final products

Use the following information to answer questions 4 and 5.

A student tested the activity of three enzymes in solutions at different pH values. The results are shown in **Figure 2**.

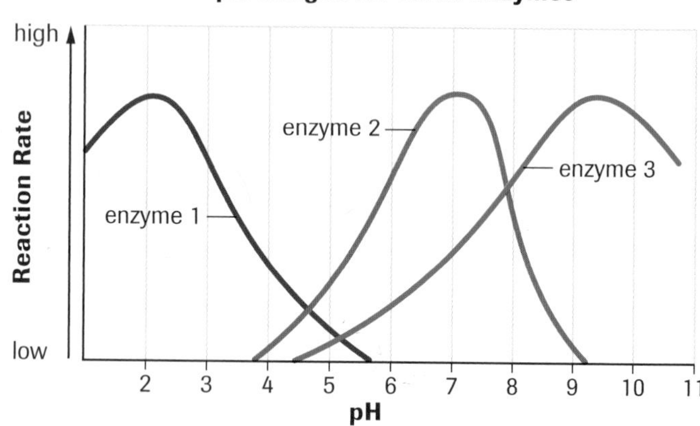

Figure 2

4. According to the data provided in the graph,
   A. enzyme 1 works best in an alkaline environment
   B. enzyme 2 works best in an acidic environment
   C. enzyme 3 works best in an alkaline environment
   D. enzymes 1 and 3 work equally well in acidic and alkaline environments

5. **Select** the optimal pH levels for enzymes 1, 2, and 3.
   A. 5; 7; 8
   B. 5.5; 4; 4.5
   C. 2; 7; 9.5
   D. 1; 9; 12

6. **Identify** why enzymes in the stomach do not digest the stomach itself.
   A. A protective mucous layer coats the stomach. Protein-digesting enzymes are stored in the inactive form.
   B. HCl is buffered to maintain a neutral pH. Fat-digesting enzymes are stored in the inactive form.
   C. A protective mucous layer coats the stomach. HCl is buffered to maintain a neutral pH.
   D. Fat-digesting enzymes are stored in the inactive form. Protein-digesting enzymes are stored in the inactive form.

Use the following information to answer questions 7 and 8.

Figure 3 shows organs of the digestive system.

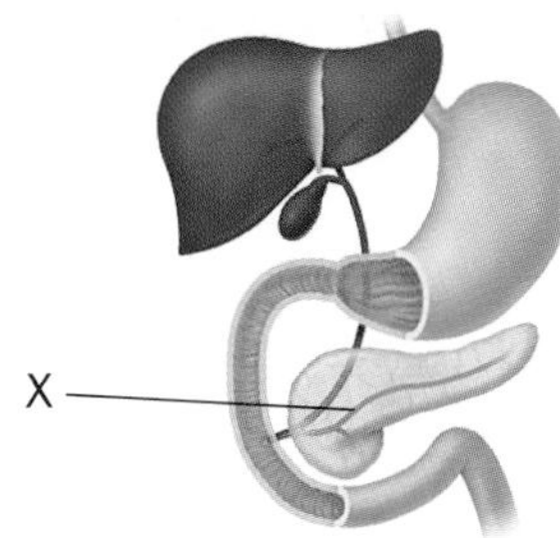

Figure 3

7. If the duct labelled X becomes blocked, the blockage would
   A. prevent pancreatic enzymes from entering the small intestine, and prevent bile salts from the liver from entering the small intestine
   B. prevent enzymes and food from the stomach from entering the small intestine, and prevent pancreatic enzymes from entering the large intestine
   C. prevent bile salts from the stomach from entering the small intestine, and prevent pancreatic enzymes from entering the small intestine
   D. prevent pancreatic enzymes from entering the large intestine, and prevent enzymes and food from the stomach from entering the small intestine

8. Identify the three food nutrients whose digestion would be impaired by the blockage of the duct.
   A. vitamins, cofactors, monosaccharides
   B. proteins, lipids, amino acids
   C. lipids, proteins, polysaccharides
   D. vitamins, amino acids, lipids

---

9.  NR The following structures are found in the digestive system:
   1. duodenum
   2. pyloric sphincter
   3. pharynx
   4. rectum

   List these structure in the order that food passes through them. (Record all four digits of your answer.)

Part 2

10. Why are phospholipids well suited for cell membranes?

11. DE Three different digestive fluids are placed in test tubes. The fluid placed in test tube 1 was extracted from the mouth. The fluids in test tubes 2 and 3 were extracted from what was believed to be the stomach. Five millilitres of olive oil are placed in each of the test tubes, along with a pH indicator. The initial colour of each of the solutions is red, indicating the presence of a slightly basic solution. The solution in test tube 3 turns clear after 10 min, but all of the other test tubes remain red. Write a unified response addressing the following aspects of this experiment.
- **Describe** the conclusions you would draw from the experiment.
- **Justify** each of the conclusions with the data provided. (*Hint:* Consider which substance is digested. What are the structural components?)

Use the following information to answer questions 12 to 14.

Data were collected from two different chemical reactions and are displayed in **Figure 4**.

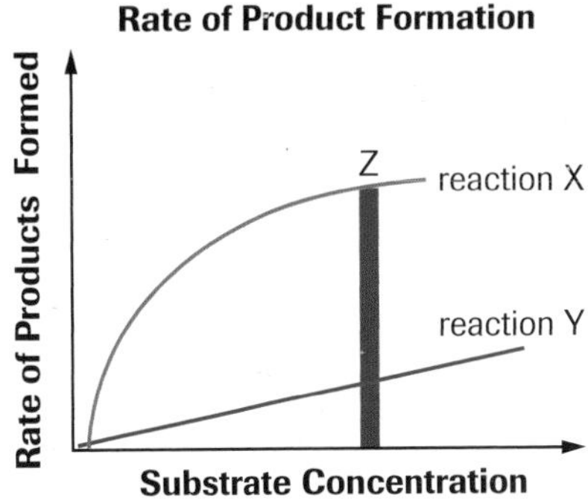

Figure 4

12. DE Identify the reaction that would most likely represent an enzyme-catalyzed reaction. **Explain** why.

13. DE **Why** does reaction X begin to level off at point Z?

14. DE **Predict** how the reaction curve would change if additional enzymes were added to both reaction X and reaction Y. **Explain** your prediction.

---

15. If a molecule similar to substrate "R" attaches itself to enzyme "r," **how** might the reaction in **Figure 5** be affected?

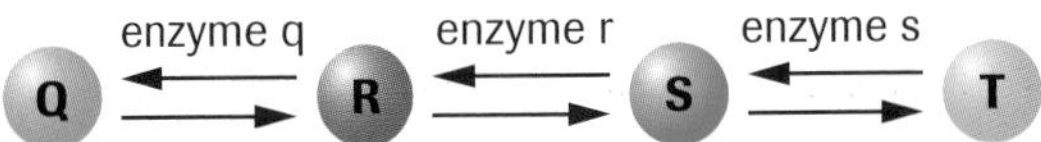

Figure 5

16. Why are pepsin and trypsin stored in inactive forms? Why can erepsins be stored in active forms?

17. Under certain abnormal conditions, the stomach does not secrete hydrochloric acid. **Identify** two functions that hydrochloric acid has in the digestive process and **describe** how the failure to secrete hydrochloric acid will affect these processes.

18. Why do individuals with gallstones experience problems digesting certain foods?

19. Why might individuals with an obstructed bile duct develop jaundice?

chapter

Respiratory System and Motor System

▶ In this chapter

- Exploration: Making a Model of the Chest Cavity
- Investigation 9.1: Determining Lung Capacity
- Chemistry Connection: Acids and Bases
- Explore an Issue: Using Erythropoietin to Increase Oxygen-Carrying Capacity
- Investigation 9.2: The Effects of Exercise on Lung Volume
- Web Activity: Dr. Malcolm King
- Web Activity: Asthma
- Web Activity: Smokeless Tobacco
- Case Study: Smoking and Lung Cancer
- Mini Investigation: Microscopic Examination of Muscle
- Mini Investigation: Effect of Low Temperature on Muscle Contraction
- Investigation 9.3: The Effects of Muscle Activity on Body Temperature

Top water polo players are superb athletes. The sport requires the strength of a rower, the endurance of a cross-country skier, and the scoring touch of a soccer player.

What separates athletes, like Waneek Horn-Miller, an Aboriginal athlete (**Figure 1**), from the majority of us? The exceptional physical fitness of an athlete depends largely on the superior ability to deliver oxygen and chemical fuels to the cells of the body. To sustain life-giving processes, all cells require nutrients and oxygen. Within the mitochondria inside the cells, oxygen is used during cellular respiration to convert organic chemicals to energy-rich ATP molecules that fuel cellular activities. In muscle cells, this energy is used for movement. Athletes also often have a superior respiratory system that provides an excellent exchange of air, ensuring plentiful oxygen for the cells.

Training can increase your ability to take in oxygen (through the respiratory system) and deliver it (through the circulatory system) to cells of the body. Training can also change the amount of muscle tissue in your body, while inactivity can cause the amount of muscle tissue to shrink.

However, not everyone who trains will become an elite athlete. Your inherited physiology may not allow for sufficient ventilation for you to excel in one sport, but may make you better suited for a different sport or activity.

In this chapter, you will first look at the respiratory system and how it works to deliver oxygen to the cells. Then, you will look at the muscles in the human motor system. The motor system supports all the systems of the human body, including the respiratory system and digestive system you read about in the previous chapter.

STARTING points

Answer these questions as best you can with your current knowledge. Then, using the concepts and skills you have learned, you will revise your answers at the end of the chapter.

1. What everyday experiences indicate the importance of providing oxygen to living cells?
2. Fitness can be measured by the body's ability to provide oxygen for the tissues of the body. Make a list of sports that you believe require great fitness. Make another list of sports that you believe require less fitness. Be prepared to justify your answers.
3. Predict how changes in oxygen level might affect muscle activity.

Career Connections:
Physiologist; Commercial Diver; Prosthetist and Orthotist

Figure 1
Waneek Horn-Miller led Canada's women's national water polo team in the 2000 Olympics in Sydney.

Exploration — Making a Model of the Chest Cavity

You can make a model of the human chest cavity. The balloons represent the lungs, and the latex glove represents the diaphragm.

Materials: empty 2-L plastic bottle, two balloons, Y-tube, rubber stopper with hole, latex surgical glove, elastic band, scissors

- Cut the bottom off the plastic bottle.
- Place the rubber stopper into the neck of the bottle.
- Place a balloon over the two ends of the Y-tube.
- Insert the Y-tube and balloons into the bottle. Twist the free end of the Y-tube into the hole in the rubber stopper.
- Stretch the glove over the bottom of the bottle and secure with the elastic band (**Figure 2**).

(a) Predict what will happen when you pull down and then push up on the glove. Test your prediction.

(b) Relate your observations to air pressure in the model.

(c) How could you improve the model?

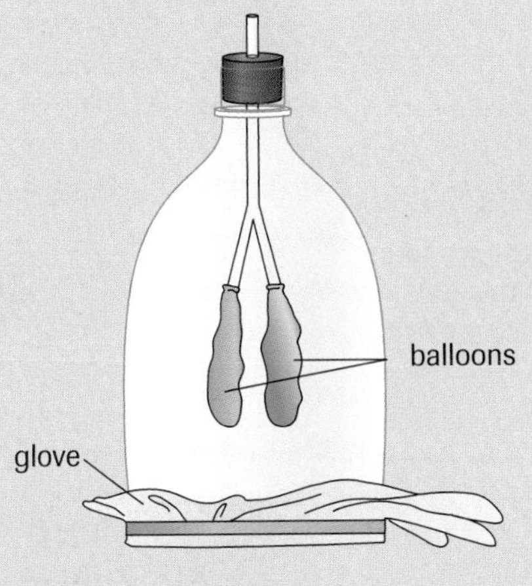

Figure 2
Model of chest cavity

9.1 The Importance of an Oxygen Delivery System

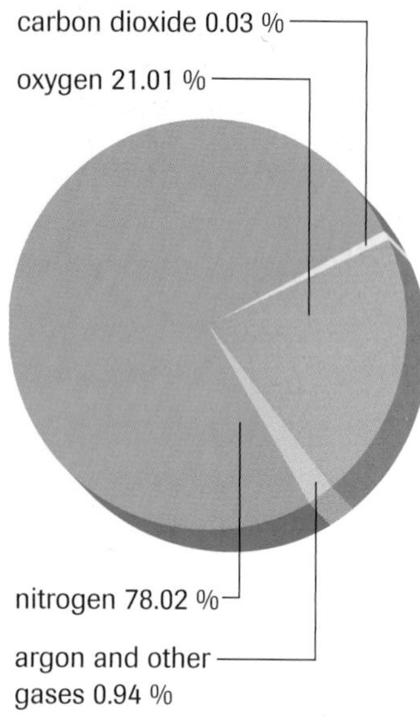

Figure 1
Nitrogen and oxygen are the two most abundant components in atmospheric air.

You live in a sea of air. Nitrogen, oxygen, carbon dioxide, and trace gases are taken into and expelled from your body with every breath. Earth's atmosphere is made up of approximately 78 % nitrogen and 21 % oxygen; the remaining gases, argon, carbon dioxide, and others, make up about 1 % (**Figure 1**). The second most abundant component, oxygen, is vital to life. Cells obtain energy through a chemical reaction called oxidation, in which organic compounds are broken down using oxygen. Although a small amount of energy can be obtained in anaerobic conditions (in the absence of oxygen), life processes in humans cannot be maintained without an adequate supply of oxygen.

Oxygen is so essential to the survival of humans that just a few minutes without it will result in death. By comparison, individuals can live for a number of days without water and several weeks without food. It has been estimated that an average adult utilizes 250 mL of oxygen every minute while resting. Oxygen consumption may increase up to 20 times with strenuous exercise.

Respiration and Breathing

Breathing, or ventilation, involves the movement of air between the external environment and the body. The uptake of oxygen and the release of carbon dioxide by cells take place across a **respiratory membrane.**

The term **respiration** can be used to describe all processes that supply oxygen to the cells of the body for the breakdown of glucose and to describe the process by which carbon dioxide is transported to the lungs for exhalation. **Figure 2** shows the processes involved in respiration.

breathing the process of the exchange of air between the lungs and the environment, including inspiration and expiration

respiratory membrane the membrane where the diffusion of oxygen and other gases occurs between the living cells of the body and the external environment (the atmosphere or water)

respiration all processes involved in the exchange of oxygen and carbon dioxide between cells and the environment, including breathing, gas exchange, and cellular respiration

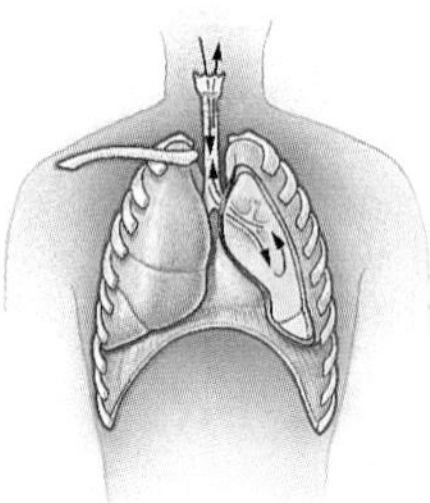

Breathing is the process by which air enters and leaves the lungs.

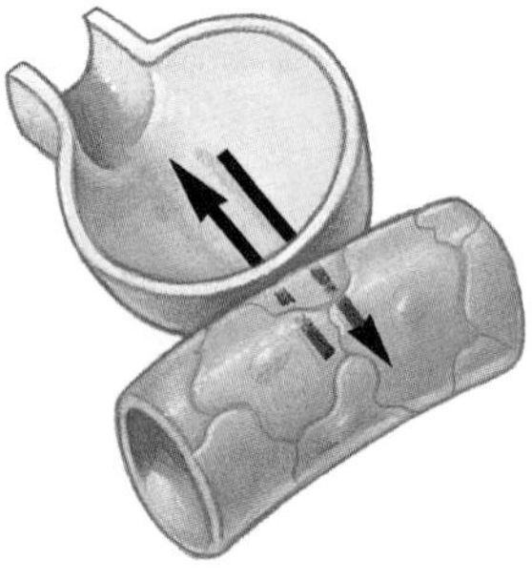

External respiration takes place in the lungs and involves the exchange of O_2 and CO_2 molecules between the air and the blood.

Internal respiration takes place within the body and involves the exchange of O_2 and CO_2 molecules between the blood and tissue fluids.

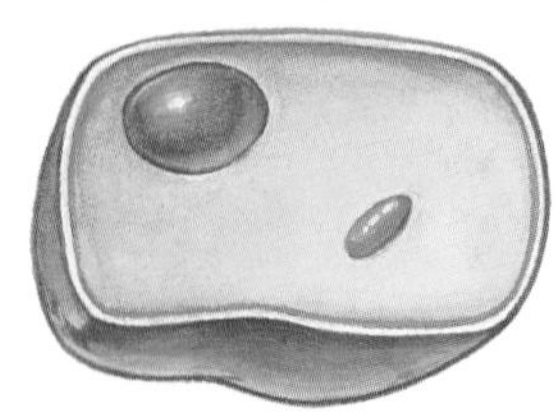

Cellular respiration involves the production of ATP in body cells.

Figure 2
The processes of respiration

Oxygen is used for cellular respiration. Organelles called mitochondria are the centres of cellular respiration. During the process of cellular respiration, oxygen and sugar molecules react, resulting in the production of carbon dioxide and water. The energy released is used to maintain cell processes, such as growth, movement, and the creation of new molecules. The concentration of oxygen in cells is much lower than in their environment because cells continuously use oxygen for cellular respiration. Oxygen must be constantly replenished if a cell is to survive.

CAREER CONNECTION

Physiologist

Physiologists study the functions of cells, organs, tissues, and their interrelationships. There are many specializations in physiology, including exercise physiology, which studies how the body responds to exercise. Physiologists may work in a laboratory, or they may teach. What education is required to become a physiologist? Explore further to find examples of the type of work physiologists do.

www.science.nelson.com 

Practice

1. Why is oxygen so essential for survival?
2. Differentiate between breathing and cellular respiration.
3. What is the function of the respiratory membrane?

The Human Respiratory System

In humans, air enters the respiratory system either through the two nasal cavities or the mouth (**Figure 3**). Foreign particles are prevented from entering the lower respiratory tract by tiny hairs lining the nasal cavities that act as a filtering system. The nasal cavities warm and moisten incoming air and contain mucus, which traps foreign particles and keeps the cells lining the cavities moist.

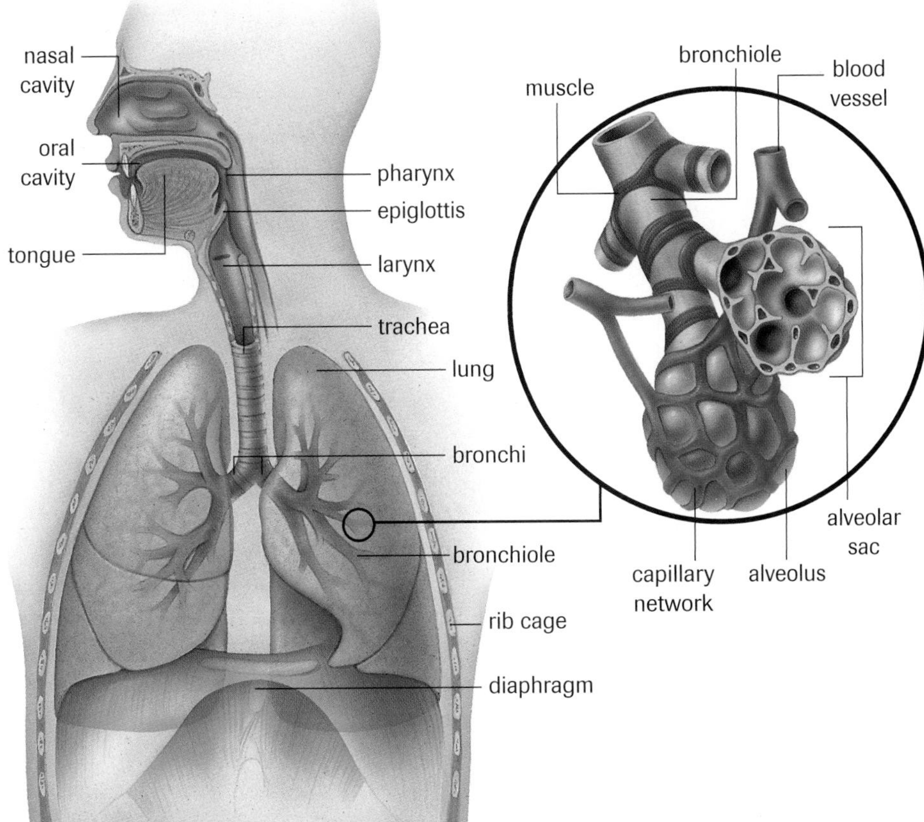

Figure 3 
The human respiratory system

EXTENSION

Structure of an Alveolus

This animation provides a cutaway view of an alveolus and takes a closer look at the respiratory membrane which separates the capillaries from the alveoli.

www.science.nelson.com 

trachea the windpipe

cilia tiny hairlike structures found on some cells that sweep away foreign debris

epiglottis the structure that covers the glottis (opening of the trachea) during swallowing

The nasal cavities open into an air-filled channel at the back of the mouth called the pharynx. Two openings branch from the pharynx: the **trachea**, or windpipe, and the esophagus, which carries food to the stomach. Mucus-producing cells, some of which are ciliated, line the trachea. The mucus traps debris that may have escaped the filters in the nasal passage. This debris is swept by the **cilia** (singular: cilium) from the windpipe back into the pharynx. The wall of the trachea is supported by bands of cartilage, which keep the trachea open. An enlarged segment of cartilage (the larynx) supports the **epiglottis**, a flaplike structure that covers the glottis, or opening of the trachea, when food is being swallowed. When food is chewed, it is forced to the roof of the mouth and pushed backward. This motion initiates a reflex action, which closes the epiglottis, allowing food to enter the esophagus rather than the trachea. If you have ever taken in food or liquids too quickly, you will know how it feels to bypass this reflex. Food or liquid entering the trachea stimulates the cilia, and particles too large to be swept out of the respiratory tract are usually expelled by a second more powerful reflex: a violent cough.

larynx the voice box

Air from the pharynx enters the **larynx**, or voice box, located at the upper end of the trachea. The larynx contains two thin sheets of elastic ligaments that form the vocal cords (**Figure 4**). The vocal cords vibrate as air is forced past them. Different sounds are produced by a change in tension on the vocal cords. Your larynx is protected by thick cartilage commonly known as the Adam's apple. Following puberty, the cartilage and larynx increase in size and thickness, more so in males than females. In the same way as a larger drum creates a lower-pitched sound, the larger voice box in males produces a deeper sound. Rapid growth of the larynx creates problems for adolescent boys, who have difficulty controlling the pitch of their voices. Have you ever noticed how your voice lowers when you have a cold? Inflammation of the vocal cords causes swelling and produces lower-frequency vibrations. Should the infection become severe and result in a condition referred to as laryngitis, you may temporarily lose your voice.

DID YOU KNOW?

What Are Hiccups?

All of us have had the hiccups at one time or another. An irritation of the diaphragm causes air to become trapped in the respiratory tract and the diaphragm experiences a muscular spasm. The hiccup sound is produced when air is taken in as the glottis closes.

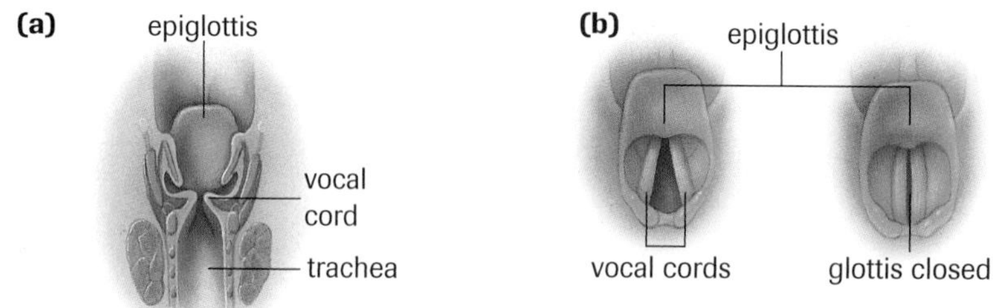

Figure 4
(a) Larynx, showing the vocal cords
(b) Position of the vocal cords when the glottis is open and closed during speech

bronchi the passages from the trachea to the left and right lung

bronchiole the smallest passageways of the respiratory tract

alveoli sacs of the lung in which gas exchange occurs

Inhaled air moves from the trachea into two **bronchi** (singular: bronchus), which, like the trachea, contain bands of cartilage. The bronchi carry air into the right and left lungs, where they branch into many smaller airways called **bronchioles**. Unlike the trachea and bronchi, the bronchioles do not contain cartilaginous bands. Muscles in the walls of the bronchioles can decrease their diameter. Any closing of the bronchioles increases the resistance of air movement and can produce a wheezing sound. Air moves from the bronchioles into tiny sacs called **alveoli** (singular: alveolus). Measuring between 0.1 and 0.2 μm (micrometres) in diameter, each alveolus is surrounded by capillaries. In the alveoli, gases diffuse between the air and blood according to concentration gradients. Oxygen and carbon dioxide both move from areas of higher concentration to areas of lower concentration. Therefore, oxygen moves from the air within alveoli into the capillaries, while carbon dioxide moves from the capillaries into the air in the alveoli. The alveoli are composed of a single layer of cells, which permits rapid gas exchange. (However, the respiratory membrane is really three layers thick.) Each lung contains about 150 million alveoli. That provides enough surface area to cover half a tennis court, or about 40 times the surface area of the human body.

Have you ever tried to pull the cover slip from a microscope slide, only to discover that it seems to be fused to the slide? This phenomenon is caused by water molecules adhering to the glass. A similar problem faces the alveoli. During inhalation the alveoli appear bulb shaped, but during exhalation the tiny sacs collapse. The two membranes touch but are prevented from sticking together by a film of fat and protein called lipoprotein. This film lines the alveoli, allowing them to pop open during inhalation. Some newborn babies, especially premature babies, do not produce enough of the lipoprotein. Extreme force is required to overcome the surface tension created, and the baby experiences tremendous difficulty inhaling. This condition, referred to as respiratory distress syndrome, often results in death.

The outer surface of the lungs is surrounded by a thin membrane called the **pleural membrane**, which also lines the inner wall of the chest cavity. These two membranes adhere to each other. This adhesion is why the lungs expand and draw in air when the volume of the chest cavity is increased. The space between the pleural membranes is filled with a small amount of fluid that reduces the friction between the lungs and the chest cavity during inhalation. Pleurisy, the inflammation of the pleural membranes, is most often caused by a viral infection or pneumonia. The inflammation may result in friction of the membranes. Sometimes, fluid builds up between the pleural membranes. This buildup of fluid puts pressure on the lungs, making expiration (exhalation) easier, but inspiration (inhalation) much more difficult and painful.

EXTENSION 

Maintaining the Alveolar Space

Why do the alveoli in your lungs stay expanded? This audio clip will explore the factors that prevent the alveoli from collapsing.

www.science.nelson.com 

pleural membrane a thin membrane that surrounds the outer surface of the lungs and lines the inner wall of the chest cavity

Practice

4. Describe the function of cilia in the respiratory tract.
5. Explain how the functions of the trachea, esophagus, and epiglottis are related.

Breathing Movements

Pressure differences between the atmosphere and the chest, or thoracic, cavity determine the movement of air into and out of the lungs. Atmospheric pressure remains relatively constant, but the pressure in the chest cavity may vary. An understanding of breathing hinges on an understanding of gas pressures.

Gases move from an area of high pressure to an area of low pressure. Inspiration occurs when pressure inside the lungs is less than that of the atmosphere, and expiration occurs when pressure inside the lungs is greater than that of the atmosphere.

The **diaphragm**, a dome-shaped sheet of muscle that separates the thoracic, or chest, cavity from the abdominal cavity, can regulate the pressure in the chest cavity. During inspiration, the diaphragm muscle contracts, or shortens, pulling downward. The chest volume increases and pressure in the lungs decreases. The atmospheric pressure is now greater than the pressure in the chest cavity, and air moves into the lungs. During expiration, the diaphragm relaxes and returns to its dome shape due to the force exerted by the organs in the abdomen. The chest volume decreases and pressure increases. The pressure in the chest cavity is now greater than the atmospheric pressure, and air moves out of the lungs.

DID YOU KNOW?

Chest Wound First-Aid

If you are injured and have a hole in your chest, one first-aid technique is to place your hand over the wound to create a seal.

diaphragm a sheet of muscle that separates the organs of the thoracic cavity from those of the abdominal cavity

intercostal muscle a muscle that raises and lowers the rib cage

The diaphragm is assisted through the action of the intercostal muscles, which cause the ribs to move (**Figure 5**). Have you ever noticed how your ribs rise when you inhale? The ribs are hinged to the vertebral column, allowing them to move up and down. Bands of muscle, the **intercostal muscles**, are found between the ribs. A nerve stimulus causes the intercostal muscles to contract, pulling the ribs upward and outward. This increases the volume of the chest, lowers the pressure in the chest cavity, and air moves into the lungs. If the intercostals are not stimulated, the muscles relax and the rib cage falls. The chest wall pushes against the lungs with greater pressure, and air is forced out of the lungs.

Air moves into the lungs.
Intercostal muscles contract; rib cage moves upward.
(a)
Diaphragm contracts and moves downward.
Air moves out of the lungs.
Intercostal muscles relax; rib cage falls.
(b)
Diaphragm relaxes and moves upward.

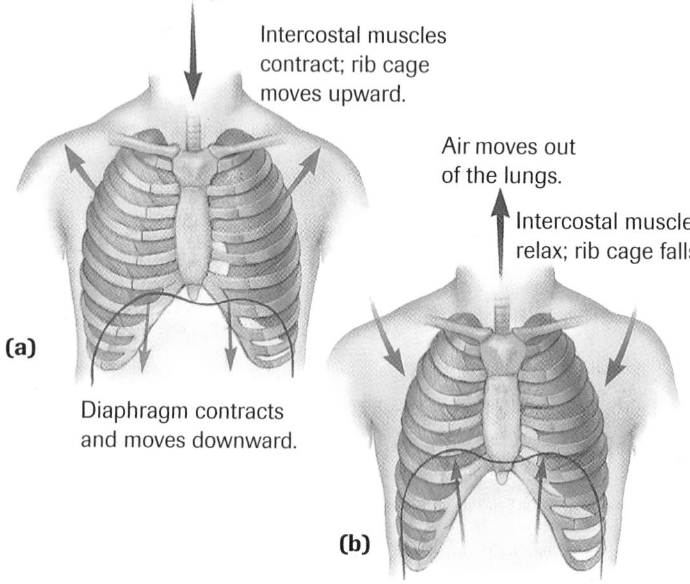

Figure 5
Changes in chest volume during inspiration and expiration
(a) The intercostal muscles contract and the rib cage pulls upward. Because pressure in the chest cavity is lower than the atmospheric pressure, air moves into the lungs.
(b) The intercostal muscles relax and the rib cage falls. Because pressure in the chest cavity is higher than the atmospheric pressure, air moves out of the lungs.

EXTENSION

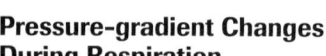

Pressure-gradient Changes During Respiration
This animation discusses ventilation and examines the relationship between atmospheric and intra-alveolar pressure.

www.science.nelson.com
GO

The importance of the pressure difference between the lungs and the atmosphere can be illustrated by a pneumothorax. A pneumothorax is an accumulation of air inside the chest in the space between the pleural membranes that line the lungs and the inner chest wall. The pressure of the air causes the lung to collapse. A traumatic pneumothorax results from a penetrating injury to the chest, such as a bullet hole or stab wound. When the diaphragm contracts and the rib cage rises, the pressure inside the chest cavity is reduced; however, air flows directly through the hole in the chest. To treat a pneumothorax, the air must be removed so that the lung can re-expand.

INVESTIGATION 9.1 *Introduction*

Determining Lung Capacity

The lungs of healthy, fit people tend to have a greater volume than the lungs of those who experience poor health or who are less fit. What is your lung capacity?

To perform this investigation, turn to page 305.

Report Checklist

- ● Purpose
- ● Problem
- ● Hypothesis
- ● Prediction
- ● Design
- ○ Materials
- ○ Procedure
- ● Evidence
- ● Analysis
- ● Evaluation
- ● Synthesis

The Importance of an Oxygen Delivery System

- The cells of the body obtain energy through oxidation. Thus, oxygen is essential to survival.
- Respiration includes all the processes involved in the exchange of oxygen and carbon dioxide between cells and the environment.
- Air enters the respiratory system through the nose or the mouth; then, it enters the pharynx, trachea, bronchi, and the bronchioles and alveoli in the lungs.
- In the alveoli, gases diffuse between air and blood according to concentration gradients. Oxygen moves into the alveoli and carbon dioxide moves out of the alveoli.
- The movement of gases into and out of the lungs is determined by the difference in pressure between the atmosphere and the thoracic cavity. Pressure in the thoracic cavity is regulated by the diaphragm. The diaphragm is assisted by the movement of the intercostal muscles.
  - During inspiration (inhalation), the intercostal muscles contract, the diaphragm flattens and pulls downward, the rib cage pulls up and outward, chest volume increases, pressure in the lungs decreases, and air moves into the lungs.
  - During expiration (exhalation), the intercostal muscles relax, the diaphragm becomes dome shaped, the rib cage falls, chest volume decreases, pressure in the lungs increases, and air moves out of the lungs.

Section 9.1 Questions

1. Describe the similarities and differences between the bronchi, bronchioles, and alveoli. How is each type of structure well suited for its purpose in the lungs?
2. Explain how and why oxygen and carbon dioxide diffuse between the alveoli and the air in the lungs.
3. Why does a throat infection cause your voice to produce lower-pitched sounds?
4. Trace the pathway of a breath of air from its point of entry to its diffusion in the lungs. Refer to the structures that the air passes by or through.
5. What is respiratory distress syndrome?
6. Why does the buildup of fluid in the chest cavity, as occurs with pleurisy, make exhalation easier but inhalation more difficult?
7. Describe the movements of the ribs and the diaphragm during inhalation and exhalation.
8. Bronchitis is an inflammation of the bronchi or bronchioles that causes them to swell. What problems would be caused as the airways swell and decrease in diameter?
9. Nicotine inhaled with cigarette smoke causes blood vessels to narrow. What problems would this cause for the cells of the body?

9.2 Gas Exchange and Transport

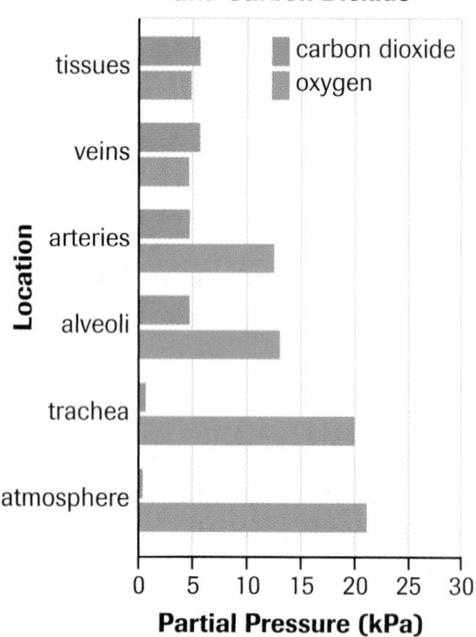

Figure 1
Partial pressures of oxygen and carbon dioxide

An understanding of gas exchange in the human body is tied to an understanding of the physical nature of gases. As mentioned in the previous section, gases diffuse from an area of higher pressure to an area of lower pressure.

Dalton's law of partial pressure states that each gas in a mixture exerts its own pressure, or partial pressure. The graph in **Figure 1** shows the partial pressures of oxygen and carbon dioxide in the body. Gases diffuse from an area of high partial pressure to an area of lower partial pressure. The highest partial pressure of oxygen is found in atmospheric air. Oxygen diffuses from the air (21.2 kPa) into the lungs (13.3 kPa for the alveoli).

The partial pressure of oxygen in the blood differs depending on location. Arteries carry blood away from the heart while veins carry it back to the heart. Arteries are connected to veins by capillaries, where gas exchange takes place and oxygen diffuses into the tissues. (Remember that energy is continuously released from nutrients by reactions within the cells that require oxygen. Oxygen will never accumulate in the cells.) Therefore, the largest change in the partial pressure of oxygen is observed as oxygen travels from the arteries (12.6 kPa) into the capillaries (5.3 kPa).

Carbon dioxide, the product of cellular respiration, follows an opposite pattern. Partial pressure of carbon dioxide is highest in the tissues and venous blood. The partial pressure of nitrogen, although not shown in the graph, remains relatively constant. Atmospheric nitrogen is not involved in cellular respiration.

Practice

1. (a) Where is the partial pressure of oxygen the highest? the lowest?
   (b) How is this related to the diffusion of oxygen into the tissues?
2. Where is the partial pressure of carbon dioxide the highest? the lowest?

Oxygen Transport

hemoglobin the oxygen-carrying molecule in red blood cells

oxyhemoglobin hemoglobin that is bound to oxygen

Oxygen (O_2) moves from the atmosphere, the area of highest partial pressure, to the alveoli. It then diffuses from the alveoli into the blood and dissolves in the plasma. Oxygen is not very soluble in blood—about 0.3 mL of oxygen per 100 mL of blood. However, even at rest, the body requires approximately 10 times that amount of oxygen. **Hemoglobin** greatly increases the oxygen-carrying capacity of the blood. The hemoglobin molecule consists of four polypeptides that are composed of heme, the iron-containing pigment, and globin, the protein component. Each heme group contains an iron atom, which binds with oxygen. When oxygen dissolves into the plasma, hemoglobin forms a weak bond with the oxygen molecule to form **oxyhemoglobin**. Once oxyhemoglobin is formed, other oxygen molecules can dissolve in the plasma. With hemoglobin, the blood can carry 20 mL of oxygen per 100 mL of blood, almost a 70-fold increase.

The amount of oxygen that combines with hemoglobin is dependent on partial pressure. The partial pressure in the lungs is approximately 13.3 kPa. Thus, blood leaving the lungs is still nearly saturated with oxygen. As blood enters the capillaries, the partial pressure drops to about 5.3 kPa. This drop in partial pressure causes the dissociation, or split, of oxygen from the hemoglobin, and oxygen diffuses into the tissues. **Figure 2** (on the next page) shows an oxygen–hemoglobin dissociation curve. You will notice that very little oxygen is released from the hemoglobin until the partial pressure of oxygen reaches 5.3 kPa. This ensures that most of the oxygen remains bound to the hemoglobin

EXTENSION

Partial Pressure Gradients
Oxygen and carbon dioxide exchange occurs across capillaries and is driven by partial pressure gradients. This animation reviews the partial pressures of CO_2 and O_2 in different regions of the body.

www.science.nelson.com 

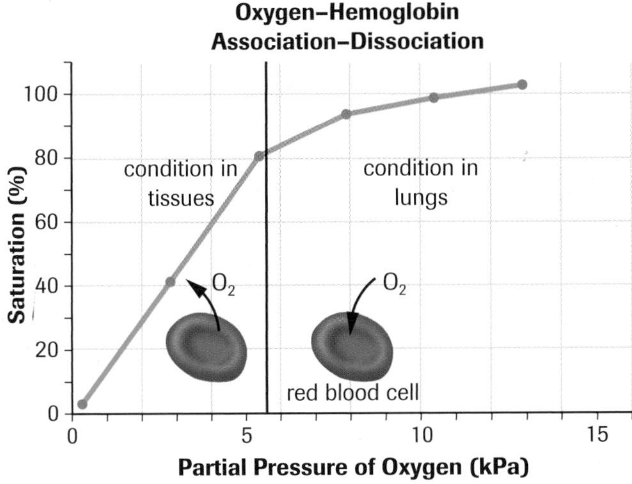

Figure 2
Oxygen–hemoglobin dissociation curve

until it gets to the tissue capillaries. Also note that venous blood still carries a rich supply of oxygen. Approximately 70 % of the hemoglobin is still saturated when blood returns to the heart.

+ EXTENSION

The Oxyhemoglobin Dissociation Curve
This audio clip analyzes the oxyhemoglobin dissociation curve and its correlation to hemoglobin's changing affinity for oxygen, as it gains and loses oxygen molecules.

www.science.nelson.com GO

Carbon Dioxide Transport

Carbon dioxide (CO_2) is about 20 times more soluble than oxygen. About 9 % of the carbon dioxide produced by the tissues of the body is carried in the plasma. Approximately 27 % of the body's carbon dioxide combines with hemoglobin to form carbaminohemoglobin. The remaining 64 % of the body's carbon dioxide combines with water from the plasma to form carbonic acid (H_2CO_3):

$$CO_2 + H_2O \rightarrow H_2CO_3$$

An enzyme called **carbonic anhydrase** increases the rate of this chemical reaction by about 250 times. The rapid conversion of free carbon dioxide into carbonic acid decreases the concentration of carbon dioxide in the plasma. This maintains a low partial pressure of carbon dioxide, ensuring that carbon dioxide continues to diffuse into the blood (**Figure 3**).

carbonic anhydrase an enzyme found in red blood cells that speeds the conversion of carbon dioxide and water to carbonic acid

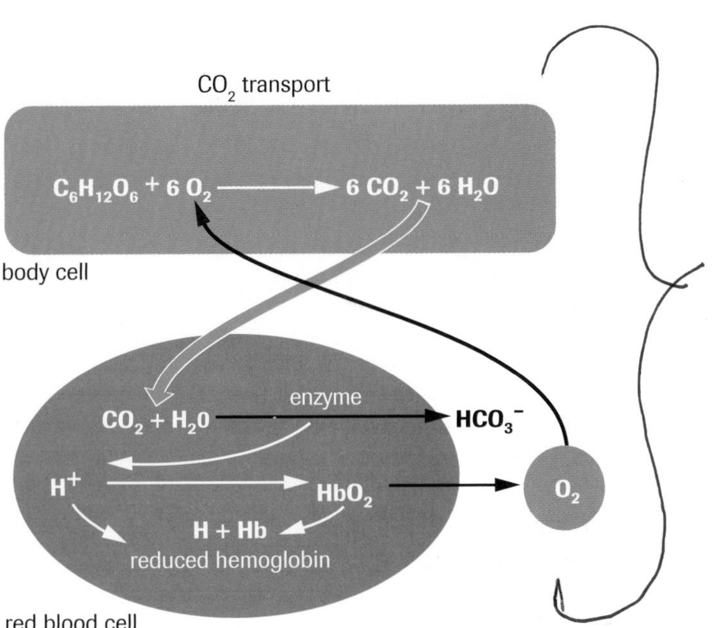

Figure 3
Under the influence of carbonic anhydrase, an enzyme found in red blood cells, carbon dioxide combines with water to form carbonic acid (H_2CO_3), which then, dissociates into H^+ and HCO_3^- ions.

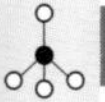

CHEMISTRY CONNECTION

Acids and Bases

When carbon dioxide dissolves in the water in plasma, it forms carbonic acid. You can learn more about acids and bases in your chemistry course.

www.science.nelson.com 

The formation of acids, such as carbonic acid, can create problems. Because acids can change the pH of the blood and eventually bring about death, they must be buffered. This is where the second function of hemoglobin comes into effect. Being unstable, the carbonic acid dissociates into bicarbonate ions (HCO_3^-) and hydrogen ions (H^+):

$$(H_2CO_3 \rightarrow H^+ + HCO_3^-)$$

The hydrogen ions help dislodge oxygen from the hemoglobin, and then combine with the hemoglobin to form reduced hemoglobin. When hemoglobin combines with the hydrogen ions, it is removing H^+ from the solution; that is, the hemoglobin is acting as a **buffer**. Meanwhile, the bicarbonate ions are transported into the plasma. Oxygen is released from its binding site and is now free to move into the body cells.

buffer a substance capable of neutralizing acids and bases, thus maintaining the original pH of the solution

Once the venous blood reaches the lungs, oxygen dislodges the hydrogen ions from the hemoglobin binding sites. Free hydrogen and bicarbonate ions combine to form carbon dioxide and water:

$$H^+ + HCO_3^- \rightarrow H_2O + CO_2$$

The highly concentrated carbon dioxide diffuses from the blood into the alveoli and is eventually eliminated during exhalation.

DID YOU KNOW ?

Andean Aboriginals

There is less air at high altitudes, than at sea level, so a person inhales fewer oxygen molecules with each breath. Andean highlanders, the Quechua and Aymara, have adapted to living high in the mountains. Their red blood cells contain more hemoglobin than people living at sea level. Although both groups breathe at the same rate, the Andean highlanders deliver oxygen to their cells more efficiently.

Maintaining Gas Levels

A variety of mechanisms exist to help maintain appropriate levels of oxygen and carbon dioxide. For example, a chemical receptor helps ensure that carbon dioxide, the waste product of cellular respiration, does not accumulate. During exercise, cellular respiration increases, causing carbon dioxide levels to increase. This stimulates chemical receptors in the brainstem. The activated nerve cells from the brain carry impulses to muscles that increase breathing movements. Increased breathing movements help flush excess carbon dioxide from the body. Other chemical receptors in the walls of the carotid artery are able to detect low levels of oxygen in the blood. A nerve is stimulated and a message is sent to the brain. The brain relays the information, by way of another nerve, to the muscles that control breathing. Thus, a system of "turning on" and "turning off" mechanisms is used to help maintain equilibrium.

EXPLORE an issue

Using Erythropoietin to Increase Oxygen-Carrying Capacity

Issue Checklist

- ○ Issue
- ● Resolution
- ○ Design
- ● Evidence
- ● Analysis
- ● Evaluation

In the past, drug use in sports was most often linked to power sports such as weightlifting and sprinting. Steroids increase muscle mass and strength.

In the late 1980s, endurance athletes turned to erythropoietin (EPO), a naturally occurring hormone that promotes the production of red blood cells in the bone marrow. By increasing red blood cell production, the oxygen-carrying capacity of the blood is improved and more oxygen can be delivered to the tissues. You know the saying about "too much of a good thing"? In the case of EPO, the problem is too many red blood cells in the blood. Although oxygen delivery is improved, the blood becomes thicker and more difficult to move through the blood vessels. This, in turn, can cause an increased incidence of stroke, heart attack, and heart failure. In 1988, EPO was linked to the death of at least 20 cyclists.

Despite the adverse effects, athletes continue to use EPO for many different sports, and deaths associated with the hormone continue. In the 2002 Olympic Games, Canadian cross-country skier Beckie Scott (**Figure 4**, next page) had her bronze medal elevated to gold when both the gold and silver medallists in the event tested positive for EPO.

Figure 4
Beckie Scott's bronze medal was elevated to a gold medal in cross-country skiing because the two other winning athletes had used performance-enhancing drugs.

Statement
Although individual athletes are banned for drug use in Olympic sports, it continues to be a problem. The ban should be extended to all athletes from that country in that particular sport for a defined number of years.

1. Form a group and research the issue.

www.science.nelson.com 

2. Discuss the issue with class members and others in preparation for a debate.
3. Write a list of points and counterpoints that your group has considered.
4. Take a stand. Decide if you agree or disagree with the statement. Should an entire country be banned from a sport for the actions of one individual?
5. Defend your position in the debate.

SUMMARY Gas Exchange and Transport

- Gases diffuse from an area of higher pressure to an area of lower pressure.
- The partial pressure of oxygen is highest in the atmosphere and lowest in the veins and tissues.
  - Oxygen diffuses from the atmosphere into alveoli and then, into the blood.
  - Hemoglobin bonds to oxygen molecules to form oxyhemoglobin. Hemoglobin and oxygen dissociate in the capillaries, and oxygen diffuses into the tissues.
- The partial pressure of carbon dioxide is highest in the tissues and veins and lowest in the atmosphere.
  - Some carbon dioxide combines with water from plasma to form carbonic acid; this decreases the carbon dioxide concentration in the blood, ensuring that carbon dioxide continues to diffuse into the blood.
  - Carbonic acid dissociates into HCO_3^- and H^+. Hemoglobin combines with H^+, releasing oxygen and acting as a buffer.
  - In the lungs, H^+ and HCO_3^- combine to form carbon dioxide and water. Carbon dioxide is highly concentrated; it diffuses from the blood into alveoli and is eliminated through exhalation.
- To help maintain equilibrium, chemical receptors detect a change in gas levels and send a message to increase or decrease breathing rate.

CAREER CONNECTION

Commercial Diver
Commercial divers need to know about the partial pressure of gases. These divers work in constructing or inspecting underwater machinery, including offshore oil and gas rigs. Breathing atmospheric concentrations of oxygen can cause problems when commercial divers do deep dives. Learn how someone would become a commercial diver, and explore the types of work done.

www.science.nelson.com 

Section 9.2 Questions

1. How does partial pressure affect the movement of oxygen from the alveoli to the blood?
2. How is carbon dioxide transported in the blood?
3. Describe the importance of hemoglobin as a buffer.
4. Trace the pathway of an oxygen molecule from the atmosphere to its combination with a hemoglobin molecule.
5. What is the function of carbonic anhydrase?

9.3 Regulation of Breathing Movements

Breathing movements are controlled by nerves from the medulla oblongata in the brain (**Figure 1**). Information about the accumulation of carbon dioxide (CO_2) and acids and the need for oxygen is detected by **chemoreceptors**. Two different types of receptors are oxygen chemoreceptors and carbon dioxide, or acid, chemoreceptors. The carbon dioxide receptors are the most sensitive and are the main regulators of breathing movements.

chemoreceptor a specialized nerve receptor that is sensitive to specific chemicals

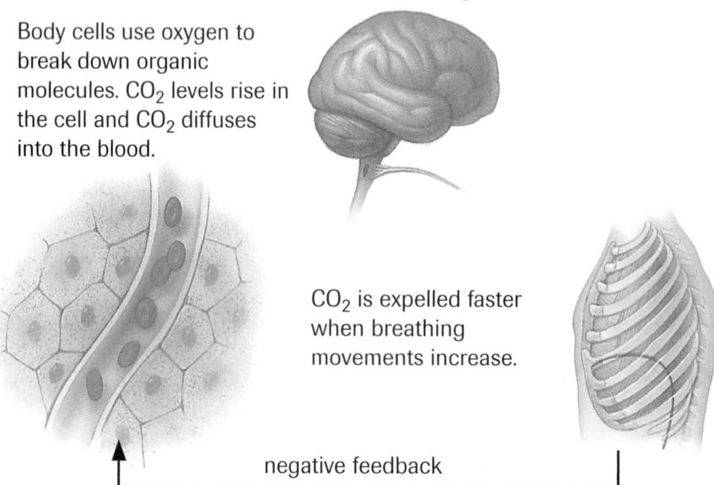

Chemoreceptors in the medulla oblongata detect high levels of CO_2. A nerve impulse is sent to the intercostal muscles and diaphragm to increase breathing movements.
Body cells use oxygen to break down organic molecules. CO_2 levels rise in the cell and CO_2 diffuses into the blood.
CO_2 is expelled faster when breathing movements increase.
negative feedback

Figure 1
Carbon dioxide control

CO_2 dissolves in the blood and forms an acid. Should the CO_2 accumulate, special chemoreceptors in the medulla oblongata become activated. Once activated, the medulla oblongata relays messages to the intercostal muscles and diaphragm to increase breathing movements. The acceleration of the breathing rate decreases the levels of CO_2 in the blood. Once CO_2 levels fall, the chemoreceptors become inactive, and the breathing rate returns to normal.

A second monitoring system, which relies on chemoreceptors sensitive to oxygen, is found in the carotid and aortic arteries (**Figure 2**). Referred to as the *carotid* and *aortic bodies*, these specialized receptors are primarily responsible for detecting low levels of oxygen. When stimulated, the oxygen receptors send a nerve impulse to the medulla oblongata. Once activated, the medulla sends nerve impulses to the intercostal muscles and diaphragm to increase breathing movements. Increased ventilation increases blood oxygen, thereby, compensating for low levels of oxygen. A secondary function of these bodies is to detect high blood CO_2 or high levels of acidity, although the medulla oblongata is the more sensitive receptor of CO_2.

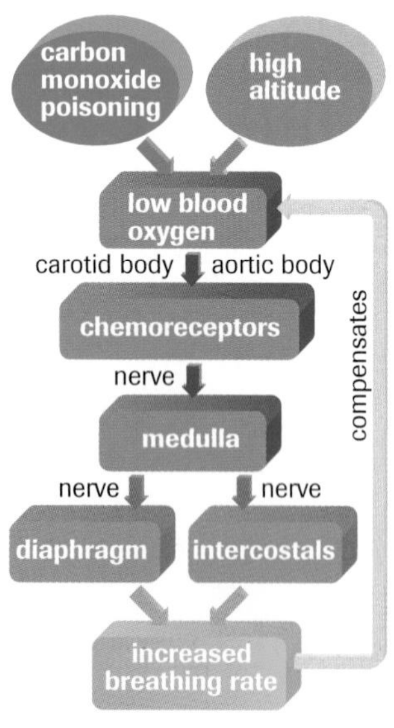

Figure 2
Low blood oxygen levels are detected by special oxygen chemoreceptors in the aorta and carotid arteries.

Because the CO_2 receptors are more sensitive to changes in blood chemistry, the oxygen receptors act as a backup system. The oxygen receptors are only called into action when oxygen levels fall and CO_2 levels remain within the normal range. For example, when you hold your breath, CO_2 levels rise and oxygen levels drop—the high CO_2 levels would initiate increased breathing movements. However, the situation differs at high altitudes, where the air is thinner and fewer oxygen molecules are found. Since low oxygen levels are not accompanied by higher CO_2 levels, the chemoreceptors in the carotid and aortic bodies stimulate breathing movements. Increased ventilation helps establish normal blood oxygen levels.

Response of the Respiratory System to Exercise

The ventilation of the alveoli can increase up to 20 times with heavy exercise to keep up with the demands for increased oxygenation and the need to expel CO_2. Although all the factors that cause increased ventilation of the lungs are not known, three factors play an important role: decreased O_2, increased CO_2, and increased H^+. **Figure 3** outlines some of the body's responses to exercise.

DID YOU KNOW?

Carbon Monoxide Poisoning

Carbon monoxide (CO) poisoning is another example of how falling blood oxygen levels stimulate increased breathing rate. Carbon monoxide competes with oxygen for the active site on the hemoglobin molecule. Unfortunately, CO gains faster access. As more hemoglobin molecules bind with CO, less oxygen is carried to the tissues. The carbon dioxide level tends not to increase. Eventually, the low oxygen level is detected by the chemoreceptors and breathing movements increase.

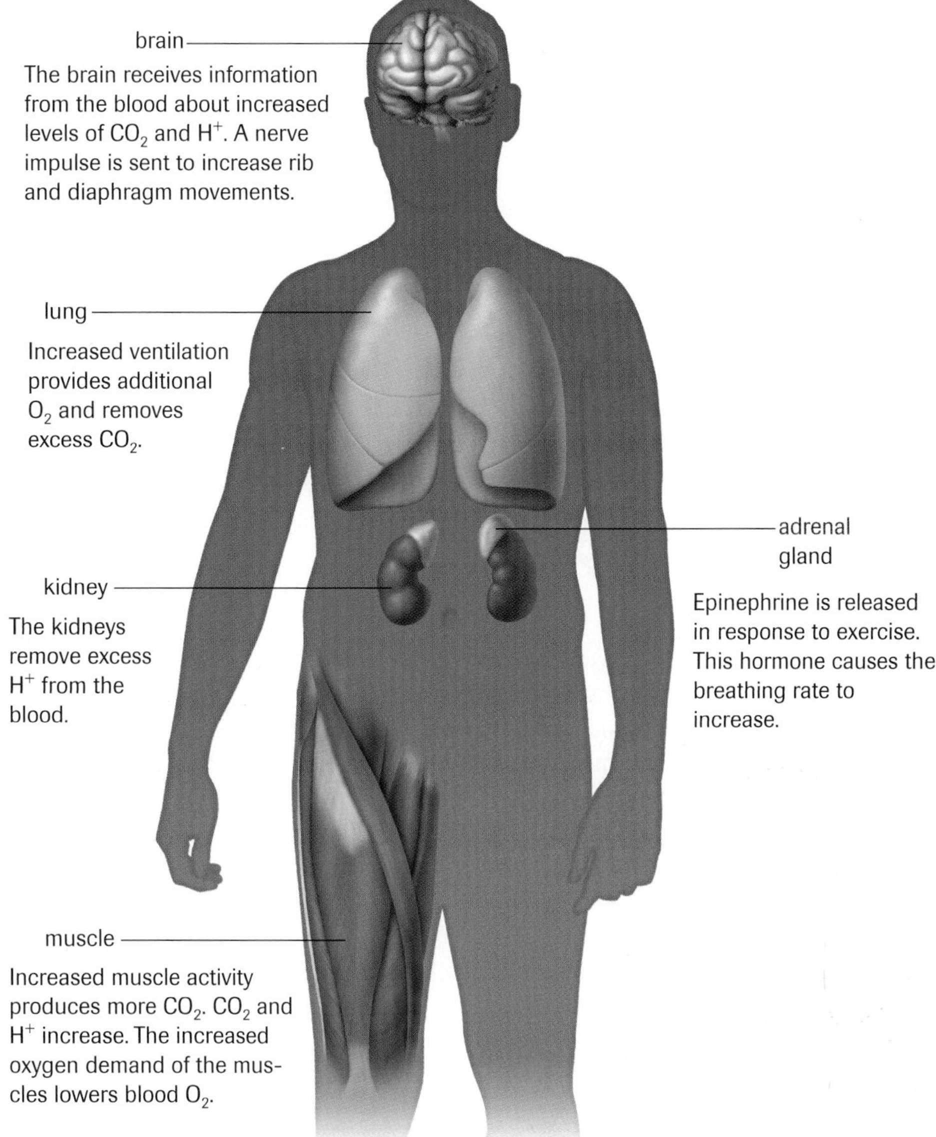

brain
The brain receives information from the blood about increased levels of CO_2 and H^+. A nerve impulse is sent to increase rib and diaphragm movements.
lung
Increased ventilation provides additional O_2 and removes excess CO_2.
kidney
The kidneys remove excess H^+ from the blood.
muscle
Increased muscle activity produces more CO_2. CO_2 and H^+ increase. The increased oxygen demand of the muscles lowers blood O_2.
adrenal gland
Epinephrine is released in response to exercise. This hormone causes the breathing rate to increase.

Figure 3
The body's response to exercise

INVESTIGATION 9.2 *Introduction*

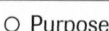

The Effects of Exercise on Lung Volume

Different factors can affect the volume of a single breath. In this investigation, you will design and carry out an experiment on how exercise affects lung volume.

Report Checklist

○ Purpose	● Design	● Analysis
● Problem	● Materials	● Evaluation
● Hypothesis	● Procedure	○ Synthesis
● Prediction	● Evidence	

To perform this investigation, turn to page 306. 

Figure 4
Dr. Malcolm King

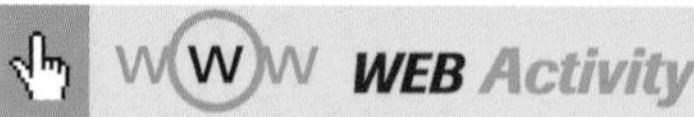

WEB Activity

Canadian Achievers—Dr. Malcolm King

Dr. Malcolm King (**Figure 4**), a Professor in the Department of Medicine at the University of Alberta, began his career as a chemist, studying polymers. He now applies this knowledge to studies of the role of mucus from the lungs in two serious disorders of the respiratory system, cystic fibrosis and chronic obstructive lung disease. Dr. King is a leader in his field, having published over 160 papers, and is the recipient of many awards. A member of the Mississaugas of the New Credit First Nation in Southern Ontario, Dr. King is also interested in training Aboriginal students in medicine, and in examining traditional medicines used to treat respiratory diseases. Conduct additional research on Dr. Malcolm King, his research, and his leadership role in science and Aboriginal issues.

www.science.nelson.com GO

Disorders of the Respiratory System

All respiratory disorders share one common characteristic: they all decrease oxygen delivery to the tissues.

bronchitis an inflammation of the bronchial tubes

emphysema a respiratory disorder characterized by an overinflation of the alveoli

Bronchitis

Bacterial or viral infections, as well as reactions to environmental chemicals, can cause a variety of respiratory problems. **Bronchitis** is an ailment characterized by narrowing of the air passages and inflammation of the mucous lining in the bronchial tubes. This leads to excess production of mucus, tissue swelling, a narrowing of the air passages, and decreased air movement through the bronchi. The condition becomes even more serious in the bronchioles. Unlike the trachea and the bronchi, the bronchioles are not supported by bands of cartilage to help keep them open.

EXTENSION

Pillow Fungus

Professor Ashley Woodcock describes her discovery of an entire ecosystem that exists in our pillows. This ecosystem includes multiple species of potentially allergenic fungus, bacteria and dust mites. While this is definitely a problem for individuals with respiratory ailments such as asthma and allergies, research continues to see if it is problem for others without any previous allergies.

www.science.nelson.com GO

Emphysema

In **emphysema**, the walls of the alveoli become inflamed. Over time, this destroys the air sacs, causing them to lose their elasticity, stretch, and eventually rupture. As a result, it becomes difficult to exhale and air becomes trapped in the lungs. The fact that there are fewer alveoli means there is less surface area for gas exchange which, in turn, leads to decreased oxygen levels. The most common cause of emphysema is smoking. Emphysema is associated with chronic bronchitis. Together they are known as chronic obstructive pulmonary disease (COPD). Like bronchitis, COPD involves an increased resistance to airflow through the bronchioles. Although air flows into the alveoli fairly easily, the decreased diameter of the bronchioles creates resistance to the movement of air out of the lungs and exhalation becomes laboured. In the body's attempt to maintain equilibrium, the breathing rate increases. The circulatory system adjusts by increasing the heart rate.

Practice

1. What is bronchitis? What are its effects on the respiratory system?
2. Describe the pressure changes that occur in the lungs during breathing for someone with emphysema.

WWW WEB Activity

Simulation–Asthma

Bronchial asthma is associated with the inflammation of the bronchioles. In asthma, greater effort is required to exhale than to inhale. The imbalance between the amount of air entering the lungs and the amount of air leaving the lungs must be met by increasing the exertion of expiration. In this activity, you will view the events that occur in the lung during an asthma attack. Why does the imbalance in the amount of air entering and leaving the lungs occur?

www.science.nelson.com 

bronchial asthma a respiratory disorder characterized by reversible narrowing of the bronchial passages

Case Study

Smoking and Lung Cancer

More Canadian men and women die from lung cancer than from any other form of the disease (**Figure 5**). As in other cancers, there is uncontrolled growth of cells. The solid mass of cancer cells in the lungs greatly decreases the surface area for diffusion. Tumours may actually block bronchioles, thereby reducing airflow to the lungs and potentially causing the lung to collapse.

In contrast to skin cancers, lung cancers are almost always fatal—the five-year survival rate is not much better than 15 %. Lung cancer is the second most common cancer, yet it is one of the most preventable. Prior to the use of tobacco, lung cancer was relatively rare. Smoking increased in popularity in the 1920s and it was usually men who smoked. In the 1940s, lung cancer began to increase at a dramatic rate, becoming the most common cancer in men. As more and more women began to smoke, lung cancer cases among women also rose significantly. In 1995, lung cancer surpassed breast cancer as the number one cancer killer of women. The World Health Organization estimates that, every year, 4 million people die as a result of smoking tobacco. This figure is expected to rise to 10 million by 2010.

When smokers quit, their risk of developing lung cancer lessens over time (**Figure 6**, next page). Also, as with most cancers, if lung cancer is detected at an early stage, there is a greater chance of survival. Some common symptoms include an unusual cough, sputum containing blood, hoarseness, and shortness of breath which is noticeable during physical activity. **Figure 7**, on the next page, shows how the bronchioles and alveoli of a smoker appear in comparison to those of a nonsmoker.

How does smoking lead to lung cancer? Cancer usually begins in the bronchi or bronchioles. Components of cigarette smoke contribute to the development of cancerous tumours. The four diagrams in **Figure 8**, on the next page, show the development and progression of lung cancer. Cigarette smoke travels through the bronchioles and irritates the cells. Special

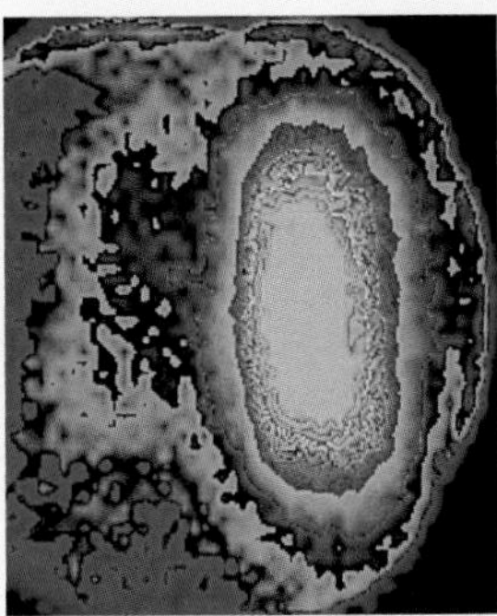
(a)

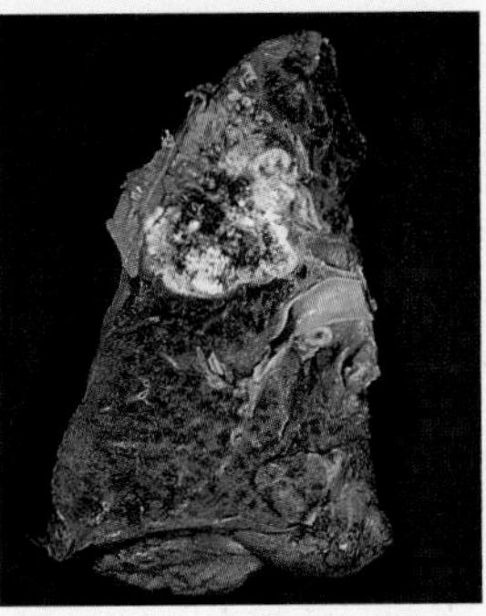
(b)

(c)

Figure 5
(a) A lung scan reveals cancer of the lung. The colours in the healthy lung indicate normal ventilation. On the left side, the absence of the normal colours and the presence of the purple colour indicate a nonfunctioning lung.
(b) Smoke descends toward the lungs.
(c) Postmortem specimen of a human lung shows a cancerous tumour of the upper lobe as a black and white area. The entire lung is permeated with black, tarry deposits, suggesting a history of heavy smoking.

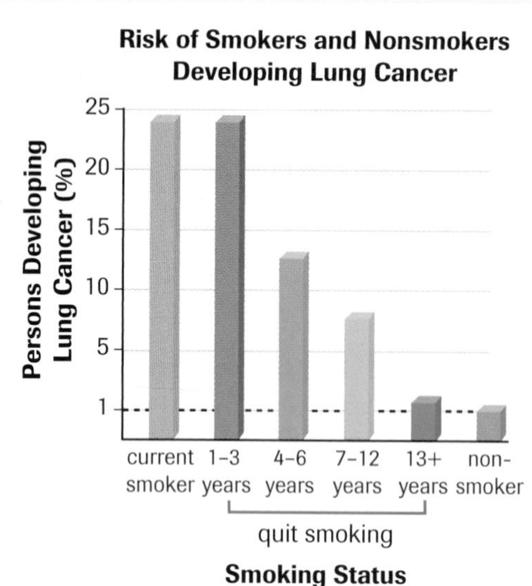

Figure 6
When smokers stop smoking, their risk of lung cancer decreases with time.

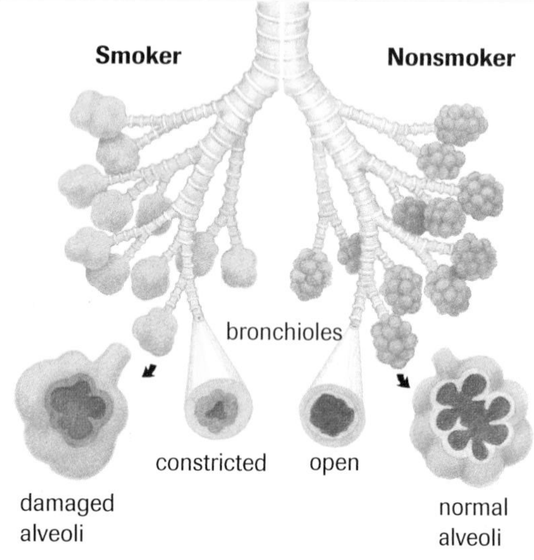

Figure 7
A comparison of the bronchioles and alveoli of a smoker and a nonsmoker

cells produce mucus, which is designed to trap foreign particles. Compare the mucous layers in **Figures 8 (a)** and **(c)**. Ciliated cells line the bronchioles. Cilia sweep away the debris trapped by the mucus. Unfortunately, the tar found in cigarette smoke slows the action of the cilia. The sludgelike tar becomes trapped in the mucus. **Figure 8 (b)** shows the beginning of a cancerous tumour and **Figure 8 (c)** shows how the tumour advances. Note the location of the tumour and its growth. While the tumour is still walled in by the basal membrane in **Figure 8 (c)**, it has broken through the membrane in **Figure 8 (d)**.

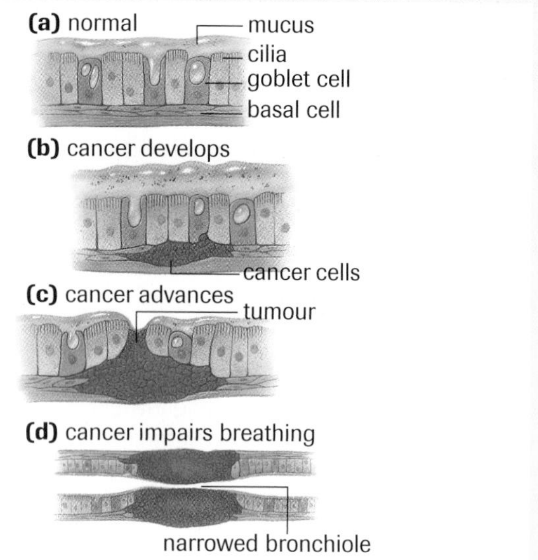

Figure 8
Development of a tumour in the tissues of the bronchiole walls

Case Study Questions

1. How does cigarette smoke affect the mucous layer in the bronchioles?
2. Why does the buildup of tar in the bronchioles limit airflow?
3. In what area does a tumour begin to develop?
4. Why has the mucous layer in **Figure 8 (c)** decreased in size?
5. Cancer cells often travel in lymph vessels to other parts of the body, where they continue to divide. Why does this characteristic make cancer especially dangerous?
6. At what stage might cells break away and cause a tumour in another area of the body?
7. The Canadian tobacco industry employs thousands of full-time and part-time workers. Thousands of seasonal workers are also employed, and thousands of wholesale and retail workers profit from the sale of tobacco products. The government also raises money through tobacco taxation, and the tobacco industry's contributions to the Canadian economy are large. However, the costs associated with smoking are also large. Do you think that the government should ban the sale of tobacco products? Defend your position.

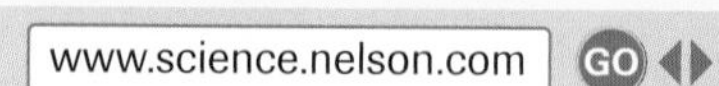

Web Quest—Smokeless Tobacco

Most people agree that smoking is bad for your health. This Web Quest takes a look at an alternative to smoking—smokeless tobacco! What are the issues surrounding the use of this drug? Is it really an acceptable alternative or is it just as unhealthy? Explore this issue and compose a letter outlining whether you agree or disagree with using federal money to support research on smokeless tobacco.

www.science.nelson.com GO

SUMMARY Regulation of Breathing Movements

- Breathing movements are regulated by the medulla and by chemoreceptors in the carotid artery and the aorta.
- All respiratory disorders decrease oxygen delivery to the tissues. Healthy lungs are much more efficient at gas exchange than unhealthy lungs are.
- Bronchitis is an inflammation of the bronchioles, which results in narrowed air passages and decreased air movement.
- Emphysema is inflammation and overinflation of the alveoli, causing them to rupture and reducing the surface area available for diffusion.
- Bronchial asthma is characterized by narrowing of the bronchial passages.
- Lung tumours reduce the surface area for diffusion.

Search for a Safe Cigarette
The tobacco industry's quest for a "safer" cigarette is filled with promise and pitfalls.

www.science.nelson.com GO

Section 9.3 Questions

1. How do CO_2 levels regulate breathing movements?
2. Why does exposure to carbon monoxide (CO) increase breathing rates?
3. How does emphysema affect the lungs?
4. How does partial pressure affect the movement of oxygen from the alveoli to the blood?
5. How is CO_2 transported in the blood?
6. Describe the importance of hemoglobin as a buffer.
7. Why is the slowing down of the cilia in smokers dangerous?
8. Nicotine, one of the components of cigarettes, slows the cilia lining the respiratory tract, causes blood vessels to constrict, and increases heart rate. Another component of cigarette smoke is carbon monoxide. Carbon monoxide competes with oxygen for binding sites on the hemoglobin molecule found in red blood cells. Analyze the data presented in this chapter, and describe the potential dangers associated with smoking.
9. Survey several people who smoke and calculate the amount of tar taken in each day. Most cigarettes contain about 15 mg of tar, with 75 % of the tar being absorbed. Show your calculations.
10. On an X ray, a cancerous tumour shows up as a white spot (**Figure 9**). A healthy lung appears dark. Why would the tumour appear white?

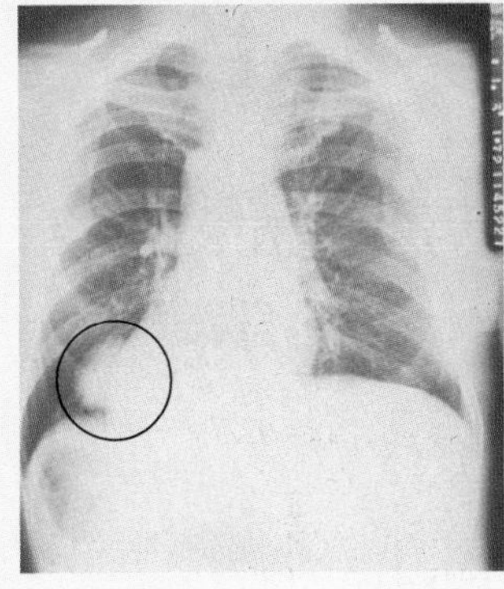

Figure 9
An X ray showing the presence of a tumour in the lower right lung

9.4 Muscles

cardiac muscle the involuntary muscle of the heart

smooth muscle the involuntary muscle found in the lining of many organs

skeletal muscle the voluntary muscle that makes the bones of the skeleton move

tendon a band of connective tissue that joins muscle to bone

antagonistic muscles a pair of skeletal muscles that are arranged in pairs and that work against each other to make a joint move

Your body has more than 600 muscles that can be divided into three basic types (**Figure 1**). **Cardiac muscle** is the muscle that makes the heart beat, and it is found only in the heart. Cardiac muscle contracts and relaxes automatically (involuntarily) because it is controlled by nerves of the autonomic nervous system. **Smooth muscle** is found in the lining of organs such as the stomach, the esophagus, the uterus, and the walls of blood vessels. Smooth muscle contractions move food through the digestive system and help push a baby through the vagina during delivery. Smooth muscle contraction is also involuntary. Unlike cardiac muscle and smooth muscle, the muscles that are attached to the bones of the skeleton are under conscious (voluntary) control, and are called **skeletal muscle**. **Figure 2**, on the next page, shows some of the main skeletal muscles of the body. These are the muscles that allow you to walk, talk, and hit a baseball with a bat. Skeletal muscles are attached to bones by **tendons**.

Muscles shorten when they contract and lengthen when they relax. A body part moves only when a contracting muscle pulls it. Many skeletal muscles are arranged in pairs that work against each other to make a joint move. These are called **antagonistic muscles**. The biceps and triceps muscles of the arm are an antagonistic pair of muscles (**Figure 3**, next page). When the biceps contracts and the triceps relaxes, the bones forming the elbow joint are brought closer together. When the biceps relaxes and the triceps contracts, the two bones are moved apart. The muscle that must contract to bend a joint is

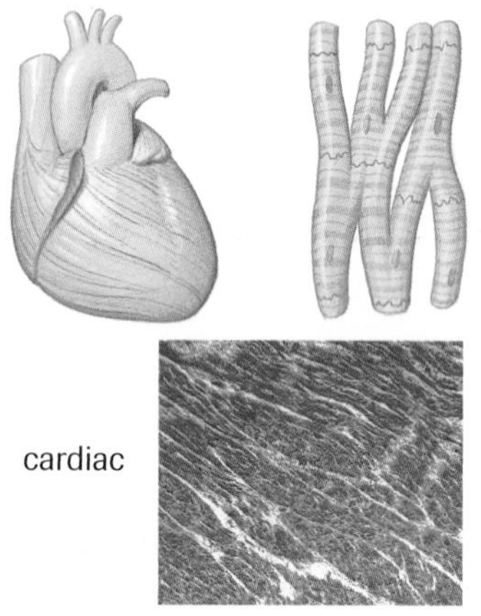

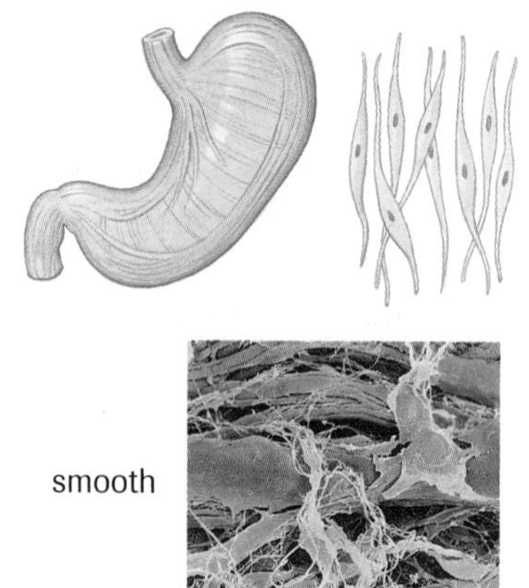

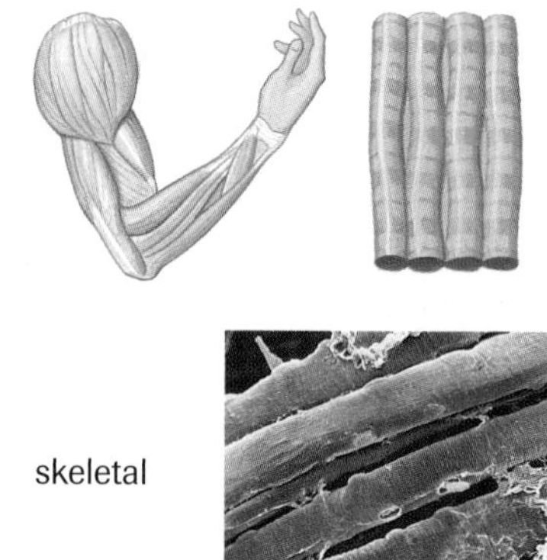

Figure 1
Types of muscle

mini *Investigation* — *Microscopic Examination of Muscle*

In this activity, you will examine and compare the structures of cardiac, smooth, and skeletal muscle.

Materials: prepared slides of cardiac, smooth, and skeletal muscle

- Examine the three types of muscle under low, medium, and high power magnification.

(a) Draw a diagram of each muscle type under low power magnification. Label the nuclei, cell membranes, and striation if visible.

(b) In a chart, describe the similarities and differences that you observed among the muscle types.

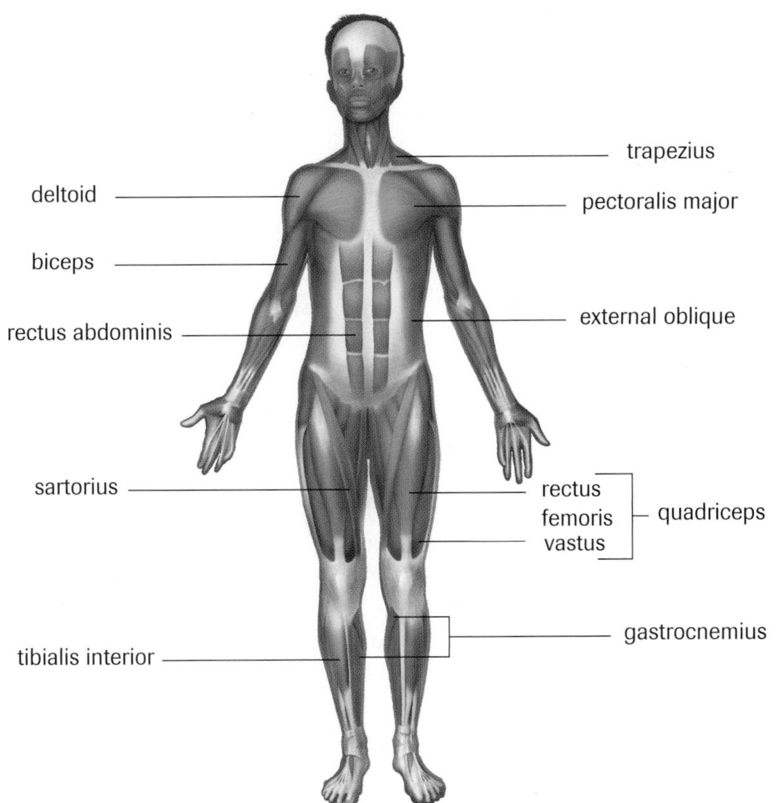

Figure 2
Some major muscles of the human body

DID YOU KNOW ?

The Triceps
Have you ever admired a bulging biceps? Although bodybuilders work hard to develop well-defined biceps muscles, it is the triceps that are used most often during sports that require throwing, such as baseball, javelin, and shot put.

called a **flexor**, so the biceps muscle is a flexor. The muscle that must contract to straighten a joint is called an **extensor**. The triceps muscle is an extensor muscle. The origin is the place where the muscle attaches to the stationary bone; the insertion is where it attaches to the moving bone.

The central nervous system ensures that the biceps and triceps do not attempt to pull against each other. Excitatory nerve impulses that cause the triceps to contract are accompanied by inhibitory nerve impulses that cause the biceps to relax.

flexor the muscle that must contract to bend a joint

extensor the muscle that must contract to straighten a joint

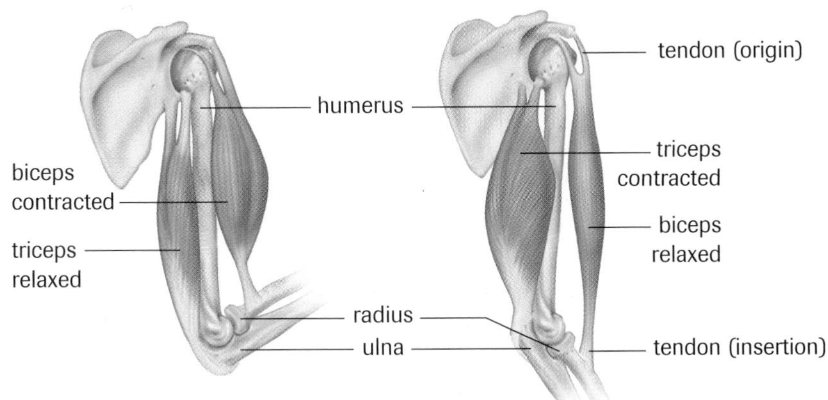

Figure 3
The biceps and triceps are an example of antagonistic muscles.

+ EXTENSION

The Role of the Skeleton
The skeleton is an important part of the motor system. Bones and muscles work together to permit movement. Go to the Nelson Web site to learn more about the role of the skeleton.

www.science.nelson.com 

mini Investigation — Effect of Low Temperature on Muscle Contraction

Materials: ice, water, large beaker, pen and paper, stopwatch

- Write your name as many times as possible in 2 min. Use a stopwatch to keep track of time. Record the number of signatures.
- Immerse your hand in ice water for as long as you can, and once again write your name as many times as possible in 2 min. Record the number of signatures.
- Rub your hand until warm and repeat the procedure.

(a) Construct a data table that compares the number of signatures to hand temperature.
(b) Compare the quality of the signatures.
(c) Why does cold water affect the muscles?

EXTENSION

General Musculo-Skeletal Anatomy
This audio clip describes the anatomical references that identify the interrelationships between muscles and the skeleton.

www.science.nelson.com

sarcolemma the delicate sheath that surrounds muscle fibres

myofilament a thread of contractile proteins found within muscle fibres

EXTENSION

Troponin and Tropomyosin
Take a closer look at actin filaments in a skeletal muscle cell, and the two proteins which aid in muscle contraction.

www.science.nelson.com

Skeletal Muscle

Bend your elbow and squeeze your fist. The muscles in your forearm and the biceps, the large muscle above the elbow, bulge. These muscles are skeletal muscles. Skeletal muscle permits movement, enables smiling, and helps keep you warm. An estimated 80 % of the energy used in skeletal muscle contraction is lost as heat. Is it any wonder that you shiver when cold?

Skeletal muscle is composed of several bundles of cells called fibres. Unlike other cells, which contain one nucleus, many nuclei are found in each muscle cell. The fibres are enclosed within a membrane called the **sarcolemma**. Within the muscle fibres are tiny **myofilaments** bundled together (**Figure 4 (a)**). Two kinds of myofilaments can be seen under the electron microscope, each composed of a different contractile protein. Thin myofilaments are composed of actin, and thick myofilaments are composed of myosin. They overlap to produce a striated, or striped, appearance.

The alternating dark and light bands of the muscle fibres can be explained by examining the arrangement of the myofilaments. The length of the muscle fibre is defined by the Z lines that anchor the actin fibres. The area between the Z lines is the *sarcomere*. The thick myosin filaments form the darker A bands, while the thinner actin filaments allow more light to penetrate and form the lighter I bands shown in **Figure 4 (b)**.

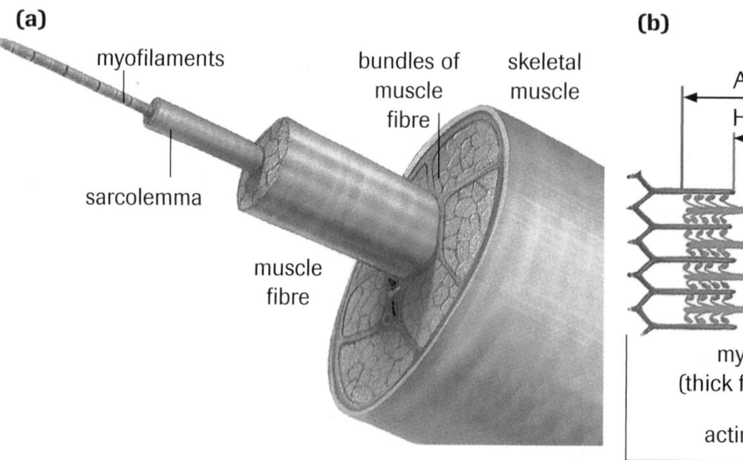

Figure 4
(a) The structure of skeletal muscle
(b) A sarcomere

The Sliding Filament Theory

As the word *theory* suggests, all is not known about muscle contraction. The sliding filament theory provides a working model that helps explain what scientists believe is happening.

Muscles cause movement by shortening. The actin filaments slide over the myosin filaments. Z lines move closer together when muscle fibres contract. As the actin and myosin filaments begin to overlap, the lighter I band becomes progressively smaller. But what causes the actin and myosin filaments to overlap? It is believed that knoblike projections on the thick myosin filaments form cross-bridges on receptor sites of the thinner actin filaments. A series of cross-bridges attach and detach as the actin filaments are drawn inward. **Figure 5** illustrates the sliding filament theory.

The energy required for muscle contraction comes from ATP, adenosine triphosphate. In the absence of ATP, the cross-bridges fail to detach and the muscle becomes rigid. A condition known as *rigor mortis* is due to the contraction of muscles following death. With death, ATP production ceases and skeletal muscle becomes fixed. The condition may last up to 60 hours after death.

The release of a transmitter chemical at the junction between the nerve and muscle initiates muscle contraction. Once the transmitter chemical reaches a specialized endoplasmic reticulum, found within the cytoplasm, calcium ions are released. The calcium ions bind to sites along the actin filaments and initiate the formation of cross-bridges with the myosin fibres. It is believed that the release of calcium ions begins the breakdown of ATP by the myosin filaments. ATP provides the energy for the filaments to slide over one another. Eventually, the calcium ions are actively taken up and stored in the specialized endoplasmic reticulum. The muscle then relaxes. When calcium ions are again released from the endoplasmic reticulum, the muscle contracts.

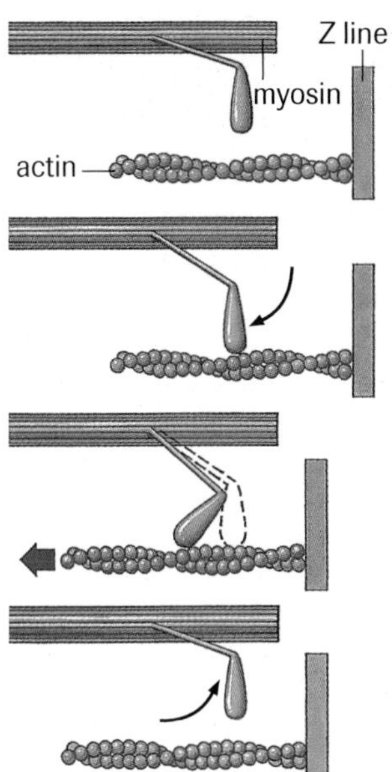

Figure 5
Sliding filament theory, showing one actin and one myosin filament

Energy Sources for Contraction
In this animation, review the metabolic routes which produce ATP in muscle cells.

www.science.nelson.com 

Muscle Fatigue

Have you ever felt your muscles begin to burn while skiing? Have your muscles ever failed you during a race? No matter how hard you try, you begin to lose control of your muscles. Muscle fatigue is caused by a lack of energy and the buildup of waste products within your muscles.

Unfortunately, very little ATP can be stored in muscle tissue. The energy demand is met by aerobic respiration. Glucose is systematically broken down by a series of enzymes found in the cytoplasm and mitochondria of your cells. Glucose is oxidized by oxygen to form ATP, carbon dioxide, and water. A high-energy compound called **creatine phosphate**, found in all muscle cells, ensures that ATP supplies remain high. Creatine phosphate supplies a phosphate to adenosine diphosphate (ADP) to replenish ATP supplies. If creatine phosphate levels remain high in muscle cells, ATP levels can be maintained.

creatine phosphate a compound in muscle cells that releases a phosphate to ADP and helps regenerate ATP supplies in muscle cells

As long as oxygen can be supplied and cellular respiration can meet the demands of muscle cells, the filaments will continue to be drawn together. However, should energy demand exceed ATP supply, lactic acid begins to accumulate. Lactic acid causes muscle pain and is associated with fatigue. The burning that you feel in your legs while skiing a difficult run or the pain the you feel in your rib muscles after prolonged heavy exercise is due to an accumulation of lactic acid. During this condition, referred to as oxygen debt, the fluids surrounding the muscles become acidic and eventually the muscle fails to contract. The rapid breathing that takes place after heavy exercise is designed to repay the oxygen debt.

CAREER CONNECTION 

Prosthetist and Orthotist
Prosthetists design and construct devices such as artificial limbs, and orthotists design and construct devices such as braces and supports. They work with physicians to improve the quality of life for patients who have injuries or deformities. Find out the educational requirements for a prosthetist and orthotist.

www.science.nelson.com 

 INVESTIGATION 9.3 *Introduction*

The Effects of Muscle Activity on Body Temperature

In this investigation, you will conduct an experiment to show the relationship between muscle activity and thermal energy.

To perform this investigation, turn to page 306.

Report Checklist

- ○ Purpose
- ● Problem
- ● Hypothesis
- ● Prediction
- ● Design
- ● Materials
- ● Procedure
- ● Evidence
- ● Analysis
- ● Evaluation
- ○ Synthesis

DID YOU KNOW ?

Muscle Spasms

Muscle spasms are caused by involuntary contractions of muscles. A pinched nerve is often responsible for the spasm.

Muscle Contraction

A muscle twitch, or contraction, occurs when a nerve impulse stimulates several muscle cells. A pause between the impulse and the muscle contraction is referred to as the *latent period* (**Figure 6 (a)**). Upon contraction, actin and myosin fibres slide over one another, causing the muscle to shorten. After the contraction phase, the actin and myosin filaments disengage and the muscle begins to relax. Once the relaxation phase is complete, each muscle cell usually returns to its original length. Should a muscle cell be stimulated once again, it will contract with equal force (**Figure 6 (b)**).

An interesting phenomenon occurs when a stimulation happens before the relaxation phase is complete. Predictably, the actin and myosin filaments slide over one another, but because the relaxation has not yet been completed, the overlap is increased and greater muscle shortening can be observed. The sum of the shortening that remains from the first muscle twitch and the shortening produced by the second muscle twitch creates a greater force of contraction. The strength of the contraction depends on how close the second stimulus is to the first stimulus. The process, shown in **Figure 6 (c)**, is referred to as **summation**. Occasionally, repeated muscle stimulation prevents any relaxation phase. The state of constant muscle contraction, known as **tetanus**, is shown in **Figure 6 (d)**.

summation increased muscle contraction produced by the combination of stimuli

tetanus the state of constant muscle contraction caused by sustained nerve impulses

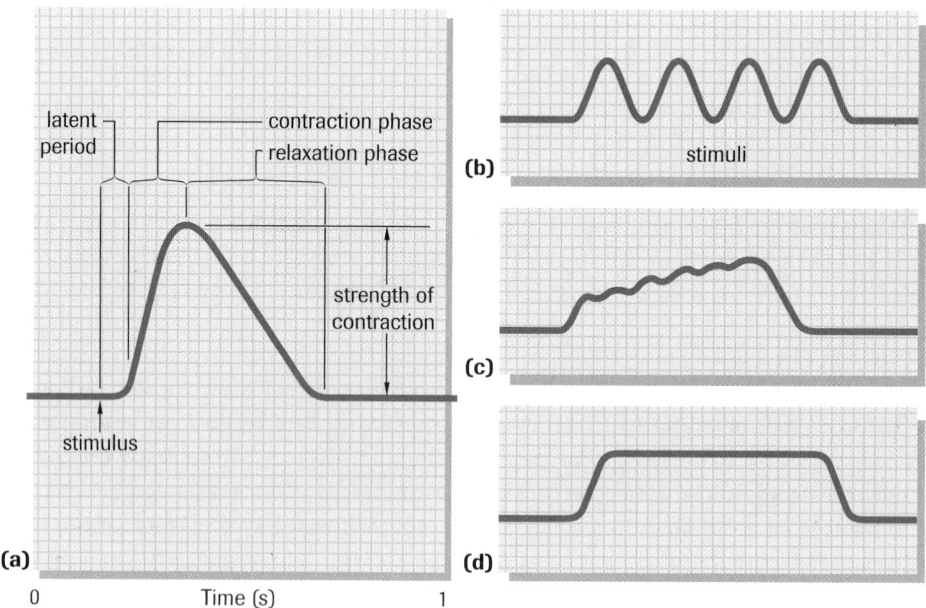

Figure 6
(a) Recording of a muscle twitch that lasts approximately 1 s
(b) Single muscle twitches approximately 1 s apart. The muscle returns to its original length before succeeding stimuli cause contractions.
(c) Summation of muscle twitches from about six stimulations every second. Following the contraction, the muscle does not have enough time to return to its original length before being stimulated again.
(d) Tetanus resulting from about 20 stimulations per second. The actin and myosin filaments remain overlapped.

Fast and Slow Twitch Muscle Fibres

It has often been said that great sprinters are born not made. Although training can improve technique, it can never make an ordinary person a world-class sprinter. The genetic factor appears too great to be overcome with increased fitness and improved technique.

Sprinters are born with a large amount of what is called fast twitch muscle fibre. It is the thick myosin filaments that determine the speed of muscle contraction. Three different forms of myosin, referred to as isomers, determine whether you have the potential to be a sprinter or a marathon runner. The fibres are referred to as type I, IIa, and IIx. Type I fibres cause slower muscle twitch and are found in greater abundance in distance runners. These fibres break down ATP slowly, but efficiently, to release energy. Type IIa and IIx fibres, the faster twitch myosin fibres, break down ATP faster, but less efficiently. The slower twitch type I fibres are required for endurance events in which aerobic metabolism is predominant. The fast twitch type IIa and IIx fibres rely predominantly on anaerobic respiration. Although all athletes have both slow and fast twitch fibres, the proportions vary dramatically, as shown in **Figure 7**.

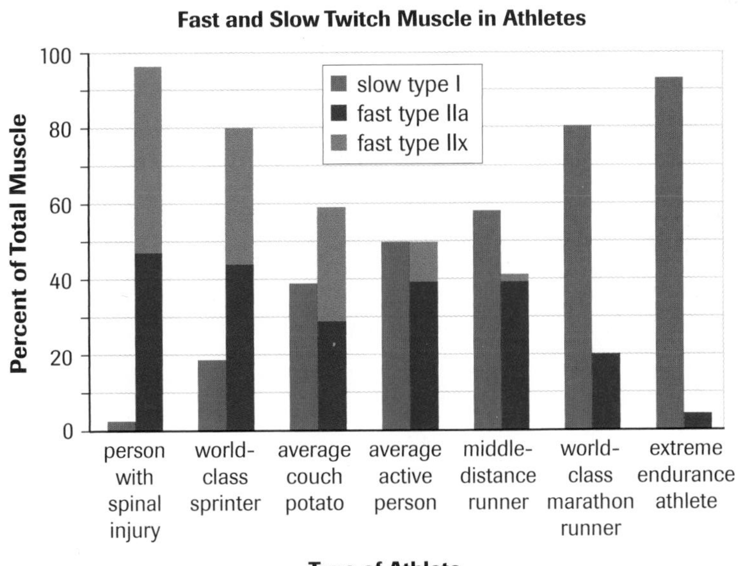

Figure 7
Different types of athletes have varying proportions of slow and fast twitch muscle fibres.

+ EXTENSION

Nervous System and Muscle Contraction
View this animation to see how signals from the nervous system control muscle contraction.

www.science.nelson.com

DID YOU KNOW ?

Red and White Muscle
There are two different types of muscle fibres. Red muscle fibres are well-suited for slow contraction, while white muscle fibres are designed for rapid contraction. Red muscle fibres appear red because they contain myoglobin, the protein that binds oxygen, which is used during cellular respiration. White fibres contain little myoglobin and, therefore, use less oxygen. They obtain energy from the breakdown of glycogen without oxygen.

Motor System Injuries

Muscles, like all living tissues, require nourishment from a balanced diet, including an adequate supply of protein. Regular exercise is necessary for maintaining healthy muscles. Studies done in the near zero-gravity environment of outer space show that astronauts lose muscle mass unless they exercise regularly.

Motor system injuries are common in people who perform heavy work or exercise. Torn muscles, stretched tendons, torn ligaments, joint sprains, and joint dislocations are common sports injuries.

Comparing Fast and Slow Twitch Muscle Fibres
This audio clip describes the physiological differences between fast and slow twitch muscle fibres.

www.science.nelson.com

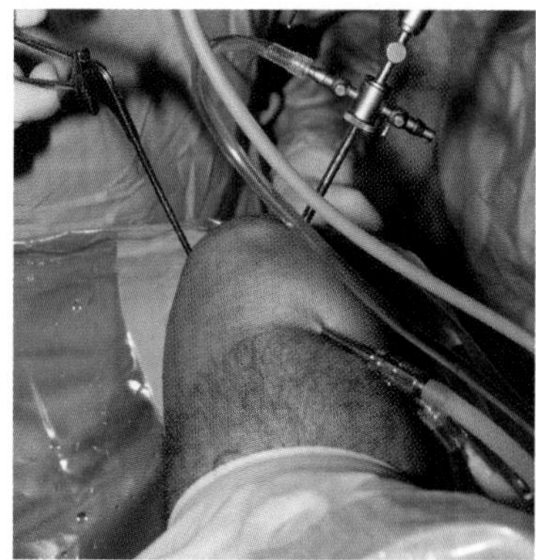

Figure 8
Arthroscopic surgery

Arthroscopic Surgery

Torn cartilage or ligament? An innovative technique called arthroscopic surgery (named after the viewing device, the arthroscope) has dramatically improved the prognosis for people who suffer knee injuries.

The first arthroscope was used in Japan in 1917—today's instruments barely resemble this early predecessor. An arthroscope is a needlelike tube, less than 2 mm wide, that is equipped with a fibreoptic light source (**Figure 8**). The needle can be inserted through a small puncture in the knee, which requires only local anesthesia. The fibreoptic lens can be linked with a television screen, providing a view of the inside of the damaged knee. The arthroscope is also fitted with thin surgical tools that can snip away unhealthy tissue. Under most circumstances, hospitalization is not required following the surgery, and activity can be resumed relatively quickly.

EXTENSION

Redesigning the Body for Motion

In this activity, you will re-engineer parts of the human body that are most susceptible to injuries from sports and aging.

www.science.nelson.com 

SUMMARY Muscles

- The body contains three types of muscle: cardiac, smooth, and skeletal.
- The movement of bones at a joint is performed by skeletal muscles, which work in antagonistic pairs.
- Skeletal muscles are composed of muscle fibres, which contain myofilaments.
- Myofilaments are threads of contractile proteins, either actin or myosin.
- The fibres of skeletal muscle are encased in a membrane called the sarcolemma.
- The energy for muscle contraction is provided by ATP.

Section 9.4 Questions

1. What is the sarcolemma?
2. Name the two myofilaments found in muscle fibres and briefly outline their function.
3. Why does skeletal muscle appear striated, or striped?
4. Why is ATP needed for muscle contraction?
5. Why is creatine phosphate required for muscle contraction?
6. Define muscle tetanus.
7. Using **Figure 9**, make predictions about which athlete would be well-suited for sprinting and which for distance running. Give reasons for your prediction.

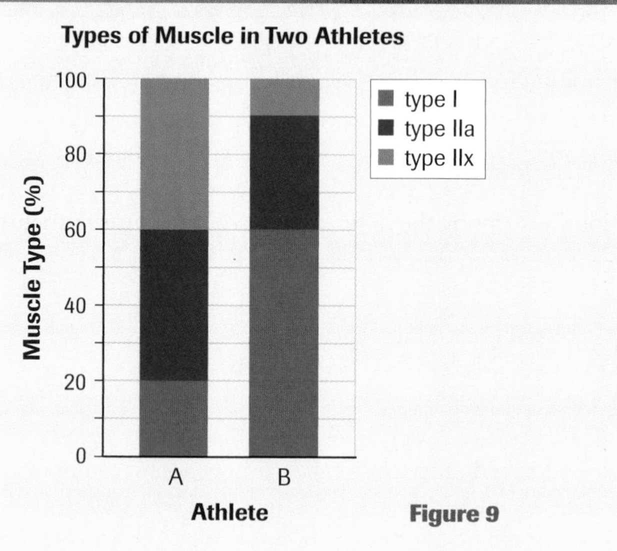

Figure 9

INVESTIGATION 9.1

Determining Lung Capacity

Healthy lungs can take in oxygen and expel carbon dioxide from the body with much greater efficiency than unhealthy lungs can. In this investigation, you will examine indicators of general respiratory health by measuring lung capacity at rest. Normal lung capacity (**Table 1**) varies with factors such as age, height, gender, and physical fitness.

Table 1 Approximate Lung Volumes for an Average 70-kg Male

Measure	Volume (L)
total lung capacity (TLC)	5
tidal volume (TV)	0.45 to 0.5
residual volume (RV)	1.5
expiratory reserve volume (ERV)	1.5
inspiratory reserve volume (IRV)	2.5

There are several measures that are important in determining lung capacity. The following four can be measured using a respirometer: Tidal volume (TV) is the amount of air inhaled and exhaled in a normal breath; expiratory reserve volume (ERV) is the amount of air that can be forcibly exhaled after a normal exhalation; and inspiratory reserve volume (IRV) is the amount of air that can be forcibly inhaled after a normal inhalation. Vital capacity (VC) is the maximum amount of air that can be exhaled after a full inhalation and is calculated from IRC, ERV, and TV.

Residual volume (RV) is the amount of air left in the lungs after a maximum exhalation. Total lung capacity (TLC) is the amount of air in the lungs after a maximum inhalation, or all the air that the lungs can hold. **Figure 1** illustrates the relationships among the different lung volume measurements.

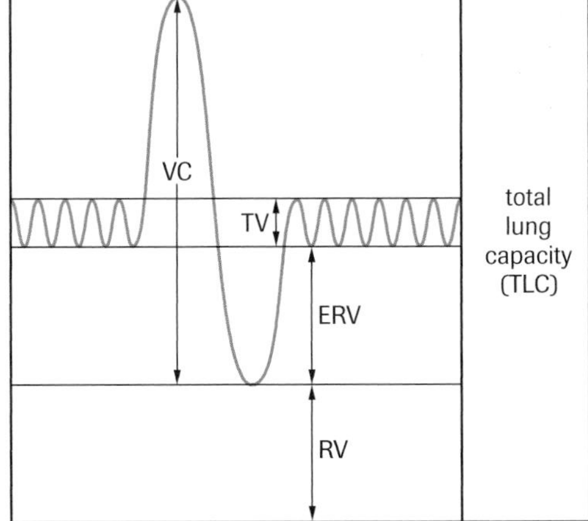

Figure 1
Lung volumes

Report Checklist

- Purpose
- Problem
- Hypothesis
- Prediction
- Design
- Materials
- Procedure
- Evidence
- Analysis
- Evaluation
- Synthesis

Materials

respirometer with disposable mouthpieces

Procedure

1. Set the gauge to zero before you place a new, unused mouthpiece in the respirometer.
2. Be careful not to inhale at any time through the mouthpiece. Develop a regular, relaxed breathing pattern so you will obtain accurate results. After inhaling normally, place the mouthpiece attached to the respirometer in your mouth and exhale normally. Read the gauge on the respirometer. Record the volume exhaled as tidal volume.
3. Reset the respirometer to zero. Inhale normally, then place the mouthpiece attached to the respirometer in your mouth and exhale normally. Read the gauge on the respirometer and then exhale forcibly. Record the difference as expiratory reserve volume.
4. Reset the respirometer to zero. Inhale as much air as possible and then exhale for as long as you can into the respirometer. Read the gauge on the respirometer. Record the value as vital capacity.
5. Repeat Steps 1 to 4 for two more trials, without changing the mouthpiece.

Analysis and Evaluation

(a) Determine your inspiratory reserve volume by using the following formula:

$$VC = IRC + ERV + TV$$

(b) Using the above formula, indicate where IRV would be in **Figure 1**.

Synthesis

(c) Predict how the tidal volume and vital capacity of a marathon runner might differ from that of the average Canadian.

(d) How might bronchitis affect your expiratory reserve volume? Provide your reasons.

(e) Predict how the respiratory volumes collected for a person with emphysema would differ from those you collected.

INVESTIGATION 9.2

The Effects of Exercise on Lung Volume

Report Checklist

- ○ Purpose
- ● Problem
- ● Hypothesis
- ● Prediction
- ● Design
- ● Materials
- ● Procedure
- ● Evidence
- ● Analysis
- ● Evaluation
- ○ Synthesis

The total lung capacity of fully grown, healthy lungs is about 5 L. However, a person normally inhales and exhales only about 0.5 L. Various factors can affect the lung volume of a single breath. In this investigation, you will design ways to test the effects of exercise on lung volume during one inhalation and exhalation.

Purpose

To determine how exercise affects lung volume during a single breath

Do not perform this activity if you are not allowed to participate in physical education classes.

Design

Design a controlled experiment that includes the following:

- a prediction and a hypothesis
- the manipulated, responding, and fixed variables
- a step-by-step description of the procedure
- a list of safety precautions
- a table to record observations

Submit your design to your teacher for approval. Then, carry out your investigation.

Analysis

(a) State how exercise affects lung volume.

Evaluation

(b) Was your prediction correct? Was your hypothesis supported?

(c) Describe any problems in carrying out the procedure.

(d) Suggest ways to improve your current design.

(e) If you were to repeat this experiment, what new factors would you investigate? Write a brief description of the new procedure.

INVESTIGATION 9.3

The Effects of Muscle Activity on Body Temperature

Report Checklist

- ○ Purpose
- ● Problem
- ● Hypothesis
- ● Prediction
- ● Design
- ● Materials
- ● Procedure
- ● Evidence
- ● Analysis
- ● Evaluation
- ○ Synthesis

Liquid crystals can be used to measure changes in body temperature. ATP supplies muscles with energy. However, some of the ATP is converted to thermal energy, which increases body temperature.

Purpose

To investigate the relationship between muscle activity and thermal energy

Do not perform this activity if you are not allowed to participate in physical education classes.

Design

Design an experiment to show the relationship between muscle activity and thermal energy. You may want to use a thermometer to calibrate the liquid crystal colours.

- Identify the controlled variables, manipulated variable, and responding variable.
- Write a prediction and a hypothesis for the experiment.
- Create a step-by-step procedure that includes any safety precautions.

Present your design to your teacher for approval. Then, conduct your experiment.

Complete an analysis and evaluation of your experiment. Communicate your results in a written report.

(a) Present your data in tables and graphically if appropriate.

(b) Present conclusions based on the data collected.

Evaluation

(c) Evaluate your experimental design.

Chapter 9 SUMMARY

Outcomes

Knowledge

- identify the principal structures of the respiratory systems, i.e., nasal passages, pharynx, larynx, epiglottis, trachea, bronchi, bronchioles, alveoli, diaphragm, rib muscles, pleural membranes (9.1)
- explain how gases and heat are exchanged between the human organism and its environment, i.e., mechanism of breathing, gas exchange, removal of foreign material (9.2, 9.3)
- explain how the motor system supports body functions, referencing smooth, cardiac, and striated muscle, i.e., digestive, circulatory, respiratory, excretory, and locomotory (9.4)
- describe, in general, the action of actin and myosin in muscle contraction and heat production (9.4)

STS

- explain that the goal of technology is to provide solutions to practical problems (9.2, 9.3, 9.4)
- explain that the products of technology are devices, systems, and processes that meet given needs; however, these products cannot solve all problems (9.3, 9.4)
- explain that concepts, models, and theories are often used in interpreting and explaining observations, and in predicting future observations (9.4)

Skills

- ask questions and plan investigations (9.1, 9.3, 9.4)
- conduct investigations and gather and record data and information (9.1, 9.3) and by identifying smooth, cardiac, and striated muscle tissue under magnification (9.4)
- analyze data and apply mathematical and conceptual models (9.1, 9.3, 9.4)
- work as members of a team and apply the skills and conventions of science (all)

Key Terms

9.1

breathing
respiratory membrane
respiration
trachea
cilia
epiglottis
larynx
bronchi
bronchiole
alveoli
pleural membrane
diaphragm
intercostal muscle

9.2

hemoglobin
oxyhemoglobin
carbonic anhydrase
buffer

9.3

chemoreceptor
bronchitis
emphysema
bronchial asthma

9.4

cardiac muscle
smooth muscle
skeletal muscle
tendon
antagonistic muscles
flexor
extensor
sarcolemma
myofilament
creatine phosphate
summation
tetanus

MAKE a summary

1. Create a flow chart or diagram that shows how the respiratory system exchanges matter and energy with the environment. Label the diagram with as many of the key terms as possible.
2. Revisit your answers to the Starting Points questions at the start of the chapter. Would you answer the questions differently now? Why?

Go To

The following components are available on the Nelson Web site. Follow the links for *Nelson Biology Alberta 20–30*.

- an interactive Self Quiz for Chapter 9
- additional Diploma Exam-style Review Questions
- Illustrated Glossary
- additional IB-related material

There is more information on the Web site wherever you see the Go icon in the chapter.

▸ Chapter 9 REVIEW

Many of these questions are in the style of the Diploma Exam. You will find guidance for writing Diploma Exams in Appendix A5. Science Directing Words used in Diploma Exams are in bold type. Exam study tips and test-taking suggestions are on the Nelson Web site.

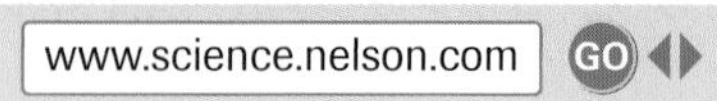

DO NOT WRITE IN THIS TEXTBOOK.

Part 1

1. The following structures are involved in respiration:
NR
1. muscle cell
2. bronchiole
3. capillary
4. trachea

List these structures in the order in which oxygen reaches them during respiration. (Record all four digits of your answer.)

2. An increase in breathing rate is caused by
A. elevated levels of blood oxygen
B. elevated levels of blood carbon dioxide
C. reduced levels of blood carbon dioxide
D. reduced levels of blood carbon monoxide

Use the following information to answer questions 3 and 4.

Changes in the partial pressure of gases in the blood were monitored at 1-second intervals and then graphed (**Figure 1**).

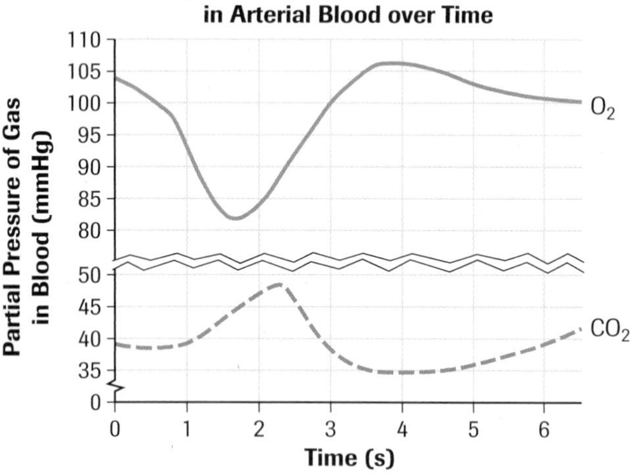

Figure 1

3. Select the time at which the chemoreceptors in the medulla will receive a message to initiate breathing movements.
A. 1.6 s
B. 2.2 s
C. 3.5 s
D. 4.0 s

4. Identify the time that would immediately follow a breathing movement and the reason why.
A. 1.7 s, because oxygen and carbon dioxide leave the blood
B. 3.5 s, because oxygen is entering the blood and carbon dioxide is leaving the blood
C. 4.5 s, because oxygen and carbon dioxide enter the blood
D. 4.5 s, because oxygen is entering the blood and carbon dioxide is entering the blood

5. Identify the factors that would increase the delivery of oxygen to the tissues.
A. high blood volume and high altitude
B. low blood volume and high altitude
C. high hemoglobin and low altitude
D. low hemoglobin and low altitude

6. Identify the diagram in **Figure 2** that correctly depicts a contracted muscle fibre.

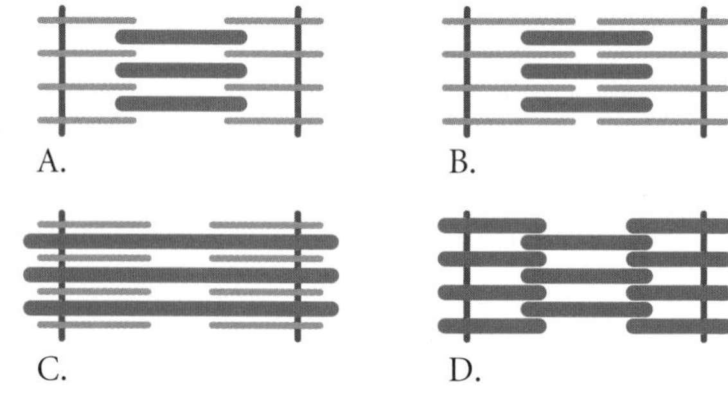

Figure 2

Use the following information to answer questions 7 and 8.

Different types of athletes have different amounts of type IIa and type IIx muscle fibres.

1. sprinter
2. marathon runner
3. average active person
4. extreme endurance athlete

7. List all of the given athletes in the order of increasing amount of type IIa and type IIx muscle fibres. (Record all four digits of your answer.)
NR

8. List all of the given athletes in the order of their increasing oxygen demand. (Record all four digits of your answer.)
NR

Part 2

Use the following information to answer questions 9 to 11.

Figure 3 shows the components of the human respiratory system.

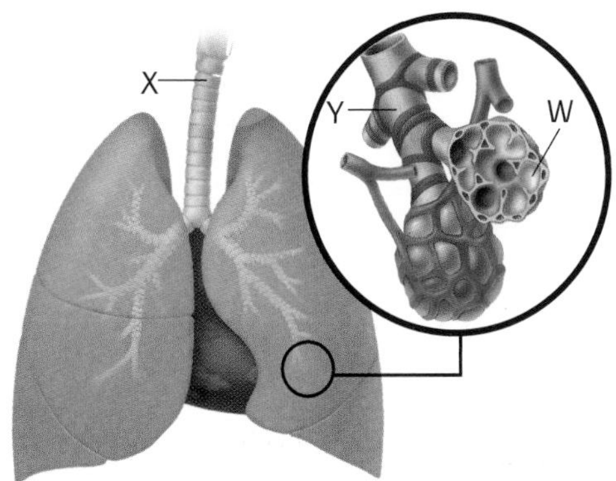

Figure 3

9. **Identify** the structures labelled W, X, and Y in **Figure 3**, and **describe** the function of each. DE

10. **Identify** the structure(s) in **Figure 3** that have cartilaginous bands. DE

11. The inflammation or restriction of airflow in one of the structures in **Figure 3** is associated with asthma. **Identify** this structure. DE

12. **Describe** the pressure changes that occur during inhalation and exhalation.

Use the following information to answer questions 13 to 15.

The composition of air was analyzed from inhaled and exhaled air (**Table 1**).

Table 1 Composition of Inhaled and Exhaled Air

Air component	Inhaled air (%)	Exhaled air (%)
oxygen	20.71	14.60
carbon dioxide	0.41	4.00
water	1.25	5.90
nitrogen	78.00	75.50

13. **Explain** why more water is found in exhaled air. DE

14. **Explain** the difference in oxygen levels in inhaled and exhaled air. DE

15. If nitrogen is not used by the cells of the body, **explain** the different composition between inhaled and exhaled air. DE

16. Changes in the partial pressure of gases in arterial blood were monitored over time as a subject began to perform light exercise (**Figure 1**, previous page).
    (a) At which time would the breathing rate likely be greatest? **Justify** your answer.
    (b) **Predict** when the subject began exercising. **Describe** your reasons.
    (c) When would the breathing rate return to normal? **Explain**.

17. According to the data shown in **Figure 4**, **identify** which hemoglobin is more effective at absorbing oxygen. **Describe** the adaptive advantage that is provided by hemoglobin that allows it to combine readily with oxygen.

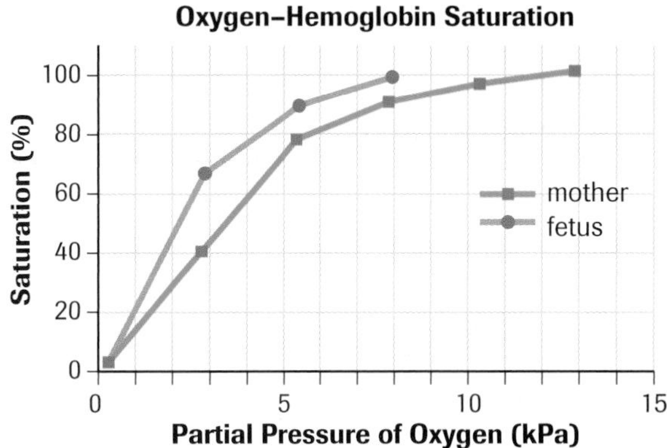

Figure 4

18. Cigarette smoke has the following effects:
    - There is destruction of many of the cilia that line the bronchi and bronchioles.
    - There is a buildup of mucus along the walls of the bronchioles. This reduces their interior diameter.
    - There is an increase in blood pressure that causes the rupturing of the walls of some of the alveoli.

    Refer to each of the effects listed above. **Describe** specific ways in which the normal functioning of the respiratory tract is altered by smoking tobacco.

19. **How** does the fact that muscles shorten when excited help support the sliding filament theory of muscle contraction?

20. **Why** does the condition of rigor mortis support the theory that ATP is required for muscle relaxation?

21. **Explain** how the motor system supports
    (a) the digestive system
    (b) the respiratory system

Extension

22. Allan Becker of the University of Manitoba studies dogs to learn more about how asthma works in people. Research how allergies have been linked with asthma. **Describe** the advantages and disadvantages of using modelling experiments on dogs.

www.science.nelson.com GO

chapter

10 Circulatory System

In this chapter

- Exploration: Listening to Heart Sounds
- Mini Investigation: Monitoring Your Pulse
- Mini Investigation: Observing Blood Flow in a Fish Tail
- Mini Investigation: Mapping Veins
- Explore an Issue: Growing a New Heart
- Investigation 10.1: Fetal Pig Dissection
- Web Activity: Observing the Movement of Blood through the Heart
- Case Study: Diagnosing Heart Conditions
- Mini Investigation: Effects of Caffeine on Heart Rate
- Investigation 10.2: Effects of Posture on Blood Pressure and Pulse
- Explore an Issue: Pre-teens and High Blood Pressure
- Investigation 10.3: Effects of Exercise on Blood Pressure and Pulse

Your circulatory system moves blood throughout your body. It carries nutrients to cells, wastes away from cells, and chemical messages from cells in one part of the body to distant target tissues. It distributes heat throughout the body and, along with the kidneys, maintains levels of body fluid.

Your circulatory system has 96 000 km of blood vessels to sustain your 100 trillion cells. No larger than the size of your fist and with a mass of about 300 g, the heart beats about 70 times/min from the beginning of life until death (**Figure 1**). During an average lifetime, the heart pumps enough blood to fill two large ocean tankers.

Every minute, 5 L of blood cycles from the heart to the lungs, picks up oxygen, and returns to the heart. Next, the heart pumps the oxygen-rich blood to the tissues of the body. The oxygen aids in breaking down high-energy glucose into low-energy compounds, which releases energy within the tissue cells. The cells use the energy to build new materials, repair existing structures, and for a variety of other energy-consuming reactions. Oxygen is necessary for these processes to occur, and the circulatory system plays a central role in providing that oxygen.

The circulatory system is also vital to human survival because it transports cellular wastes and helps defend against invading organisms. It permits the transport of immune cells throughout the body. You will learn about the immune system in the next chapter.

STARTING points

Answer these questions as best you can with your current knowledge. Then, using the concepts and skills you have learned, you will revise your answers at the end of the chapter.

1. People with heart problems often experience a racing and pounding heart even after mild exercise. Why does this occur?
2. Elite athletes literally have "big hearts." How would the resting heart rate of someone with cardiovascular disease compare to that of an athlete? Suggest a reason for the difference.
3. If scientists wanted to grow a heart, would it be best to obtain cells from the individual who had the heart problem or another individual? Explain.
4. Although scientists have successfully grown cells to form certain heart components, these tissue cultures lack the arteries and veins found in a normal heart. Why are blood vessels necessary?

Career Connections:
Cardiology Technologist, Registered Nurse

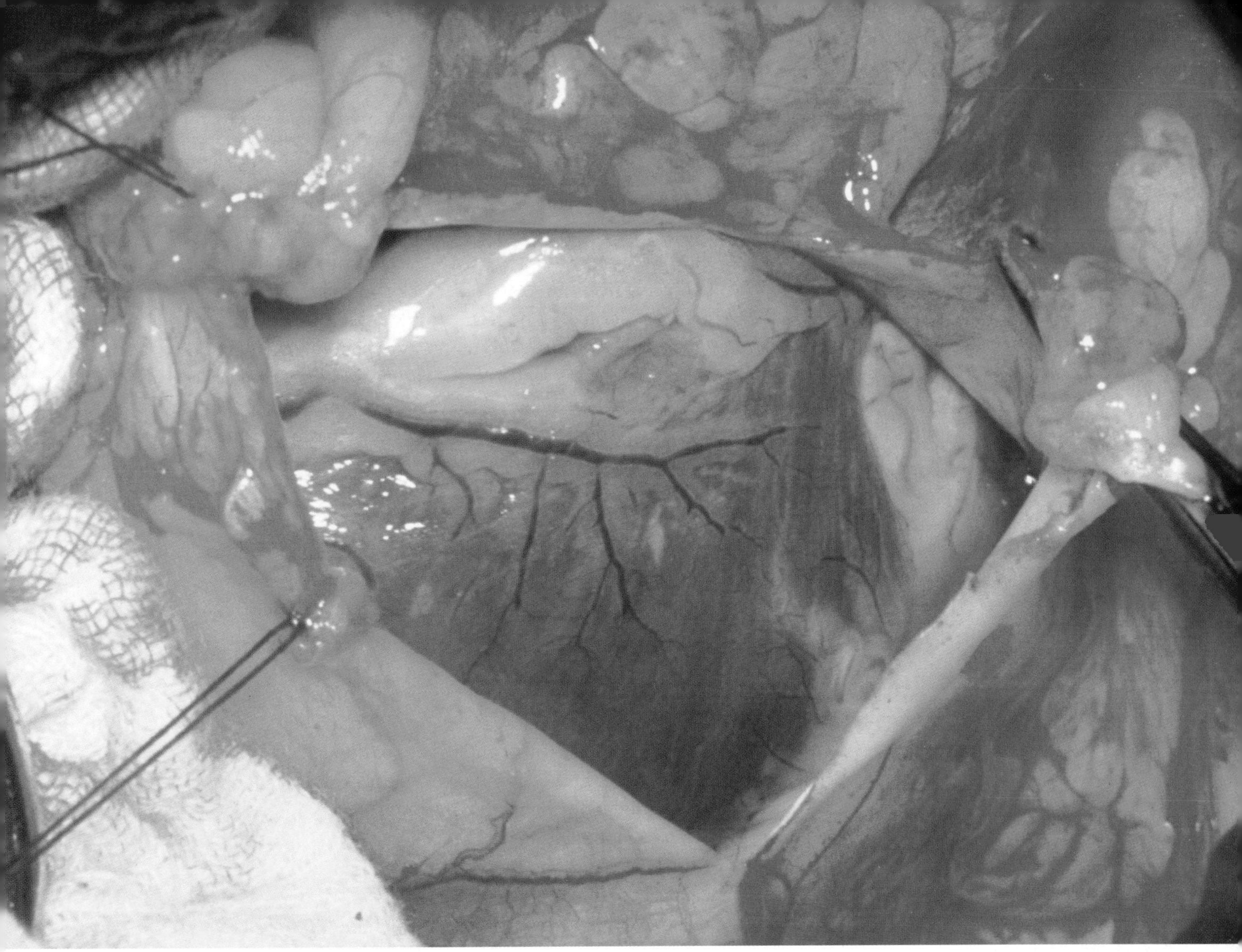

Figure 1
In this photo of a heart during surgery, you can see the coronary artery that supplies the muscle cells of the heart with the oxygen and nutrients they require. A blocked coronary artery can greatly reduce the ability of the heart to function.

Exploration Listening to Heart Sounds

Medical workers use stethoscopes to measure blood pressure and to listen to the heart, lungs, and intestines. You will use a stethoscope to listen to your heart.

Disinfect the earpieces of the stethoscope with rubbing alcohol before and after use.

- Place a stethoscope on your own chest and listen for a heart sound (**Figure 2**). Locate the area where the heart sounds are loudest and clearest.
- After 1 min of moderate exercise (e.g., walking on the spot), listen for your heart sounds again.

(a) Draw a diagram of a chest showing where you located the clearest sound.
(b) Did the sound of your heartbeat change after exercise? Describe what differences you heard.

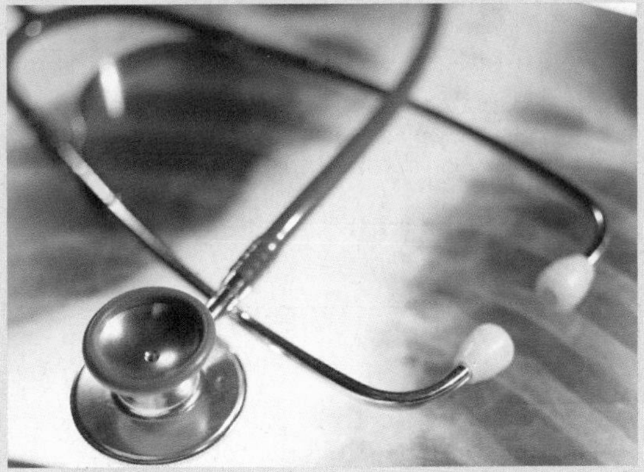

Figure 2
A stethoscope

10.1 Blood Vessels

Figure 1
William Harvey (1578–1657)

The ancient Greeks believed that the heart was the centre of human intelligence, an "innate heat" that generated four humours: black and yellow bile, phlegm, and blood. Galen, the personal physician of Roman emperor Marcus Aurelius in the second century C.E., influenced early physiology. Although he provided many enlightening theories, Galen is best known for steering scientists in the wrong direction. Galen believed that blood did not circulate. Although he believed that blood might ebb like the tides, he never thought of the heart as a pump. Galen's theory was generally accepted until the 17th century. Some science historians have suggested that his failure to consider the pumping action of the heart could be attributed to a lack of a technical model: the water pump had not been invented when Galen applied his theory.

William Harvey (1578–1657), the great English physiologist (**Figure 1**), questioned Galen's hypothesis. Harvey, like many Europeans during that period, was influenced by the astronomer Galileo. Galileo's new principles of dynamics became the foundation of Harvey's work. By applying Galileo's theories of fluid movement to blood, Harvey reasoned that blood must circulate.

Harvey attempted to quantify the amount of blood pumped by the heart each minute. He began his research by dissecting cadavers and observing blood vessels. Using mathematics, he calculated that the heart contains approximately 57 mL of blood. Harvey then concluded that 14.8 L must be pumped from the heart each hour. However, much less blood could be found in the body; the heart must be pumping the same blood over and over again. Harvey's estimates were at best conservative—he greatly underestimated the capacity of the heart to pump blood. However, by using empirical data, Harvey tested and challenged a theory that had been accepted for 1400 years.

Although William Harvey was convinced that blood must pass from the arteries to the veins, there was no visible evidence of how this was accomplished. He speculated that blood vessels too small to be seen by the human eye might explain how blood circulates. Four years after his death, an Italian physiologist, Marcello Malpighi, used a microscope to observe the tiniest blood vessels, the capillaries (from Latin, meaning "hairlike"). Malpighi's observations confirmed Harvey's theory of circulation. **Figure 2**, on the next page, shows the major blood vessels of the circulatory system, as they are known today.

DID YOU KNOW ?

Was Harvey First?
Evidence from an ancient Egyptian papyrus discovered in the 19th century suggests that the Egyptians correctly mapped the flow of blood from the heart 3300 years before William Harvey.

Arteries and Arterioles

artery a blood vessel that carries blood away from the heart

pulse change in the diameter of the arteries following heart contractions

Arteries are the blood vessels that carry blood away from the heart. They have thick walls composed of distinct layers. The outer and inner layers are primarily connective tissue, while the middle layers are made up of muscle fibres and elastic connective tissue, as shown in **Figure 3 (a)**, on page 314. Every time the heart contracts, blood surges from the heart and enters the arteries. The arteries stretch to accommodate the inrush of blood. The **pulse** you can feel near your wrist and on either side of your neck is created by changes in the diameter of the arteries following heart contractions. Heart contraction is followed by a relaxation phase. During this phase, pressure drops and elastic fibres in the walls of the artery recoil. It is interesting to note that the many cells of the artery are themselves supplied with blood vessels that provide nourishment. Blood from the arteries passes into smaller arteries, called arterioles. The middle layer of arterioles is composed of elastic fibres and smooth muscle.

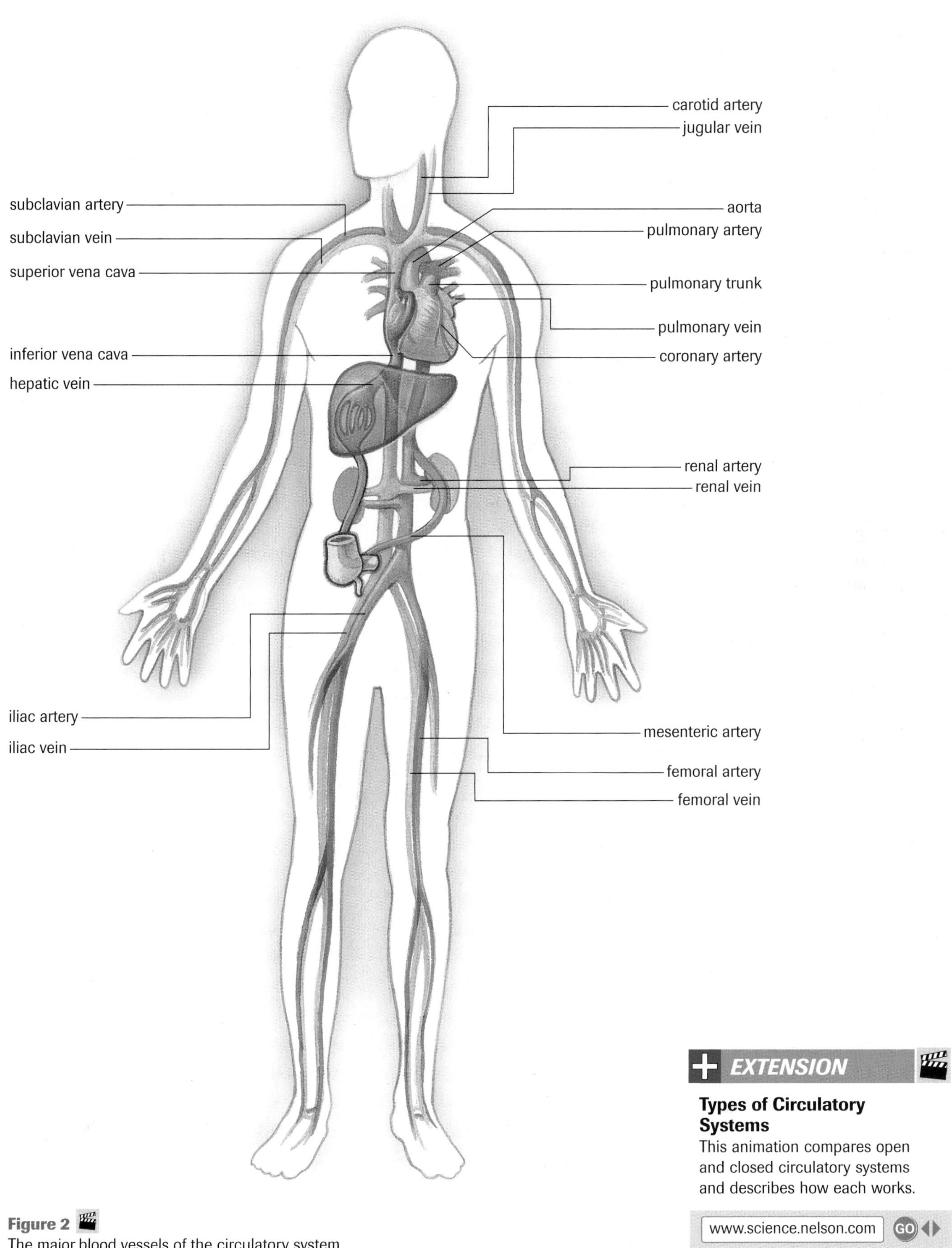

Figure 2
The major blood vessels of the circulatory system

EXTENSION

Types of Circulatory Systems
This animation compares open and closed circulatory systems and describes how each works.

www.science.nelson.com GO

Figure 3
(a) Arteries have strong walls capable of withstanding great pressure. The middle layer of arteries contains both muscle tissue and elastic connective tissue. The low-pressure veins have a thinner middle layer.
(b) The photo shows a cross section of an artery and a vein.

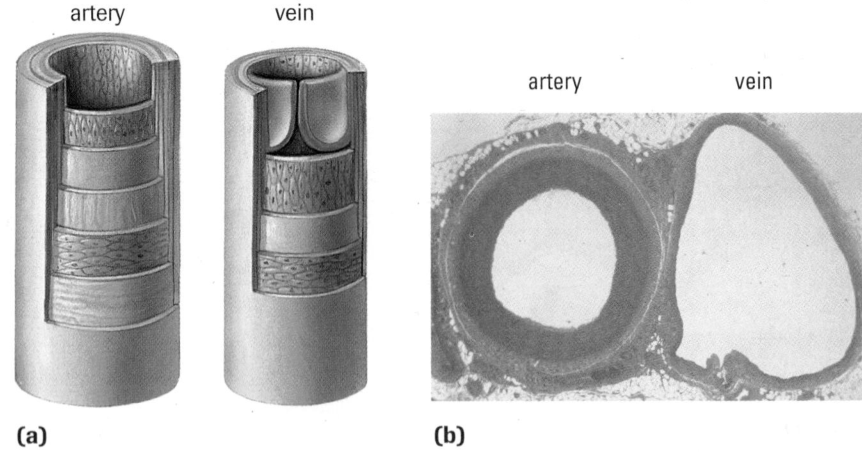

autonomic nervous system the part of the nervous system that controls the motor nerves that regulate equilibrium, and that is not under conscious control

vasoconstriction the narrowing of blood vessels, allowing less blood to the tissues

vasodilation the widening of blood vessels, allowing more blood to the tissues

The **autonomic nervous system**, which controls the motor nerves that maintain equilibrium, regulates the diameter of the arterioles. A nerve impulse causes smooth muscle in the arterioles to contract, reducing the diameter of the blood vessel. This process is called **vasoconstriction**. Vasoconstriction decreases blood flow to tissues. Relaxation of the smooth muscle causes dilation of the arterioles, and blood flow increases. This process, called **vasodilation**, increases the delivery of blood to tissues. This, in turn, permits the cells in that localized area to perform energy-consuming tasks.

Precapillary sphincter muscles regulate the movement of blood from the arterioles into capillaries. Blushing is caused by vasodilation of the arterioles leading to skin capillaries. Red blood cells close to the surface of the skin produce the pink colour. Vasodilation helps the body release some excess heat that is produced when you become nervous. Have you ever noticed someone's face turn a paler shade when they are frightened? The constriction of the arteriolar muscles diverts blood away from the outer capillaries of the skin toward the muscles. The increased blood flow to the muscles provides more oxygen and glucose to meet the energy demands of a response to a threat or danger.

Arterioles leading to capillaries open only when cells in that area require blood. It has been estimated that the body would need 200 L of blood if all the arterioles were open at one time. Although the majority of brain capillaries remain open, as few as one fiftieth of the capillaries in resting muscle remain open.

+ EXTENSION

Atherosclerosis and the Positive Feedback Cycle
Listen to this audio clip to understand the accelerating influence that positive feedback has on the development of atherosclerotic plaque and coronary artery disease.

www.science.nelson.com 

Atherosclerosis

Anyone who has ever washed dishes is aware of how fat floats on water. You may have noticed that when one fat droplet meets another, they stick together and form a larger droplet. Unfortunately, the same thing can happen in your arteries. Excess lipid in your blood is deposited in the walls of the arteries, slowly narrowing the inside diameter of the blood vessel. Calcium and other minerals deposit on top of the lipid, forming plaque. This condition is known as **atherosclerosis**, the most common form of a group of disorders called **arteriosclerosis,** or arterial disease. Arteriosclerosis can narrow arteries and lead to high blood pressure (**Figure 4**, next page). To make matters worse, blood clots, which are normally a life-saving property of blood, form in the blood vessel when the plaque gets so big that it bursts through the wall of the artery. This can totally block the artery and cut off blood flow. In the heart, as the arteries become narrowed and blocked, inadequate amounts of blood and oxygen are delivered to the heart muscle, resulting in chest pains and possibly a heart attack.

atherosclerosis a degeneration of blood vessels caused by the accumulation of fat deposits in the inner wall

arteriosclerosis a group of disorders that cause the blood vessels to thicken, harden, and lose their elasticity

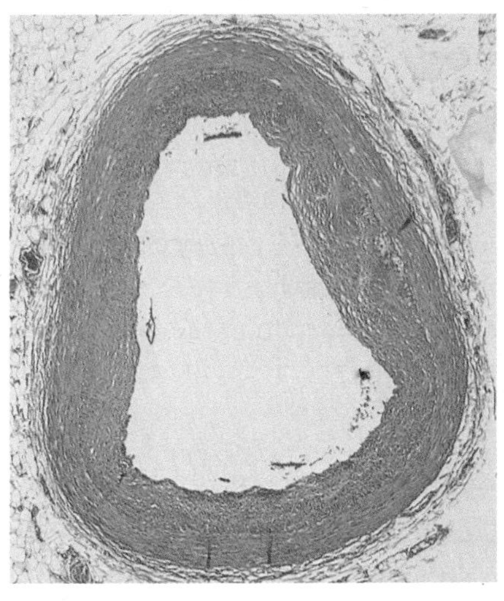

(a)

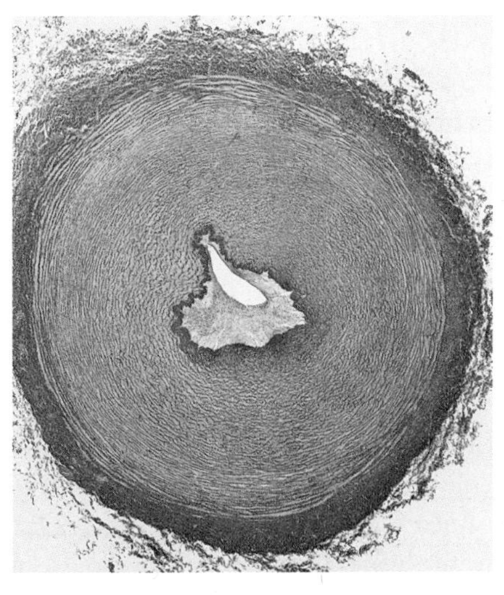

(b)

Figure 4
(a) Cross section of a normal artery
(b) Cross section of an artery from a person with atherosclerosis. Notice that fat deposits have narrowed the passageway.

Every year heart disease kills more Canadians than any other disease. Lifestyle changes must accompany any medical treatment. A low-fat diet plus regular exercise are keys to prevention.

Aneurysm

An **aneurysm** is a bulge that forms in the wall of a weakened blood vessel, usually an artery. The most common sites are the aorta of the heart, the abdominal aorta, and arteries in the brain. Aneurysms are often due to atherosclerosis. In much the same way as the weakened wall of an inner tube begins to bulge, the weakened segment of the artery protrudes as blood pulses through. The thinner wall offers less support and eventually ruptures. Less oxygen and nutrients are delivered to the tissues, resulting in cell death. An aneurysm in the brain is one of the conditions that can cause a stroke.

aneurysm a bulge in the weakened wall of a blood vessel, usually an artery

mini *Investigation* — *Monitoring Your Pulse*

Walking or mild exercise will increase your heart rate by 20 % to 30 %. For those in good health, increased energy demands during extreme exercise can raise the heart rate to an incredible 200 beats per minute. Although few individuals can sustain such a rapid heart rate, it indicates the capacity of the heart to adjust to changing situations.

Do not perform this activity if you are not allowed to participate in physical education classes.

- While sitting still, place your index and middle finger near your wrist, as shown in **Figure 5**. The pulse you feel is blood rushing through the brachial artery in your arm. Count the number of heartbeats in 30 s. Record your pulse at rest and then calculate the heart rate as beats per min.
- Remain sitting quietly and place your index finger and middle finger on the side of your neck just to the side your trachea. You will feel blood pulse through the carotid artery, which is an artery that carries blood to the head. Take your pulse for 30 s and then calculate the heart rate for 1 min.
- Run on the spot for approximately 2 min.
- Take your pulse immediately after exercise using either the carotid artery or the brachial artery. Record your heart rate.

(a) Compare the strength of the pulse in the carotid artery with that in your arm.
(b) Compare your heart rate before and after exercise.
(c) Do you think the difference between resting heart rate and the heart rate after exercise would be greater for athletes? Explain your answer.

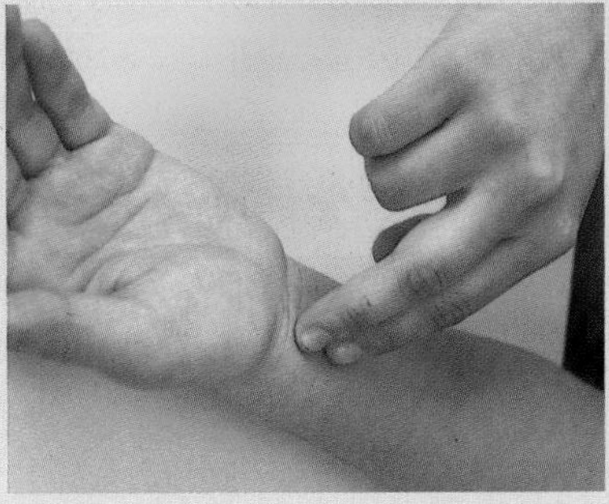

Figure 5
Arteries near the surface permit taking of the pulse.

Capillaries

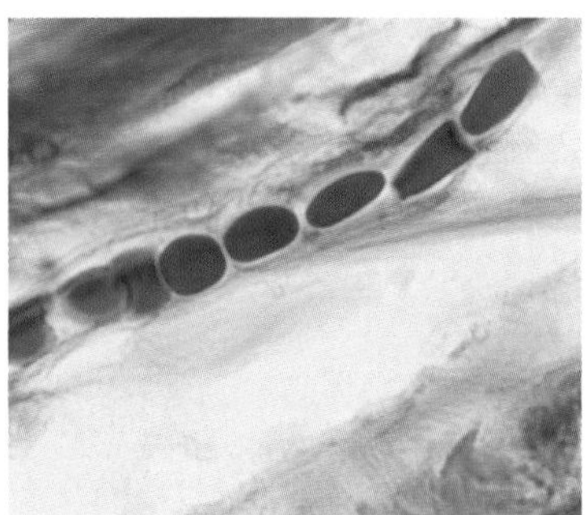

Figure 6
Red blood cells in a capillary. Notice that the capillary is only wide enough for cells to pass through one at a time.

Capillaries, composed of a single layer of cells, are the sites of fluid and gas exchange between blood and body cells. Many active cells, such as muscle cells, may be supplied by more than one capillary. Most capillaries are between 0.4 and 1.0 mm long with a diameter of less than 0.005 mm. The diameter is so small that red blood cells must travel through capillaries in single file (**Figure 6**). The single cell layer of capillaries, although ideal for diffusion, creates problems. Capillary beds are easily destroyed. High blood pressure or any impact, such as that caused by a punch, can rupture the thin-layered capillary. Bruising occurs when blood rushes into the spaces between tissues.

Oxygen diffuses from the blood into the surrounding tissues through the thin walls of the capillaries into the body cells. Oxygenated (oxygen-rich) blood appears red in colour, while deoxygenated (oxygen-poor) blood appears purple-blue as it leaves the capillary. The deoxygenated blood collects in small veins called venules and is carried back to the heart. Some protein is also exchanged, but this process is not believed to involve diffusion. Water-soluble ions and vitamins are believed to pass through spaces in the walls of the capillary vessels. Because some spaces are wider than others, some capillaries may be more permeable than others.

mini *Investigation* — *Observing Blood Flow in a Fish Tail*

William Harvey described the movement of blood through vessels in the early 1600s. He concluded that blood carried nutrients to tissues and transported wastes away from tissues to specialized organs. Unable to see capillaries, Harvey speculated that tiny blood vessels were the sites of diffusion of wastes and nutrients between cells and the circulating blood.

Materials: goldfish, net, absorbent cotton, Petri dish, cover slip, light microscope

- Using the net, carefully remove a small goldfish from the aquarium and place it in the Petri dish.
- Cover the goldfish, except the head and tail, with absorbent cotton that has been soaked with aquarium water. Place enough cotton to completely cover the fish. The gills must be covered and soaked with water.
- Add a cover slip to the tail (**Figure 7**).
- Position the Petri dish on the stage of a light microscope and observe the fish tail under low-power magnification.
- When you have completed your observations, gently remove the cotton and submerge the Petri dish into the aquarium to release the fish unharmed.

(a) Describe the movement of blood in arterioles, capillaries, and venules.

(b) Explain why capillary walls are much thinner than those of the arterioles or venules.

(c) Blood cells squeeze through capillaries, moving in single file. Explain the advantage of single-file motion and the slowing of blood cells through the capillary.

(d) Where would you expect to find more capillaries: muscle tissue or fat tissue? Give reasons for your answer.

(e) Live animals are used in many research experiments. Comment of the use of live animals in research.

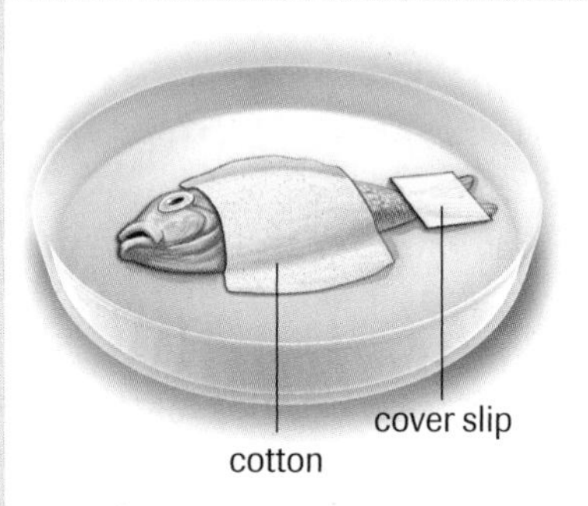

Figure 7
Experimental setup

Practice

1. What causes a pulse?
2. Define vasodilation and vasoconstriction.
3. What are the functions of capillaries?

Veins and Venules

Capillaries merge and become progressively larger vessels, called venules. Unlike capillaries, the walls of venules contain smooth muscle. Venules merge into **veins**, which have greater diameter. Gradually, the diameter of the veins increases as they approach the heart. However, the process of returning the blood to the heart is difficult. As blood flows from arteries to arterioles to capillaries, blood flow is greatly reduced. As blood passes through a greater number of narrower vessels with weaker walls, fluid pressure is reduced. (See **Figure 3** on page 314 for a comparison of the walls of arteries and veins.) By the time blood enters the venules, the pressure is between 15 mmHg and 20 mmHg. This pressure is not enough to drive the blood back to the heart, especially from the lower limbs.

vein a blood vessel that carries blood toward the heart

How then does blood get back to the heart? William Harvey, the English physiologist, conducted experiments to answer that question. In one experiment, he tied a band around the arm of one of his subjects, restricting venous blood flow. The veins soon became engorged with blood and swelled. Harvey then placed his finger on the vein and pushed blood toward the heart. The vein closed up or collapsed. Harvey repeated the procedure, but this time he pushed the blood back toward the hand. Bulges appeared in the vein at regular intervals. What caused the bulges? Dissection of the veins confirmed the existence of valves.

The valves open in one direction, steering blood toward the heart. They do not allow blood to flow back in the other direction (**Figure 8 (a)**). When Harvey tried to push blood toward the hand, the valves closed, causing blood to pool in front of the valves and distend the vein. When he directed blood toward the heart, the valves opened and blood flowed from one compartment into the next. The vein collapsed because the band tied around the arm prevented the blood from passing.

Skeletal muscles also aid venous blood flow. Venous pressure increases when skeletal muscles contract and push against the vein. The muscles bulge when they contract, thereby reducing the vein's diameter. Pressure inside the vein increases and the valves open, allowing blood to flow toward the heart. Sequential contractions of skeletal muscle create a massaging action that moves blood back to the heart (**Figure 8 (b)**). This may explain why you feel like stretching first thing in the morning. It also provides a reason why some people faint after standing still for long periods of time. Blood begins to pool in the lower limbs and cannot move back to the heart without movement of the leg muscles.

(a)

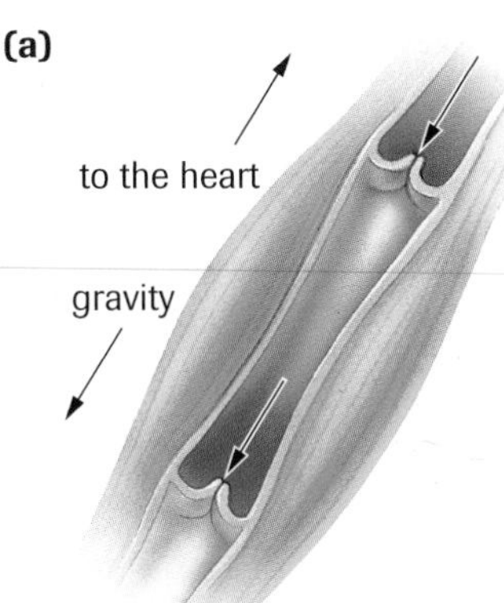

(b)

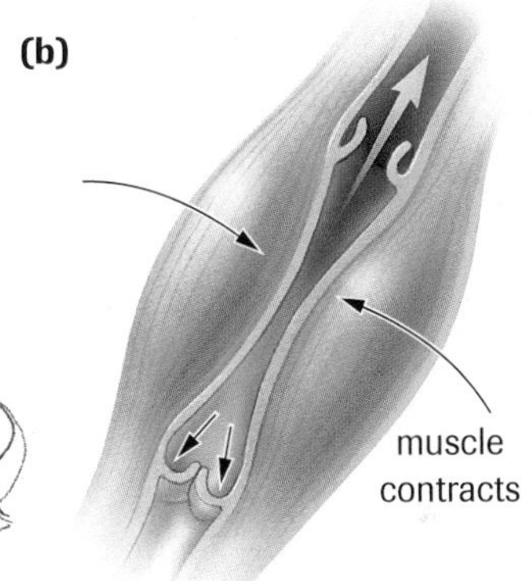

Figure 8
Venous valves and skeletal muscle work together in a low-pressure system to move blood back to the heart.

The veins serve as more than just low-pressure transport canals; they are also important blood reservoirs. As much as 65 % of your total blood volume can be found in the veins. During times of stress, venous blood flow can be increased to help you meet increased energy demands. Nerve impulses cause smooth muscle in the walls of the veins to contract, increasing fluid pressure. Increased pressure drives more blood to the heart.

Unfortunately, veins, like other blood vessels, are subject to problems. Large volumes of blood can distend the veins. In most cases, veins return to normal diameter, but if the pooling of blood occurs over a long period of time, the one-way valves are damaged. Without proper functioning of the valves, gravity carries blood toward the feet and greater pooling occurs. Surface veins gradually become larger and begin to bulge. This disorder is known as varicose veins. Although there is a genetic link to weakness in the vein walls, lifestyle can accelerate the damage. Prolonged standing, especially with restricted movement, increases pooling of blood. Prolonged compression of the superficial veins in the leg can also contribute to varicose veins.

mini Investigation — Mapping Veins

CAUTION: Do not leave the sphygmomanometer inflated past 30 mmHg or on longer than 5 min.

- Place a pressure cuff (sphygmomanometer) over a subject's upper arm and inflate it to 30 mmHg.
- Locate one of the veins on the inside of the subject's arm and use your index finger to push blood in the vein toward the elbow.
- Describe the appearance of the vein. Draw a diagram to illustrate your description.
- Now push the blood in the vein toward the fingers.
- Describe the appearance of the vein. Draw a diagram to illustrate your description.

(a) How do you know that the blood vessel is a vein and not an artery?

SUMMARY — Blood Vessels

- Arteries carry blood away from the heart.
- Vasoconstriction is a reduction in the diameter of the blood vessel, decreasing blood flow and the amount of oxygen to the tissues. Vasodilation is an increase in the diameter of the blood vessel, increasing blood flow and the amount of oxygen to the tissues.
- Atherosclerosis is a narrowing of the arteries due to a buildup of plaque that contains fat.
- Capillaries are the site of fluid and gas exchange between the blood and the cells.
- Veins carry blood toward the heart.
  - Pressure in the veins is much lower than in the arteries.
  - One-way valves and skeletal muscles help venous blood flow.

Section 10.1 Questions

1. Explain what happens in the blood vessels when someone blushes. Why does this happen?
2. Are all the capillaries open all the time? Why or why not? What determines whether a capillary is open?
3. What are the advantages and disadvantages of capillaries being composed of a single cell layer?
4. Explain the importance of William Harvey's theory of blood circulation.
5. Why are aneurysms dangerous?
6. Prepare a table comparing arteries and veins.
7. Fluid pressure is very low in the veins. Explain how blood gets back to the heart.
8. What causes varicose veins? What lifestyle changes could prevent the development of varicose veins?
9. Atherosclerosis is a disease caused by the buildup of plaque inside an artery.
   (a) Explain how it occurs.
   (b) What problems can be created by the buildup of plaque?
   (c) Suggest a treatment for the disorder.

The heart is a muscular organ that pumps to circulate blood throughout the body. A fluid-filled membrane called the pericardium surrounds the heart. The fluid bathes the heart, preventing friction between its outer wall and the covering membrane.

The heart consists of two parallel pumps separated by the **septum**. The pumping action is synchronized; muscle contractions on the right side mirror those on the left. The pump on the right receives deoxygenated blood from the body tissues and pumps it to the lungs. The pump on the left receives oxygenated blood from the lungs and pumps it to the cells of the body. Vessels that carry blood to and from the lungs make up the **pulmonary circulatory system**. Vessels that carry blood to and from the body make up the **systemic circulatory system**. **Figure 1** illustrates the two systems.

The four-chambered human heart is composed of two thin-walled **atria** (singular: **atrium**) and two thick-walled **ventricles**. Blood from the systemic system enters the right atrium, and blood from the pulmonary system enters the left atrium. The stronger, more muscular ventricles pump the blood to distant tissues.

septum a wall of muscle that separates the right and left sides of the heart

pulmonary circulatory system the system of blood vessels that carries deoxygenated blood to the lungs and oxygenated blood back to the heart

systemic circulatory system the system of blood vessels that carries oxygenated blood to the tissues of the body and deoxygenated blood back to the heart

atrium (plural: **atria**) a thin-walled chamber of the heart that receives blood from veins

ventricle a muscular, thick-walled chamber of the heart that delivers blood to the arteries

Pulmonary Circuit

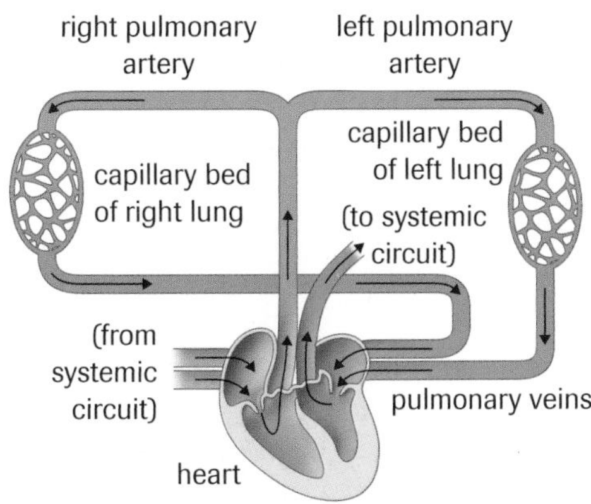

Systemic Circuit

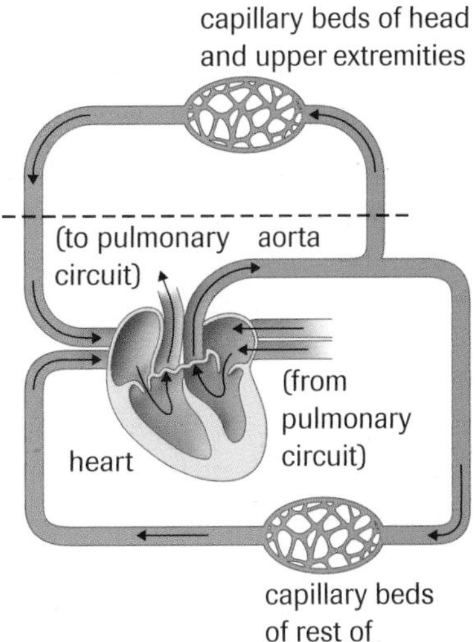

Figure 1
The pulmonary and systemic circuits of the circulatory system. The blood vessels carrying oxygenated blood are in red; the vessels carrying deoxygenated blood are in blue.

One-Way Blood Flow

Blood is carried to the heart by veins. The superior vena cava carries deoxygenated blood from the head and upper body to the right atrium. The inferior vena cava carries deoxygenated blood from all veins below the diaphragm to the same atrium. Oxygenated blood flowing from the lungs enters the left atrium by way of the pulmonary veins. Blood from both atria is eventually pumped into the ventricles.

Valves called **atrioventricular (AV) valves** separate the atria from the ventricles. In much the same way as the valves within veins ensure one-directional flow, the AV valves prevent the flow of blood from the ventricles back into the atria. The AV valves are supported by bands of connective tissue called chordae tendinae. A second set of valves, called **semilunar valves**, separate the ventricles from the arteries. These valves are half-moon shaped (hence, the name *semilunar*), and they prevent blood that has entered the arteries from flowing back into the ventricles (**Figure 2**, next page).

atrioventricular (AV) valve a heart valve that prevents the backflow of blood from a ventricle into an atrium

semilunar valve a valve that prevents the backflow of blood from an artery into a ventricle

Figure 2
Anatomy of the human heart

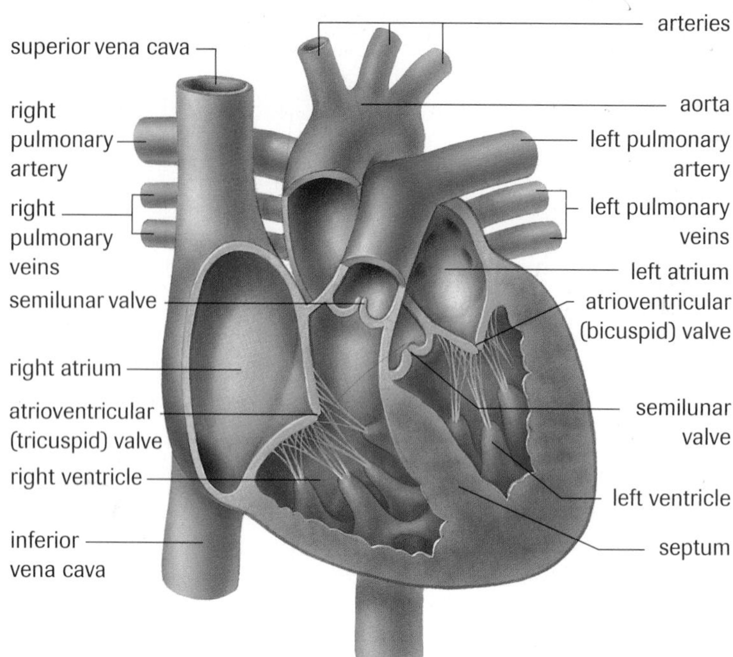

aorta the largest artery in the body; carries oxygenated blood to the tissues

coronary artery an artery that supplies the cardiac muscle with oxygen and nutrients

Blood is carried away from the heart by arteries. The **aorta**, the largest artery in your body, carries oxygenated blood away from the heart. The **coronary arteries**, arteries that form an important branch of the aorta, supply the muscle cells of the heart with oxygen and nutrients. A blocked artery illustrates the importance of proper coronary circulation. Chest pain, or angina, occurs when too little oxygen reaches the heart. The heart, unlike other organs that slow down if they cannot receive enough nutrients, must continue beating no matter what demands are placed on it. It has been estimated that the heart may use 20 % of the body's total blood oxygen during times of stress.

As with other arteries, fat deposits and plaque can collect inside coronary arteries. Medications are often used to increase blood flow, but in severe situations blood flow must be rerouted. A coronary bypass operation involves removing a vein from another part of the patient's body and grafting it into the heart (**Figure 3**). However, for the vein to be grafted, the heart must be temporarily stopped. During the operation, the patient's heart is cooled and a heart–lung machine is used to supply oxygen and push blood to the tissues of the body.

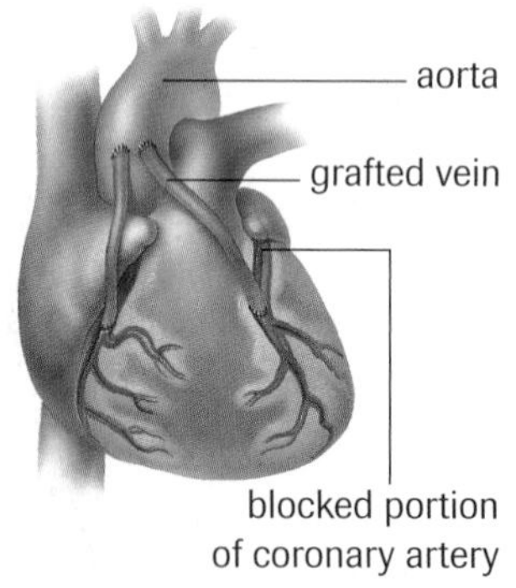

Figure 3
Coronary bypass operation. Blood flow is rerouted around the blockage.

Practice

1. Differentiate between the systemic and the pulmonary circulatory systems.
2. What is the function of the AV valves and the semilunar valves?
3. What is angina and what causes it?
4. What is a coronary bypass operation and why is it performed?

EXPLORE an issue

Issue Checklist

- ○ Issue
- ● Resolution
- ○ Design
- ● Evidence
- ● Analysis
- ● Evaluation

Growing a New Heart

Cardiovascular disease is the leading cause of death in North America. About 44 000 Canadians, 40 % of them younger than 65 years, die each year from heart disease. Over 4000 patients in Canada and the United States are on the waiting list for a new heart. Only the sickest patients make the list, and not all of them will receive a new heart—some will die waiting. Aggressive campaigns to educate people about the importance of organ donation have resulted in increased numbers of donors. However, it may not be enough. Over the past few years, the demand for organs has been rising by about 15 % per year, and this rate will likely increase. Fewer than 3000 patients worldwide receive heart transplants annually.

Dr. Michael Sefton (**Figure 4**), director of the Institute of Biomaterials and Biomedical Engineering at the University of Toronto, has a solution that would provide an almost unlimited number of hearts for transplant. What Sefton calls a "heart in a box" is a transplantable heart that can be grown in the laboratory.

First, researchers must create scaffolding that the cells will grow around (**Table 1**). Typically, biodegradable plastics are used. The next step is to seed the scaffolding with living cells. The scaffolding and cells are then placed in a bioreactor—a sort of incubator that maintains constant temperature and provides the nutrients and oxygen required to support cell division. The cells secrete proteins and growth factors that bind them together to form living tissues. Although researchers have not yet been able to grow a complete living heart, they have successfully grown components of the heart.

Statement

Individuals who adopt unhealthy lifestyle choices that are dangerous to the health of their heart should not have the opportunity to have another one grown for them.

Figure 4
Dr. Michael Sefton

1. Form a group and research the issue.

www.science.nelson.com 

2. Discuss the issue with class members and others in preparation for a debate.
3. Write a list of points and counterpoints that your group has considered.
4. Take a stand. Decide if you agree or disagree with the statement.
5. Defend your position in the debate.
6. Should this technology be used to support people who have an unhealthy lifestyle?

Table 1 Procedure for Growing a Heart

1. Cells are placed on plastic scaffolding.	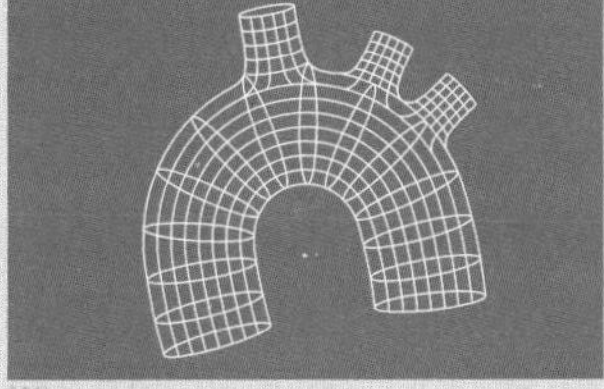	2. The scaffolding, seeded with cells, is placed in a bioreactor that provides nutrients and oxygen.	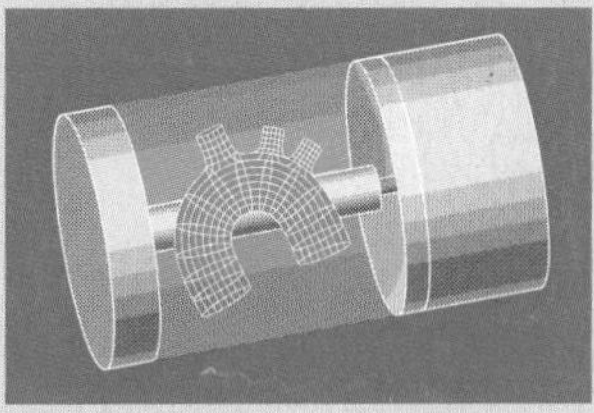
3. The cells divide and fill the open spaces of the scaffolding.	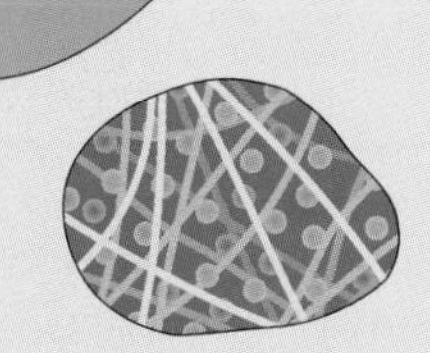	4. This technique can be used to grow parts of the heart and perhaps, eventually, the entire organ.	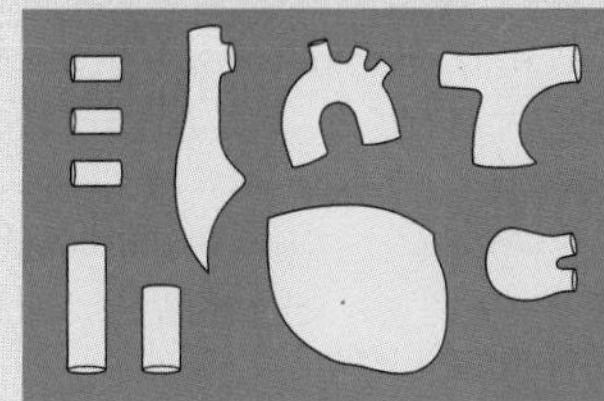

INVESTIGATION 10.1 *Introduction*

Fetal Pig Dissection

The organ systems of humans and pigs are arranged in the body in very similar ways. In this investigation, you will explore the arrangement of the digestive, respiratory, and circulatory systems that you have learned about in this unit.

To perform this investigation, turn to page 340.

Report Checklist

● Purpose	● Design	● Analysis
● Problem	○ Materials	● Evaluation
● Hypothesis	○ Procedure	○ Synthesis
● Prediction	● Evidence	

WEB Activity

Simulation—Observing the Movement of Blood through the Heart

In this activity, you will follow the movement of blood through a virtual beating heart. Before you begin, write or draw a description of how you think blood moves through the heart. After you have finished, make any changes that are needed.

www.science.nelson.com 

Cardiac Catheterization

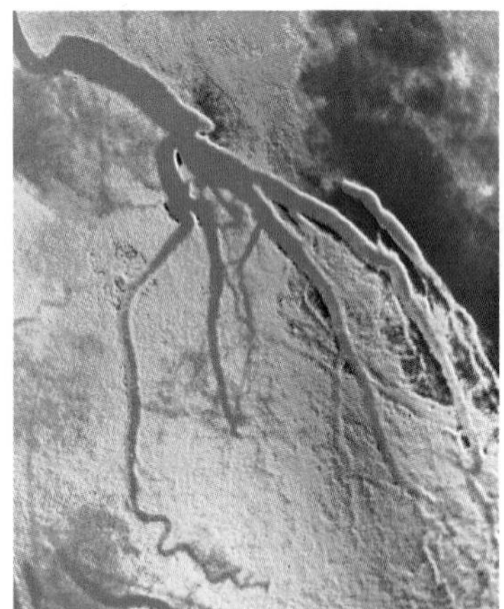

Figure 5
Dye showing the coronary arteries

At one time, doctors had to rely on external symptoms to detect coronary artery blockage. An inability to sustain physical activity, rapid breathing, and a general lack of energy are three of the symptoms of coronary distress. However, these same symptoms can also indicate a wide variety of other circulatory and respiratory diseases. One way to determine whether or not a patient is suffering from coronary artery problems is to perform surgery. Unfortunately, the surgery is not without risks. Clearly, less invasive means for diagnosing the problem would be desirable.

One of the most useful techniques to detect coronary artery blockage is cardiac catheterization. In this procedure, a small, thin hollow tube, called a catheter, is passed into an artery in the groin as the patient lies on an examination table. The catheter is then pushed up through the aorta and into the heart. A dye visible on X-ray film is then injected into the catheter. The dye travels through the blood vessels while its image is traced by a fluoroscope (a fluorescent screen). The image can also be projected on a television monitor (**Figure 5**). An area of restricted blood flow pinpoints the region of blockage. The catheter helps direct the surgeon to the problem prior to surgery. In a technique known as angioplasty, the catheter has a tiny balloon attached that can be inflated to open up the blocked blood vessel.

Blood samples can also be taken with the catheter to determine how much oxygen is in the blood in the different chambers. This tells the physician how well the blood is being oxygenated in the lungs. Low levels of oxygen in the left side of the heart can provide information about whether the circulatory and respiratory systems are working together efficiently. The catheter can even be used to monitor pressures in each of the heart chambers.

Setting the Heart's Tempo

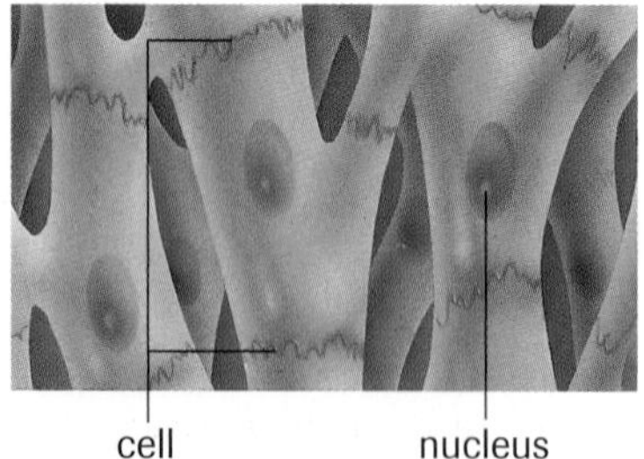

Figure 6
The heart is composed of cardiac muscle, which has a unique branching pattern.

Heart, or cardiac, muscle differs from other types of muscle. Like skeletal muscle, cardiac muscle appears striated (striped) when viewed under a microscope. But unlike skeletal muscle, cardiac muscle displays a branching pattern (**Figure 6**). The greatest difference stems from the ability of this muscle to contract without being stimulated by external nerves. Muscle with this ability, called **myogenic muscle**, explains why the heart will continue to beat, at least for a short time, when removed from the body.

myogenic muscle muscle that contracts without external nerve stimulation

The remarkable capacity of the heart to beat can be illustrated by a simple experiment. When a frog's heart is removed and sliced into small pieces while in a salt solution that simulates the minerals found within the body, each of the pieces continues to beat, although not at the same speed. Muscle tissue from the ventricles follows a slower rhythm than muscle tissue from the atria. Muscle tissue closest to where the venae cavae enter the heart has the fastest tempo. The unique nature of the heart becomes evident when two separated pieces are brought together. The united fragments assume a single beat. The slower muscle tissue assumes the tempo set by the muscle tissue that beats more rapidly.

The heart's tempo or beat rate is set by the **sinoatrial (SA) node** (Figure 7). This bundle of specialized nerves and muscles is located in the upper right atrium. The SA node acts as a pacemaker, setting a rhythm of about 70 beats per minute for the heart. Nerve impulses are carried from the pacemaker to other muscle cells by modified muscle tissue. Originating in the atria, the contractions travel to a second node, the **atrioventricular (AV) node**. The AV node serves as a conductor, passing nerve impulses via two large nerve fibres, called **Purkinje fibres**, through the septum toward the ventricles. The Purkinje fibres run along the septum that separates the right and left ventricles, carrying impulses from the AV node to the bottom tip of the heart. From here, these branching fibres carry impulses up along the outer walls of the ventricles back toward the atria. A wave of cardiac contraction follows the nerve pathway. Both the right and left atria contract prior to the right and left ventricles. One of the greatest challenges for surgeons performing open-heart surgery is to make incisions at the appropriate location. A scalpel placed in the wrong spot could cut fibres that conduct nerve impulses.

Heart rate is influenced by autonomic nerves. Two regulatory nervous systems—the **sympathetic** and **parasympathetic nervous systems**—conduct impulses from the brain to the SA node. Stimulated during times of stress, the sympathetic nerves increase heart rate. This increases blood flow to tissues, enabling the body to meet increased energy demands. When the heart rate exceeds 100 beats per min, this is referred to as tachycardia. Tachycardia can result from exercise or from the consumption of such drugs as caffeine or nicotine. During times of relaxation, the parasympathetic nerves are stimulated to slow the heart rate.

sinoatrial (SA) node a small mass of tissue in the right atrium that originates the impulses stimulating the heartbeat

atrioventricular (AV) node a small mass of tissue in the right atrioventricular region through which impulses from the sinoatrial node are passed to the ventricles

Purkinje fibre a nerve fibre that branches and carries electrical impulses throughout the ventricles

sympathetic nervous system a division of the autonomic nervous system that prepares the body for stress

parasympathetic nervous system a division of the autonomic nervous system that returns the body to normal resting levels following adjustments to stress

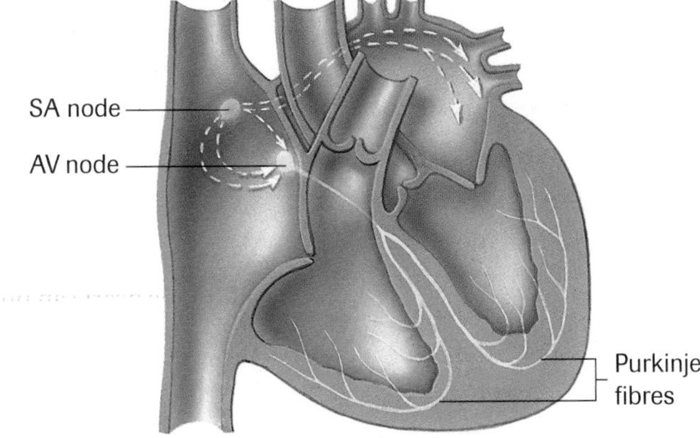

Figure 7
The SA node initiates heart contractions. Modified muscle tissue passes a nerve impulse from the pacemaker down the dividing septum toward the ventricles.

Practice

5. What is myogenic muscle?
6. What is the difference between the sympathetic and the parasympathetic nervous systems?

Case Study

Diagnosing Heart Conditions

Physicians can use electrocardiographs, which map electrical fields within the heart, to make tracings to diagnose certain heart problems. Electrodes that can detect the electrical impulses of the heart are placed on the body surface are connected to a recording device. The electrical impulses are displayed on a graph called an electrocardiogram (ECG) (**Figure 8**). Changes in electrical current reveal normal or abnormal events of the cardiac cycle. The first wave, referred to as the P wave, represents the electrical impulse that causes atrial contraction. The larger spike, referred to as the QRS wave, represents the electrical impulse that causes ventricular contraction. A final T wave signals that the ventricles have recovered. A patch of dead heart tissue, for example, will not conduct impulses and produces abnormal line tracings (**Figure 9**). By comparing the tracings, physicians are able to locate the area of the heart that is damaged.

The electrocardiograph is especially useful for monitoring the body's response to exercise. Stress tests are performed by monitoring a subject who is riding a stationary bike or running on a treadmill. Some heart malfunctions remain hidden during rest, but can be detected during vigorous exercise.

Physicians often refer to an irregular heartbeat as arrhythmia (**Figure 10**). One cause of arrhythmia is a blocked coronary artery. When a coronary artery is blocked, it delivers less blood and can cause the heart to beat in an irregular pattern. The buildup of toxic products associated with poor oxygen delivery can initiate contractions of the heart muscle. Rather than synchronized heartbeats, where muscle cells within the ventricles pick up electrical signals from surrounding muscle fibres, each cell within the ventricle responds to the toxins surrounding it and begins to contract wildly. This is referred to as ventricular fibrillation.

As the heart fibrillates, blood is not pumped in a coordinated fashion. The twitching heart pushes blood back and forth, reducing its ability to deliver needed oxygen. The heart responds by beating faster, but without a controlled pattern of muscle contraction, blood delivery to the tissues will not improve.

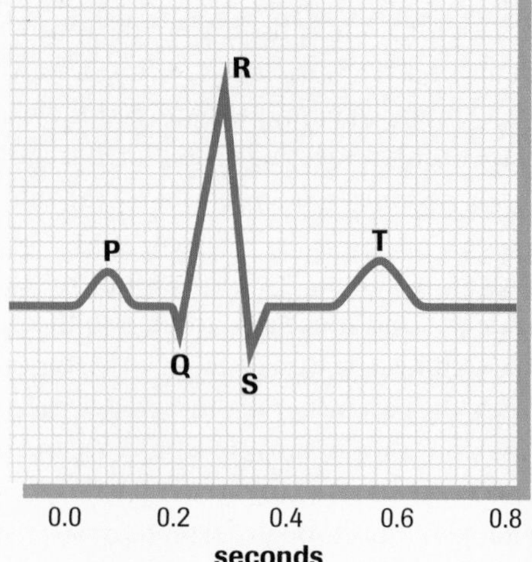

Figure 8
Electrocardiogram (ECG) showing the duration of a single beat. The flat lines show the resting period between beats.

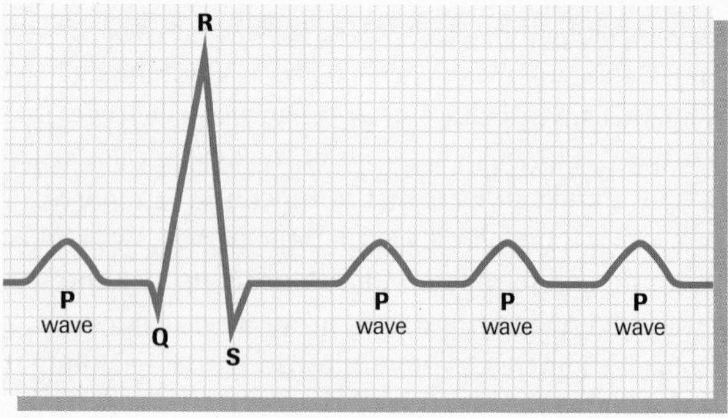

Figure 9
An abnormal electrocardiogram

Case Study Questions

1. What do the repetitive P waves in **Figure 9** indicate?
2. What would a small QRS wave indicate?
3. What is arrythmia?
4. Why is ventricular fibrillation dangerous?

Figure 10
Not all arrhythmias are abnormal. The ECG in **(a)** is a slowed heart rate associated with athletes. The ECG in **(b)** shows an uncontrolled heart rate, or ventricular fibrillation.

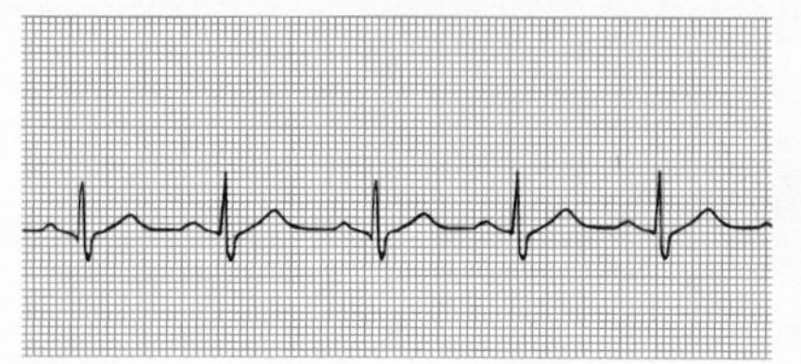

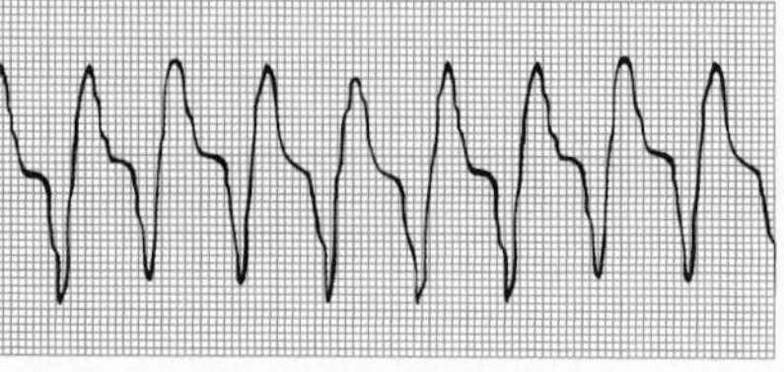

(a) **(b)**

Heart Sounds

The familiar *lubb-dubb* heart sounds are caused by the closing of the heart valves. The period of relaxation of the heart is called diastole, during which both the atria and the ventricles are relaxed. When the atria are relaxed, they fill with blood (**Figure 11 (a)**). The atria then contract, increasing fluid pressure and forcing the AV valves open. Blood flows from the atria into the ventricles (**Figure 11 (b)**). In turn, the filled ventricles contract. The pressure forces the AV valves shut, producing a heavy *lubb* sound and pushing blood through the semilunar valves and into the arteries (**Figure 11 (a)**). The period of contraction is called **systole**. The ventricles then relax, and their volume increases. With increased volume, pressure in the ventricles decreases and blood tends to be drawn from the arteries toward the area of lower pressure; however, the blood is prevented from re-entering the ventricles by the semilunar valves. The closing of the semilunar valves creates the lighter *dubb* sound.

diastole relaxation (dilation) of the heart, during which the atria fill with blood

systole contraction of the heart, during which blood is pushed out of the heart

Occasionally, the valves do not close completely. This condition is one cause of heart murmurs. The heart murmur occurs when blood leaks past the closed heart valve because of an improper seal. The AV valves, especially the left AV valve (the bicuspid valve), are especially susceptible to defects. The rush of blood from the ventricle back into the atrium produces a gurgling sound that can be detected with a stethoscope. Blood flowing back toward the atrium is inefficient because it is not directed to the systemic or pulmonary systems. The hearts of individuals who experience these murmurs compensate for decreased oxygen delivery by beating faster and eventually enlarging.

A second mechanism helps compensate for decreased blood flow in people with leaky heart valves. Like an elastic band, the more cardiac muscle is stretched, the stronger is the force of contraction. When blood flows from the ventricle back into the atrium, blood volume in the atrium increases. The atrium accepts the normal volume and the additional blood from the ventricle. The extra volume stretches the atrium and drives blood to the ventricle with greater force. The increased blood volume in the ventricle causes it to contract with greater force, driving more blood to the tissues.

DID YOU KNOW ?

The First Stethoscope

In 1816, René Laennec, a young physician, was examining a patient for heart distress. The practice at the time was for the doctor to place his ear on the patient's chest and listen for the *lubb-dubb* sounds. However, Laennec decided to try another approach. He rolled up a paper and placed it to the patient's chest. The heart sounds became clearer. Later, wooden cylinders were used, eventually to be replaced by the modern Y-shaped stethoscope.

(a)

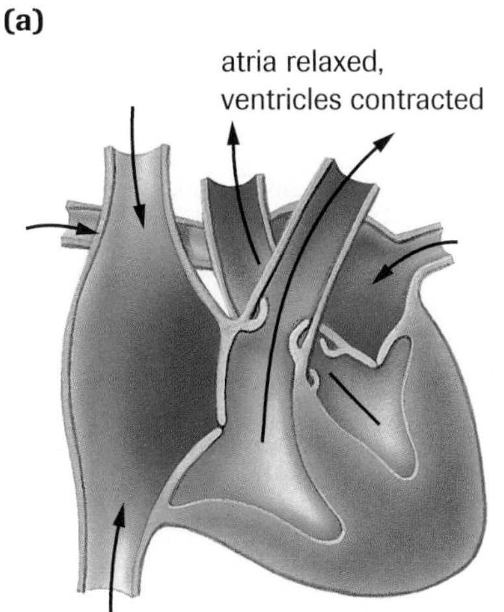

(b)

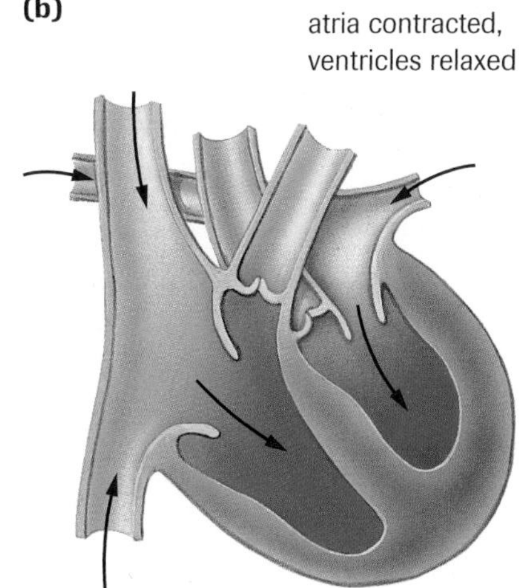

Figure 11

(a) The relaxed atria fill with blood. Ventricular contractions close the AV valves and open the semilunar valves.

(b) The relaxation of the ventricles lowers pressure and the right and left atria contract in unison, pushing blood into the right and left ventricles. The closing of the semilunar valves prevents blood from re-entering the ventricles.

Practice

7. Explain the terms *diastole* and *systole.*
8. What causes the characteristic heart sounds?
9. What is one cause of heart murmurs?

CBC radioONE

QUIRKS & QUARKS

The State of Statins

Researchers interviewed in this clip support the use of a class of drugs called statins to treat individuals with high cholesterol, to reduce the risk of heart disease. However, using drugs on otherwise healthy people, particularly before they change their eating and exercise habits, is controversial.

www.science.nelson.com 

Medications and the Heart

Many traditional homeopathic medical treatments are now being supported by science. Foxglove *(Digitalis purpurea)*, a popular garden plant in Britain, has long been used in tea as a tonic. Scientists have found that the active ingredient in the plant, digitalis, initiates strong, regular heart contractions, and it is now used to treat congestive heart failure. Nitroglycerin, an explosive, has also been used to prevent heart attacks. It works by relaxing smooth muscle and dilating blood vessels.

Medical therapy for heart failure has improved greatly with the development of beta-blockers. These drugs are especially important for people with irregular heartbeats or who display the effects of high blood pressure.

Receptor sites located on the surface of cells receive molecules, such as hormones, that affect the way cells behave. Epinephrine, a stress hormone, attaches to receptors on the heart and blood vessels, increasing heart rate and narrowing the blood vessels. Both effects lead to an increase in blood pressure. Beta-blockers tie up receptor sites that accept epinephrine.

There are two types of beta-receptors on cell surfaces, beta 1 and beta 2. Beta 1 receptors are found on the surface of the cardiac muscle. These affect the speed and strength of heart contractions and directly influence blood pressure. Beta 2 receptors are found primarily in the blood vessels and the bronchioles leading into the lungs. When the effects of the stress hormone are blocked, the heart rate slows and blood vessels relax, leading to a reduction in blood pressure.

Like most medications, beta-blockers can have side effects. Since they reduce the effects of stress hormones by slowing the heart, patients may feel tired, be less able to exercise vigorously, or experience lightheadedness or dizziness due to low blood pressure.

mini Investigation — Effects of Caffeine on Heart Rate

Materials: concave depression slide, glycerin, cover slip, *Daphnia* culture, strong coffee (not hot), medicine dropper, pencil, paper, watch

- Place a few drops of glycerin into the depression slide.
- Using a medicine dropper, place a small drop of the *Daphnia* culture onto the glycerin.
- Prepare a wet mount by adding a cover slip and observe under low magnification.
- While observing the beating heart, have your lab partner indicate a start time and a stop time 30 s later. Mark with your pencil on a piece of paper every time the heart beats.
- Record the heart rate for *Daphnia*. Conduct two more trials.
- Remove the cover slip and add a drop of coffee. Replace the cover slip and repeat the same procedure.

(a) Record the data you have collected in a data table.

(b) Calculate the mean heart rate for the control and the caffeine.

(c) Present the data you have collected using a graph.

(d) How did caffeine affect heart rate?

(e) It was noted that two different groups did not have exactly the same data. Identify variables that could affect the heart rate.

(f) What changes would you suggest to produce repeatable data?

SUMMARY The Heart

- The pulmonary circulatory system is the system of blood vessels that carries blood to and from the lungs. The systemic circulatory system is the system of blood vessels that carries blood to and from the body.
- The heart consists of two parallel pumps separated by the septum.
  - Blood enters the heart through the atria.
  - Ventricles pump the blood to the body tissues.
  - Atrioventricular valves prevent the flow of blood from the ventricles back into the atria.
  - Semilunar valves prevent blood the flow of blood from arteries back into the ventricles.
  - Coronary arteries supply the heart with oxygen and nutrients.
- The heart rate is set by the sinoatrial (SA) node. Contractions in the SA node travel to the atrioventricular (AV) node and then travel along the Purkinje fibres to the rest of the heart.
- Diastole is heart relaxation. Systole is heart contraction.
- The *lubb-dubb* sound is caused by the AV valves and the semilunar valves closing in turn as blood is pushed from the atria through the ventricles and out of the heart. If the valves do not close completely, the heart compensates by beating faster and pumping blood with more force.

+ EXTENSION

Operation: Heart Transplant

Enter the virtual NOVA operating theatre, where you will be given a scalpel and perform a heart transplant.

www.science.nelson.com

Section 10.2 Questions

1. What are the atria and the ventricles? How do they differ in structure and function?
2. In what sense is blood flow in the body one way?
3. Draw and label the major blood vessels and chambers of the heart. Trace the flow of deoxygenated and oxygenated blood through the heart.
4. Describe cardiac catheterization and explain its usefulness.
5. Explain differences in the strength of a pulse between the carotid artery (neck area) and the brachial artery (wrist area).
6. Explain changes in the pulse after exercise.
7. Describe the pathway of nerve impulses through the heart. Refer to the terms *sinoatrial node, atrioventricular node,* and *Purkinje fibres.*
8. How does the heart compensate for the improper function of the AV valves?
9. What is an electrocardiogram? Why is it useful? Explain what the different waves of an electrocardiogram indicate.
10. Draw a flow chart or diagram to show how a beta-blocker works.
11. When researching the impact of scientific knowledge or technology on society, what kinds of sources do you consult? Do you think that medical or scientific sources will give an impartial point of view? Explain.
12. Medical technologies are often patented, bringing in great profits to the owners. Using print or electronic media, find out about some of these technologies. Do you think that technology such as an artificial heart should be owned? What are the social and moral implications of such ownership?

    www.science.nelson.com

13. Predict some advantages and disadvantages of artificial hearts over donor hearts.
14. All drugs that block beta 2 receptors also block beta 1 receptors. Some drugs work selectively by blocking beta 1 receptors without affecting the beta 2 receptors. Indicate which drug, a beta 2 nonselective or beta 1 selective drug, would produce fewer side effects. Give your reasons.

10.3 Regulation of Blood Flow

Blood surges through the arteries with every beat of the heart. Elastic connective tissue and smooth muscle in the walls of the arteries stretch to accommodate the increase in fluid pressure. The arterial walls recoil much like an elastic band as the heart begins the relaxation phase characterized by lower pressure. Even the recoil forces help push blood through arterioles toward the tissues.

Cardiac Output

cardiac output the amount of blood pumped from the heart each minute

stroke volume the quantity of blood pumped with each beat of the heart

Cardiac output is defined as the amount of blood that flows from the heart per minute. Unless some dysfunction occurs, the amount of blood pumped from the right side of the heart is equal to the amount of blood pumped from the left side of the heart. Two factors affect cardiac output: stroke volume and heart rate.

Stroke volume is the quantity of blood pumped with each beat of the heart. The stronger the heart contraction, the greater the stroke volume. Approximately 70 mL of blood per beat leave each ventricle while you are resting. *Heart rate* is the number of times the heart beats per minute. The equation below shows how cardiac output is determined using stroke volume and heart rate.

$$\begin{aligned}\text{cardiac output} &= \text{stroke volume} \times \text{heart rate}\\ &= 70\ \text{mL/beat} \times 70\ \text{beats/min}\\ \text{cardiac output} &= 4900\ \text{mL/min}\end{aligned}$$

DID YOU KNOW?

What's Your Resting Heart Rate?

Due to greater stroke volume, some athletes have much slower heart rates. The tennis player Bjorn Borg once demonstrated a resting heart rate of 35 beats/min.

Individuals who have a mass of 70 kg must pump approximately 5 L of blood per minute. Smaller individuals require less blood and, therefore, have lower cardiac outputs. Naturally, cardiac output must be adjusted to meet energy needs. During exercise, heart rate increases to meet increased energy demands.

The cardiac output equation provides a basis for comparing individual fitness. Why do two people with the same body mass have different heart rates? If you assume that both people are at rest, both should require the same quantity of oxygen each minute. For example, Tom, who has a heart rate of 100 beats per minute, has a lower stroke volume. Lee, who has a heart rate of 50 beats per minute, has a higher stroke volume.

Table 1 Cardiac Output of Two People

Person	Stroke volume (mL/beat)	Heart rate (beats/min)	Cardiac output (stroke volume × heart rate)
Tom	50	100	5 L
Lee	100	50	5 L

Lee's lower heart rate indicates a higher stroke volume. Strong hearts can pump greater volumes of blood with each beat. This is why athletes often have low heart rates. Hearts that are less strong are unable to pump as much blood per beat, but compensate by increasing heart rate to meet the body's energy demands. It is important to recognize that heart rate is only one factor that determines physical fitness. You may also find that your heart rate will fluctuate throughout the day. Various kinds of food, stress, or a host of other factors can affect your heart rate.

Blood Pressure

Blood pressure is the force of the blood on the walls of the arteries. It can be measured indirectly with an instrument called a **sphygmomanometer** (**Figure 1**). A cuff with an air bladder is wrapped around the arm. A small pump is used to inflate the air bladder, thereby closing off blood flow through the brachial artery, one of the major arteries of the arm. A stethoscope is placed below the cuff and air is slowly released from the bladder until a low-pitched sound can be detected. The sound is caused by blood entering the previously closed artery.

sphygmomanometer a device used to measure blood pressure

Each time the heart contracts, the sound is heard. A gauge on the sphygmomanometer measures the pressure exerted by the blood during ventricular contraction. This pressure is called systolic blood pressure. Normal systolic blood pressure is less than 120 mmHg (**Table 2**). (Blood pressure is measured in the non-SI units of millimetres of mercury, or mmHg.) The cuff is then deflated even more, until the sound disappears. At this point, blood flows into the artery during ventricular relaxation, or filling. This pressure is called diastolic blood pressure. Normal diastolic blood pressure is less than 80 mmHg. A systolic pressure of 120 mmHg and a diastolic pressure of 80 mmHg would be reported as 120/80 (120 over 80). Reduced filling, such as that caused by an internal hemorrhage, will cause diastolic blood pressure to fall. **Figure 2** shows that fluid pressure decreases with distance from the ventricles; thus, blood pressure readings are not the same in all arteries.

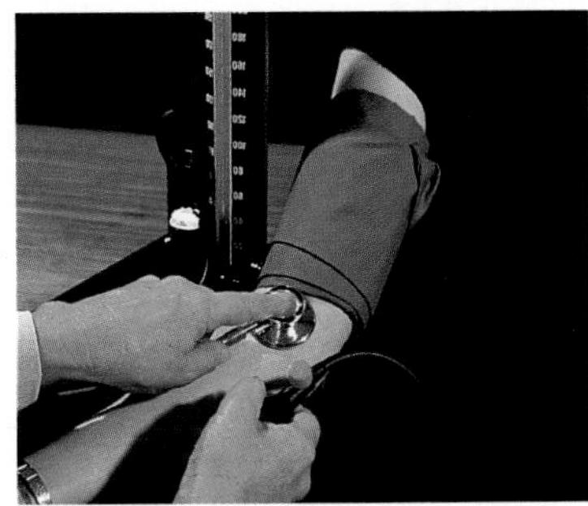

Figure 1
A sphygmomanometer

Table 2 Blood Pressure Categories (for 18 years and older)

	Blood Pressure (mmHg)	
Category	**Systolic**	**Diastolic**
normal	< 120	< 80
pre-hypertensive	120 to 139	80 to 89
hypertensive		
stage 1	140 to 159	90 to 99
stage 2	≥ 160	≥ 100

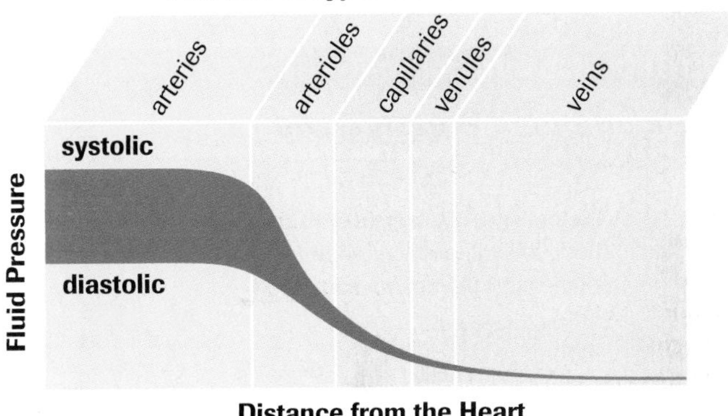

Figure 2
Fluid pressure decreases the farther blood moves from the heart.

Blood pressure depends on two factors. The first is cardiac output. Any increase in cardiac output will increase blood pressure. Another factor is arteriolar resistance. The diameter of the arteriole is regulated by smooth muscles. Constriction of the smooth muscles surrounding the arteriole closes the opening and reduces blood flow through the arteriole. With this reduced blood flow, more blood is left in the artery. The increased blood volume in the artery produces higher blood pressure. Conversely, factors that cause arteriolar dilation increase blood flow from the arterioles, thereby reducing blood pressure.

The smooth muscles in the walls of the arterioles respond to neural and hormonal controls that regulate blood pressure. The diameter of the arterioles also adjusts in response to metabolic products, such as those produced during the breakdown of glucose. When there is sufficient oxygen to break down glucose, carbon dioxide and water are produced. When there is insufficient oxygen, lactic acid is produced. Accumulation of carbon dioxide and lactic acid causes the relaxation of smooth muscles in the walls of the arterioles, dilating them. The dilated arterioles increase blood flow to local tissues, delivering more oxygen. Arteriolar dilation in response to increased metabolic

DID YOU KNOW?

Blood Pressure Units
The SI metric unit for blood pressure is the kilopascal (kPa). However, in medicine, blood pressure is still measured in millimetres of mercury (mmHg). (1 mmHg = 0.133 322 4 kPa)

Adjustment of Blood Flow

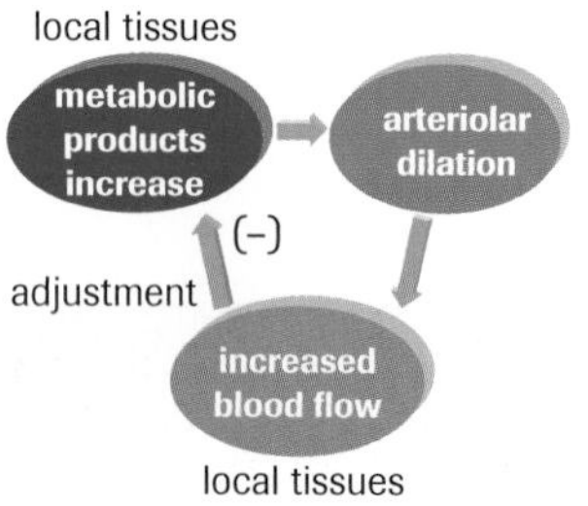

local tissues

metabolic products increase → arteriolar dilation → increased blood flow

(–) adjustment

local tissues

Figure 3
Control of arteriolar dilation

products is a good example of how the body maintains equilibrium (**Figure 3**). Activities such as exercise cause an increase in metabolic products. Because these products accumulate in the most active tissues, the increased blood flow helps provide greater nutrient supply and carries the potentially toxic materials away. Tissues that are less active produce fewer metabolic products. These arterioles remain closed until the products accumulate.

Hypertension: The Silent Killer

Hypertension (high blood pressure) is caused by increased resistance to blood flow, which results in a sustained increase in blood pressure. If blood pressure remains high, blood vessels are often weakened and may rupture. The body attempts to compensate for weakened vessels by increasing the support provided by connective tissues. Unfortunately, when the body increases the amount of connective tissue, arteries often become hard and less elastic. During systole, as blood pulses through these reinforced vessels, blood pressure increases more than usual, which in turn causes further stress and greater weakening.

Although hypertension is sometimes hereditary, diet is often a primary factor in the development of the disease. For example, in susceptible individuals, using too much salt can cause blood pressure to rise and the heart to work harder. Hypertension is often described as a silent killer because symptoms are usually not noticeable until the situation becomes very serious. A heart attack or stroke can be the first indication that something is wrong.

INVESTIGATION 10.2 ***Introduction***

Effects of Posture on Blood Pressure and Pulse

Blood pressure is affected by factors such as exercise, drugs, and even posture. In this investigation, you will explore whether changes in body position cause measurable changes in blood pressure and/or pulse.

Report Checklist

○ Purpose	● Design	● Analysis
● Problem	○ Materials	● Evaluation
● Hypothesis	○ Procedure	○ Synthesis
● Prediction	● Evidence	

To perform this investigation, turn to page 344. 

Regulation of Blood Pressure

Regulation of blood pressure is essential since low blood pressure reduces your capacity to transport blood. The problem is particularly acute for tissues in the head, where blood pressure works against the force of gravity. High blood pressure creates equally serious problems. High fluid pressure can weaken an artery and eventually result in its rupture.

Special blood pressure receptors are located in the walls of the aorta and the carotid arteries, which are major arteries found on either side of the neck. These receptors are sensitive to high pressures. When blood pressure exceeds acceptable levels, the receptors respond to the increased pressure on the wall of the artery. A nerve impulse travels to the medulla oblongata, the blood pressure regulator located in the brainstem. Sympathetic (stress) nerve impulses are decreased and parasympathetic (relaxation) nerve impulses are increased. In reponse to decreasing sympathetic nerve stimulation, arterioles dilate, increasing the outflow of blood from the artery. Stimulation of the parasympathetic nerve causes heart rate and stroke volume to decrease. The decreased cardiac output slows the movement of blood into the arteries, lowering blood pressure.

CAREER CONNECTION

Cardiology Technologist

Cardiology technologists carry out diagnostic testing and monitoring of the heart, and ensure that pacemakers are working properly. They operate equipment during electrocardiograms, exercise stress tests, and echocardiograms. Are you interested in a career as a cardiology technologist?

www.science.nelson.com 

Low blood pressure is adjusted by the sympathetic nerves. Without nerve information from the pressure receptors of the carotid artery and aorta, the sympathetic nerves will continue to be stimulated, causing cardiac output to increase and arterioles to constrict. The increased flow of blood into the artery accompanied by decreased outflow raises blood pressure to acceptable levels.

EXPLORE an issue

Pre-teens and High Blood Pressure

Issue Checklist

- ○ Issue
- ○ Design
- ● Analysis
- ● Resolution
- ● Evidence
- ● Evaluation

For many years, high blood pressure was associated primarily with men over 40 years of age. High blood pressure creates health problems due to the stress exerted on blood vessels and the heart itself. Heart disease is the number one killer of North Americans over age 40. Insufficient physical exercise, increased daily stress, and poor eating habits have made hypertension more common in women and younger adults.

Ironically, in an era when we know more about the causes and effects of high blood pressure, more people seem to be at risk of developing future health problems.

What is even more disturbing is that younger people today are likely even more susceptible to high blood pressure than their grandparents. A survey of 5000 pre-teens conducted by the Heart and Stroke Foundation indicated that most of them were aware of the benefits of physical exercise and of eating five to ten portions of fruit and vegetables each day. The vast majority also identified smoking as harmful for the heart. However, that same survey indicated that just over 50 % had engaged in some physical exercise that day, nearly 33 % had been exposed to second-hand smoke, and only 14 % had consumed four or more servings of fruit and vegetables. Virtual computer games were identified as the main competition for physical games, and fast foods were preferred to fruit and vegetables.

The rate of obesity among pre-teen boys nearly tripled between 1981 and 1996, while the obesity rate for girls more than doubled during the same time frame. The heart must work harder to pump blood through extra blood vessels in order to provide oxygen and nutrients to the new fat cells.

High blood pressure and obesity contribute to the development of type 2 diabetes. Aboriginal peoples have an increased risk of diabetes compared to the general population. Knowing the risk factors is important for everyone. Researchers have shown that type 2 diabetes, once associated with middle-aged men and women, is now found in overweight adolescents.

Statement

Health ministers across Canada know that money spent on prevention to change lifestyle behaviours is less costly than treating disease. Some people have even speculated about providing tax credits for leading a healthy lifestyle. How can a healthy lifestyle be promoted? Should people receive tax credits or pay less medical insurance? What responsibility do governments have in promoting a healthy lifestyle?

1. Form a group and research the issue.

www.science.nelson.com 

2. Discuss the issue with class members and others in preparation for a debate.
3. Write a list of points and counterpoints that your group has considered.
4. Take a stand. Decide if you agree or disagree with the statements.
5. Defend your position in the debate.

Response of the Circulatory System to Exercise

Your body's response to exercise is an excellent example of how the body maintains equilibrium. Exercise places considerable demands on the circulatory system, but this system does not act alone in monitoring the needs of tissues or in ensuring that adequate levels of oxygen and nutrients are delivered to the active cells. The nervous and hormonal systems also play important roles in adjustment.

During times of stress, the sympathetic nerves stimulate the adrenal glands. The hormone epinephrine (adrenaline) is released from the adrenal gland and travels in the blood to other organs of the body. Epinephrine stimulates the release of red blood cells from the spleen. Although the significance of the response is not yet understood, it is clear that increased numbers of red blood cells aid oxygen delivery. Epinephrine and direct stimulation from the sympathetic nerves increase heart rate and breathing rate. The increased heart rate provides for faster oxygen transport, while the increased breathing rate ensures that the blood contains higher levels of oxygen. Both systems work together to improve oxygen delivery to active tissues. A secondary but important function is the increased efficiency of waste removal from the active tissues.

Blood cannot flow to all capillaries of the body simultaneously. The effect of dilating all arterioles at one time would be disastrous—blood pressure would plunge. Only the most active tissues receive priority in times of stress. As a result, epinephrine causes vasodilation of the arterioles leading to the heart, brain, and muscles, preparing the organism for the flight-or-fight reaction. At the same time, the blood vessels leading to the kidney, stomach, and intestines constrict, depriving these areas of blood until the stress situation has been overcome.

Practice

1. What is hypertension?
2. How does exercise affect your heart rate? Provide an explanation for any change.
3. How does exercise affect your blood pressure? Provide an explanation for any change.
4. How is it possible that two different people have different pulses after doing exactly the same exercise?

INVESTIGATION 10.3 *Introduction*

Effects of Exercise on Blood Pressure and Pulse

How do you predict exercise will affect blood pressure and pulse? In this investigation, you will design and carry out a controlled experiment to test your prediction.

To perform this investigation, turn to page 344. 

Report Checklist

- ○ Purpose
- ● Problem
- ● Hypothesis
- ● Prediction
- ● Design
- ● Materials
- ● Procedure
- ● Evidence
- ● Analysis
- ● Evaluation
- ○ Synthesis

Regulating Body Temperature

thermoregulation maintenance of body temperature within a range that enables cells to function efficiently

Thermoregulation is the maintenance of body temperature within a range that enables cells to function efficiently. Different species of animals are adapted to different temperature ranges, and each animal has an optimal temperature range. To understand the mechanisms of temperature regulation, we first need to consider the exchange of heat between the body and the environment.

Humans are able to maintain a constant body temperature regardless of their surroundings. The body adjusts to decreases in environmental temperatures by increasing the rate of cellular respiration to generate heat. In humans, normal body temperature is usually 37 °C; however, there is variation within any population. Studies indicate that body temperatures vary slightly during the day. Temperature in most individuals falls slightly during the night. It should also be noted that core temperatures and peripheral temperatures of the body tend to vary from each other. Core temperatures, found in the chest cavity, the abdominal cavity, and the central nervous system, remain relatively constant and are usually higher than 37 °C. The peripheral temperatures can be as much as 4 °C lower on very cold days.

DID YOU KNOW ?

Does Alcohol Warm You Up?

Many people believe that a drink of alcohol will warm them up on a cold day. Alcohol causes dilation of the arterioles leading to the skin capillaries, causing the sensation of warmth. However, the sensation is misleading. The dilation of these arterioles increases blood flow to the skin, which increases heat loss and speeds cooling.

Response to Temperature Stress

How does the body protect itself against excessive heat caused by exercise or high environmental temperatures? **Figure 4** shows what it does. When sensors in the brain detect a rise in body temperature, a nerve impulse is coordinated within the **hypothalamus**, and a signal is sent to the sweat glands to initiate sweating. The evaporation of perspiration from the skin causes cooling. At the same time, a nerve message is sent to the blood vessels in the skin, causing them to dilate. This allows more blood flow to the skin. Since the skin has been cooled by the evaporation of sweat, the blood loses heat to the skin. When blood from the skin returns to the core of the body, it cools the internal organs. Along with water, valuable salts are also carried to the skin's surface and lost with perspiration.

hypothalamus region of a vertebrate's brain responsible for coordinating many nerve and hormone functions

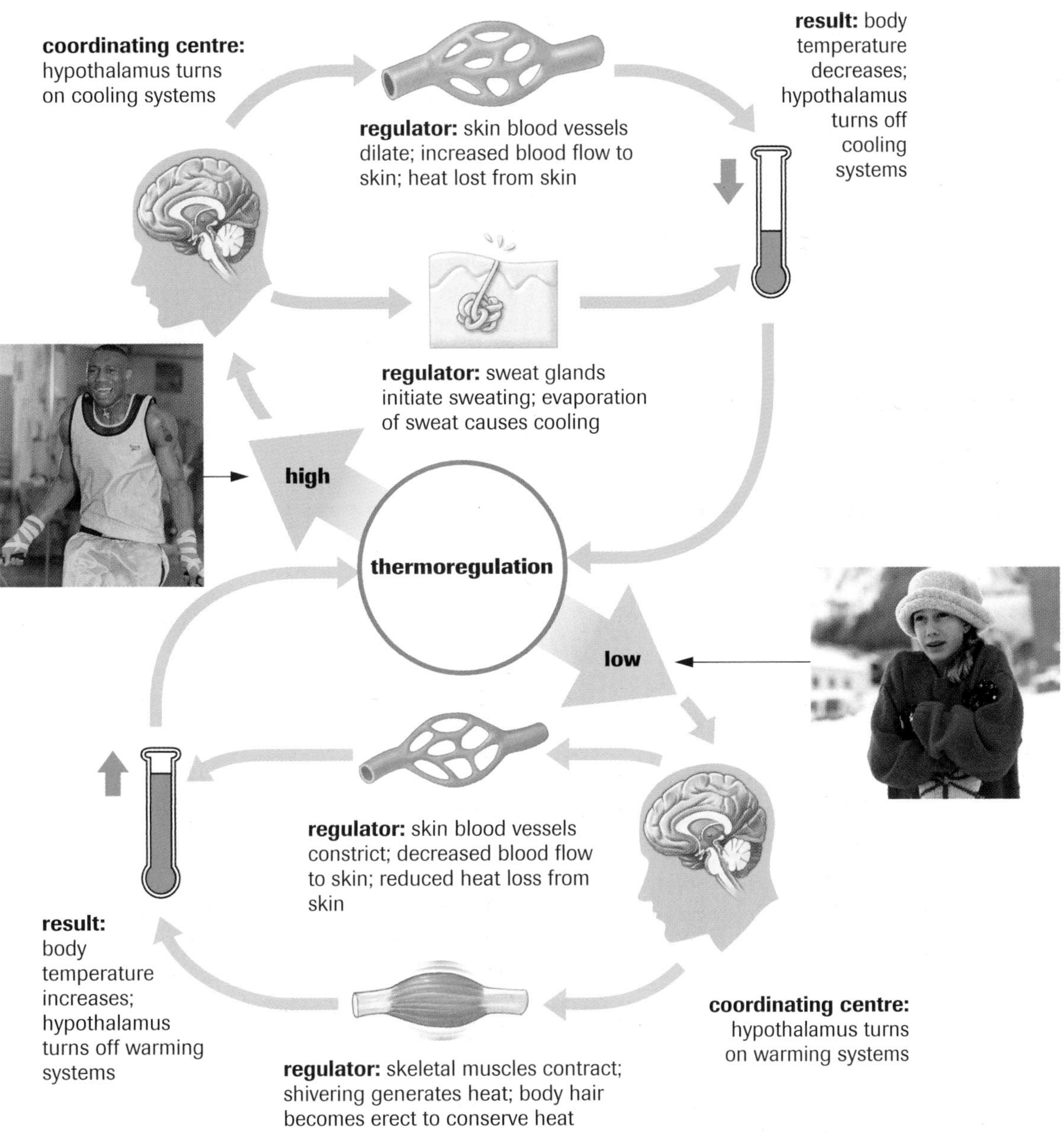
coordinating centre: hypothalamus turns on cooling systems
regulator: skin blood vessels dilate; increased blood flow to skin; heat lost from skin
result: body temperature decreases; hypothalamus turns off cooling systems
regulator: sweat glands initiate sweating; evaporation of sweat causes cooling
high
thermoregulation
low
regulator: skin blood vessels constrict; decreased blood flow to skin; reduced heat loss from skin
result: body temperature increases; hypothalamus turns off warming systems
coordinating centre: hypothalamus turns on warming systems
regulator: skeletal muscles contract; shivering generates heat; body hair becomes erect to conserve heat

Figure 4
The evaporation of sweat and dilation of blood vessels provide a negative feedback response that cools the body. The constriction of blood vessels, shivering, and erection of the body hairs provide a negative feedback response that helps conserve heat.

In many ways, your response to cold mirrors your response to heat (**Figure 4**, previous page). When external temperatures drop, thermoreceptors in the skin send a message to the hypothalamus. Acting as a coordinating centre, the hypothalamus sends messages to the organs and tissues to increase body temperature. Nerves going to the arterioles of the skin cause smooth muscles to contract and the arterioles to constrict, limiting blood flow. This reduces heat loss from the skin and retains heat in the core of the body.

Nerve messages are also carried to the smooth muscle that surrounds the hair follicles in your skin, causing the hair to stand on end. The small bump made by the contraction of the muscle attached to the hair is often called a "goosebump." The erect hair traps warm, still air next to the surface of your skin and helps reduce heat loss. This response is particularly effective in mammals with a thick coat of body hair.

In addition, the hypothalamus also sends nerve messages that initiate shivering. The shivering response is a rhythmic contraction of skeletal muscle. Cycles of rapid muscle contractions of between 10 and 20 times per minute generate heat production by increasing metabolism.

Prolonged exposure to cold can create a hormonal response that also elevates metabolism. This type of heat production is most often associated with special adipose tissue called brown fat. Although its role in humans remains controversial, brown fat is especially capable of converting chemical energy into heat. Brown fat is important in newborns because they lack the ability to shiver. Babies have a small amount of brown fat in their neck and armpits and near their kidneys that insulates and generates heat.

Hypothermia is a condition in which the body's core temperature falls below the normal range. A drop in temperature of only a few degrees can lead to a coma and possibly death. However, some people, mainly small children, have survived sustained exposure to cold temperatures. This is often explained by the mammalian diving reflex. When a mammal is submerged in cold water, the heart rate slows and blood is diverted to the brain and other vital organs to conserve heat.

DID YOU KNOW?

Self-Healing Behaviour

It has been discovered that sick lizards can intentionally give themselves a fever by resting in hot, sunny places. This behaviour raises their temperature to a slightly higher level, and the resulting fever helps fight infection.

SUMMARY Regulation of Blood Flow

- Cardiac output is the amount of blood the heart can pump each minute.
- Blood pressure is the force of blood on the walls of the arteries. It is measured as systolic and diastolic blood pressure in millimetres of mercury (mmHg).
- Blood pressure is higher in vessels closer to the heart.
- Increased cardiac output increases blood pressure. If arteries are constricted, blood flow is slower and blood pressure is higher.

Table 3 Summary of Stimulus–Response in Thermoregulation

Stimulus	Physiological response	Result
decreased environmental temperature	• constriction of blood vessels in skin • body hairs become erect • shivering	• heat is conserved • more heat is generated by increased metabolism
increased environmental temperature	• dilation of blood vessels of skin • sweating	• heat is dissipated

Section 10.3 Questions

1. How does stroke volume affect cardiac output?
2. How do metabolic products affect blood flow through arterioles? What causes the accumulation of metabolic products and where is accumulation most likely to occur?
3. Referring to the sympathetic and parasympathetic nerves, outline the adjustments to high blood pressure that help maintain equilibrium.
4. Would you expect blood pressure readings in all the major arteries to be the same? Explain your answer.
5. Why is systolic pressure lower when you are lying down than when you are standing up?
6. Why might diastolic blood pressure decrease as heart rate increases?
7. How do "goosebumps" help protect against rapid cooling?
8. What behavioural adjustments affect thermoregulation?
9. Explain why oral and rectal thermometers can give different readings.
10. Heat exhaustion caused by a person's exposure to heat can result in weakness or collapse. It usually involves a decrease in blood pressure. Explain why the thermoregulatory adjustment to heat can cause a drop in blood pressure.
11. The maximum suggested temperature of the water in a hot tub is about 38 °C. A higher temperature can seriously increase the risk of heat stroke. Explain why people will collapse in a hot tub set at 45 °C, but can survive temperatures of over 120 °C in heated rooms.
12. In **Figure 5 (a)**, beginning at the box labelled "increase in body temperature," replace the letters with the following feedback mechanisms for temperature control by the body: sweating, shivering, adjustment, evaporation. Do the same in **Figure 5 (b)**, beginning at the box labelled "decrease in body temperature."

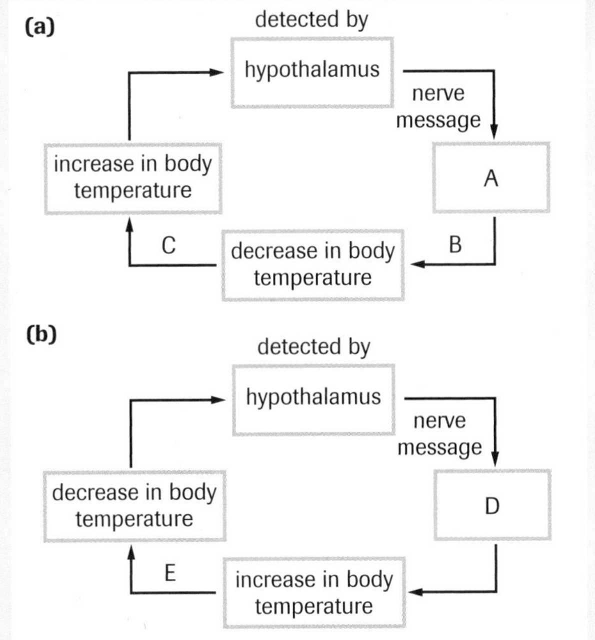

Figure 5

13. Arteriosclerosis is a group of disorders that can cause high blood pressure. How could lifestyle choices (e.g., related to nutrition or exercise) be changed to lessen a person's likelihood of getting the disorder?
14. Use the Internet or library to research how rapid cooling of the organs and tissues is used for surgery.

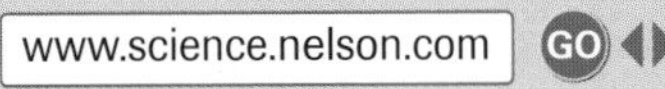

15. Drugs such as ecstasy interfere with the feedback mechanism that helps maintain a constant body temperature. Explain why these drugs are dangerous.

10.4 Capillary Fluid Exchange

extracellular fluid (ECF) fluid that occupies the spaces between cells and tissues; includes plasma and interstitial fluid

filtration the selective movement of materials through capillary walls by a pressure gradient

It is estimated that nearly every tissue of the body is within 0.1 mm of a capillary. Capillaries provide cells with oxygen, glucose, and amino acids and are associated with fluid exchange between the blood and surrounding **extracellular fluid (ECF)**. Most fluids simply diffuse through capillaries, whose cell membranes are also permeable to oxygen and carbon dioxide. Water and certain ions are thought to pass through spaces between the cells of the capillary while larger molecules and a very small number of proteins are believed to be exchanged by endocytosis or exocytosis. This section will focus on the movement of water molecules.

Two forces regulate the movement of water between the blood and ECF: fluid pressure and osmotic pressure. The force that blood exerts on the wall of a capillary is about 35 mmHg at the arteriole end of the capillary and approximately 15 mmHg at the venous end. The reservoir of blood in the arteries creates pressure on the inner wall of the capillary. Much lower pressure is found in the ECF. Although fluid bathes the cells, no force drives the extracellular fluid. Water moves from an area of higher pressure, the capillary, into an area of lower pressure, the ECF (**Figure 1**). The outward flow of water and small mineral ions is known as **filtration**. Because capillaries are selectively permeable, large materials such as proteins, red blood cells, and white blood cells remain in the capillary.

The movement of fluid out of the capillary must be balanced with a force that moves fluid into the capillary. The fact that large proteins are found in the blood but not in the ECF may provide a hint as to the nature of the second force. Osmotic pressure draws water back into the capillary. The large protein molecules of the blood and dissolved minerals are primarily responsible for the movement of fluid into capillaries. The movement of fluid into capillaries is called absorption. Osmotic pressure in the capillaries is usually about 25 mmHg, but it is important to note that the concentration of solutes can change with fluid intake or excess fluid loss caused by perspiration, vomiting, or diarrhea.

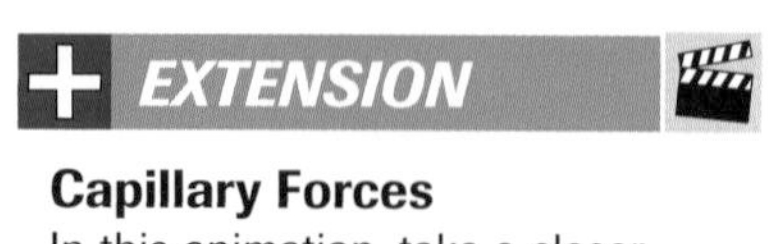

Capillary Forces

In this animation, take a closer look at how fluid is moved in and out of capillaries by various forces.

www.science.nelson.com 

arteriolar end–
water moves out

venous end–
water moves in

arteriole

venule

fluid pressure
35 mmHg

fluid pressure
15 mmHg

osmotic pressure 25 mmHg

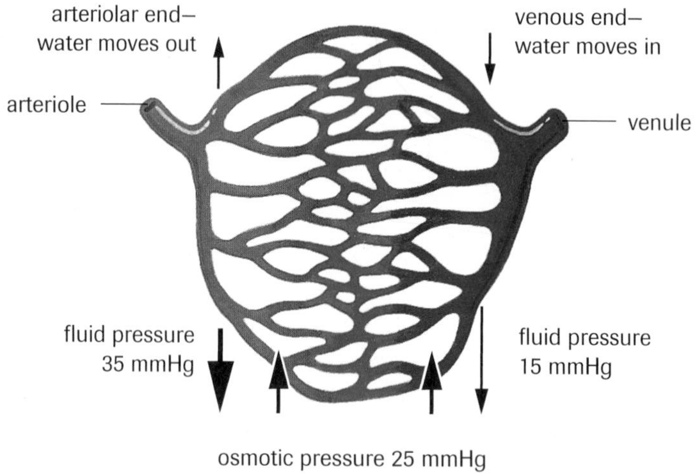

Arteriolar end	
osmotic pressure	25 mmHg
fluid pressure	35 mmHg
absorption	−10 mmHg

Venous end	
osmotic pressure	25 mmHg
fluid pressure	15 mmHg
absorption	+10 mmHg

Figure 1
Fluid movement into and out of the capillaries

Application of the capillary exchange model provides a foundation for understanding adjustments that maintain equilibrium (**Figure 2**). The balance between osmotic pressure and fluid pressure is upset during a hemorrhage (excessive bleeding). The decrease in blood volume resulting from the hemorrhage lowers blood pressure. Although proteins are lost with the hemorrhage, so are fluids. Fewer proteins are present, but the concentration has not been changed. The force that drives fluid from the capillaries diminishes, but the osmotic pressure, which draws water into the capillaries, is not altered. The force drawing water from the tissues and ECF is greater than the force pushing water from the capillary. The net movement of water into the capillaries maintains equilibrium. As water moves into the capillaries, fluid volume is restored.

EXTENSION

Nutrient and Waste Exchange

Fluid movement into and out of the capillaries greatly improves the efficiency of nutrient and waste exchange between the blood and the tissues. Listen to this audio clip for a better understanding of this process.

www.science.nelson.com GO

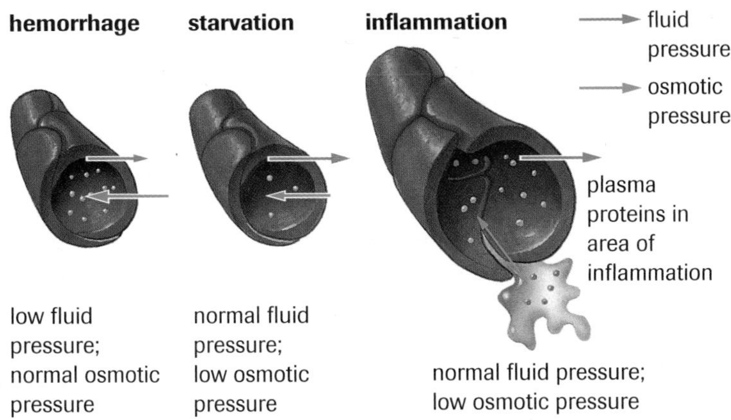

Figure 2
The balance between osmotic pressure and fluid pressure is upset during a hemorrhage, starvation, or inflammation.

Individuals who are suffering from starvation often display tissue swelling, or edema. Plasma proteins are often mobilized as one of the last sources of energy. The decrease in concentration of plasma proteins has a dramatic effect on osmotic pressure, which draws fluids from the tissues and ECF into the capillaries. The decreased number of proteins lowers osmotic pressure, thereby decreasing absorption. More water enters the tissue spaces than is pulled back into the capillaries, causing swelling.

Practice

1. Is fluid pressure greater in the arterioles or in the venules? Give reasons.
2. Is fluid pressure inside the capillary greater or less than the pressure in the ECF? How does this affect the movement of water?
3. What process allows water to flow out of the capillary but keeps proteins, red blood cells, and white blood cells inside the capillary?

The Lymphatic System

Normally, a small amount of protein leaks from capillaries to tissue spaces. Despite the fact that the leak is very slow, the accumulation of proteins in the ECF would create a major problem: osmotic pressure would decrease and tissues would swell.

The proteins are drained from the ECF and returned to the circulatory system by way of another network of vessels: the lymphatic system (**Figure 3**, next page). **Lymph**, a fluid similar to blood plasma, is transported in open-ended lymph vessels that are similar to veins. This low-pressure return system operates by slow muscle contractions against the vessels, which are supplied with flaplike valves that prevent the backflow of fluids. Eventually, lymph is returned to the venous system via the right and left subclavian veins.

lymph the fluid found in lymph vessels that contains some proteins that have leaked through capillary walls

lymph node a mass of tissue that stores lymphocytes and removes bacteria and foreign particles from the lymph

lymphocyte a white blood cell that produces antibodies

Enlargements called **lymph nodes** are located at intervals along the lymph vessel (**Figure 3**). These house white blood cells that, by the process of phagocytosis, filter out any bacteria that might be present. The lymph nodes also filter damaged cells and debris from the lymph and store **lymphocytes**. The lymph nodes in your neck sometimes swell when you have a sore throat.

Lymphoid Organs

Red bone marrow (**Figure 3**) is where all types of blood cells are produced. Stem cells, which are contained in the marrow, divide at incredible rates and differentiate into different types of white blood cells to meet the needs of the body. These specialized blood cells enter the circulatory system from a variety of sinuses. In children, red bone marrow is found in most bones; by adulthood, however, the cranium, sternum (breastbone), ribs, spinal column, and the long bones of the arms and legs have become the primary locations for blood cell production.

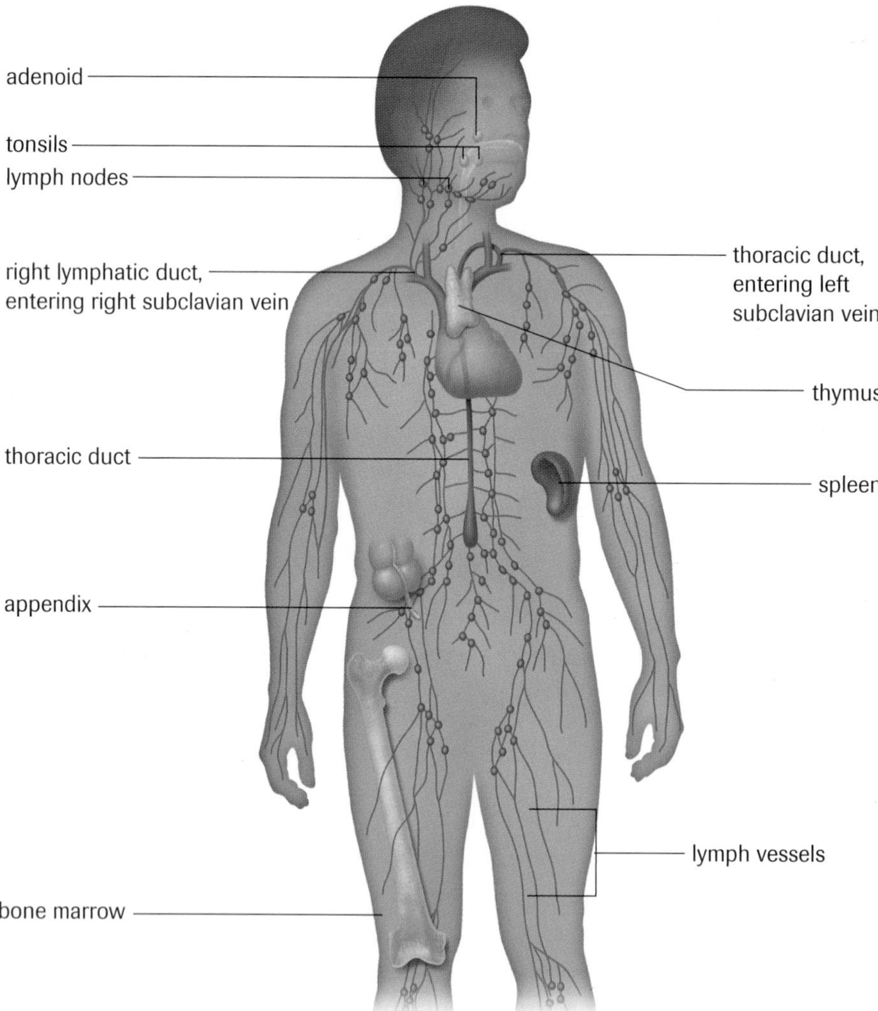

Figure 3

The lymphatic system. Debris is filtered out from the lymph, and the lymph is returned to the circulatory system.

CAREER CONNECTION

Registered Nurse

Registered nurses perform many duties, including administering medications, assisting surgeons, supervising nursing programs, treating illness and injury, and assessing/monitoring patient symptoms and reactions. Find out more about this exciting and challenging career.

www.science.nelson.com

The **spleen** is one of the body's largest lymphoid organs (**Figure 3**, previous page). Located in the upper left side of the abdominal cavity, just below the diaphragm, the spleen is richly supplied with blood sinuses. The sinuses allow the spleen to hold approximately 150 mL of blood, making it an excellent blood reservoir. The spleen releases red blood cells in response to low blood pressure or when blood oxygen levels drop dramatically.

spleen a lymphoid organ that acts as a reservoir for blood and a filtering site for lymph

The **thymus gland** is one of the few glands that tends to get smaller with age. Located in front of the trachea, just above the heart, the thymus gland is where T lymphocytes, or T cells, mature (**Figure 3**). The T cells that are released from the thymus gland have been selected to ensure that they will not initiate an immune response against the body's own proteins.

thymus gland a lymphoid organ in which T lymphocytes mature

SUMMARY *Capillary Fluid Exchange*

- Capillaries are associated with fluid exchange between blood and the extracellular fluid (ECF).
- The movement of water between blood and the ECF is regulated by fluid pressure and by osmotic pressure.
  - Water moves from an area of high fluid pressure, the capillary, to an area of low fluid pressure, the ECF.
  - Proteins and dissolved minerals in the blood cause fluid from the ECF to move into the blood by osmosis.
- Proteins in the ECF are returned to the circulatory system by the lymphatic system.
- Lymph nodes house white blood cells that filter bacteria.
- Red bone marrow is where all types of blood cells are produced.
- The spleen stores and purifies blood. The spleen releases red blood cells in response to low blood pressure or low oxygen levels in blood.

Section 10.4 Questions

1. What two factors regulate the exchange of fluid between capillaries and ECF?
2. Use the capillary exchange model to explain how the body maintains equilibrium following a hemorrhage.
3. Why does a low concentration of plasma protein cause edema?
4. What are lymph vessels and how are they related to the circulatory system?
5. What is lymph? How is lymph transported in the body? Where does lymph eventually go?
6. Why are lymphocytes important to the immune system?
7. What is the importance of the spleen?

INVESTIGATION 10.1

Fetal Pig Dissection

Report Checklist

- ● Purpose
- ● Problem
- ● Hypothesis
- ● Prediction
- ● Design
- ○ Materials
- ○ Procedure
- ● Evidence
- ● Analysis
- ● Evaluation
- ○ Synthesis

Like humans, the pig is a placental mammal, meaning that the fetus receives nourishment from the mother through the umbilical cord. Because the anatomy of the fetal pig resembles that of other placentals, this laboratory serves two important functions. It provides an overview of vertebrate anatomy and provides the framework for understanding functioning body systems.

Read and follow the procedure carefully. Accompanying diagrams are included for reference only. Use the appropriate dissecting instruments. This activity has been designed to minimize the use of a scalpel.

Materials

safety goggles	string	dissecting pins
lab apron	scalpel	scissors
dissecting gloves	hand lens	ruler
preserved fetal pig	dissecting tray	forceps and probe

Wear safety goggles and an apron at all times.

Wear plastic gloves when handling the preserved specimen and when performing a dissection to prevent any chemicals from coming in contact with your skin.

Wash all splashes of preservative from your skin and clothing immediately. If you get any chemical in your eyes, rinse for at least 15 min.

Work in a well-ventilated area. To reduce your exposure to any fumes from the preservative, make sure to avoid placing your face directly over the dissecting tray.

When you have finished the activity, clean your work area, wash your hands thoroughly, and dispose of all specimens, chemicals, and materials as instructed by your teacher.

Procedure

Part I: External Anatomy

1. Place your pig in a dissecting tray. Use **Figure 1** to help you identify the four regions of the pig's body: the head, the neck, the trunk, and the tail.
2. Place the pig on its back (dorsal surface) and observe the umbilical cord.

Part II: Abdominal Cavity

During the dissection, you will be directed to examine specific organs as they become visible. Remove only those organs indicated by the dissection procedure. Proceed cautiously to prevent damaging underlying structures.

3. With the pig still on its dorsal surface, attach one piece of string to one of the pig's hind legs, pull it under the dissecting pan, and tie it to the other hind leg. Repeat the procedure for the fore legs.
4. Using scissors, make the incision indicated as 1 in **Figure 2**. Start by cutting around the umbilical cord, and then cut straight toward the anterior (head) of the pig.

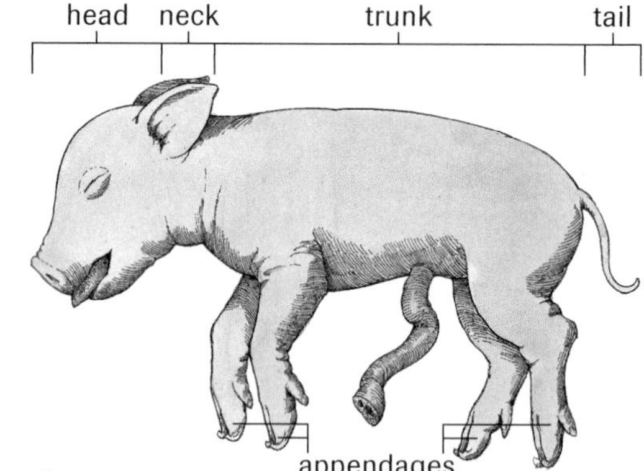

Figure 1
Regions of the body

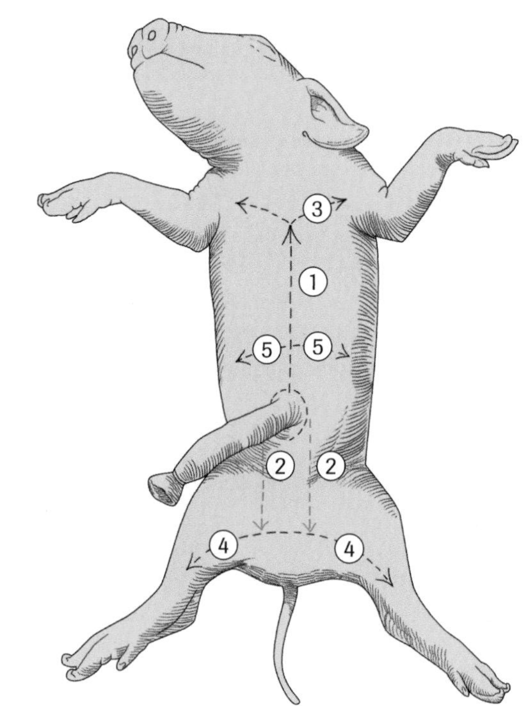

Figure 2
Ventral view of a fetal pig

5. Make incision 2 toward the posterior (tail) of the pig. Make incision 3 near the neck, and then incision 4. Make lateral incision 5; this incision runs parallel to the diaphragm, which separates the thoracic (chest) cavity from the abdominal cavity.
6. Pull apart the flaps along incision 5, exposing the abdominal cavity (**Figure 3**). Use the probe to open the connective tissue (peritoneum) that holds the internal organs to the lining of the body cavity. Now pull apart the flaps of skin covering incision 4 to expose the posterior portion of the abdominal cavity. Use pins to hold back the flaps of skin.
7. Locate the liver near the anterior of the abdominal cavity. Record the number of lobes in the liver.
8. Using a probe, lift the lobes and locate the saclike gallbladder. Describe the location of the gallbladder.
9. Follow the thin duct from the gallbladder to the coiled small intestine. Bile salts, produced in the liver, are stored in the gallbladder. The bile duct conducts the fat-emulsifying bile salt to the small intestine.
10. Locate the J-shaped stomach beneath the liver. Using forceps and a probe, lift the stomach and locate the esophagus attached near its anterior end. Locate the small intestine at the posterior junction of the stomach. The coiled small intestine is held in place by mesentery (a thin, somewhat transparent, connective tissue). Note the blood vessels that transport digested nutrients from the intestine to the liver.
11. Using a probe and forceps, lift the junction between the stomach and small intestine, removing supporting tissue. Uncoil the junction and locate the creamy-white pancreas. The pancreas produces a number of digestive enzymes and a hormone called insulin, which helps regulate blood sugar. Describe the appearance of the pancreas.
12. Locate the spleen, the elongated organ found around the outer curvature of the stomach. The spleen stores red and white blood cells. The spleen also removes damaged red blood cells from the circulatory system.
13. Using a scalpel, remove the stomach from the pig by making transverse (crosswise) cuts near the junction of the stomach and the esophagus, and near the junction of the stomach and small intestine. Make a cut along the midline of the stomach, and open the cavity. Rinse as instructed by your teacher. View the stomach under a hand lens. Describe the appearance of the inner lining of the stomach.

Part III: Thoracic Cavity

14. Carefully fold back the flaps of skin that cover the thoracic cavity. You may use dissecting pins to attach the ribs to the dissecting tray. List the organs found in the thoracic cavity (**Figure 4**, next page).
15. Locate the heart. The coronary vessels carry blood to and from the heart itself (**Figure 5 (a)**, next page). Using forceps and a probe, remove the pericardium (a thin connective tissue covering the heart) from the outer surface of the heart.

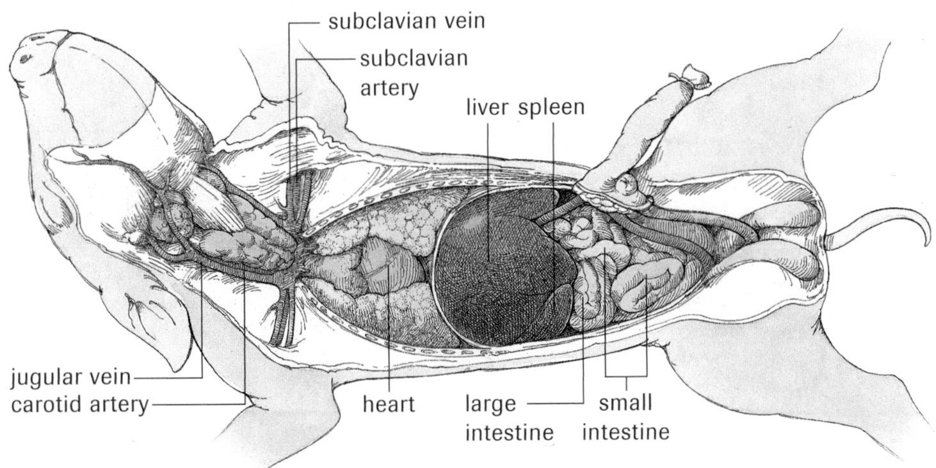

Figure 3
Abdominal cavity and thoracic cavity of the fetal pig. Organs of the digestive system and circulatory system are highlighted in the diagram.

Figure 4
Thoracic cavity and urogenital system

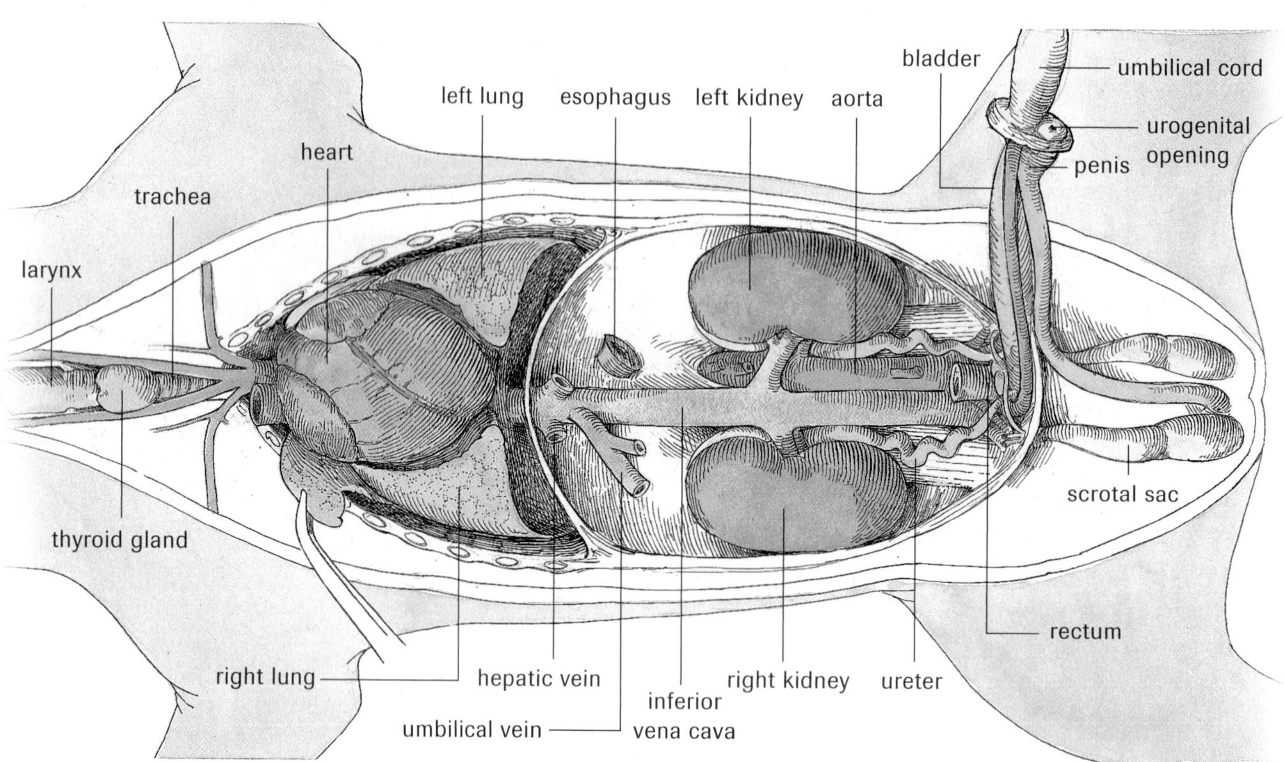

16. Blood from the head and upper body enters the right side of the heart through the superior vena cava. The large blood vessel that carries blood from the lower parts of the body to the right side of the heart is called the inferior vena cava (**Figure 5 (b)**). (The right side refers to the pig's right side.) Both the superior and inferior venae cavae are considered to be veins because they bring blood to the heart.

Figure 5
(a) Ventral view of the heart
(b) Dorsal view of the heart

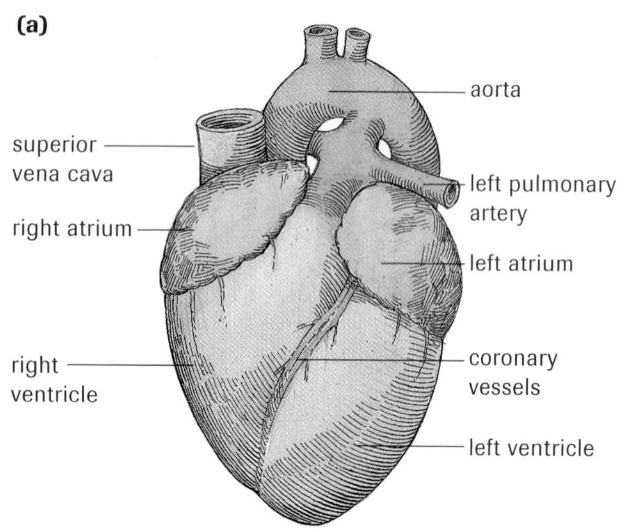

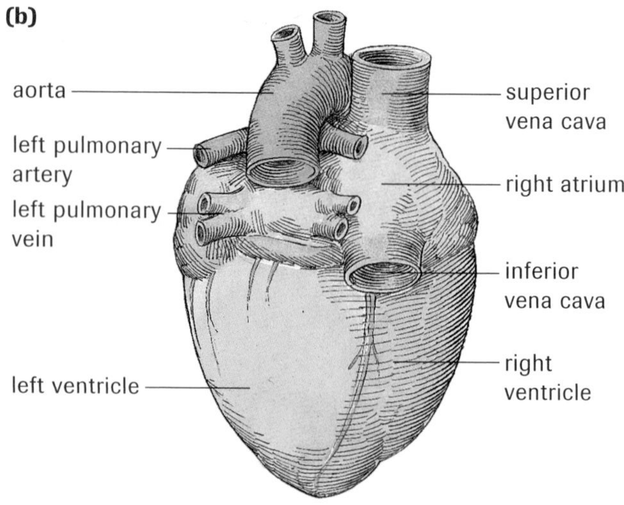

17. Trace blood flow through the heart. Blood entering the right side of the heart collects in the right atrium. Blood from the right atrium is pumped into the right ventricle. Upon contraction of the right ventricle, blood flows to the lungs by way of the pulmonary artery. Arteries carry blood away from the heart. Blood, rich in oxygen, returns from the lungs by way of the pulmonary veins and enters the left atrium. Blood is pumped from the left atrium to the left ventricle and out the aorta.
18. Make a diagonal incision across the heart and expose the heart chambers. Compare the thickness of the wall of a ventricle to that of an atrium.
19. Locate the spongy lungs on either side of the heart and find the trachea leading into the lungs (**Figure 6**).
20. Place your index finger on the trachea and push downward. Describe what happens.

Analysis and Evaluation

(a) What is the function of the umbilical cord?

(b) State the function of the following organs: stomach, liver, small intestine, gallbladder, pancreas, large intestine, and spleen.

(c) What is the function of the mesentery?

(d) Why does the left ventricle contain more muscle than the right ventricle?

(e) Why do the lungs feel spongy?

(f) What function do the cartilaginous rings of the trachea serve?

(g) Make labelled diagrams of the following:
- digestive system
- heart and the blood vessels associated with it
- respiratory system

(h) Write a report in which you point out the similarities and differences between the anatomy of a pig and a human.

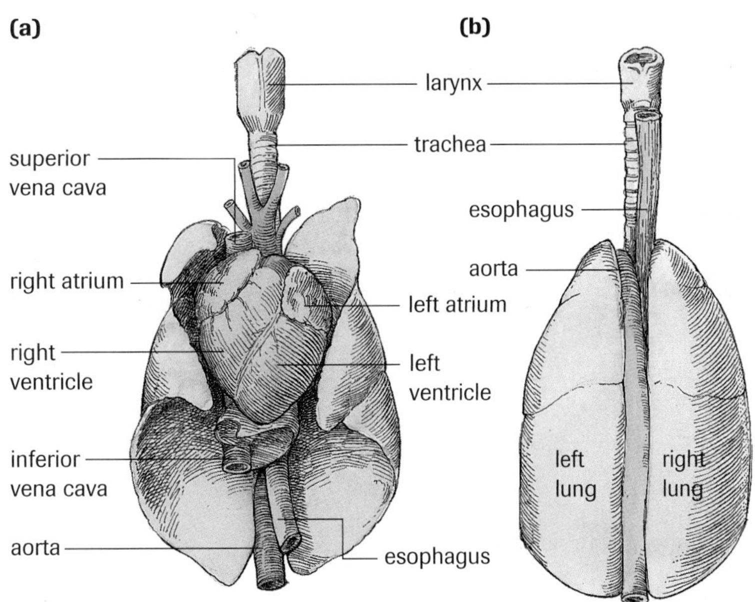

Figure 6
(a) Ventral view of heart and lungs
(b) Dorsal view of lungs

INVESTIGATION 10.2

Effects of Posture on Blood Pressure and Pulse

Blood pressure is affected by factors such as exercise, drugs, and even posture.

Purpose
To determine the effect of posture on blood pressure and pulse

Materials
sphygmomanometer watch with second hand

Procedure
1. Ask your partner to sit quietly for 1 min.
2. Expose your partner's arm and place the cuff of the sphygmomanometer just above the elbow.
3. Close the valve on the rubber bulb. Inflate the cuff by squeezing the rubber bulb until a pressure of 180 mmHg registers.
4. Release the pressure by opening the valve on the sphygmomanometer and watch the readout. Record the systolic and diastolic blood pressures.

Report Checklist

- ○ Purpose
- ● Problem
- ● Hypothesis
- ● Prediction
- ● Design
- ○ Materials
- ○ Procedure
- ● Evidence
- ● Analysis
- ● Evaluation
- ○ Synthesis

Do not leave the pressure on for longer than 1 min. If you are unsuccessful, release the pressure and try again on the opposite arm.

5. Completely deflate the cuff. If you are not using an electronic sphygmomanometer that provides the pulse, take and record your partner's pulse. Place your index and middle fingers on the inside arm near the wrist. Count the number of pulses in 1 min.
6. Repeat Steps 2 to 5 while your partner is in a standing position and then in a lying position.

Analysis
(a) Which varied more with the change in posture: systolic blood pressure or diastolic blood pressure? Explain.

(b) What factors other than posture might have contributed to the change in blood pressure?

INVESTIGATION 10.3

Effects of Exercise on Blood Pressure and Pulse

In this investigation, you will design and perform a controlled experiment to test the effects of exercise on blood pressure and pulse. Once your teacher has approved your design, carry out your procedure and record the evidence. You will then analyze the evidence to state how exercise affected blood pressure and pulse. In your lab report, include answers to the Evaluation questions.

Do not perform this activity if you are not allowed to participate in physical education classes.

Purpose
To determine the effects of exercise on blood pressure and pulse

Report Checklist

- ○ Purpose
- ● Problem
- ● Hypothesis
- ● Prediction
- ● Design
- ● Materials
- ● Procedure
- ● Evidence
- ● Analysis
- ● Evaluation
- ○ Synthesis

Design
Your design must include:

- descriptions of the manipulated, responding, and controlled variables
- a step-by-step procedure
- a list of safety precautions
- an appropriate method to record the evidence

Evaluation
(a) Describe any problems or difficulties in carrying out the procedure.

(b) How could you improve your current design?

Chapter 10 SUMMARY

Outcomes

Knowledge

- identify the principal structures of the heart and associated blood vessels, i.e., atria, ventricles, septa, valves, aorta, vena cavae, pulmonary arteries and veins, and sinoatrial node, atrioventricular node, Purkinje fibres (10.2)
- describe the action of the heart, blood pressure, and the general circulation of the blood through coronary, pulmonary, and systemic pathways (10.2)
- describe the structure and function of blood vessels, i.e., arteries, veins, and capillaries (10.1)
- explain the role of the circulatory system at the capillary level in aiding the digestive, excretory, respiratory, and motor systems' exchange of energy and matter with the environment (10.3)
- explain the role of blood in regulating body temperature (10.3)
- explain how the motor system supports body functions, i.e., circulatory (10.1)
- describe and explain, in general terms, the function of the lymphatic system (10.4)

STS

- explain how Canadian society supports scientific research and technological development (10.2)
- explain that decisions regarding the application of scientific and technological developments involve a variety of perspectives, including social, cultural, environmental, ethical, and economic considerations (10.2)

Skills

- ask questions and plan investigations (10.3)
- conduct investigations and gather and record data and information by: measuring blood pressure (10.3) and observing blood flow in capillaries in a living organism or through demonstration in a virtual lab (10.1); selecting and integrating information to observe the principal features of a mammalian circulatory system and the direction of blood flow, and identifying structures from drawings (10.2) and; observing, through dissection or computer simulations, the respiratory and digestive systems of a representative mammal and identifying the major structural components (10.2)
- work as members of a team and apply the skills and conventions of science (all)

Key Terms

10.1

artery
pulse
autonomic nervous system
vasoconstriction
vasodilation
atherosclerosis
arteriosclerosis
aneurysm
vein

10.2

septum
pulmonary circulatory system
systemic circulatory system
atrium
ventricle
atrioventricular (AV) valve
semilunar valves
aorta
coronary artery
myogenic muscle
sinoatrial (SA) node
atrioventricular (AV) node
Purkinje fibre
sympathetic nervous system
parasympathetic nervous system
diastole
systole

10.3

cardiac output
stroke volume
sphygmomanometer
thermoregulation
hypothalamus

10.4

extracellular fluid (ECF)
filtration
lymph
lymph node
lymphocyte
spleen
thymus gland

MAKE a summary

1. Create a concept map that shows how the circulatory system maintains an internal equilibrium. Label the concept map with as many of the key terms as possible.
2. Revisit your answers to the Starting Points questions at the start of the chapter. Would you answer the questions differently now? Why?

Go To

The following components are available on the Nelson Web site. Follow the links for *Nelson Biology Alberta 20–30*.

- an interactive Self Quiz for Chapter 10
- additional Diploma Exam-style Review Questions
- Illustrated Glossary
- additional IB-related material

There is more information on the Web site wherever you see the Go icon in the chapter.

Many of these questions are in the style of the Diploma Exam. You will find guidance for writing Diploma Exams in Appendix A5. Science Directing Words used in Diploma Exams are in bold type. Exam study tips and test-taking suggestions are on the Nelson Web site.

www.science.nelson.com 

DO NOT WRITE IN THIS TEXTBOOK.

Part 1

1. The pacemaker of the heart is the
   A. Purkinje fibres
   B. sinoatrial node
   C. atrioventricular node
   D. semilunar node

2. The pulmonary artery
   A. carries oxygenated blood to the heart from the lungs
   B. carries deoxygenated blood to the heart from the lungs
   C. carries oxygenated blood away from the heart to the lungs
   D. carries deoxygenated blood away from the heart to the lungs

Use the following information to answer questions 3 and 4.

The oxygen content of the blood was monitored in different blood vessels as blood moved away from the heart. The results of the study are shown in **Figure 1**.

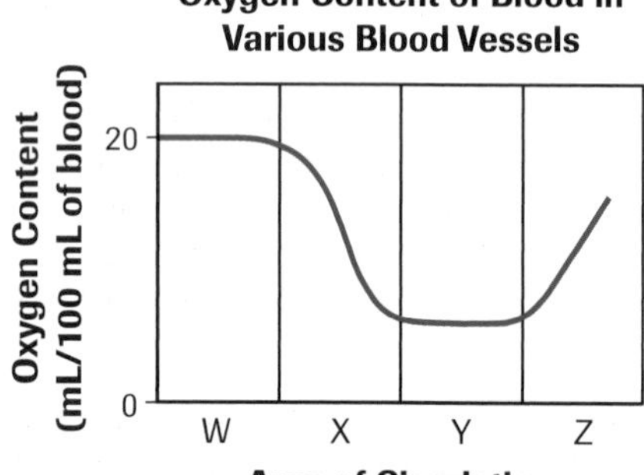

Figure 1

3. The area of the graph in **Figure 1** that would most likely represent capillaries within muscle cells would be
   A. W
   B. X
   C. Y
   D. Z

4. Identify the area of the graph in **Figure 1** where you would expect to find blood within a vein inside the brain.
   A. W
   B. X
   C. Y
   D. Z

Use the following information to answer questions 5 to 7.

Capillaries were observed within the tail of a fish. The capillaries were subjected to treatment with different chemicals, and the flow of blood cells through the capillary was observed 30 seconds later. **Table 1** shows the data that was collected.

Table 1 Blood Flow in Fish Tail Capillaries

Treatment	Average blood flow after treatment (cells/min)
control	60
epinephrine	40
lactic acid	90
alcohol	80
temperature reduced by 20 °C	30
nicotine	25

5. The number of blood cells that would normally pass through capillaries of the fish's tail at room temperature is
   A. 60 cells/min
   B. 40 cells/min
   C. 80 cells/min
   D. 30 cells/min

6. Nicotine is a drug found in cigarettes. Select the conclusion that is supported by the data provided in **Table 1**.
   A. Nicotine causes arteriolar constriction. Fewer blood cells move through capillaries after the treatment.
   B. Nicotine causes arteriolar constriction. More blood cells move through capillaries after the treatment.
   C. Nicotine causes constriction of the capillaries. Fewer blood cells move through capillaries after the treatment.
   D. Nicotine causes constriction of the capillaries. More blood cells move through capillaries after the treatment.

7. Lactic acid is produced in muscles during anaerobic respiration. Select the conclusion about lactic acid treatment that is supported by the data provided in **Table 1**.
   A. Lactic acid decreases blood flow to tissues. More oxygen is delivered to tissues, which decreases the amount of lactic acid in the blood.
   B. Lactic acid decreases blood flow to tissues. More oxygen is delivered to tissues, which increases the amount of lactic acid in the blood.
   C. Lactic acid increases blood flow to tissues. More oxygen is delivered to tissues, which decreases the amount of lactic acid in the blood.
   D. Lactic acid increases blood flow to tissues. More oxygen is delivered to tissues, which increases the amount of lactic acid in the blood.

8. Calculate the stroke volume of a person with a heart rate NR of 82 beats/min and a cardiac output of 4.6 L. (Record your answer as a value rounded to two decimal places.)

Part 2

Use the following information to answer questions 9 to 11.

Figure 2 shows the chambers of the heart, and blood vessels entering and exiting the heart.

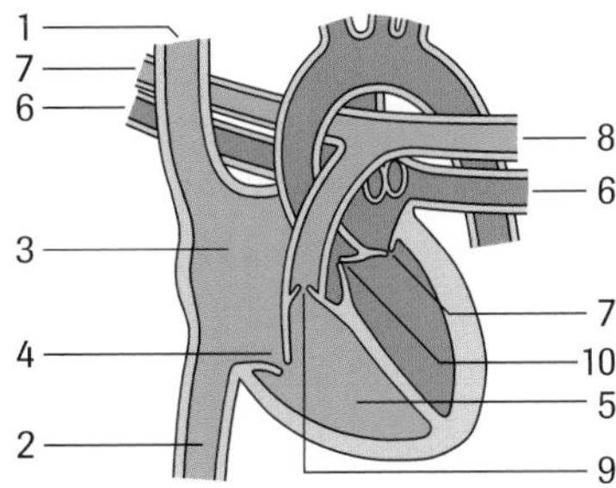

Figure 2

9. **Identify** the number(s) of the vein(s) that return blood to DE the heart from the body.
10. **Identify** the number of the ventricle that contains DE deoxygenated blood.
11. **Identify** the number of the heart valves that produce the DE *lubb* sound when closing.

12. **Identify** differences in the structures of veins, arteries, and capillaries and **describe** how they are related to the functions of each vessel.
13. "Oxygenated blood is found in all arteries of the body." Is this statement true or false? Give reasons to **explain** your answer.
14. **Why** does the left ventricle contain more muscle than the right ventricle?
15. Arteriosclerosis is a condition referred to as "hardening of the arteries." It results from a reduction in the elasticity of the arteries. **Describe** two circulatory problems that might arise from this effect on the vessels.
16. The victim of an accident has had a large blood vessel severed and bleeding is severe. **How** does excessive bleeding endanger life? **Outline** in a list two physiological responses that will help the victim to survive.
17. **Why** does the blockage of a lymph vessel in the left leg cause swelling in that area?

Use the following information to answer questions 18 and 19.

Table 2 is a record of a person's blood pressure taken in a sitting position before and after exercise.

Table 2 Effect of Exercise on Blood Pressure and Pulse

Condition	Systolic blood pressure (mmHg)	Diastolic blood pressure (mmHg)	Pulse (beats/min)
resting	120	80	70
after exercise	180	45	160

18. **Why** does systolic blood pressure increase after exercise? DE
19. **Why** does diastolic blood pressure decrease after exercise? DE

20. **How** does the respiratory system depend on the circulatory system?
21. Nicotine causes the constriction of arterioles. Write a DE unified response that addresses the following aspects of smoking during pregnancy.
    - **Explain why** pregnant women are advised not to smoke.
    - Mothers who smoke give birth to babies who are, on average, 1 kg smaller than normal. **Describe** a possible relationship between the effects of nicotine on the mother's circulatory system and the lower body mass of babies.
22. Heart disease is currently the number one killer of middle-aged males, accounting for billions of dollars every year in medical expenses and productivity loss. Should males be required by law to undergo heart examinations? **Justify** your answer. Consider the social and moral implications of such a law.
23. Caffeine causes heart rate to accelerate; however, a scientist who works for a coffee company has suggested that blood pressure will not increase due to coffee consumption. This scientist states that equilibrium adjustment mechanisms ensure that blood pressure readings will remain within an acceptable range. **Design** an experiment that will test the scientist's hypothesis. What other reasons might the scientist have for suggesting that caffeine does not increase blood pressure?

chapter

11 Blood and the Immune System

In this chapter

- Exploration: Tracing an Infection
- Investigation 11.1: Diagnosing Disease by Examining Blood Cells
- Web Activity: Blood Typing
- Mini Investigation: Observing Phagocytosis
- Case Study: Bovine Spongiform Encephalopathy
- Web Activity: Virtual Immunology Laboratory
- Explore an Issue: The Future of Stem Cell Research

To appreciate the importance of the immune system, consider severe combined immunodeficiency (SCID), also known as the "boy in the plastic bubble" syndrome after David Vetter, an American boy who had to live in a sterile plastic bubble. SCID is a rare disease of the immune system, and those affected must live in a virtually germ-free environment or risk contracting life-threatening infections. In 2006, a baby in Ontario was born with SCID. Treatments for SCID include bone marrow transplants and gene therapy.

Unlike familiar infectious diseases caused by viruses and bacteria, bovine spongiform encephalopathy (BSE) is caused by a neurological invader that does not contain nucleic acids. The disease is caused by a *prion*, an abnormal infectious version of a protein. During the 1980s and early 1990s, thousands of people in Britain ate beef from cattle that had BSE, often called mad cow disease (**Figure 1**). By the mid-1990s, the human version of mad cow disease, known as variant Creutzfeldt–Jakob disease, surfaced, and scientists considered the possibility that the disease could be transmitted from cows to people through the food chain.

STARTING points

Answer these questions as best you can with your current knowledge. Then, using the concepts and skills you have learned, you will revise your answers at the end of the chapter.

1. How do you think the idea that a protein can cause an infectious disease has altered the way we think about disease?
2. Which of the following medical conditions have been linked with bacteria, viruses, or prions?
   (a) heart attack
   (b) ulcers
   (c) AIDS
   (d) measles
   (e) diabetes mellitus
3 Allergies are caused by an over-reaction of your immune system. Harmless agents, such as proteins in peanut butter, are recognized as harmful invaders and an immune response is mobilized. What other mistakes of the immune system can cause problems?

Career Connections:
Medical Laboratory Technologist; Pathologist

Figure 1
A prion causes BSE in cattle.

Exploration Tracing an Infection

In this activity, you will simulate the spread of an infection. Each member of your class will be provided with a numbered plastic cup filled with a mystery fluid. One of these cups will contain an "infection."

Safety goggles and a lab apron must be worn for the entire laboratory.

Materials: index card, pen or pencil, numbered plastic cup of mystery fluid, dropper bottle of phenolphthalein indicator

- Write your name and cup number on your index card.
- Share your mystery fluid with a classmate. Pour all of your fluid into your partner's cup. Then, have your partner pour half of the combined fluids back into your cup. Both you and your partner then record the other person's cup number on your index card.
- Repeat the previous step until you have shared fluids with exactly three other students. Note that every class member will share fluids with three other students.
- Once all exchanges have occurred, your teacher will add a drop of phenolphthalein indicator to each of the cups. A pink colour indicates an infection.

(a) Can you identify the origin of the infection?
(b) If so, then identify the source. If not, why not?

11.1 Components of Blood

DID YOU KNOW ?

Water Content of Blood
Blood is not the most watery tissue of your body. It has been estimated that the grey matter of your brain is 85 % water.

plasma the fluid portion of the blood

The average 70-kg individual is nourished and protected by about 5 L of blood. Approximately 55 % of the blood is fluid; the remaining 45 % is composed of blood cells (**Figure 1**). All blood cells are produced by the bone marrow (**Figure 2**). The percentage of red blood cells in the blood is called the hematocrit. The fluid portion of the blood is referred to as the **plasma**, which is about 90 % water, allowing it to be described as a fluid tissue. As in other tissues, the individual cells in the blood work together for a common purpose.

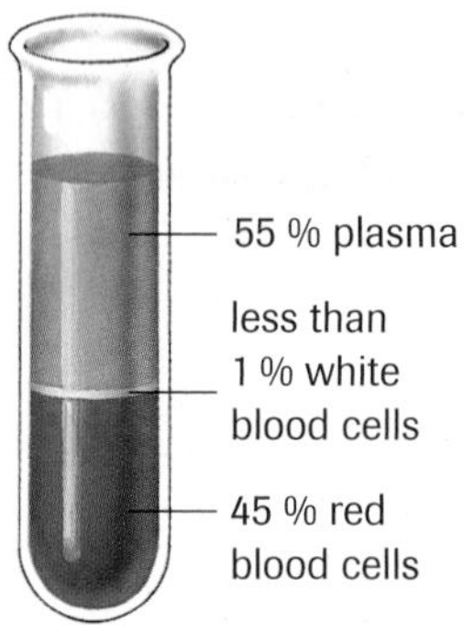

Figure 1
Proportions of fluid and cells in blood

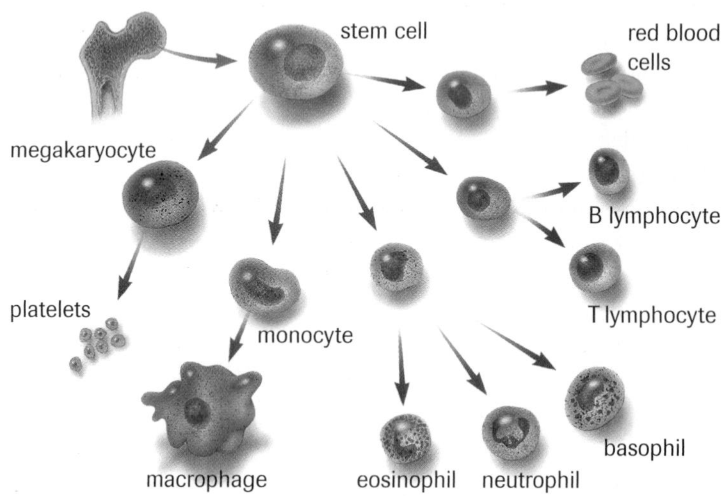

Figure 2
Stem cells of the bone marrow give rise to blood cells. The agranulocytes include the monocytes and lymphocytes. The granulocytes include the eosinophils, basophils, and neutrophils.

Table 1 Plasma Proteins

Type	Function
albumins	osmotic balance
globulins	antibodies, immunity
fibrinogens	blood clotting

The plasma also contains blood proteins, glucose, vitamins, minerals, dissolved gases, and waste products of cellular metabolism. The large plasma proteins help maintain homeostasis. One group of proteins is called the albumins; they, along with inorganic minerals, establish an osmotic pressure that draws water back into capillaries and helps maintain body fluid levels. A second group of proteins, the globulins, help provide protection against invading microbes. Fibrinogens, the third group of proteins, are important in blood clotting. **Table 1** summarizes the types of plasma proteins and their functions.

Erythrocytes

erythrocyte a red blood cell that contains hemoglobin and carries oxygen

The primary function of **erythrocytes**, red blood cells, is the transport of oxygen. Although some oxygen diffuses into the plasma, the presence of hemoglobin increases the ability of the blood to carry oxygen by a factor of almost 70. Without hemoglobin, your red blood cells would supply only enough oxygen to maintain life for approximately 4.5 s. With hemoglobin, humans can survive without oxygen for a few minutes. This is not much time, but remember that the blood returns to the heart and is pumped to the lungs, where oxygen supplies are continuously replenished. This might indicate why people survive even when the heart stops for short periods of time. Children who have been immersed in cold water for longer than a few minutes have survived with comparatively minor cell damage because colder temperatures slow body metabolism and decrease oxygen demand.

An estimated 280 million hemoglobin molecules are found in a single red blood cell. The hemoglobin is composed of heme, the iron-containing pigment, and globin, the protein structure. Four heme groups, each containing an iron atom, attach to the folded protein structure and bind with oxygen molecules. The oxyhemoglobin complex gives blood its red colour. Once oxygen is given up to cells of the body, the shape of the hemoglobin molecule changes, causing the reflection of blue light. This explains why blood appears blue in the veins.

Red blood cells are biconcave (concave on both sides) disks approximately 7 μm in diameter. This shape provides a greater surface area for gas exchange—between 20 % and 30 % more surface area than a sphere. The outer membranes of red blood cells become brittle with age, causing them to rupture as they file through the narrow capillaries. Since red blood cells live only about 120 days, cell reproduction is essential. One estimate suggests that at least five million red blood cells are produced every minute of the day.

Red blood cells do not contain a nucleus when mature, which allows more room for the cell to carry hemoglobin. This enucleated condition raises two important questions. First, since cells, by definition, contain a nucleus or nuclear material, are red blood cells actually cells? The second question addresses cell reproduction: how do cells without a nucleus and chromosomes reproduce? The answer to both of the above questions can be found in bone marrow, where red blood cells are produced by nucleated stem cells. The young cells lose their nuclei as they are discharged into the bloodstream.

The average male has about 5.5 billion red blood cells per millilitre of blood, while the average female has about 4.5 billion. Individuals living at high altitudes can have red cell counts as high as 8 billion per millilitre. How does the body ensure that adequate numbers of red blood cells are maintained? Specialized white blood cells, located primarily in the spleen and liver, monitor the age of red blood cells and remove debris from the circulatory system. Following the breakdown of red blood cells, the hemoglobin is released. Iron is recovered and stored in the liver and bone marrow for production of new red blood cells. The heme is transformed into bile pigments.

A deficiency in hemoglobin or red blood cells decreases oxygen delivery to the tissues. This condition, known as **anemia**, is characterized by low energy levels. The most common cause of a low red blood cell count is hemorrhage. Physical injury, bleeding due to ulcers, or hemorrhage in the lungs due to tuberculosis can cause anemia. If more than 40 % of the blood is lost, the body is incapable of coping. Anemia may also be associated with a dietary deficiency of iron, which is an important component of hemoglobin. The red blood cells must be packed with sufficient numbers of hemoglobin molecules to ensure adequate oxygen delivery. Raisins and liver are two foods rich in iron.

Leukocytes

White blood cells, or **leukocytes**, are much less numerous than red blood cells. It has been estimated that red blood cells outnumber white blood cells by a ratio of 700 to 1. White blood cells have a nucleus, making them easily distinguishable from red blood cells. In fact, the shape and size of the nucleus, along with the granules in the cytoplasm, have been used to identify different types of leukocytes (**Figure 2**, previous page). The granulocytes are classified according to small granules in the cytoplasm that become visible when stained. The agranulocytes are white blood cells that do not have granules in their cytoplasm. Granulocytes and agranulocytes are both produced in the bone marrow, but agranulocytes are modified in the lymph nodes. The function of some leukocytes is to destroy invading microbes by phagocytosis; they squeeze out of capillaries and move toward the microbe like an amoeba. Once the microbe has been engulfed, the leukocyte releases enzymes that digest the microbe and the leukocyte itself. The function of other white blood cells is to form special proteins, called antibodies, which interfere with invading microbes and toxins.

DID YOU KNOW ?

Colour of Blood

The word *erythrocyte* comes from the Greek *erythros*, meaning "red." However, a single red blood cell does not appear red but pale orange–the composite of many red blood cells produces the red colour.

DID YOU KNOW ?

How Old Is Your Blood?

Because red blood cells live only 120 days, they are continually breaking down and being replenished. The misconception that "young blood" is better than "old blood" persists even today. The blood of elderly people is virtually the same as the blood of young people.

anemia the reduction in blood oxygen due to low levels of hemoglobin or poor red blood cell production

leukocyte a white blood cell

DID YOU KNOW ?

Average Blood Volume

The average male contains an estimated 80 mL of blood for every kilogram of body mass. The average female contains an estimated 65 mL of blood for every kilogram of body mass.

 **INVESTIGATION 11.1** *Introduction*

Diagnosing Disease by Examining Blood Cells

White blood cells often provide physicians with information used in diagnosing disease. In this investigation, you will examine and count different types of white blood cells, then relate this information to disease diagnosis.

To perform this investigation, turn to page 369.

Report Checklist

● Purpose	● Design	● Analysis
● Problem	○ Materials	● Evaluation
● Hypothesis	○ Procedure	● Synthesis
● Prediction	● Evidence	

Platelets

platelet a component of blood responsible for initiating blood clotting

Platelets, or thrombocytes, do not contain a nucleus and are produced from large nucleated cells in the bone marrow. Small fragments of cytoplasm break from the large megakaryocyte, a large cell in the bone marrow, to form platelets. Platelets play an important role in blood clotting. When a blood vessel is damaged, the cells of the vessel wall release a substance that makes them sticky, and platelets begin to stick to the injured site. As the platelets build up, they form a plug to stop the bleeding. The platelets change shape from round to spiny, and they release substances that trap more platelets and cause clotting proteins to form.

Practice

1. Name the two major components of blood.
2. List three plasma proteins and indicate the function of each.
3. What is the function of hemoglobin?
4. List factors that initiate red blood cell production.
5. What is anemia?
6. What is the role of platelets?

Blood Clotting

Blood clotting maintains equilibrium by preventing the loss of blood from torn or ruptured blood vessels. Blood clots also forestall the rupture of weakened blood vessels by providing additional support.

Trillions of platelets move through the blood vessels. When a blood vessel is damaged, platelets are activated and clump together to form a plug to stop the bleeding. The platelets release a protein called thromboplastin (**Figure 3**).

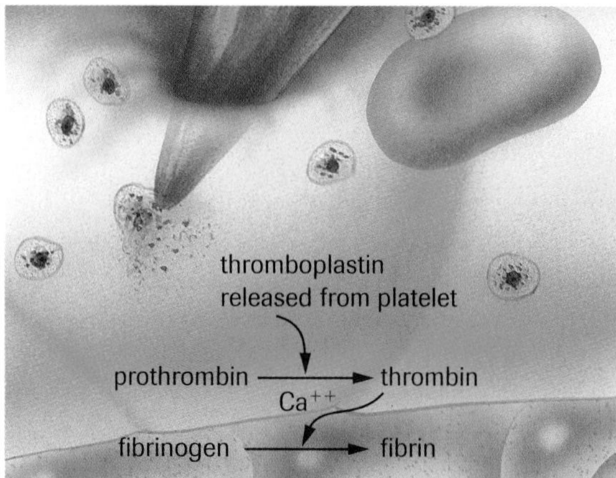

Figure 3
The thromboplastin released from the platelet initiates a series of reactions that produce a blood clot.

The thromboplastin, along with calcium ions present in the blood, activates a plasma protein called prothrombin. Prothrombin, along with another plasma protein, called fibrinogen, is produced by the liver. Under the influence of thromboplastin, prothrombin is transformed into thrombin. In turn, thrombin acts as an enzyme by splicing two amino acids from the fibrinogen molecule. Fibrinogen is converted into fibrin threads, which wrap around the damaged area, trapping red blood cells and more platelets to form a clot and stop bleeding (**Figure 4**).

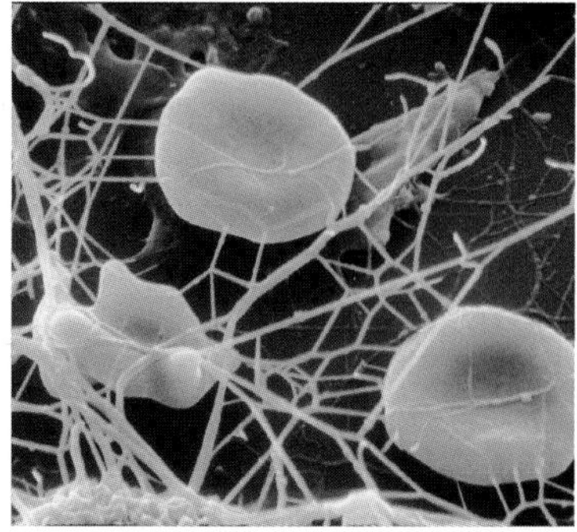

Figure 4
Formation of a blood clot. Red blood cells are caught in a mesh of fibrin.

Although blood clotting preserves life, it can also result in life-threatening situations. A **thrombus** is a blood clot that blocks a blood vessel. Because blood will not pass through the area, local tissues are not supplied with oxygen and nutrients. If a clot forms in the brain, cerebral thrombosis can cause a stroke. Coronary thrombosis—a clot in a coronary artery of the heart—can be equally dangerous.

Should a blood clot dislodge, it becomes an **embolus**. The embolus may travel through the body to lodge in a vital organ. Cerebral embolisms, coronary embolisms, and pulmonary embolisms can be life-threatening. What causes an embolus or thrombus is not completely understood, but scientists believe that genetic factors may be involved. It is known, however, that the incidence of thrombi and emboli increases as people get older.

thrombus a blood clot that forms within a blood vessel and blocks it

embolus a blood clot that dislodges and is carried by the circulatory system to another part of the body

Artificial Blood

On March 1, 1982, a precedent-setting legal case brought attention to an emerging medical technology. A man and woman, trying to push their car, were critically injured when they were hit by another car. For personal reasons, the couple chose not to have a blood transfusion. During the legal dispute that ensued, the wife died, and the courts ruled that action must be taken to save the husband's life. Five litres of fluosol—artificial blood—were transfused into the man over a period of five days. Doctors believed that the artificial blood could maintain adequate oxygen levels until the man's bone marrow began replenishing red blood cells.

Fluosol, a non-toxic liquid that contains fluorine, was developed in Japan. Fluosol carries both oxygen and carbon dioxide. It requires no blood matching, and when frozen, can be stored for long periods of time. Artificial blood, unlike human blood, does not have to undergo expensive screening procedures before being used in transfusions. Artificial blood will not carry human immunodeficiency virus (HIV), hepatitis, or any other virus. However, despite its advantages, artificial blood is not as good as the real thing. Although it carries oxygen, it is ill-suited for many of the other functions associated with blood, such as blood clotting and immunity. The real value of artificial blood is that it provides time until human blood can be administered. It could also serve as a supplement for patients with diseases like thalassemia (Cooley's anemia) or aplastic anemia, which require the patients to undergo multiple transfusions.

CAREER CONNECTION 

Medical Laboratory Technologist

One of the many duties medical laboratory technologists (MLTs) perform is drawing blood for analysis. They also conduct routine lab tests and set up, clean, and maintain lab equipment. Survey Web sites for job opportunities for MLTs. Report on your findings.

www.science.nelson.com 

ABO Blood Groups

In the 17th century, Jean-Baptiste Denis performed the first blood transfusion by injecting lamb's blood into a young boy. The youth survived, but a repeat of the experiment, on an older man, proved disastrous—the man died almost immediately. Denis attempted to explain what went wrong, but he lacked crucial information. Why do some transfusions help, while others kill?

At the turn of the 20th century, Karl Landsteiner discovered that different blood types exist. Therefore, the secret to successful transfusion was the correct matching of blood types. Markers called glycoproteins are located on the membrane of some of the red blood cells. Individuals with blood type A have a glycoprotein, the A marker, attached to their cell membrane. Individuals with blood type B have a glycoprotein, the B marker,

antigen a substance, usually protein, that stimulates the formation of an antibody

antibody a protein formed within the blood that reacts with an antigen

attached to their cell membrane. Individuals with blood type AB have both A and B markers attached to their cell membrane. Blood type O has neither marker.

Should an individual with blood type O receive blood from an individual with blood type A, the type O blood would recognize the A marker as a foreign invader (**Figure 5**). The A marker acts as an **antigen** in the body of the individual with blood type O. Special proteins, called **antibodies**, are produced in response to a foreign invader. The antibodies attach to the antigen markers and cause the blood to clump. It is important to note that antigen A would not cause the same immune response if transfused into the body of an individual with blood type A. The marker associated with blood type A would not be a foreign invader because A-type antigens are found on that individual's red blood cells. **Table 2** summarizes the antigens and antibodies for the four ABO blood groups.

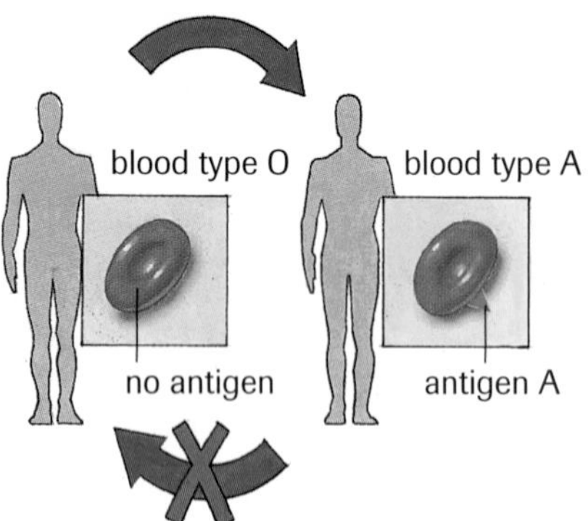

Figure 5
Individuals with blood type A can receive blood type O during a transfusion. However, individuals with blood type O cannot receive blood type A during a transfusion.

Table 2 Antigens and Antibodies Found in Blood Groups

Blood group	Antigen on red blood cell	Antibody in serum
O	none	A and B
A	A	B
B	B	A
AB	A and B	none

agglutination the clumping of blood cells caused by antigens and antibodies

The antibodies produced by the recipient act on the invading antigens. As shown in **Figure 6**, the antibodies cause **agglutination**, or clumping, of the blood. The importance of the correct transfusion is emphasized by the fact that agglutinated blood can no longer pass through the tiny capillaries. The agglutinated blood therefore clogs the capillaries and prevents the delivery of oxygen and nutrients. Individuals with type AB blood possess both antigens and, therefore, are able to receive blood from any donor. Blood type AB is the universal recipient. Blood type O is referred to as the universal donor because it can be donated to individuals of all blood types. Blood type O contains no antigen. Although antibodies will not be produced against type O, the immune system of individuals with blood type O can recognize antigens on other blood cells. Blood

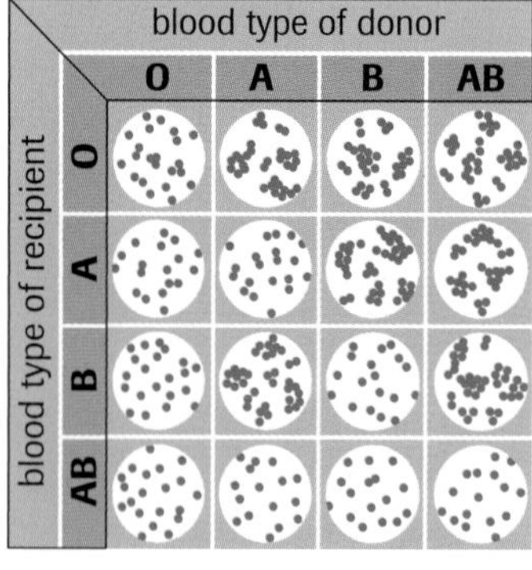

(a)

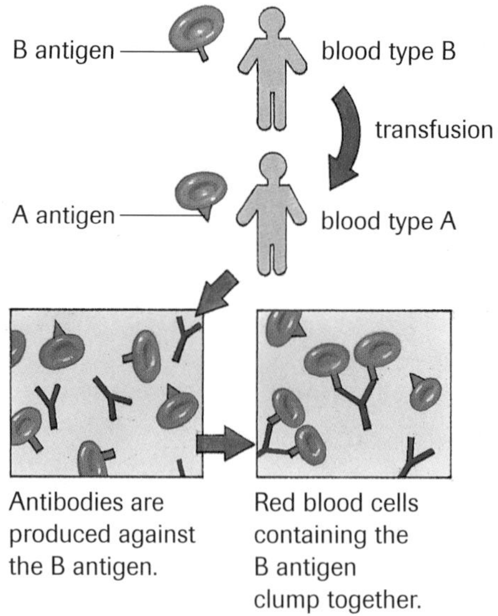

(b)

Figure 6
(a) Agglutination response of ABO blood groups
(b) Agglutination response of blood type A (recipient) to blood type B (donor)

type O, despite being the universal donor, may only accept blood from individuals with blood type O. Blood type AB, despite being the universal recipient, may only donate blood to individuals with blood type AB.

Simulation—Blood Typing

Blood transfusions may be required during surgery or when a person loses blood due to trauma. Identifying a patient's blood type is critical to ensuring that the appropriate type of blood is provided. In this activity, you will follow an interactive animation in which you must identify the blood type of virtual patients and then give them a blood transfusion. You will also find additional information on the biology of blood types.

Rhesus Factor

During the 1940s scientists discovered another antigen on the red blood cell—the rhesus factor. Like the ABO blood groups, the rhesus factor is inherited. Individuals who have this antigen are said to be Rhesus positive (Rh+). Approximately 85 % of Canadians have the antigen. The remaining 15 % of individuals who do not have the antigen are said to be Rhesus negative (Rh–). Individuals who are Rh– may donate blood to Rh+ individuals, but should not receive Rh+ blood. The human body has no natural antibodies against Rh factors, but antibodies can be produced following a transfusion. Although Rh antibodies are produced in response to antigens, it should be pointed out that the immune reaction is subdued compared with that of the ABO group.

Rhesus-factor incompatibilities become important for Rh+ babies of Rh– mothers. If the baby inherits the Rh+ factor from the father, a condition called erythroblastosis fetalis can occur with the second and subsequent pregnancies. The first child is spared because the blood of the mother and baby are separated by the placenta (a membrane inside the uterus that exchanges materials between mother and baby). During birth, the placenta is shed from the uterus. Capillary beds rupture, and, for the first time, the blood of the baby comes into contact with the blood of the mother. The mother's immune system recognizes the Rh+ antigens and triggers the production of antibodies. But, by the time the antibodies are produced, the first baby is no longer connected to the placenta and has escaped the potentially dangerous situation. However, a second pregnancy presents problems if the fetus is Rh+. The mother retains many of the antibodies from her first encounter with Rh+ blood. If antibodies cross the placenta, they attach to the antigen on the red blood cells of the fetus, causing them to be destroyed. Symptoms of erythroblastosis fetalis include anemia, jaundice, and an enlarged liver.

SUMMARY Components of Blood

- Blood is composed mainly of plasma and blood cells.
- Plasma proteins play roles in maintaining homeostasis, in producing antibodies, and in blood clotting.

- Erythrocytes function primarily to transport oxygen.
  - Erythrocytes contain hemoglobin, which increases the amount of oxygen that can be carried in the blood.
  - Erythrocytes are produced in the bone marrow; once they leave, they have no nucleus and cannot reproduce.
- Leukocytes are an important part of the immune system.
- Platelets are cell fragments that clump together at the site of a damaged blood vessel to form a clot.
- Blood type A has the A antigen, type B has the B antigen, type AB has both, and type O has neither.
- Blood types must be matched before giving a blood transfusion.
  - An incompatible marker acts as an antigen in the recipient's body.
  - The recipient will produce antibodies against the antigen, causing agglutination.
  - AB is the universal recipient, and O is the universal donor.
- The Rhesus (Rh) factor is another potential source of blood incompatibility.

Section 11.1 Questions

1. What are erythrocytes and what is their primary function?
2. Explain the mechanism by which hemoglobin increases the ability of blood to carry oxygen.
3. Are erythrocytes true cells? Why or why not?
4. State two situations that result in a deficiency of hemoglobin.
5. How do white blood cells differ from red blood cells?
6. State two major functions associated with leukocytes.
7. How do platelets contribute to the formation of blood clots?
8. Differentiate between an embolus and a thrombus.
9. List the advantages and disadvantages associated with using artificial blood.
10. Cancer of the white blood cells is called leukemia. Like other cancers, leukemia is associated with rapid and uncontrolled cell production. Examine the test tubes shown in **Figure 7** and predict which subject might be suffering from leukemia. Give your reasons.
11. Most physicians would not diagnose leukemia on the basis of one test. What other conditions might explain the appearance of the test tube you chose in question 10? Give your reasons.
12. Lead poisoning can cause bone marrow destruction. Which of the subjects in **Figure 7** might have lead poisoning? Give your reasons.
13. Which subject in **Figure 7** lives at a high altitude? Give your reasons.

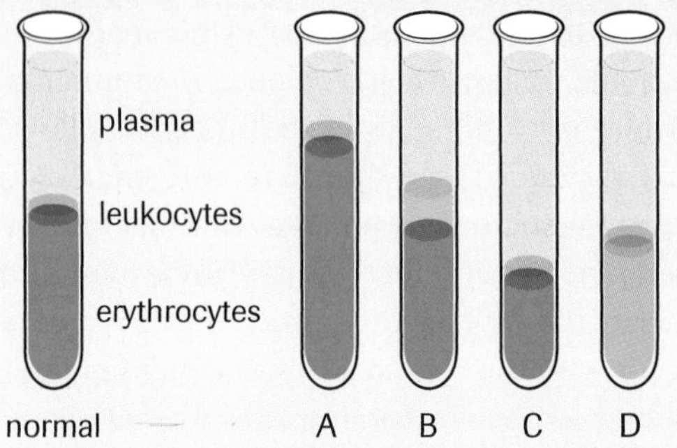

Figure 7

14. Athletes can take unfair advantage of the benefits of extra red blood cells. Two weeks prior to a competition, a blood sample is taken and centrifuged, and the red blood cell component is stored. A few days before the event, the red blood cells are injected into the athlete. Why would athletes remove red blood cells only to return them to their body later?
15. How does Rh+ blood differ from Rh- blood?
16. Explain why type O blood is considered the universal donor. Why is type AB the universal recipient?
17. What would happen if blood type A was transfused into people with blood types A, B, O, and AB? Provide an explanation for each case.
18. Why does a fetus with erythroblastosis fetalis develop anemia?

The Body's Lines of Defence 11.2

The human body must constantly defend itself against the many unwelcome intruders it encounters in the air, in food, and in water. It must also deal with abnormal body cells that sometimes turn into cancer. Three lines of defence have evolved to help resist infection and possible death from fatal illnesses. The first two lines of defence are considered nonspecific immune responses, meaning that they do not distinguish one microbe from another. The third line of defence—the immune system—is a specific immune response that reacts in specialized ways to various invaders. All the cells involved in the immune system develop from the bone marrow. (These cells were illustrated in **Figure 2**, Section 11.1, on page 350.)

DID YOU KNOW ?

The Skin Is the Largest Organ

The skin is the largest organ of the body, accounting for as much as 15 % of the body's total mass. An area no larger than a dime will contain approximately 10 hairs, 15 oil glands, 3 blood vessels, 100 sweat glands, and 200 neurons.

The First Line of Defence

The body's first line of defence against foreign invaders is largely physical. Like a medieval city that used walls and moats to defend against attack from outsiders, the skin and mucous membranes defend against viral and bacterial invaders. Intact skin provides a protective barrier that cannot normally be penetrated by bacteria or viruses. The skin also has chemical defences in the form of acidic secretions, which keep it within a pH range of 3 to 5, acidic enough to inhibit the growth of microbes. Lysozyme, an antimicrobial enzyme secreted in human tears, saliva, mucous secretions, and perspiration, destroys the cell walls of bacteria, killing them.

In the respiratory tract, invading microbes and foreign debris become trapped in a layer of mucus and are filtered by tiny hairlike structures called cilia (**Figure 1**). The cilia move in waves, sweeping particles up toward the throat where coughing can expel them. Corrosive acids in the stomach and protein-digesting enzymes destroy most of the invading microbes carried into the body with food.

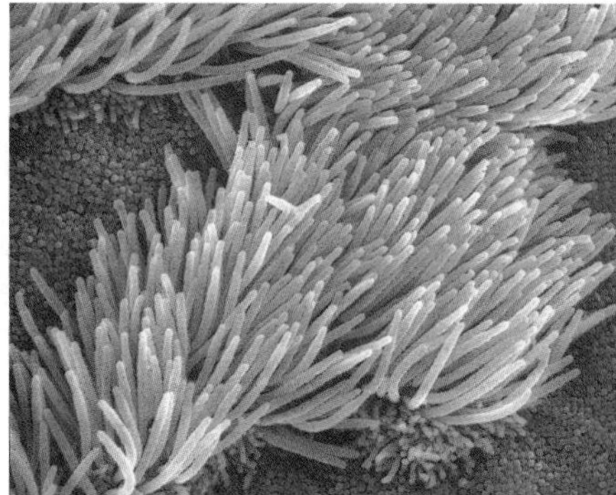

Figure 1
Cilia in the respiratory tract

The Second Line of Defence

A second line of defence can be mobilized if the invader takes up residence within the body. Leukocytes, or white blood cells, may engulf invading microbes or produce antibodies.

The body's nonspecific defence mechanisms rely mainly on the process of **phagocytosis**, the ingestion of invading microbes by certain types of white blood cells. When a foreign particle penetrates the skin through an injury, special leukocytes, known as *monocytes*, migrate from the blood into the tissues, where they develop into **macrophages** (meaning "big eaters"). The macrophages extend long protrusions, called *pseudopods*, that attach to the surface of the invading microbe; the microbe is then engulfed and destroyed by enzymes within the macrophage.

In another phagocytic response, white blood cells called *neutrophils* are attracted to chemical signals given off by cells that have been damaged by microbes. In a process called *chemotaxis*, the neutrophils squeeze out of capillaries and migrate toward the infected tissue. The neutrophils then engulf the microbe and release lysosomal enzymes that digest both the microbe and the leukocyte. The remaining fragments of protein, dead white blood cells, and the digested invader are called **pus**. Tissue damage due to physical injury also initiates a localized **inflammatory response**—a nonspecific immune response resulting in swelling, redness, heat, and pain (**Figure 2**, next page). Pus and accompanying inflammation are sure signs that the second line of defence has been at work.

phagocytosis the process by which a white blood cell engulfs and chemically destroys a microbe

macrophage a phagocytic white blood cells found in lymph nodes, bone marrow, and the spleen and liver

pus a thick liquid composed of protein fragments from digested leukocytes and microbes

inflammatory response localized nonspecific response triggered when tissue cells are injured by bacteria or physical injury, characterized by swelling, heat, redness, and pain

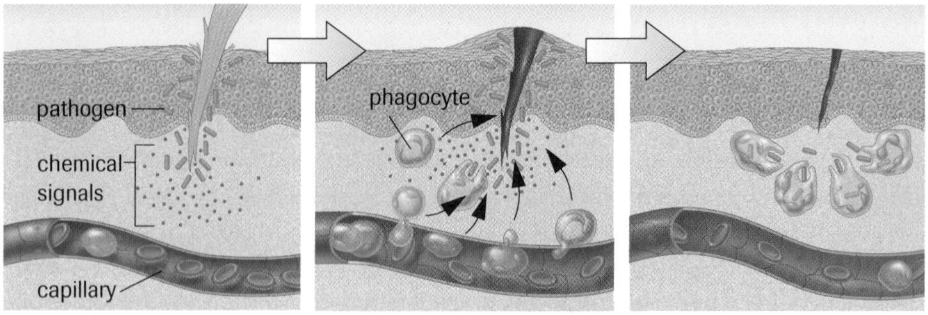

pathogen
chemical signals
capillary
phagocyte

(a) At the first sign of injury, chemical signals are released by the foreign invader. Other chemicals–histamines and prostaglandins–are released by the cells of the body.

(b) Chemical signals cause the capillaries to dilate. Blood flow increases and the capillaries become more permeable. Other chemicals attract phagocytic cells and specialized white blood cells.

(c) Phagocytes engulf and digest the invaders and cellular debris, which promotes healing of the tissues.

Figure 2
Damage to tissue cells by bacteria or physical injury initiates a localized inflammatory response.

The body's nonspecific defence system responds to localized injuries, like a cut or puncture, but it can also respond with a system-wide defence to more severe damage or infection. Injured cells emit chemicals that stimulate the production of phagocytic white blood cells and increase their release into the bloodstream.

A fever is an example of the body's system-wide response to infection. When infectious organisms spread throughout your body, such as when you have a cold or flu, neutrophils and macrophages digest the invaders and release chemicals into your bloodstream. When these chemicals reach your hypothalamus, they reset the body's thermostat to a higher temperature—about 40 °C. A fever makes it difficult for harmful bacteria to survive; thus, the fever helps to prevent the proliferation of the infectious organisms. Reducing your fever by taking aspirin may actually prolong the infection. However, if your body temperature rises above 40 °C, it can be unsafe. For example, a fever of 41 °C may cause convulsions, especially in young children. Human cells cannot survive above 43 °C because proteins start to denature.

mini *Investigation* *Observing Phagocytosis*

Protist models can be used to observe phagocytosis, the process by which macrophages engulf invaders (**Figure 3**).

Materials: prepared slide of amoeba, light microscope, medicine dropper, slide, cover slip, live amoeba culture, live yeast culture

- Obtain a prepared slide of amoeba that shows phagocytosis, and use a light microscope to look at it under high-power magnification.

(a) Draw what you see. Label the extension of false feet as "pseudopods" and indicate the food vacuole (if present).

- Using a medicine dropper, make a wet mount from a live amoeba culture. Observe the movement of the amoeba.
- Remove the cover slip from the slide and use a medicine dropper to add a drop of live yeast culture. Replace the cover slip and observe for phagocytosis.

(b) Describe the movement of the amoeba.
(c) Describe the process of phagocytosis.

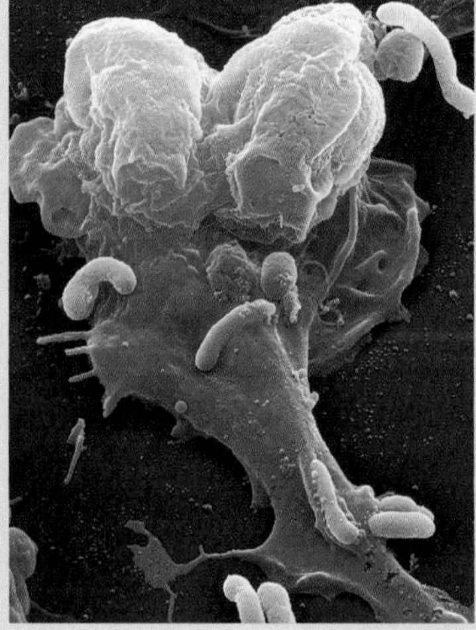

Figure 3
The macrophage has long, sticky extensions of cytoplasm that draw bacteria toward the macrophage. Once the bacteria come in contact with the macrophage, they are engulfed and destroyed.

The Immune Response (The Third Line of Defence)

Although some macrophages migrate throughout the body, others reside permanently in body tissues, such as the brain, lungs, kidneys, liver, and connective tissues. The fixed macrophages that reside in the spleen, lymph nodes, and other tissues of the lymphatic system trap and filter out microorganisms and foreign invaders that enter the blood. (Refer to **Figure 3**, Section 10.4, on page 338, for an illustration of the lymphatic system.)

The appearance of foreign organisms in the body activates antimicrobial plasma proteins, called **complement proteins**. There are about 20 known types of complement proteins. Under normal conditions, these proteins are present in the circulatory system in an inactive form. Marker proteins from invading microbes activate the complement proteins, which, in turn, serve as messengers. The proteins aggregate to initiate an attack on the cell membranes of fungal or bacterial cells. Some of the activated proteins trigger the formation of a protective coating around the invader, as shown in **Figure 4 (a)**. This coating seals the invading cell, immobilizing it. A second group punctures the cell membrane, as seen in **Figure 4 (b)**. Water enters the cell through the pore created by the protein, causing the cell to swell and burst. A third group of proteins attaches to the invader, as illustrated in **Figure 4 (c)**, making it more susceptible to phagocytosis by leukocytes.

complement protein a plasma protein that helps defend against invading microbes by tagging the microbe for phagocytosis, puncturing cell membranes, or triggering the formation of a mucous coating

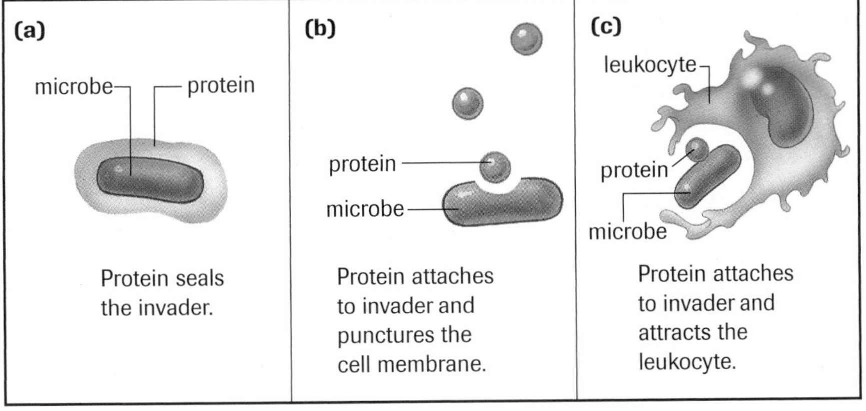

(a)
microbe
protein
Protein seals the invader.
(b)
protein
microbe
Protein attaches to invader and punctures the cell membrane.
(c)
leukocyte
protein
microbe
Protein attaches to invader and attracts the leukocyte.

Figure 4
Complement proteins aid the immune response.

T cell a lymphocyte, manufactured in the bone marrow and processed by the thymus gland, that identifies and attacks foreign substances

B cell a lymphocyte, made and processed in the bone marrow, that produces antibodies

Also involved in the immune response are lymphocytes, a type of white blood cell that produces antibodies. An antibody is a protein molecule that protects the body from invaders. All cells have special markers located on their cell membranes. Normally, the immune system does not react to the body's own markers. However, intruding cells or foreign proteins activate the production of antibodies. The cell membrane of a bacterium and the outer coat of a virus contain many different antigens. The antigen (a term derived from antibody generator) may even be a toxin produced by moulds, bacteria, or algae. The toxin presents a danger to the cells of the body because it interferes with normal cell metabolism.

Two different types of lymphocytes are found in the immune system. The first is the **T cell**, which is produced in the bone marrow and stored in the thymus gland, from which the T cell receives its name. The T cell's mission is to seek out the intruder and signal the attack. Acting much like a sentry, one type of T cell identifies the invader by its antigen markers (**Figure 5**), which are located on the cell membrane. Once the antigen is identified, another T cell passes this information on to the antibody-producing **B cell**.

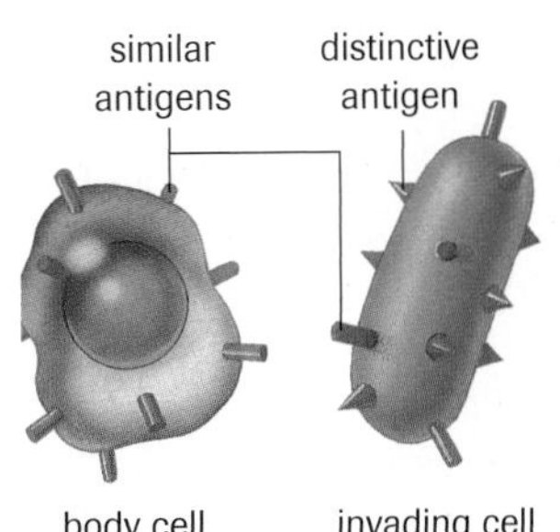

similar antigens
distinctive antigen
body cell
invading cell

Figure 5
Sugar-protein complexes located on the cell membrane act as markers. T cells distinguish the markers on the body's cells from those of invading cells.

Producing Monoclonal Antibodies

Have you ever wondered where synthetic antibodies come from? This audio clip provides a step-by-step analysis of the synthetic process used by industry to produce large quantities of identical antibodies.

www.science.nelson.com 

B cells multiply and produce molecular weapons: the antibodies. Each B cell produces a single type of antibody, which is displayed along its cell membrane. Eventually, the B cells are released from the bone marrow and enter the circulatory system. Some B cells differentiate into super-antibody-producing cells called *plasma cells.* These plasma cells can produce as many as 2000 antibody molecules every second.

Antigen–Antibody Reactions

Antibodies are Y-shaped proteins engineered to target foreign invaders. Antibodies are specific; this means that an antibody produced against the influenza virus, for example, is not effective against HIV, the virus that causes acquired immunodeficiency syndrome (AIDS). The tails of these Y-shaped proteins are very similar regardless of the type of antibody. Variations exist only at the outer edge of each arm, the area in which the antibody combines with the antigen (**Figure 6**). Antigen markers found on the influenza virus are different from those found on HIV. Each antibody has a shape that is complementary to its specific antigen. Thus, the binding site of an antibody produced in response to the influenza virus will not complement HIV.

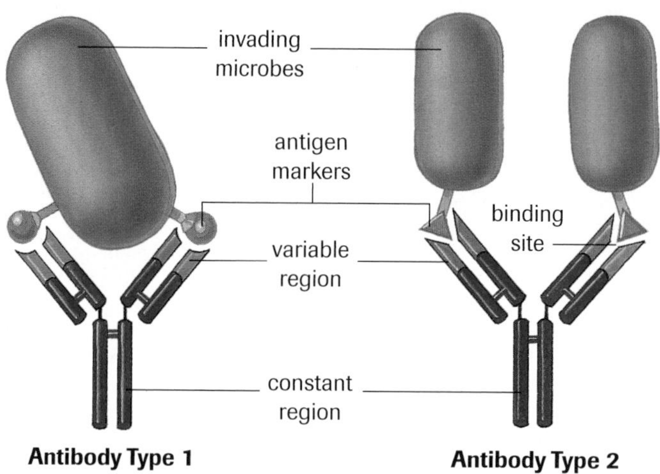

Figure 6

Each type of antibody will combine only with the appropriate antigen.

receptor site a port along a cell membrane into which hormones, nutrients, and other needed materials fit

Many different antigen markers are located on the membrane of a virus or bacterium. Although different antibodies can attach to the invader, each antibody attaches only to its complementary marker. The attachment of antibodies to the antigens creates an antigen–antibody complex, which is larger and more conspicuous and, therefore, more easily engulfed and destroyed by the circulating macrophages.

How do antibodies prevent poisons, or toxins, from destroying cells? Specialized **receptor sites** are found on different cells, which may explain why some poisons affect the nervous system while others affect the digestive or circulatory system. The receptor site is designed to accommodate either a hormone or a specific nutrient. Unfortunately, the toxin has a shape similar to a hormone or nutrient that allows it to become attached to the receptor sites on cell membranes. Once attached, the poison is engulfed by the cell, which assumes that it is actually a needed substance. Antibodies interfere with the attachment of toxins to the cell membranes' receptor sites by binding to the toxins, as shown in **Figure 7**.

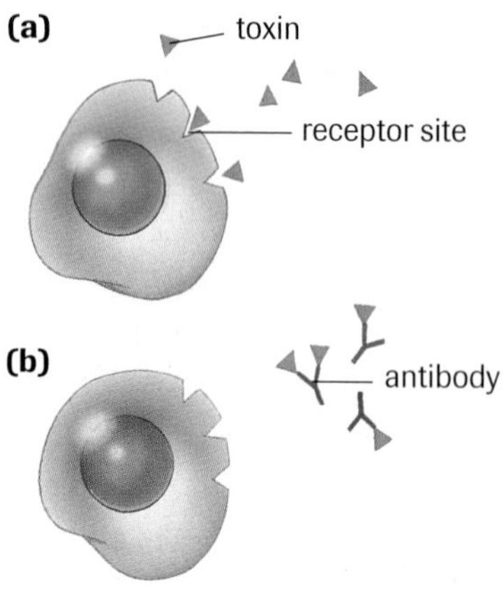

Figure 7
(a) Toxin binds to receptor.
(b) Antibody binds to toxin.

Viruses also use receptor sites as entry ports. The virus injects its hereditary material into the cell, but most often leaves the outer protein coat in the receptor site. Because of this outer coat, different viruses attach to different types of cells. For example, the outer coat of the cold virus has a geometry that enables it to attach to lung cells. HIV attaches to the receptor sites of the T cell (**Figure 8**). Once attached, the virus is engulfed by a T cell, creating another problem for the immune system. Antibody production requires a blueprint of the invader, but the protein coat of the virus hides inside the very cells assigned as sentries for invading antigens. Does this provide a clue as to why the body experiences difficulty defeating HIV?

Antibodies attach themselves to invading viruses, thereby preventing the viruses from binding to receptor sites on cells. For some viruses, the antibody will cause the virus to change shape, so it cannot bind to a cell. Occasionally, the outer coat of an invader will change shape slightly because of mutations. The mutated viruses can still gain access to a receptor site but are not tied up by an antibody.

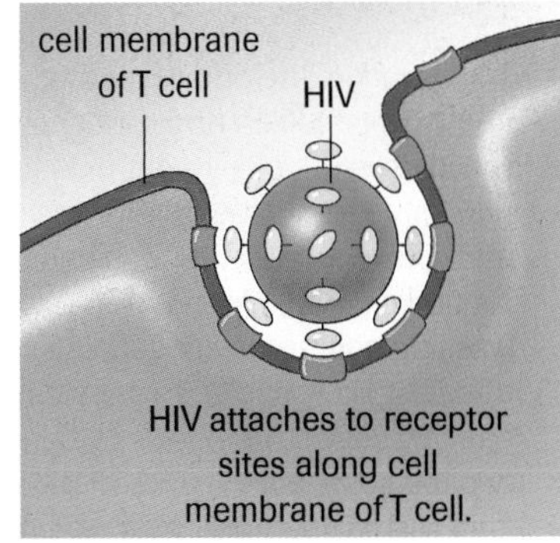
cell membrane of T cell
HIV
HIV attaches to receptor sites along cell membrane of T cell.

Figure 8
HIV has a shape that provides access to the T cell. The T cell engulfs HIV, unlike most other viruses.

Case Study

Bovine Spongiform Encephalopathy

Bovine spongiform encephalopathy (BSE) belongs to a larger group of transmissible spongiform encephalopathy (TSE) diseases that are characterized by the spongy deterioration of the brain. Transmissible means that the disease can pass from one animal to another. Eventually, BSE destroys the nervous system and causes death.

Spongiform encephalopathy is found in animals other than cattle. Scrapie affects sheep and goats. Chronic wasting disease (CWD) affects mule deer, white-tailed deer, and elk. Creutzfeldt-Jakob Disease (CJD) is a rare and fatal form of TSE that affects humans. Variant Creutzfeldt-Jakob disease (vCJD) has been diagnosed since 1996 and is thought to be linked to the consumption of meat products derived from BSE cattle.

What Causes the Disease?

The most widely accepted theory is that an agent, called a prion (**Figure 9**), infects the host and causes the conversion of normal proteins into abnormal proteins, which accumulate in the brain tissue and change its structure to a spongy form.

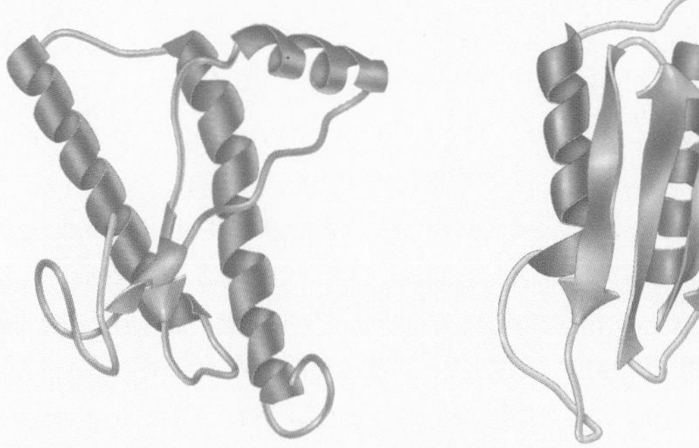

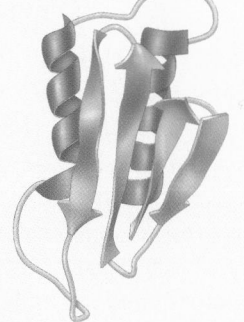

Figure 9
A normal prion (left) compared to the infectious form (right) that causes BSE. The structures of the proteins are shown using the ribbon model for ease of comparison.

Prions have caused the scientific community to examine disease in a new manner. Prions are proteins that are self-replicating, but, unlike other disease-causing agents, prions do not contain genetic material. Most prions are highly resistant to heat, freezing, and chemical sterilization.

The Origin of the Disease

Different and sometimes competing theories about the origin of this disease propose the possibility that BSE occurred at undetectable levels long before it was identified in British cattle in 1986. Many experts believe that BSE may have been caused by feeding ruminant (cattle, sheep, goats, deer, elk, bison) protein products to cattle. The prion could have been introduced to cattle from infected feed. One theory suggests that the protein may have come from another TSE, such as scrapie. Scrapie in sheep has been in existence for hundreds of years. When the protein from the sheep changed shape, it may have jumped species to the cow.

The recycling of proteins such as brain tissue and bone within cattle feed seems to be the problem. This practice dates back at least to the 1920s. It was originally seen as an inexpensive way to boost milk production and increase weight gain in cattle. The recycling of animal protein, known as rendering, is still regarded as an efficient way to utilize nutritious materials that would otherwise be wasted. Rendering serves the public interest by

- controlling the spread of pathogens that grow on waste tissues.
- reducing air pollution. Incinerating animal wastes as another means of disposal would reduce air quality.
- reducing wastes from packing plants. Approximately 50 % of every cow and about 30 % of every pig are not consumed by humans.

Understanding the Threat

Many scientists believe the disease began long before the first case of BSE was recorded in 1986 in England. A long incubation period (4 to 5 years) before the disease manifests itself indicates that it may have appeared in the 1970s.

In Canada, the first case of BSE was reported in 1993, in a beef cow imported from Britain in 1987. In 1997, feed-practice controls were put in place by the federal government of Canada. High-risk tissues such as cow brain and spinal cord could not be added to cattle feed. The second case was found in Alberta on May 20, 2003. The herd was immediately destroyed. Infected feed was identified as the most likely cause. The United States, along with other nations, closed the border to Canadian beef. In January 2005, two more Canadian cases of BSE were confirmed.

In March 1996, vCJD was diagnosed in people living in Britain and France. In August 2002, doctors confirmed that a Saskatchewan man died from vCJD, the human counterpart to BSE. The man was known to have spent time in Britain and may have acquired the disease there.

Evaluating Safety

- Canada had 13.5 million cows in 2005, with about 5.7 million (42 %) in Alberta.
- There had been four confirmed cases by January 2005, but one was from an imported cow. Only three cases were from cows native to Canada.
- To prevent prions from entering the food chain, rendering plants do not use sheep infected with scrapie, elk or deer infected with CWD, or high-risk cattle. Brain and spinal cord tissue are not used in feed.
- All ruminant products from countries that pose a risk of BSE are banned from Canada.
- All rendered proteins from cattle were banned from cattle feed in 1997.
- Feed practices are similar in the United States and Canada. Feed products are exported and imported between the two countries.
- BSE prions have never been found in dairy products.
- Random testing of beef cattle for BSE is routinely conducted. The testing frequency increased dramatically in 2003.

Case Study Questions

1. According to the map provided by the European Commission in 2002 (**Figure 10**), assess the risk presented for Canada.
2. According to the evidence presented, do cattle from Canada present higher levels of risk than those from the United States? Give your reasons.
3. According to the data provided, make a prediction about the country that might have been the original site of this disease. Give your reason.
4. Explain why it is difficult to provide a worldwide perspective on the spread of BSE.
5. How are prions unlike viruses and bacteria?
6. What would normally happen to a protein exposed to extreme heat?
7. Why would prion resistance to heat cause concern among humans?

Geographical BSE Risk

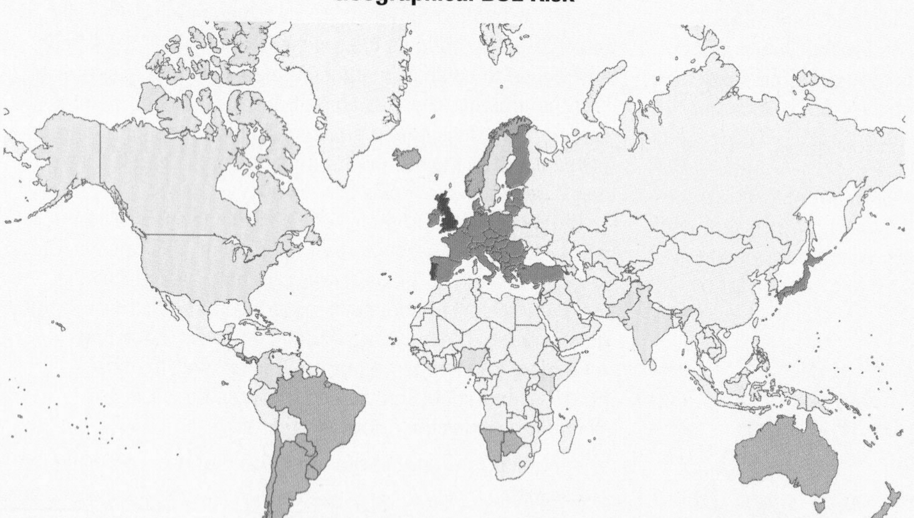

The geographical BSE risk (GBR) is a qualitative indicator of the likelihood of one or more cattle being infected with BSE, pre-clinically as well as clinically, at a given point in time.

no data: | Category 1: highly unlikely | Category 2: unlikely but not excluded | Category 3: likely but not confirmed or confirmed at a lower level | Category 4: confirmed, at a higher level

Source: European Commission, Scientific Steering Committee on the Geographical Risk of BSE (GBR), August 2002

Figure 10
BSE risk by country

8. Suggest a way of controlling the disease.
9. Explain why beef cattle under three years of age pose less threat.
10. Compare the BSE trends in and outside the UK using the graphs in **Figure 11**.
11. According to **Figure 11 (b)**, what was the worst year for BSE cases within the UK? What was the total number of cases?
12. Why would government officials want to know the age of infected cows?
13. Make two generalizations from the graph presented in **Figure 12**.
14. The decline in vCJD deaths from 2000 to 2001 (**Figure 12**) indicates fewer cases; however, it may not indicate that the disease is being eradicated. Why should caution be used in claiming that vCJD has been conquered?
15. Assess the risk of eating beef for humans.
16. What additional safety measures would you suggest?

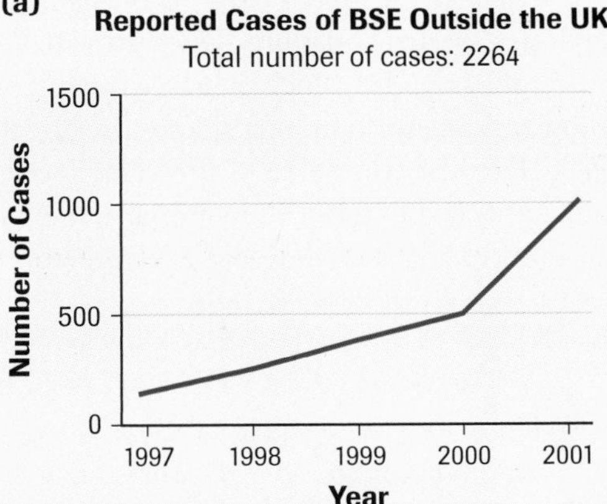

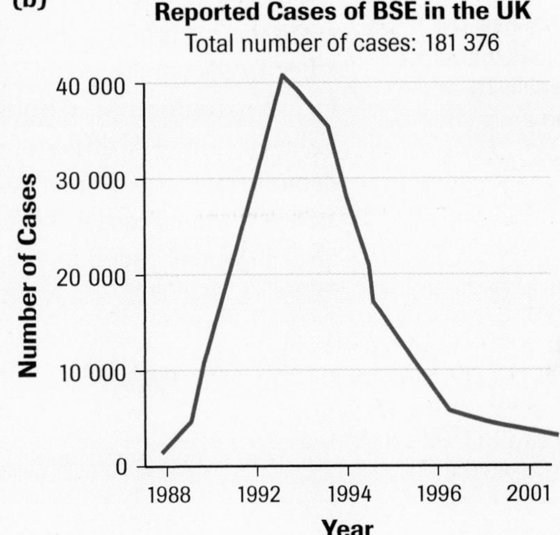

Figure 11
Reported cases of BSE

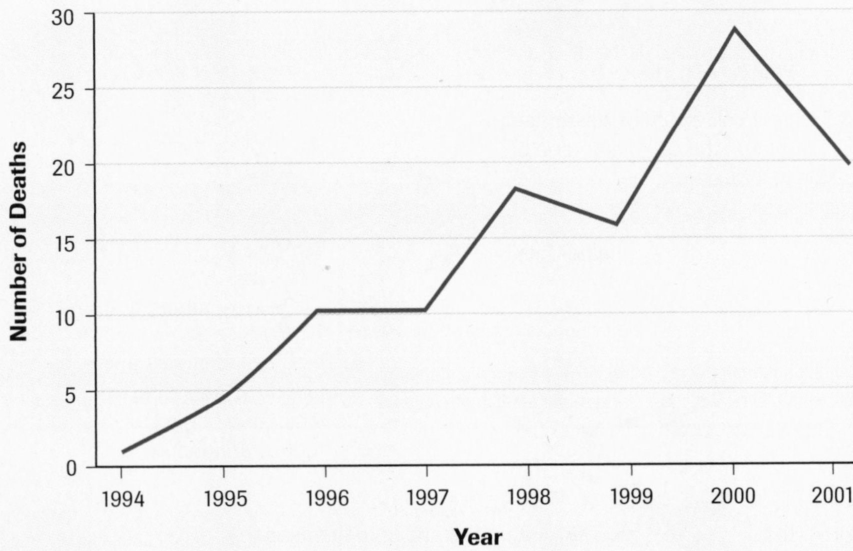

Figure 12
Global deaths from vCJD

Recognizing Harmful Antigens

Figure 13 illustrates how the body recognizes harmful antigens. The T cells roam the body in search of foreign invaders that pose a threat to survival. The macrophages attack the invaders and engulf them. The foreign antigen markers are not destroyed with the invader but are pushed to the cell membrane of the macrophage. Pressing the antigens into its cell membrane, the macrophage couples with T cells referred to as **helper T cells**. The T cells read the antigen's shape and release a chemical messenger called **lymphokine**. The lymphokine causes the B cells to divide into identical cells called clones. Later, a second message is sent from the helper T cells to the B cells, triggering the production of antibodies. Each B cell produces a specific type of antibody. By the time the B cells enter the circulatory system, many antibodies are attached to their cell membranes.

The helper T cells activate an additional defender, the **killer T cells**. As the name suggests, these lymphocytes carry out search-and-destroy missions. Once activated, the killer T cells puncture the cell membrane of the intruder, which may be a fungus, protozoan parasite, or bacterium. Viruses, however, are much more insidious because they hide within the confines of the host cell. Here, the true value of the killer T cells is demonstrated. Once the viral coat is found attached to the cell's membrane, the T cell attacks the infected cell. By destroying the infected body cell, the killer T cell prevents the virus from reproducing.

helper T cell a T cell with receptors that bind to fragments of antigens

lymphokine a protein produced by the T cells that acts as a chemical messenger between other T cells and B cells

killer T cell a T cell that destroys microbes, body cells infected with viruses, and mutated cells by puncturing cell membranes

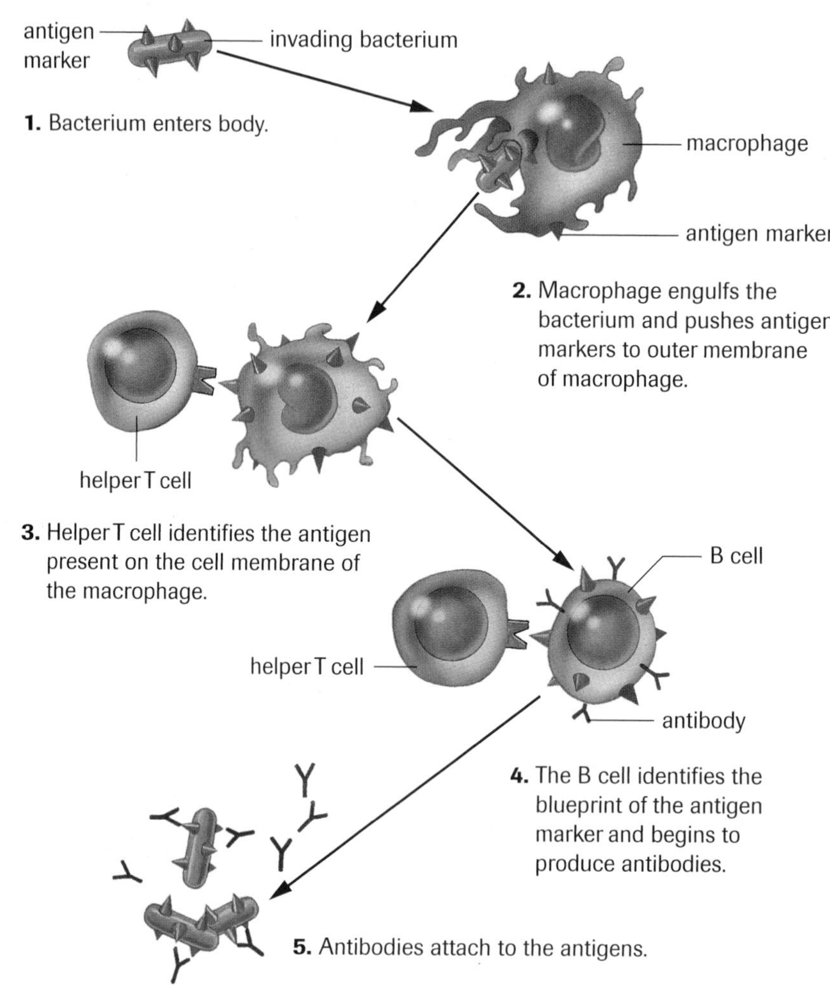

antigen marker
invading bacterium
1. Bacterium enters body.
macrophage
antigen marker
2. Macrophage engulfs the bacterium and pushes antigen markers to outer membrane of macrophage.
helper T cell
3. Helper T cell identifies the antigen present on the cell membrane of the macrophage.
B cell
helper T cell
antibody
4. The B cell identifies the blueprint of the antigen marker and begins to produce antibodies.
5. Antibodies attach to the antigens.

Figure 13
The immune system recognizes harmful antigens.

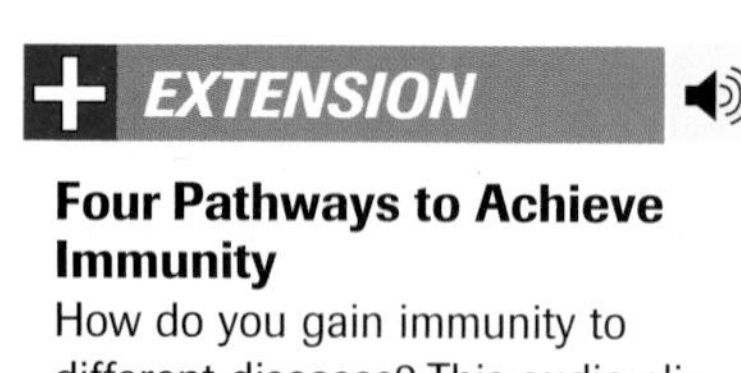

EXTENSION

Four Pathways to Achieve Immunity

How do you gain immunity to different diseases? This audio clip will discuss the four different ways to acquire immunity to specific diseases.

www.science.nelson.com

GO

Killer T cells also destroy mutated cells (**Figure 14**). This is an extremely important process because some of the altered cells may be cancerous. Many experts believe that everyone develops cancerous cells, but, in most cases, the T cells eliminate them before a tumour forms. Killer T cells may also account for the body's rejection of transplanted organs. Antigen markers on the cell membranes of the donor will be different from those of the recipient. Once the foreign markers of the transplanted tissue are recognized, the recipient's killer T cells initiate an assault. Immunosuppressant drugs, such as cyclosporin, can slow the killer T cells. Unfortunately, individuals who receive these drugs become susceptible to bacterial infections. One of the leading causes of death for an organ transplant patient is pneumonia.

Once the battle against foreign invaders has been won, another T cell, the **suppressor T cell**, inhibits the immune system response. Communication between the helper T cells and the suppressor T cells ensures that the body maintains adequate numbers of antibodies to contain the invading antigen. Most of the B cells and T cells will die off within a few days after the battle, but a small contingent will remain long after to guard the site. Phagocytes survey the area, cleaning up the debris left from dead and injured cells.

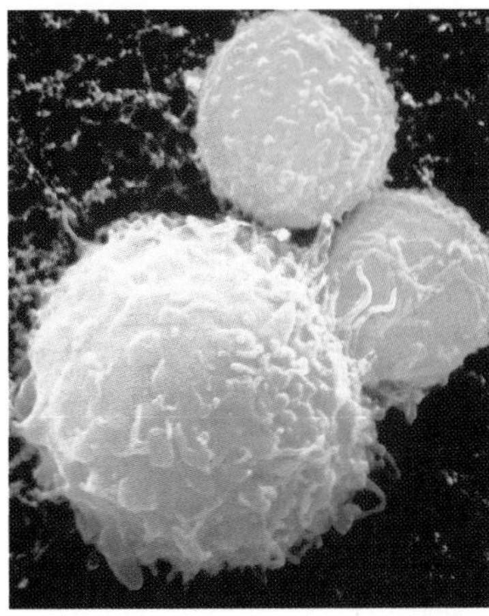

Figure 14
Killer T cells bind with a tumour cell.

suppressor T cell a T cell that turns off the immune system

The Immune System's Memory

The Aboriginal population of Hawaii was nearly annihilated by measles in the late 18th and early 19th centuries after British explorer James Cook and his sailors unwittingly introduced the disease when they arrived at the Hawaiian Islands. In North America, the Aboriginal population was decimated by epidemics of smallpox. Because neither group had been exposed to these viruses before, they had no antibodies to fight infection. At this time, Europeans and Asians, unlike the Aboriginal populations of Hawaii and North America, had long been exposed to many types of viruses and were better able to produce antibodies to fight them.

As mentioned earlier, the helper T cells must read a blueprint of the invader before B cells produce antibodies. This blueprint is stored even after the invader is destroyed so that subsequent infections can be stopped before the microbe gains a foothold. Immunity is based on maintaining an adequate number of antibodies. It is believed that a **memory B cell** is generated during the infection. Like helper T cells, the memory B cells hold an imprint of the antigen that characterizes the invader. Most T cells and B cells produced to fight the infection die within a few days; however, the memory B cells remain. During a subsequent infection, the memory B cells identify the invader and quickly mobilize antibody-producing B cells. Invading pathogens are defeated before they become established. As long as the memory B cell survives, the individual is immune.

Immune Memory

Watch this brief simulation of how B cells help the body respond faster to antigens the body has encountered before.

www.science.nelson.com GO

memory B cell a B cell that retains information about the shape of an antigen

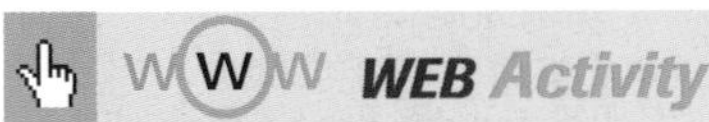

Simulation—Virtual Immunology Laboratory

How does your immune system respond to foreign invaders? How do antibodies know which antigen to attack? Can the formation of antibodies be used to diagnose disease? In this activity, you will use an ELISA (enzyme-linked immunosorbent assay) to detect either the antigen or antibody associated with a disease-causing agent. After you have finished the simulation, create a model to depict how the main components of the immune system function.

www.science.nelson.com GO

SUMMARY The Body's Lines of Defence

- Skin and mucous membranes provide physical barriers that prevent most infectious organisms from entering the body.
- Leukocytes (white blood cells), produced in the bone marrow, fight infection in a variety of ways. Phagocytosis of invading microbes is one of the main methods used by certain leukocytes to combat infection.
- Tissue damage due to physical injury initiates the inflammatory response, which is a nonspecific immune response resulting in swelling, redness, heat, and pain.
- Antibodies attach to foreign antigens, such as microbes and toxins. Each antibody is specific and can only bind its complementary antigen.

Table 1 Lymphocytes Involved in the Immune Response

Cell	Function
helper T cells	act as sentries to identify foreign invading substances
B cells	produce antibodies
killer T cells	puncture cell membranes of infected cells, thereby killing the cell
suppressor T cells	turn off the immune system
memory B cells	retain information about the shape of an antigen

Section 11.2 Questions

1. How does lysozyme protect the body against invading microbes?
2. Outline protective mechanisms provided by the respiratory tract.
3. How do monocytes protect against microbes?
4. Explain why swelling and pus at the site of an injury are signs that the immune system is functioning.
5. Define and contrast these terms: antigen, antibody; T cell lymphocytes, B cell lymphocytes; macrophages, lymphocytes.
6. Explain how B cell, helper T cell, and killer T cell lymphocytes provide immunity.
7. How do antibodies defeat antigens? Describe four contributions that antibodies make to the immune system.
8. How do memory B cells provide continuing immunity?
9. A patient displaying a high fever may be asked by the physician to have blood tests done. One of these tests would likely be a white blood cell count. Explain what an abnormal result might indicate.
10. A research group has begun testing on a potential cure for type 1 diabetes, an inherited disease caused by the destruction of the insulin-producing cells in the pancreas by one's own immune system. An immunosuppressant drug is administered twice daily to a test group of 150 people.
    (a) Why can the immunosuppressant drug prevent diabetes?
    (b) Researchers found that the drug wasn't effective once symptoms for diabetes were expressed in test subjects. What conclusions can you draw about this?
    (c) Explain why researchers are working on a test to identify antibodies that destroy insulin-producing cells.
    (d) List three important research questions that remain to be answered.

Malfunctions of the Immune System 11.3

Abnormal functioning of the immune system can cause two types of problems: immunodeficiency diseases and inappropriate attacks of the immune system against nonthreatening agents. Immunodeficiency diseases may be caused by a foreign agent, such as HIV, which attacks T cells, or a hereditary condition, such as severe combined immunodeficiency (SCID). The gene mutation that causes SCID results in the inability to produce B cells and T cells. Cancer therapy or prolonged exposure to anti-inflammatory drugs, such as cortisol, can also reduce the effectiveness of the immune system.

Inappropriate or exaggerated immune responses can also create problems. A hypersensitivity to harmless agents (an allergy) or a response in which the immune system begins to attack normal cells in one's own body (an autoimmune disease) can destroy tissues and organs.

Allergies

Allergies occur when your immune system mistakes harmless antigens for harmful invaders. If you are allergic to peanuts, your immune system recognizes one of the proteins in the peanut as dangerous. Although the protein is quite safe, your body mobilizes the antibody strike force against it. Tissue swelling and mucus secretion and, sometimes, constricted air passages are part of the immune response. Dust, ragweed, strawberries, and leaf moulds do not pose any direct threat to life, but the immune response to these agents can sometimes be so severe that it becomes life threatening.

A severe allergic reaction is an anaphylactic reaction (**Figure 1**), which involves the respiratory and circulatory systems. It often is accompanied by swelling of different body parts, hives, and itching. When you ingest something, like food or medicine, to which you are allergic, cells that "believe" they are endangered release a chemical messenger, called *bradykinin,* which stimulates the release of another chemical, *histamine.* Histamine is produced by the circulating white blood cells known as basophils and by mast cells found in connective tissues. Histamine changes the cells of the capillaries, increasing

DID YOU KNOW ?

Peanut Allergy

Peanut allergy is the most common cause of food anaphylaxis (anaphylactic shock from foods). Ingesting minute amounts can lead to a rapid reaction resulting in death within minutes. Because a reaction may recur even after an initial epinephrine injection, the affected person must be immediately hospitalized. Traces of peanut from a knife, plate, countertop, or even from kissing someone who has eaten peanuts can trigger a reaction. For those who are sensitive to peanuts, avoiding peanut products is crucial but also difficult. In Canada, annual peanut butter consumption is estimated to be about 3 kg per person. Many processed foods contain the ingredient "hydrolyzed vegetable protein," which may contain peanut protein.

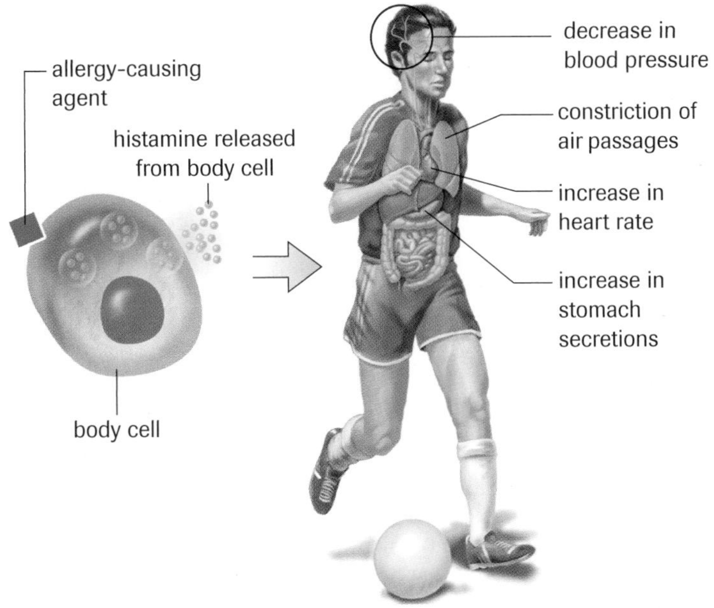

Figure 1
The body's response to an allergy-causing agent

permeability. The enlarged capillary causes the area to redden. Proteins and white blood cells leave the capillary in search of the foreign invader, but, in doing so, they alter the osmotic pressure. The proteins in the extracellular fluid create another osmotic force that opposes the osmotic force in the capillaries. Less water is absorbed into the capillaries, and tissues swell. These reactions can be brought on by drugs, vaccines, and some foods (peanuts, shellfish, eggs, berries, and milk) in individuals who are sensitive to these substances. Anaphylactic shock can occur very quickly. Weakness, sweating, and difficulty breathing are indicators of the condition. Nausea, diarrhea, and a drop in blood pressure may also occur. Medical precautions may range from carrying a kit with epinephrine to carrying antihistamines. People with severe food allergies should wear a medical alert bracelet or necklace and read all food labels carefully.

Autoimmune Diseases

The immune system can make mistakes. As you have already learned, allergies are caused when the immune system perceives harmless substances to be dangerous. The immune system can also go awry and launch an attack on the body's own cells. The renegade lymphocytes treat the body's cells as foreign and make antibodies to attach to their cell membranes. Many researchers believe that most people have mutated T cells and B cells that are capable of attacking the body; however, the renegade cells are usually held in check. The suppressor T cells play an important role in recognizing and intercepting the renegade T cells and B cells. One theory suggests that the suppressors secrete a substance that tells the macrophages to engulf the renegade cells.

The failure of the suppressor T cells to control the renegade cells can be seen in autoimmune diseases such as rheumatoid arthritis, in which an immune response is mounted against the connective tissues of the joints. Rheumatic fever, another autoimmune disorder, results from an exaggerated immune response that scars the heart muscle. Type 1 diabetes is caused by an immune reaction against the insulin-producing cells of the pancreas, and lupus is caused by the accumulation of antigen–antibody complexes that build up in the walls of blood vessels, joints, kidneys, and skin. Multiple sclerosis (MS) is an autoimmune disease in which T cells of the body initiate an attack on the myelin sheath of nerve cells. In the advanced stages of MS, paralysis results from the destruction of the insulation of the nerve cell provided by the myelin sheath.

Drugs or serious infections can weaken the suppressor T cells, leaving the body vulnerable to autoimmune diseases. We know that the number of suppressor T cells declines with age, increasing the incidence of rheumatoid arthritis and other autoimmune diseases. Some individuals are born with defective suppressor T cells. Although no single cure exists, immune-suppressing drugs have been developed that reduce the intensity of the attack by the renegade cells.

CAREER CONNECTION

Pathologist
Pathologists are medical doctors who diagnose diseases and advise other physicians and surgeons about the treatment of diseases such as cancer. Pathologists perform tests on human tissue and blood to determine the type and extent of disease. Forensic pathologists specialize in determining the cause of death in forensic investigations. Find out if this is a career direction for you.

www.science.nelson.com 

DID YOU KNOW ?

Organ Donation in Canada
Canada's organ donation rate is among the lowest of all the developed countries—more than 3000 Canadians are waiting for an organ transplant. One organ donor can donate numerous organs and tissues including lungs, heart, liver, kidneys, pancreas, bowel, eye tissue, skin, heart valves, bone, tendons, veins, and ligaments. You can indicate your wish to become an organ donor on your health card. Discuss this decision with your family so your wishes are known.

Organ Transplant Rejection

The main challenge with any tissue or organ transplant is the immune response of the recipient—that is, the immune system's ability to distinguish between "self" and "nonself." The donor organ is often identified as a foreign invader by distinctive protein markers on its cell membranes. The distinctive marker (known as major histocompatability complex, or MHC) is a protein fingerprint unique to each individual. The recipient makes antibodies designed to destroy the foreign invader.

Kidney transplants can be used as an example. Living donor kidneys account for about 15 % of all kidney transplants. Because humans are born with two kidneys, the donor is able to give one kidney without significant effects on quality of life. A single kidney can carry out the filtering and osmoregulatory functions of the body. To reduce rejections, attempts are made to match the MHC of the tissues of donors and recipients as closely as possible. For living donor transplants, physicians usually look to close relatives because the MHC is genetically controlled. The better the match, the greater the chances of long-term success.

Kidney transplants from recently deceased donors account for the vast majority of transplants. However, the need for organs far surpasses supply (**Figure 2**). Again, as with living donors, close matching is essential. Not every donor kidney is appropriate for a specific recipient. To help reduce rejection, even for close matches, immunosuppressant drugs can be given. However, a drug that minimizes the fight against foreign tissues will also reduce the immune system's ability to fight off invading viruses and bacteria. These drugs place patients at risk of infections.

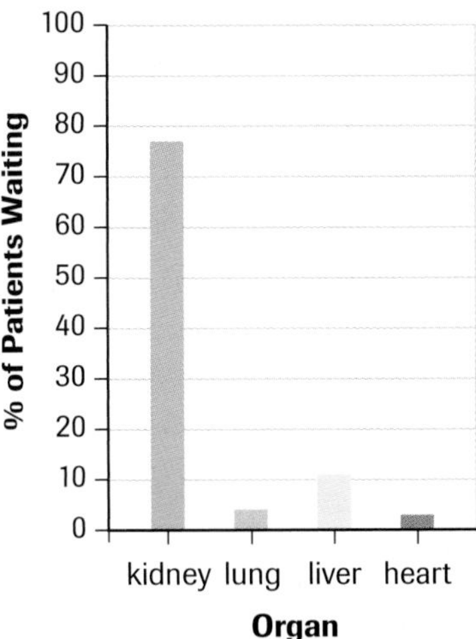

Figure 2
Percentage of all patients waiting for a transplant, by organ type. Kidney transplants are the second most common transplant in Canada (corneal transplants rank number one) and the most common organ transplant.

Organ Transplants in Alberta

Alberta's Capital Health Regional Transplant Program, located at the University of Alberta Hospital and Stollery Children's Hospital in Edmonton, provides transplants for adults and children from Alberta, Saskatchewan, the Northwest Territories, and British Columbia (**Table 1**). Its survival rates are among the best in Canada, and it is the only program in the country that provides all types of organ and tissue transplants.

The HOPE (Human Organ Procurement and Exchange) Program is responsible for the coordination, recovery, and distribution of organs in Alberta. HOPE also promotes awareness of organ and tissue donation. The Comprehensive Tissue Centre is one of only two accredited tissue banks in Canada. Transplanted tissues include eyes (cornea and sclera), skin, heart valves, and bone.

Table 1 Alberta's Capital Health Regional Transplant Program, 2004

Organ transplanted	Quantity
heart	28
heart/lung	1
lung	24
liver	71
kidney	84
kidney/pancreas	13
pancreas	1

Stem Cell Research

The answer for replacing damaged tissues and organs may lie in stem cell research rather than transplantation. Stem cells can develop into a variety of different tissues such as epithelial, muscle, or nerve. Intestinal stem cells reline the gut; skin stem cells replace cells that are continuously sloughed off; and stem cells in the bone marrow give rise to a wide range of blood cells. Stem cells are **pluripotent cells**, meaning they can give rise to different types of body cells.

In 1998, James Thomson, a researcher at the University of Wisconsin, demonstrated that human stem cells could transform into a variety of cells, such as those that form the bone marrow, brain, muscle, skin, pancreas, liver, or practically any human tissue. If it were possible to regulate the development of human stem cells, the cells could replace destroyed islet cells that produce insulin, repair damaged cartilage, or repair cardiac tissue that has been destroyed by heart disease.

Dr. Freda Miller and colleagues at the Montreal Neurological Institute (MNI) have discovered multipotent stem cells in adult skin. These skin cells can be directed to become neurons or even muscle cells.

pluripotent cell a cell that is capable of developing into a number of specialized cell, such as neuron or muscle cell

EXPLORE an issue

The Future of Stem Cell Research

Issue Checklist

- ○ Issue
- ● Resolution
- ○ Design
- ● Evidence
- ● Analysis
- ● Evaluation

The greatest challenge of organ transplants is to trick the recipient's immune system into accepting the new organ. Finding someone with a close tissue match to donate an organ can be extremely difficult. What if the person who needs a transplant could use his or her own stem cells to repair the damaged organ?

Statement

Governments should redirect some funding from organ transplant research to autologous (i.e., originating from the same individual) stem cell research.

1. Investigate this rapidly changing field of research. Search for information in newspapers, periodicals, CD-ROMs, and on the Internet.

www.science.nelson.com 

2. Prepare a list of points and counterpoints. You might consider these questions:
   (i) Researchers are working on ways to use mature cells as a source for stem cells. How will this change the prospects for successful treatment?
   (ii) Companies have applied for patents on specific stem cells and techniques used to culture stem cells. These companies will own a medical procedure and collect huge royalties. Should this be allowed?
   (iii) Speculate why many people object to stem cell research.
   (iv) Why are governments regulating this field of research?
3. Decide whether you agree or disagree with the statement.
   (a) Prepare an outline.
   (b) Write your position paper.
   (c) Prepare to defend your position in class.

SUMMARY Malfunctions of the Immune System

- Abnormal functioning of the immune system can cause two types of problems: immunodeficiency diseases and inappropriate immune responses (allergic reactions and autoimmune diseases).
- Allergies occur when the immune system mistakes harmless antigens for harmful invaders.
- Autoimmune diseases occur when lymphocytes treat the body's cells as foreign.

Section 11.3 Questions

1. What are allergies?
2. Explain how an allergic reaction to peanuts can be life threatening.
3. Why is epinephrine administered as a treatment for a severe allergic reaction?
4. What causes autoimmune diseases?
5. What evidence suggests that suppressor T cells may be a significant factor in autoimmune diseases?
6. Why do donor organs have to be matched to the recipients?
7. Select an autoimmune disease and research the latest medical advance toward a cure. Search for information in newspapers, periodicals, CD-ROMs, and on the Internet.

www.science.nelson.com 

8. Research the role of histamines in an allergic reaction.

INVESTIGATION 11.1

Report Checklist

● Purpose	● Design	● Analysis
● Problem	○ Materials	● Evaluation
● Hypothesis	○ Procedure	● Synthesis
● Prediction	● Evidence	

Diagnosing Disease by Examining Blood Cells

White blood cell counts can be used as clues in the diagnosis of disease. In this activity, you will examine prepared slides to identify different types of white blood cells and to determine how changes in blood cell counts are used to diagnose disease.

The slides have been prepared using Wright's stain, which allows you to clearly view cells and many types of microorganisms. Wright's and similar stains for blood and bone marrow smears are mixtures of acidic and basic dyes. According to the number of acid and basic groups present, cell components absorb the dyes from the mixture in various proportions.

Materials

prepared slide of human blood
light microscope
lens paper

Procedure

1. Before beginning the investigation, clean all microscope lenses with lens paper and rotate the nosepiece to the low-power objective. Place the slide of blood on the stage, and focus under low power. Locate an area in which individual blood cells can be seen.
2. Rotate the revolving nosepiece to the medium-power objective and focus. Red blood cells greatly outnumber white blood cells.

(a) Draw a single human red blood cell.

(b) Estimate the size of the human red blood cell. Show your calculation.

3. Scan the field of view for different white blood cells. Using the classification of leukocytes provided in **Table 1**, classify the leukocytes and record your results.
4. Repeat the procedure by scanning 10 different visual fields. Record the data in your table.

Analysis

(c) Explain why few blood tests provide a diagnosis of disease.

Table 1 Classification of Leukocytes

Type	Description	Normal proportion (%)	Observed number	Observed proportion (%)
Granulocyte	granular cytoplasm			
neutrophil	3-lobed nucleus, 10 μm (Wright's stain: purple nucleus, pink granules)	65		
eosinophil	2-lobed nucleus, 13 μm (Wright's stain: blue nucleus, red granules)	2–4		
basophil	2-lobed nucleus, 14 μm (Wright's stain: blue-black nucleus, blue-black granules)	0.5		
Agranulocyte	nongranular cytoplasm			
monocyte	U-shaped nucleus, 15 μm (Wright's stain: light bluish-purple nucleus, no granules)	4–7		
lymphocyte (small)	large nucleus, 7 μm (Wright's stain: dark bluish-purple nucleus, no granules)	2–3		
lymphocyte (large)	large nucleus, 10 μm (Wright's stain: dark bluish-purple nucleus, no granules)	20–25		

Synthesis

Blood tests are used to help diagnose disease. **Table 2** shows some changes in leukocyte counts and the conditions associated with those changes. Use **Table 2** to answer the following questions:

(d) Why would a physician not diagnose leukemia based on a single blood test?

(e) What information might a blood test provide about a patient being treated for the lung disease tuberculosis? Why would blood tests be taken even after the disease has been diagnosed?

(f) Leukemia can be caused by the uncontrolled division of cells from two different sites: the bone marrow or lymph nodes. Indicate how blood tests could be used to determine which site harbours the cancerous tumour.

(g) Do blood donors need to have their blood counts taken? Why or why not?

Table 2 Health Conditions Associated with Abnormal Leukocytes

Leukocyte change	Associated conditions
increased eosinophils	allergic condition, cholera, scarlet fever, granulocytic leukemia
increased neutrophils	toxic chemical, newborn acidosis, hemorrhage, rheumatic fever, severe burns, acidosis
decreased neutrophils	pernicious anemia, protozoan infection, malnutrition, aplastic anemia
increased monocytes	tuberculosis (active), monocytic leukemia, protozoan infection, mononucleosis
increased lymphocytes	tuberculosis (healing), lymphocytic leukemia, mumps

Chapter 11 SUMMARY

Outcomes

Knowledge

- describe the main components of blood and their role in transport, blood clotting, and in resisting the influence of pathogens, i.e., erythrocytes, leukocytes, platelets, plasma (11.1, 11.2)
- describe the ABO and Rh blood groups on the basis of antigens and antibodies (11.1)
- explain the sequence of the blood clotting process (11.1)
- describe and explain, in general terms, the function of the lymphatic system (11.2)
- list the main cellular and non-cellular components of the human defence system and describe their role, i.e., skin, macrophage, helper T cell, B cell, killer T cell, suppressor T cell, and memory B cell (11.2)

STS

- explain how Canadian society supports scientific research and technological development that help achieve a sustainable society, economy, and environment (11.2)
- explain that decisions regarding the application of scientific and technological developments involve a variety of perspectives (11.3)

Skills

- conduct investigations and gather and record data and information by: determining the morphology and abundance of cellular components in a prepared human blood slide (11.1) and; researching and designing a simulation or model of the functioning of the main components of the human immune system (11.2)
- analyze data and apply mathematical and conceptual models (11.2)
- work as members of a team and apply the skills and conventions of science (all)

Key Terms

11.1

plasma
erythrocyte
anemia
leukocyte
platelet
thrombus
embolus
antigen
antibody
agglutination

11.2

phagocytosis
macrophage
pus
inflammatory response
complement protein
T cell
B cell
receptor sites
helper T cell
lymphokine
killer T cell
suppressor T cell
memory B cell

11.3

pluripotent cell

MAKE a summary

1. Imagine a microbe entering your blood. Create a flow chart or diagram that shows how the immune system would respond to this potentially dangerous situation. Label the diagram with as many of the key terms as possible.
2. Revisit your answers to the Starting Points questions at the start of the chapter. Would you answer the questions differently now? Why?

Go To

The following components are available on the Nelson Web site. Follow the links for *Nelson Biology Alberta 20–30.*

- an interactive Self Quiz for Chapter 11
- additional Diploma Exam-style Review Questions
- Illustrated Glossary
- additional IB-related material

There is more information on the Web site wherever you see the Go icon in the chapter.

EXTENSION

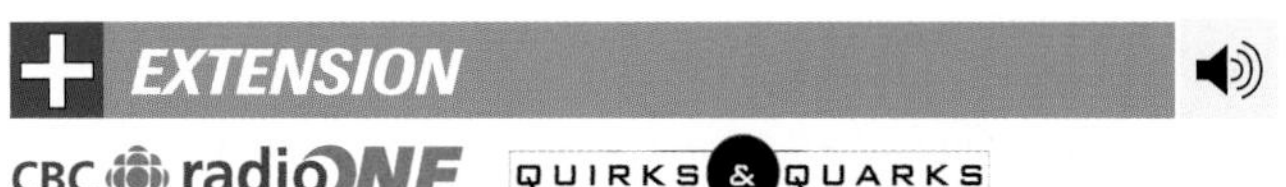

The Path of Least Resistance: Alternatives to Antibiotics

More and more strains of bacteria are appearing that are resistant to antibiotics. Three researchers, Dr. Tania Watts (University of Toronto), Dr. Bob Hancock (University of British Columbia), and Dr. Gregor Reid (University of Western Ontario), discuss their research into alternatives to antibiotics.

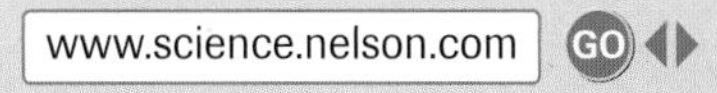

EXTENSION

Pandemic Flu

Will the virus that causes bird flu develop the ability to move from person to person?

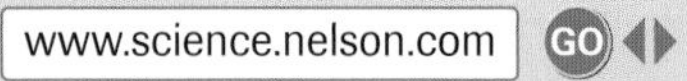

Many of these questions are in the style of the Diploma Exam. You will find guidance for writing Diploma Exams in Appendix A5. Science Directing Words used in Diploma Exams are in bold type. Exam study tips and test-taking suggestions are on the Nelson Web site.

www.science.nelson.com 

DO NOT WRITE IN THIS TEXTBOOK.

Part 1

1. The introduction of a microbe into the bloodstream will result in the production of (1) _____________ by (2) _____________.
   A. (1) antigens, (2) erythrocytes
   B. (1) antibodies, (2) erythrocytes
   C. (1) antigens, (2) leukocytes
   D. (1) antibodies, (2) leukocytes

2. **Identify** two functions of proteins found in the plasma.
   A. acting as antigens and blood clotting
   B. acting as antibodies and maintaining osmotic balance
   C. carrying oxygen and clotting blood
   D. phagocytosis and acting as antibodies

3. The ability of blood to clot can be reduced by
   A. ruptured platelets
   B. low calcium concentration in the blood
   C. high levels of thrombin
   D. high levels of iron in red blood cells

4. **Identify** which of the following is not involved in the body's defence system.
   A. skin
   B. erythrocytes
   C. macrophages
   D. cilia

Use the following information to answer questions 5 and 6.

A kinesiologist measured the factors related to circulation shown in **Table 1** in four different subjects.

Table 1 Cardiovascular Measurements of Four Subjects

Measurement	Subject W (normal)	Subject X	Subject Y	Subject Z
cardiac output (L/min)	5.1	7.2	5.4	4.0
white blood cell count (per mm^3 of blood)	8000	7900	15 000	8200
O_2 content of arterial blood (mL/100 mL of blood)	19.5	10.2	19.0	17.5

5. Which subject is most likely suffering from a bacterial infection?
   A. Subject X: low levels of oxygen in the blood occur when someone has an infection
   B. Subject Y: higher leukocyte levels produce more antibodies
   C. Subject Z: lower cardiac output conserves energy
   D. Subject Y or Subject Z: both have higher cardiac output to deliver more nutrients to tissues

6. Which subject is most likely suffering from anemia?
   A. Subject X: low levels of oxygen occur in the blood when someone has an infection
   B. Subject X: low levels of oxygen occur with a deficiency of hemoglobin
   C. Subject Y: higher leukocyte levels produce more antibodies
   D. Subject Z: low cardiac output conserves energy

Use the information in **Figure 1** to answer questions 7 and 8.

Antigens and Antibodies of Four Blood Groups

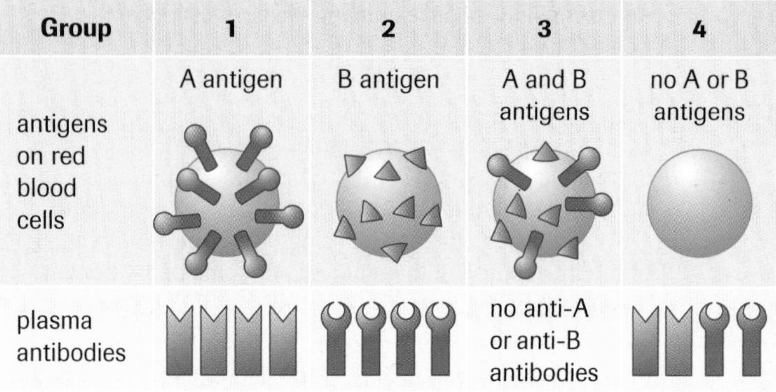

Group	1	2	3	4
antigens on red blood cells	A antigen	B antigen	A and B antigens	no A or B antigens
plasma antibodies			no anti-A or anti-B antibodies	

Figure 1

7. According to **Figure 1**, blood type A would be represented by
   A. group 1
   B. group 2
   C. group 3
   D. group 4

8. Blood group 3 has
   A. no antibodies because you do not produce antibodies against your own antigens.
   B. no antigens because you do not produce antigens against your own antibodies.
   C. no antibodies because you do not produce antigens against your own antibodies.
   D. no antigens because you do not produce antibodies against your own antibodies.

9. The following are steps involved in the immune response:
NR
1. Suppressor T cells inhibit the immune system.
2. Antibodies attach to antigens on bacterial cells.
3. B cells produce antibodies.
4. Bacterial cells enter the body and are engulfed by macrophages.

Give the numbers of the steps in the order that they occur, from first to last. (Record all four digits of your answer.)

Part 2

10. (a) **Sketch** an antibody, showing how it attaches to specific antigens.
(b) Label the receptor sites on the cell membrane.
(c) Use the diagram to **explain why** an antibody produced in response to the mumps virus would have no effect against influenza.
(d) Use the diagram to **explain** how antibodies target antigens for phagocytosis.

11. **Explain why** the second time an organism invades the body, the person is not likely to get seriously ill.

12. **Distinguish** between T cell lymphocytes and B cell lymphocytes.

13. **How** do viruses use the receptor sites to gain access into the cell?

14. **Explain why** T cells have difficulty identifying antigens from HIV.

15. **Describe** the function of lymphokine.

16. **Describe** in your own words the function of each of the following:
(a) killer T cells
(b) helper T cells
(c) suppressor T cells
(d) memory B cells

17. **Explain why** the Hawaiian population was so severely affected by measles and the Aboriginal population of North America was so much more susceptible to smallpox than Europeans were.

18. **Define** pluripotent cells.

19. **Why** does the likelihood of autoimmune disease increase with age?

20. **Explain** how a food allergy can threaten life.

Use the following information to answer questions 21 to 23.

The data in **Table 2** were collected from three patients.

Table 2 Blood Cell Counts and Temperature of Three Patients

Patient	Red blood cell count (cells/μL)	White blood cell count (cells/μL)	Body temperature (°C)
normal	5.0×10^6	7 000	37.0
X	2.0×10^6	3 000	37.0
Y	2.5×10^6	10 000	36.5
Z	5.1×10^6	15 000	39.0

21. Lead poisoning is characterized by a destruction of bone marrow. Which patient would you suspect has lead poisoning? **Justify** your choice.
DE

22. **Predict** which patient has a viral infection. Explain your answer.
DE

23. Leukemia is a cancer characterized by the proliferation of white blood cells. Which patient would you suspect has leukemia? **Justify** your choice.
DE

Use the following information to answer questions 24 and 25.

Before the work of Dr. Barry J. Marshall and Dr. Robert Warren of Perth, Australia, most doctors believed that stress was the cause of ulcers. In 1983, Marshall and Warren reported that *Helicobacter pylori*, a bacterium living in the stomach, is the most common cause of ulcers. Today, researchers around the world are turning to another bacterium, *Chlamydia pneumonia*, as the main culprit in triggering coronary heart disease.

24. If coronary heart disease is caused by a bacterium, **how** might this affect the search for treatment?
DE

25. **Explain why** physicians attempting to diagnose coronary heart disease may be monitoring antibodies.
DE

chapter 12 Excretory System

In this chapter

- Exploration: Making a Model of a Filtering Excretory System
- Lab Exercise 12.A: Comparing Solutes in the Plasma, Nephron, and Urine
- Web Activity: Kidney Function
- Investigation 12.1: Do Sports Drinks Really Work?
- Investigation 12.2: Diagnosis of Kidney Disorders
- Explore an Issue: Xenotransplants

In August 2000, Canadians Peter Reid and Lori Bowden won the Ironman Canada Triathlon men's and women's titles, completing the gruelling 226-km swim–cycle–run in 8 h, 29 min, and 49 s and 9 h, 17 min, and 23 s, respectively (**Figure 1**). The husband-and-wife team, dubbed "the world's fittest couple," went on to further victories: Peter once again won the Ironman Canada Triathlon in August 2001, and Lori won her third straight women's crown at the Australian Ironman competition in April 2001.

Imagine completing a 4-km swim and a 180-km bicycle ride only to have a 42-km marathon ahead of you. To meet the demands of this challenging competition, the body undergoes a series of adjustments to continue operating. One such adjustment is an increase in the rate of cellular respiration; another is a decrease in urine output.

The oxidation of glucose during cellular respiration generates waste energy in the form of heat. During severe strenuous exercise, body temperature can increase to more than 39 °C. To dissipate heat, sweat is produced.

The evaporation of sweat is a cooling process. The loss of water alters the volume of body fluids, which can cause a drop in blood pressure. The heart and circulatory system respond to changes in blood pressure, while the kidneys conserve water in an attempt to maintain fluid volume.

Water is not the only thing lost with sweating; many ions essential for nerve function and muscle contraction are carried to the skin with the perspiration. The kidneys are also responsible for maintaining the body's electrolyte balance.

STARTING points

Answer these questions as best you can with your current knowledge. Then, using the concepts and skills you have learned, you will revise your answers at the end of the chapter.

1. What dangers exist if your body is unable to regulate the fluid balance of your tissues?
2. What challenges would the body have to respond to if the kidneys failed to work?
3. Explain how the circulatory system and excretory system interact during exercise.

Career Connections:
Urologist; Emergency Medical Technician

Figure 1
Lori Bowden finished first in the women's Ironman Canada triathlon in 2000.

Exploration — Making a Model of a Filtering Excretory System

You can create a model of a filtering excretory system.

Materials: funnel, aquarium charcoal, 2 small beakers, food colouring, non-absorbent cotton, ring stand

- Place a small piece of non-absorbent cotton in a funnel. Fill the funnel with aquarium charcoal, and put a small beaker beneath the funnel. Fill a second beaker with about 25 mL of water, and add five drops of food colouring.
- Pour the coloured water through the funnel and collect it in the beaker beneath as shown in **Figure 2**.

(a) Compare the colour of the filtered water with the original coloured water.
(b) Predict what will happen if the water is filtered once again. Test your prediction.
(c) How would you improve the filter?

Figure 2
Model of a filtering excretory system

12.1 Waste Excretion and Internal Equilibrium

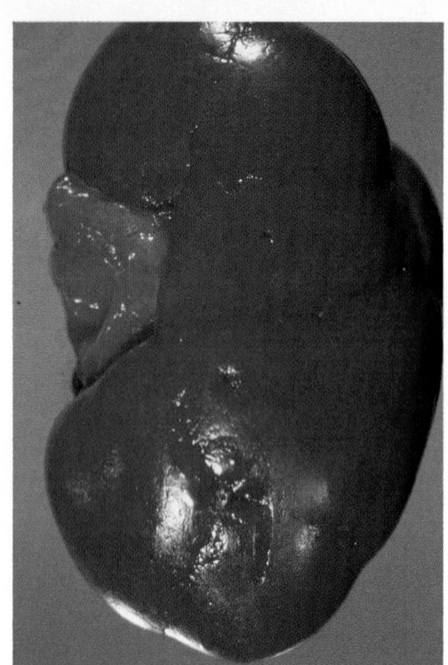

Figure 1 The human kidney is about the size of a fist and weighs approximately 0.5 kg.

The cells of the body obtain energy by converting complex organic compounds into simpler compounds. However, many of these simpler compounds can be harmful. To maintain life processes, the body must eliminate waste products. The lungs eliminate carbon dioxide, one of the products of cellular respiration. The liver transforms ingested toxins, such as alcohol and heavy metals, into soluble compounds that can be eliminated by the kidneys. The liver also transforms the hazardous products of protein metabolism into metabolites, which are then eliminated by the kidneys (**Figure 1**). In fact, the kidneys play a crucial role in removing waste, balancing blood pH, and maintaining water balance.

The average Canadian consumes more protein than is required to maintain tissues and promote cell growth. Excess protein is often converted into carbohydrates. Protein, unlike carbohydrates, contains nitrogen. The amino group (NH_2) that is characteristic of amino acids must be discarded by the body.

This process, referred to as **deamination**, occurs in the liver. The byproduct of deamination is ammonia, a water-soluble gas. However, ammonia is extremely toxic—a buildup of as little as 0.005 mg can kill humans. Fish are able to avoid ammonia buildup by continually releasing it through their gills. Land animals, however, do not have the ability to release small quantities of ammonia throughout the day—it must be stored. Once again, the liver is called into action. In the liver, two molecules of ammonia combine with another waste product, carbon dioxide, to form **urea**. Urea is 100 000 times less toxic than ammonia. The blood can dissolve 33 mg of urea per 100 mL of blood. A second waste product, **uric acid**, is formed by the breakdown of nucleic acids. **Table 1** summarizes the roles of various organs in the removal of metabolic waste.

The kidneys help maintain water balance. Although it is possible to survive for weeks without food, humans cannot survive for more than a few days without water. Humans deplete their water reserves faster than their food reserves. The average adult loses about 2 L of water every day through urine, perspiration, and exhaled air. Greater volumes are lost when physical activity increases. For the body to maintain water balance, humans must consume 2 L of fluids daily. A drop in fluid intake by as little as 1 % of your body mass will cause thirst, a decrease of 5 % will bring about extreme pain and collapse, while a decrease of 10 % will cause death.

deamination removal of an amino group from an organic compound

urea nitrogen waste formed from two molecules of ammonia and one molecule of carbon dioxide

uric acid a waste product formed from the breakdown of nucleic acids

Water and Solute Balance
This animation discusses the processes that influence water and solute balance in mammals.

www.science.nelson.com

DID YOU KNOW?

Uric Acid
Uric acid is found in the urine of only a few mammals: humans, higher apes, and Dalmatian dogs. The uric acid molecule has a structure similar to that of caffeine.

Table 1 Removal of Metabolic Waste

Waste product	Origin	Organ of excretion
ammonia	• deamination of amino acids by the liver	kidneys
urea	• deamination of amino acids by the liver • ammonia combined with carbon dioxide	kidneys; skin (small amounts)
uric acid	• product of the breakdown of nucleic acids, such as DNA	kidneys
carbon dioxide	• waste product of cellular respiration	lungs
bile pigments	• breakdown of red blood cell pigment hemoglobin	liver
lactic acid	• product of anaerobic respiration	liver

Anatomy of the Urinary System

Renal arteries branch from the abdominal aorta and carry blood to the kidneys. With a mass of about 0.5 kg each, the fist-shaped kidneys may hold as much as 25 % of the body's blood at any given time. **Figure 2** shows the position of the kidneys and other organs of the urinary system in the body. Wastes are filtered from the blood by the kidneys and conducted to the urinary bladder by **ureters.** A urinary sphincter muscle located at the base of the bladder acts as a valve, permitting the storage of urine. When approximately 200 mL of urine has been collected, the bladder stretches slightly and nerves send a signal to the brain. When the bladder fills to about 400 mL, more stretch receptors are activated and the message becomes more urgent. If a person continues to ignore the messages, the bladder continues to fill. After about 600 mL of urine has accumulated, voluntary control is lost. The sphincter relaxes, urine enters the **urethra**, and it is voided.

The cross section of the kidney in **Figure 2** reveals three structures. An outer layer of connective tissue, the **cortex**, encircles the kidney. An inner layer, the **medulla**, is found beneath the cortex. A hollow chamber, the **renal pelvis**, joins the kidney with the ureter.

ureter a tube that conducts urine from the kidney to the bladder

urethra the tube that carries urine from the bladder to the exterior of the body

cortex the outer layer of the kidney

medulla the area inside of the cortex

renal pelvis the hollow area where the kidney joins the ureter

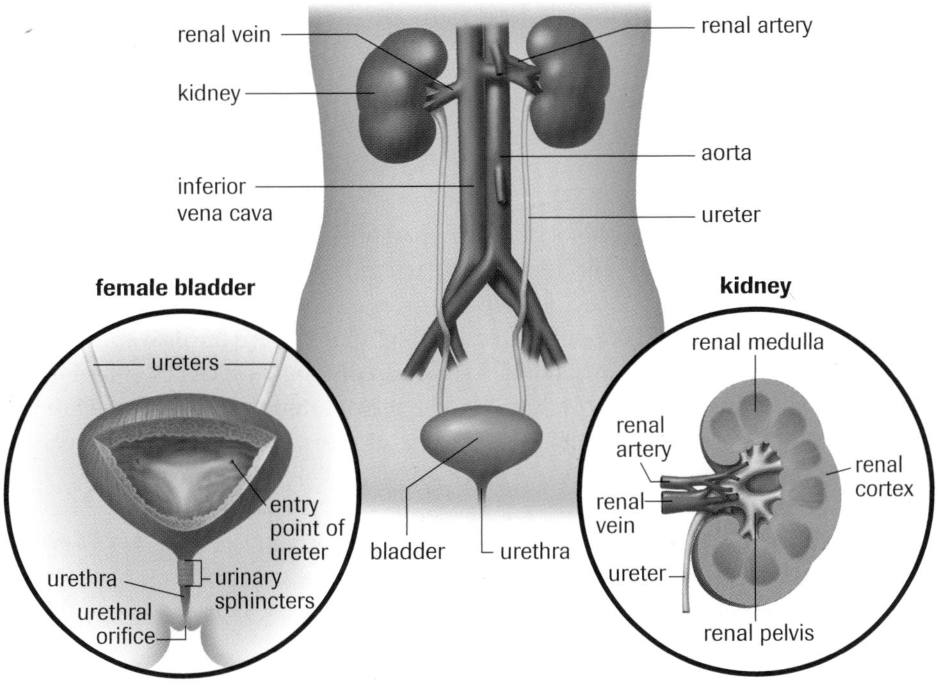

Figure 2
The human urinary system

Nephrons

Approximately one million slender tubules, called **nephrons**, are the functional units of the kidneys (**Figure 3**, next page). Small branches from the renal artery, the **afferent arterioles**, supply the nephrons with blood. The afferent arterioles branch into a capillary bed, called the **glomerulus.** Unlike other capillaries, the glomerulus does not transfer blood to a venule. Blood leaves the glomerulus by way of other arterioles, the **efferent arterioles**. Blood is carried from the efferent arterioles to a net of capillaries called **peritubular capillaries** that wrap around the kidney tubule. Blood leaves the nephron via a venule that joins the renal vein.

nephron a functional unit of the kidney

afferent arteriole a small branch of the renal artery that carries blood to the glomerulus

glomerulus the high-pressure capillary bed that is the site of filtration

efferent arteriole a small branch of the renal artery that carries blood away from the glomerulus to the peritubular capillaries

peritubular capillary a member of the network of small blood vessels that surround the tubule of the nephron

Figure 3
Diagram of a nephron showing the glomerulus and Bowman's capsule

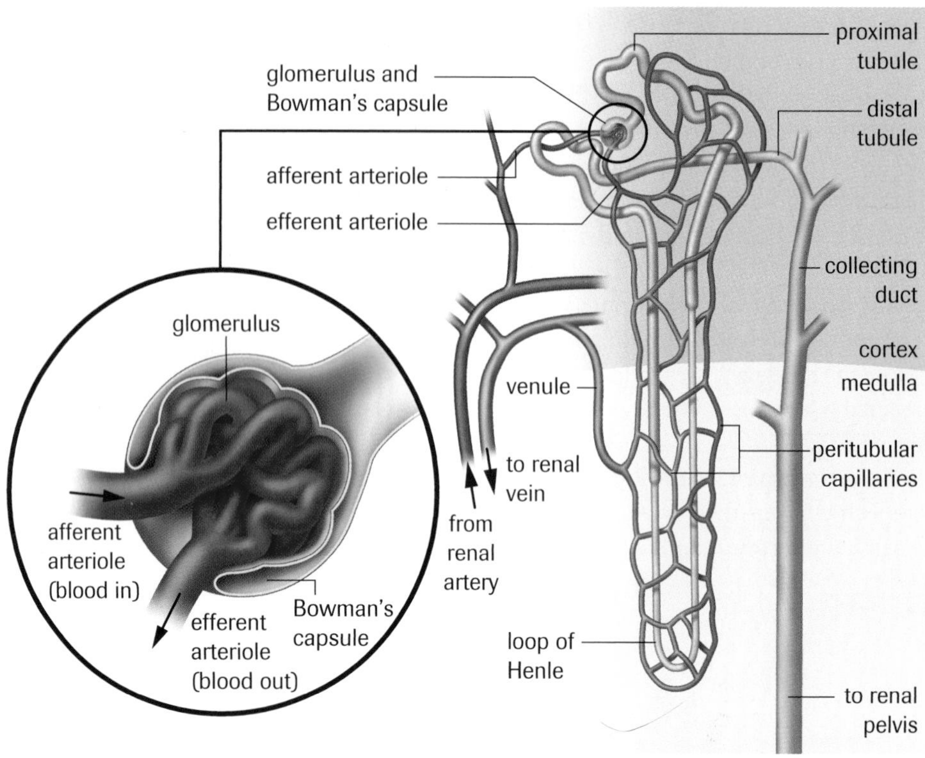

Bowman's capsule the cuplike structure that surrounds the glomerulus

proximal tubule the section of the nephron joining the Bowman's capsule with the loop of Henle

loop of Henle the section of the tubule that carries filtrate from the proximal tubule to the distal tubule

distal tubule conducts urine from the loop of Henle to the collecting duct

collecting duct a tube that carries urine from nephrons to the renal pelvis

The glomerulus is surrounded by a funnel-like part of the nephron called the **Bowman's capsule**. The Bowman's capsule, the afferent arteriole, and the efferent arteriole are located in the cortex of the kidney. Fluid to be processed into urine enters the Bowman's capsule from the blood. The capsule tapers to a thin tubule, called the **proximal tubule**. Urine is carried from the proximal tubule to the **loop of Henle**, which descends into the medulla of the kidney. Urine moves through the **distal tubule**, the last segment of the nephron, into the **collecting ducts**. As the name suggests, the collecting ducts collect urine from many nephrons that, in turn, merge in the pelvis of the kidney.

Practice

1. Describe the two main functions of the kidneys.
2. What is deamination and why is it an important process?
3. How does the formation of urea prevent poisoning?

Formation of Urine

Urine formation depends on three functions. Filtration is accomplished by the movement of fluid from the blood into the Bowman's capsule. Reabsorption involves the transfer of essential solutes and water from the nephron back into the blood. Secretion involves the transport of materials from the blood into the nephron.

Filtration

Each nephron of the kidney has an independent blood supply. Blood moves through the afferent arteriole into the glomerulus, a high-pressure filter. Normally, pressure in a capillary bed is about 25 mmHg. The pressure in the glomerulus is about 65 mmHg.

Structure of the Glomerulus
This animation provides a closer look at the structure of the glomerulus, and its role in urine formation (filtration).

www.science.nelson.com 

Dissolved solutes pass through the walls of the glomerulus into the Bowman's capsule. Although materials move from areas of high pressure to areas of low pressure, not all materials enter the capsule. Scientists have extracted fluid from the glomerulus and Bowman's capsule using a thin glass tube called a micropipette. **Table 2** compares sample solutes extracted from the glomerulus and Bowman's capsule.

Plasma protein, blood cells, and platelets are too large to move through the walls of the glomerulus. Smaller molecules pass through the cell membranes and enter the nephron.

Table 2 Comparison of Solutes

Solute	Glomerulus	Bowman's capsule
water	yes	yes
sodium chloride	yes	yes
glucose	yes	yes
amino acids	yes	yes
hydrogen ions	yes	yes
urea	yes	yes
plasma proteins	yes	no
erythrocytes	yes	no
platelets	yes	no

Reabsorption

On average, about 600 mL of fluid flows through the kidneys every minute. Approximately 20 % of the fluid, or about 120 mL, is filtered into the nephrons. Imagine what would happen if none of the filtrate were reabsorbed back into the blood. You would form 120 mL of urine each minute. You would also have to consume at least 1 L of fluid every 10 min to maintain equilibrium. Much of your day would be concerned with regulating water balance. Fortunately, only 1 mL of urine is formed for every 120 mL of fluid filtered into the nephron. The remaining 119 mL of fluid and solutes is reabsorbed. Aldosterone is a hormone that increases the reabsorption of Na^+ ions and water by the kidneys, thereby helping to maintain body fluid levels.

Selective reabsorption occurs by both active and passive transport. Carrier molecules move Na^+ ions across the cell membranes of the cells that line the nephron. Negative ions, such as Cl^- and HCO_3^-, follow the positive Na^+ ions by charge attraction (**Figure 4** on next page). Numerous mitochondria supply the energy necessary for active transport. However, the energy supply is limited. Reabsorption occurs until the **threshold level** of a substance is reached. Excess NaCl remains in the nephron and is excreted with the urine.

Other molecules are actively transported from the proximal tubule. Glucose and amino acids attach to specific carrier molecules, which shuttle them out of the nephron and into the blood. However, the amount of solute that can be reabsorbed is limited. For example, excess glucose will not be shuttled out of the nephron by the carrier molecules. This means that individuals with high blood glucose and those who consume large amounts of simple sugars will excrete only some of the excess glucose.

The solutes that are actively transported out of the nephron create an osmotic gradient that draws water from the nephron. A second osmotic force, created by the proteins not filtered into the nephron, also helps reabsorption. The proteins remain in the bloodstream and draw water from the **interstitial fluid** into the blood. As water is reabsorbed from the nephron, the remaining solutes become more concentrated. Molecules such as urea and uric acid will diffuse from the nephron back into the blood, although less is reabsorbed than was originally filtered.

+ EXTENSION 

Kidney Filtration and Exercise

This audio clip will explore the factors that contribute to lower levels of kidney filtration during exercise and relate these factors to the changes in blood chemistry during exercise.

www.science.nelson.com 

CAREER CONNECTION 

Urologist

Urology is a medical specialty that deals with the urinary system. What types of things do urologists do? Do they ever perform kidney transplants? Find out what training is needed to become a urologist.

www.science.nelson.com 

threshold level the maximum amount of a substance that can be moved across the nephron

+ EXTENSION 

Tubular Reabsorption

This animation illustrates how solutes and water are reabsorbed from the nephron back into the blood.

www.science.nelson.com 

interstitial fluid the fluid that surrounds the body cells

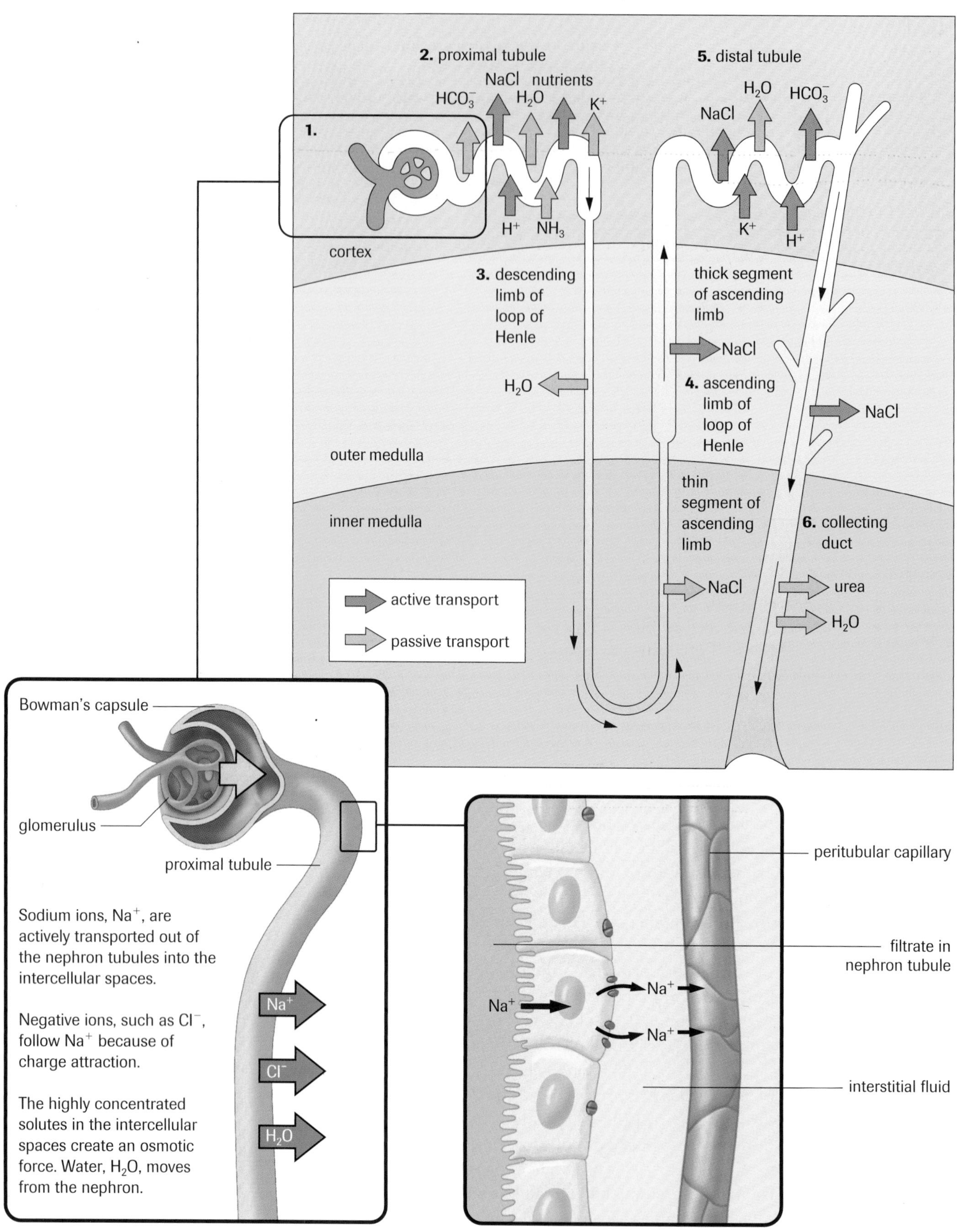

Figure 4

Overview of the steps in urine formation. The numbers in the diagram match the processes in **Table 3**, on the next page.

Secretion

Secretion is the movement of wastes from the blood into the nephron. Ammonia, excess H^+ ions, and minerals such as K^+ ions are examples of substances secreted. Even drugs such as penicillin can be secreted. Cells loaded with mitochondria line the distal tubule. As in reabsorption, tubular secretion occurs by active transport, but, unlike in reabsorption, molecules are shuttled from the blood into the nephron. **Table 3** summarizes the events in urine formation.

Table 3 Urine Formation

Site	Description of process	Substances transported
1. glomerulus and Bowman's capsule	• Filtration of water and dissolved solutes occurs as blood is forced through walls of glomerulus into Bowman's capsule by fluid pressure in capillaries.	• sodium ions (Na^+), chloride ions (Cl^-), water (H_2O), hydrogen ions (H^+), glucose, amino acids, vitamins, minerals, urea, uric acid
2. proximal tubule	• Selective reabsorption of nutrients from filtrate back into blood occurs by active and passive transport. • Within proximal tubule, pH is controlled by secretion of hydrogen ions (H^+) and reabsorption of bicarbonate ions (HCO_3^-).	• bicarbonate ions (HCO_3^-), salt (NaCl), water (H_2O), potassium ions (K^+), hydrogen ions (H^+), ammonia (NH_3), glucose, amino acids, vitamins, urea
3. descending limb of loop of Henle	• The descending limb of loop of Henle is permeable to water, resulting in loss of water from the filtrate by osmosis. • Salt (NaCl) becomes concentrated in the filtrate as descending limb penetrates inner medulla of kidney.	• water (H_2O)
4. ascending limb of loop of Henle	• A thin segment of ascending limb of loop of Henle is permeable to salt, resulting in the diffusion of salt out of ascending limb. • Salt continues to pass from filtrate to interstitial fluid in the thick segment of ascending limb.	• salt (NaCl)
5. distal tubule	• Selective reabsorption of nutrients from blood into nephron occurs by active transport. Distal tubule helps regulate potassium (K^+) and salt (NaCl) concentration of body fluids. • As in the proximal tubule, pH is controlled by tubular secretion of hydrogen ions (H^+) and reabsorption of bicarbonate ions (HCO_3^-).	• salt (NaCl), potassium ions (K^+), water (H_2O), hydrogen ions (H^+), bicarbonate ions (HCO_3^-), uric acid, ammonia (NH_3)
6. collecting duct	• Urine formation	• water (H_2O), salt (NaCl), urea, uric acid, minerals

Practice

4. State the function of each part of the nephron: Bowman's capsule, proximal tubule, loop of Henle, distal tubule, and collecting duct.
5. Describe the three main processes that are involved in urine formation.

LAB EXERCISE 12.A

Comparing Solutes in the Plasma, Nephron, and Urine

Report Checklist

- ○ Purpose
- ○ Problem
- ○ Hypothesis
- ○ Prediction
- ○ Design
- ○ Materials
- ○ Procedure
- ○ Evidence
- ● Analysis
- ○ Evaluation
- ○ Synthesis

Micropipettes were used to draw fluid from the Bowman's capsule, the glomerulus, the loop of Henle, and the collecting duct. Solutes in the fluids were measured. The resulting data are displayed in **Table 4**.

Analysis

(a) Which of the solutes was not filtered into the nephron? Explain your answer.

(b) The test for glucose was not completed for the sample taken from the glomerulus. Predict whether glucose would be found in the glomerulus. Provide reasons for your prediction.

(c) Why do urea and ammonia levels increase after filtration occurs?

(d) Chloride ions, Cl^-, follow actively transported Na^+ ions from the nephron into the blood. Therefore, you would expect the Cl^- concentration to decrease as fluids are extracted along the nephron. What causes the discrepancy?

(e) Is it correct to say that veins carry blood with high concentrations of waste products and arteries carry blood with high concentrations of nutrients? Explain.

(f) Compare the blood found in a renal artery and a renal vein with respect to urea and glucose.

Table 4 Solute Concentrations in Various Parts of the Kidney

Solute	Bowman's capsule	Glomerulus	Loop of Henle	Collecting duct
protein	0	0.8	0	0
urea	0.05	0.05	1.50	2.00
glucose	0.10	no data	0	0
chloride ions	0.37	no data	no data	0.6
ammonia	0.0001	0.0001	0.0001	0.04
substance X	0	9.15	0	0

Quantities are in g/100 mL.

WWW **WEB Activity**

Simulation—Kidney Function

In this activity, you can follow the links to a number of computer-generated simulations of kidney function. Trace the pathway of fluid through the different parts of the kidney. You can also find other diagrams and descriptions of kidney function. Research and create a flow chart to show how the excretory system maintains water and ions in equilibrium.

www.science.nelson.com GO

INVESTIGATION 12.1 *Introduction*

Do Sports Drinks Really Work?

Report Checklist

- ○ Purpose
- ● Problem
- ● Hypothesis
- ● Prediction
- ● Design
- ● Materials
- ● Procedure
- ● Evidence
- ● Analysis
- ● Evaluation
- ○ Synthesis

Are sports drinks any better than water and sugar? How can you determine whether a sports drink is able to restore the electrolytes essential for the operation of nerves and muscles?

To perform this investigation, turn to page 393. 

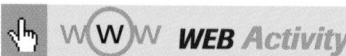

pH Balance

In addition to regulating body fluid volumes and maintaining the composition of salts in the blood, the kidneys maintain pH balance. Despite the variety of foods and fluids consumed with varying pH levels, the pH of the body remains relatively constant, between 7.3 and 7.5. In addition, during cellular respiration, cells produce carbon dioxide, which forms carbonic acid. Carbonic acid and other excess acids ionize to produce H^+ ions. The buildup of H^+ ions lowers pH.

An acid–base balance is maintained by buffer systems that absorb excess H^+ ions or ions that act as bases. Excess H^+ ions from metabolic processes are buffered by bicarbonate ions in the blood. Bicarbonate ions, HCO_3^-, eliminate the excess H^+ ions, preventing a change in pH. Carbonic acid, a weak acid, is produced. In turn, the carbonic acid breaks down to form carbon dioxide and water. The carbon dioxide is then transported to the lungs where much of it is exhaled. The following reaction shows one type of buffer system, called the bicarbonate–carbon dioxide buffer system (**Figure 5**):

$$HCO_3^- + H^+ \rightleftharpoons \underset{\text{carbonic acid}}{H_2CO_3} \rightleftharpoons H_2O + CO_2$$

The buffer system of the blood removes excess H^+ ions; however, the buffer must be restored if the body is to be protected. The kidneys help restore the buffer by reversing the reaction. As shown in **Figure 5**, carbon dioxide is actively transported from the peritubular capillaries, which surround the nephron, into the cells that line the nephron. The carbon dioxide combines with water to initiate the reverse reaction, generating HCO_3^- and H^+ ions. The bicarbonate ions diffuse back into the blood, thereby restoring the buffer. The H^+ ions recombine with either phosphate ions or ammonia and are excreted with the filtrate from the nephron.

CAREER CONNECTION

Emergency Medical Technician

Emergency medical technicians (EMTs), or paramedics, deliver pre-hospital emergency care. Their responsibilities include cardiopulmonary resuscitation, monitoring vital signs, starting intravenous lines, administering drugs, assisting in childbirth, and immobilizing patients. Discover more about the technical training programs EMTs receive.

www.science.nelson.com 

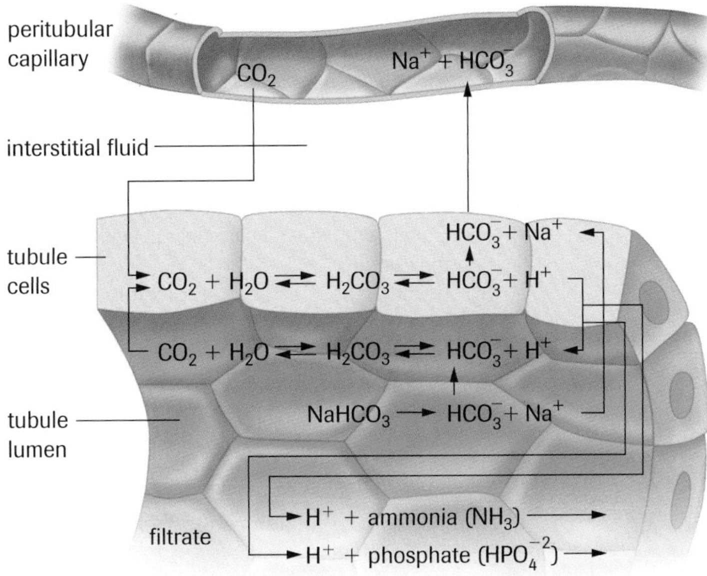

Figure 5
The bicarbonate–carbon dioxide buffer system maintains the pH balance.

SUMMARY Waste Excretion and Internal Equilibrium

- The kidneys filter waste from the blood and help maintain water balance.
- The liver helps to eliminate toxic nitrogen groups from the body by deamination.
- Nephrons are the functional units of the kidneys.
- Urine formation depends on three functions: filtration, reabsorption, and secretion.
- The glomerulus acts as a high-pressure filter.
- Selective reabsorption occurs by both active and passive transport.
- Secretion is the active transport of waste from the blood into the nephron.
- Kidneys help maintain pH by excreting excess H^+ ions and restoring HCO_3^- ions to the blood.

Table 5 Summary of Nephron Structure and Function

Structure	Function
afferent arteriole	carries blood to the glomerulus
glomerulus	a high-pressure capillary bed enclosed by the Bowman's capsule that is the site of filtration
efferent arteriole	carries blood away from the glomerulus
peritubular capillary bed	capillaries that network around the nephron
venule	carries filtered blood out of the nephron

Section 12.1 Questions

1. Why do you think it is beneficial to humans to have two kidneys rather than one? Explain your answer.
2. Explain the function of nephrons.
3. Use the diagram in **Figure 6** to identify the following:
   (a) the structure that filters blood
   (b) the structure that carries urine from the kidney
   (c) the structure that carries blood containing urea into the kidney
   (d) the structure that stores urine

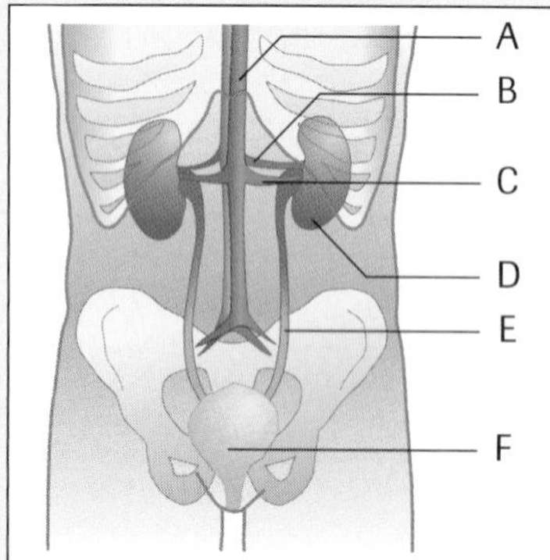

Figure 6

4. An adult under normal conditions will eliminate about 1.5 L of urine daily. Design an experiment that will test how urine output is affected by the consumption of a food containing caffeine (e.g., coffee, tea, chocolate, cola).
5. Explain why individuals who consume large amounts of sugars might do the following:
   (a) excrete large amounts of glucose in the urine
   (b) excrete large amounts of urine
6. Marine fish, such as herring and cod, live in a hypertonic environment. These fish lose water through their gills by osmosis. To replace the water, the fish drink seawater.
   (a) Explain why these fish must actively transport salt from their bodies.
   (b) Because these fish excrete salt through their gills, kidney function is affected. Explain the effect on the volume of urine excreted and the concentration of solutes in the urine.
7. Explain why the regulation of salt is important for people with renal hypertension.
8. What role do the kidneys serve in maintaining pH?
9. Using the HCO_3^- buffering system, explain what would happen if the kidneys failed to excrete H^+ ions.
10. Using the Internet and other resources, conduct research to explain how urine might be recycled on a space flight.

www.science.nelson.com

Kidney Dysfunction 12.2

Proper functioning of the kidneys is essential for the body to maintain equilibrium. The multifunctional kidneys are affected when other systems break down; conversely, kidney dysfunction affects other systems. Many kidney disorders can be detected by urinalysis (**Figure 1**).

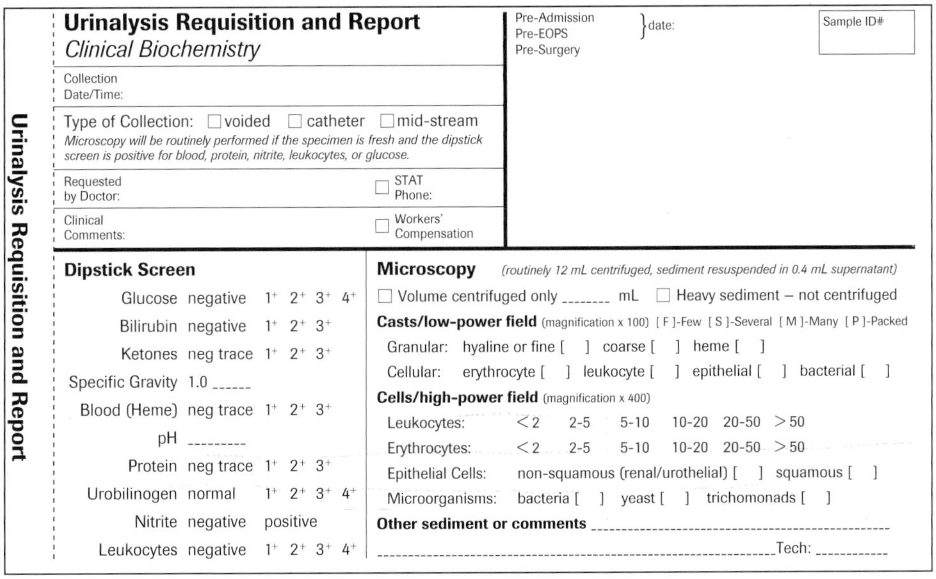

Urinalysis Requisition and Report

Urinalysis Requisition and Report
Clinical Biochemistry

Pre-Admission / Pre-EOPS / Pre-Surgery } date:

Sample ID#

Collection Date/Time:

Type of Collection: ☐ voided ☐ catheter ☐ mid-stream
Microscopy will be routinely performed if the specimen is fresh and the dipstick screen is positive for blood, protein, nitrite, leukocytes, or glucose.

Requested by Doctor: ☐ STAT Phone:

Clinical Comments: ☐ Workers' Compensation

Dipstick Screen

Glucose	negative 1+ 2+ 3+ 4+
Bilirubin	negative 1+ 2+ 3+
Ketones	neg trace 1+ 2+ 3+
Specific Gravity	1.0 ______
Blood (Heme)	neg trace 1+ 2+ 3+
pH	_________
Protein	neg trace 1+ 2+ 3+
Urobilinogen	normal 1+ 2+ 3+ 4+
Nitrite	negative positive
Leukocytes	negative 1+ 2+ 3+ 4+

Microscopy *(routinely 12 mL centrifuged, sediment resuspended in 0.4 mL supernatant)*

☐ Volume centrifuged only ________ mL ☐ Heavy sediment – not centrifuged

Casts/low-power field (magnification x 100) [F]-Few [S]-Several [M]-Many [P]-Packed

Granular: hyaline or fine [ ] coarse [ ] heme [ ]

Cellular: erythrocyte [ ] leukocyte [ ] epithelial [ ] bacterial [ ]

Cells/high-power field (magnification x 400)

Leukocytes:	<2	2-5	5-10	10-20	20-50	>50
Erythrocytes:	<2	2-5	5-10	10-20	20-50	>50

Epithelial Cells: non-squamous (renal/urothelial) [ ] squamous [ ]

Microorganisms: bacteria [ ] yeast [ ] trichomonads [ ]

Other sediment or comments ________________________________

________________________________ Tech: ___________

Figure 1
Many kidney problems can be diagnosed by analyzing a urine sample.

Diabetes Mellitus

Diabetes mellitus is caused by inadequate secretion of insulin from islet cells in the pancreas. Without insulin, blood glucose levels tend to rise. Some people with diabetes mellitus need insulin injections to regulate their blood glucose levels. The cells of the proximal tubule are supplied with enough ATP to reabsorb 0.1 % blood glucose, but in diabetes mellitus much higher blood glucose concentrations are found. The excess glucose remains in the nephron and is excreted in the urine. This excess glucose provides an osmotic pressure that opposes the osmotic pressure created by other solutes that have been actively transported out of the nephron. Water remains in the nephron and is lost with the urine. Individuals with untreated diabetes mellitus void large volumes of urine, which explains why they are often thirsty. The water lost with the excreted sugar must be replenished.

Another form of diabetes, diabetes insipidus, results from a defect in a different hormone—antidiuretic hormone (ADH), which regulates water reabsorption in the nephron. A person with this form of diabetes produces large volumes of dilute urine.

Osmoregulation in the Collecting Duct

This audio clip examines how antidiuretic hormone (ADH) impacts the cells of the collecting duct in the kidney and influences the amount of water that is re-absorbed from the filtrate.

www.science.nelson.com 

Nephritis

Nephritis is not a single disease but a broad description of many diseases characterized by inflammation of the nephrons. One type of nephritis affects the tiny blood vessels of the glomerulus. It is believed that toxins produced by invading microbes destroy the tiny blood vessels, altering the permeability of the nephron. Proteins and other large molecules are able to pass into the nephron. Because no mechanism is designed to reabsorb protein, the proteins remain in the nephron and create an osmotic pressure that draws water into the nephron. The movement of water into the nephron increases the output of urine. Nephritis can lead to irreversible kidney damage and kidney failure.

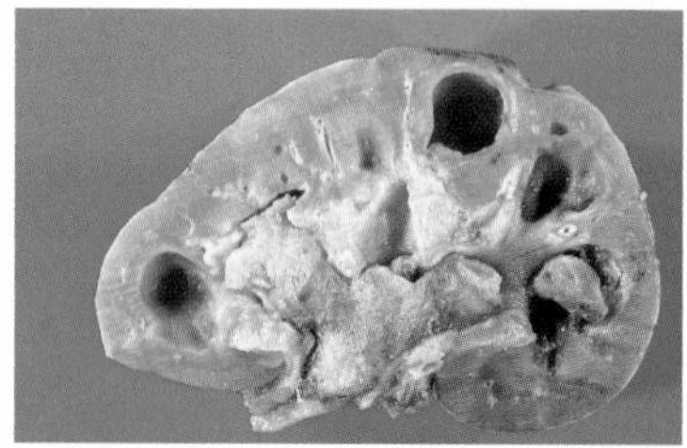

Figure 2
This kidney contains several large stones. Most stones consist mainly of calcium oxalate, calcium phosphate, or both.

Kidney Stones

Kidney stones (**Figure 2**) are caused by the precipitation of mineral solutes from the blood. The sharp-sided stones can lodge in the renal pelvis, or they may move down the ureter into the bladder and be passed out of the body with the urine. Delicate tissues are torn as the stone moves toward the bladder, causing excruciating pain. Larger stones may even lodge in the ureter, which requires medical attention.

Blasting Kidney Stones

The traditional treatment for unpassable kidney stones has been surgical removal followed by a period of convalescence. A technique developed by German urologist Dr. Christian Chaussy, called extracorporeal shock-wave lithotripsy (ESWL), has greatly improved prospects for kidney stone patients with stones less than 2 cm in size.

The nonsurgical technique uses high-energy shock waves to break the kidney stones into small fragments. The shock waves pass through soft tissue and strike the stone. After a few days, tiny granules from the stone can be voided through the excretory system.

Not all stones can be eliminated by shock-wave treatment. The size of the stone, its location in the urinary tract, and its composition all determine whether ESWL is an appropriate treatment. In most cases, this technique can be performed on an outpatient basis, and recovery time is greatly reduced from that of surgical removal.

INVESTIGATION 12.2 *Introduction*

Diagnosis of Kidney Disorders

How is urinalysis used to detect various kidney disorders? In this investigation, you will test simulated urine for kidney disease.

Report Checklist

○ Purpose	● Design	● Analysis
● Problem	○ Materials	● Evaluation
● Hypothesis	○ Procedure	● Synthesis
● Prediction	● Evidence	

To perform this investigation, turn to page 394. 

Dialysis Technology

For people whose kidneys cannot effectively process bodily wastes, a dialysis machine can restore the proper solute balance. Dialysis is defined as the exchange of substances across a semipermeable membrane. Like a kidney that is functioning normally, a dialysis machine operates on the principles of diffusion and blood pressure. However, unlike a kidney, a dialysis machine cannot perform active transport.

There are two types of dialysis: hemodialysis and peritoneal dialysis (**Figure 3**, next page). In hemodialysis, the machine is connected to the patient's circulatory system by a vein. Blood is pumped through a series of dialysis tubes that are submerged in a bath of various solutes. Glucose and a mixture of salts set up concentration gradients. For example, HCO_3^- ions will move from the bath into the blood if it is too acidic. Because the dialysis fluids have no urea, this solute always moves from the blood into the dialysis fluid. Urea will move from the blood into the dialysis fluid until equal concentrations are established. By continually flushing expended dialysis solution and replacing it, the process continually removes urea and other waste solutes. During hemodialysis, the body also receives the hormones the kidneys are unable to produce.

An alternative is peritoneal dialysis, sometimes referred to as continuous ambulatory peritoneal dialysis (CAPD). With this method, 2 L of dialysis fluid is pumped into the abdominal cavity, and the membranes of the cavity selectively filter wastes from the blood. Urea and other wastes diffuse from the plasma into the peritoneum and into the dialysis fluid. Wastes accumulate in the dialysis fluid, which can be drained off and

DID YOU KNOW?

Earliest Treatment of Kidney Stones

Operations to remove kidney stones were performed in the time of Hippocrates, the Greek physician considered to be the father of medicine (c. 460–377 B.C.E.).

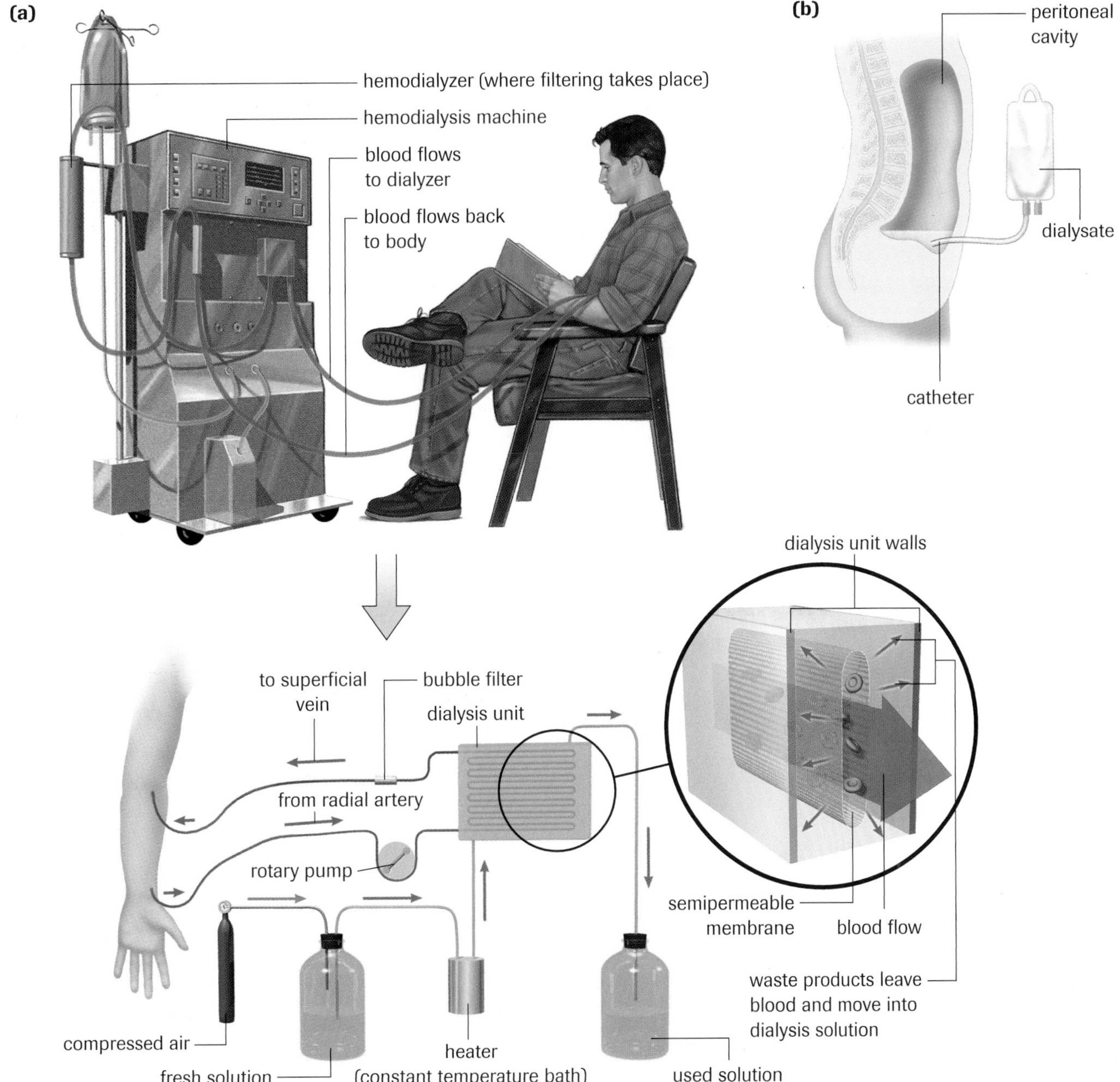

Figure 3
(a) In hemodialysis, a unit called a dialyzer mimics the action of the nephron. For hemodialysis treatments, a person must first have a minor surgical procedure to create an access, a shunt, for the needles and tubing needed to connect the circulatory system to the dialysis machine. Most people need three weekly dialysis sessions of about four hours each.
(b) Peritoneal dialysis is done through the peritoneal membrane, which is the lining of the abdominal cavity. In a minor surgical procedure, a catheter (a thin tube) is first inserted. A solution called the dialysate is then fed into the abdominal cavity through the catheter. The dialysate remains in this cavity for two to six hours. Then, the dialysate fluid is drained from the abdomen via the catheter. Once the fluid is drained, new fluid is placed to begin the process anew.

Kidney Dialysis

This animation explains in more detail how hemodialysis and peritoneal dialysis work to restore proper solute balance in place of functioning kidneys.

www.science.nelson.com 

replaced several times a day. As dialysis occurs, the patient may continue with non-strenuous activities. Peritoneal dialysis allows for greater independence because patients can perform the procedure in their own home.

Although dialysis technology can remove toxic wastes from the body and maintain electrolyte balance, it is unable to accomplish other tasks of the kidneys. Dialysis equipment is not able to produce hormones, such as erythropoietin and renin, nor is it able to activate vitamin D.

A new and promising technique involves the transplant of kidney cells from a pig into a dialysis machine. The living cells not only produce renal hormones but seem to be much better at regulating electrolytes and pH.

Kidney Transplants

According to the Kidney Foundation of Canada, a patient diagnosed with end-stage renal disease (kidney failure) in the 1960s had little chance of surviving. By the 1970s, renal dialysis had changed life expectancy dramatically, but the patient had to spend up to 36 hours each week in treatment. By the 1980s, hemodialysis had reduced treatments to 12 hours a week.

Although dialysis machines are effective, nothing can surpass the workings of a real kidney. Today, kidney transplants are 85 % successful and the preferred treatment for many patients (**Figure 4**). A transplanted kidney produces hormones and responds to the homeostatic adjustments of other body systems. The main disadvantage with any transplant is the immune response of the recipient. The donor kidney is often identified as a foreign invader, and the recipient's immune system springs into action in an attempt to destroy it. (See "Recognizing Harmful Antigens," Section 11.2, page 364.)

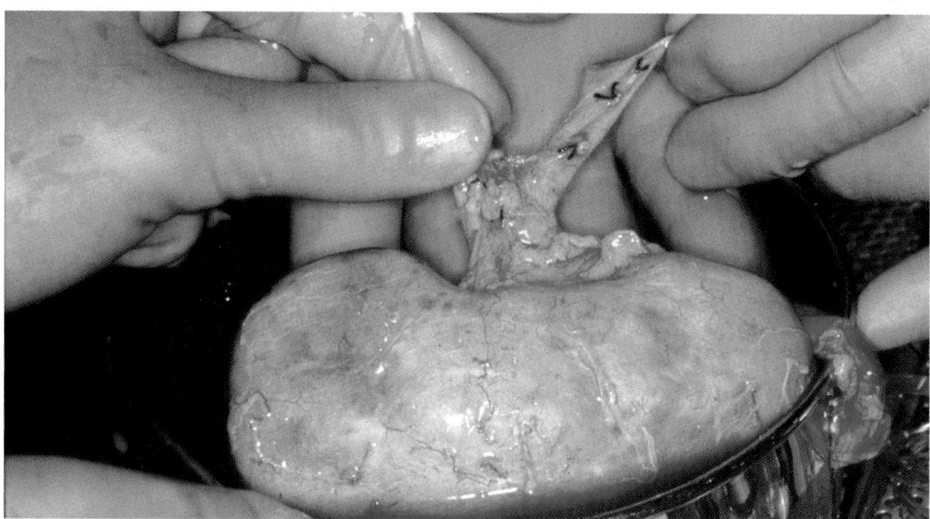

Figure 4
A human kidney being prepared for transplant

A kidney transplant involves placing a new kidney and ureter in the lower abdomen near the groin, where they are surgically attached to the blood vessels and bladder (**Figure 5**). The operation usually takes two to four hours. The old kidneys are not usually removed unless they are very large or chronically infected. After surgery, a catheter is inserted into the bladder for several days to drain the urine produced by the new kidney. Sometimes dialysis is required after the transplant until the new kidney can fully function. Immunosuppresive drugs are given after the transplant to help prevent rejection of the new organ.

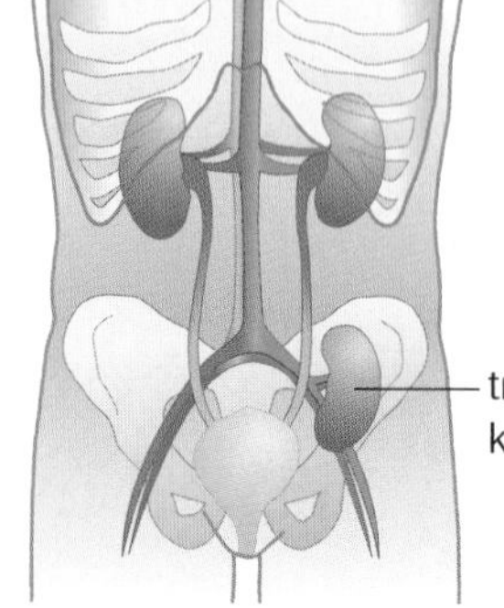

Figure 5
Location of new kidney

EXPLORE an issue

Issue Checklist

- ○ Issue
- ● Resolution
- ○ Design
- ● Evidence
- ● Analysis
- ● Evaluation

Xenotransplants

A survey of Canadians in the year 2000 found that

- 94 % agreed that organ donation was a positive outcome of a person's death;
- 81 % indicated a willingness to donate organs; and
- 65 % reported having had a discussion about organ donation with loved ones.

In spite of public education, the organ donation rate in Canada is less than 40 %. The shortage of organs has spurred scientists to explore new and creative solutions for the many patients awaiting new organs. Xenotransplants are transplants from one species to another (*xeno* means strange or foreign). Xenotransplants from animals to humans have been attempted for several decades, but scientists have yet to successfully solve the problem of organ rejection. Improvements in immunosuppressive drugs have extended the boundaries of possibility and could relieve the wait for thousands of patients.

A second advance, the placement of human genes into animals by genetic engineering, has made xenotransplantation even more viable. Transgenic animals are animals that have genes from other species inserted into their DNA. Because transgenic animals possess not only their own genes but also those of humans, the chances of rejection are reduced. The immune system of the recipient will recognize the human marker on cell membranes as being related to their own tissues.

Although primates were once used as the primary source for xenotransplants, pigs have become the most common animal (**Figure 6**). The organs of the pig resemble those of humans in both size and structure. In addition, pigs are easier and less expensive to breed. Baboons, the early primate of choice, were found to harbour many viruses that can easily be transferred to humans.

As of 2003, xenotransplants were not allowed in Canada. One of the fears is the introduction of new viruses into humans. Microbes that might be harmless in their natural animal host could be deadly in a human. Could xenotransplants cause an outbreak of a deadly disease?

Figure 6
Pigs have become the animal of choice for xenotransplants.

Statement

The government should allow xenotransplants in Canada.

(a) In your group, research the issue. Search for information in newspapers, periodicals, CD-ROMs, and the Internet.

www.science.nelson.com 

(b) Discuss the issue with class members and others in preparation for the debate.

(c) Write a list of points and counterpoints that your group considered.

(d) Decide whether your group agrees or disagrees with the statement.

(e) Prepare to defend your group's position in a class discussion.

(f) What responsibilities do governments have to ensure that all groups have a voice in the debate?

SUMMARY *Kidney Dysfunction*

- Proper functioning of the kidneys is essential for maintaining equilibrium.
- Many kidney diseases can be detected by urinalysis.
- A number of kidney diseases affect proper kidney function, including diabetes mellitus, diabetes insipidus, nephritis, and kidney stones.
- Dialysis and transplants are the most common treatments for kidney disease.

Section 12.2 Questions

1. What are kidney stones?
2. Explain why people with diabetes become dehydrated.
3. Why isn't there a cure for nephritis?
4. Sketch a diagram of a kidney dialysis machine and explain how it works.
5. Identify advantages of peritoneal dialysis over hemodialysis.
6. Complete **Table 1** in your notebook.

Table 1 Types of Kidney Dysfunction

Kidney dysfunction	Cause	Problem created	Recommended treatment
diabetes mellitus	lack of insulin production	glucose in urine will cause dehydration	
diabetes insipidus			ADH provided by injection
nephritis			
kidney stones			

7. What is the most difficult challenge to overcome in achieving successful kidney transplants? Provide a reason.
8. Tests were performed on patients A, B, C, and D. Results from the tests are provided in **Table 2**. The results obtained for patient A are considered normal.

Table 2 Test Results for Four Patients

Patient	Blood pressure (mmHg)	Cardiac output (L/min)	Glucose in urine (g/100 mL)	Urine output (mL/24 h)
A	120/70	5.0	0.00	1500
B	130/80	5.5	0.00	1700
C	115/70	4.5	0.06	1950
D	90/55	3.0	0.00	500

(a) Which patient could have a circulatory problem?
(b) Explain how a circulatory problem could affect urine output.
(c) Explain why the urine output of patient C is elevated.

9. Alcohol is a diuretic, a substance that increases the production of urine. Alcohol suppresses the production and release of ADH. Should people who are prone to developing kidney stones consume alcohol? Explain.
10. In some countries, kidneys are sold for transplant. Do you believe that this practice is acceptable? Explain your answer.

INVESTIGATION 12.1

Do Sports Drinks Really Work?

Report Checklist

○ Purpose	● Design	● Analysis
● Problem	● Materials	● Evaluation
● Hypothesis	● Procedure	○ Synthesis
● Prediction	● Evidence	

Sweating helps to cool the body while exercising. Drinking water during and after exercising helps to restore water balance, but does not, according to many sports drinks advertisers, enable the body to continue operating at peak athletic performance. Sugar and electrolyte levels must be restored. Sugars provide the fuel for cellular respiration. Electrolytes, such as K^+ and Ca^{2+}, are essential for nerve and muscle function.

Nerve and muscle function can be measured by monitoring changes in reaction time. In this investigation, you will design ways to test the effects of a sports drink on reaction time.

Purpose

To determine the effect of sports drinks on reaction time

Hypothesis/Prediction

(a) Predict what effects, if any, that sports drinks will have on reaction time. Record your prediction, and describe the criteria you used in making your prediction.

Design

(b) Design a controlled experiment to test your hypothesis. Include the following in your design:
- descriptions of the manipulated, responding, and controlled variables
- a step-by-step description of the procedure, including the steps for measuring reaction time (one possibility for measuring reaction time is given below)
- a list of safety precautions
- a table to record observations

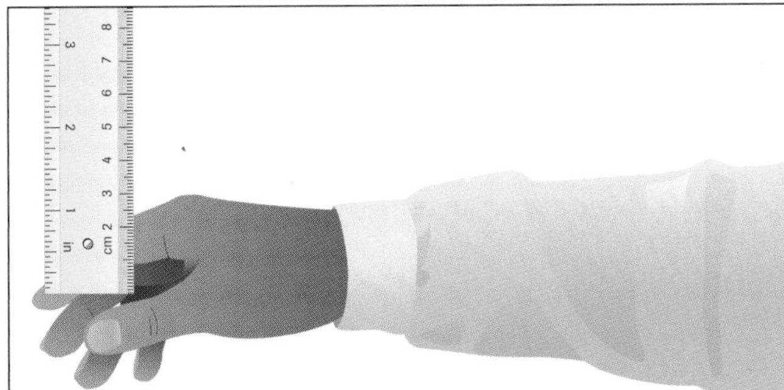

Figure 1
Starting position of ruler

Procedure

1. Submit your procedure, safety precautions, data table, and list of materials and apparatus to your teacher for approval. The procedure for measuring reaction time is given below. For the rest of the procedure, use your own approved design.

Measuring Reaction Time

2. Ask your subject to place his or her forearm flat on the surface of a desk. The subject's entire hand should be extended over the edge of the desk.
3. Ask the subject to place his or her index finger and thumb approximately 2 cm apart. Hold a 30-cm ruler vertically between the thumb and forefinger of the subject. The lower end of the ruler should be even with the top of the thumb and forefinger (**Figure 1**).
4. Indicate when ready, and release the ruler within the next 30 s. Measure the distance the ruler falls before being caught between the subject's thumb and forefinger. Repeat twice more and calculate the average. Repeat the procedure for the left hand. Record your data in a table.

Analysis

(c) Explain how the sports drink affected reaction time.

(d) Explain how the data confirmed or disproved your prediction.

Evaluation

(e) Describe any problems you encountered while carrying out the procedure.

(f) Describe how you could improve your current design.

(g) Reaction time is affected by other factors, such as anticipation. If you were to repeat this experiment, what new factors would you investigate? Write a brief description of the new procedure.

INVESTIGATION 12.2

Report Checklist		
○ Purpose	● Design	● Analysis
● Problem	○ Materials	● Evaluation
● Hypothesis	○ Proceduree	● Synthesis
● Prediction	● Evidence	

Diagnosis of Kidney Disorders

The identification of proteins and sugars in urine samples can reveal kidney disease. This investigation will involve the use of simulated urine samples to test for indications of disease.

Biuret reagent can be used to identify proteins. It reacts with the peptide bonds joining amino acids together, producing colour changes from blue, indicating no protein, to pink or purple.

Benedict's solution can be used to identify reducing sugars. In this investigation, it will be used to detect glucose in the urine. **Table 1** summarizes the quantitative results obtained when reducing sugars, such as glucose, react with Benedict's solution.

Table 1 Reducing Sugar and Benedict's Solution Reactions

Colour of Benedict's solution	Approximate % of sugar
blue	negative
light green	0.5–1.0
green to yellow	1.0–1.5
orange	1.5–2.0
red to red-brown	> 2.0

Purpose

To determine which of the samples have characteristics that indicate kidney disease

Materials

- safety goggles
- laboratory apron
- 4 urine samples (simulated), labelled W, X, Y, and Z in dropper bottles
- 4 small test tubes
- wax pencil
- distilled water in wash bottle
- Benedict's solution (in small dropper bottle)
- test-tube clamp
- hot water bath
- test-tube brush
- Biuret reagent (in small dropper bottle)
- hydronium pH paper

Safety goggles and a laboratory apron must be worn for the entire laboratory. Handle hot objects and their contents carefully to avoid burns.

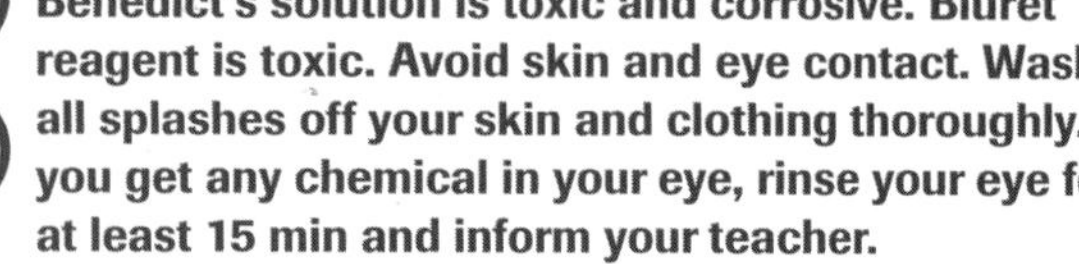

Benedict's solution is toxic and corrosive. Biuret reagent is toxic. Avoid skin and eye contact. Wash all splashes off your skin and clothing thoroughly. If you get any chemical in your eye, rinse your eye for at least 15 min and inform your teacher.

Procedure

1. Label four test tubes W, X, Y, and Z. Place 20 drops of urine sample W in test tube W. Repeat the procedure for samples X, Y, and Z in their respective test tubes.
2. Add 10 drops of Benedict's solution to each test tube and, using a test-tube clamp, place the test tubes in a hot water bath (approximately 80 °C).
3. Observe for 6 min. Record any colour changes in a table. Use **Table 1** to identify the values for each sample. Record the values in the table.
4. Wash each of the test tubes and dry them before beginning the protein test.
5. Use your four labelled test tubes. Place 20 drops of each urine sample in its respective test tube. Add 20 drops of Biuret reagent to each of the test tubes, then tap the test tubes with your fingers to mix the contents. Record your results in a table.
6. Use hydronium paper to determine the pH of each sample. A chart is usually located on the pH paper dispenser. Record your results in the table.
7. Clean up your work space. Dispose of all chemicals as directed by your teacher.
8. Wash your hands thoroughly.

Analysis

(a) Which sample indicates diabetes mellitus? Provide your reasons.

(b) Which sample indicates diabetes insipidus? Give reasons for your response.

(c) Which sample indicates nephritis? Provide reasons for your answer.

(d) Which sample indicates a tremendous loss of body water while exercising? Provide your reasons.

Synthesis

(e) What are recommended treatments for diabetes mellitus and diabetes insipidus?

(f) Why is nephritis difficult to treat?

Chapter 12 SUMMARY

Outcomes

Knowledge

- identify the principal structures of the excretory system, i.e., kidneys, ureters, urinary bladder, and urethra (12.1)
- explain the structure and function of the nephron, including the glomerulus, Bowman's capsule, tubules, loop of Henle, collecting duct, afferent and efferent arterioles, and capillary net, and explain their functions in maintaining plasma compositions, i.e., water, pH, and ions (12.1)
- describe the function of the kidney in excreting metabolic wastes and expelling them into the environment (12.1)
- identify the role of antidiuretic hormone (ADH) and aldosterone in water reabsorption and excretion (12.1, 12.2)

STS

- explain that the goal of science is knowledge about the natural world (12.2)
- identify the role of antidiuretic hormone (ADH) and aldosterone in water reabsorption and excretion (12.1, 12.2)

Skills

- ask questions and plan investigations (12.1, 12.2)
- conduct investigations and gather and record data and information by researching and creating a flow chart to describe how humans maintain homeostasis with respect to water and ions (12.1)
- analyze data and apply mathematical and conceptual models by: observing the principal features of a mammalian excretory system and identifying structures from drawings obtained from various print and electronic sources (12.1); collecting and interpreting data in analysis of simulated urine, identifying limitations of data, comparing to theoretical values, and producing a generalization (12.1, 12.2); and making analogies between kidney function and renal and peritoneal dialysis (12.2)
- work as members of a team and apply the skills and conventions of science (all)

Key Terms

12.1

deamination	glomerulus
urea	efferent arteriole
uric acid	peritubular capillary
ureter	Bowman's capsule
urethra	proximal tubule
cortex	loop of Henle
medulla	distal tubule
renal pelvis	collecting duct
nephron	threshold level
afferent arteriole	interstitial fluid

MAKE a summary

1. Create a flow chart or diagram that shows how the excretory system maintains an internal equilibrium through the exchange of matter and energy with the environment. Label the diagram with as many of the key terms as possible. Check other flow diagrams and use appropriate designs to make your sketch clear.
2. Revisit your answers to the Starting Points questions at the start of the chapter. Would you answer the questions differently now? Why?

Go To

The following components are available on the Nelson Web site. Follow the links for *Nelson Biology Alberta 20–30.*

- an interactive Self Quiz for Chapter 12
- additional Diploma Exam-style Review Questions
- Illustrated Glossary
- additional IB-related material

There is more information on the Web site wherever you see the Go icon in the chapter.

EXTENSION

Pig Cell Transplants

Dr. David White discusses the controversy of a new technique of transplanting insulin-producing islet cells into diabetics. The procedure would allow diabetics to cut down, or even stop their daily shots. The controversy stems from the fact that the islet cells come from seven-day-old piglets.

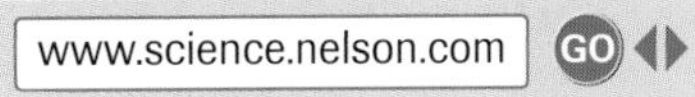

UNIT 20 D PERFORMANCE TASK

Determining Fitness Level

In this Performance Task, you will design and carry out a fitness test. This test will indirectly indicate the amount of oxygen being delivered to your tissues.

www.science.nelson.com GO

Many of these questions are in the style of the Diploma Exam. You will find guidance for writing Diploma Exams in Appendix A5. Science Directing Words used in Diploma Exams are in bold type. Exam study tips and test-taking suggestions are on the Nelson Web site.

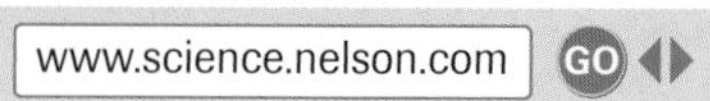

DO NOT WRITE IN THIS TEXTBOOK.

Part 1

1. The site of filtration in the kidney occurs between the
   A. renal artery and renal vein
   B. glomerulus and Bowman's capsule
   C. distal tubule and collecting duct
   D. renal artery and glomerulus

2. The normal sequence of processes in the formation of urine is
   A. reabsorption, secretion, filtration
   B. secretion, reabsorption, filtration
   C. filtration, reabsorption, secretion
   D. active transport, reabsorption, filtration

3. Identify the area in **Figure 1** in which the reabsorption of glucose takes place.
   A. W
   B. Y
   C. X
   D. Z

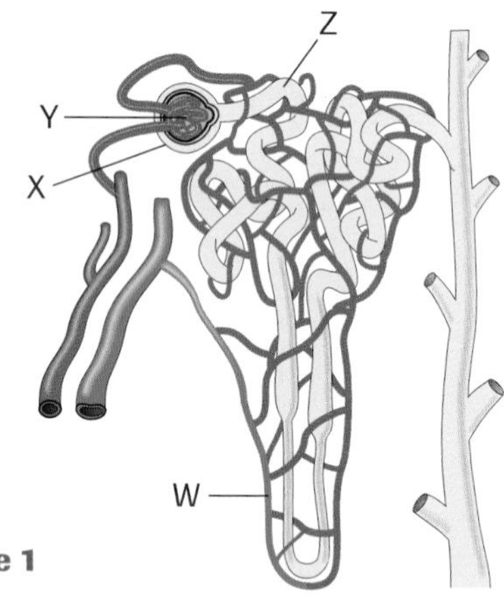

Figure 1

4. The following are structures of the excretory system:

   1. ascending limb of the loop of Henle
   2. ureter
   3. renal pelvis
   4. Bowman's capsule

   List the numbers of the structures in the order in which urine passes through them. (Record all four digits of your answer.)

Part 2

5. **Sketch** a labelled diagram that shows the following parts of the excretory system: kidney, renal artery, renal vein, ureter, bladder, and urethra. **Describe** the function of each organ.

6. **Figure 2** is a diagram of a nephron. Write a unified response that addresses the following aspects of this structure:
   DE
   - **Identify** which letters indicate the afferent and efferent arterioles.
   - **Explain** how an increase in blood pressure in B would affect the functioning of the kidney.
   - **Explain** why proteins and blood cells are found in B but not in D.
   - **Identify** the area of the nephron where you would expect to find the greatest concentration of glucose.
   - **Identify** the area(s) in which Na^+ ions are actively transported.
   - **Identify** the area of secretion.
   - **Identify** the area(s) of the nephron where you would expect to find urea?
   - In which area of the nephron would you expect to find cells with a great number of mitochondria? **Justify** your answer.

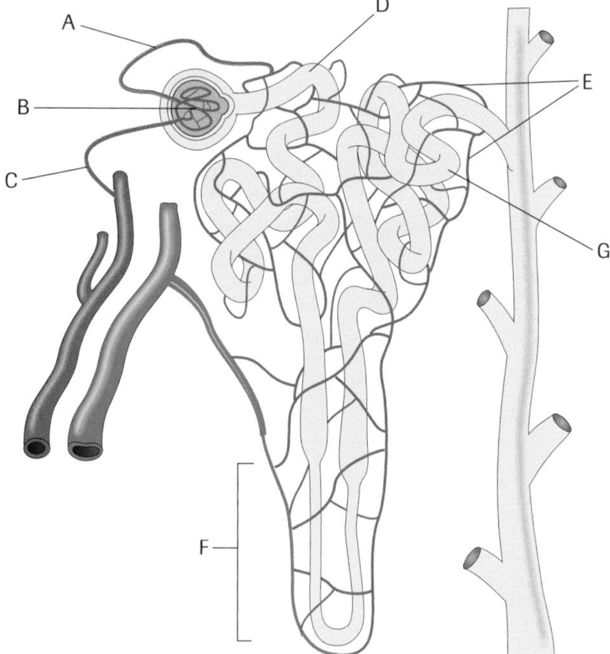

Figure 2

7. The following processes occur in the formation and excretion of urine once the blood has entered the kidney. List these subsequent processes in the order in which they occur.
   (a) urine is stored in the bladder
   (b) blood enters the afferent arteriole
   (c) fluids pass from the glomerulus into the Bowman's capsule
   (d) urine is excreted by the urethra
   (e) Na^+ ions, glucose, and amino acids are actively transported from the nephron
   (f) urine passes from the kidneys into the ureters

Use the following information to answer questions 8 to 10.

A micropipette was used to extract fluids from various structures within the kidney. The data in **Table 1** show an analysis of the fluids.

Table 1 Concentration of Substances in Kidney Fluids

Substance found in fluid	Blood plasma from afferent arteriole	Glomerular filtrate from Bowman's capsule	Urine
protein	7.00	0.00	0.00
urea 0.04	0.04	2.00	
glucose	0.10	0.10	0.00
sodium ions	0.32	0.32	0.35
chloride ions	0.38	0.38	0.60

Quantities are in g/100 mL.

8. According to the data provided, which substance is not filtered from the blood into the Bowman's capsule? **Justify** your answer. DE

9. Which substance provides evidence of secretion? **Justify** your response. DE

10. Which substance provides evidence of reabsorption? **Justify** your answer. DE

11. A pH analysis reveals that the urine of humans fluctuates between acidic and basic depending on the diet. **How** does the kidney help to maintain a constant blood pH?

12. A drug causes dilation of the afferent arteriole and constriction of the efferent arteriole. **Describe how** the drug will affect urine production.

13. **Why** do the walls of the proximal tubule contain so many mitochondria?

14. Athletes now undergo random urine testing for drugs. From your knowledge of excretion, **describe** the pathway of substances such as drugs through the urinary system, from the time they enter the glomerulus until they are excreted in the urine.

15. A drug that inhibits the formation of ATP by the cells of the proximal tubule is introduced into the nephron. **How** will the drug affect urine formation? Provide a complete physiological explanation.

16. A blood clot lodges in the renal artery and restricts blood flow to the kidney. **Explain why** this condition leads to high blood pressure.

17. For every 100 mL of salt water consumed, 150 mL of body water is lost. The solute concentration found in seawater is greater than that found in the blood. **Explain** in physiological terms **why** this loss of body water occurs. (*Hint:* Consider the threshold level for salt reabsorption by the cells of the nephron.)

18. **Predict** how a drop in blood pressure would affect urine output. **Justify** your prediction.

19. **Outline** in a chart the advantages and disadvantages of the following:
   (a) hemodialysis
   (b) peritoneal dialysis
   (c) kidney transplants by living donors and cadaver donors

Use the following information to answer questions 20 and 21.

Figure 3 outlines a dialysis procedure.

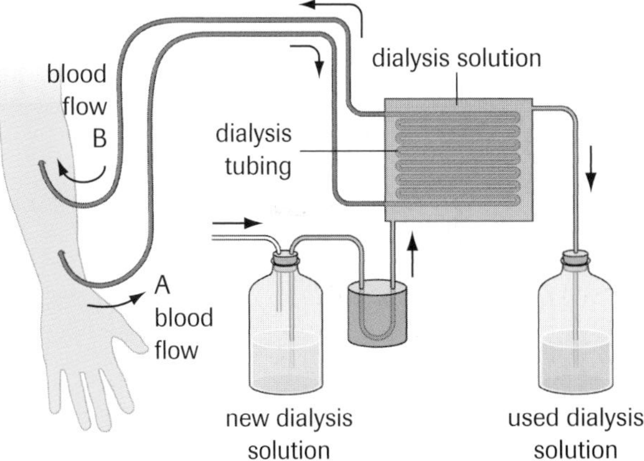

Figure 3

20. **Describe** what happens to the concentration of urea in the blood in **Figure 3**, as blood moves through blood vessel A, through the dialysis tubing, and into blood vessel B. DE

21. For effective dialysis to occur in **Figure 3**, will wastes move by active transport or by diffusion? **Identify** which fluid must contain the lower concentration of wastes: the blood or the dialysis solution. DE

Extension

22. **Design** an efficient kidney for an animal living in a desert.

Many of these questions are in the style of the Diploma Exam. You will find guidance for writing Diploma Exams in Appendix A5. Science Directing Words used in Diploma Exams are in bold type. Exam study tips and test-taking suggestions are on the Nelson Web site.

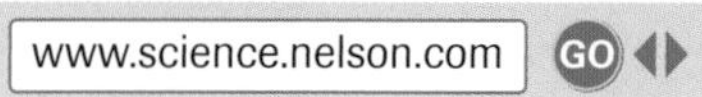

DO NOT WRITE IN THIS TEXTBOOK.

Part 1

Use the following information to answer questions 1 and 2.

In a study, a volunteer fasted for 12 hours, and was then given 300 g of food. Blood samples were taken before she ate, then once an hour for 9 h. The concentrations of fatty acids, glucose, and amino acids in the blood were determined. **Figure 1** is a graph of this data.

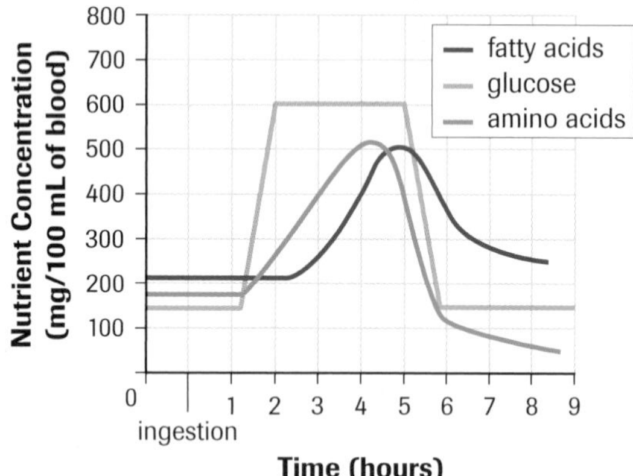

Figure 1

1. According to the data in **Figure 1**, the most difficult food to chemically break down and use for energy is
   A. fat
   B. protein
   C. carbohydrate
   D. amino acids

2. Identify how long after ingestion the maximum concentration of amino acids and fats in the blood occurred.
   A. amino acids, 1h; fats, 3h
   B. amino acids, 2h; fats, 4h
   C. amino acids, 4h; fats, 5h
   D. amino acids, 5h; fats, 8h

3. Identify the reason why the backwash of bile salts into the stomach can lead to stomach ulcers.
   A. Bile salts are very acidic and corrosive to cells. Cells that line the stomach are destroyed by acids.
   B. Bile salts can emulsify the mucosal layer, which is composed of proteins and lipids. Unprotected cells are digested.
   C. Bile salts convert pepsinogen into pepsin, which begins digesting proteins in the cells of the stomach's lining.
   D. Bile salts can digest the mucosal layer, which is composed of proteins and vitamins. Unprotected cells are digested.

4. Correctly complete the following statement: A heart attack will result from lack of nutrients and oxygen to the heart muscle, due to a blockage by atherosclerosis of the
   A. pulmonary arteries
   B. coronary arteries
   C. pulmonary veins
   D. coronary veins

5. Identify which of the following respiratory volumes cannot be measured directly using a respirometer.
   A. tidal volume
   B. expiratory reserve volume
   C. inspiratory reserve volume
   D. vital capacity

6. Identify which of the following is not involved in the immune system's second line of defence.
   A. helper T cells
   B. chemotaxis
   C. phagocytosis
   D. pseudopods

7. Identify the process by which gases move from the alveoli into the capillaries.
   A. active transport
   B. osmosis
   C. filtration
   D. diffusion

8. Correctly complete the following statement: Complete separation of the pulmonary and systemic circulation systems is necessary to provide
   A. increased cardiac output
   B. more efficient operation of the lungs
   C. more efficient oxygenation of the blood
   D. increased ventricular contractions

9. Identify the statement that correctly describes how breathing rate is regulated.
   A. The heart controls the breathing rate by monitoring oxygen levels.
   B. The heart controls the breathing rate by monitoring carbon dioxide levels.
   C. The brain controls the breathing rate by monitoring oxygen levels.
   D. The brain controls the breathing rate by monitoring carbon dioxide levels.

Use the following information to answer questions 10 and 11.

Fluid samples were taken from different parts of the nephron (samples W, X, and Y). The concentration of urea, glucose, and protein in each sample was then determined, and recorded in **Table 1**.

Table 1 Composition of Fluid Samples from Nephron

Component	Sample W (g/100 mL)	Sample X (g/100 mL)	Sample Y (g/100 mL)
urea	0.03	0.03	2.00
glucose	0.10	0.10	0.00
protein	0.007	7.00	0.00

10. Identify the part of the nephron from which sample X was likely taken.

A. The glomerulus: there is a higher protein concentration because very few proteins pass through the glomerulus.

B. The distal tubule: there is a lower concentration of urea because most of the water is absorbed in the distal tubule.

C. The collecting duct: there is a lower concentration of urea because water is not reabsorbed.

D. The proximal tubule: glucose is found in the proximal tubule because the glomerulus is permeable to glucose.

11. Identify the parts of the nephron from which samples W and Y were taken.

A. Sample W is from the distal tubule; sample Y is from the collecting duct.

B. Sample W is from the loop of Henle; sample Y is from Bowman's capsule.

C. Sample W is from the loop of Henle; sample Y is from the distal tubule.

D. Sample W is from Bowman's capsule; sample Y is from the collecting duct.

12. During muscle contraction

A. the sarcomeres lengthen, and actin and myosin fibres shorten

B. the sarcomeres shorten, and actin and myosin fibres lengthen

C. the sarcomeres lengthen, but actin and myosin fibres do not change in length

D. the sarcomeres shorten, but actin and myosin fibres do not change in length

Use the following information to answer questions 13 and 14.

These four numbered structures are examples of different classes of nutrients used by the human body.

1

$^{+}H-N(H)(H)-C(H)-C(=O)-N(H)-C(H)-C(=O)-O^{-}$ (gly, ile)

2

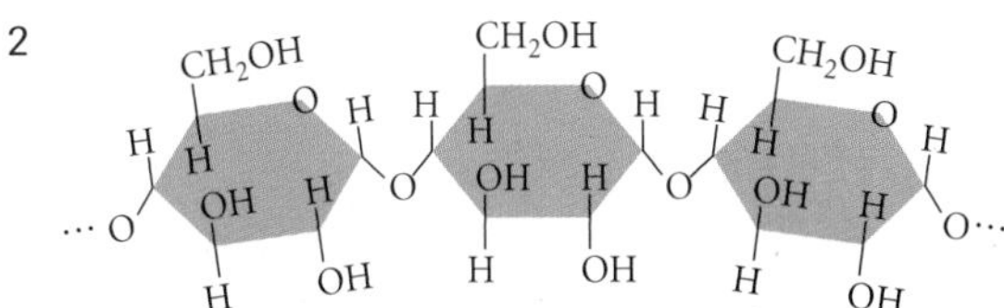

3

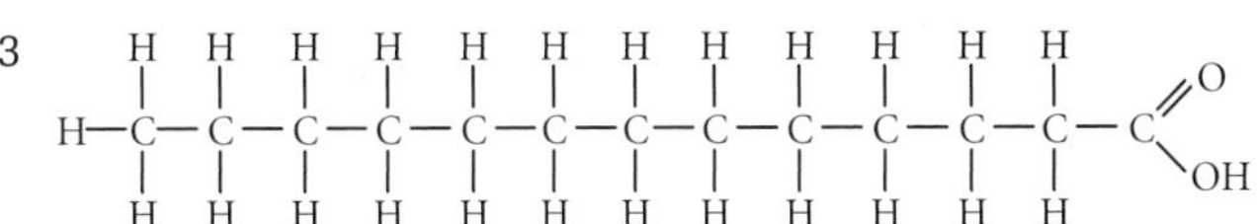

4

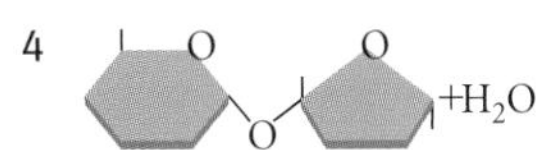

13. NR Match the number of each of the structures with its description. Use each number only once. (Record all four digits of your answer.)

_____ disaccharide _____ fat _____ dipeptide _____ polysaccharide

14. NR Match the number of each of the structures with its enzyme below. Use each number only once. (Record all four digits of your answer.)

_____ sucrase _____ amylase _____ lipase _____ protease

Part 2

15. Identify the blood vessel that is being referred to in each of the following statements:

(a) This blood vessel is the site of diffusion of oxygen and nutrients.

(b) This blood vessel has the highest blood pressure.

16. Figure 2 (next page) shows the components of the human respiratory system. **Identify** the structure by number and name that is described in each of the following statements:

(a) This muscular structure relaxes during exhalation, causing the volume of the chest cavity to decrease.

(b) This structure conducts air into the left lung.

(c) This structure prevents food from entering the trachea.

(d) Inhalation and exhalation are indicated by pressure changes within these structures.

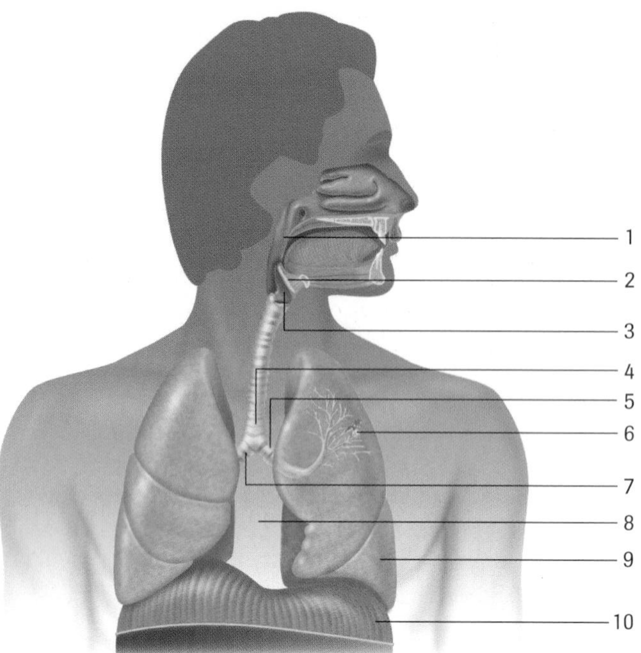

Figure 2

Use the following information to answer questions 17 and 18.

Amylase digestion of starch is tested by the experiment shown in **Figure 3**. Each of the flasks is filled with 100 mL of 4 % starch suspension. A 1 % amylase solution is added to flask 1. The amylase solution is boiled for 2 min then added to flask 3.

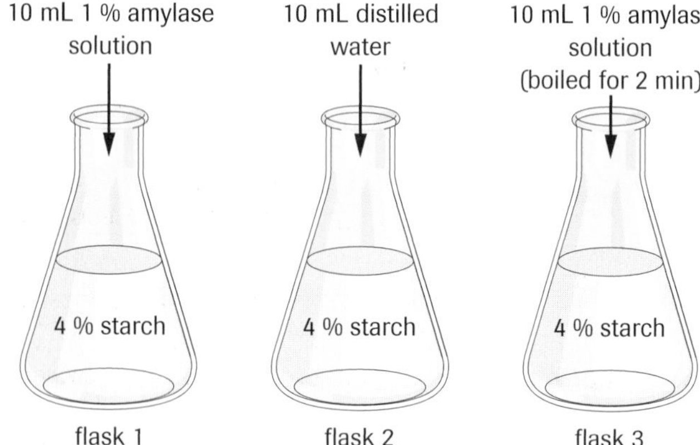

Figure 3

17. **Identify** the control in this experiment.
DE

18. Iodine was added to the flasks after 10 min. **Predict** in which flask(s) the blue-black colour, indicating the presence of starch, would likely be observed. **Explain why**.
DE

19. The money spent on cancer treatment continues to escalate every year. One politician has suggested that medical problems caused by inappropriate lifestyle choices should be given a lower priority for treatment. Write a unified response that addresses the following aspects of life style and health.
DE
    - **Identify** two diseases that could be reduced by changing lifestyles.
    - **Evaluate** the politician's statement. Should money be used first to treat people who have not contributed to their own health problem? **Justify** your answer.

Use the following information to answer questions 20 to 23.

Pancreatin is a commercially prepared mixture of the components of the pancreas, including trypsin and lipase. An experiment was conducted to determine the effect of pancreatin and bile on the digestion of egg yolk. Egg yolk contains lipids and proteins. The scientist placed 10 g of egg yolk in each of four test tubes and incubated them at 37 °C for 24 h. As shown in **Table 2**, the pH of the solution was recorded at the beginning of the experiment and after 24 h. The degree of digestion is indicated by plus signs (+).

Table 2 Experimental Data for the Digestion of Egg Yolk

Test tube	Initial pH	Pancreatin	Bile	pH after 24 h	Amount of digestion
1	9	no	no	9	none
2	9	✓	no	7	+++
3	9	no	✓	9	+
4	9	✓	✓	6	++++

20. **Identify** which test tube acted as a control. **Describe** what the control indicates.
DE

21. **Explain why** the pH of the solution changes after 24 h in test tubes 2 and 4.
DE

22. **Explain why** test tube 4 shows a greater amount of digestion than test tube 2.
DE

23. **Interpret** the results of test tube 3.
DE

Use the following information to answer questions 24 to 27.

Hemoglobin and myoglobin are two proteins that carry oxygen. Myoglobin, found in muscle cells, has the ability to combine with one molecule of oxygen. Hemoglobin, found in red blood cells, has the ability to combine with four oxygen molecules. **Figure 4**, on the next page, shows the ability of hemoglobin and myoglobin to combine with oxygen at varying partial pressures.

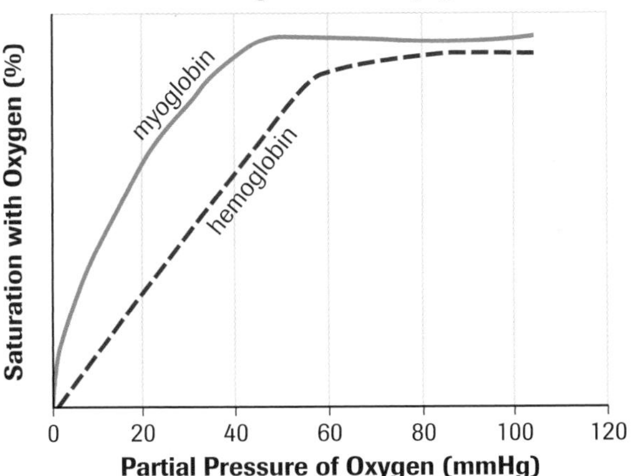

Figure 4

24. **Identify** the protein that accepts oxygen more readily. DE

25. **Identify** the partial pressure at which hemoglobin becomes saturated. DE

26. **Identify** the partial pressure at which myoglobin becomes saturated. DE

27. **Describe** the adaptation for exercise by comparing the saturation curves for hemoglobin and myoglobin. DE

---

28. **List** all types of T and B lymphocytes and explain the role of each in the immune response.

29. A glass of milk contains lactose, proteins, butterfat (mostly triglycerides), vitamins, and minerals. **Describe** what happens to each component in your digestive tract.

30. Often, holiday meals are larger than regular meals and have a higher fat content. After eating a holiday meal, you may feel uncomfortably full for longer than normal. Based on what you have learned about digestion, **describe** in biochemical terms the cause of the discomfort.

31. DE In some forms of heart failure, the left side of the heart is the weaker and fails to perform properly, while the right side continues to pump blood into the lungs with near normal vigour. Write a unified response addressing the following aspects of this form of heart failure:
    - **Explain why** fluid flows from the lung capillaries into the alveoli and bronchioles of the lungs, resulting in a condition called pulmonary edema.
    - **Describe** the effect of pulmonary edema on the normal functioning of the lungs.
    - **Describe** a possible technological solution for this condition.

32. DE Prolonged starvation reduces the amount of protein in the blood. One consequence of this is an increased amount of tissue fluid, which tends to gather in the abdomen and lower limbs. Write a unified response addressing the following aspects of this increase in tissue fluid:
    - **How** is this related to capillary fluid exchange?
    - Indicate a possible reason **why** scientists have been unable to solve the problem.

33. **Define** muscle tetanus.

Use the following information to answer questions 34 to 37.

Lung cancer is the leading cause of cancer death in both men and women in Canada. It is also a disease that can be prevented. Controllable environmental factors seem to stimulate cancer-causing genes over a period of time to become active, causing cells to develop into lung cancer. Interpret the information presented in **Figure 5**.

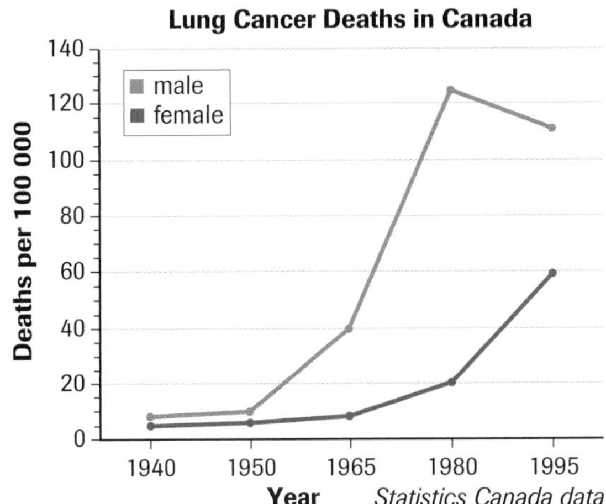

Figure 5

34. DE In the early 1920s, shortly after the First World War, smoking became fashionable for men. **Hypothesize** why lung cancer rates did not increase until the 1950s.

35. DE Suggest a reason **why** no comparable increase occurred in lung cancer in women during the same period. **Justify** your answer.

36. **Predict** trends in lung cancer over the next 10 to 20 years. DE

37. DE **Compare** the trends between males and females between 1980 and 1995.

---

38. About 80 % of runners land on the outer part of their foot and roll inward. This action helps absorb the shock, but for people whose foot bends more than 10 degrees, the action can lead to problems. Conduct research on running shoes that correct for pronation, or excessive foot roll. **How** have running shoe manufacturers attempted to prevent injuries?

    www.science.nelson.com GO

39. Review the focusing questions on page 236. Using the knowledge you have gained from this unit, briefly **outline** a response to each of these questions.

unit

30 A

Nervous and Endocrine Systems

Organs do not work independently; rather, they work in coordinated systems that continuously respond and adjust to changing environments. The nervous system senses changes in the internal and external environment, and relays this information through neurons, such as those shown here. The body then responds to these messages. In many cases, it is the endocrine that responds, by changing levels of hormones.

Researchers are investigating artificial substitutes for many human organs and cells. Artificial cells that mimic the biological processes of natural cells could one day be used to help build artificial kidneys and livers. Synthetic fabric could temporarily serve as artificial skin for burn victims. A bioartificial pancreas that is currently being tested in animals at the University of Alberta could one day provide a cure for diabetes. To be able to function properly, an artificial organ must also be able to communicate with and act together with the body's own cells. What characteristics do these substitutes need to function effectively in the body? In this unit, you will study how the nervous and endocrine systems work together to coordinate the functions of all the organs of the body and help maintain homeostasis, the body's attempt to adjust to a fluctuating external environment.

As you progress through the unit, think about these focusing questions:

- How does the human body maintain equilibrium between its internal and external environments?
- What physiological processes and control systems are involved in maintaining homeostasis?

UNIT 30 A PERFORMANCE TASK

Determining the Effects of Caffeine on Homeostasis

Caffeine is one of the world's most widely used drugs. In this Performance Task, you will investigate the effects caffeine has on human systems and demonstrate how the homeostatic feedback adjustment works. You will use an invertebrate or a protist as a model to provide information that may be applicable to human physiological systems. At the end of this unit, you may apply your skills and knowledge to complete this Performance Task.

www.science.nelson.com 

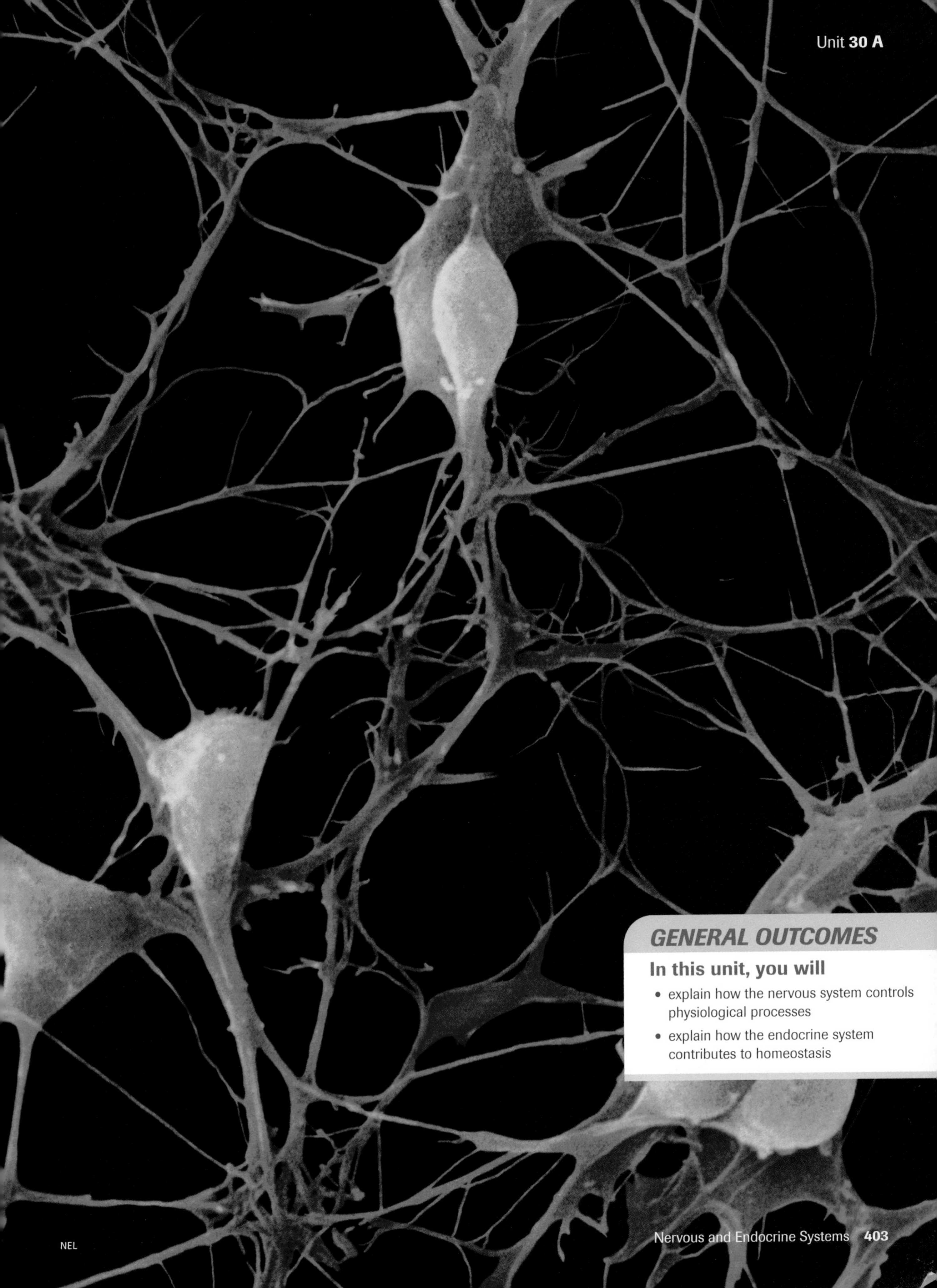

GENERAL OUTCOMES

In this unit, you will

- explain how the nervous system controls physiological processes
- explain how the endocrine system contributes to homeostasis

Unit 30 A

Nervous and Endocrine Systems

ARE YOU READY?

These questions will help you find out what you already know, and what you need to review, before you continue with this unit.

Prerequisites

Concepts

- cellular structures and functions
- kidney function
- immune response

Skills

- ask questions about observed relationships
- plan investigations of questions, ideas, and problems
- analyze data and apply mathematical concepts and conceptual models to develop and assess possible solutions

You can review prerequisite concepts and skills on the Nelson Web site and in the Appendices.

A Unit Pre-Test is also available online.

www.science.nelson.com 

Knowledge

1. Place the following terms from smallest to largest and provide an example of each term:
   - chromosome
   - tissue
   - organ system
   - cell
   - gene
   - organ

2. Which statement is the best description of negative feedback?
   (a) A series of receptors that respond to changes in the internal environment of the body by inhibiting the release of hormones.
   (b) A control system that prevents imbalances in the body by compensating for any changes with a new change in the opposite direction.
   (c) A mechanism that responds to changes in the internal and external environments of the body by stimulating the release of hormones.
   (d) A biological system that prevents the body from responding to changes in the external environment, releasing hormones, or using nerves to shut down organs.

3. Use the diagram of negative feedback in **Figure 1** to explain how the body maintains homeostasis when water intake decreases. (*Hint:* The excretory system was covered in your Biology 20 studies.)

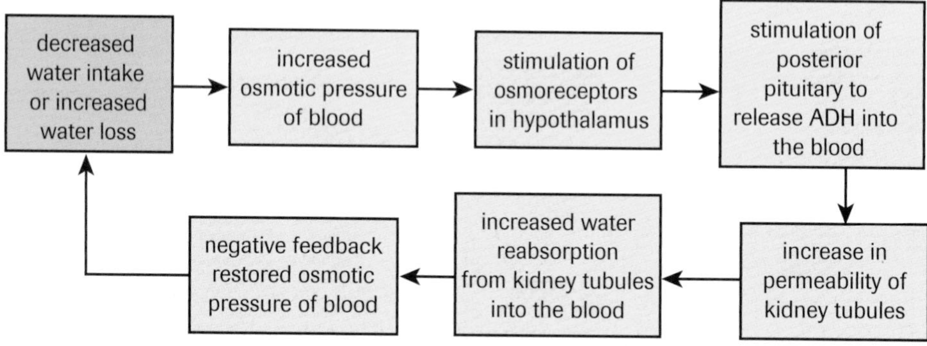

Figure 1

4. From the physiology you studied in Biology 20, provide an example of how cells communicate with each other to protect the body from invading microbes.

5. From the physiology you studied in Biology 20, provide an example of how cells in one part of the body communicate with cells in another part of the body to release hormones.

Skills and STS Connections

6. A cell is placed in a beaker and the concentration of Na^+ ions and sugar ($C_6H_{12}O_6$) is monitored after 10 s and 60 s (**Figure 2**).
   (a) By examining both the cell and the beaker after 10 s, what evidence supports the hypothesis that the cell membrane is permeable to sugar?
   (b) By examining both the cell and the beaker after 10 s, what evidence supports the hypothesis that Na^+ ions move by diffusion?
   (c) By examining both the cell and the beaker after 60 s, what evidence supports the hypothesis that sugar is actively transported?
   (d) By examining both the cell and the beaker after 60 s, provide a hypothesis that helps explain why the total number of sugar molecules has decreased.

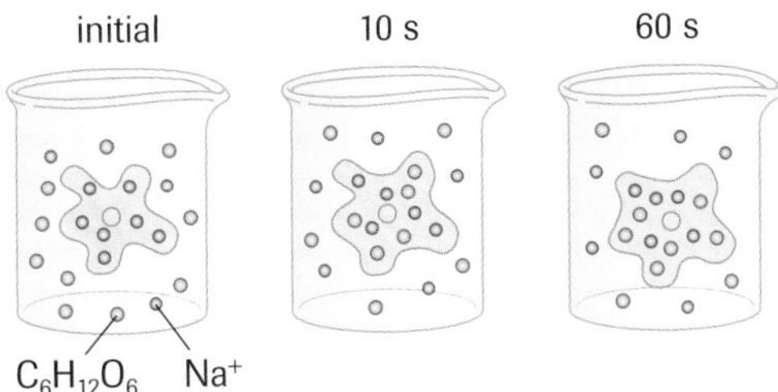

Figure 2

7. A research team wishes to show the negative effects of consuming alcohol on driving. Knowing that alcohol impairs reaction times, the researcher needs to design an investigation that will test their hypothesis.
   (a) Create a hypothesis for the experiment.
   (b) Present the experimental design.
   (c) Write a multi-step procedure for the experiment.
   (d) Identify the independent and dependent variables for the experiment.
   (e) What variables must be controlled to get reliable results?
   (f) Design a data table for the experiment.
   (g) Would you expect identical data from different subjects? Explain your answer.
   (h) What practical information could be provided by the experiment?

chapter

13 Nervous System

In this chapter

- Exploration: Stimulus and Response in Invertebrates
- Investigation 13.1: Reflex Arcs
- Chemistry Connection: Electrolytes
- Mini Investigation: Examining Neurons
- Case Study: Drugs and the Synapse
- Web Activity: Spinal Cord Research
- Investigation 13.2: Brain Dissection
- Web Activity: Wilder G. Penfield
- Case Study: Phineas Gage
- Web Activity: Neuroimaging

In 1998, Michael J. Fox (**Figure 1**) announced that he was leaving a popular television sitcom because of Parkinson's disease. Fox was diagnosed with early stages of Parkinson's disease in 1991, when he noticed a twitch in a finger. Over the next seven years the disease progressed, making acting very difficult.

Parkinson's disease is a progressive degenerative nerve disorder that affects muscle activity. Cells in two areas of the brain, the substantia nigra and the locus cerulus, degenerate and die. These cells secrete dopamine and norepinephrine. Any reduction in these chemicals affects muscle movement. Early symptoms include muscle tremors, slow body movements, rigidity in the joints, and an inability to regain one's balance. As the disease progresses, the symptoms become more pronounced and daily activities become extremely difficult.

The cause of the disease is not known. In about 15 % of cases, heredity plays a role. A person can inherit one of two genes that produce proteins that destroy the brain cells. In the remaining 85 % of cases, scientists believe that a dormant gene is triggered. Unfortunately, the actual trigger and how the gene is triggered is unknown. Although the disease usually occurs in people over 50, Parkinson's can also affect younger adults.

STARTING Points

Answer these questions as best you can with your current knowledge. Then, using the concepts and skills you have learned, you will revise your answers at the end of the chapter.

1. Do nerves carry electrical current? Explain.
2. Does a nerve that carries information from your eye, function any differently from a nerve that sends information to a muscle?
3. A woman touches a hot object and quickly moves her finger away. Does the brain coordinate the movement of the finger away from the hot object?
4. A cougar jumps from behind a bush and startles a man standing nearby. The information is passed to the man's brain. Explain how the nervous system, endocrine system, and urinary system prepare his body for stress.
5. Endurance athletes, such as Alex Decoteau (**Figure 2**, next page), a great long-distance runner from the Red Pheasant reserve in Saskatchewan, have to endure a lot of pain. He was able fight back the pain and win four races in one day. What allows one person to withstand more pain than another person?

Career Connections: Mental Health Worker; Chiropractor

Figure 1
Canadian actor Michael J. Fox

Figure 2
In 1910, Alex Decoteau won the half-mile, one mile, two mile, and five mile races at a meet in Fort Saskatchewan.

Exploration — Stimulus and Response in Invertebrates

Invertebrates such as worms and leeches have a distinct top and bottom, front and back, and head and tail. In this activity, you will observe the response of an invertebrate to a simple stimulus.

Materials: medicine dropper, invertebrate, microscope slide, paper towel

- Gently touch the head of the invertebrate with a piece of paper towel and note its response.
  (a) Explain why the invertebrate responded as it did.
  (b) What can you infer about the nervous system of the invertebrate?
  (c) How do you think an invertebrate would respond to a concentration of salt added to its environment?

13.1 The Importance of the Nervous System

Prisoners have often been isolated and placed in dark rooms as a means of punishment. Imagine how you would be affected if you didn't know whether it was day or night, or if you couldn't hear a sound for days.

Even in these extreme conditions, however, your nervous system remains active. Information about your depth of breathing, the physical condition of the breathing muscles, and the amount of water contained in the respiratory tract is continually relayed to the brain for processing and storage. Other nerve cells detect air temperature, light intensity, and odours. Pressure receptors in the skin—known as baroreceptors—inform you of the fit of your clothes and can detect an insect scurrying across your leg. Blinking your eyes or scratching your nose requires coordinated nerve impulses. Memories of happy times and hopes for your future reside in the nervous system.

The nervous system is an elaborate communication system that contains more than 100 billion nerve cells in the brain alone. That number exceeds the number of visible stars in the Milky Way galaxy.

central nervous system (CNS) the body's coordinating centre for mechanical and chemical actions; made up of the brain and spinal cord

peripheral nervous system (PNS) all parts of the nervous system, excluding brain and spinal cord, that relay information between the central nervous system and other parts of the body

Organization of the Nervous System

The nervous system has two main divisions: the **central nervous system (CNS)** and the **peripheral nervous system (PNS)** (Figure 1). The central nervous system consists of the nerves of the brain and spinal cord and acts as a coordinating centre for incoming and outgoing information. The peripheral nervous system consists of nerves that carry information between the organs of the body and the central nervous system.

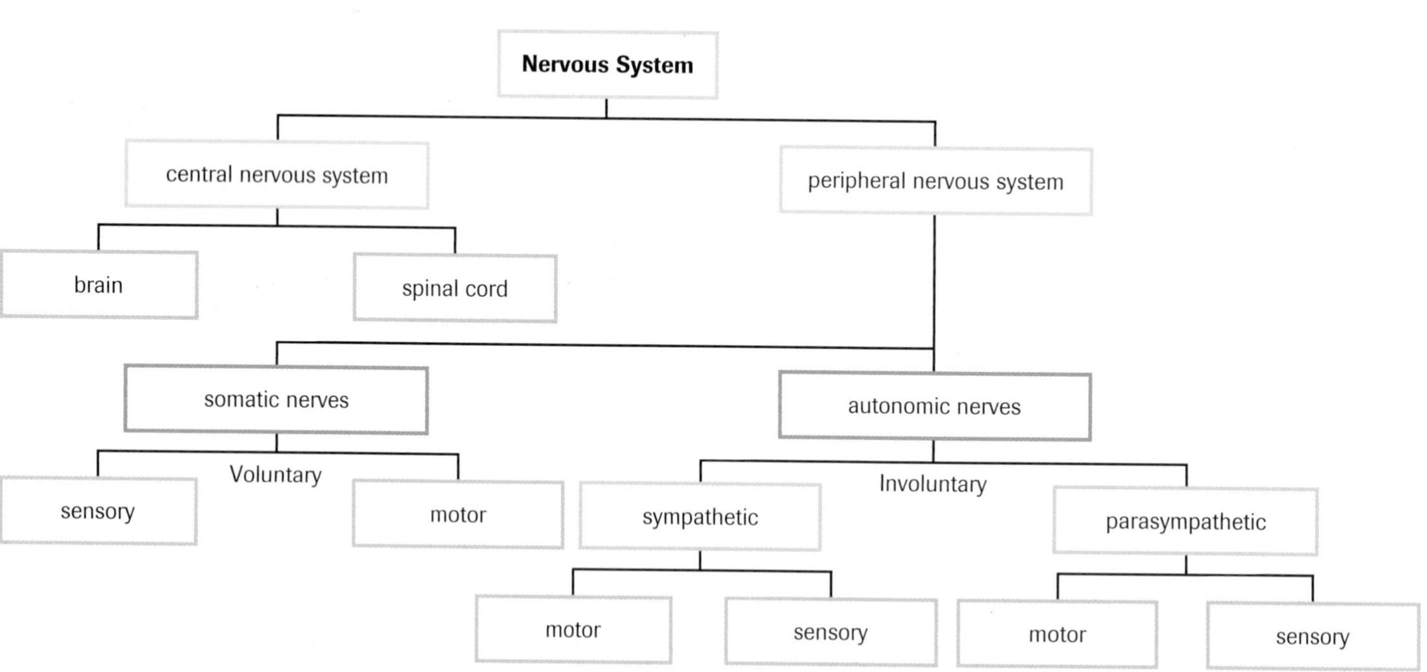

Figure 1
The main divisions of the nervous system

The peripheral nervous system can be further subdivided into somatic and autonomic nerves. The somatic nervous system controls the skeletal muscle, bones, and skin. Sensory somatic nerves relay information about the environment to the central nervous system, while motor somatic nerves initiate an appropriate response. The autonomic nervous system contains special motor nerves that control the internal organs of the body. The two divisions of the autonomic system—the sympathetic nervous system and the parasympathetic nervous system—often operate as "on–off" switches. These two systems will be discussed later in the chapter.

Anatomy of a Nerve Cell

Two different types of cells—glial cells and neurons—are found in the nervous system. **Glial cells**, often called neuroglial cells, are nonconducting cells and are important for the structural support and metabolism of the nerve cells. **Neurons** are the functional units of the nervous system (**Figure 2**). All neurons contain dendrites, cell bodies, and axons. The **dendrites** receive information, either from the environment or from other neurons. Like all living cells, neurons contain a nucleus (in a neuron, the nucleus is within the cell body). Dendrites conduct nerve impulses toward the cell body. An extension of cytoplasm, called the **axon**, conducts nerve impulses away from the cell body. A neuron has only one axon, though it may form many branches. In humans, the axon is extremely thin; more than 100 axons could be placed inside the shaft of a single human hair. The axon carries the nerve impulse toward other neurons or to effectors. A close examination of most nerves shows that they are comprised of many axons held together by connective tissue (**Figure 3**, next page).

glial cell nonconducting cell important for structural support and metabolism of the nerve cells

neuron nerve cell that conducts nerve impulses

dendrite projection of cytoplasm that carries impulses toward the cell body

axon extension of cytoplasm that carries nerve impulses away from the cell body

Many axons are covered with a glistening white coat of a fatty protein called the **myelin sheath**, which acts as insulation for the neurons. Axons that have a myelin covering are said to be myelinated. Formed by special glial cells called **Schwann cells**, the myelin sheath insulates by preventing the loss of charged ions from the nerve cell. The areas between the sections of myelin sheath are known as the **nodes of Ranvier**. Nerve impulses jump from one node to another, thereby speeding the movement of nerve impulses. Not surprisingly, nerve impulses move much faster along myelinated nerve fibres than nonmyelinated ones. The speed of the impulse along the nerve fibre is also affected by the diameter of the axon. Generally, the larger the diameter of the axon, the faster the speed of the nerve impulse.

myelin sheath insulated covering over the axon of a nerve cell

Schwann cell special type of glial cell that produces the myelin sheath

nodes of Ranvier regularly occurring gaps between sections of myelin sheath along the axon

All nerve fibres found within the peripheral nervous system have a thin outer membrane called the **neurilemma**, which surrounds the axon. The neurilemma is formed by the Schwann cells and promotes the regeneration of damaged axons. This explains why feeling gradually returns to your finger following a paper cut—severed neurons can be rejoined. However, not all nerve cells that have a myelin sheath have a neurilemma. Nerves within the brain that contain myelinated fibres are called white matter because the myelinated axons are whitish in appearance. Other nerve cells within the brain and

neurilemma delicate membrane that surrounds the axon of some nerve cells

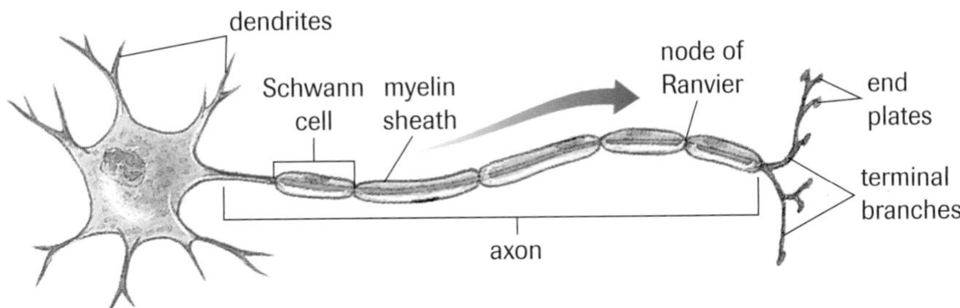

Figure 2
Structure of a neuron. The arrow shows the direction in which a nerve impulse travels.

DID YOU KNOW?

Multiple Sclerosis

Multiple sclerosis is caused by the destruction of the myelin sheath that surrounds the nerve axons. The myelinated nerves in the brain and spinal cord are gradually destroyed as the myelin sheath hardens and forms scars, or plaques. This scarlike tissue prevents normal impulse transmission. Often referred to as MS, multiple sclerosis can produce symptoms of double vision, speech difficulty, jerky limb movements, and partial paralysis of the voluntary muscles. First identified by a French neurologist in 1868, MS is the most common neurological disease affecting young adults in Canada.

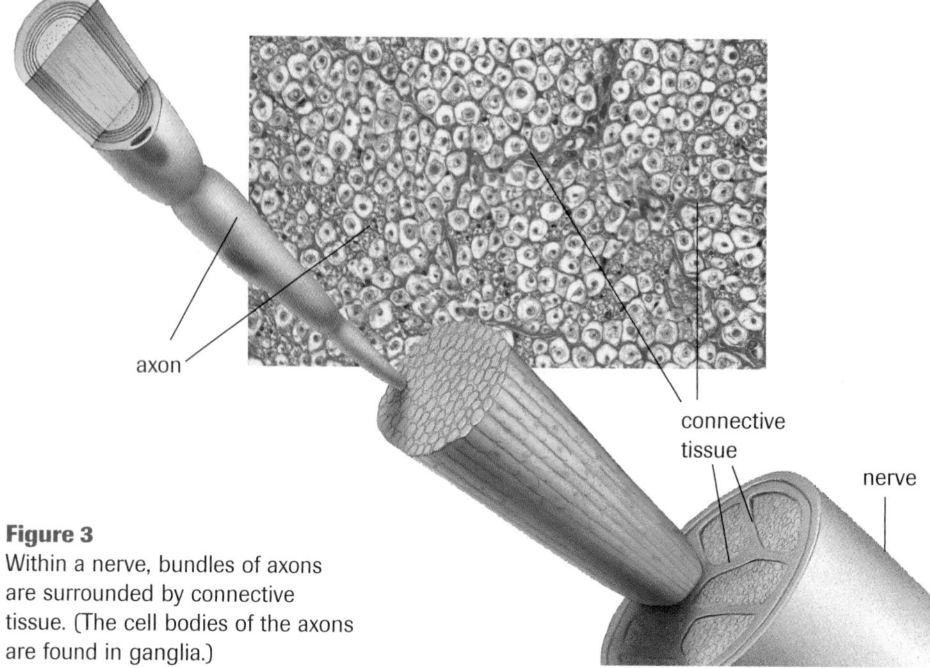

Figure 3
Within a nerve, bundles of axons are surrounded by connective tissue. (The cell bodies of the axons are found in ganglia.)

spinal cord, referred to as the grey matter, lack a myelin sheath. Cells of the white and grey matter of the central nervous system lack neurilemmas. That is why damage to the central nervous system tends to be permanent.

Neurons are categorized into three groups: the sensory neurons, interneurons, and motor neurons. **Sensory neurons** (also known as afferent neurons) relay information (or stimuli) received by **sensory receptors** about the external or internal environment to the central nervous system for processing. The cell bodies of sensory neurons are located in clusters called **ganglia** (singular, **ganglion**) located outside of the spinal cord.

Interneurons, as the name suggests, link neurons to other neurons. Found only in the brain and spinal cord, the interneurons (also known as association neurons) integrate and interpret the sensory information and connect sensory neurons to outgoing motor neurons. **Motor neurons** (also known as efferent neurons) relay information to the **effectors**, which is the cell or organ that responds to the stimulus. Muscles, organs, and glands are classified as effectors because they produce responses.

sensory neuron neuron that carries impulses to the central nervous system; also known as afferent neuron

sensory receptor highly modified dendrites of a sensory neuron that are activated by an environmental stimulus

ganglion (plural **ganglia**) collections of nerve cell bodies located outside the central nervous system

interneuron a neuron of the central nervous system that connects with sensory, motor, and other interneurons to integrate sensory input with motor output; also known as association neuron

motor neuron neuron that carries impulses from the central nervous system to an effector; also known as efferent neuron

effector a cell or organ that produces a physiological response when stimulated by a nerve impulse

Practice

1. Differentiate between the peripheral nervous system (PNS) and central nervous system (CNS).
2. Differentiate between sensory nerves and motor nerves.
3. Briefly describe the function of the following parts of a neuron: dendrites, myelin sheath, Schwann cells, cell body, and axon.
4. What is the relationship between the speed of a nerve impulse and the size of the axon along which it travels?

Repairing Damaged Nerves

For years, scientists have been puzzled about why the central nervous system does not support nerve growth in the same way as the peripheral nervous system. New surgical procedures, the identification of factors that inhibit nerve cell regeneration in the central nervous system, and emerging work with stem cells provide hope for the many people who are paralyzed by spinal cord injury (SCI) (**Figure 4**).

In Norrtalje, Sweden, 25-year-old Thomas Westburg sustained a serious spinal cord injury while snowmobiling. Four nerves were torn from the spinal cord in the area of the neck. The injury left Westburg's left shoulder, arm, and hand completely paralyzed. Surgeons at the Karolinska Hospital in Stockholm reattached two of the nerves. Remarkably, the repair job provided a channel along which new nerves began to grow from cell bodies in Westburg's spinal cord. The slow growth of nerve cells finally connected the spinal cord with muscles that move the arm. In Westburg's case, about 40 % of mobility was restored.

Some promising research comes from the use of stem cells. Stem cells are cells that have not yet specialized into tissue cells, such as skin, bone, muscle, or nerve cells. Scientists are experimenting with the possibility of replacing cells that have been damaged by disease or trauma, such as in cases of spinal cord injury or Parkinson's disease.

In October 2000, scientists announced that they had reconnected severed nerves in the spinal cords of rats using spore-like cells from the nervous system of adult rats. Only 3 μm (micrometres) in diameter, these repair cells are so small that some researchers first regarded them as cellular debris. The spore-like cells can be frozen for more than a month and still be retrieved for use. Properly incubated, they grow easily and can withstand a decrease in nutrients and changes of temperature. Placed in the body of a mammal, they are able to survive with limited amounts of oxygen for several days until blood vessels grow into the area. These spore-like cells can only transform into cells associated with nerve conduction.

Scientists harvested the spore-like nerve cells from the spines of healthy adult rats and seeded them into the spinal cords of injured rats. Quickly the new cells began to grow in the area of the severed cord. After 10 days, researchers recorded small twitches in the toes of the rats. Within three months, some of the rats could stand on their hind legs. The use of adult stem cells has also been proposed for this purpose. However, further research is required to determine whether these cells could be used to treat neurological diseases and injuries.

Figure 4
Snowmobile accidents account for a high number of spinal cord injuries in Canada.

DID YOU KNOW ?

Spinal Cord Injury in Canada
According to the Canadian Paraplegic Association (CPA), about 1000 new injuries a year result in some level of permanent paralysis or neurological deficit. Spinal cord injury is most common in males in the 15–34 age group.

+ EXTENSION

CBC radioONE
QUIRKS & QUARKS

Brain Band-Aid
Dr. Rutledge Ellis-Behnke (professor in the Department of Brain and Cognitive Sciences at the Massachusetts Institute of Technology) and colleagues have been working to overcome the body's natural defence systems that prevent damaged neurons from growing back and repairing. In research trials in hamsters, severed nerves have been regrown and function has been restored.

www.science.nelson.com 

The Reflex Arc

If you accidentally touch a hot stove, you probably do not think about how your nervous system tells you that it is hot. The sensation of heat is detected by specialized temperature receptors in your skin, and a nerve impulse is carried to the spinal cord. The sensory neuron passes the impulse on to an interneuron, which, in turn, relays the impulse to a motor neuron. The motor neuron causes the muscles in the hand to contract and the hand to pull away. All this happens in less than a second, before the information even travels to the brain. Very quickly, the sensation of pain becomes noticeable and you may let out a scream.

Reflexes are involuntary and often unconscious. Imagine how badly you could burn yourself if you had to wait for the sensation of pain before removing your hand from the hot stove. The damage would be much worse if you had to go through the process of gauging the intensity of the pain and then contemplating the appropriate action. Even the small amount of time required for nerve impulses to move through the many circuits of the brain and back to the muscle would increase the damage.

reflex arc neural circuit through the spinal cord that provides a framework for a reflex action

The simplest nerve pathway is the **reflex arc**. Most reflexes occur through a reflex arc, which do not involve coordination by the brain. Reflex arcs contain five essential components: the sensory receptor, the sensory neuron, the interneuron (most often found in the spinal cord, but in some reflex arcs, in the brain), the motor neuron, and the effector (**Figure 5**).

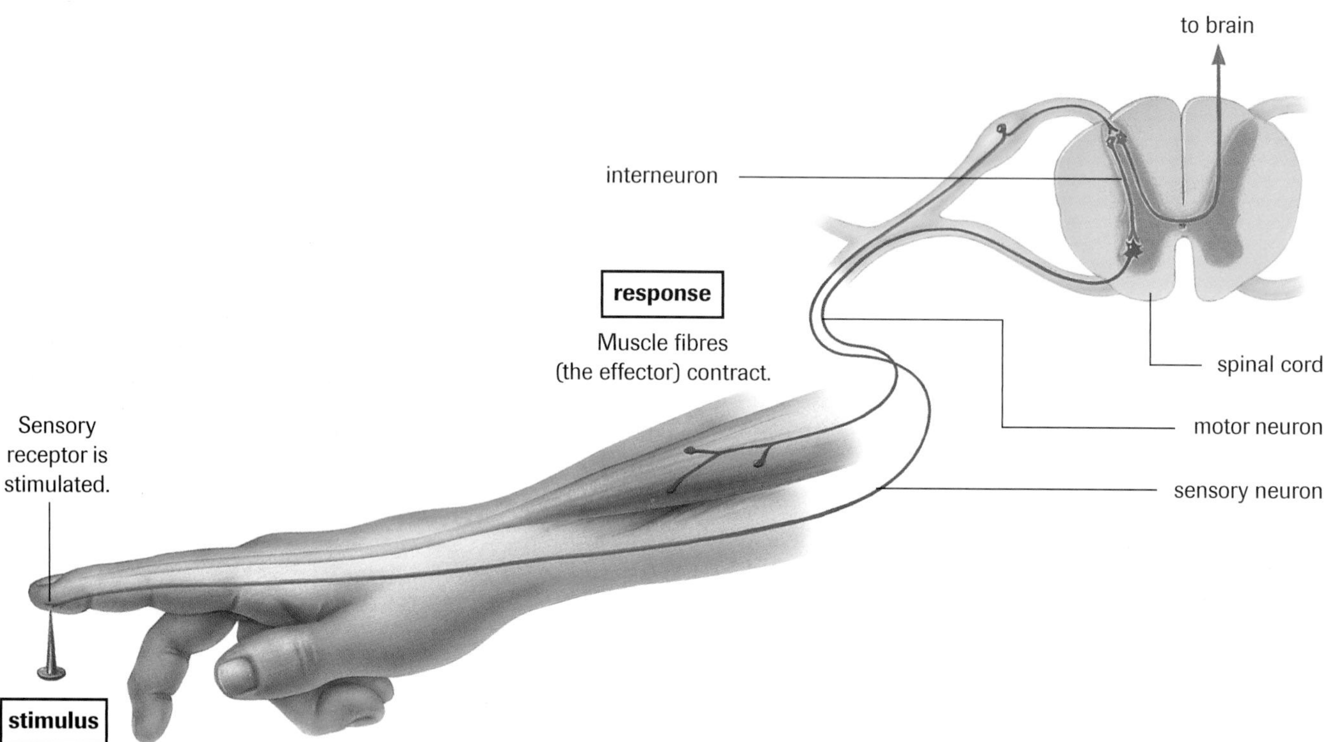

Figure 5
A reflex arc begins when the touch receptor in the finger senses the tack. Sensory information is relayed from the sensory neuron (purple) to the spinal cord. Interneurons in the spinal cord (green) receive the information from the sensory neuron and relay it to the motor neuron (red). The motor neuron activates the muscle cell (the effector), causing it to contract. The brain also receives sensory information from a sensory neuron, which registers as pain. This step is not part of the reflex arc.

Physicians may stimulate a reflex arc to test the health and functioning of parts of the nervous system. For example, the patellar reflex is stimulated by gently tapping the tendon below the kneecap. Sensory receptors detect the slight stretching of the tendon and relay an impulse to a sensory neuron (**Figure 6**, next page). The impulse travels down the sensory neuron to the spinal cord. The message has now travelled from the peripheral nervous system to the central nervous system. The central nervous system then relays a message back out to the peripheral nervous system, along two motor neurons that connect with the muscles on the upper and lower thigh (the quadriceps and hamstrings, respectively). The impulses from these motor neurons simultaneously cause the quadriceps to contract and the hamstrings to relax. As a result, the lower leg rises. This all takes place so quickly as to seem instantaneous.

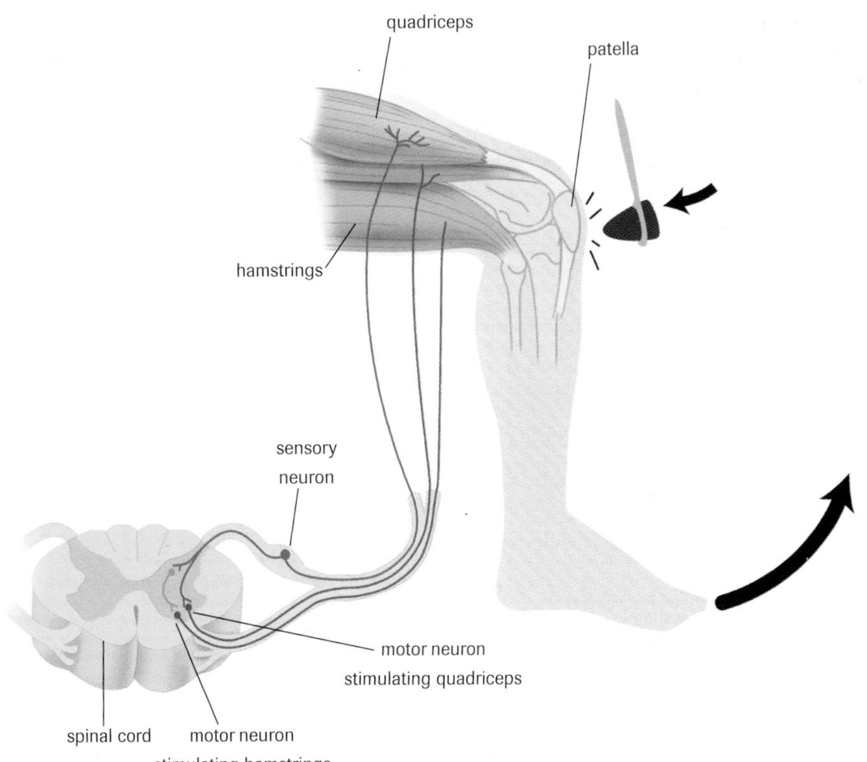

Figure 6
The patellar reflex is commonly known as the "knee-jerk response." Tapping on the ligament under the knee cap causes the lower leg to raise in response.

You may have experienced a physician quickly shining a small penlight in one eye during an examination. In this exam, the physician is looking for your pupils to constrict (become smaller) in response to the light. (This should never be done with a bright light, since it could damage the eye.) This is called the pupillary reflex. Sensors in the eye detect the light and pass an impulse to a sensory neuron. In this case, the impulse is carried to the brain. This is the point at which the message is relayed from the peripheral nervous system to the central nervous system in this reflex arc. As with the patellar reflex, the central nervous system relays a message to two motor neurons in the peripheral nervous system, one for each eye. These neurons carry an impulse to muscles in the eye that cause the pupil to contract. As a result, when a light is shone in one eye of a person with a healthy nervous system, the pupils of both eyes will respond simultaneously.

INVESTIGATION 13.1 ***Introduction***

Reflex Arcs

Reflex arcs provide a framework for reflex actions. Simple physical tests can be performed to test reflexes. In this investigation, you will observe the presence and strength of a number of reflex arcs. You will also design an experiment to investigate a reflex arc.

Report Checklist

- ● Purpose
- ○ Problem
- ● Hypothesis
- ● Prediction
- ● Design
- ● Materials
- ● Procedure
- ● Evidence
- ● Analysis
- ● Evaluation
- ● Synthesis

To perform this investigation, turn to page 436.

SUMMARY The Importance of the Nervous System

Table 1 Parts of the Nervous System

Structure	Function
neuron	• nerve cell that conducts nerve impulses
sensory neuron (afferent neuron)	• carries impulses to the central nervous system
interneuron	• carries impulses within the central nervous system
motor neuron (efferent neuron)	• carries impulses from the central nervous system to effectors
dendrite	• projection of cytoplasm that carries impulses toward the cell body
axon	• extension of cytoplasm that carries nerve impulses away from the cell body
myelin sheath	• covering over the axon of a nerve cell that is composed of Schwann cells and insulates the axon
nodes of Ranvier	• regularly occurring gaps between sections of myelin sheath that speed transmission of nerve impulses
neurilemma	• delicate membrane surrounding the axons of some nerve cells that promotes nerve regeneration
reflex arc	• neural circuit that travels through the spinal cord • provides a framework for a reflex action

Section 13.1 Questions

1. Name the essential components of a reflex arc and the function of each.
2. What would happen if neuron I in **Figure 7** was severed?
3. In **Figure 7**, what is the order in which an impulse travels along a reflex arc?
4. Primitive sporelike repair cells have been extracted from adult rats. Discuss some of the benefits of using mature repair cells.
5. The incidence of multiple sclerosis (MS) varies among different regions of Canada. Provide a possible explanation for different distributions of the disease.
6. A study on severed optic nerves showed that neurons from the peripheral nervous system grafted into the stalk of the optic nerve regrew approximately 10 % of the retinal ganglions. No reconnections were seen when severed optic-nerve neurons were left alone. What do these findings suggest?

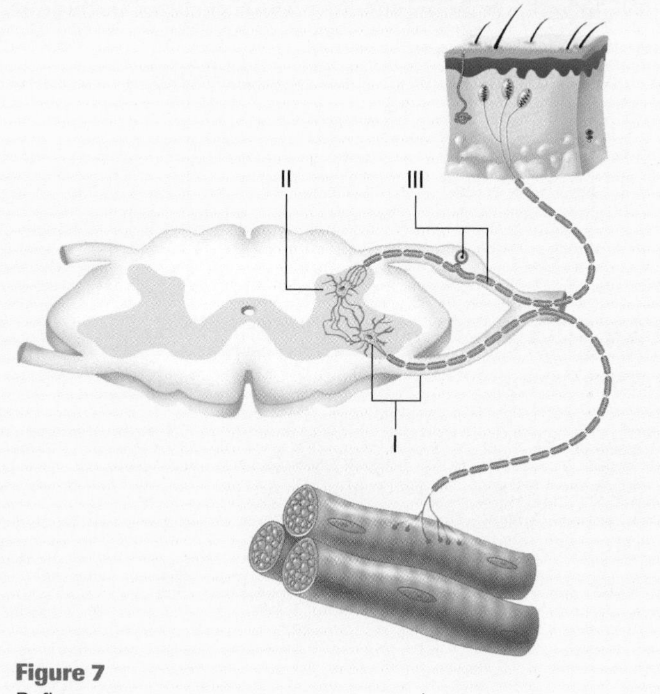

Figure 7
Reflex arc

Electrochemical Impulse 13.2

As early as 1900, German physiologist Julius Bernstein suggested that nerve impulses were an electrochemical message created by the movement of ions through the nerve cell membrane. Evidence supporting Bernstein's theory was provided in 1939 when two researchers at Columbia University, K.S. Cole and H.J. Curtis, placed a tiny electrode inside the large nerve cell of a squid (**Figure 1**). A rapid change in the electrical potential difference—commonly called the potential—across the membrane was detected every time the nerve became excited. The resting membrane normally had a potential somewhere near −70 mV (millivolts); however, when the nerve became excited, the potential on the inside of the membrane registered +40 mV. This reversal of potential is described as an **action potential**. Cole and Curtis noticed that the +40 mV did not last more than a few milliseconds (ms) before the potential on the inside of the nerve cell returned to −70 mV, the **resting potential**.

action potential the voltage difference across a nerve cell membrane when the nerve is excited

resting potential voltage difference across a nerve cell membrane when it is not transmitting a nerve impulse (usually negative)

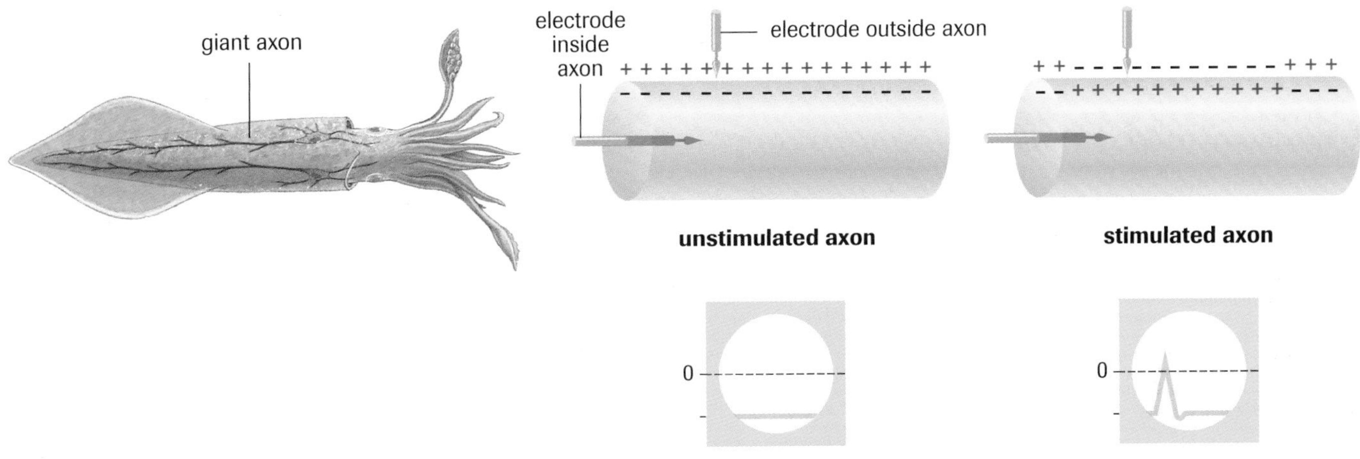

Figure 1
A miniature electrode is placed inside the giant axon of a squid. The inside of the resting membrane is negative with respect to the outside of the membrane. When stimulated, the charges across the nerve membrane temporarily reverse.

The Resting Potential

The plasma membrane of almost all cells has an electrical potential of about –70 mV. In neurons, this electrical potential is called the resting potential. What gives plasma membranes this electrical potential? If we examine the neuron on a molecular level, we can find the answer. Like almost all cells, neurons have a rich supply of positive and negative ions on both sides of the cell membrane (**Figure 2**). There is a higher concentration of potassium ions (K^+) inside the cell and a higher concentration of sodium ions (Na^+) outside the cell. The movement of K^+ is mainly responsible for creating the electrical potential.

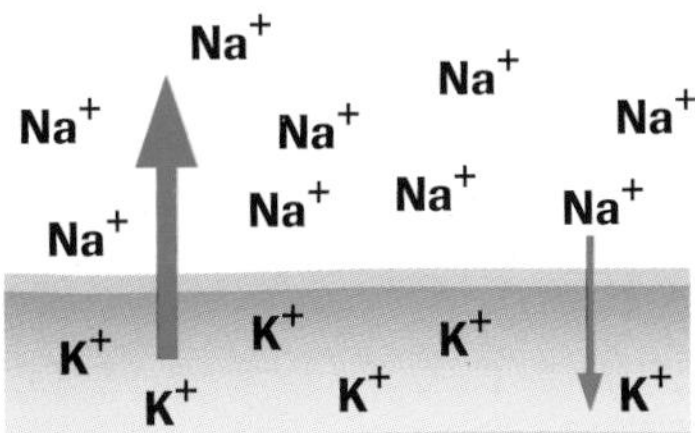

Figure 2
The K^+ concentration is higher inside the cell and the Na^+ concentration is higher outside the cell.

facilitated diffusion transport of substances across cell membrane down a concentration gradient by a carrier in the membrane; does not use energy

gated ion channel a pore in the cell membrane that allows ions to move in and out of the cell by opening and closing

sodium-potassium pump a transporter in the cell membrane that moves potassium ions into the cytoplasm while simultaneously removing sodium ions from the cytoplasm to the extracellular fluid

active transport movement of substances across cell membranes that uses energy; often moves substances against a concentration gradient

CHEMISTRY CONNECTION

Electrolytes

An electrolyte is an aqueous electrical conductor. As in nerve cells, it is the ions in an electrolyte solution that transfer electric charge within an electric cell. Your *Chemistry 20–30* textbook will provide more information on ions and electric cells.

www.science.nelson.com 

polarized membrane membrane charged by unequal distribution of positively charged ions inside and outside the nerve cell

The plasma membrane of all cells, including neurons, is composed of a phospholipid bilayer. Plasma membranes are selectively permeable; ions cannot cross the bilayer by simple diffusion. Instead, they enter cells by **facilitated diffusion**, passing through **gated ion channels** that span the bilayer. Ion channels are specific to particular ions, such as K^+ or Na^+ ions.

There are many more K^+ channels than Na^+ channels in the membrane, so more K^+ diffuse out of the cell than Na^+ diffuse in (**Figure 3**). As K^+ leaves the cell, it transfers its positive charge outside the cell. The negatively charged ions are trapped inside the cell, and so an electrical charge builds up across the membrane, creating an electrical gradient. (If ion concentrations were determined only by diffusion, eventually the concentrations of sodium and potassium would equalize across the membrane. This does not happen because the **sodium-potassium pump** in the membrane moves potassium back into the cell and sodium back out of the cell through **active transport**.)

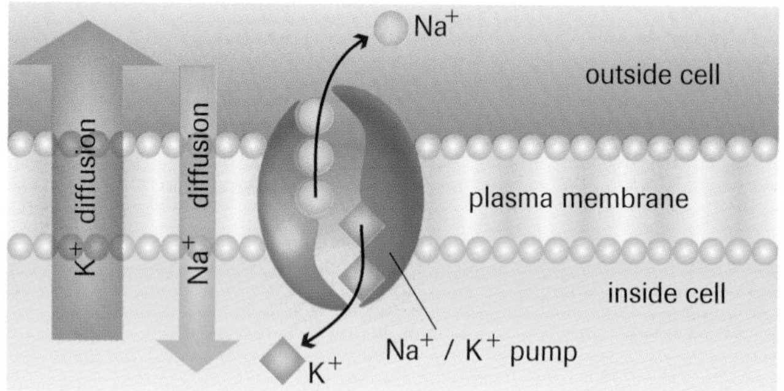

Figure 3

As potassium and sodium diffuse down their concentration gradients across the cell membrane through facilitated diffusion, the sodium-potassium pump actively transports them against the gradients.

Excess positive ions accumulate along the outside of the nerve membrane, while excess negative ions accumulate along the inside of the membrane. The resting membrane is said to be charged and is called a **polarized membrane**. The separation of electrical charges by a membrane has the potential to do work, which is expressed in millivolts (mV). A charge of −70 mV indicates the difference between the number of positive charges found on the inside of the nerve membrane relative to the outside. (A charge of −90 mV on the inside of the nerve membrane would indicate even fewer positive ions inside the membrane relative to the outside.)

The Action Potential

A nerve impulse is an action potential. When a neuron receives a stimulus, the cell membrane becomes more permeable to sodium than potassium. Scientists believe that sodium channels are opened in the membrane, while potassium channels close. The highly concentrated sodium ions rush into the cell by diffusion and by charge attraction. The rapid inflow of sodium reverses the charge on both sides of the membrane.

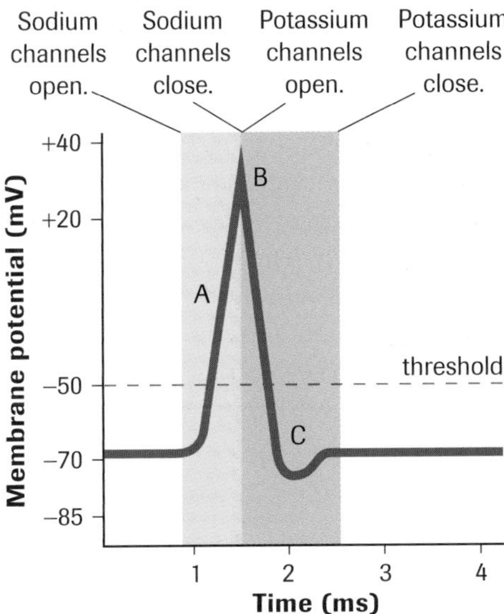

Figure 4
The phases of an action potential

depolarization diffusion of sodium ions into the nerve cell resulting in a charge reversal

repolarization process of restoring the original polarity of the nerve membrane

hyperpolarization condition in which the inside of the nerve cell membrane has a greater negative charge than the resting membrane; caused by excessive diffusion of potassium ions out of the cell

refractory period recovery time required before a neuron can produce another action potential

This charge reversal is referred to as **depolarization** (A on **Figure 4**). Once the voltage inside the cell becomes positive, the sodium channels slam closed, stopping the inflow of sodium. The potassium channels then open and potassium ions diffuse out of the cell and the charge outside the cell becomes positive again. The process of restoring the original polarity of the nerve membrane is called **repolarization** (B). However, the potassium gates close relatively slowly and the outside of the cell becomes even more positively charged than the resting membrane (and the inside more negatively charged) as more and more potassium ions move out of the cell. This is called **hyperpolarization** (C). The sodium-potassium pump restores the condition of the resting membrane by transporting sodium ions out of, and potassium ions into, the cell. The time taken for the membrane to return to the resting potential after repolarization is called the **refractory period**, which lasts 1 to 10 ms. The membrane must return to the resting potential before it can generate another action potential.

Movement of the Action Potential

An action potential happens at a specific point on the nerve cell membrane. But how does it move along the cell membrane? In fact, an action potential does not move. Many action potentials are generated one after another along the cell membrane, causing a wave of depolarization. It is similar to a falling domino. When the first domino falls, it causes the domino next to it to fall, and so on.

The first action potential is generated as sodium ions rush into the cell, causing a depolarization of the membrane. The positively charged ions that rush into the nerve cell are then attracted to the adjacent negative ions, which are aligned along the inside of the nerve membrane (**Figure 5**). Similarly, the positively charged sodium ions on the outside of the resting membrane are attracted to the negative charge that has accumulated along the outside of the membrane in the area of the action potential.

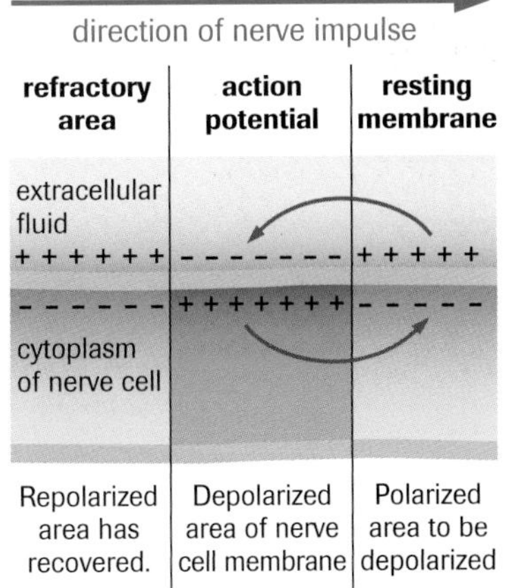

Figure 5
The movement of a nerve impulse. Red arrows indicate ions attracted to adjacent ions with opposite charges.

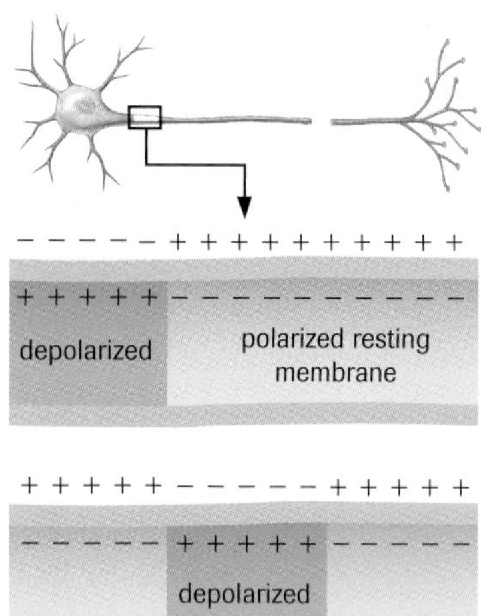

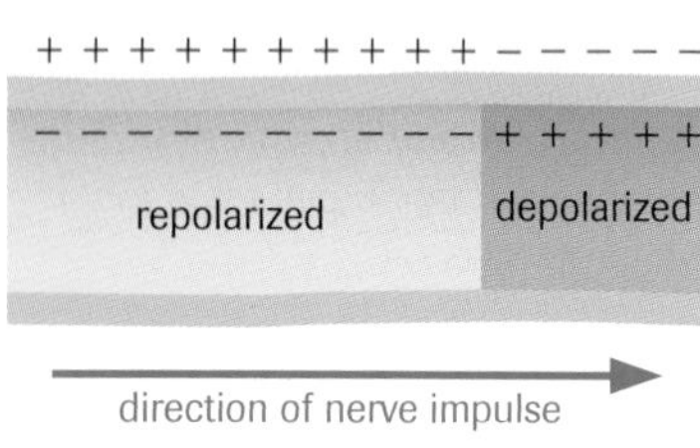

+ + + + + + + + + + – – – – –
– – – – – – – – – – + + + + +
repolarized
depolarized

direction of nerve impulse

Figure 6
Successive action potentials along a section of axon cause a wave of depolarization along the cell membrane.

The flow of positively charged ions from the depolarized area toward the adjacent resting membrane causes an electrical disturbance. This electrical stimulus causes the sodium channels in the adjacent resting membrane to open, triggering an action potential next to the first action potential. The cycle keeps repeating and the action potentials cause a wave of depolarization along the membrane (**Figure 6**).

What stops the action potentials from going backwards along the cell membrane? Recall that the membrane can only produce another action potential when it is at the resting potential. Thus, during the refractory period right after an action potential, the cell membrane cannot produce another action potential because it is hyperpolarized. So, a new action potential can only be triggered at the leading edge of the first depolarized area.

When axons are myelinated, nerve impulses travel by **saltatory conduction**. In myelinated axons, the gated ion channels are concentrated at the nodes of Ranvier. The flow of ions across the cell membrane can only happen at the nodes and so action potentials have to "jump" from node to node. This causes a nerve signal to be transmitted down an axon much faster (**Figure 7**).

saltatory conduction generation of action potentials only at nodes of Ranvier in myelinated axons, resulting in rapid transmission of nerve impulses

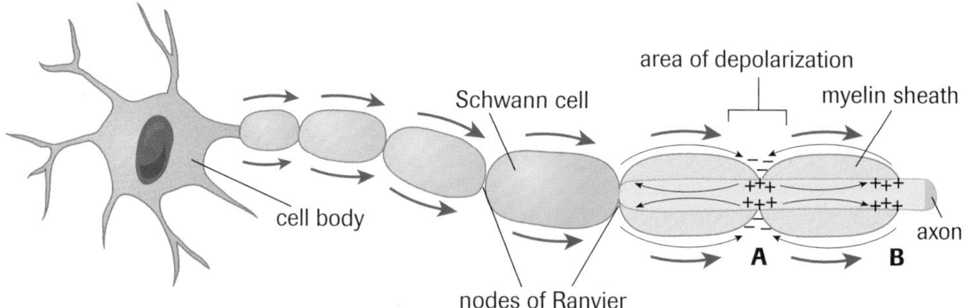

Figure 7
In myelinated axons, depolarization happens only at the nodes (**A**) and an action potential jumps to the next node (**B**). The red arrows show the direction of the nerve impulse and the black arrows show the flow of ions.

Practice

1. What is a polarized membrane?
2. What causes the inside of a neuron to become negatively charged?
3. Why does the polarity of a cell membrane reverse during an action potential?
4. Why do nerve impulses move faster along myelinated nerve fibres?

Threshold Levels and the All-or-None Response

In a classic experiment, a single neuron leading to a muscle is isolated and a mild electrical shock is applied to the neuron. A special recorder measures the strength of muscle contraction. **Figure 8**, on the next page, shows sample data for this experiment. In this example, stimuli of less than 2 mV does not produce any muscle contraction. A potential stimulus must be above a critical value to produce a response. The critical intensity of the stimulus is known as the **threshold level**. Stimuli below threshold levels do not initiate a response. In **Figure 8**, although a threshold level of 2 mV is required to produce a response, threshold levels are different for each neuron.

threshold level minimum level of a stimulus required to produce a response

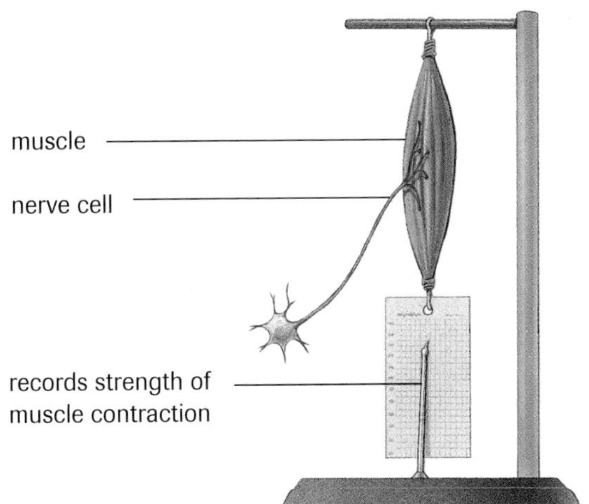

Table 1 Stimulus Strength and Force of Muscle Contraction

Strength of stimuli	Force of contraction
1 mV	–
2 mV	3 N
3 mV	3 N
10 mV	3 N

Figure 8
The threshold level for this neuron is 2 mV. Different neurons have different threshold levels.

The Threshold Potential of a Neuron

Listen to this audio discussion of the reaction of a neuron to stimulus once its membrane potential has reached the threshold level.

www.science.nelson.com 

A second, but equally important, conclusion can be drawn from the experimental data in **Table 1**. Increasing the intensity of the stimuli above the critical threshold value will not produce an increased response—the intensity of the nerve impulse and speed of transmission remain the same. In what is referred to as the **all-or-none response**, neurons either fire maximally or not at all.

all-or-none response a nerve or muscle fibre responds completely or not at all to a stimulus

How do animals detect the intensity of stimuli if nerve fibres either fire completely or not at all? Experience tells you that you are capable of differentiating between a warm object and one that is hot. To explain the apparent anomaly, we must examine the manner in which the brain interprets nerve impulses. Although stimuli above threshold levels produce nerve impulses of identical speed and intensity, variation with respect to frequency does occur. The more intense the stimulus, the greater the frequency of impulses. Therefore, when a warm glass rod is placed on your hand, sensory impulses may be sent to the brain at a slow rate. A hot glass rod placed on the same tissue also causes the nerve to fire, but the frequency of impulses is greatly increased—a difference the brain recognizes.

The different threshold levels of neurons provide a second way for the intensity of stimuli to be detected. Each nerve is composed of many individual nerve cells or neurons. A glass rod at 40 °C may cause a single neuron to reach threshold level, but the same glass rod at 50 °C will cause two or more neurons to fire (**Figure 9**). The second neuron has a higher threshold level. The greater the number of impulses reaching the brain, the greater the intensity of the response.

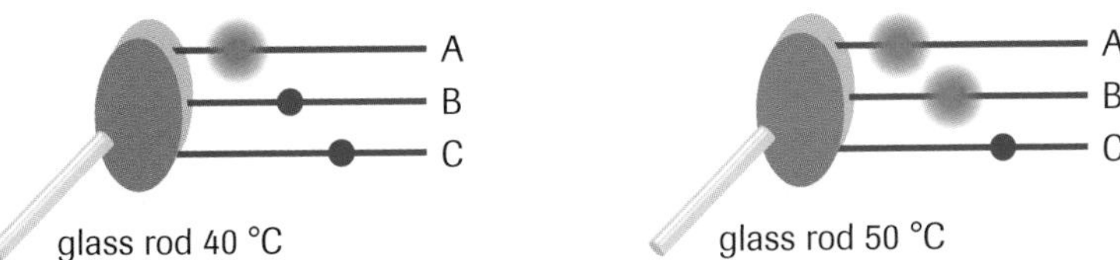

Figure 9
Neuron B has a higher threshold level than neuron A and will not fire until the glass rod is heated above 40 °C. The brain interprets both the number of neurons excited and the frequency of impulses.

Synaptic Transmission

synapse a region between neurons, or between neurons and effectors; also known as the synaptic cleft

neurotransmitter chemical messenger released by the presynaptic neuron that binds to receptors on the postsynaptic neuron

presynaptic neuron neuron that carries impulses to the synapse

postsynaptic neuron neuron that carries impulses away from the synapse

Small spaces between neurons, or between neurons and effectors, are known as **synapses**. The terminal branches of a single neuron allow it to join with many different neurons (**Figure 10**). Synapses rarely involve just two neurons. Small vesicles containing chemicals called **neurotransmitters** are located in the end plates of axons. The impulse moves along the axon and releases neurotransmitters from the end plate. The neurotransmitters are released from the **presynaptic neuron** and diffuse across the synapse, or synaptic cleft, creating a depolarization of the dendrites of the **postsynaptic neuron** when the neurotransmitters bind to receptors. Although the space between neurons is very small—approximately 20 nm (nanometres)—the nerve transmission slows across the synapse. Diffusion is a slow process. Not surprisingly, the greater the number of synapses over a specified distance, the slower the speed of transmission. This may explain why you react so quickly to a stimulus in a reflex arc, which has few synapses, while solving biology problems, which involves many more synapses, requires more time.

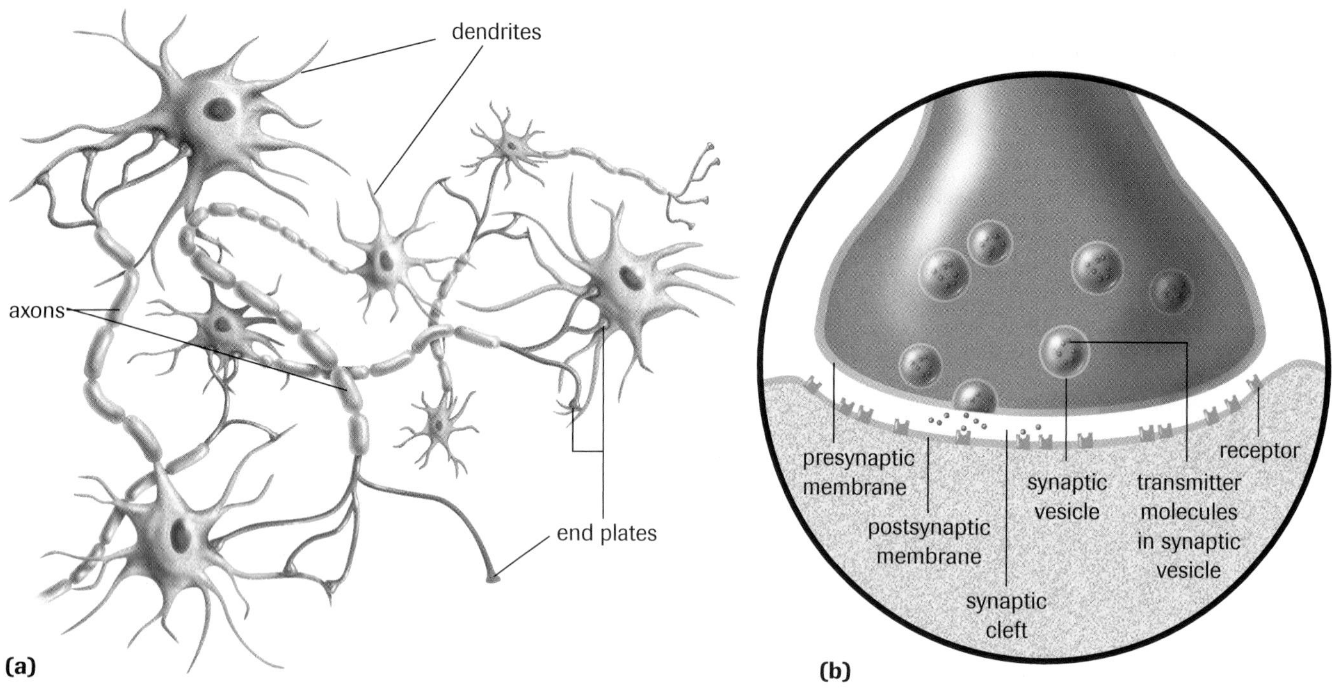

Figure 10
(a) The end plates of terminal branches synapse with the cell bodies and dendrites of many different neurons.
(b) Synaptic vesicles in the end plate of the presynaptic neuron release neurotransmitters into the synaptic cleft. The neurotransmitters attach themselves to receptors on the postsynaptic membrane, causing it to depolarize. The action potential continues along the postsynaptic neuron.

Practice

5. Some people report they have a high pain tolerance. Explain this in terms of threshold levels.
6. What is the all-or-none response?
7. Describe the path of a nerve impulse across a synapse.

mini *Investigation* Examining Neurons

1. Using a light microscope, examine a longitudinal view of a neuron.
   (a) Describe the appearance of the neuron.
   (b) Estimate the diameter of the neuron.
2. Follow the nerve cell to the synapse.
   (a) Describe the appearance of the synapse and draw a diagram of it.
   (b) Estimate the distance between the presynaptic neuron and the postsynaptic neuron.

Calculation of Scale
Listen to this review of calculation of scale in microscopic measurements.

www.science.nelson.com 

3. Refer to the Nelson Web site to view different scientific models of synapses and photomicrographs of synapses taken from scanning electron microscopes and electron microscopes.

www.science.nelson.com 

   (a) What additional information about synapses is revealed by observing these high-magnification, high-resolution photomicrographs?
   (b) How do the scientific models help explain the functioning of the synapse?

Neurotransmitters

Neurotransmitters alter the membrane potentials of postsynaptic neurons. **Acetylcholine** is a neurotransmitter found in the end plates of many nerve cells. Acetylcholine acts as an excitatory neurotransmitter on many postsynaptic neurons by opening the sodium ion channels. Once the channels are opened, the sodium ions rush into the postsynaptic neuron, causing depolarization. The reversal of charge causes the action potential. However, the continued presence of acetylcholine also presents a problem. With the sodium channels open, the postsynaptic neuron would remain in a constant state of depolarization. How can the nerve respond to the next impulse if it never recovers? The presynaptic membrane releases the enzyme **cholinesterase**, which destroys acetylcholine. Once acetylcholine is destroyed, the sodium channels close, and the neuron begins its recovery phase. Many insecticides take advantage of the synapse by blocking cholinesterase. The heart of an insect, unlike the human heart, is totally under nerve control. An insecticide causes the insect's heart to respond to the nerve message by contracting but never relaxing.

acetylcholine neurotransmitter released from vesicles in the end plates of neurons, which makes the postsynaptic membranes more permeable to Na^+ ions

cholinesterase enzyme, which breaks down acetylcholine, that is released from presynaptic membranes in the end plates of neurons shortly after acetylcholine

Not all neurotransmitters are excitatory. For example, although acetylcholine can act as an excitatory neurotransmitter on some postsynaptic membranes, it can act as an inhibitory neurotransmitter on others. Inhibitory neurotransmitters make the postsynaptic membrane more permeable to potassium. By opening even more potassium gates, the potassium ions inside the neuron follow the concentration gradient and diffuse out of the neuron. The rush of potassium out of the cell increases the number of positive ions outside the cell relative to the number found inside the cell, and the cell membrane becomes hyperpolarized, inhibiting any action potentials. As the name suggests, these inhibitory neurotransmitters prevent postsynaptic neurons from becoming active.

DID YOU KNOW ?

Myasthenia Gravis
Drugs that temporarily keep the enzyme cholinesterase from working are used to treat myasthenia gravis, a disease of progressive fatigue and muscle weakness caused by the impaired transmission of nerve impulses.

Figure 11, on the next page, shows a model of a typical neural pathway. Neurotransmitters released from neurons A and B are both excitatory, but neither neuron is capable of causing sufficient depolarization to initiate an action potential in neuron D. However, when both neurons A and B fire at the same time, a sufficient amount of neurotransmitter is released to cause depolarization of the postsynaptic membrane. The production of an action potential in neuron D requires the sum of two excitatory neurons. This principle is referred to as **summation**.

summation effect produced by the accumulation of neurotransmitters from two or more neurons

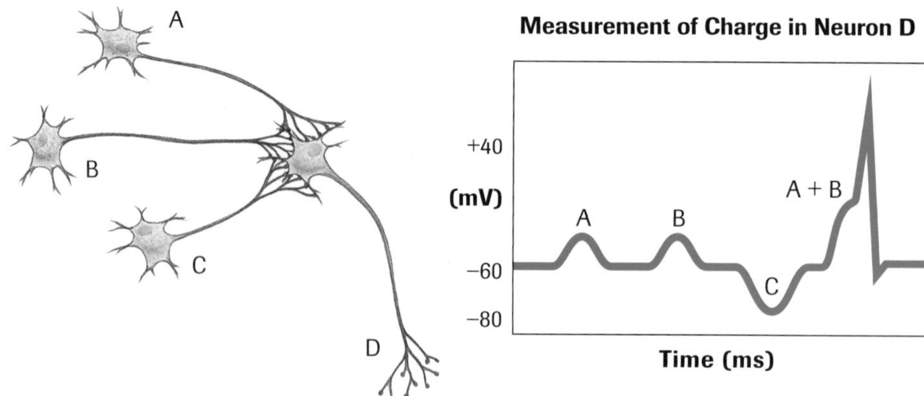

Figure 11 Action potentials must occur simultaneously in A and B to reach the threshold level in D.

The neurotransmitter released from neuron C produces a dramatically different response. Neuron D becomes more negatively charged when neuron C is activated. You may have already concluded that neuron C must release an inhibitory neurotransmitter.

The interaction of excitatory and inhibitory neurotransmitters is what allows you to throw a ball. As the triceps muscle on the back of your upper arm receives excitatory impulses and contracts, the biceps muscle on the front of your arm receives inhibitory impulses and relaxes. By coordinating excitatory and inhibitory impulses, the two muscles of the arm do not pull against each other.

Many different neurotransmitters have been identified in the nervous system. Some common ones are summarized in **Table 1**.

CAREER CONNECTION

Mental Health Worker

Mental health workers must have an extensive knowledge about how the nervous system works. Chemical imbalances in neurotransmitters may contribute to mental health issues, such as depression and other disorders, so these health care providers must be able to identify potential problems and assess patient needs. If helping people and diagnosing problems interests you, becoming a mental health worker might be the career for you.

www.science.nelson.com 

Table 1 Common Neurotransmitters

Neurotransmitter	Action	Secretion sites	Major effects
acetylcholine	excitatory to skeletal muscles; excitatory or inhibitory at other locations	neuromuscular functions; CNS, PNS	skeletal muscle contraction
norepinephrine	excitatory or inhibitory	CNS, PNS	wakefulness
dopamine	generally excitatory	CNS, PNS	voluntary movement and emotions
serotonin	generally inhibitory	CNS	sleep
GABA (gamma-aminobutyric acid)	inhibitory	CNS	motor behaviour

Inhibitory impulses in your central nervous system are very important. Sensory information is received by the brain and is prioritized. Much of the less important information is ignored so that you can devote your attention to the more important sensory information. For example, during a biology lecture, your sensory information should be directed at the sounds coming from your teacher, the visual images that appear on the chalkboard, and the sensations produced as you move your pen across the page. Although your temperature receptors may signal a slight chill in the air and the pressure receptors in your skin may provide the reassuring information that you are indeed wearing clothes, the information from these sensory nerves is suppressed. Inhibitory impulses help you prioritize information. That is why the inhibitory neurotransmitter GABA is the most abundant neurotransmitter in the brain.

Various disorders have been associated with neurotransmitters. Parkinson's disease, characterized by involuntary muscle contractions and tremors, is caused by inadequate production of dopamine. Alzheimer's disease, associated with the deterioration of memory and mental capacity, has been related to decreased production of acetylcholine.

Case Study

Drugs and the Synapse

Psychoactive drugs are a group of legal and illegal drugs that exert their effect on the nervous system, disrupting its ability to receive information about the external or internal environment. Because the nervous system is the primary way in which your body receives information about changes in your internal and external environment, anything that distorts the nervous system's operation will create problems.

Under normal circumstances, impulses are relayed between nerve cells in the brain by neurotransmitters. A neurotransmitter released from the presynaptic neuron attaches to receptor sites on the postsynaptic neuron. When enough receptor sites have been filled by the transmitter chemicals, the nerve cell membrane is disrupted and an impulse is initiated—the nerve cell fires. Psychoactive drugs interfere with either the movement of these transmitter molecules or their attachment to the receptor sites.

Depressants, such as tranquillizers, opiates, barbiturates, and alcohol, are a group of psychoactive drugs that slow down the action of the central nervous system. Some depressants delay the effect of transmitter chemicals by slowing the reaction of connecting nerves. Stimulants, such as cocaine, nicotine, amphetamines, and caffeine, are psychoactive drugs that speed up the action of the central nervous system. Some stimulants prevent the neurotransmitters from being broken down or recycled once they have left the receptors. The neurotransmitters remain longer than they normally would and they keep the receptor sites on the postsynaptic neuron full, resulting in more frequent firing of the neuron.

Different drugs act at different points in the normal sequence of events to affect neurotransmission. They may have stimulant or depressant effects by any of the mechanisms listed below.

Effects of a Stimulant on Neurotransmission

(a) A drug mimics the neurotransmitter and stimulates the receptor at the receptor site ((**2**) in **Figure 12**).

(b) A drug decreases the rate of breakdown or diffusion of the neurotransmitter from the receptor site.

(c) A drug increases the rate of release of the neurotransmitter from storage at the presynaptic neuron (**1**).

Effects of a Depressant on Neurotransmission

(a) A drug blocks the receptor site and so the normal neurotransmitter cannot interact with the receptor (**2**) and send an impulse.

(b) A drug decreases synthesis and storage of the neurotransmitter at the presynaptic neuron (**5**).

(c) A drug increases the rate of breakdown of the neurotransmitter on the postsynaptic membrane (**3**) or in the synaptic cleft (**4**).

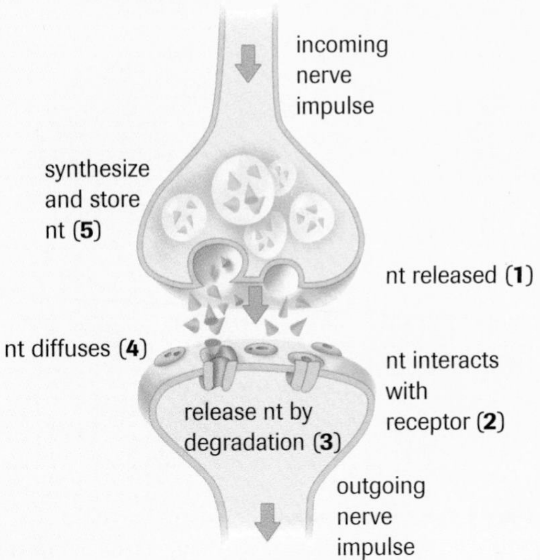

Figure 12
The path of neurotransmitters (nt) in the synapse

Opiates

In the 1970s, scientists discovered that the brain had receptors for opiates such as codeine, morphine, and heroin. These receptors were located in parts of the brain important for breathing, pain, and emotions. Scientists wondered why the brain had these receptors. Later it was discovered that opiates have a similar chemical structure to endorphins, naturally occurring painkillers that the brain manufactures. Endorphins are always in the brain, but they are released in greater amounts when a person is in pain or under stress. Pain is interpreted by specialized cells in the dorsal part of the spinal cord. When stimulated, these cells produce a neurotransmitter that "informs" the injured area of the damage. Increasing the amount of the pain neurostransmitter released increases the perception of pain. Endorphins block the production of pain neurotransmitters and so can block feelings of pain or stress. When people take opiates, the main effect is relief from pain.

In addition to pain relief, opiates cause other effects: euphoria, drowsiness, and reduced anxiety. Not all of the mechanisms by which opiates produce these effects are known. It is generally believed that opiates stimulate the reward pathway in the brain (**Figure 13**, next page). The reward pathway is designed to reinforce behaviours that are essential to survival, such as drinking when thirsty. Stimulating neurons in these pathways brings on pleasant, happy feelings that encourage repetition of the behaviour that led to the stimulation of the pathway. The neurons in the reward pathway use the neurotransmitter dopamine. One theory is that stimulating opiate receptors inhibits the release of the neurotransmitter GABA, which normally inhibits the release of dopamine, so dopamine release is increased in the reward pathway.

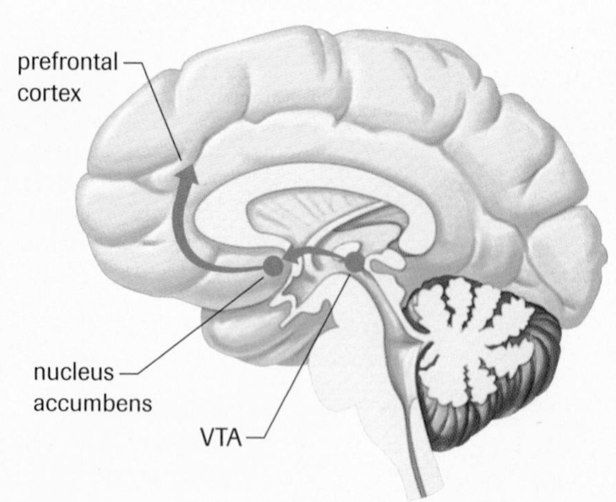

Figure 13
The reward pathway involves three different parts of the brain: the ventral tegmental area (VTA), nucleus accumbens, and the prefrontal cortex.

Alcohol

Alcohol, a depressant, is one of the most widely used and abused of the psychoactive drugs. It affects the central nervous system in many different ways. It enhances the effects of the neurotransmitter GABA, which is an inhibitory transmitter. It also weakens the effect of the neurotransmitter glutamine, which is an excitatory transmitter. Weakening an excitatory transmitter has the same effect as enhancing an inhibitory transmitter: both make a person sluggish. Alcohol does this by interacting with receptors for these neurotransmitters on the postsynaptic membrane. Alcohol also increases the production of endorphins.

Alcohol affects different areas of the brain. In the cerebral cortex, alcohol depresses behavioural inhibitory centres, slows down the processing of information from the senses, and inhibits thought processes. Alcohol affects the hippocampus, causing exaggerated emotions. By acting on the cerebellum, which controls fine motor movement, alcohol inhibits coordination.

Nicotine

Nicotine is one of the most widely used, and most addictive, stimulants. A component of the tobacco plant, it is commonly taken in with cigarette smoke. When inhaled, nicotine reaches the brain in approximately 10 seconds. Nicotine mimics acetylcholine and binds to acetylcholine receptors. This leads to an increase in energy level, heart rate, and breathing rate. When nicotine binds to certain receptor sites, it stimulates the production of endorphins, which promotes the release of the neurotransmitter dopamine in the reward pathway.

Cocaine

Made from a plant called *Erythroxylon coca*, cocaine is a stimulant. It can be taken by chewing on coca leaves, smoked, inhaled ("snorted"), or injected. When cocaine reaches the brain, it causes feelings of euphoria, excitement, reduced hunger, and strength. It also increases heart rate and blood pressure. Cocaine prevents the reuptake of norepinephrine, seratonin, and dopamine, so these remain in the synaptic cleft for a longer time.

Cocaine stimulates neurons in the reward pathway, among other areas of the brain. By stimulating the reward pathway, the user has a feeling of well-being, which reinforces use of the drug.

Addiction

Prolonged use of all these drugs can lead to **addiction**. Addiction is a behavioural phenomenon: a person who is addicted loses self-control. Addicts focus their attention on the drug over all other things, even when they are harming themselves. Addiction also involves two other physical phenomena: physical dependence and tolerance. Physical dependence means that if a person suddenly stops taking the drug, she or he goes through withdrawal. Tolerance means that, over time, a person needs an increased amount of the drug in order to produce the desired effect.

Case Study Questions

1. (a) Provide a diagram that shows how a psychoactive drug interferes with receptor sites on the postsynaptic neuron.
   (b) Why are such diagrams, known as scientific models, useful?
2. Alcohol also decreases the production of acetylcholine. Link decreased production of acetylcholine production to decreased reaction times.
3. Describe the behaviour of a person who has had too much to drink and relate each symptom to events in the central nervous system.
4. Why might someone take opiates?
5. Draw a diagram that shows how an opiate affects the synapse.
6. What is the result of having increased levels of dopamine in the synapses of the reward pathway?
7. During the mid-1990s, the death of two elite basketball players was linked to the use of cocaine. Explain why using a stimulant prior to exercise is dangerous.
8. How might an understanding of the effects of depressants and stimulants affect a person's decisions about whether to take these kinds of drugs?
9. Amphetamines are drugs that are often abused. Find out how amphetamines affect the synapse and the effects they have on the brain.

www.science.nelson.com 

SUMMARY Electrochemical Impulse

- Nerves conduct electrochemical impulses from the dendrites along the axon to the end plates of the neuron.
- Active transport and diffusion of sodium and potassium ions establish a polarized membrane.
- An action potential is caused by the inflow of sodium ions.
- Nerve cells exhibit an all-or-none response.
- Neurotransmitters allow the nerve message to move across synapses.

+ EXTENSION

In Pursuit of Ecstasy

This brief video shows how the recreational drug ecstasy affects neurotransmitters in the brain, and how these changes can have serious side-effects, including permanent changes in brain chemistry and, in a few cases, death.

www.science.nelson.com

Section 13.2 Questions

1. Why was the squid axon particularly appropriate for nerve research?
2. What changes take place along a nerve cell membrane as it moves from a resting potential to an action potential to a refractory period?
3. In **Figure 14**, which area(s) of the graph indicate(s) the opening of Na^+ ion channels and the diffusion of Na^+ ions into the nerve cells? Explain your answer.

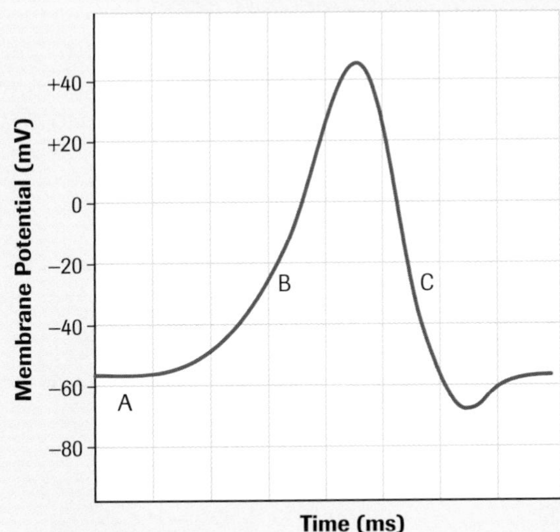

Figure 14
Action potential

4. In **Figure 14**, repolarization occurs in which areas? Explain your answer.
5. Use the synapse model in **Figure 15** to explain why nerve impulses move from neuron A to neuron B, but not from neuron B back to neuron A.

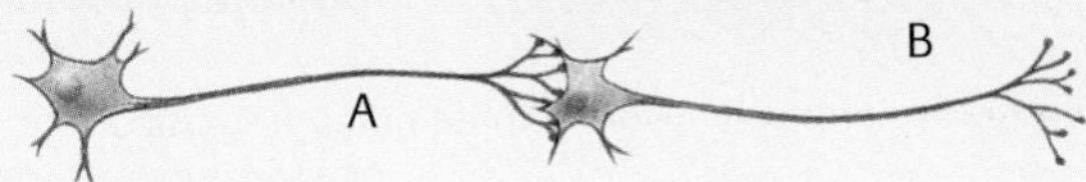

Figure 15
Nerve pathway

6. Explain the functions of acetylcholine and cholinesterase in the transmission of nerve impulses.
7. The action of many psychoactive drugs can be explained in terms of neurotransmitters. Valium, a depressant, interacts with gamma-amino-butyric acid (GABA) transmitter–receptor sites on postsynaptic membranes. The greater the number of receptor sites that are occupied, the more effective the neurotransmitter. LSD and mescaline, both hallucinogenic drugs, are thought to interact with the receptor sites of serotonin.
   (a) Draw a diagram that shows how Valium and hallucinogenic drugs work.
   (b) What dangers exist from taking drugs that interfere with naturally produced neurotransmitter chemicals?
8. The neurotransmitter serotonin is normally involved in temperature regulation, sensory perception, and mood control. A class of compounds known as selective serotonin reuptake inhibitors (SSRIs) has proven highly successful in the treatment of depression, anxiety, and obsessive-compulsive disorder (OCD). (The drug Prozac is a commonly prescribed SSRI.) How do these therapeutic drugs affect serotonin? Are there any risks involved? Search for information in newspapers, periodicals, CD-ROMs, and on the Internet.

www.science.nelson.com

13.3 The Central Nervous System

The central nervous system consists of the brain and spinal cord. The brain is formed from a concentration of nerve tissue in the anterior portion of animals and acts as the coordinating centre of the nervous system. Enclosed within the skull, the brain is surrounded by a tough three-layer protective membrane known as the **meninges**. The outer membrane is called the *dura mater*, the middle layer is the *arachnoid mater*, and the inner layer is the *pia mater*. These three membrane layers protect the brain.

meninges protective membranes that surround the brain and spinal cord

cerebrospinal fluid cushioning fluid that circulates between the innermost and middle membranes of the brain and spinal cord; it provides a connection between neural and endocrine systems

Cerebrospinal fluid circulates between the innermost and middle meninges of the brain and through the central canal of the spinal cord. The cerebrospinal fluid acts both as a shock absorber and a transport medium, carrying nutrients to brain cells while relaying wastes from the cells to the blood. Physicians can extract cerebrospinal fluid from the spinal cord to diagnose bacterial or viral infection. The technique, referred to as a lumbar puncture or spinal tap, is used to identify poliomyelitis and meningitis.

The Spinal Cord

The spinal cord carries sensory nerve messages from receptors to the brain and relays motor nerve messages from the brain to muscles, organs, and glands. Emerging from the skull through an opening called the foramen magnum, the spinal cord extends downward through a canal within the backbone (**Figure 1**). A cross section of the spinal cord reveals the two types of nerve tissue introduced earlier in this chapter: white matter and grey matter. Although the central grey matter consists of nonmyelinated interneurons, the surrounding white matter is composed of myelinated nerve fibres from the sensory and motor neurons. The interneurons are organized into nerve tracts that connect the spinal cord with the brain. A dorsal root brings sensory information into the spinal cord, while a ventral root carries motor information from the spinal cord to the peripheral muscles, organs, and glands (effectors).

DID YOU KNOW?

Meningitis

Meningitis is caused by a bacterial or viral infection of the outer membranes of the brain. Its symptoms include fever, vomiting, an intense headache, and a stiff neck. If left untreated, bacterial meningitis can lead to death.

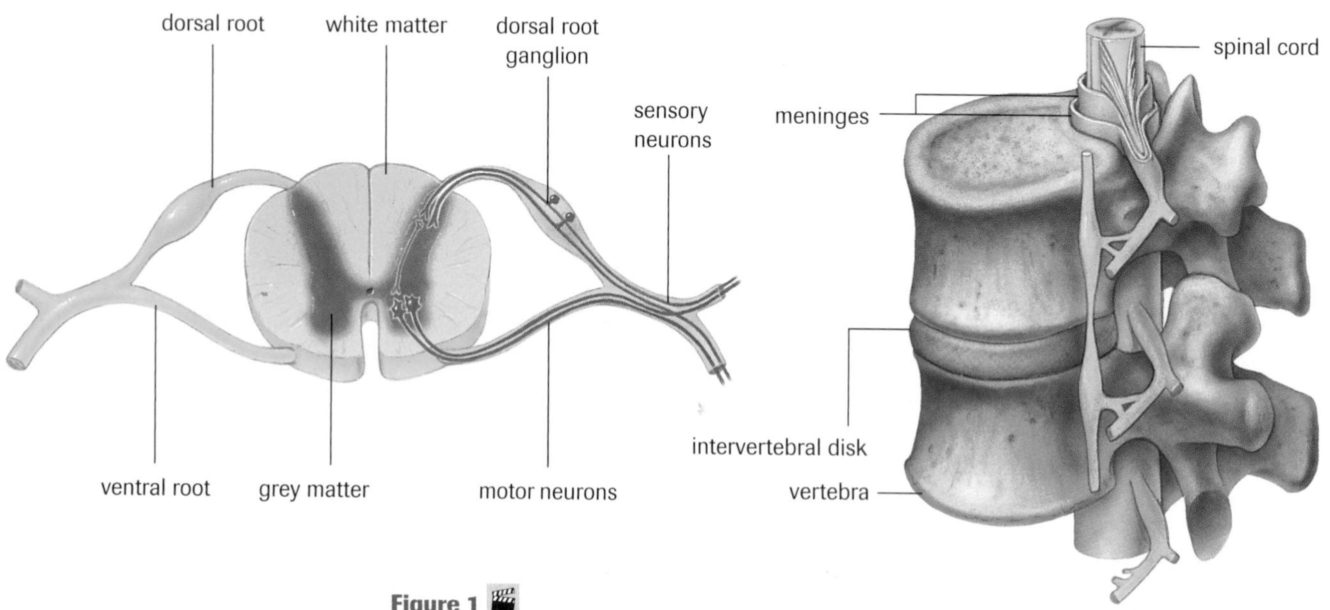

Figure 1

The spinal cord is protected by the vertebral column. Sensory nerves enter the spinal cord through the dorsal root, and motor nerves leave through the ventral root.

Web Quest—Spinal Cord Research

Spinal cord injuries can be devastating, although most individuals go on to live very complete and active lives. Thanks to advances in spinal cord research, people living with these injuries have more technology and research than ever to support them. This Web Quest takes you deep into the world of spinal cord injury research. You will be required to come up with a persuasive argument for increased funding in one of several remarkable directions, including healing damaged spinal columns, re-growing new cells and even changing the way the body uses the spinal cord.

www.science.nelson.com GO

Brain Structure and Function

What makes *Homo sapiens* unique is intellect and the reasoning functions of the brain. However, despite its apparent uniqueness, the human brain has developmental links with other chordates (**Figure 2**). As in primitive vertebrates, the human brain comprises three distinct regions: the forebrain, the midbrain, and the hindbrain.

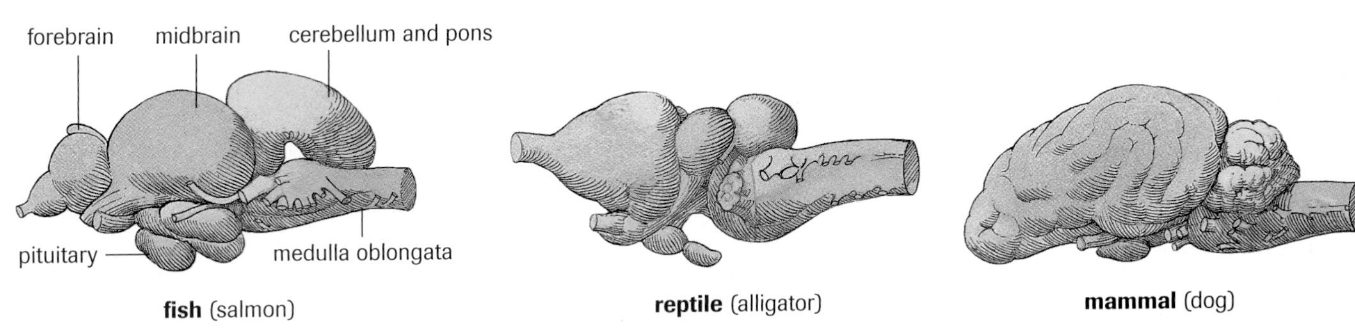

Figure 2
The greatest evolutionary changes in the human brain have occurred in the forebrain. Coloured in blue, the forebrain is the site of reason, intellect, memory, language, and personality.

In humans, the forebrain is greatly enlarged and is comprised of many regions. The **cerebrum** forms the largest part of the forebrain and is divided into left and right hemispheres. These two giant hemispheres act as the major coordinating centre from which sensory information and accompanying motor actions originate. Speech, reasoning, memory, and even personality reside within these paired cerebral hemispheres. The surface of the cerebrum is known as the **cerebral cortex**. Composed of grey matter, the cortex has many folds that increase surface area. The deep folds are known as fissures.

cerebrum largest and most highly developed part of the human brain, which stores sensory information and initiates voluntary motor activities

cerebral cortex outer layer of the cerebral hemispheres

Each hemisphere can be further subdivided into four lobes (**Figure 3**, next page): the frontal lobe, the temporal lobe, the occipital lobe, and the parietal lobe. **Table 1**, on the next page, lists the functions of each of the lobes.

Stimulation of the motor cortex by electrical probes can trigger muscles in various parts of the body. Not surprisingly, the number of nerve tracts leading to the thumb and fingers is greater than the number leading to the arms or legs, since the thumb and fingers are capable of many delicate motor movements. Wrist and arm movements, by contrast, are limited and, therefore, regulated by fewer nerves. **Figure 4**, on the next page, shows parts of the human body drawn in proportion to the number of motor nerves that control them. Note the size of the tongue and mouth. Human speech depends on subtle changes in the position of the tongue and mouth.

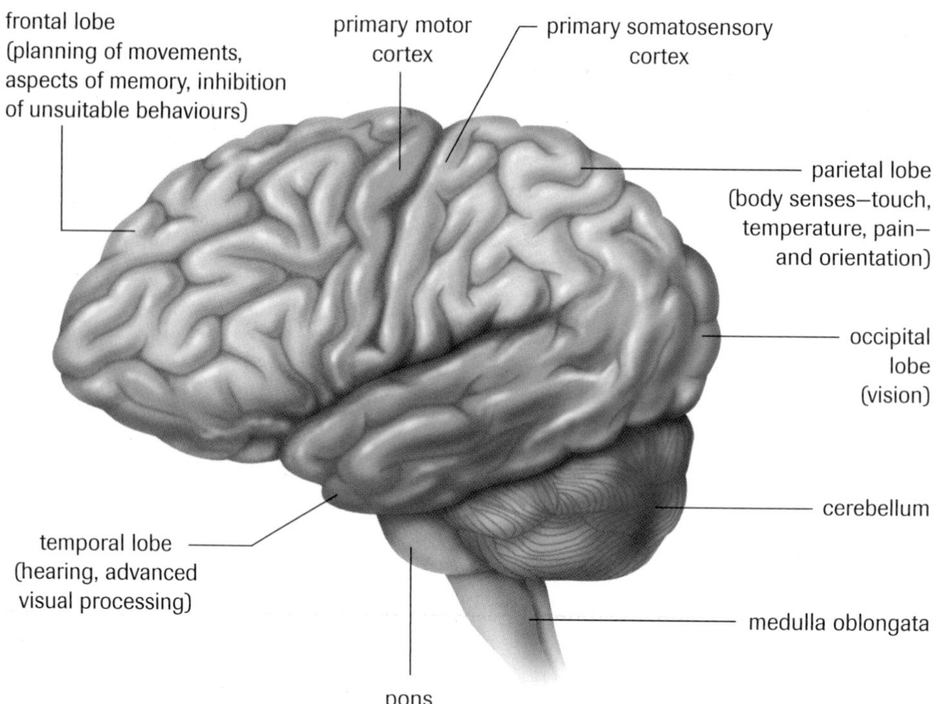

Figure 3 Primary receiving and integrating centres of the human cerebral cortex. Primary cortical areas receive signals from receptors on the body's periphery. Association areas coordinate and process sensory input from different receptors.

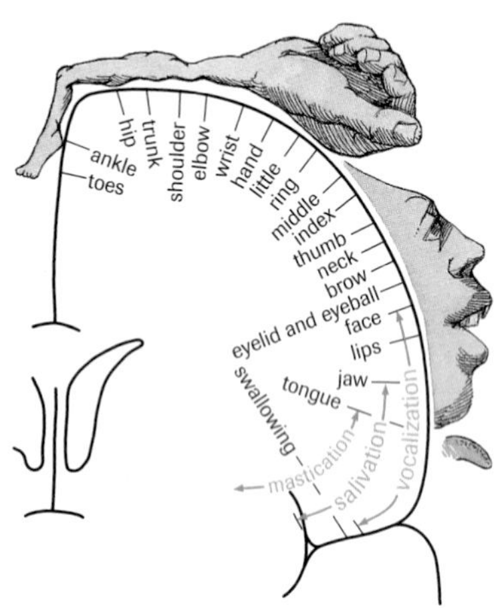

Figure 4 Regions of the body are drawn in proportion to the area of the motor cortex required to control the region.

Table 1 The Lobes of the Cerebrum

Lobe	Function
frontal lobe	• Motor areas control movement of voluntary muscles (e.g., walking and speech). • Association areas are linked to intellectual activities and personality.
temporal lobe	• Sensory areas are associated with vision and hearing. • Association areas are linked to memory and interpretation of sensory information.
parietal lobe	• Sensory areas are associated with touch and temperature awareness. • Association areas have been linked to emotions and interpreting speech.
occipital lobe	• Sensory areas are associated with vision. • Association areas interpret visual information.

corpus callosum nerve tract that joins the two cerebral hemispheres

thalamus area of brain that coordinates and interprets sensory information and directs it to the cerebrum

hypothalamus area of the brain that coordinates many nerve and hormone functions

Research has demonstrated that information stored in one side of the brain is not necessarily present in the other. The right side of the brain has been associated with visual patterns or spatial awareness; the left side of the brain is linked to verbal skills. Your ability to learn may be related to the dominance of one of the hemispheres. A bundle of nerves called the **corpus callosum** (**Figure 5**, next page) allows communication between the two hemispheres.

The thalamus, hypothalamus, and olfactory bulbs are also part of the forebrain. The **thalamus** acts as a relay station, directing incoming sensory information to the appropriate parts of the cerebrum for interpretation. The **hypothalamus** is a small part of the brain but it plays a large role in maintaining the body's internal equilibrium. A direct connection between the hypothalamus and the pituitary gland unites the nervous system with the endocrine system. (The role of the hypothalamus and the endocrine system will be discussed in greater detail in chapter 15.) Located on the bottom of the temporal lobes, the **olfactory bulbs** receive and interpret information about smell.

olfactory bulb area of the brain that processes information about smell; one bulb in each hemisphere

The midbrain lies just below the thalamus. Consisting of four spheres of grey matter, the midbrain acts as a relay centre for some eye and ear reflexes. The hindbrain, as the name suggests, is found posterior to the midbrain and joins with the spinal cord. The cerebellum, pons, and medulla oblongata are the major regions of the hindbrain. The **cerebellum**, located immediately beneath the two cerebral hemispheres, is the largest section of the hindbrain. The cerebellum controls limb movements, balance, and muscle tone. Have you ever considered the number of coördinated muscle actions required to pick up a pencil? The hand must be opened before it touches the pencil; the synchronous movement of thumb and fingers requires coordination of both excitatory and inhibitory nerve impulses.

cerebellum part of the hindbrain that controls limb movements, balance, and muscle tone

The **pons**, meaning "bridge," is largely a relay station that passes information between the two regions of the cerebellum and between the cerebellum and the medulla. The posterior region of the hindbrain is the **medulla oblongata**. Nerve tracts from the spinal cord and higher brain centres run through the medulla, which acts as the connection between the peripheral and central nervous systems. The medulla oblongata controls involuntary muscle action. Breathing movements, the diameter of the blood vessels, and heart rate are but a few things regulated by this area of the hindbrain. The medulla oblongata also acts as the coordinating centre for the autonomic nervous system.

pons region of the brain that acts as a relay station by sending nerve messages between the cerebellum and the medulla

medulla oblongata region of the hindbrain that joins the spinal cord to the cerebellum; one of the most important sites of autonomic nerve control

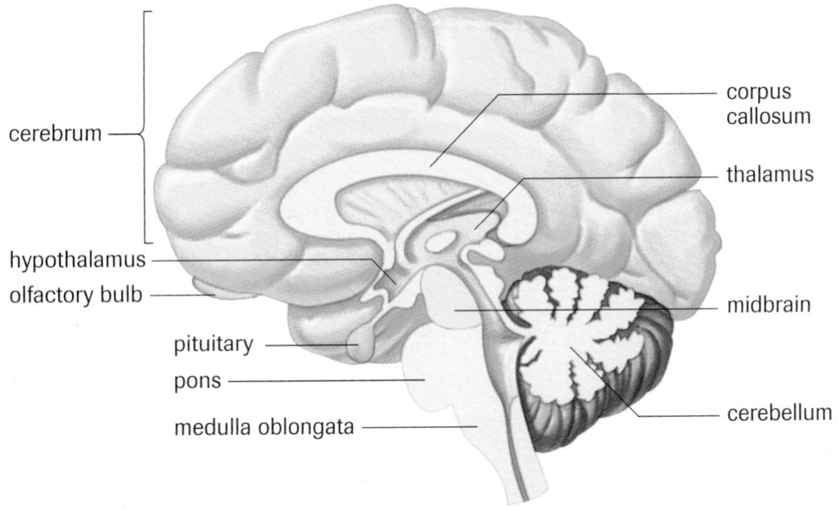

cerebrum

corpus callosum

thalamus

hypothalamus

olfactory bulb

midbrain

pituitary

pons

medulla oblongata

cerebellum

Figure 5
The human brain cut lengthwise between the two cerebral hemispheres

Practice

1. List the parts of the forebrain.
2. List the parts of the hindbrain.
3. What is the structure that connects the two cerebral hemispheres?
4. What is the function of the pons?

INVESTIGATION 13.2 *Introduction*

Brain Dissection

In this investigation you will perform a dissection of a sheep's brain to identify principal brain structures and relate them to human brain structures.

Report Checklist

● Purpose	● Design	● Analysis
○ Problem	● Materials	○ Evaluation
○ Hypothesis	○ Procedure	○ Synthesis
○ Prediction	● Evidence	

To perform this investigation, turn to page 437. 

Figure 6
In the 1940s and early 1950s, Dr. Wilder G. Penfield studied brain structure and function in living humans using a surgical procedure.

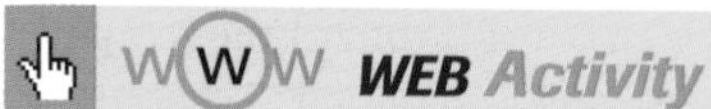

Canadian Achievers—Dr. Wilder G. Penfield

Dr. Wilder G. Penfield (1891–1976), founder of the Montreal Neurological Institute, was the foremost pioneer in brain mapping. Using electrical probes, Penfield (**Figure 6**) located three speech areas within the cerebral cortex. Interestingly, the predominant speech areas reside on the left side of the brain. Penfield's finding dismissed the once-held notion that the two hemispheres were mirror images of each other. Penfield also spent a great deal of his time mapping the cerebral cortex of people with epilepsy. Penfield developed a surgical technique that involved removing a section of the skull and probing the brain with electrodes to locate the diseased area. Find out more about Dr. Penfield and how his research improved understanding and treatment of this brain disorder.

www.science.nelson.com 

Case Study

Phineas Gage

In September 1848, a thunderous explosion shook the ground near the small town of Cavendish, Vermont. Phineas Gage, the 25-year-old foreman of a railway construction crew, lay on the ground impaled by a tamping iron. Apparently Gage had accidentally set off blasting caps by tamping them with a large iron bar. A closer examination revealed that the metre-long bar had entered his skull immediately below the left eye and exited through the top of the skull (**Figure 7**). Incredible as it may seem, Phineas Gage recovered from the explosion and lived for another 12 years. He showed no signs of physical impairment. His vision, hearing, balance, and speech remained intact. However, he did experience one change: the once quiet and thoughtful Phineas became irresponsible and short-tempered. Spontaneous temper tantrums would send him into a fit of profanity. What could have triggered such changes?

Case Study Questions

1. Which lobe of Gage's brain was damaged?
2. Provide a hypothesis to explain why Phineas Gage's personality changed. How would you test your hypothesis?
3. In 1949, Portuguese neurologist Antonio Egas Moniz received the Nobel Prize for his surgical procedure—known as prefrontal leukotomy—in which some of the nerve tract between the thalamus and the frontal lobes is severed. Why might a physician attempt such an operation?

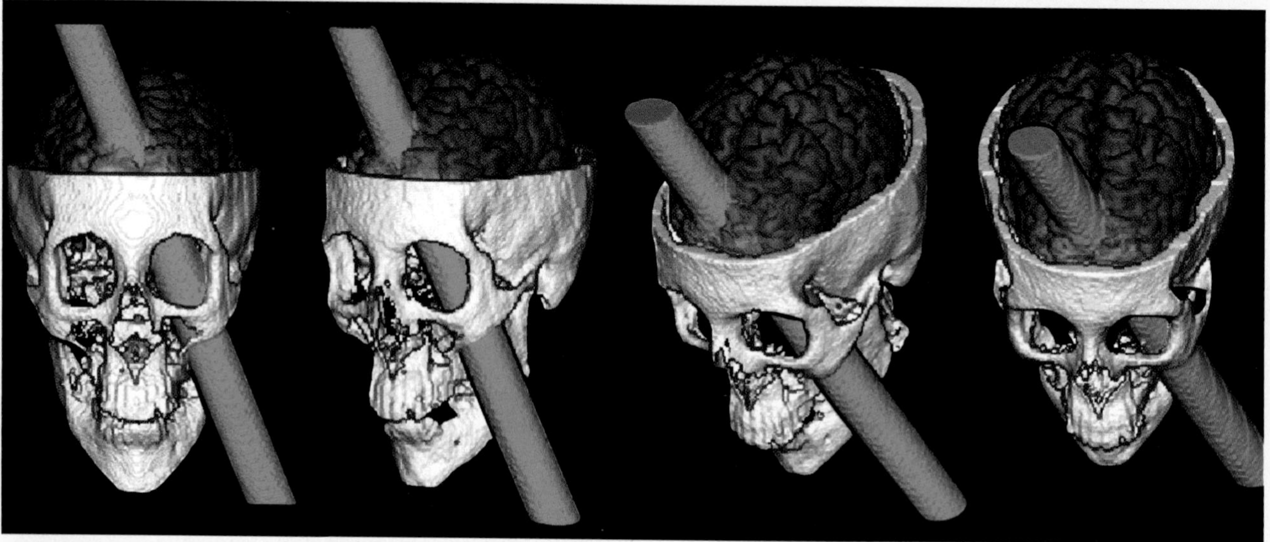

Figure 7
Computer model of the skull of Phineas Gage shown from four angles

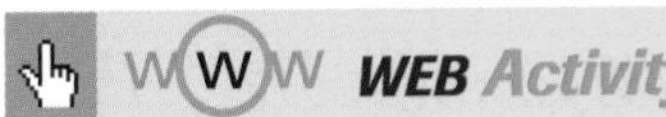

Case Study—Neuroimaging

Non-invasive imaging techniques are now available to researchers studying normal body functions and to physicians diagnosing various disorders, including cancer. These techniques are especially useful in neuroimaging—viewing the brain. Visit the Nelson Web site to learn more about positron-emission tomography (PET scans) and magnetic resonance imaging (MRI) (**Figure 8**) and other techniques. How do these techniques work and what can they reveal about the brain?

www.science.nelson.com 

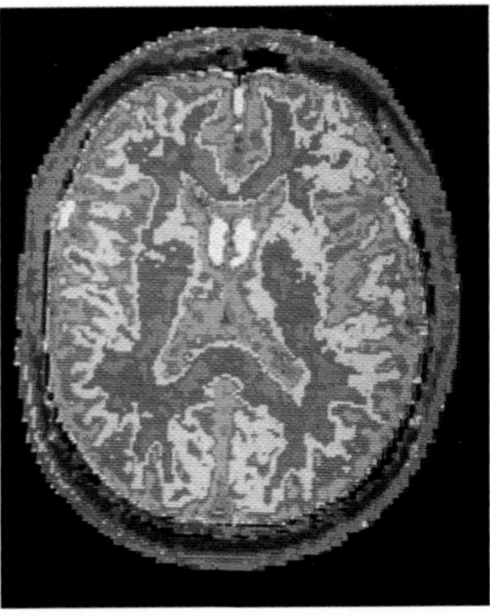

Figure 8
MRI image of a normal human brain

Research into Treatments for Alzheimer's Disease

Alzheimer's disease is a progressive, degenerative neurological disease often linked with aging. The most common symptoms are deterioration of thinking and of memory. Although it is more common in people over 65 years of age, it can affect people in their 40s. The cause of Alzheimer's disease is unknown. While family history puts individuals at a slightly higher risk, there is no clear genetic cause. Scientists currently believe that environmental factors, such as water or air pollution, may play a greater role in the development of the disease. In 2005, an estimated 280 000 Canadians over the age of 65 had Alzheimer's disease. By the year 2031, experts predict that the number will rise to 509 000.

One of the characteristics of brain tissue of Alzheimer's patients is the production of plaques and tangles (**Figure 9**). Plaques are created when a normal process goes awry. Healthy brains have microscopic deposits that contain a protein called beta amyloid. The beta amyloid has been split off from a larger protein by enzymes called secretases. In the brain of an Alzheimer's patient, secretases appear to work too well and produce too much beta amyloid. The large amounts of beta amyloid are deposited as amyloid plaques, which destroy neurons. Tangles form when healthy neurons begin to grow and behave abnormally. These tangles eventually choke and kill the neuron. As more neurons die, the patient loses brain tissue.

Knowing the biological basis of the disease gives researchers ideas about how to treat it. One of the most ambitious research efforts has been directed toward finding a vaccine to prevent the disease. By injecting antibodies against beta amyloids, researchers hope to reduce abnormal levels in Alzheimer's patients.

+ EXTENSION 

Profile: Erich Jarvis

The work of neuroscientist Erich Jarvis demonstrates the power of open-mindedness in the lab. Find out why he chose a career in science over dance, why he calls himself a scientific artist, and why he finds bird brains so interesting.

www.science.nelson.com 

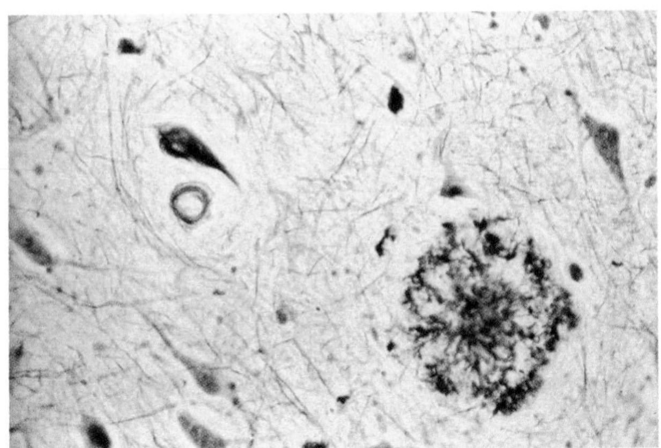

Figure 9
The large dark patch, lower right, is a beta amyloid plaque. The dark triangle, upper left, is a neuron filled with tangles.

Secrets of the Mind: Probe the Brain

Canadian brain surgeon Wilder Penfield mapped the brain's motor cortex by applying mild electric currents to the exposed brains of patients.

In this simulation, you will apply a virtual electric probe to an exposed brain. You will apply small shocks and observe how the body responds.

www.science.nelson.com 

The Central Nervous System

Table 2 Function of the Main Structures of the Central Nervous System

Structure	Function
meninges	• protective membranes that surround the brain and spinal cord
cerebrospinal fluid	• circulates between the innermost and middle membranes of the brain and spinal cord • acts as a transport medium and shock absorber (cushion)
cerebrum	• the largest and most highly developed part of the human brain • stores sensory information and initiates voluntary motor activities
cerebral cortex	• the outer layer of the cerebral hemispheres
corpus callosum	• a nerve tract that allows communication between the two cerebral hemispheres
cerebellum	• the region of the brain that coordinates muscle movement
hypothalamus	• maintains the body's internal equilibrium
pons	• the region of the brain that acts as a relay station by sending nerve messages between the cerebellum and the medulla
medulla oblongata	• the hindbrain region that joins the spinal cord to the cerebellum • the site of autonomic nerve control

Section 13.3 Questions

1. List the four regions of the cerebral cortex and state the function of each.
2. Name the different areas of the brain labelled on **Figure 10** and indicate the functions of the different areas.

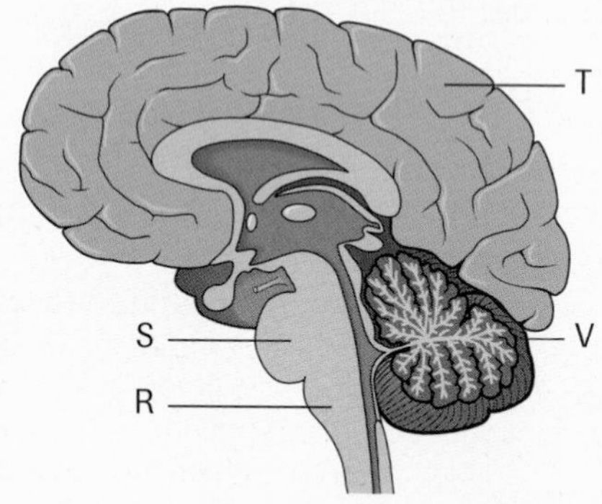

Figure 10
Human brain

3. A physician makes an incision completely through the corpus callosum. How might this affect the patient?
4. Compare the evolutionary development of the human brain to that of a fish's brain. What special advancements are noted in the human brain?
5. The old saying that "an elephant never forgets" seems to have some basis. What area of the brain would you examine to begin researching this question? Explain why.
6. Studies have been conducted to attempt to demonstrate the mental or reasoning superiority of some people based on skull size. Critique these studies.
7. Conduct an information search on strokes, including the causes, risk factors, warning signs, and effects on the various body systems. Include statistics on the incidence of strokes in Canada and on some lifestyle strategies for reducing the risk of stroke. Prepare a poster summarizing your research results in the form of charts, graphs, and tables. Be prepared to share your findings with your class. Search for information in newspapers, periodicals, CD-ROMs, and on the Internet.

   www.science.nelson.com 

8. The EEG has been used to legally determine death. Although the heart may continue to beat, the cessation of brain activity signals legal death. Ethical problems arise when some brain activity remains despite massive damage. Artificial resuscitators can assume the responsibilities of the medulla oblongata and regulate breathing movements. Feeding tubes can supply food, and catheters can remove wastes when voluntary muscles can no longer be controlled. The question of whether life should be sustained by artificial means has often been raised. Should a machine like the EEG be used to define the end of life? Explain your answer.

The Peripheral Nervous System 13.4

The peripheral nervous system is composed of two divisions, the sensory-somatic and the autonomic nervous system. Both of these systems are composed of sensory neurons, which run from stimulus receptors to the central nervous system (CNS), and motor neurons, which run from the CNS to muscles or organs that take action. The sensory-somatic nervous system senses and responds to external stimuli, and the autonomic nervous system responds to internal stimuli (**Figure 1**).

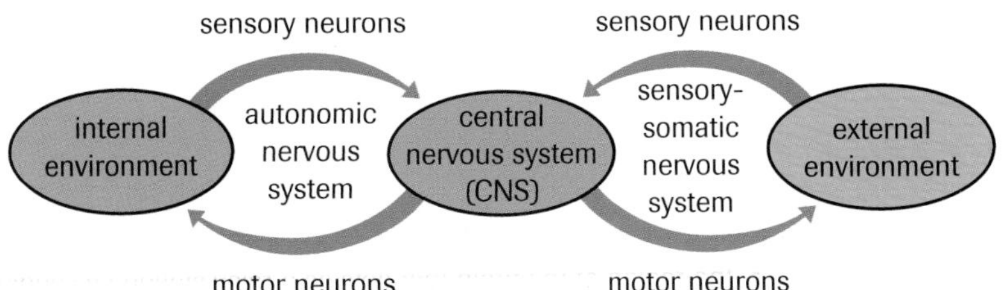

Figure 1
Both divisions of the peripheral nervous system interact with the central nervous system.

The Sensory-Somatic System

The sensory-somatic nervous system brings information about the external environment to the CNS and sends information back to the skeletal muscles. The sensory-somatic nervous system is considered to be under voluntary (somatic) control because you can, for the most part, control the movement of your muscles. However, reflex arcs, which are involuntary, also fall under the sensory-somatic nervous system.

This system is composed of 12 pairs of cranial nerves (nerves that originate in the brain) and 31 pairs of spinal nerves. Some of these nerves have only sensory neurons, others have motor neurons, and others have both sensory and motor neurons. The cranial nerves control vision, hearing and balance, taste and smell, facial and tongue movements, and muscles of the head and neck among other things. The spinal nerves innervate the skeletal muscles for the rest of the body. All our conscious awareness of our surroundings and all our actions to cope with them operate through the sensory-somatic nervous system.

The Autonomic Nervous System

The autonomic nervous system brings information about the body's internal environment to the CNS and carries signals back to regulate the internal environment. So the autonomic nervous system controls smooth muscle, cardiac muscle, the internal organs, and glands. Unlike the sensory-somatic nervous system, this control is involuntary. For example, rarely do you consciously direct your breathing movements. Blood oxygen levels are monitored throughout the body. If levels fall below the normal range, autonomic nerves act to restore oxygen levels by increasing your breathing rate and heart rate.

The autonomic nervous system also differs anatomically from the sensory-somatic nervous system. It uses two groups of motor neurons to stimulate the target effectors (muscles, organs, or glands). The first group, the preganglionic neurons, run from the CNS to a ganglion where they connect with a second group, the postganglionic neurons, which then run to the target organ, muscle, or gland.

DID YOU KNOW ?

How Polygraphs Work

Lie detectors (also known as polygraphs) monitor changes in the activity of the sympathetic nervous system. One component of a lie detector, the galvanic skin response, checks for small changes in perspiration. In theory, a stressful situation, such as lying, would cause the stimulation of sympathetic nerves, which, in turn, would activate the sweat glands. Increased breathing and pulse rates are also monitored by lie detectors. Because lie detectors cannot always differentiate between lying and other stressful situations, they are not considered 100 % accurate.

sympathetic nervous system nerve cells of the autonomic nervous system that prepare the body for stress

parasympathetic nervous system nerve cells of the autonomic nervous system that return the body to normal resting levels after adjustments to stress

The autonomic system is made up of two distinct, and often opposing, units, the **sympathetic nervous system** and **parasympathetic nervous system** (**Figure 2**). The sympathetic system prepares the body for stress, while the parasympathetic system reverses the effects of the sympathetic nervous system and restores the body to normal. **Table 1**, on the next page, summarizes the effects of the autonomic nervous system. Sympathetic and parasympathetic nerves also differ in anatomy. Sympathetic nerves have a short preganglionic nerve and a longer postganglionic nerve; the parasympathetic nerves have a long preganglionic nerve and a shorter postganglionic nerve. The preganglionic nerves of both systems release acetylcholine, but the postganglionic nerve from the sympathetic system releases norepinephrine. The postganglionic nerves from the parasympathetic system release acetylcholine and nitric oxide. The sympathetic nerves

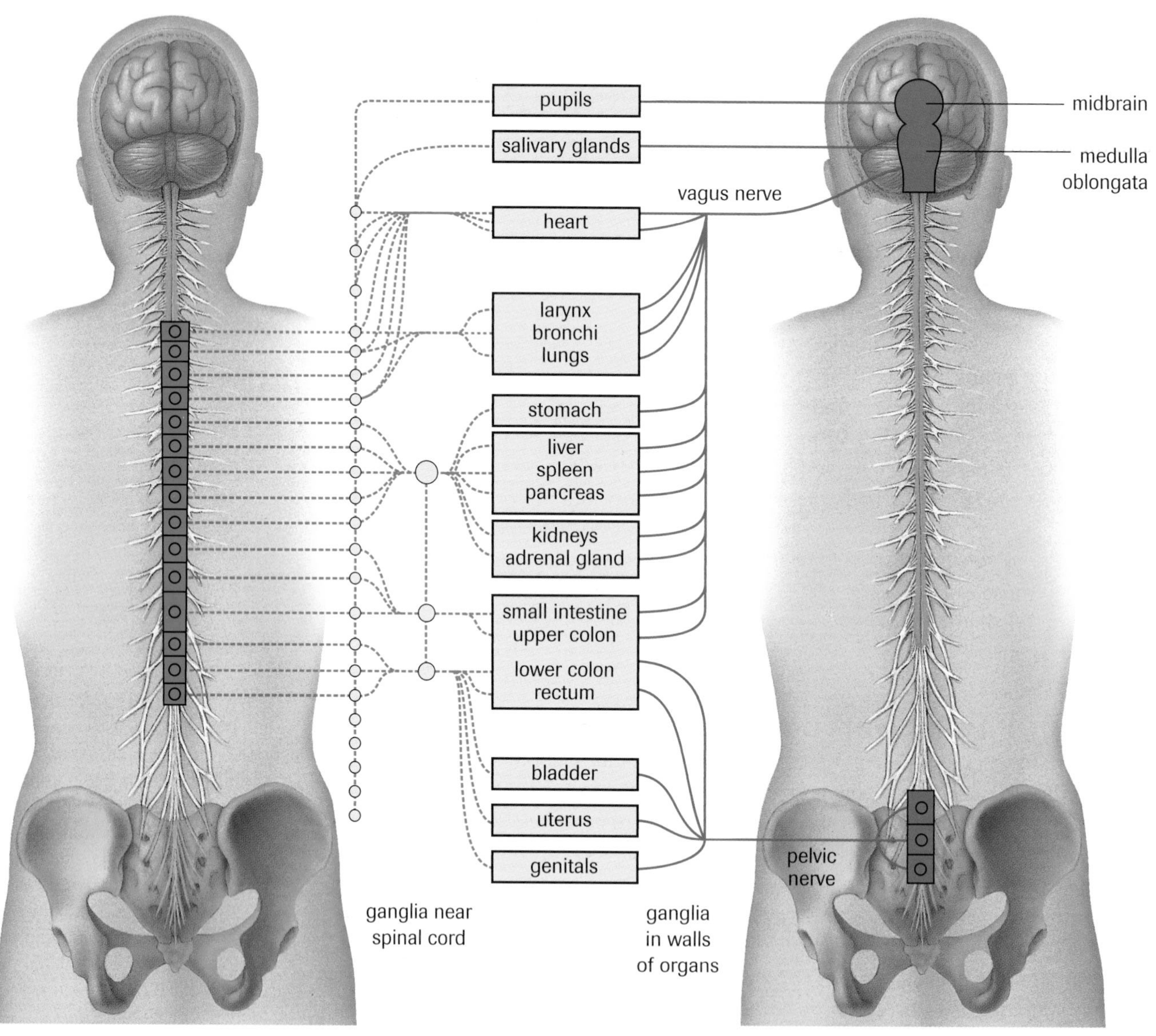

Figure 2
The sympathetic nerves are shown in green, and the parasympathetic nerves are shown in purple.

Table 1 Some Effects of the Autonomic Nervous System

Organ	Sympathetic	Parasympathetic
heart	increases heart rate	decreases heart rate
digestive tract	decreases peristalsis	increases peristalsis
liver	increases the release of glucose	stores glucose
eyes	dilates pupils	constricts pupils
bladder	relaxes sphincter	contracts sphincter
skin	increases blood flow	decreases blood flow
adrenal gland	causes release of epinephrine	no effect

CAREER CONNECTION

Chiropractor

Chiropractors treat disorders of the musculoskeletal system by manipulating the spinal column. They often work with massage therapists, physiotherapists, and physicians and may interpret X-rays, make diagnoses, and develop treatment plans.

www.science.nelson.com 

come from the thoracic vertebrae (ribs) and lumbar vertebrae (small of the back). The parasympathetic nerves exit directly from the brain or from either the cervical (the neck area) or caudal (tailbone) sections of the spinal cord. An important cranial nerve of the parasympathetic system is the **vagus nerve** (*vagus* meaning "wandering"). Branches of the vagus nerve innervate the heart, bronchi of the lungs, liver, pancreas, and the digestive tract.

vagus nerve major cranial nerve that is part of the parasympathetic nervous system

SUMMARY The Peripheral Nervous System

- The peripheral nervous system is made up of the sensory-somatic and the autonomic nervous systems. Together they sense and respond to external and internal stimuli.
- The autonomic nervous system consists of the sympathetic and parasympathetic systems. The sympathetic system prepares the body for stress; the parasympathetic system returns the body to a resting state.

Section 13.4 Questions

1. State the similarities and differences between the two divisions of the peripheral nervous system.
2. State the two divisions of the autonomic nervous system and compare their structures and functions.
3. What are the functions of the vagus nerve?
4. How do sympathetic and parasympathetic nerves differ from one another?
5. Many prescription drugs affect the autonomic nervous system. **Table 2** describes the action of four different drugs.
   (a) Which drug should not be taken by someone who has high blood pressure? Give reasons for your answer.
   (b) A patient who has taken too much neostigmine is admitted to hospital. What symptoms would be displayed?

Table 2 Drug Actions

Drug	Action
pilocarpine	produces effects similar to the parasympathetic nervous system
resperine	inhibits the activity of the sympathetic nervous system
ephedrine	stimulates the release of norepinephrine from postganglionic nerves
neostigmine	blocks the action of cholinesterase at synapses

INVESTIGATION 13.1

Report Checklist		
● Purpose	● Design	● Analysis
○ Problem	● Materials	● Evaluation
● Hypothesis	● Procedure	● Synthesis
● Prediction	● Evidence	

Reflex Arcs

Reflex arcs make up the neural circuit that travels through the spinal cord, providing a framework for reflex actions. Simple physical tests are used to check reflexes. In this investigation, you will observe the presence and strength of a number of reflex arcs and design an investigation about the blink reflex. Read through the investigation, then write a prediction on what will happen in each part of the procedure. Then, formulate and record a hypothesis to explain your predictions. Make sure you make clear notes of all your observations as you gather evidence for the investigation.

Problem

What is the advantage of being able to test different reflexes?

Materials

rubber reflex hammer
penlight

Procedure

Part 1: Knee Jerk

1. Find a partner. You will act as each other's subjects.
2. Have your subject sit on a chair with his or her legs crossed. The subject's upper leg should remain relaxed.
3. Locate the position of the kneecap and find the large tendon below the midline of the kneecap.
4. Using a reflex hammer, gently strike the tendon below the kneecap.
5. Ask the subject to clench a book with both hands, then strike the tendon of the upper leg once again.

Part 2: Achilles Reflex

6. Have the subject remove a shoe. Ask your subject to kneel on a chair so that his or her feet hang over the edge of the chair. Push the toes toward the legs of the chair and then lightly tap the Achilles tendon with the reflex hammer.

Part 3: Babinski Reflex

7. Now ask the subject to remove a sock. Have the subject sit in a chair, then place the heel of the bare foot on another chair for support. Quickly slide the reflex hammer along the sole of the subject's foot, beginning at the heel and moving toward the toes.

Part 4: Pupillary Reflex

8. Have the subject close one eye for approximately 1 min. Ask him or her to open the closed eye. Compare the size of the pupils.
9. Ask the subject to close both eyes for 1 min, then open both eyes. Shine a penlight in one of the eyes.
10. Select a student with light-coloured eyes to be the subject. With at least two observers carefully watching the subject's eyes, gently stroke the fine hairs on the nape of the subject's neck.

Part 5: The Blink Reflex

11. The eye blinks when an object moves toward the eye. Design an experiment to investigate conditions that initiate the reflex. Consider any of the following questions.
    - What size of object is required to initiate the blink reflex?
    - At what speed must the object move to cause the reflex?
    - At what distance from the eye is the reflex initiated?

(a) Present your design to your teacher for approval prior to conducting your investigation.

Caution: Be careful when moving objects close to the eyes to avoid injury.

Analysis

(b) From your observations, formulate a hypothesis about the sequence of events that occur in the nervous system in each part of the procedure.

(c) How does the knee-jerk reflex change when the subject is clenching the book? Why do you think this is?

(d) What is the purpose of testing different reflexes?

(e) What conclusions, if any, can you draw from the data from your investigation of the blink reflex?

INVESTIGATION 13.1 *continued*

Synthesis

(f) Explain why the knee-jerk and Achilles reflexes are important in walking.

(g) A person touches a stove, withdraws his or her hand, and then yells. Why does the yelling occur after the hand is withdrawn? Does the person become aware of the pain before the hand is withdrawn?

INVESTIGATION 13.2

Brain Dissection

An examination of the preserved brain of a sheep or any other mammal will provide enough similarities to be useful for structural and general functional comparisons to be made between it and the human brain. The main difference between the human and most other mammalian brains is the larger human cerebrum.

Report Checklist

● Purpose	● Design	● Analysis
○ Problem	● Materials	○ Evaluation
○ Hypothesis	○ Procedure	○ Synthesis
○ Prediction	● Evidence	

Purpose

To examine the structures of a mammalian brain and relate those structures to the functions of the human brain.

Materials

safety goggles
lab apron
latex gloves
dissecting tray
forceps
scalpel
probe
model of human brain and diagrams showing different sheep brain views

See Appendix B2 for notes on lab safety during a dissection. Take particular care when using a scalpel.

Procedure

Part 1: External Structure

1. Obtain a sheep brain, examine the dorsal, lateral, and ventral views (**Figure 1**), and identify the three major structures that are easily seen:
   - The large cerebrum is composed of the two cerebral hemispheres. They form the largest part of the brain and also make up the largest part of the forebrain.
   - The cerebellum is the highly convoluted structure behind the cerebrum and above the brain stem. The cerebellum is part of the hindbrain.
   - The brain stem extends from the spinal cord (the cut region) through the base and part of the central interior of the brain. Because the brain stem extends the length of the brain, it includes a portion of the hindbrain, the forebrain, and all of the midbrain.

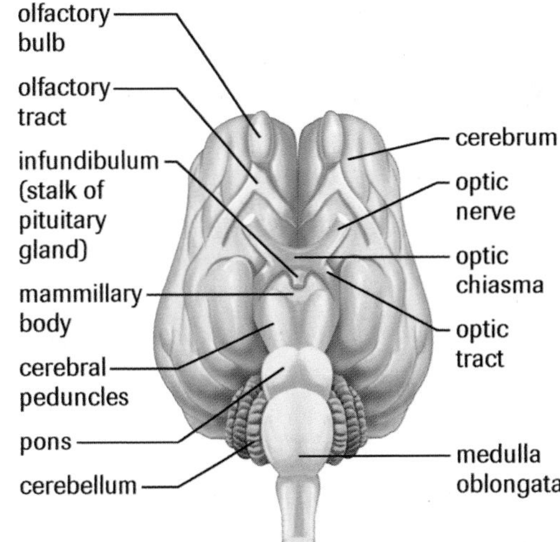

Figure 1
Sheep's brain, ventral view

INVESTIGATION 13.2 *continued*

2. Examine the cerebrum and note the convoluted appearance of its surface. A membrane called the meninges covers the surface of the cerebrum. (Depending on the preservation technique, the meninges may or may not be present.)

(a) Name and describe the functions of the three membranes that make up the meninges.

3. The convolutions are formed by the raised areas or ridges, called gyri, and the depressed areas, called fissures. The major fissures divide the important lobes of the cerebrum. The mammalian cerebrum is much more convoluted than the brains of other vertebrates, such as birds, reptiles, amphibians, and fish.

(b) What is the significance of these convolutions? How do they provide mammals with an advantage?

4. Refer to a model or diagrams of the human brain to help you locate the corresponding fissures and lobes of the sheep cerebrum. Note any differences and similarities in the cerebrums.
   - The longitudinal fissure divides the two cerebral (right and left) hemispheres.
   - The central fissure extends from the top of each cerebral hemisphere to the lateral fissure.
   - The parieto-occipital fissure is not visible externally, but is found near the back of the cerebrum deep in each cerebral hemisphere.
   - The frontal lobe is in front of the central fissure and the parietal lobe is behind this fissure, extending to the region of the parieto-occipital fissure.
   - Behind the parieto-occipital fissure is the occipital lobe.
   - Below the lateral fissure and extending to the occipital lobe is the temporal lobe.

(c) List the cerebral lobes and describe the major human functions located in each. Gently move the cerebral hemispheres apart to expose the corpus callosum.

(d) Describe the function of the corpus callosum.

5. Locate the highly convoluted cerebellum, which lies posterior to the cerebral hemispheres. Compare the cerebellum of the sheep brain with a model or diagrams of the human brain. Note that the sheep brain is not divided longitudinally, as is the human cerebellum.

(e) What is the function of the cerebellum?

6. Examine the ventral surface of the sheep brain and locate the medulla oblongata, which begins where the spinal cord widens, just below the cerebellum. The medulla oblongata contains regions where motor nerves from the right side of the cerebrum cross over to the left side of the spinal cord, and vice versa. Some sensory nerves travelling to the brain also cross over in the medulla, and others cross over where the nerve enters the spinal cord.

(f) What centres that control vital autonomic functions are located in the medulla oblongata?

7. While holding the occipital lobes, gently pull down and back on the cerebellum. In the cavity toward the centre of the brain a small, bulbous mass will be seen. This is the pineal gland of the forebrain, which secretes the hormone melatonin. The pineal gland has nerve connections with the eyes. Melatonin regulates reproductive functions related to light and changes in the seasons, marked by the amount of daylight. The precise role of melatonin and the pineal gland and how they regulate biological rhythms associated with reproduction in humans is uncertain.

(g) Research the role of melatonin and the pineal gland in their regulation of biological rhythms in other vertebrates.

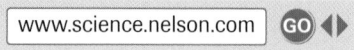

www.science.nelson.com GO

8. Just below the pineal gland are four rounded structures of the midbrain called the corpora quadrigemina. The two upper structures carry nerve impulses from the eyes and are involved with reflex responses to visual stimuli. The lower two structures relay impulses from the ears to the auditory areas of the cerebrum.

9. Examine the ventral surface of the brain. Moving forward from the spinal cord, note that just in front of the medulla oblongata is a rounded structure called the pons.

(h) What is the function of the pons?

Anterior to the pons are the rounded cerebral peduncles, which carry nerve tracts to and from the medulla oblongata and the cerebral hemispheres. The mammillary body is a rounded structure in front of the cerebral peduncles and below the hypothalamus. In the sheep brain, the mammillary body is a single structure, whereas in humans it is double. The mammillary body is a relay station for olfactory neurons.

INVESTIGATION 13.2 *continued*

(i) Describe the functions of the hypothalamus.

Below the hypothalamus and in front of the mammillary body is the infundibulum, the stalk to which the pituitary gland is attached. The pituitary gland may not be present, as it is sometimes broken off during preparation of the brain.

10. The optic chiasma forms an X in front of the infundibulum.

(j) Explain the significance of the optic chiasma in relation to the right and left retinas and the right and left occipital lobes.

Locate the olfactory bulbs in front of the optic chiasma, at the base of the frontal lobes of the cerebrum.

(k) Describe the function of the olfactory bulbs.

Part 2: Internal Structure

11. Observe the internal view (**Figure 2**) of a sheep brain that has been dissected in the sagittal plane. If the brain has not already been dissected, use your scalpel to cut vertically down the midline of the brain. Locate the following structures that were seen in the dorsal and ventral views of the whole brain: cerebrum, corpus callosum, cerebellum, medulla oblongata, spinal cord; pineal gland, corpora quadrigemina; pons, cerebral peduncle, mammillary body, infundibulum, optic chiasma, and olfactory bulb.

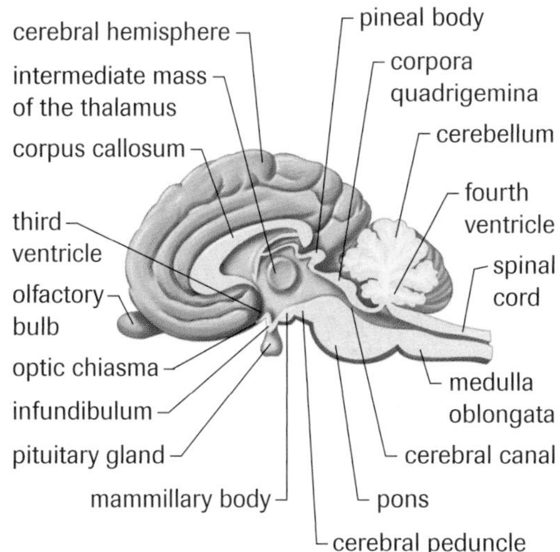

Figure 2
Sheep's brain, internal view

12. Note the difference in colour of the outer and inner regions of the cerebellum. Note also how this colour difference follows the convolutions. This is also characteristic of the cerebrum.

(l) Explain the significance of the difference in colour and its relationship to the convolutions.

(m) Explain why the corpus callosum is only one colour.

13. Locate the four ventricles of the brain. These ventricles develop from an enlargement of the cavity in the embryonic neural tube. The ventricles are filled with cerebrospinal fluid, which also surrounds the brain and the spinal cord beneath the meninges.

(n) Describe the composition of the cerebrospinal fluid.

The two lateral ventricles (the first and second ventricles) extend mostly into the parietal lobe and partly into the frontal and occipital lobes of the cerebral hemispheres, beginning from a region beneath the corpus callosum. Insert a blunt probe into the small opening below the corpus callosum to explore one of the lateral ventricles. A thin membrane on the surface of each ventricle contains a network of capillaries called the choroid plexus. These membranes and the choroid plexus capillaries produce the cerebrospinal fluid. This fluid drains from the lateral ventricles into the third ventricle, which is between the right and left masses of the thalamus. The thalamus is above the mammillary body and the hypothalamus. The hypothalamus forms the floor of the third ventricle. The third ventricle drains posteriorly through a narrow canal above the cerebral peduncle. This canal enlarges between the medulla oblongata and the cerebellum to form the fourth ventricle. Continuing posteriorly, the fourth ventricle forms a narrow canal called the central spinal canal. Where this canal begins is considered to be the beginning of the spinal cord. The cerebrospinal fluid also flows from the fourth ventricle along the dorsal surface of the spinal cord and around to its ventral surface. From the ventral surface it then begins to flow anteriorly until it reaches the brain. As the cerebrospinal fluid flows over the brain, it is reabsorbed into blood capillaries in the arachnoid layer of the meninges.

(o) Describe the functions of the ventricles and the cerebrospinal fluid.

Chapter 13 SUMMARY

Outcomes

Knowledge

- describe a neuron and myelin sheath, explaining the formation and transmission of an action potential and the transmission of a signal across a synapse and the main chemicals and transmitters involved (13.1, 13.2)
- identify structures of the central and peripheral nervous systems and explain their functions in regulating the voluntary (somatic) and involuntary (autonomic) systems, (13.1, 13.3, 13.4)
- describe the organization of neurons into nerves and simple reflex arcs (13.1)

STS

- explain that scientific knowledge and theories develop through hypotheses, collection of experimental evidence and by providing explanations (13.1)
- explain that scientific investigation includes analyzing evidence and providing explanations based on scientific theories and concepts (13.2)
- explain that the goal of technology is to provide solutions to practical problems (13.3)

Skills

- conduct investigations and record data by: investigating the physiology of reflex arcs (13.1); observing neurons and synapses (13.3); and observing a mammalian brain and identifying structures (13.3)
- analyze data and apply concepts (13.1, 13.3)
- work as members of a team (all)

Key Terms

13.1

central nervous system (CNS)
peripheral nervous system (PNS)
glial cell
neuron
dendrite
axon
myelin sheath
Schwann cell
nodes of Ranvier
neurilemma
sensory neuron
sensory receptor
ganglion
interneuron
motor neuron
effector
reflex arc

13.2

action potential
resting potential
facilitated diffusion
gated ion channel
sodium-potassium pump
active transport
polarized membrane
depolarization
repolarization
hyperpolarization
refractory period
saltatory conduction
threshold level
all-or-none response
synapse
neurotransmitter
presynaptic neuron
postsynaptic neuron
acetylcholine
cholinesterase
summation
addiction

13.3

meninges
cerebrospinal fluid
cerebrum
cerebral cortex
corpus callosum
thalamus
hypothalamus
olfactory bulb
cerebellum
pons
medulla oblongata

13.4

sympathetic nervous system
parasympathetic nervous system
vagus nerve

MAKE a summary

1. Construct a mind map of the nervous system by linking key terms. Begin with **Figure 1**, page 408, in Section 13.1.
2. Revisit your answers to the Starting Points questions at the start of the chapter. Would you answer the questions differently now? Why?

Go To

The following components are available on the Nelson Web site. Follow the links for *Nelson Biology Alberta 20–30.*

- an interactive Self Quiz for Chapter 13
- additional Diploma Exam-style Review Questions
- Illustrated Glossary
- additional IB-related material

There is more information on the Web site wherever you see the Go icon in the chapter.

EXTENSION

Mirror Neurons

A recently discovered system in the brain may help explain why we humans can get so worked up watching other people.

www.science.nelson.com GO

▸ Chapter 13 REVIEW

Many of these questions are in the style of the Diploma Exam. You will find guidance for writing Diploma Exams in Appendix A5. Science Directing Words used in Diploma Exams are in bold type. Exam study tips and test-taking suggestions are on the Nelson Web site.

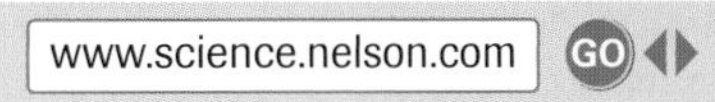

DO NOT WRITE IN THIS TEXTBOOK.

Part 1

1. The nervous and endocrine systems are similar, in that they both
   A. regulate body movement
   B. have prolonged effects on target organs
   C. respond to changes in equilibrium to maintain homeostasis
   D. respond to changes in the external environment, but do not respond to changes in the internal environment

2. The primary function of the myelin sheath is to
   A. supply nutrients to the axon
   B. increase the speed at which nerve impulses travel
   C. conduct active transport of potassium ions
   D. regulate the diffusion of sodium ions across the synapse

Use the following information to answer questions 3 and 4.

Figure 1 shows a reflex arc. The neurons that make up the arc are labelled with roman numerals.

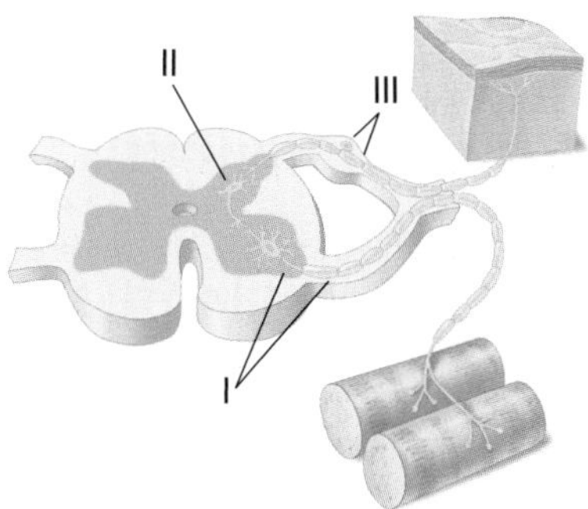

Figure 1

3. If neuron I were severed,
   A. the sensory receptor would detect touch, but the muscle would not contract
   B. the muscle would still be capable of contracting, but sensory information would not be relayed to the CNS
   C. the reflex arc would not work because sensory information is not received by the CNS
   D. it would be impossible for the information received by the sensory neuron to travel to the brain

4. The order in which an impulse travels along the reflex arc is
   A. I, II, and III
   B. II, I, and III
   C. III, II, and I
   D. III, I, and II

5. An impulse can move from one neuron to an adjacent neuron because
   A. the axon of one neuron always touches the axon of the adjacent neuron
   B. dendrites of one neuron always touch the axon of the adjacent neuron
   C. chemical transmitters are released from the dendrites of one neuron and diffuse to the axon terminal of the adjacent neuron
   D. chemical transmitters are released from the axon terminal of one neuron and diffuse to the dendrites of the adjacent neuron

Use the following information to answer questions 6 and 7.

Figure 2 shows the change in the membrane potential of a neuron as it undergoes an action potential.

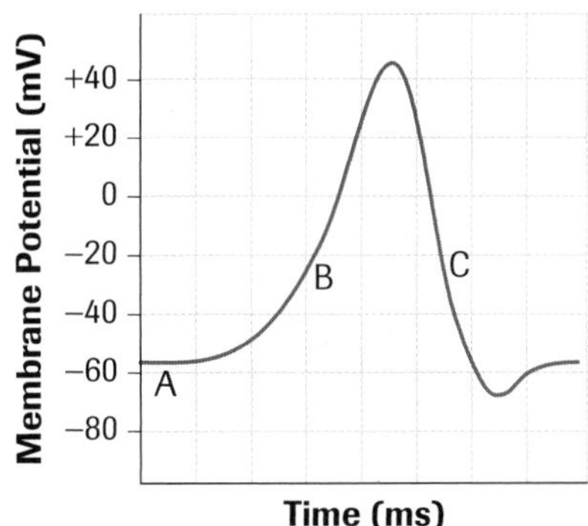

Figure 2

6. The area of the graph that indicates the opening of Na^+ ion channels and the diffusion of Na^+ ions into the nerve cells is
   A. area A, which represents polarization of the membrane
   B. area B, which represents depolarization of the membrane
   C. area C, which represents repolarization of the membrane
   D. areas B and C, which represent depolarization of the membrane

7. Repolarization occurs in
   A. area B because more K^+ ions enter the cell than Na^+ leave
   B. area B because more Na^+ ions enter the cell than K^+ leave
   C. area C because of diffusion of K^+ ions out of the axon
   D. area C because of diffusion of Na^+ ions out of the axon

8. A stroke results in a loss of speech, difficulty in using the right arm, and an inability to solve mathematical equations. Which area of the brain is damaged?
   A. left cerebellum
   B. right cerebellum
   C. left cerebral hemisphere
   D. right cerebral hemisphere

9. NR Place the following events involved in nerve transmission across a synapse in the order in which they occur. (Record all four digits of your answer.)
   1. Cholinesterase attaches to acetylcholine.
   2. Acetylcholine is released from the vesicles in the presynaptic neuron.
   3. The electrochemical impulse reaches the end plate of the presynaptic neuron.
   4. Sodium channels are opened along the postsynaptic neuron.

10. NR In **Figure 3**, which number represents the segment of the neuron that is: depolarized, polarized (resting membrane), repolarized (refractory period), and more permeable to Na^+ ions? (Record all four digits of your answer.)

________	________	________	________
depolarized	polarized	repolarized	more permeable to Na^+ ions

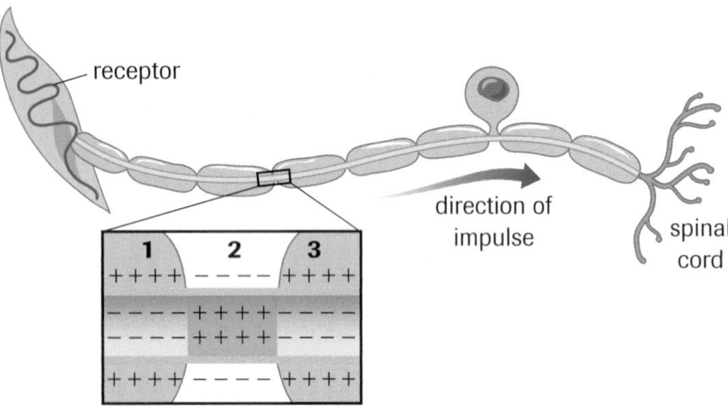

Figure 3
Myelinated neuron

11. NR From the list, identify the statements about the synapse that are correct. (Record all four digits of your answer in lowest-to-highest numerical order.)
   1. Nerve impulses speed up as they cross the synapse.
   2. Synapses occur only between two neurons.
   3. Destruction of the synaptic vesicles in neuron #1 will prevent depolarization in neuron #2.
   4. Neurotransmitters released from neuron #1 attach to the postsynaptic membrane of neuron #2.
   5. Neurotransmitters diffuse across the synapse.
   6. All neurotransmitters cause the depolarization of the postsynaptic membrane.
   7. Neurotransmitters from neuron #1 are destroyed by enzymes.

Part 2

12. Use what you have learned about threshold levels to **explain why** some individuals can tolerate more pain than others.

13. In **Figure 4**, the neurotransmitter released from neuron X causes the postsynaptic membrane of nerve Y to become more permeable to sodium. However, the neurotransmitter released from nerve W causes the postsynaptic membrane of nerve Y to become less permeable to sodium but more permeable to potassium. **Explain why** the stimulation of neuron X produces an action potential in neuron Y, but the stimulation of neuron X and W together fails to produce an action potential.

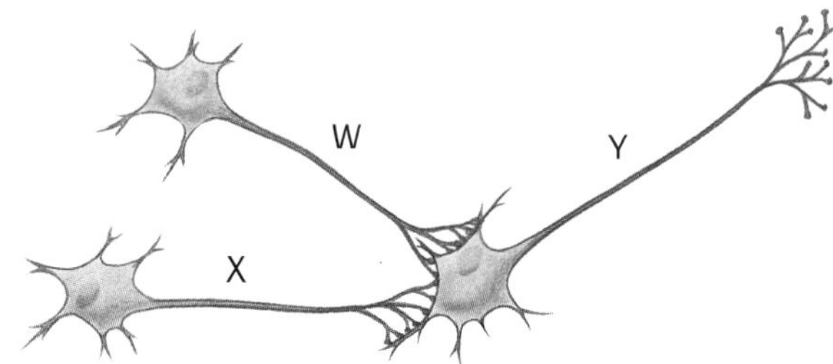

Figure 4
Nerve pathway

14. Botulism (a toxin produced by bacteria that causes food poisoning) and curare (a natural poison) inhibit the action of acetylcholine. **Describe** the symptoms you would expect to find in someone exposed to botulism or curare. **Explain** the symptoms.

15. A patient complains of losing his sense of balance. A marked decrease in muscle coordination is also mentioned. **Identify** which area of the brain a physician might look at for the cause of the symptoms.

Use the following information to answer questions 16 and 17.

A nerve cell that synapses in a muscle is stimulated by electrical current. The strength of the stimulus is increased and the force of muscle contraction is recorded. The results are recorded in **Table 1**.

Table 1 Stimulus Strength and Force of Muscle Contraction

Trial	Strength of stimulus (mV)	Force of contraction of muscle (N)
1	0	none
2	10	none
3	20	4
4	30	not measured

16. **Predict** the force of muscle contraction in trial 4. Give your DE reasons.

17. **Identify** the threshold level from the experiment.

Use the following information to answer questions 18 and 19.

Three different neurons synapse on a single neuron, as shown in **Figure 5**. The experimental data is recorded in **Table 2**.

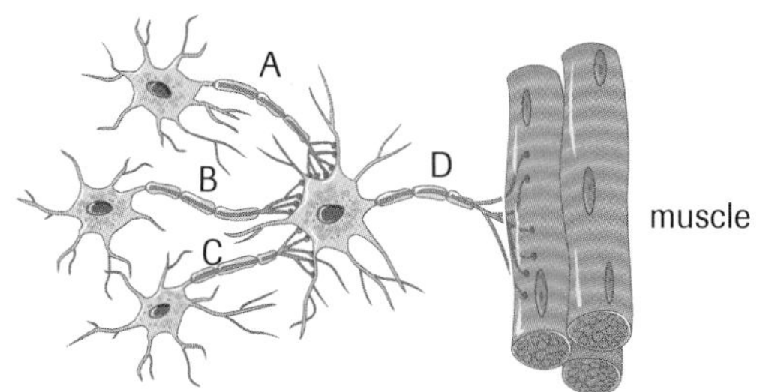

Figure 5

Table 2 Effects of Stimulating Neurons A, B, and C

Neuron stimulated	Effect on muscle
A	contraction
A and B	no contraction
B	no contraction
A and C	contraction
C	no contraction
B and C	no contraction

18. From the experimental data, **infer** which neuron releases DE an inhibitory neurotransmitter.

19. **Explain** the principle of summation using the experimental DE data.

---

20. During World War I, physicians noted a phenomenon called "phantom pains." Soldiers with amputated limbs complained of pain or itching in the missing limb. Use your knowledge of sensory nerves and the central nervous system to **explain** this phenomenon.

21. Scientists continue to look for chemical factors that both DE stimulate and inhibit the growth of new nerve cells. One such factor is myelin-associated glycoprotein (MAG), which is abundant in the myelin sheath of neurons in the central nervous system, but is scarce in the myelin of peripheral nervous system neurons. Write a unified response addressing the following aspects of research into MAG:
    - **Predict** whether MAG is a growth stimulator or growth inhibitor? **Justify** your answer.
    - **Why** might scientists be interested in developing drugs that would turn on or turn off MAG?

22. People with Parkinson's disease have low levels of the neurotransmitter dopamine. Researchers have been able to coax rat embryonic stem cells to develop into dopamine neurons. When these neurons were implanted into rats with a rodent version of Parkinson's, the characteristic tremor of the disease disappeared. Conduct research to **identify** the latest information concerning treatment of Parkinson's disease.

    www.science.nelson.com GO

23. For hundreds of years, people in China have believed that DE drinking herbal tea can improve one's memory. Researchers have isolated a compound from the tea that inhibits the action of cholinesterase. The compound, called huperzine A, is believed to be the active ingredient. Researchers are now exploring whether huperzine A affects symptoms of Alzheimer's disease. Write a unified response addressing the following aspects of huperzine A and Alzheimer's disease:
    - **Why** are researchers exploring the use of huperzine A for Alzheimer's patients?
    - **Why** do you think that some Western scientists have been reluctant to research medicinal effects of herbal teas?
    - **How** do you think the research into herbal teas will be received once the action of hyperzine A is known?

24. Individuals with spinal cord injuries often report loss of sensation and muscle paralysis. Recently, researchers have found that Id proteins, proteins in cancer cells which promote tumour growth, may be used to help re-grow damaged axons in the CNS. Investigate Id proteins and their potential to regenerate axons.
    (a) **Explain why** a person with a spinal cord injury might experience a loss of sensation.
    (b) **Describe** the significance of using Id proteins to stimulate the repair of damaged axons.
    (c) **Why** is it unlikely that the Id proteins might cause brain cancer if introduced into neurons?

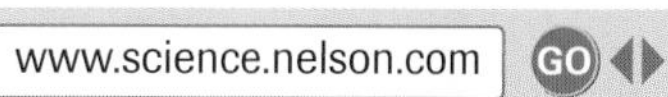
www.science.nelson.com GO

25. Use what you know about the transmission of nerve impulses to **hypothesize** (formulate a hypothesis) about how local and general anaesthetics work.

    www.science.nelson.com GO

chapter 14 The Senses

In this chapter

- Exploration: Detecting Temperature Changes
- Investigation 14.1: Mapping Sensory Receptors
- Investigation 14.2: Eye Dissection
- Mini Investigation: Afterimages
- Mini Investigation: Testing for Astigmatism
- Web Activity: Corneal Surgery
- Investigation 14.3: Hearing and Equilibrium
- Web Activity: Ear Structure and Function

David Hume, the great Scottish philosopher, once concluded that humans are nothing more than the sum of their experiences. Elders in Aboriginal societies are revered because of their experiences. Our experiences, or what some philosophers call reality, exist because of a sensory nervous system. Environmental stimuli such as the flash of lightning (**Figure 1**), the sound of thunder, the chill of a cold day, and the smells of food are relayed to the brain by sensory neurons.

As you learned in the previous chapter, sensory neurons supply the central nervous system with information about the external environment and our internal environment. Whether it is information gathered by the sensory receptors of the eye or from those of the ear, it is carried to the brain along neurons as electrochemical impulses. Different parts of the brain process auditory information and visual information. How sensory information is perceived depends on which part of the brain receives the impulse. For example, if a visual sensory neuron were instead routed to the processing site for auditory information, you might hear lightning!

STARTING Points

Answer these questions as best you can with your current knowledge. Then, using the concepts and skills you have learned, you will revise your answers at the end of the chapter.

1. Imagine if neurons carrying sensory information about sound were surgically moved from the sound interpreting area in the temporal lobe to the vision interpreting area in the occipital lobe.
   (a) How would the brain interpret a loud sound?
   (b) Would moving the nerve ending to another part of the visual area of the occipital lobe cause a different interpretation of the stimulus? Explain why or why not.
2. When you first walk into a kitchen where fish is cooking, the smell is strong and distinctive, yet after a few minutes the smell disappears.
   (a) Why does the smell seem to disappear?
   (b) What advantage is gained from having the smell disappear?
3. Predict which of the following areas of the body are most sensitive to touch by placing them in order. Provide reasons for the order you have chosen.
   - back of the neck
   - lips
   - face
   - fingertips
   - palms of hand
   - shoulder

Career Connections: Optometrist; Audiologist

Figure 1
The central nervous system processes environmental stimuli.

▶ Exploration Detecting Temperature Changes

Heat and cold receptors, rather than detecting specific temperatures as does a thermostat, are adapted to signal *changes* in environmental temperatures.

Materials: 3 bowls or large beakers, warm water, room-temperature water, cold water

- Fill three bowls or large beakers with water—one with warm, one with room-temperature, and one with cold water.
- Place your right hand in the cold water and your left hand in the warm water (**Figure 2**). Allow your hands to adjust to the temperature and then transfer both hands to the bowl that contains room-temperature water.
  (a) Describe what happens.
  (b) Explain why you might feel a chill when you step out of a warm shower even though room temperature is comfortable.
  (c) Explain the following observations: When a frog is placed in a beaker of water above 40 °C, the frog will leap out immediately. When the frog is placed in room-temperature water and the temperature is slowly elevated, the frog will remain in the beaker.

Figure 2

14.1 Sensory Information

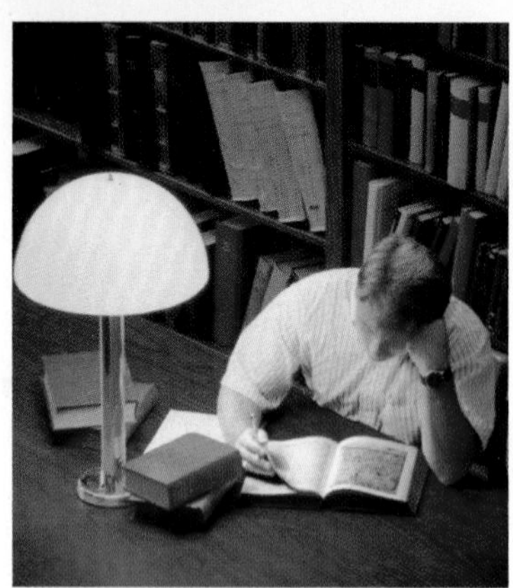

Figure 1
In order for us to see, visual receptors in the eye must be stimulated by light.

Sensory neurons supply the central nervous system with information about the external environment and the quality of our internal environment. Light-sensitive receptors within the retina of the eye are stimulated by light, not sound (**Figure 1**). A group of specialized temperature receptors in the skin identify cold, while other ones identify heat. Specialized chemoreceptors in the carotid artery provide the central nervous system with information about blood carbon dioxide and oxygen levels. Special osmoregulators in the hypothalamus monitor water concentration in the blood, and highly modified stretch receptors monitor blood pressure in arteries. How do different receptors respond to different stimuli? How are different stimuli converted into electrochemical events? How do you identify the intensity of different stimuli? How does the brain interpret stimuli?

A stimulus is a form of energy. Sensory receptors convert one source of energy into another. For example, taste receptors in your tongue convert chemical energy into a nerve action potential, a form of electrical energy. Light receptors in the eye convert light energy into electrical energy. Balance receptors of the inner ear convert gravitational energy and mechanical energy into electrical energy.

As you learned in section 13.1, sensory receptors are highly modified dendrites of sensory neurons. Often, different sensory receptors and connective tissues are grouped within specialized sensory organs, such as the eye or ear. This grouping of different receptors often amplifies the energy of the stimulus to ensure that the stimulus reaches threshold levels. **Table 1** lists different types of sensory receptors found within the body, classified by the type of stimulus to which they respond.

Table 1 The Body's Sensory Receptors

Receptor Type	Stimulus	Information provided
taste	chemical	presence of specific chemicals (identified by taste buds)
smell	chemical	presence of chemicals (detected by olfactory cells)
pressure	mechanical	movement of the skin or changes in the body surface
proprioceptor	mechanical	movement of the limbs
balance	mechanical	body movement
audio	sound	sound waves
visual	light	changes in light intensity, movement, and colour
thermoreceptor	temperature changes	flow of heat

A network of touch, heat, cold, pressure, and pain receptors are found throughout the skin (**Figure 2**, next page). Pain receptors have naked dendrites in the epidermis. Pain receptors are extremely important because the sensation of pain makes you move away from whatever is causing the stimulus, which protects you from harm. A simple experiment indicates that sensations occur in the brain and not the receptor itself. This phenomenon is supported by brain-mapping experiments. When the neurotransmitter released by the sensory neuron is blocked, the sensation stops. Thus the brain registers and interprets the sensation. When the sensory region of the cerebral cortex is excited by mild electrical shock at the appropriate spot, the sensation returns even in the absence of the stimulus.

DID YOU KNOW?

Seeing Stars
Occasionally a sensory receptor can be activated by stimuli that it was not designed to detect. Boxers who receive a blow to the eye often see stars. The pressure of the blow stimulates the visual receptors at the back of the eye, and the blow is interpreted as light. Similarly, a blow near the temporal lobe can often be interpreted as a bell ringing.

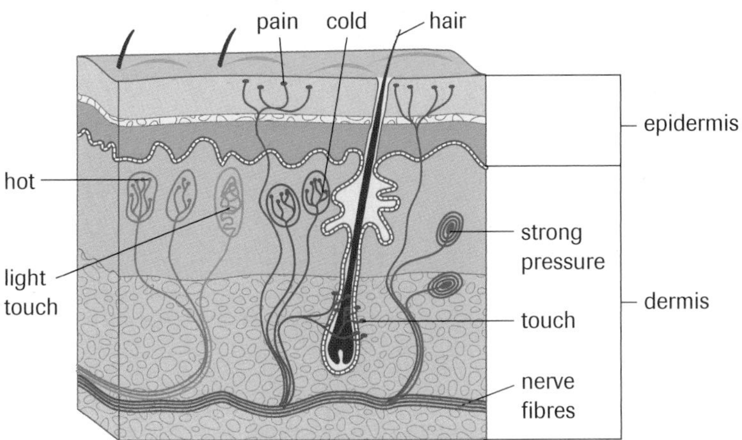

Figure 2 Each sensory receptor in the skin has dendrites modified in a different way.

Despite an incredible collection of specialized sensory receptors, much of your environment remains undetected. What you detect are stimuli relevant to your survival. For example, consider the stimuli from the electromagnetic spectrum. You experience no sensation from radio waves, or from infrared or ultraviolet wavelengths. Humans can only detect light of wavelengths between 350 nm and 800 nm. Your range of hearing, compared with that of many other species, is also limited.

Thermoreceptors do not act as thermometers, which detect specific temperatures. Hot and cold receptors are adapted to signal changes in environmental temperatures. Most animals can tolerate a wide range of temperatures, but are often harmed by rapid temperature changes. For example, a rapid change in temperature of 4 °C will kill some fish. Humans have also died from an unexpected plunge in very cold or very hot water. This principle was introduced in the Exploration at the start of Chapter 14 with the description of the "hot frog" experiment. If a frog is placed in a beaker of water above 40 °C, the frog will leap out immediately. However, if the frog is placed in room-temperature water, and the temperature is slowly elevated, it will remain in the beaker. The frog's thermoreceptors have had time to adjust.

sensory adaptation occurs once you have adjusted to a change in the environment; sensory receptors become less sensitive when stimulated repeatedly

Sensory adaptation occurs once the receptor becomes accustomed to the stimulus. The neuron ceases to fire even though the stimulus is still present. The adaptation seems to indicate that the new environmental condition is not dangerous. The same principle of adaptation can be applied to touch receptors in the skin. Generally, the receptors are only stimulated when clothes are put on or taken off. Sensory information assuring you that your clothes are still on your body is usually not required.

Taste and Smell

Taste receptors allow you to differentiate between things that are edible and things that are inedible. Taste receptors are found in different locations in different species. For example, octopuses have taste receptors on their tentacles. In humans, taste receptors are concentrated in the taste buds on the tongue (**Figure 3**). Specific chemicals dissolve on the tongue and stimulate receptors in the taste buds. There are five main types of taste: sweet, sour, salt, bitter, and savoury (also called umami). Each is associated with molecular shapes or charges. For example, salty taste is associated with the positive sodium ion, and savoury taste is associated with salts of glutamic acid. For example, table salt (sodium chloride) is a common salty food enhancer in foods such as potato chips and canned foods, and monosodium glutamate is a common savoury food enhancer in Asian cuisine and processed foods. A taste bud contains 1 to 200 cells. Each cell can

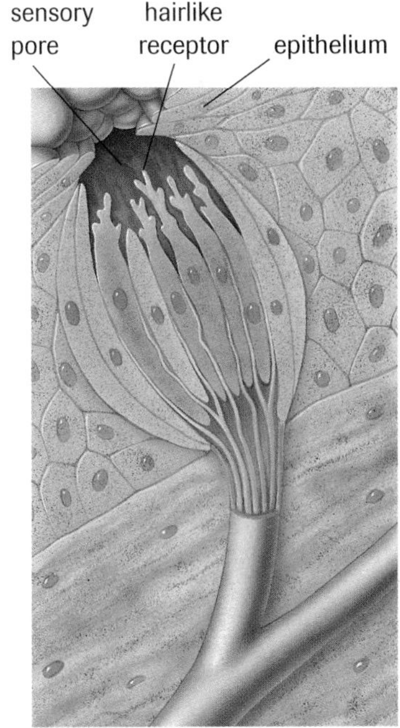

Figure 3 Dissolved chemicals enter the taste pore where they are detected by receptor cells. There are more than 10 000 taste buds in a human mouth.

DID YOU KNOW ?

Taste + Smell + Irritation = Flavour

When you describe how a food "tastes" you are really describing its flavour, which is actually the combination of its taste, smell, and chemical irritation. Chemical irritants, such as the burn of chili peppers or the cool of menthol, add to the way things feel in your mouth.

respond to chemicals responsible for all the taste types, but it tends to be more responsive to one particular chemical. When you bite into an orange slice, the brain processes information from all the different cells and perceives a complex flavour.

Experience tells you that your sense of taste and smell (olfaction) work together. Have you ever noticed that when you have a cold, your ability to taste food is reduced? Clogged nasal passages reduce the effectiveness of olfactory cells (located in the nasal cavity). Since you use both types of receptors to experience food, the diminished taste you experience is actually the result of your reduced capacity to smell the food. The main difference between taste and smell is that smell detects airborne chemicals and taste detects dissolved chemicals.

INVESTIGATION 14.1 *Introduction*

Mapping Sensory Receptors

Sensory receptors are specialized structures designed to respond to specific stimuli from the internal or external environment. Receptors convert information about changing environments to electrochemical impulses, which are transmitted to the central nervous system. In this investigation you will map the position of several sensory receptors in the skin.

Report Checklist

- ○ Purpose
- ● Problem
- ● Hypothesis
- ● Prediction
- ● Design
- ○ Materials
- ○ Procedure
- ● Evidence
- ● Analysis
- ● Evaluation
- ● Synthesis

To perform this investigation, turn to page 462. 

SUMMARY *Sensory Information*

- Sensory receptors are highly modified dendrites of sensory neurons that detect information about the external or internal environment.
- Sensory receptors convert one form of energy into another. For example, the eye converts light energy into an electrochemical impulse.
- Taste receptors detect dissolved chemicals; olfactory receptors detect airborne chemicals. Taste and olfactory receptors act together to create the perception of taste.

Section 14.1 Questions

1. Identify a sensory receptor for each of the following stimuli: chemical energy, mechanical energy, heat, light energy, and sound energy.
2. Do sensory receptors identify all environmental stimuli? Give examples to back up your answer.
3. Explain the concept of sensory adaptation by using examples of olfactory stimuli and auditory stimuli.
4. Explain why you are less able to taste food when you have a cold.

The Structure of the Eye 14.2

One of the primary ways humans gather information about their environment is through the visual information supplied by the sensory receptors in the eye. The structure of the eye allows for sensory information to be gathered and transmitted to the brain efficiently. The eye comprises three separate layers: the sclera, the choroid layer, and the retina (**Figure 1**). The **sclera** is the outermost layer of the eye. Essentially a protective layer, the white fibrous sclera maintains the eye's shape. The front of the sclera is the clear, bulging **cornea**, which acts as the window to the eye by bending light toward the pupil. Like all tissues, the cornea requires oxygen and nutrients. However, the cornea is not supplied with blood vessels, which would cloud the transparent cornea. Most of the oxygen is absorbed from gases dissolved in tears. Nutrients are supplied by the **aqueous humour**, a transparent fluid in a chamber behind the cornea.

sclera outer covering of the eye that supports and protects the eye's inner layers; usually referred to as the white of the eye

cornea transparent part of the sclera that protects the eye and refracts light toward the pupil of the eye

aqueous humour watery liquid that protects the lens of the eye and supplies the cornea with nutrients

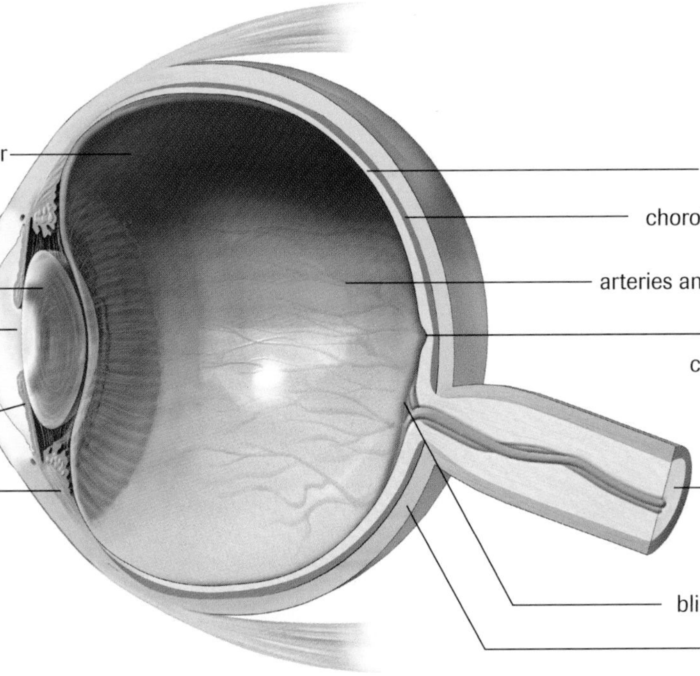

Figure 1
Simplified diagram of the human eye

EXTENSION

Focusing Light on the Retina
Listen to this description of the structures of the eye that actively and passively refract light so that it can be focused with high resolution on the surface of the retina.

www.science.nelson.com 

The middle layer of the eye is called the **choroid layer**. Toward the front of the choroid layer is the **iris**. The iris is composed of a thin circular muscle that acts as a diaphragm, controlling the size of the pupil, the opening formed by the iris that allows light into the eye. The lens, which focuses the image on the retina, is found in the area immediately behind the iris. Ciliary muscles, attached to ligaments suspended from the dorsal and ventral ends of the lens, alter the shape of the lens. A large chamber behind the lens, called the vitreous humour, contains a cloudy, jellylike material that maintains the shape of the eyeball and permits light transmission to the retina.

choroid layer middle layer of tissue in the eye that contains blood vessels that nourish the retina

iris opaque disk of tissue surrounding the pupil that regulates amount of light entering the eye

retina innermost layer of tissue at the back of the eye containing photoreceptors

rods photoreceptors that operate in dim light to detect light in black and white

cones photoreceptors that operate in bright light to identify colour

The innermost layer of the eye is the **retina**, which comprises four different layers of cells: pigmented epithelium, light-sensitive cells, bipolar cells, and cells of the optic nerve. The pigmented epithelium is positioned between the choroid layer and the light-sensitive cells. Pigmented granules in this layer prevent light that has entered the eye from scattering. There are two different types of light-sensitive cells: the **rods** and the **cones** (**Figure 2**). The rods respond to low-intensity light; the cones, which require high-intensity light, identify colour. Both rods and cones act as the sensory receptors. Once excited, the nerve message is passed from the rods and cones to the bipolar cells, which, in turn, relay the message to the cells of the optic nerve. The optic nerve carries the impulse to the central nervous system (**Figure 3**).

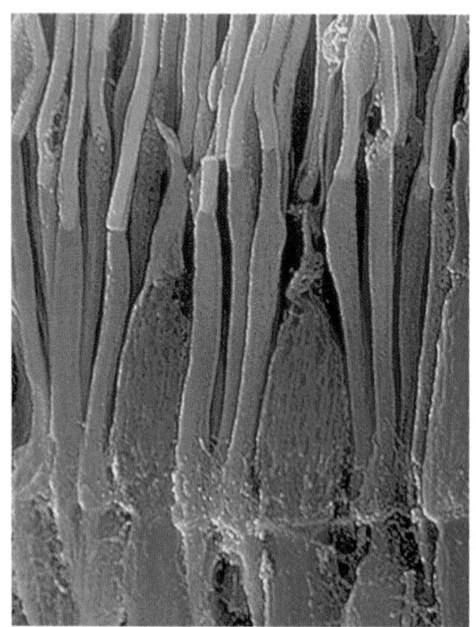

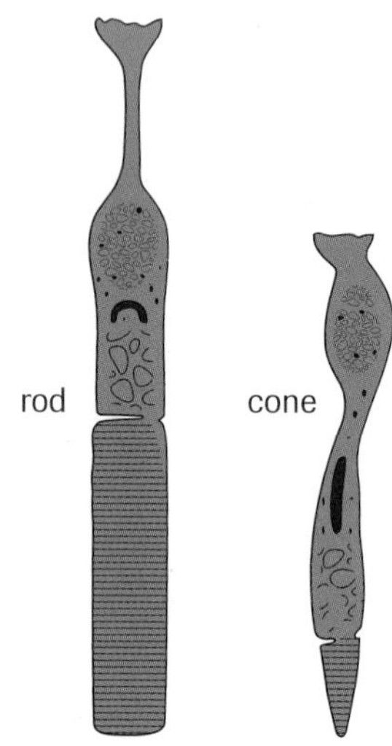

Figure 2
In humans, there are about 18 times as many rods (orange) as cones (red) in the retina.

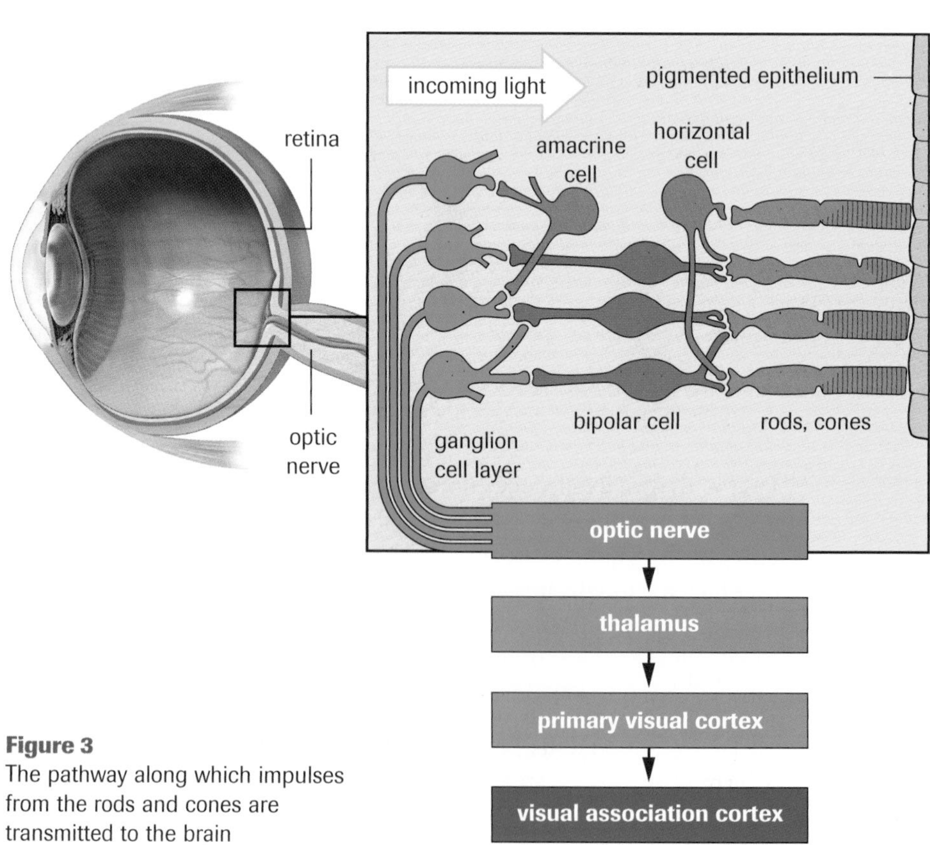

Figure 3
The pathway along which impulses from the rods and cones are transmitted to the brain

Rods and cones are unevenly distributed on the retina. In the centre of the retina is a tiny depression referred to as the **fovea centralis**. The most sensitive area of the eye, it contains cones packed very close together. When you look at an object, most of the light rays fall on the fovea centralis. Rods surround the fovea, which could explain why you may see an object from the periphery of your visual field without identifying its colour. There are no rods or cones in the area in which the optic nerve comes in contact with the retina. Because of this absence of photosensitive cells, this area is appropriately called the blind spot. **Table 1** summarizes the different parts of the eye.

fovea centralis area at centre of retina where cones are most dense and vision is sharpest

Table 1 Parts of the Eye

Structure	Function
sclera	• supports and protects delicate photocells
cornea	• refracts light toward the pupil
aqueous humour	• supplies cornea with nutrients and refracts light
choroid layer	• contains blood vessels that nourish the retina
iris	• regulates the amount of light entering the eye
vitreous humour	• maintains the shape of the eyeball and permits light transmission to the retina
lens	• focuses the image on the retina
pupil	• the opening in the iris that allows light into the eye
retina	• contains rods used for viewing in dim light and cones used for identifying colour
fovea centralis	• most light-sensitive area of the retina • contains only cones
blind spot	• where the optic nerve attaches to the retina

CAREER CONNECTION 

Optometrist

Does the biology of the eye fascinate you? Understanding how the complex parts of the eye work together to produce vision is essential for treating eye and health-related disorders, such as glaucoma. Optometrists are eye specialists who conduct examinations, diagnose disease, evaluate eye structure, and prescribe drugs, eyeglasses and contact lenses. Find out more about this career choice.

www.science.nelson.com 

Simulation—Principal Features of the Eye

In this animation, you will observe the structure of the human eye while listening and reading about the function of each structure. At the end of the animation, you will complete an interactive quiz to test your understanding.

www.science.nelson.com 

Practice

1. List the three layers of the eye and describe the function of each layer.
2. Compare rods and cones in terms of location, structure, and function.

INVESTIGATION 14.2 *Introduction*

Eye Dissection

The eyes of most mammals have very similar anatomy. Dissection of a cow eye can therefore help you better understand the structures of the human eye. In this investigation, you will dissect a cow eye and describe the structures you observe.

To perform this investigation, turn to page 463. 

Report Checklist

- ○ Purpose
- ● Problem
- ○ Hypothesis
- ○ Prediction
- ● Design
- ○ Materials
- ○ Procedure
- ● Evidence
- ● Analysis
- ○ Evaluation
- ○ Synthesis

Chemistry of Vision

An estimated 160 million rods surround the colour-sensitive cones in the centre of the retina. The rods contain a light-sensitive pigment called **rhodopsin**, or "visual purple." The cones contain similar pigments, but they are less sensitive to light. Rhodopsin is composed of a form of vitamin A and a large protein molecule called opsin. When a single photon, the smallest unit of light, strikes a rhodopsin molecule, it divides into

rhodopsin the pigment found in the rods of the eye

two components: retinene, the pigment portion, and opsin, the protein portion. This division alters the cell membrane of the rods and produces an action potential. Neurotransmitters are released from the end plates of the rods, and the nerve message is conducted across synapses to the bipolar cells and to a neuron of the optic nerve. For the rods to continue to work, rhodopsin levels must be maintained. A long-term vitamin A deficiency can permanently damage the rods.

The extreme sensitivity of rhodopsin to light creates a problem. In bright light, rhodopsin breaks down faster than it can be restored. The opsins used for colour vision are much less sensitive to light and, therefore, operate best with greater light intensity. Since only the rods are active during periods of limited light intensity, images appear as shades of grey. Not surprisingly, the rods are most effective at dusk and dawn.

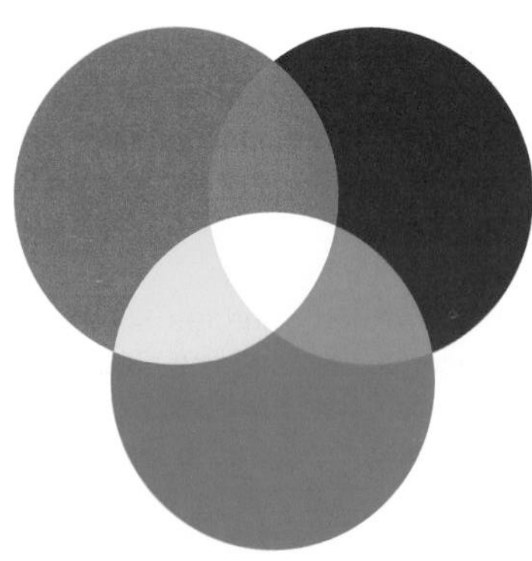

Figure 4
The three primary colours for source light are red, blue, and green. Each cone is sensitive to one of these three colours.

Colour Perception

The cones are responsible for colour vision. Each cone is sensitive to one of the three primary colours of source light: red, blue, and green. (Do not confuse the primary colours of source light with the primary colours of reflected light: magenta, cyan, and yellow.) When combinations of cones are stimulated by incoming light, the brain perceives different colours (**Figure 4**). For example, yellow is perceived when cones sensitive to both green and red wavelengths are stimulated. Purple is perceived when cones sensitive to both red and blue wavelengths are stimulated. Cyan (blue-green) is perceived when cones sensitive to blue and green wavelengths are stimulated. White is perceived when cones sensitive to all three wavelengths are stimulated. The three types of cones firing in different combinations allow humans to see millions of different shades of colour.

Colour blindness occurs when one or more types of cones are defective. The most common type of colour blindness, red-green colour blindness, occurs when the cones containing the red-sensitive pigment fail to work properly. The defect is genetic and more common in males than females.

DID YOU KNOW ?

Seeing Ultraviolet Light
The lens of the eye is not clear. A slight yellow coloration blocks out rays from the ultraviolet end of the electromagnetic spectrum. As you age, your lenses become thicker and more yellow, making you less able to see wavelengths from the ultraviolet end of the spectrum.

Afterimages

Have you ever noticed a trailing blue or green line that stays in your vision after you look into a camera flash? What you see is an afterimage. There are two different types of afterimages: positive and negative. The positive afterimage occurs after you look into a bright light and then close your eyes. The image of the light can still be seen even though your eyes are closed. The more dramatic negative afterimage occurs when the eye is exposed to bright coloured light for an extended period of time.

mini *Investigation* — *Afterimages*

Stare at the cross in **Figure 5** with one eye for 30 s, and then stare at a bright white surface for at least 30 s. The colours will reverse. The afterimage is believed to be caused by fatigue of that particular type of cone in that area of the retina. The horizontal red cones become fatigued, but the complementary green cones continue to fire. The opposite effect occurs for the vertical bar.

Figure 5
The red bar produces a green afterimage; the green bar produces a red afterimage.

Focusing the Image

As light enters the eye, it is first bent toward the pupil by the cornea. Light waves normally travel in straight lines and slow down when they enter more dense materials like the cornea. The slowing of light by a denser medium causes bending, which is called refraction. The cornea directs light inward toward the lens, resulting in further bending. Because the lens is thicker in the centre than at its outer edges, light is bent to a focal point. An inverted image is projected on the light-sensitive retina.

Ciliary muscles control the shape of the lens, and suspensory ligaments maintain a constant tension. When close objects are viewed, the ciliary muscle contracts, and the lens becomes thicker. The thicker lens provides additional bending of light for near vision. For objects that are farther away, relaxation of the ciliary muscles causes the lens to become thinner. The adjustment of the lens to objects near and far is referred to as **accommodation**. Objects 6 m from the viewer need no accommodation.

The importance of the accommodation reflex becomes more pronounced with age. Layers of transparent protein covering the lens increase throughout your life, making the lens harder. As the lens hardens, it loses its flexibility. By the time you reach age 40, near-point accommodation has diminished and may begin to hinder reading.

A secondary adjustment occurs during the accommodation reflex. When objects are viewed from a distance, the pupil dilates in an attempt to capture as much light as possible. When objects are viewed close up, the pupil constricts in an attempt to bring the image into sharp focus. Test this for yourself by looking at the print on this page with one eye. Move your head toward the book until the print gets very blurry. Now crook your finger until you have a small opening and look through it. Gradually make the opening smaller. The image becomes sharper. Light passes through a small opening and falls on the most sensitive part of the retina, the fovea centralis. Inuit were aware of this principle when they made eyeglasses by drilling holes in whalebone. Light passing through the narrow openings resulted in a sharper focus.

+ EXTENSION 

Hyperpolarization

In this audio clip, you will hear about a mechanism called hyperpolarization, which is involved in creating a nerve impulse that plays a role in detection of light in the retina.

www.science.nelson.com 

accommodation adjustments made by the lens and pupil of the eye for near and distant objects

+ EXTENSION 

Visual Accommodation

Watch the eye change during accommodation in this interactive animation.

www.science.nelson.com 

Vision Defects

Glaucoma is caused by a buildup of aqueous humour in the anterior chamber of the eye. Although a small amount of the fluid is produced each day, under normal conditions tiny ducts drain any excess. When these drainage ducts become blocked, fluid builds up in the anterior chamber. As the fluid builds up, the pressure inside the eye rises. The retinal ganglion cells slowly die from this increased pressure, which leads to vision loss.

Problems may arise with the lens. Occasionally, the lens becomes opaque and prevents some of the light from passing through. The condition is known as a **cataract**. A traditional solution to the problem has been to remove the lens and to fit the patient with strong eyeglasses.

In most people, the lens and cornea are symmetrical. Incoming light is refracted along identical angles for both the dorsal (back) and ventral (front) surfaces, forming a sharp focal point. In some individuals, however, the lens or cornea is irregularly shaped. This condition is called **astigmatism**.

glaucoma disease of the eye in which increased pressure within the eyeball causes a gradual loss of sight

cataract condition that occurs when the lens or cornea becomes opaque, preventing light from passing through

astigmatism vision defect caused by abnormal curvature of surface of the lens or cornea

▶ mini Investigation — Testing for Astigmatism

The chart in **Figure 6** will help you determine whether you have astigmatism. Cover one eye and look at the chart. If you have cornea astigmatism, the lines along one plane will appear sharp, but those at right angles will appear fuzzy. Repeat the test with the other eye.

(a) In your own words, describe what causes astigmatism.

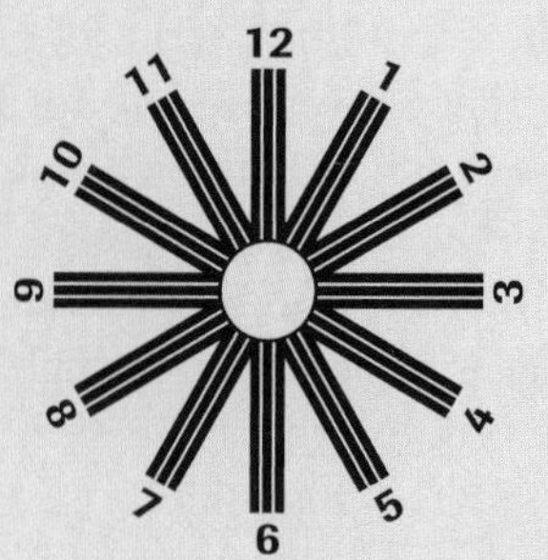

Figure 6
A test for corneal astigmatism

nearsightedness condition that occurs when the image is focused in front of the retina

farsightedness condition that occurs when the image is focused behind the retina

Two of the more common vision defects are **nearsightedness** (also known as myopia) and **farsightedness** (hyperopia). Nearsightedness occurs when the eyeball is too long. Since the lens cannot flatten enough to project the image on the retina, the distant image is instead brought into focus in front of the retina. Someone who is nearsighted is able to focus on close objects, but has difficulty seeing objects that are distant. Glasses that contain a concave lens can correct nearsightedness (**Figure 7**). Farsightedness is caused by an eyeball that is too short, causing distant images to be brought into focus behind the retina, instead of on it. A farsighted person is able to focus on distant objects, but has trouble seeing objects that are close up. Farsightedness can be corrected by glasses that have a convex lens.

Nearsightedness (myopia)

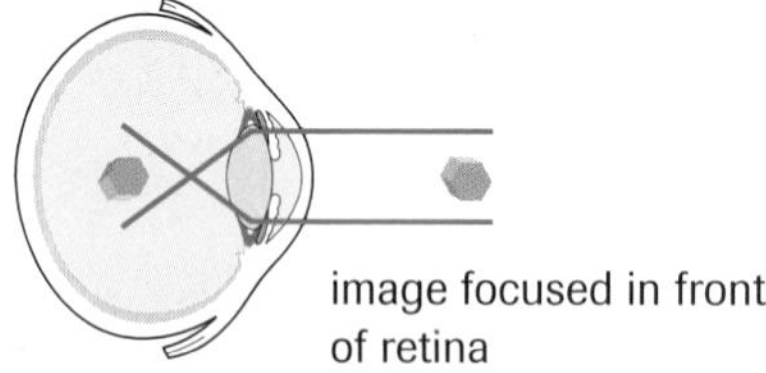

Correction for nearsightedness

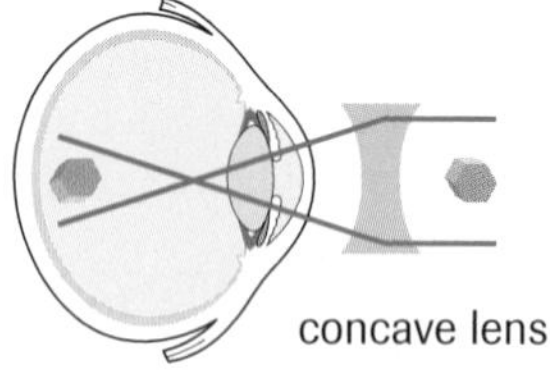

Astigmatism

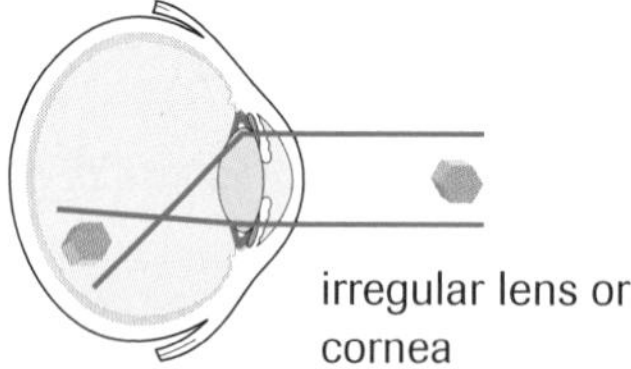

Correction for astigmatism

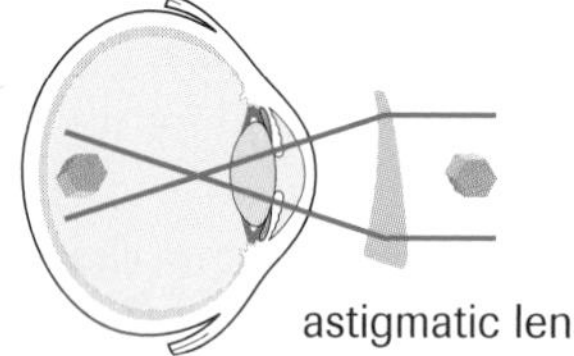

Farsightedness (hyperopia)

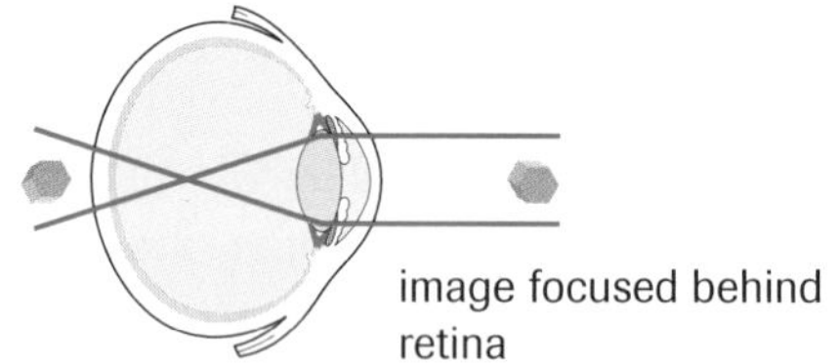

Correction for farsightedness

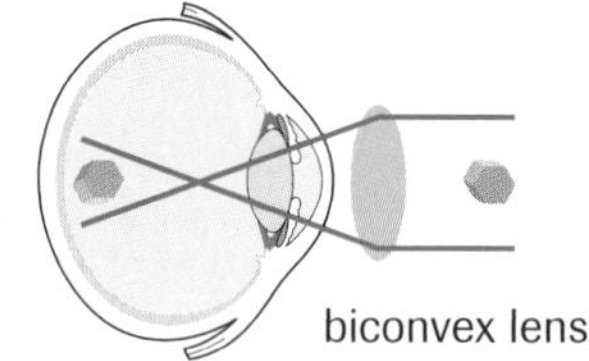

Figure 7
Visual defects can be improved with corrective lenses.

WEB Activity

Case Study—Corneal Surgery

Surgery for treating nearsightedness was first developed in Russia in the mid-1970s by Dr. Svyatoslav Fyodorov. He was inspired by a Russian teenager whose glasses had shattered during a fight, badly cutting his cornea. Remarkably, the eye healed and the boy's myopia seemed cured. An alteration of the cornea had corrected the myopia. Dr. Fyodorov soon developed a procedure called radial keratotomy for correcting myopia.

With the development of laser surgery in the early 1980s, new, less invasive, procedures were developed, including photorefractive keratotomy (PRK) and laser in-situ keratomileusis (LASIK) (**Figure 8**). Find out how these procedures work. Also, investigate corneal ring implants and implantable contact lenses. What are the pros and cons of these two new procedures?

www.science.nelson.com 

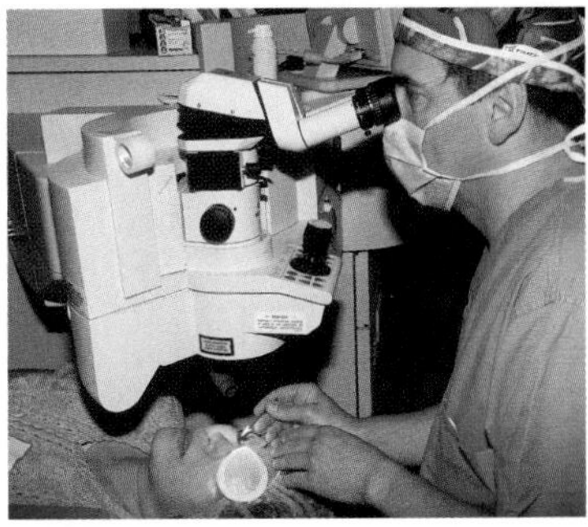

Figure 8
Laser eye surgery

SUMMARY The Structure of the Eye

- Images are displayed on the retina. Rods are photosensitive receptors that detect images in dull light. Cones are photosensitive receptors that distinguish colour in bright light.
- Ciliary muscles change the shape of the lens. A thicker lens permits the greater bending of light for viewing near objects, while a more flattened lens is used to view distant objects.

Section 14.2 Questions

1. Indicate the function of each of the following parts of the eye: vitreous humour, aqueous humour, cornea, pupil, iris, rods, cones, fovea centralis, and blind spot.
2. What are accommodation reflexes?
3. Why do rods not function effectively in bright light?
4. Identify the causes for each of the following eye disorders: glaucoma, cataract, astigmatism, nearsightedness, and farsightedness.
5. Illustrate how corrective lenses provide for normal vision.
6. Laser surgery can provide a cure for myopia (shortsightedness), but skeptics argue that surgery has risks and that shortsightedness can be corrected with glasses. A "halo effect" (circles of light that can distort night vision) may result from laser surgery.
   (a) Research the halo effect. How often does it occur after laser surgery?
   (b) Should people who experience the halo effect be allowed to drive at night? Why or why not?
   (c) Do you believe that surgery should be attempted? Explain your answer.
   (d) Do you think this surgery should be covered by medicare? Justify your answer.
7. Nearsightedness, or myopia, is experienced by up to about one-third of the population. Nearsighted people have difficulty reading highway signs and seeing other objects at a distance, but can see for up-close tasks such as reading.
   (a) Draw a diagram of an eye for a person with myopia.
   (b) Refractive surgery can reduce or even eliminate the need for glasses or contacts. The most common procedures are performed with a laser. The laser removes a layer of corneal tissue, which flattens the cornea and allows light rays to focus closer to or even on the retina. Refer to the Nelson website to research different laser techniques that can be used.

   www.science.nelson.com 
8. Hawks and eagles depend upon their excellent vision for hunting. In addition to the central fovea found in most birds, hawks and eagles have a second "lateral" fovea placed to one side of the central fovea. Explain how having a lateral fovea might help hawks and eagles hunt.

14.3 Hearing and Equilibrium

DID YOU KNOW ?

The Smallest Bones
The ear ossicles are the smallest bones in the body. They are fully developed at birth.

The ear (**Figure 1**) is associated with two separate functions: hearing and equilibrium. The ear can be divided into three sections for study: the outer ear, the middle ear, and the inner ear. The outer ear comprises the **pinna**, the external ear flap, which collects the sound, and the **auditory canal**, which carries sound to the eardrum. The auditory canal is lined with specialized sweat glands that produce earwax, a substance that traps foreign particles and prevents them from entering the ear.

pinna outer part of the ear that acts like a funnel, taking sound from a large area and channelling it into a small canal

auditory canal carries sound waves to the eardrum

tympanic membrane thin layer of tissue that receives sound vibrations, also known as the eardrum

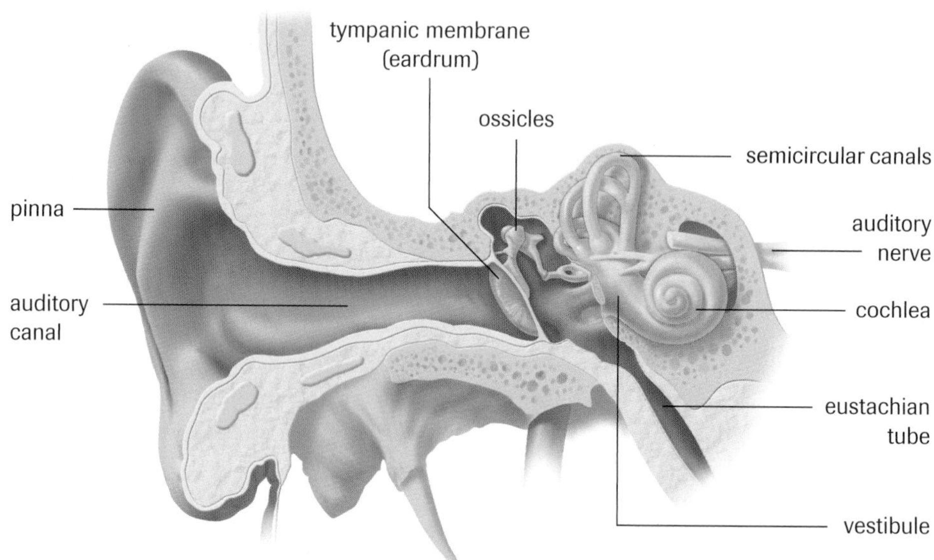

Figure 1
Anatomy of the human ear

ossicles tiny bones that amplify and carry sound in the middle ear

oval window oval-shaped hole in the vestibule of the inner ear, covered by a thin layer of tissue

eustachian tube air-filled tube of the middle ear that equalizes pressure between the external and internal ear

vestibule chamber found at the base of the semicircular canals that provides information about static equilibrium

semicircular canals fluid-filled structures within the inner ear that provide information about dynamic equilibrium

cochlea coiled structure of the inner ear that responds to various sound waves and converts them into nerve impulses

The middle ear begins at the **tympanic membrane**, and extends toward the oval and round windows. The air-filled chamber of the middle ear contains three small bones, called **ossicles**, which include the malleus (the hammer), the incus (the anvil), and the stapes (the stirrup). Sound vibrations that strike the eardrum are first concentrated within the solid malleus, and then transmitted to the incus, and finally to the stapes. The stapes strikes the membrane covering the **oval window** in the inner wall of the middle ear. Sound is amplified by concentrating the sound energy from the large tympanic membrane to the smaller oval window.

The **eustachian tube** extends from the middle ear to the mouth and the chambers of the nose. Approximately 40 mm in length and 3 mm in diameter, the eustachian tube permits the equalization of air pressure on either side of the eardrum. Have you ever noticed how your ears seem to pop when you go up in a plane? Yawning, swallowing, and chewing gum allow air to leave the middle ear through the eustachian tube. An ear infection can block the eustachian tube and create inequalities in air pressure. Discomfort, temporary deafness, and poor balance can result.

The inner ear has three distinct structures: the vestibule and the semicircular canals, which are involved with balance, and the cochlea, which is connected with hearing (**Figure 2**, next page). The **vestibule**, connected to the middle ear by the oval window, houses two small sacs, the utricle and saccule, which establish head position. There are three **semicircular canals**, arranged at different angles, and the movement of fluid in these canals helps you identify body movement. The **cochlea** is shaped like a spiralling snail's shell and contains rows of specialized hair cells that run the length of the inner canal. The hair cells respond to sound waves and convert them into nerve impulses.

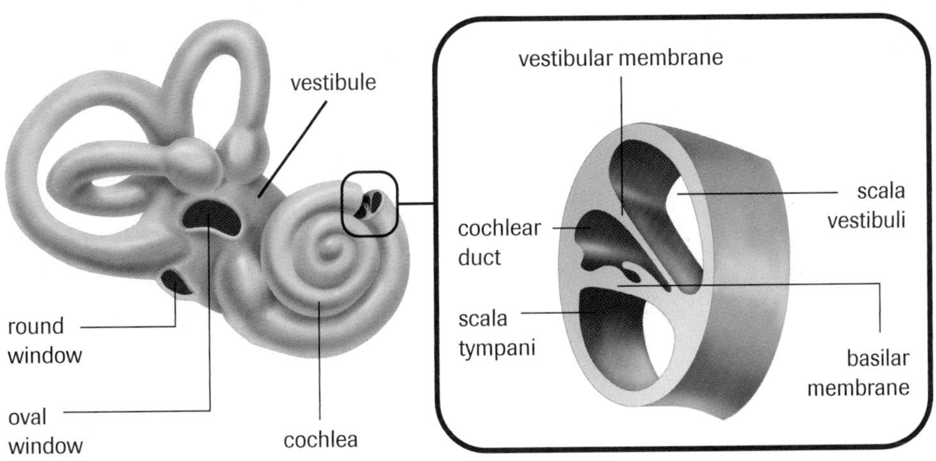

Figure 2
Sound waves are transformed into membrane vibrations in the cochlea.

Hearing and Sound

Sound is a form of energy. Like light, thermal energy, and various forms of chemical energy, sound energy must be converted into an electrical impulse before you can interpret it. The sensitivity of the ear can be illustrated by the fact that you can hear a mosquito outside your window, even though the energy reaching your ear is less than one quadrillionth of a watt. The average light in a house uses 60 W of energy.

Hearing begins when sound waves push against the eardrum, or tympanic membrane. The vibrations of the eardrum are passed on to the three bones of the middle ear: the malleus, the incus, and the stapes. Arranged in a lever system, the three bones are held together by muscles and ligaments. The bones concentrate and amplify the vibrations received from the tympanic membrane. The ossicles can triple the force of vibration from the eardrum; they move a shorter distance but exert greater force by concentrating the energy in a very small area.

Muscles that join the bones of the middle ear act as a safety net protecting the inner ear against excessive noise. Intense sound causes the tiny muscles—the smallest in your body—to contract, restricting the movement of the malleus and reducing the intensity of movement. At the same time, a second muscle contracts, pulling the stapes away from the oval window, thereby protecting the inner ear from powerful vibrations. Occasionally, the safety mechanism doesn't work quickly enough. The sudden blast from a firecracker can send the ossicles into wild vibrations before the protective reflex can be activated.

The oval window receives vibrations from the ossicles. As the oval window is pushed inward, the round window, located immediately below the oval window, moves outward. This triggers waves of fluid within the inner ear. The cochlea receives the fluid waves and converts them into electrical impulses, which you interpret as sound. The hearing apparatus within the cochlea is known as the **organ of Corti** and comprises a single inner row and three outer rows of specialized hair cells (**Figure 3**, next page), anchored to the **basilar membrane**. The hair cells respond to vibrations of the basilar membrane. Vibrations in the fluid on either side of the basilar membrane cause the membrane to move, and the hairs on the cells bend as they brush against the tectorial membrane. The movement of the hair cells, in turn, stimulates sensory nerves in the basilar membrane. Auditory information is then sent to the temporal lobe of the cerebrum via the auditory nerves.

The inner ear is able to identify both pitch and loudness because of the structure of the cochlea. Close to the oval window, the basilar membrane is narrow and stiff. Further into the cochlea, the basilar membrane widens and becomes more flexible. The narrowest area is activated by high-frequency sound waves, which contain enough energy

CAREER CONNECTION 

Audiologist

Audiologists work with people who have hearing, balance, and related ear problems. Employment opportunities are expected to grow rapidly—as the population ages, more people will have hearing problems. What type of work do audiologists do? Why is the work important? What academic requirements must be met?

www.science.nelson.com 

organ of Corti primary sound receptor in the cochlea

basilar membrane anchors the receptor hair cells in the organ of Corti

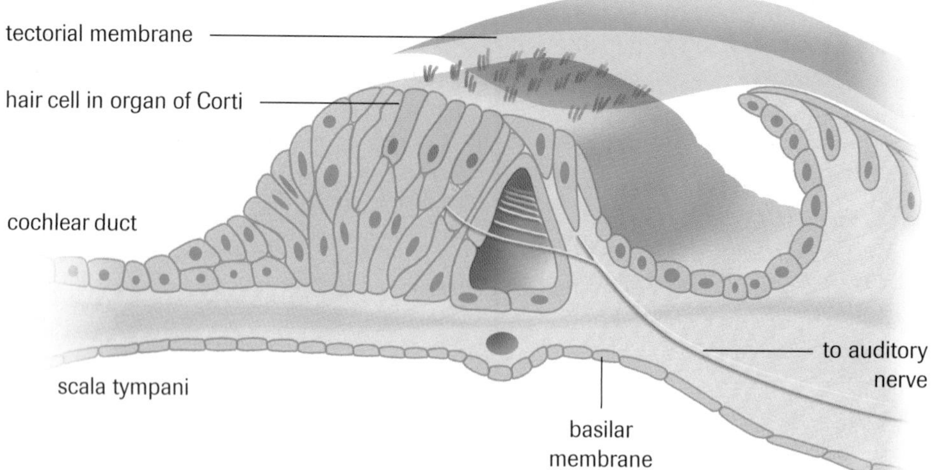

Figure 3
The organ of Corti is a ridge of cells that runs along the basilar membrane. The top of the organ of Corti meets the tectorial membrane.

to move the membrane. The high-frequency waves are transformed into basilar membrane vibrations, which, in turn, cause the hair cells to move. The hair cells trigger an action potential, which is carried to the area of the brain that registers high-pitched sounds. The high-frequency waves caused by a police siren die out quickly in the narrow, rigid part of the cochlea. However, low-frequency waves move farther along the cochlea, causing the hair cells in the wider, more elastic area to vibrate (**Figure 4**). The stimulation of nerve cells in different parts of the cochlea enables you to differentiate sounds of different pitch. Each frequency or pitch terminates in a specific part of the auditory section in the temporal lobe of the brain.

In addition to responding directly to sound energy, the basilar membrane can respond directly to mechanical stimulation. A jarring blow to the skull sets up vibrations that are passed on toward the cochlea. Aside from the sound created by the blow, the resulting mechanical vibrations of the skull can also be interpreted as sound.

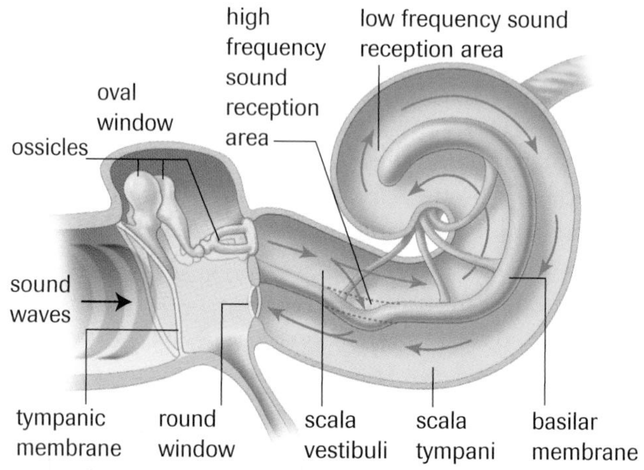

Figure 4
Here the cochlea has been uncoiled. High-frequency sounds are picked up at the base of the cochlea and low-frequency sounds are picked up towards the tip of the cochlea.

Practice

1. What function do the tympanic membrane, ossicles, and oval window serve in sound transmission?
2. Categorize the following structures of the inner ear according to whether their functions relate to balance or hearing: organ of Corti, cochlea, vestibule, saccule, ampulla, semicircular canals, oval window, and round window.

Equilibrium

Balance consists of two components: static equilibrium and dynamic equilibrium. Static equilibrium involves movement along one plane, such as horizontal or vertical. Head position is monitored by two fluid-filled sacs called the saccule and the utricle. Tiny hair cells line the saccule and utricle. Cilia from the hair cells are suspended in a gelatinous material that contains small calcium carbonate granules called **otoliths**. When the head is in the normal position, the otoliths do not move; however, when the head is bent forward, gravitational force acts on the otoliths, pulling them downward. The otoliths cause the gelatinous material to shift, and the cilia to bend (**Figure 5**). The movement of the cilia stimulates the sensory nerve, and information about head position is relayed to the cerebellum for interpretation.

otoliths tiny stones of calcium carbonate embedded in a gelatinous coating within the saccule and utricle

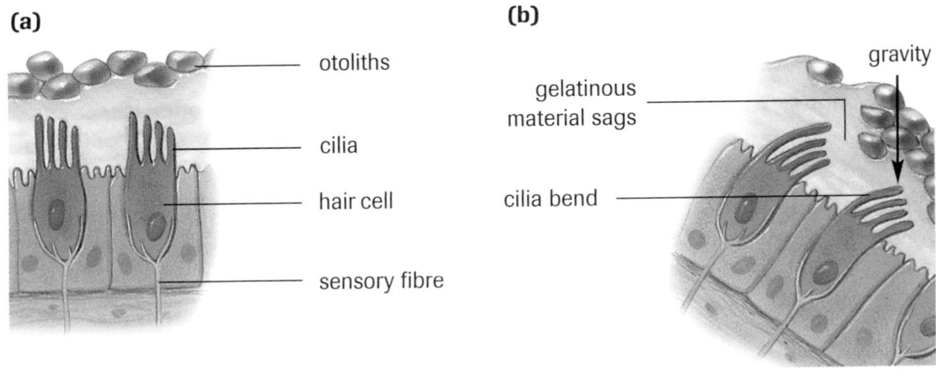

Figure 5
(a) When the head is in the erect position, the cilia from the hair cells remain erect.
(b) Movement of the head causes movement of the hair cells. Any movement of the cilia from the hair cells initiates nerve impulses.

The second aspect of balance, referred to as dynamic equilibrium, provides information during movement. While you are moving, balance is maintained by the three fluid-filled semicircular canals (**Figure 6**). Each of the canals is equipped with a pocket called an ampulla, which holds a cupula. Rotational stimuli cause the fluid in the semicircular canals to move, bending the cilia attached to hair cells in the cupulas. Once the hair cells bend, they initiate nerve impulses, which are carried to the cerebellum. It is believed that rapid continuous movement of the fluids within the semicircular canals is the cause of motion sickness.

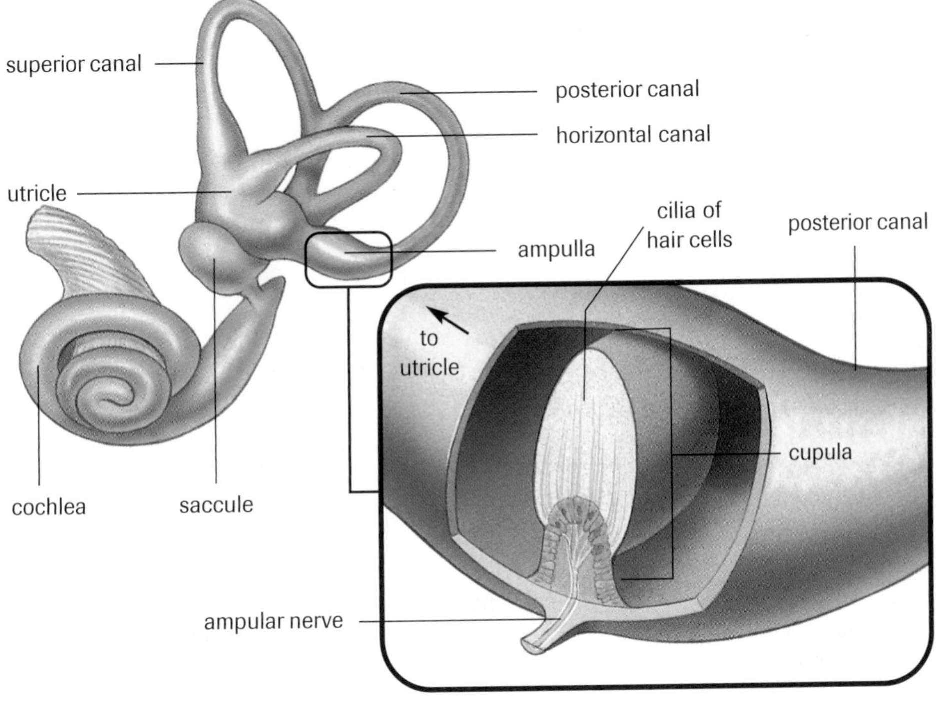

Figure 6
Three semicircular canals provide information about motion. Cilia attached to hair cells in the cupula respond to the movement of fluid in the semicircular canals.

INVESTIGATION 14.3 *Introduction*

Hearing and Equilibrium

Have you ever wondered how good your hearing actually is? Do you have trouble with motion sickness? Investigation 14.2 will help you learn more about hearing and equilibrium.

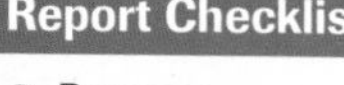

Report Checklist

● Purpose	● Design	● Analysis
○ Problem	○ Materials	● Evaluation
● Hypothesis	○ Procedure	○ Synthesis
● Prediction	● Evidence	

To perform this investigation, turn to page 464.

Treatments for Hearing Loss

One type of hearing loss is conductive hearing loss. In this type, sound waves have trouble entering the inner ear. This can be caused by wax buildup in the outer ear, middle ear infections, or a punctured eardrum. Conductive hearing loss can often be corrected by medical or surgical procedures. Another type of hearing loss is sensorineural hearing loss, where the auditory nerve is severed or damaged or the hair cells of the cochlea are damaged or dead. It can be caused by aging, exposure to loud noises, head trauma, or genetic conditions. Often hearing loss can be a mixture of the two types.

A large variety of hearing aids exist but they all work on the same principle: they all amplify sound and transmit it to the eardrum. Hearing aids have a microphone to pick up sound, an amplifier to increase the loudness of the sound, and a speaker to transmit the sound to the eardrum. However, no amount of amplification will help if the hair cells or the auditory nerve are not working, since no vibrations are being transmitted to the brain.

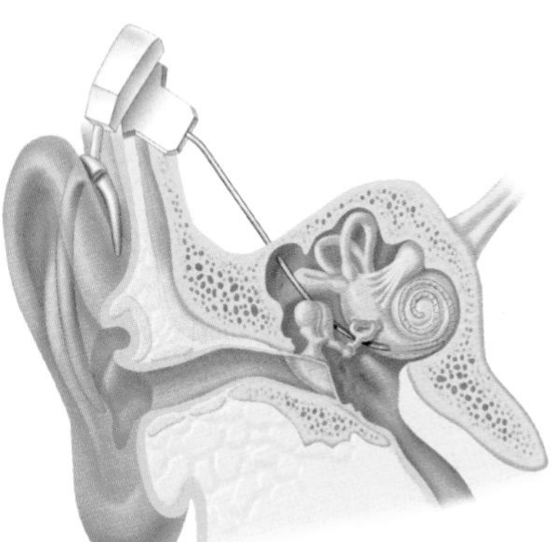

Figure 7
Unlike conventional hearing aids, cochlear implants have to be surgically implanted into the skull. Electrodes are placed in the cochlea (the grey line in the cochlea) and are connected to an external microphone placed above the ear.

Cochlear implants are devices that can restore a type of hearing to those with severe sensorineural hearing loss. A cochlear implant does not make sounds louder or clearer. The device bypasses the damaged parts of the inner ear and converts sounds into electrical impulses that are sent directly to the auditory nerve (**Figure 7**). A cochlear implant has a microphone that picks up sounds from the environment and a speech processor that selects and arranges sounds. A transmitter and a receiver/stimulator receive signals from the speech processor and convert them into electrical impulses. Electrodes then send the electrical impulses to the auditory nerves. The nerves send the coded signals to the brain, where they are interpreted as sound. Rather than restoring normal hearing by replicating the same exact sounds, the implant provides the person with sounds that enable them to interpret the environment around them. Over time the person learns to decipher what the different impulses mean and can eventually understand speech.

Simulation—Ear Structure and Function

In this simulation, you will follow sound as it travels from the outside environment through the structures of the human ear. You will look at the structures in the inner ear and how they translate the pressure changes due to sound waves into action potentials. At the end of the animation, you will complete an interactive quiz to test your understanding.

www.science.nelson.com 

SUMMARY Hearing and Equilibrium

Table 1 Parts of the Ear

Structure	Function
External ear	
pinna	• outer part of the external ear amplifies sound by funnelling it from a large area into the narrower auditory canal
auditory canal	• carries sound waves to the tympanic membrane
Middle ear	
ossicles	• tiny bones that amplify and carry sound in the middle ear
tympanic membrane	• also called the eardrum, it receives sound waves
oval window	• receives sound waves from the ossicles
eustachian tube	• air-filled tube of the middle ear that equalizes pressure between the outer and middle ear
Inner ear	
vestibule	• chamber at the base of the semicircular canals that provides information concerning static equilibrium
semicircular canals	• fluid-filled structures that provide information concerning dynamic equilibrium
cochlea	• coiled tube within the inner ear that receives sound waves and converts them into nerve impulses

Section 14.3 Questions

1. Briefly outline how the external ear, middle ear, and inner ear contribute to hearing.
2. Differentiate between static and dynamic equilibrium.
3. How do the saccule and utricle provide information about head position?
4. Describe how the semicircular canals provide information about body movement.
5. A scientist replaces ear ossicles with larger, lightweight bones. Would this procedure improve hearing? Support your answer.
6. Cochlear implants are expensive. The surgery to insert cochlear implants is covered by public health-care plans, but the cochlear implant device is not. Should patients be required to pay for their own devices?
7. Should individuals who refuse to wear ear protection while working around noisy machinery be eligible for medical coverage for the cost of hearing aids? What about rock musicians or other individuals who knowingly play a part in the loss of their own hearing? Justify your position.
8. In 1660, Robert Boyle discovered that sound cannot travel in a vacuum. Research and describe his famous experiment.

9. Research motion sickness, including its probable causes and some current solutions. You can begin your research on the Internet.

www.science.nelson.com 

10. Frequency is the number of vibrations produced per second and is measured in hertz. One hertz is equal to one vibration per second. Low-frequency sounds have low pitches and high-frequency sounds have high pitches. The hearing ranges for different species are listed in **Table 1**.

Table 1 Hearing Range of Various Species

Species	Approximate range (HZ)
human	64–23,000
dog	67–45,000
cat	45–64,000
horse	55–33,000
beluga whale	1000–123,000
goldfish	20–3000

(a) Which animal has the greatest hearing range?
(b) Provide a hypothesis as to why this animal has such a large range.

INVESTIGATION 14.1

Mapping Sensory Receptors

Your ability to feel objects is determined by the information that touch receptors provide your brain. Areas that are very sensitive have a great number of touch receptors. To distinguish between the touch of two pinpoints in an area, that area must contain two touch receptors. The body has different receptors for both hot and cold. Many times these receptors are very close to each other, but occasionally you may find one area that has only one of the receptors.

Report Checklist

○ Purpose	● Design	● Analysis
● Problem	○ Materials	● Evaluation
● Hypothesis	○ Procedure	● Synthesis
● Prediction	● Evidence	

Purpose

To map touch receptors in different parts of the body and to map the hot and cold receptors in a given area of the body

Materials

divider	ice
ruler	red and blue felt markers
two 50 mL beakers	paper towel
10 finishing nails	

Part 1: Touch Discrimination

Procedure

1. Using a ruler, move the points on the divider 20 mm apart and place the points on the back of a subject's hand (**Figure 1**).

Figure 1

Caution: The points on the divider are sharp. Be careful when placing the divider on skin. Do not press too hard as it may cause injury.

(a) Can the subject feel both points?

2. Have the subject look away from the area being investigated. Progressively decrease the distance between the points. Occasionally, touch with only one of the points to keep the results reliable.

(b) Record the minimum distance at which the subject can still distinguish two different points.

3. Predict which of the following areas of the body has the greatest number of touch receptors. (For example, predict minimum distance between two points that can be detected on the fingertip, and then test your prediction.)
   - palm of hand
   - fingertip
   - back of hand
   - calf
   - back of neck
   - lips

Analysis

(c) Compare your predicted and observed results.

(d) Explain why the fingertips are more sensitive than the back of the hand.

(e) Explain why the body part that you found to have the greatest number of receptors has that many receptors.

Synthesis

(f) Not every touch by an object can be felt. Design an investigation to measure the minimum pressure necessary to stimulate a touch receptor. If your lab has the necessary equipment, conduct your experiment after having your procedure approved by your teacher.

+ EXTENSION

Action Potentials

In this simulation, observe the relationship between different amounts of pressure and the frequency of action potentials from pressure sensors in the human hand.

www.science.nelson.com 

INVESTIGATION 14.1 *continued*

Part 2: Temperature Receptors

Prediction

(g) Predict whether you are more sensitive to hot or cold. Do you believe you have more hot or more cold receptors?

Procedure

4. Fill a beaker with warm water and another with iced water. Place five finishing nails in each beaker. Allow the nails to sit in the cold or warm water for at least 2 min between tests.
5. Draw a square 5 cm by 5 cm on the back of a subject's hand. While the subject looks away from the test area, remove one of the nails, wipe off excess water, and lightly touch the point of the nail on the skin inside the test area. Ask the subject whether the nail is hot or cold. Then return the nail to the beaker.
6. If the subject identifies the temperature correctly, place a small dot where the nail touched the hand. Use a blue water-soluble marker for cold receptors and red water-soluble marker for heat receptors.
7. Alternate between hot and cold nails when conducting your test. (And occasionally, change the order.) Map the area within the square. Do at least 20 trials for each temperature.

Analysis

(h) Compare your observed data to the prediction that you made. What conclusions can you draw from the evidence?

Synthesis

(i) Air temperatures usually range between −30 °C and +35 °C. Body temperature is about 37 °C. Using this information, explain why temperature receptors are not evenly distributed.

INVESTIGATION 14.2

Eye Dissection

The eyes of most mammals have very similar anatomy. By dissecting a cow eye, you can therefore better understand the structures of the human eye. Use the diagram in **Figure 1** on page 449 to help you to identify the structures. As you perform the dissection, record your observations in written notes and/or in biological drawings. Refer to Appendix A4 for a review of biological drawings.

Report Checklist

- ○ Purpose
- ● Problem
- ○ Hypothesis
- ○ Prediction
- ● Design
- ○ Materials
- ○ Procedure
- ● Evidence
- ● Analysis
- ○ Evaluation
- ○ Synthesis

Problem

To observe the principal features of a mammalian eye and identify the major structures

Materials

cow eye
safety goggles
lab apron
dissecting gloves
scissors
forceps
dissecting tray
hand lens
a sheet of newspaper

Wear safety goggles and an apron at all times. When you have finished the activity, clean your work area, wash your hands thoroughly, and dispose of all specimens and materials as instructed by your teacher.

Procedure, Evidence, and Analysis

1. Examine the outside of the eye.

(a) Identify as many structures as possible.

2. Using scissors and forceps, remove as much fat and muscle from the eye as possible.
3. Identify the sclera and the iris. With the scissors, carefully cut into the sclera, in a circle along the outside of the iris.

(b) Note and record how the sclera feels as you cut it.

4. Remove the front part of the eye.

(c) Identify and describe the aqueous humour and the vitreous humour.

5. Using forceps, remove the lens from the eye. Place the lens on the sheet of newspaper.

(d) Describe your observations.

INVESTIGATION 14.2 *continued*

6. Locate the ciliary muscles. These can be found where the lens was and appear black or very dark in colour and have ridges. The layer inside of the eye is the choroids layer.

(e) Describe the choroids layer.

7. Using forceps, remove the retina from the back of the eye.

(f) Describe the appearance of the retina, and the location of the blind spot in the retina.

INVESTIGATION 14.3

Hearing and Equilibrium

In this investigation, you will test the effects of environmental factors on both hearing and equilibrium. Begin by reading over the procedure, then predict what will happen in each Part. Formulate a hypothesis and explain your predictions. In Part I, gather evidence by recording the direction from which the sound seems to come and describing any changes in the intensity of the sound. In Part 2, record the direction in which the subject leans and his or her description of any sensations when standing after the chair has stopped.

Report Checklist

● Purpose	● Design	● Analysis
○ Problem	○ Materials	● Evaluation
● Hypothesis	○ Procedure	○ Synthesis
● Prediction	● Evidence	

Problem

What effect will environmental factors have on hearing? on equilibrium?

Materials

tuning fork	metre stick
rubber hammer	swivel chair

Procedure

Part 1: Factors That Affect Hearing

1. Strike a tuning fork with a rubber hammer and listen to the sound. Holding the tuning fork in your left hand, place the *stem* (not the prongs!) of the tuning fork on your forehead. Place the palm of your right hand over your right ear.
2. Repeat the procedure, but this time hold the tuning fork in your right hand and place your left hand over your left ear.
3. Repeat the procedure a third time, but ask your lab partner to cover both of your ears.
4. Strike the tuning fork with a rubber hammer and hold it approximately 1 m from your ear.
5. Ask your lab partner to place a metre stick gently on the bony bump immediately behind your ear. Then, ask him or her to place the stem of the tuning fork on the metre stick.

Part 2: Equilibrium

6. Ask your lab partner to sit in a swivel chair. Have your partner elevate his or her legs and begin slowly rotating the chair in a clockwise direction. After 20 rotations, have the subject stand. (Be prepared to support your partner!)
7. After 3 min, repeat the process, but rotate the swivel chair in a counterclockwise direction.
8. Ask your lab partner to tilt his or her head to the right, and begin a clockwise rotation of the swivel chair. After 20 rotations, ask the subject to hold his or her head erect and to stand up. (Again, be prepared to catch your lab partner.)

Analysis and Evaluation

(a) Provide explanations for the data collected.

(b) Using the data collected, provide evidence to suggest that sound intensity is greater in fluids than in air.

(c) Provide evidence that the fluid in the semicircular canals continues to move even after rotational stimuli cease.

(d) What causes the falling sensation produced in step 8?

(e) Describe the manner in which the semicircular canals detect changes in motion during a roller-coaster ride.

Chapter 14 SUMMARY

Outcomes

Knowledge

- describe the structure and function of the human eye (i.e., cornea, lens, sclera, choroid, retina, rods and cones, pupil, iris, and optic nerve) (14.2)
- describe the structure and function of the human ear (i.e., pinna, auditory canal, tympanum, ossicles, cochlea, organ of Corti, auditory nerve, utricle and saccule, semicircular canals, and eustachian tube) (14.3)
- explain other ways that human organisms sense their environment and spatial orientation (14.1, 14.3)

STS

- explain that scientific knowledge and theories develop through hypotheses, collection of evidence through experimentation, and provision of explanations (14.2)
- explain that the goal of technology is to provide solutions to practical problems (14.2, 14.3)

Skills

- ask questions and plan investigations by designing an experiment to investigate heat, cold, pressure, and touch receptors (14.1)
- conduct investigations and gather and record data and information by performing experiments to measure the ability to discriminate objects visually and to hear a range of sounds (14.2, 14.3) and by observing the principal features of an ear and eye and identifying the major visible structures of those organs (14.2, 14.3)
- analyze data and apply mathematical and conceptual models (all)
- work as members of a team and apply the skills and conventions of science (all)

Key Terms

14.1

sensory adaptation

14.2

sclera
cornea
aqueous humour
choroid layer
iris
retina
rods
cones
fovea centralis
rhodopsin
accommodation
glaucoma
cataract
astigmatism
nearsightedness
farsightedness

14.3

pinna
auditory canal
tympanic membrane
ossicles
oval window
eustachian tube
vestibule
semicircular canals
cochlea
organ of Corti
basilar membrane
otoliths

MAKE a summary

1. Imagine a cougar or bear suddenly walks in your path. Create a flow chart or diagram that shows how your nervous system would respond to this stressful situation. Label the diagram with as many key terms as possible.
2. Revisit your answers to the Starting Points questions at the start of the chapter. Would you answer the questions differently now? Why?

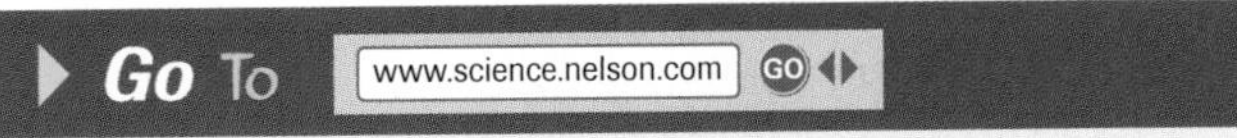

The following components are available on the Nelson Web site. Follow the links for *Nelson Biology Alberta 20–30.*

- an interactive Self Quiz for Chapter 14
- additional Diploma Exam-style Review Questions
- Illustrated Glossary
- additional IB-related material

There is more information on the Web site wherever you see the Go icon in the chapter.

EXTENSION

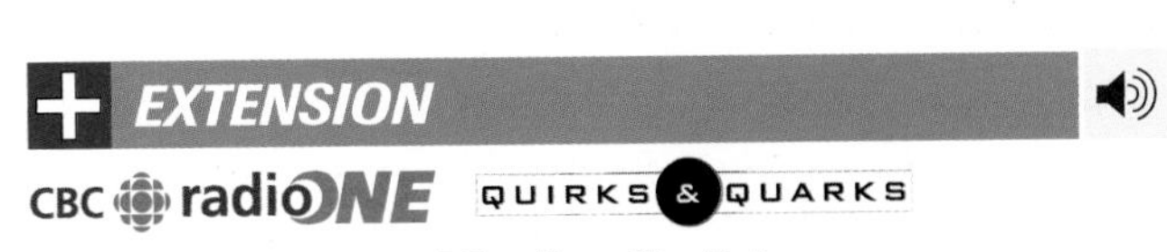

Blind, Naked, and Feeling No Pain

Listen to this interview with Dr. Tom Park, who has discovered that naked mole-rats don't feel pain through their skin. The animals otherwise seem to have normal sensation in their skin. Studying mole-rats may help us to better understand pain.

www.science.nelson.com GO

▸ Chapter 14 REVIEW

Many of these questions are in the style of the Diploma Exam. You will find guidance for writing Diploma Exams in Appendix A5. Science Directing Words used in Diploma Exams are in bold type. Exam study tips and test-taking suggestions are on the Nelson Web site.

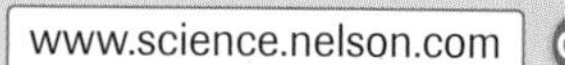

DO NOT WRITE IN THIS TEXTBOOK.

Part 1

1. The *action* and *purpose* of sensory receptors, respectively, is to
   A. increase the energy of the stimulus above the threshold level and to provide the CNS with information about the external environment only
   B. decrease the energy of the stimulus below the threshold level and to provide the CNS with information about the external environment only
   C. convert the energy of a response into an action potential and to provide the CNS with information about changes in the external environment or within the internal environment
   D. convert the energy of a stimulus into an action potential and to provide the CNS with information about changes in the external environment or within the internal environment

Use the following information to answer questions 2 and 3.

Figure 1 shows a cross section of a human eye. Structures are labelled with a letter.

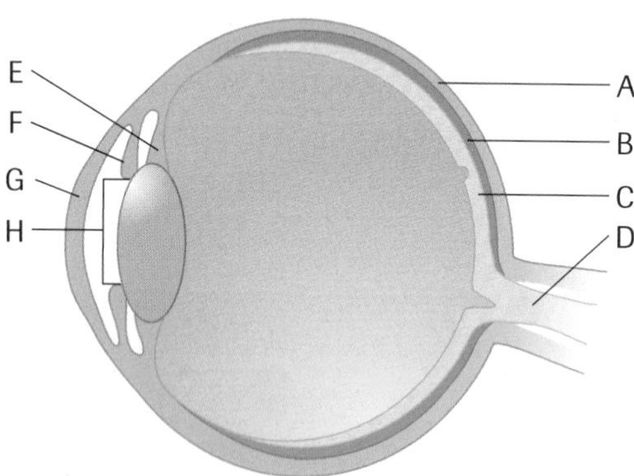

Figure 1

2. Which choice gives all three labels correctly for the given structures?
   A. A = sclera, C = retina, G = cornea
   B. B = sclera, C = retina, H = cornea
   C. C = sclera, G = retina, D = cornea
   D. F = sclera, E = retina, H = cornea

3. Identify the statement that is incorrect.
   A. Light enters through the cornea (G on the diagram).
   B. Light enters through the pupil (H on the diagram).
   C. The choroid layer (B on the diagram) prevents light from scattering.
   D. The aqueous humour (A on the diagram) prevents light from scattering.

Use the following information to answer questions 4 and 5.

Figure 2 shows the internal structures of the human ear. The structures are labelled with a number.

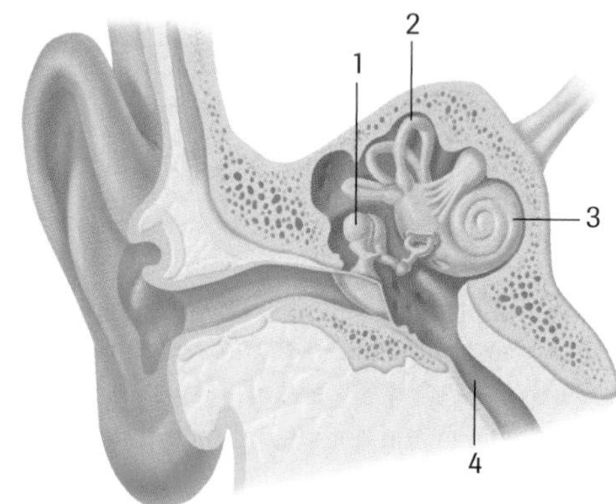

Figure 2

4. NR Match the following structures with the labels shown on **Figure 2**. (Record all four digits of your answer.)

___	___	___	___
eustacian tube	semicircular canals	ossicles	cochlea

5. The structure that is primarily responsible for maintaining dynamic equilibrium is labelled with which number?
   A. 1
   B. 2
   C. 3
   D. 4

6. A person who has colour blindness would have a gene defect expressed in this part of the eye.
   A. optic nerve
   B. vestibule
   C. cones
   D. cornea

7. NR Place the following structures in order as light passes through the eye. (Record all four digits of your answer.)
   1. aqueous humor
   2. lens
   3. cornea
   4. fovea

8. Should the curvature of the cornea along the horizontal axis of the eye be greater than the curvature along the vertical axis, the result would be
   A. glaucoma
   B. night blindness
   C. astigmatism
   D. farsightedness

9. Sensorineural deafness may be caused by
   A. the blockage of the eustachian tube
   B. damage to the basilar membrane
   C. damage to the ossicles
   D. damage to the tympanic membrane

10. NR Place the following events in the correct sequence after the initial event. (Record all four digits of your answer.)

    Initial event: Sound waves push against the eardrum or tympanic membrane.

    1. Tiny hair-like cells in the organ of Corti respond to vibrations by stimulating nerve cells in the basilar membrane.
    2. Vibrations are passed along to three bones in the middle ear: the malleus, incus, and stapes.
    3. The cochlea receives waves within the inner ear.
    4. The oval window receives vibrations from the ossicles.

Part 2

Use the following information to answer questions 11 to 14.

In an experiment, skin was exposed to different temperatures. The frequency of firing of action potentials from temperature receptors was recorded. The average frequency was then used to sketch the graph in **Figure 1**.

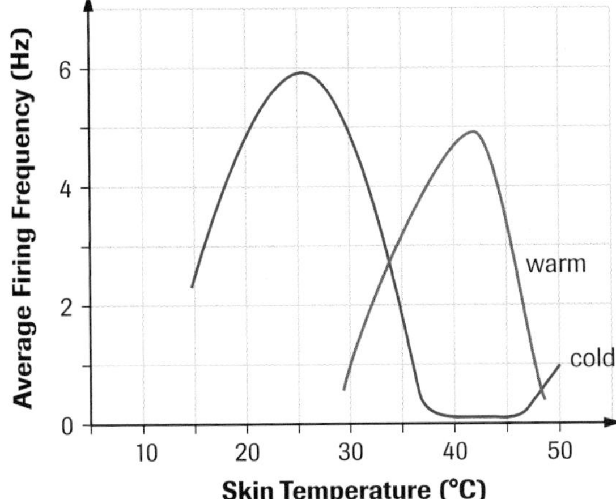

Figure 1

11. DE **Identify** the temperature at which cold temperature receptors fire most frequently.

12. DE **Identify** the temperature at which hot temperature receptors fire most frequently.

13. DE **Conclude** whether the body is more sensitive to warm or cold stimuli. **Justify** your conclusion.

14. DE **Hypothesize** why cold temperature receptors show an increased sensitivity at 50 °C.

---

15. The retina of a chicken is composed of many cones very close together. **Explain** the advantages and disadvantages associated with this type of eye.

16. DE Myopia is thought to be caused by a combination of genetic and environmental factors, but there are some differences in opinion. Write a unified response addressing the following aspects of myopia.
    - It was once believed that excessive reading might cause myopia. **How** might this theory be tested?
    - **How** might the link between myopia and genetics be established?

17. **Why** do people often require reading glasses after they reach the age of 40?

18. When the hearing of a rock musician was tested, the results revealed a general deterioration of hearing as well as total deafness for particular frequencies. **Why** is the loss of hearing not equal for all frequencies?

19. One theory suggests that painters use less purple and blue in their paintings as they age because layers of protein build up on the lens in their eyes. As the buildup gradually becomes thicker and more yellow, the shorter ultraviolet wavelengths from the ultraviolet end of the spectrum are filtered. **How** would you test the theory?

Use the following information to answer questions 20 to 23.

The data in **Table 1** were collected from an experiment.

Table 1 Changes in Near-point Accommodation with Age

Age	Near-point accommodation (cm)
10	7.5
20	10.2
30	11.3
40	17.2
50	56.8
60	87.3

20. DE **Identify** the problem that was being investigated in the experiment.

21. DE **Hypothesize** how the variables under investigation are related.

22. DE **Conclude** the age at which near-point accommodation is most affected.

23. DE **Explain** what causes the change in near-point accommodation. How does it affect people?

chapter

15 Endocrine System

In this chapter

- Exploration: Chemical Signals and Sports
- Investigation 15.1: Identification of Hyperglycemia
- Web Activity: Banting and Best
- Web Activity: Diabetes
- Lab Exercise 15.A: Effects of Hormones on Blood Sugar Levels
- Web Activity: Homeostasis and Space Travel
- Explore an Issue: Protecting Athletes

Olga Yegorova upset reigning 5000 m champion Gabriela Szabo at the 2001 World Track and Field Championships held in Edmonton. The usually polite Canadian audience booed Yegorova as she crossed the finish line. The Russian distance runner was booed for what was perceived to be an unfair advantage—taking the banned chemical hormone, erythropoietin (EPO). Following a competition in Paris, Yegorova had tested positive for erythropoietin, but she had been reinstated just before the world championships on a technicality. Although EPO was detected in Yegorova's urine, the Paris track meet organizers failed to do the required follow-up blood test. By the time Yegorova was tested again, abnormally high levels of EPO could no longer be identified.

Erythropoietin is a naturally occurring hormone produced by the kidneys. It boosts red blood cell production, increasing oxygen transport to the tissues. More oxygen means greater energy for endurance athletes. Tests have shown that athletic enhancement gained by using EPO for four weeks matches that of several years of training. But EPO is dangerous. Increased red blood cell production makes the blood thicker and more difficult to pump. Very high red blood cell counts can increase blood clotting and overwork the heart. According to some doping experts, the deaths of 20 European cyclists between 1988 and 1998 can be linked directly to EPO use.

Since the body produces EPO, it is difficult to detect. New tests that analyze blood for abnormally high red blood cell volume and analyze for unusually high EPO levels are being used to detect its use. Unfortunately, athletes can still avoid getting caught by stopping EPO treatments a few weeks before the tests.

STARTING Points

Answer these questions as best you can with your current knowledge. Then, using the concepts and skills you have learned, you will revise your answers at the end of the chapter.

1. Explain how hormones help the body adjust to stress.
2. Antidiuretic hormone (ADH) and aldosterone are hormones that affect the kidney. Explain why the regulatory systems for osmotic pressure of fluids and for body fluid volumes are controlled by chemicals carried by blood, rather than by nerves.

Career Connections:
Licensed Practical Nurse; Pharmacist

Figure 1
Gabriela Szabo of Romania leads Olga Yegorova in a race.

Exploration Chemical Signals and Sports

Find out more about the use of banned drugs in sports.

(a) Choose one banned drug and explain the unfair advantage it provides.

(b) What are some of the health risks associated with its use?

(c) Identify some of the technologies used to detect whether an athlete is using the drug.

www.science.nelson.com 

15.1 Homeostasis, Hormones, and the Endocrine System

The human body works best at a temperature of 37 °C, with a 0.1 % blood glucose level and a blood pH of 7.35. However, the external environment does not always provide the ideal conditions for life. Air temperatures in Canada can fluctuate between –40 °C and +40 °C. Rarely do foods consist of 0.1 % glucose and have a pH of 7.35. You also place different demands on your body when you take part in various activities, such as playing racquetball, swimming, or digesting a large meal. Your body systems must adjust to these variations to maintain a stable internal environment. **Homeostasis** refers to the body's attempt to adjust to a fluctuating environment. The body maintains a constant balance, or steady state, through a series of adjustments. This system of balance requires constant monitoring and feedback about body conditions (**Figure 1**). An increase in heart rate during exercise and the release of glucose from the liver to restore blood sugar levels are a couple of examples of the adjustments made. The concept of homeostasis is central to how the endocrine system operates.

homeostasis the process by which a constant internal environment is maintained despite changes in the environment

DID YOU KNOW ?

Discovering Homeostasis

The word *homeostasis* was coined in 1932 when Walter Cannon, a physiology professor at Harvard University, published the book *Wisdom of the Body.* Aided by new X-ray equipment, Cannon was able to mix food with barium sulfate and follow it toward the stomach. He noted that the waves of contraction that pushed along the digestive tract could be suspended if the animal were frightened. Cannon surmised that higher mammals have a complex system of self-regulatory mechanisms that keep the body stable under various physical and emotional circumstances.

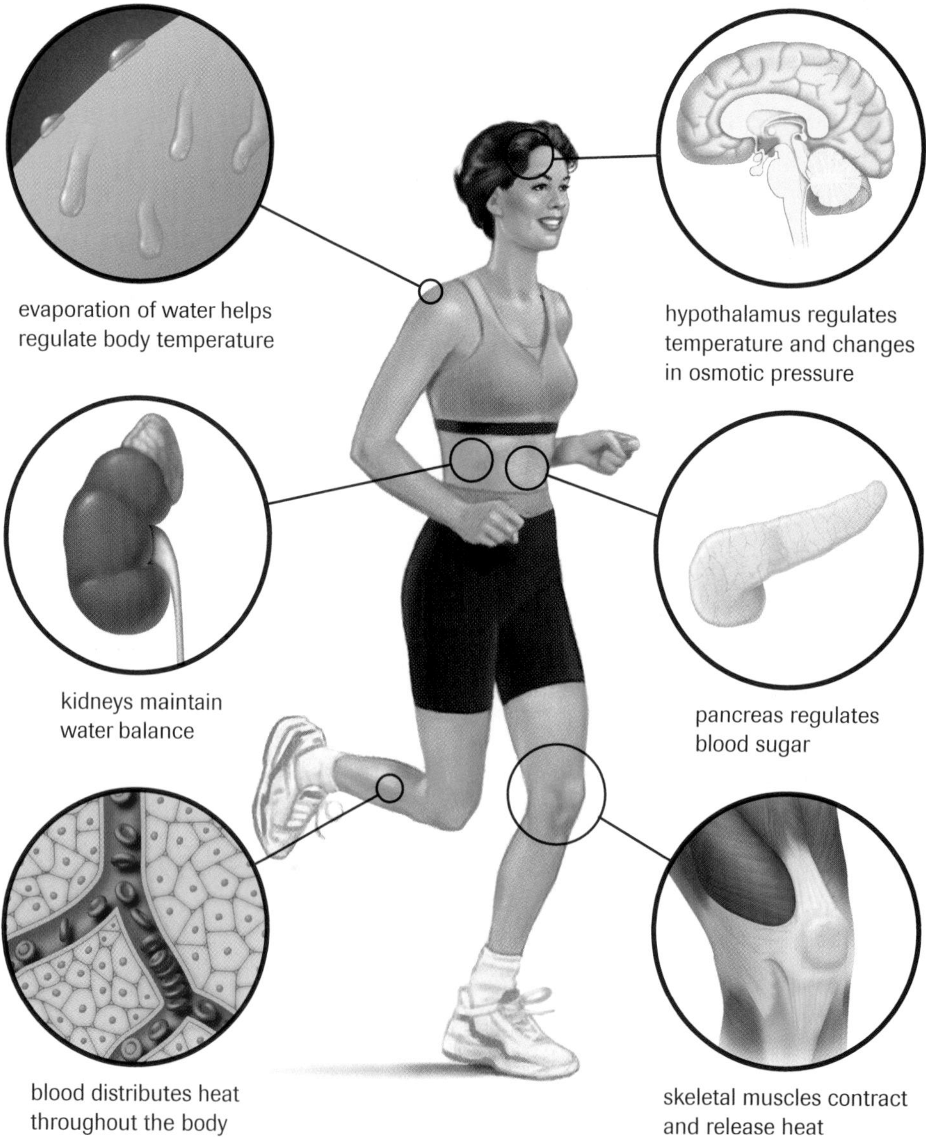
evaporation of water helps regulate body temperature
hypothalamus regulates temperature and changes in osmotic pressure
kidneys maintain water balance
pancreas regulates blood sugar
blood distributes heat throughout the body
skeletal muscles contract and release heat

Figure 1
Homeostasis requires the interaction of several regulatory systems. Information about blood sugar, fluid balance, body temperature, oxygen levels, and blood pressure is relayed to a nerve coordinating centre. Once their levels move outside the normal limits, regulators bring about the needed adjustments.

All homeostatic control systems have three functional components: a receptor, a coordinating centre, and an effector (**Figure 2**). Special receptors located in the organs of the body signal a coordinating centre once an organ begins to operate outside its normal limits. The coordinating centre relays the information to the appropriate effector, which helps to restore the normal balance. For example, when carbon dioxide levels increase during exercise, chemical receptors in the brainstem are stimulated. Nerve cells from the brain then carry impulses to effector muscles, which increase the depth and rate of breathing. The increased breathing movements help flush excess carbon dioxide from the body.

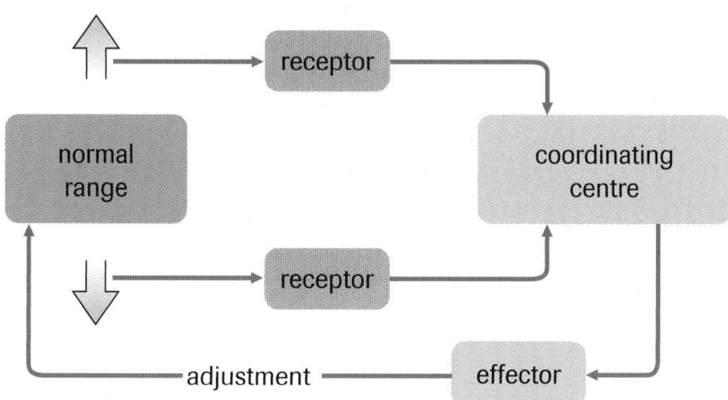

Figure 2
A schematic diagram of a control system

A group of chemical receptors in the arteries in the neck can detect low levels of oxygen in the blood. A nerve is excited and sends a message to the brain, which relays the information by way of another nerve to the muscles that control breathing movements. This system ensures that oxygen levels are maintained within an acceptable range. Homeostasis is often referred to as a **dynamic equilibrium**. Although there are fluctuations in blood glucose, body temperature, blood pressure, and blood pH, the homeostatic mechanism ensures that all body systems function within an acceptable range to sustain life (**Figure 3**).

dynamic equilibrium a state of stability within fluctuating limits

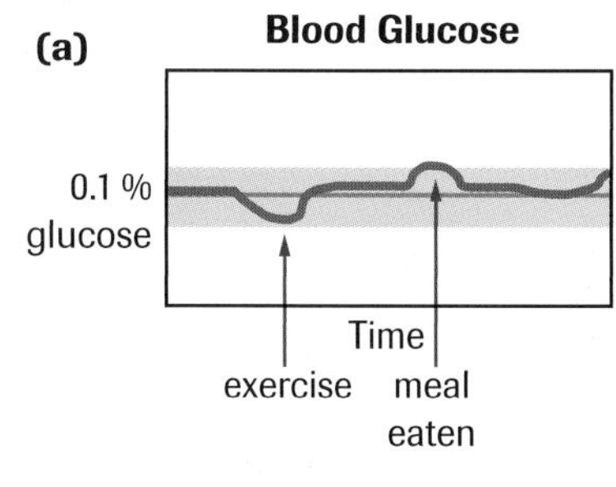

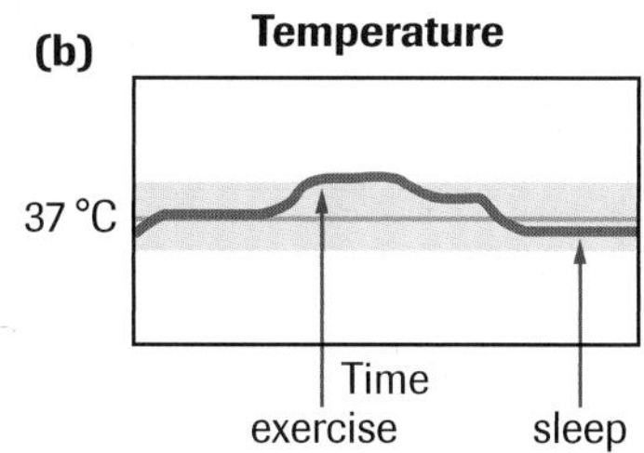

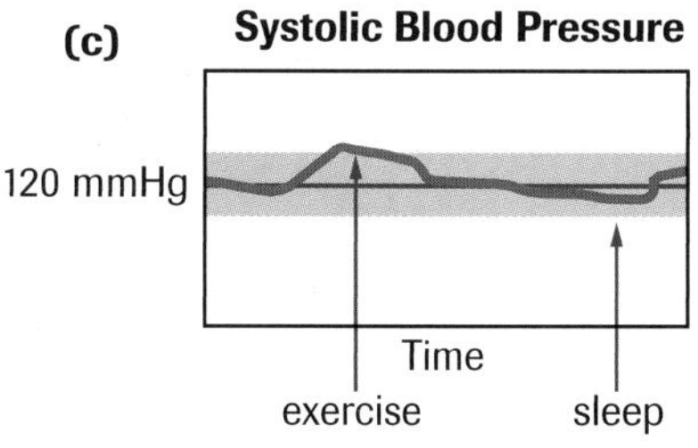

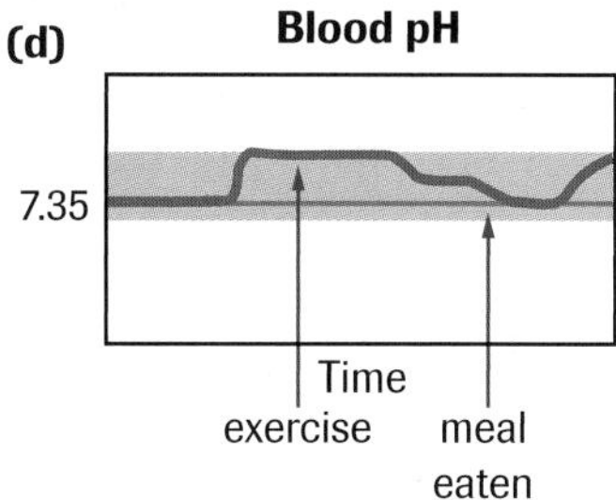

Figure 3
Blood glucose **(a)** is maintained within a narrow range and movement outside of the range can signal disease. Body temperature **(b)** can fluctuate by +2 °C with exercise and −2 °C with sleep. Systolic blood pressure **(c)** is usually near 120 mmHg but can move as high as 240 mmHg in a very fit athlete for a limited time during strenuous exercise. Blood pH **(d)** operates within a narrow range, and changes of ±0.2 can lead to death.

Homeostasis and Feedback Systems

negative feedback the process by which a mechanism is activated to restore conditions to their original state

Mechanisms that make adjustments to bring the body back within an acceptable range are referred to as **negative feedback** systems. The household thermostat is an example of such a system (**Figure 4**). In this case, the coordinating centre, called a thermostat, also contains the receptor (a thermometer). When the room temperature falls below a set point, say 20 °C, the thermostat switches on the effector (the furnace). When the thermometer detects a temperature above the set point, the thermostat switches off the furnace. This type of control circuit is called negative feedback because a change in the variable being monitored (e.g., temperature) triggers the control mechanism to counteract any further change in the same direction. Negative feedback mechanisms prevent small changes from becoming too large. Most homeostatic mechanisms in animals operate on this principle of negative feedback.

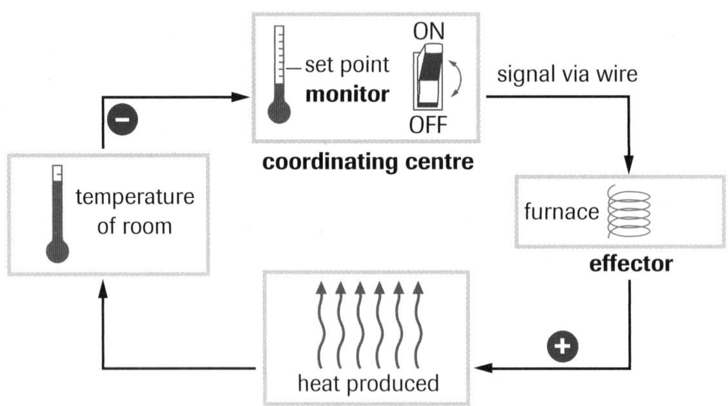

Figure 4
The household thermostat illustrates a negative feedback system. When the variable (temperature) exceeds the set point, the coordinating centre turns the effector off. The + indicates "stimulation" or "activation," and the − indicates "inhibition" or "turning off."

positive feedback the process by which a small effect is amplified

Positive feedback systems are less common in the body. Whereas negative feedback systems are designed to resist change, positive feedback systems reinforce change. Positive feedback systems move the controlled variable away from a steady state. The value of a positive feedback system is that it allows a discrete physiological event to be accomplished rapidly. Once this event is accomplished, the feedback system stops.

Practice

1. Define homeostasis.
2. Use the example of a thermostat to explain homeostasis.
3. Explain the negative feedback system shown in **Figure 5**.

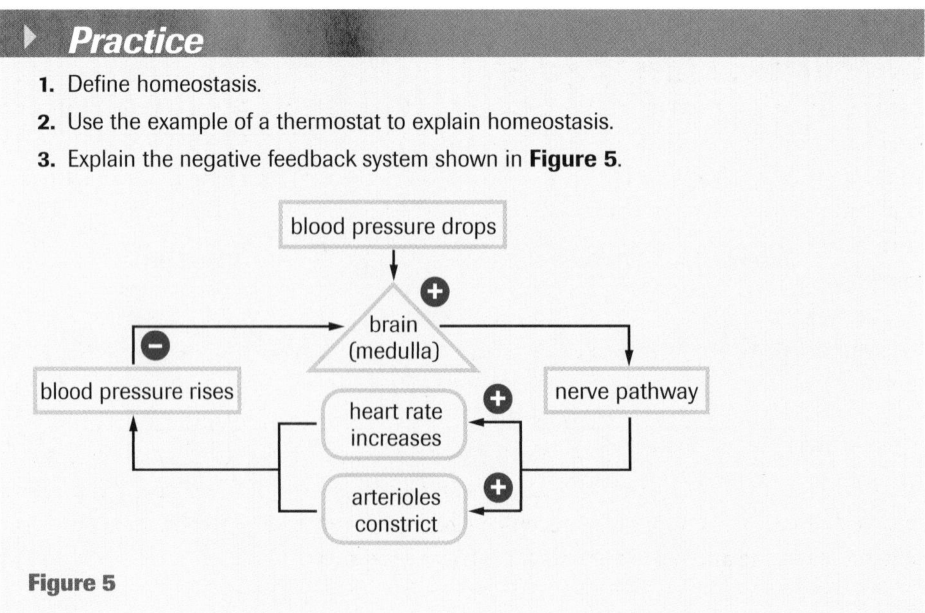

Figure 5

Hormones

The trillions of cells of the body all interact with each other—no cell operates in isolation. The integration of body functions depends on chemical controls. **Hormones** are chemical regulators produced by cells in one part of the body that affect cells in another part of the body. The word *hormone* comes from the Greek *hormon*, meaning "to excite or set into motion." Hormones serve as regulators, speeding up or slowing down certain bodily processes. Only a small amount of a hormone is required to alter cell metabolism. Chemicals produced by endocrine glands (**Figure 6**) and secreted directly into the blood are referred to as **endocrine hormones** (**Figure 7**). The circulatory system carries these hormones to the various organs of the body.

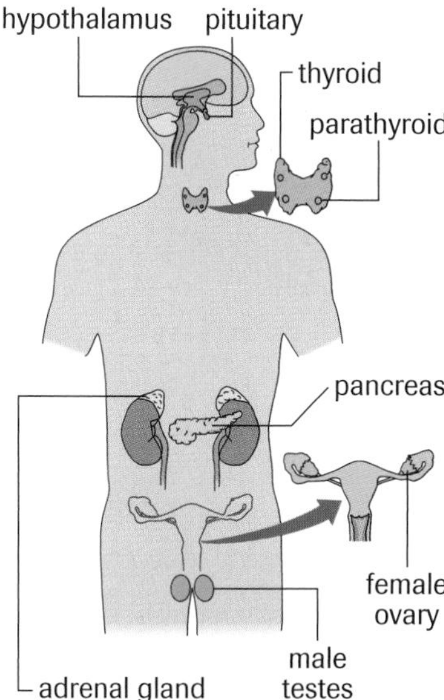

Figure 6
The location and appearance of some important endocrine glands in the human body. Hidden within the thyroid gland are four small glands—the parathyroid glands.

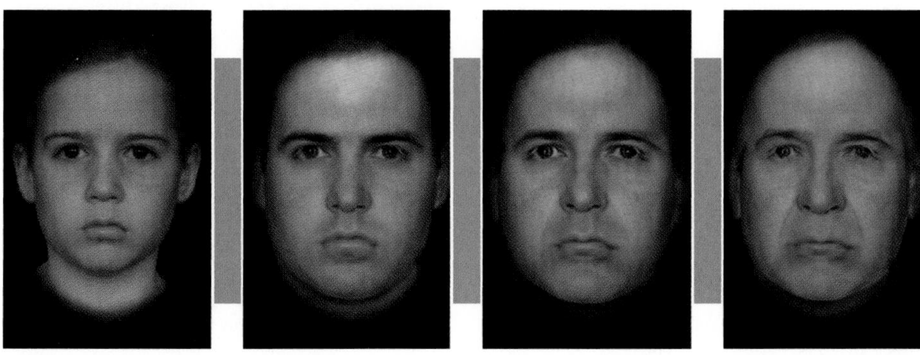

Figure 7
Endocrine hormones are chemical controls involved in the regulation of growth, development, and homeostasis. This sequence of photos is a computer simulation of the aging process based on statistical data.

hormones chemicals released by cells that affect cells in other parts of the body

endocrine hormones chemicals secreted by endocrine glands directly into the blood

insulin hormone produced by the islets of Langerhans in the pancreas; insulin is secreted when blood sugar levels are high

human growth hormone (hGH) hormone produced by the pituitary gland that stimulates growth of the body; also known as somatotropin (STH)

epinephrine (adrenaline) hormone, produced in the adrenal medulla that accelerates heart rate and body reactions during a crisis (the fight-or-flight response)

Hormones can be classified according to their activation site. Some hormones are called nontarget hormones. They affect many cells or tissues throughout the body. For example, **insulin** makes practically all cells in the body permeable to glucose and makes liver cells to convert glucose to glycogen. **Human growth hormone (hGH)** and **epinephrine** are also non-target hormones. Other hormones affect specific cells or target tissues. For example, gastrin stimulates only certain stomach cells, which then produce digestive enzymes.

Chemical Control Systems

Along with the nervous system, the endocrine system provides integration and control of the organs and tissues to maintain homeostasis. The nervous system enables the body to adjust quickly to changes in the environment. The endocrine system is designed to maintain control over a longer duration. Hormones such as growth hormone and the various hormones involved in reproduction, for example, regulate and sustain development for many years.

The division between the nervous system and endocrine system is most subtle in the hypothalamus. The hypothalamus regulates the pituitary gland through nerve stimulation as well as by releasing hormones. However, the endocrine glands, stimulated by the pituitary, secrete chemicals that affect the nerve activity of the hypothalamus.

Hormones do not affect all cells. Cells may have receptors for one hormone, but not another. The number of receptors on individual cells may also vary. For example, liver cells and muscle cells have many receptor sites for the hormone insulin, but less active cells such as bone and cartilage cells have fewer receptors.

Hormones may also be classified by their chemical nature. Most hormones are water-soluble, and are proteins, peptides, or amino acid derivatives. Water-soluble hormones act from outside the cell by binding to receptor sites on the cell membrane, which activates enzymes in the cytoplasm to carry out specific functions (**Figure 8 (a)**). The second class of hormones is fat-soluble hormones, which are also called steroids. Steroids act from inside the cell, by diffusing into a specific cell and binding with receptor molecules in the cytoplasm, which signals the cell to produce a specific protein (**Figure 8 (b)**). You will learn more about specific members of these two classes in the rest of this unit and in Unit 30 B.

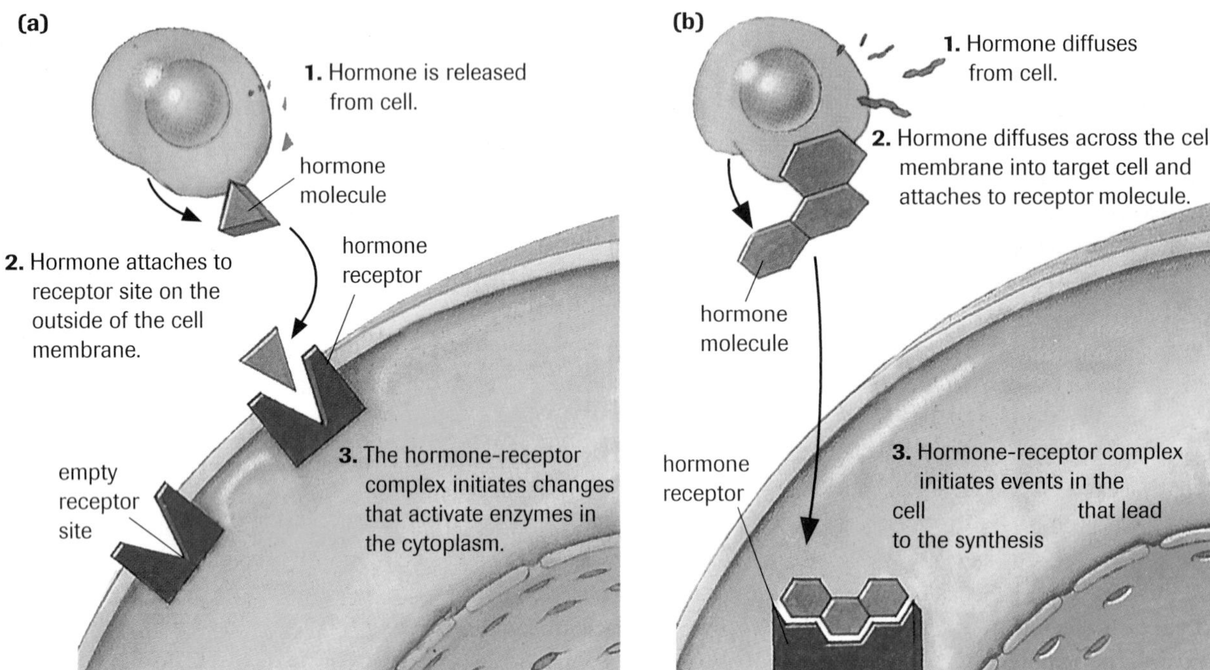

(a)
1. Hormone is released from cell.
hormone molecule
2. Hormone attaches to receptor site on the outside of the cell membrane.
hormone receptor
empty receptor site
3. The hormone-receptor complex initiates changes that activate enzymes in the cytoplasm.
(b)
1. Hormone diffuses from cell.
2. Hormone diffuses across the cell membrane into target cell and attaches to receptor molecule.
hormone molecule
hormone receptor
3. Hormone-receptor complex initiates events in the cell that lead to the synthesis

Figure 8
(a) A water-soluble hormone molecule combines with its receptor on the cell membrane. This triggers events in the cell that lead to the activation of enzymes in the cytoplasm.
(b) A fat-soluble (steroid) hormone molecule passes through the cell membrane of the target cell and combines with its receptor in the cytoplasm. This triggers events in the cell that lead to the production of a specific protein.

DID YOU KNOW ?

Exocrine Glands

Exocrine glands, unlike the endocrine glands, are glands that secrete substances through ducts or tubes onto a body surface or into a cavity. Most of the body's glands are exocrine glands. Digestive, mucous, sebaceous, and sweat glands are included in this category. The pancreas is considered both an exocrine gland and an endocrine gland.

Regulating Hormones

Hormone production must be regulated. Once a hormone produces the desired effect, production of that hormone must be decreased to maintain normal body functioning.

Consider, for example, the hormone epinephrine (adrenaline). Epinephrine enables the body to respond to stressful situations. Among other responses, the hormone causes pulse and breathing rates to accelerate and blood sugar levels to rise. All actions are designed to allow the body to respond to stress in what has come to be known as the "flight-or-fight" response. However, once the stressful situation is gone, the body returns to normal resting levels. Once again, negative-feedback action is required to restore homeostasis. Throughout this chapter, you will study other specific examples of negative feedback.

Practice

4. Define an endocrine hormone.
5. Do hormones affect every cell in the body? Explain why or why not.
6. Explain why hormones must be regulated.

DID YOU KNOW ?

Unused Protein Hormones
Protein hormones that do not attach to receptor molecules on target cells are removed from the body by the liver or kidney. The presence of these hormones can be monitored by urinalysis.

The Pituitary Gland: The Master Gland

The **pituitary gland** is often referred to as the "master gland," because it exercises control over other endocrine glands. This small, sac-like structure is connected by a stalk to the hypothalamus, the area of the brain associated with homeostasis. The interaction between the nervous system and endocrine system is evident in the hypothalamus–pituitary complex (**Figure 9**, next page). The pituitary gland produces and stores hormones. The hypothalamus stimulates the release of hormones by the pituitary gland by way of nerves and by releasing hormones.

pituitary gland gland at the base of the brain that, together with the hypothalamus, functions as a control centre, coordinating the endocrine and nervous systems

Releasing hormones (also called releasing factors) are peptides that stimulate the pituitary to release a stored hormone.

releasing hormone a peptide produced by the hypothalamus that stimulates the anterior pituitary gland to release a stored hormone; also called a releasing factor

The posterior lobe of the pituitary does not synthesize hormones. Instead, it stores and releases hormones that have been synthesized by the hypothalamus, such as antidiuretic hormone (ADH). You learned in Unit 20 D that this hormone acts on the kidneys and helps regulate body water. The ADH travels from the hypothalamus to the pituitary by way of specialized nerve cells (**Figure 9 (a)**, next page). Once at the posterior pituitary lobe, the ADH is stored until it is needed, at which time it is released into the blood.

In contrast, the anterior lobe of the pituitary synthesizes its own hormones. The secretion of the pituitary hormones by the posterior lobe, such as hGH (**Figure 9 (b)**, next page), is governed by factors secreted by the hypothalamus. Releasing factors stimulate the pituitary to secrete its hormones, and **inhibiting factors** stop pituitary secretions. These factors travel from the hypothalamus to the pituitary by a series of blood vessels.

inhibiting factor chemical that inhibits production of a hormone by the anterior pituitary gland

Table 1 summarizes the hormones produced by the pituitary gland. Most of the pituitary hormones will be discussed in detail in the following sections.

Table 1 Pituitary Hormones

Hormone	Target
Anterior lobe	
thyroid-stimulating hormone (TSH)	thyroid gland
adrenocorticotropic hormone (ACTH)	adrenal cortex
human growth hormone (hGH)	most cells
follicle-stimulating hormone (FSH)	ovaries, testes
luteinizing hormone (LH)	ovaries, testes
prolactin (PRL)	mammary glands
melanocyte-stimulating hormone (MSH)	melanocytes in skin
Posterior lobe	
oxytocin	uterus, mammary glands
antidiuretic hormone (ADH)	kidneys

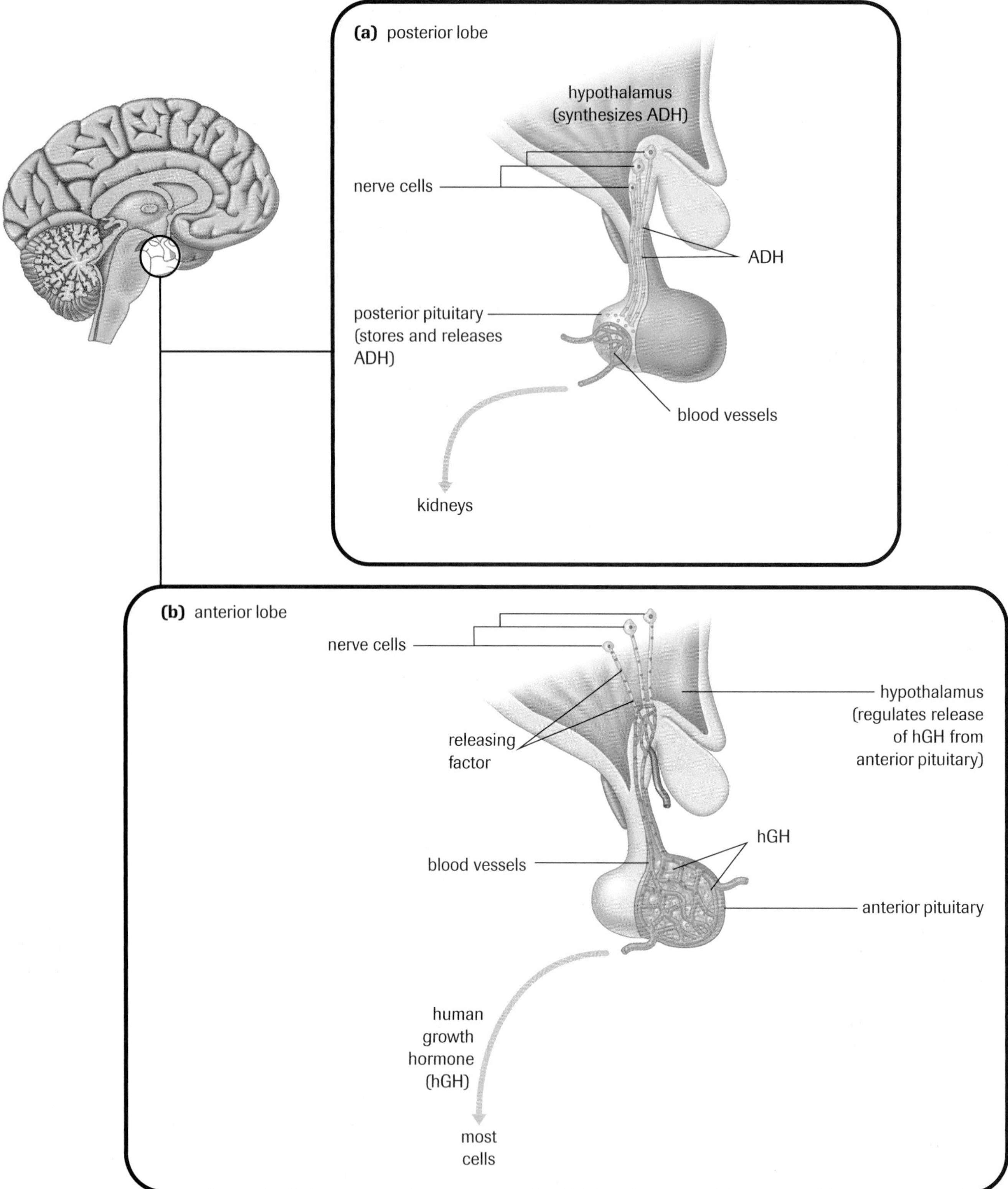

Figure 9
The pituitary gland is composed of two separate lobes: the posterior lobe and the anterior lobe.

(a) In this example, the cells of the hypothalamus synthesize antidiuretic hormone (ADH), which travels from the hypothalamus to the pituitary along specialized nerve cells. The ADH molecules remain in the pituitary gland and are released into the blood when they are needed.

(b) Releasing and inhibiting factors secreted by nerve cells of the hypothalamus travel along blood vessels to the anterior pituitary where they regulate the secretion of hormones such as hGH.

Using Recombinant DNA Technology to Produce Hormones

Genetic engineering involves extracting genes from human chromosomes and inserting them into bacteria, which then synthesize the human gene product. Recombinant DNA technology has been widely used by drug companies to produce human hormones.

Human growth hormone (hGH) can be produced by this technology. Normally produced by the pituitary, hGH primarily promotes the growth of bone and muscle. Lower than normal concentrations can cause dwarfism, extreme fatigue, anxiety, and malaise. One estimate indicates that 3 in 10 000 people have a serious deficiency of hGH.

Humans do not respond to animal growth hormone, and hGH has to be extracted from cadavers, of which there is a limited supply. Only a minute quantity of hGH can actually be extracted from the pituitary of a cadaver. In addition, the brain tissue from a cadaver might have been infected with a disease-causing agent such as the infectious protein that causes Creutzfeldt-Jacob disease, the human equivalent of mad cow disease. In 1985, recombinant DNA human growth hormone (rhGH) first became available.

Although rhGH provides a ready supply of hormone, its use has raised many ethical questions. Should rhGH be available only to children who have dwarfism or to any child that might want to be taller? Should dwarfism be treated as a disease, or viewed as one part of human diversity?

SUMMARY Homeostasis, Hormones and the Endocrine System

- Homeostasis is the body's attempt to keep all its systems operating within normal limits in a fluctuating environment.
- The endocrine system and nervous system work together to maintain homeostasis.
- All homeostatic control systems have three functional components: a receptor, a coordinating centre, and an effector.
- Negative feedback mechanisms trigger a response that reverses the changed condition; positive feedback mechanisms move the controlled variable even farther away from a steady state.
- The hypothalamus controls the production of pituitary hormones.

Section 15.1 Questions

1. Differentiate between positive and negative feedback systems.
2. Use **Figure 10** to explain homeostasis.

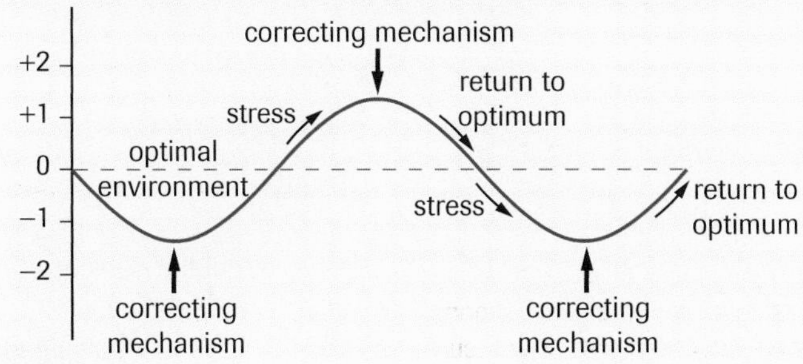

Figure 10

3. What are target tissues or organs?
4. Explain how the nervous system and endocrine system are specialized to maintain homeostasis.
5. Compare water-soluble and fat-soluble hormones.
6. Compare the anterior and posterior lobes of the pituitary. How are they similar and how are they different?
7. Some scientists have speculated that certain young female Olympic gymnasts may have been given growth hormone inhibitors. Why might the gymnasts have been given growth inhibitors? Do you think hormone levels should be altered to regulate growth patterns?
8. Compare the cells of the hypothalamus to cells of the pituitary.

15.2 Hormones That Affect Blood Sugar

islets of Langerhans hormone-producing cells of the pancreas; these cells are part of the endocrine system

glucagon hormone produced by the pancreas; when blood sugar levels are low, glucagon promotes conversion of glycogen to glucose

Two members of the endocrine system affect blood sugar levels in humans: specific cells in the pancreas and the adrenal glands. The pancreas contains two types of cells: one type that produces digestive enzymes and a second type that produces hormones. The hormone-producing cells are located in structures called the **islets of Langerhans**, named after their discoverer, German scientist Paul Langerhans. More than 200 000 tiny islets, each containing thousands of cells, are scattered throughout the pancreas. The islets contain beta and alpha cells that are responsible for the production of two hormones: insulin and **glucagon**.

Insulin is produced in the beta cells of the islets of Langerhans and is released when the blood sugar level increases. After a meal, the blood sugar level rises and an appropriate amount of insulin is released (**Figure 1**). The insulin causes cells of the muscles, the liver, and other organs to become permeable to the glucose. Also, in the liver, glucose is

EXTENSION

Hormones and Blood Glucose Regulation

In this audio clip, you can hear a discussion of how specific hormones work together to maintain blood glucose homeostasis.

www.science.nelson.com GO

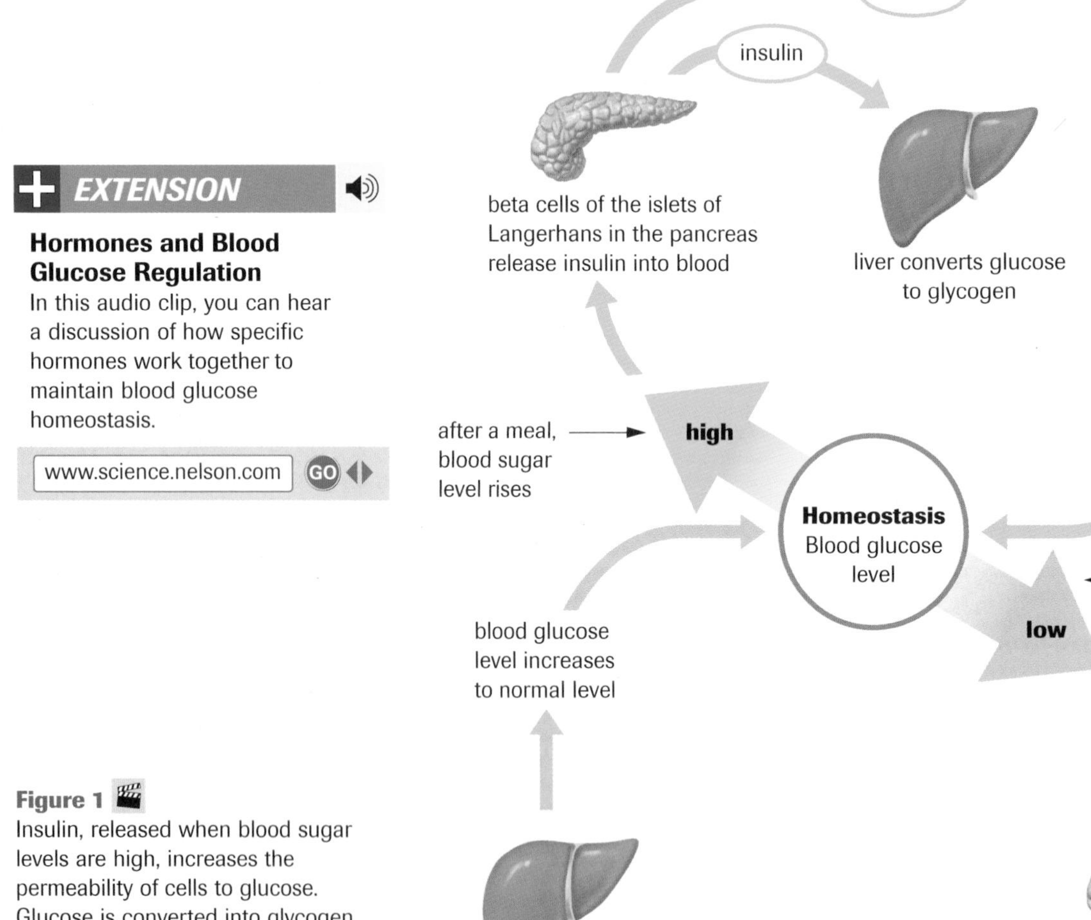
insulin
insulin
beta cells of the islets of Langerhans in the pancreas release insulin into blood
liver converts glucose to glycogen
body cells become permeable to glucose
blood glucose level decreases to normal level
after a meal, blood sugar level rises
high
Homeostasis
Blood glucose level
low
after fasting, blood sugar level is low
blood glucose level increases to normal level
liver converts glycogen to glucose and releases it into blood
alpha cells of the islets of Langerhans in the pancreas release glucagon into blood
glucagon

Figure 1
Insulin, released when blood sugar levels are high, increases the permeability of cells to glucose. Glucose is converted into glycogen within the liver, thereby restoring blood sugar levels. Glucagon, released when blood sugar levels are low, promotes the conversion of liver glycogen into glucose, thereby restoring blood sugar levels.

converted into glycogen, the primary storage form for glucose. This enables the blood sugar level to return to normal. In this way, insulin helps maintain homeostasis.

Glucagon and insulin work in a complementary fashion. Insulin causes a decrease in the blood sugar level, and glucagon causes an increase in the blood sugar level. Produced by the alpha cells of the islets of Langerhans, glucagon is released when blood sugar levels are low, such as after periods of fasting. Glucagon promotes the conversion of glycogen to glucose, which is released into the blood. As glycogen is converted to glucose in the liver, the blood sugar level returns to normal.

Diabetes

Diabetes is a chronic disease with no cure that affects more than two million Canadians. It is caused by insufficient production or use of insulin. When left untreated, it can cause blindness, kidney failure, nerve damage, and nontraumatic limb amputation.

diabetes chronic disease in which the body cannot produce any insulin or enough insulin, or is unable to use properly the insulin it does make

Without adequate levels of insulin, blood sugar levels rise very sharply following meals. This condition is known as hyperglycemia, or high blood sugar (from *hyper*, meaning "too much"; *glyco*, meaning "sugar"; and *emia* referring to a condition of the blood). The kidneys are unable to reabsorb all the blood glucose that is filtered through them, so the glucose appears in the urine. Since high concentrations of glucose in the nephrons draw water out of the plasma by osmosis, people with diabetes excrete unusually large volumes of urine and are often thirsty.

People with diabetes often feel tired. Remember that insulin causes cells to become permeable to glucose. Despite the abundance of glucose in the blood, little is able to move into the cells. The cells must turn to other sources of energy. Fats and proteins can be metabolized for energy, but, unlike carbohydrates, they are not an easily accessible energy source. The switch to these other energy sources creates a host of problems. Acetone, an intermediate product of excessive fat metabolism, can be produced. In severe cases, the smell of acetone can be detected on the breath of these people.

There are three main types of diabetes mellitus. Type 1 diabetes (formerly known as juvenile-onset diabetes) occurs when the pancreas is unable to produce insulin because of the early degeneration of the beta cells in the islets of Langerhans. It is usually diagnosed in childhood, and people who have it must take insulin to live (**Figure 2**). Approximately 10 % of people with diabetes have type 1 diabetes.

Type 2 diabetes (sometimes referred to as adult-onset diabetes) is associated with decreased insulin production or ineffective use of the insulin that the body does produce. It is usually diagnosed in adulthood and can be controlled with diet, exercise, and oral drugs known as sulfonamides (which are ineffective against type 1 diabetes). About 90 % of people with diabetes have type 2 diabetes.

A third type of diabetes, gestational diabetes, is a temporary condition that occurs in 2 % to 4 % of pregnancies. It increases the risk of type 2 diabetes in both mother and child.

DID YOU KNOW ?

Hypoglycemia

When the blood sugar level falls below normal, a condition known as hypoglycemia occurs. Hypoglycemia can be caused by too much insulin or too little glucagon.

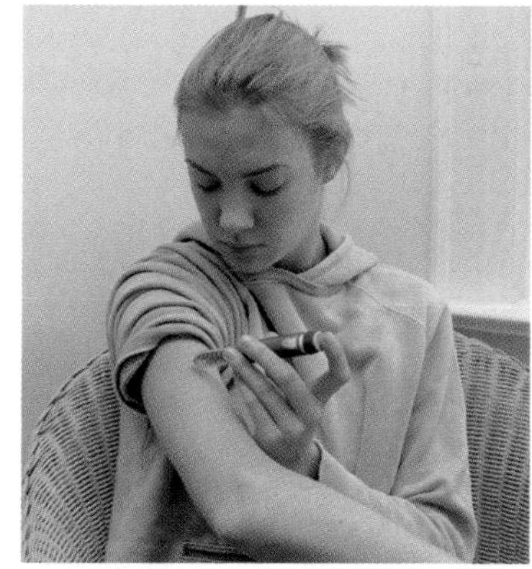

Figure 2
The pen is the newest way of injecting insulin. It is portable, accurate, and easy to use.

Practice

1. How does insulin regulate blood sugar levels?
2. How does glucagon regulate blood sugar levels?
3. Using a flow chart, show a homeostatic adjustment for a person who has consumed a significant amount of carbohydrates in the past hour.

INVESTIGATION 15.1 *Introduction*

Identification of Hyperglycemia

How is urinalysis used to identify diabetes? In this investigation, you will use simulated urine samples to identify diabetes.

Report Checklist

- Purpose
- Problem
- Hypothesis
- Prediction
- Design
- Materials
- Procedure
- Evidence
- Analysis
- Evaluation
- Synthesis

To perform this investigation, turn to page 498. 

Figure 3
Dr. Charles Best (left) and Dr. Frederick Banting (right)

WEB Activity

Canadian Achievers—Banting and Best

Working together at the University of Toronto, Dr. Frederick Banting and Dr. Charles Best (**Figure 3**) were able to isolate insulin and to then use the hormone as the first successful treatment of diabetes. Follow the links on the Nelson Web site to learn more about the remarkable work of these two scientists.

www.science.nelson.com 

Islet Cell Transplants

Type 1 diabetes is the second leading cause of blindness in Canada. Other side effects of the disease, such as kidney and heart failure, stroke, and peripheral nerve damage, affect more than 50 000 Canadians. Although insulin injections provide some regulation of blood sugar, they do not necessarily prevent many of the serious complications of diabetes.

Transplanted islet cells, however, could replace the body's natural mechanism for monitoring and producing insulin. Unlike insulin therapy, islet cell transplantation holds the potential to reverse the effects of diabetes. One of the main barriers to successful clinical islet transplantation is immune rejection. Current anti-rejection drugs are toxic and harmful to islet function, and immunosuppression leaves the recipients susceptible to invading microbes.

Researchers around the world are searching for solutions. A team of researchers at the University of Alberta has pioneered a treatment—known as the Edmonton Protocol—designed by Dr. James Shapiro, director and head of the Clinical Islet Transplant Program (**Figure 4**, next page). The treatment uses a combination of three drugs to prevent rejection of the transplanted islets and to prevent diabetes from returning. The success of the treatment depends on new methods of isolating and transplanting pancreatic cells.

Unlike other types of transplant surgery, the technique used for islet transplants presents few risks. Islet cells are extracted from the pancreas of a donor and infused into the recipient's liver by way of a large vein. The surgeon uses ultrasound to see the vein leading into the liver, the skin is frozen, and a syringe is used to put the new cells in place. The patient can usually return home the next day. The liver is used because, when damaged, it is able to regenerate itself by building new blood vessels and cells. New blood vessels and nerve cells connect to the transplanted islets in the liver and eventually produce enough insulin to control blood sugar.

CAREER CONNECTION

Licensed Practical Nurse

Licensed Practical Nurses provide health care in a variety of community care facilities such as schools, health units, nursing homes, and hospitals. Specialized training can be obtained and combined with clinical experience to further career advancement for these health care professionals.

Do you have a caring attitude with excellent communication and interpersonal skills? Above average employment turnover is expected in this career area!

www.science.nelson.com 

Figure 4
Members of the Edmonton Protocol at the University of Alberta. The research team is also working on a procedure that would permit the transplant of islet cells into people with type 1 diabetes before the onset of physical complications, such as renal failure. A challenge regarding these transplants is finding an affordable supply of insulin-producing cells. At present, cadavers provide the only source of cells and the cost of processing islets from donors is formidable.

Web Quest—Diabetes

Diabetes is on the rise in Canada and is becoming one of the leading causes of death. Having diabetes affects individuals, their families, as well as the health-care system. In this Web Quest, you will design a primer aimed at people recently diagnosed with diabetes. Your completed primer will explore the disease, current treatments, and the latest research.

www.science.nelson.com 

Adrenal Glands

The adrenal glands are located above each kidney. (The word adrenal comes from the Latin *ad*, meaning "to" or "at," and *renes*, meaning "kidneys.") Each adrenal gland is made up of two glands encased in one shell. The inner gland, the **adrenal medulla**, is surrounded by an outer casing, called the **adrenal cortex**. The medulla is regulated by the nervous system, while hormones regulate the adrenal cortex.

The adrenal medulla produces two hormones: epinephrine (also known as adrenaline) and **norepinephrine** (noradrenaline). The nervous system and the adrenal medulla are linked by the fact that both produce epinephrine. The hormone-producing cells within the adrenal medulla are stimulated by sympathetic nerves in times of stress.

In a stressful situation, epinephrine and norepinephrine are released from the adrenal medulla into the blood. Under their influence, the blood sugar level rises. Glycogen, a carbohydrate storage compound in the liver and muscles, is converted into glucose, a readily usable form of energy. The increased blood sugar level ensures that a greater energy reserve will be available for the tissues of the body. These hormones also increase heart rate, breathing rate, and cell metabolism. Blood vessels dilate, allowing more oxygen and nutrients to reach the tissues. Even the iris of the eye dilates, allowing more light to reach the retina—in a stress situation, the body attempts to get as much visual information as possible.

The adrenal cortex produces three different types of steroid hormones: the **glucocorticoids**, the **mineralocorticoids**, and small amounts of **sex hormones**. The glucocorticoids are associated with blood glucose levels. One of the most important of the glucocorticoids, **cortisol**, increases the level of amino acids in the blood in an attempt to help the body recover from stress. The amino acids are converted into glucose by the liver, thereby raising the level of blood sugar. Increased glucose levels provide a greater

adrenal medulla found at the core of the adrenal gland, produces epinephrine and norepinephrine

adrenal cortex outer region of the adrenal gland that produces glucocorticoids and mineralocorticoids

norepinephrine also known as noradrenaline, it initiates the fight-or-flight response by increasing heart rate and blood sugar

glucocorticoid any of the steroids produced by the adrenal cortex that help to regulate electrolyte and water balance

mineralocorticoid any of the sterioids produced by the adrenal cortex that regulate carbohydrate, lipid, and protein metabolism and inhibit the release of corticotrophin

sex hormone any hormone that affects the development and growth of sex organs

cortisol hormone that stimulates the conversion of amino acids to glucose by the liver

Control of Cortisol Secretion
This animation shows how cortisol secretion is regulated by a negative feedback system.

www.science.nelson.com 

adrenocorticotropic hormone (ACTH) pituitary hormone that promotes cortisol release by the adrenal cortex; also called corticotropin

tropic hormone hormone that stimulates a specific target gland to secrete other hormones

energy source, which helps cell recovery. Any of the amino acids not converted into glucose are available for protein synthesis. The proteins can be used to repair damaged cells. In addition, fats in adipose tissue are broken down into fatty acids. Thus, a second source of energy is provided, helping conserve glucose in times of fasting. Under the influence of cortisol, blood glucose uptake is inhibited in many tissues, especially in the muscles. The brain is not affected though, since any significant decrease in glucose absorption of the brain would lead to convulsions.

Short-term and long-term stress responses are shown in **Figure 5**. The brain identifies stressful situations. The hypothalamus sends a releasing hormone to the anterior lobe of the pituitary, stimulating the pituitary to secrete **adrenocorticotropic hormone (ACTH)** (also called corticotropin). ACTH is a **tropic hormone**, which is a hormone that targets another endocrine gland. The blood carries the ACTH to the target cells in the adrenal cortex. Under the influence of ACTH, the cells of the adrenal cortex secrete mineralocorticoids and glucocorticoids (among them cortisol), which are

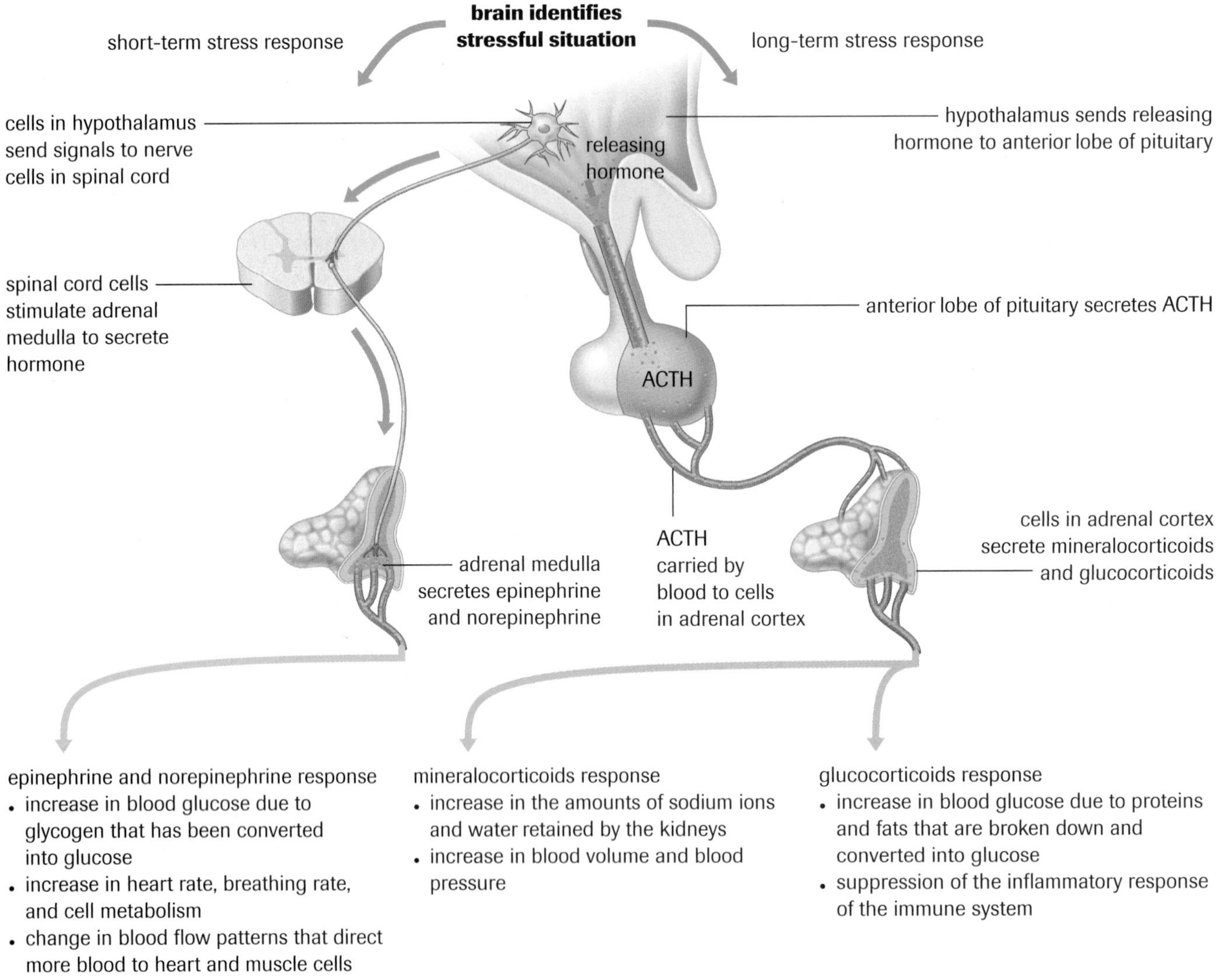

brain identifies stressful situation

short-term stress response

long-term stress response

cells in hypothalamus send signals to nerve cells in spinal cord

releasing hormone

hypothalamus sends releasing hormone to anterior lobe of pituitary

spinal cord cells stimulate adrenal medulla to secrete hormone

anterior lobe of pituitary secretes ACTH

ACTH

adrenal medulla secretes epinephrine and norepinephrine

ACTH carried by blood to cells in adrenal cortex

cells in adrenal cortex secrete mineralocorticoids and glucocorticoids

epinephrine and norepinephrine response
- increase in blood glucose due to glycogen that has been converted into glucose
- increase in heart rate, breathing rate, and cell metabolism
- change in blood flow patterns that direct more blood to heart and muscle cells

mineralocorticoids response
- increase in the amounts of sodium ions and water retained by the kidneys
- increase in blood volume and blood pressure

glucocorticoids response
- increase in blood glucose due to proteins and fats that are broken down and converted into glucose
- suppression of the inflammatory response of the immune system

Figure 5
Most of the hormones released by the adrenal cortex in response to stress affect blood sugar levels. However, mineralocorticoids do not. They affect sodium and water levels in the blood.

carried to target cells in the liver and muscles. As cortisol levels rise, cells within the hypothalamus and pituitary decrease the production of regulatory hormones, and, eventually, the levels of cortisol begin to fall. This process is called a long-term stress response. The short-term stress response is regulated by the adrenal medulla, which secretes epinephrine and norepinephrine.

Aldosterone is the most important of the mineralocorticoids. Secretion of aldosterone increases sodium retention and water reabsorption by the kidneys, thereby helping to maintain body fluid levels. You will learn more about this hormone in Section 15.3. (You will explore the third type of hormone secreted by the adrenal cortex, sex hormones, in Unit 30 B.)

aldosterone hormone produced by the adrenal cortex that helps regulate water balance by increasing sodium retention and water reabsorption by the kidneys

Practice

4. What are the similarities and differences of the adrenal cortex and the adrenal medulla?
5. What are the effects of epinephrine and norepinephrine?
6. What is the effect of cortisol?

LAB EXERCISE 15.A

Effects of Hormones on Blood Sugar Levels

Report Checklist

- ○ Purpose
- ○ Problem
- ○ Hypothesis
- ○ Prediction
- ○ Design
- ○ Materials
- ○ Procedure
- ○ Evidence
- ● Analysis
- ○ Evaluation
- ○ Synthesis

Blood sugar levels of a person with diabetes mellitus and a person without were monitored over a period of 12 h. Both ate an identical meal and performed 1 h of similar exercise.

Evidence

Use the data in **Figure 6** to answer the questions below.

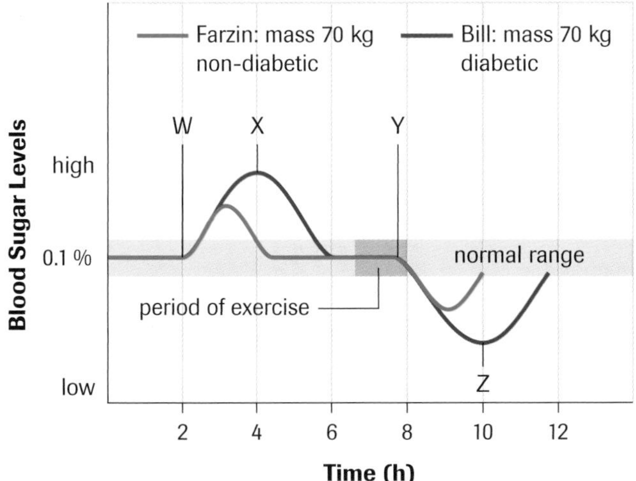

Figure 6
Blood sugar was monitored over 12 h.

Analysis

1. Which hormone injection did Bill receive at the time labelled X? Provide reasons for your answer.
2. What might have happened to Bill's blood sugar level if hormone X had not been injected? Justify your answer.
3. Explain why blood sugar levels rose at time W for Bill and Farzin.
4. Explain why their blood sugar levels begin to fall after time Y.
5. What hormone might Bill have received at time Z? Explain your answer.
6. Why is it important to note that both Farzin and Bill have the same body mass?
7. What differences in blood sugar levels are illustrated by the data collected from Bill and Farzin?
8. Formulate a hypothesis to explain why Bill and Farzin responded differently to the same environmental factors.

Hormones That Affect Blood Sugar

Table 1 Role of Hormones that Regulate Blood Sugar

Hormone	Location of hormone production	Effect
insulin	islets of Langerhans (pancreas)	• increases permeability of cells to glucose; increases glucose uptake • allows for the conversion of glucose to glycogen • brings about a decrease in blood sugar
glucagon	islets of Langerhans (pancreas)	• promotes the conversion of glycogen to glucose • brings about an increase in blood sugar
epinephrine and norepinephrine	adrenal medulla	• promotes the conversion of glycogen to glucose • brings about an increase in blood sugar • brings about an increase in heart rate and cell metabolism
cortisol (a type of glucocorticoid)	adrenal cortex	• promotes the conversion of amino acids to glucose • promotes the breakdown of fats to fatty acids • decreases glucose uptake by the muscles (not by the brain) • brings about an increase in blood sugar in response to stress

Section 15.2 Questions

1. List the hormones released from the pancreas and the adrenal glands, and indicate their control mechanisms.
2. What advantage is provided by increasing blood sugar above normal levels in times of stress?
3. How would high levels of adrenocorticotropic hormone (ACTH) affect secretions of cortisol from the adrenal glands? How would high levels of cortisol affect ACTH?
4. A number of laboratory experiments were conducted on laboratory mice. The endocrine system of mice is similar to that of humans. Brief summaries of the procedures are provided in **Table 2**.
   (a) In procedure 1, identify the gland that was removed and explain why the levels of ACTH increased.
   (b) In procedure 2, identify the hormone that was injected and explain why blood sugar levels decreased.
   (c) In procedure 3, identify the hormone that was affected and explain why urine production increased.
   (d) In procedure 4, identify the hormone that was injected and explain why blood glucose levels increased.
5. The incidence of diabetes in North America has risen dramatically in the last few decades. Research how changes in diet have affected the incidence of diabetes in the Aboriginal population.

   www.science.nelson.com 

6. The North American lifestyle and diet are believed to be major contributors to type 2 diabetes. Many companies know that foods can be made more palatable to consumers by adding fats and sugars. Discuss the practice of adding fats and sugars to food products to increase sales.
7. Cortisol levels fluctuate throughout the day. Speculate why cortisol levels might be highest in the morning and lowest around midnight.

Table 2 Experiments Conducted on Laboratory Mice

Number	Procedure	Observation
1	gland removed	• urine output increased • Na^+ ion concentration in urine increased • ACTH level increased in blood
2	hormone injected	• blood glucose levels decreased
3	blood flow from the posterior pituitary reduced	• urine production increased
4	hormone injected	• glycogen converted to glucose in the liver • blood glucose increased

Hormones That Affect Metabolism 15.3

In this section, you will explore three different glands that affect metabolism: the **thyroid gland**, which produces the hormones triiodothyronine, thyroxine, and calcitonin; the **parathyroid glands**, which produce parathyroid hormone; and the anterior pituitary gland, which produces growth hormone (among many other regulatory hormones). The thyroid gland helps regulate body metabolism, or the rate at which glucose is oxidized. The parathyroid glands help regulate calcium levels in the blood and lower phosphate levels. Growth hormone (hGH) is one of a multitude of hormones produced by the anterior pituitary gland and influences the growth of long bones and accelerates protein synthesis.

thyroid gland a two-lobed gland at the base of the neck that regulates metabolic processes

parathyroid glands four pea-sized glands in the thyroid gland that produce parathyroid hormone to regulate blood calcium and phosphate levels

Thyroid Gland

Have you ever wondered why some people seem to be able to consume fantastic amounts without any weight change, while others appear to gain weight at the mere sight of food? Thyroid hormones and the regulation of metabolic rate can partly explain this anomaly. Approximately 60 % of the glucose oxidized in the body is released as heat. The remaining 40 % is transferred to ATP, the storage form for cell energy. This added energy reserve is often consumed during activity. Individuals who secrete higher levels of thyroid hormones oxidize sugars and other nutrients at a faster rate. Therefore, these individuals tend not to gain weight and tend to feel warm.

Individuals who have lower levels of thyroid hormones do not oxidize nutrients as quickly, and therefore tend not to break down sugars as quickly. Excess blood sugar is eventually converted into liver and muscle glycogen. However, once the glycogen stores are filled, excess sugar is converted into fat. It follows that the slower the blood sugar is used, the faster the fat stores are built up. People who secrete low amounts of thyroid hormones often experience muscle weakness, cold intolerance, and dry skin and hair. Not all types of weight gain are due to hypothyroidism (low thyroid secretions). In many cases, weight gain reflects a poor diet, lack of exercise, or genetics.

The thyroid gland (**Figure 1**) is located at the base of the neck, immediately in front of the trachea or windpipe. This gland produces two hormones, **thyroxine (T4)** and **triiodothyronine (T3)**, that regulate body metabolism and the growth and differentiation of tissues. Although both hormones appear to have the same function, approximately 65 % of thyroid secretions are thyroxine. In addition to thyroid hormones, the thyroid gland produces **calcitonin**, a hormone that acts on the bone cells to lower the level of calcium found in the blood.

DID YOU KNOW ?

Hyperthyroidism

The overproduction of thyroxine by the thyroid gland results in hyperthyroidism. In hyperthyroidism, the fast oxidation of nutrients causes weight loss, elevated body temperature, and nervous behaviour. The most common cause of hyperthyroidism in Canada is an inherited disorder known as Graves' disease, or thyrotoxicosis. The condition is more common in females than in males.

thyroxine (T4) hormone produced by the thyroid gland that increases metabolism and regulates growth

triiodothyronine (T3) hormone produced by the thyroid gland that increases metabolism and regulates growth; contains three iodine atoms

calcitonin hormone produced by the thyroid gland that lowers calcium levels in the blood

(a)

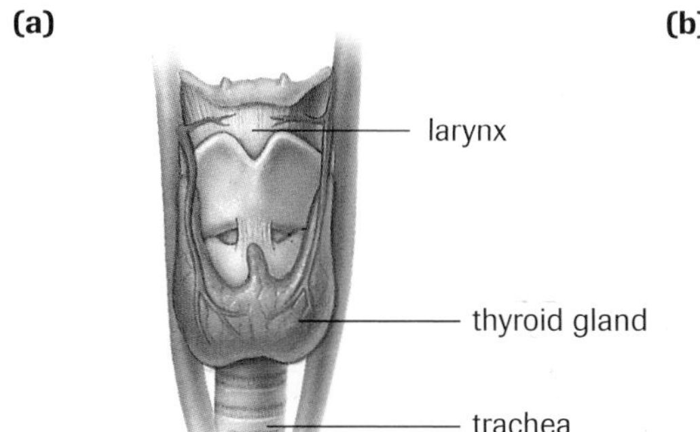

(b)

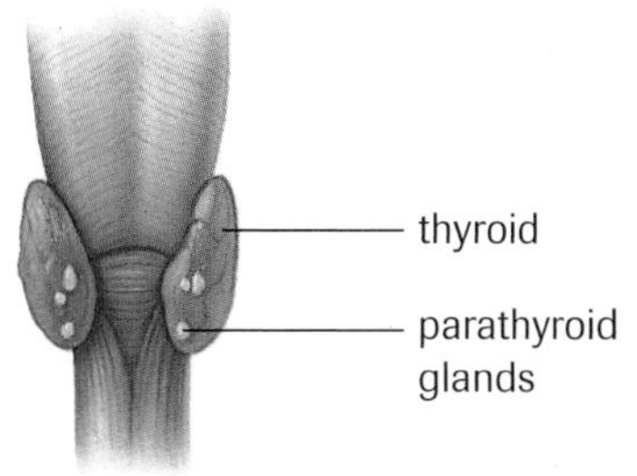

Figure 1
(a) anterior view of thyroid gland
(b) posterior view of thyroid gland

EXTENSION

Hormonal Control of Metamorphosis
In amphibians, thyroid hormones regulate the rate at which metamorphosis occurs. In this activity, you will analyze and evaluate data from five different investigations and draw conclusions about the hormonal control of metamorphosis in three species of amphibian.

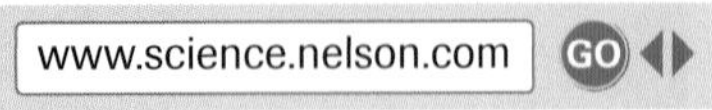

Control of thyroid hormones, like many other hormones, is accomplished by negative feedback (**Figure 2**). Should the metabolic rate decrease, receptors in the hypothalamus are activated. Nerve cells in the hypothalamus secrete thyroid-releasing hormone (TRH), which stimulates the pituitary to release thyroid-stimulating hormone (TSH). Thyroid-stimulating hormone is carried by the blood to the thyroid gland, which, in turn, releases T3 and T4. T3 and T4 raise metabolism by stimulating increased use of sugar by body cells. Higher levels of T3 and T4 and TSH cause the pathway to be "turned off." T3, T4, and TSH inhibit the release of TRH from the hypothalamus, thus turning off the production of TSH from the pituitary.

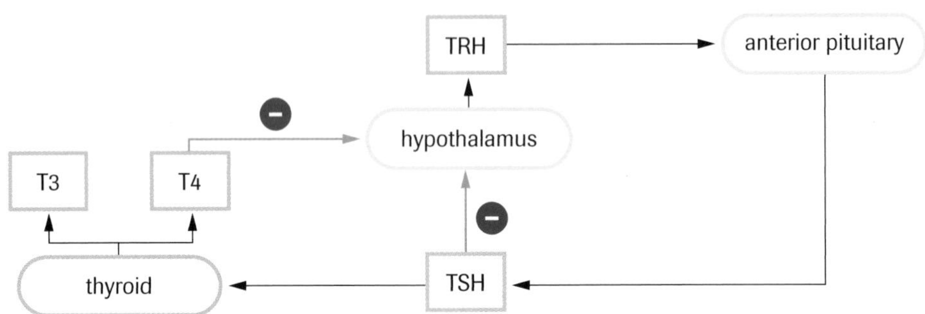

Figure 2
Feedback control loops in the secretion of thyroid hormones

Iodine is an important component of both thyroid hormones. A normal component of the diet, iodine is actively transported from the blood into the follicle cells of the thyroid. The concentration of iodine in the cells can be 25 times greater than that in the blood. Problems arise when iodine levels begin to fall. When inadequate amounts of iodine are obtained from the diet, the thyroid enlarges, producing a **goiter** (**Figure 3**).

goiter disorder that causes an enlargement of the thyroid gland

The presence of a goiter emphasizes the importance of a negative feedback control system. Without iodine, thyroid production and secretion of thyroxine drops. This causes more and more TSH to be produced and, consequently, the thyroid is stimulated more and more. Under the relentless influence of TSH, cells of the thyroid continue to develop, and the thyroid enlarges. In regions where the diet lacks iodine, the incidence of goiter remains high. In many countries, iodine is added to table salt to prevent this condition.

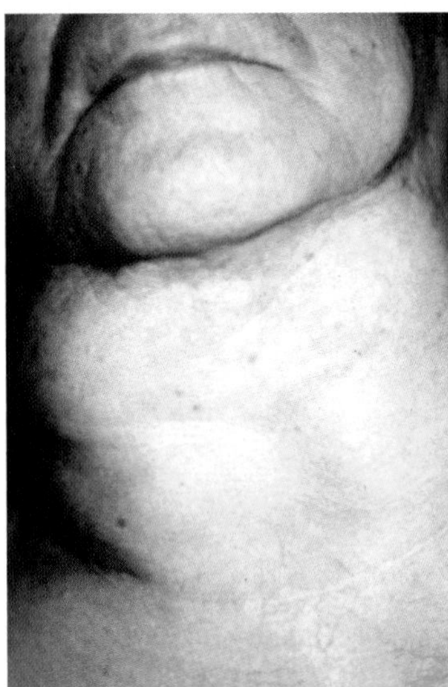

Figure 3
A goiter appears as a swelling in the neck area.

Practice

1. How does thyroxine affect blood sugar?
2. List the symptoms associated with hypothyroidism and hyperthyroidism.

Parathyroid Glands

Four small parathyroid glands are hidden within the larger thyroid gland. Before these glands were discovered, surgeons treating goiters mistakenly removed the parathyroid glands along with sections of a hyperactive thyroid gland. Although the surgery relieved symptoms associated with an overly developed thyroid gland, the patients developed more serious problems. Rapid, uncontrolled muscle twitching, referred to as tetanus, signalled abnormal calcium levels. Tetanus occurs because the nerves become easily excited.

In most cases, nerves or other hormones regulate the endocrine glands. The parathyroid glands are one of the exceptions. The parathyroid glands respond directly to chemical changes in their immediate surroundings. With involvement from the thyroid glands, the parathyroid glands keep calcium levels in homeostasis.

Low calcium levels in the blood stimulate the release of **parathyroid hormone (PTH)** from the parathyroid glands and inhibits release of calcitonin from the thyroid (**Figure 4**). A rise in PTH levels causes the calcium levels in the blood to increase and phosphate levels to decrease. The hormone does this by acting on three different organs: the kidneys, the intestines, and the bones. PTH causes the kidneys and intestines to absorb more calcium while promoting calcium release from bone. (Approximately 98 % of the body's calcium is held in storage by the skeletal system.) The bone cells break down, and calcium is separated from phosphate ions. The calcium is reabsorbed and returned to the blood, while the phosphate is excreted in the urine. This helps conserve much of the body's calcium that is dissolved in plasma. PTH also enhances the absorption of calcium from undigested foods in the intestine. So, as PTH levels increase, the absorption of calcium ions also increases.

parathyroid hormone (PTH) hormone produced by the parathyroid glands, which will increase calcium levels in the blood and lower the levels of phosphates

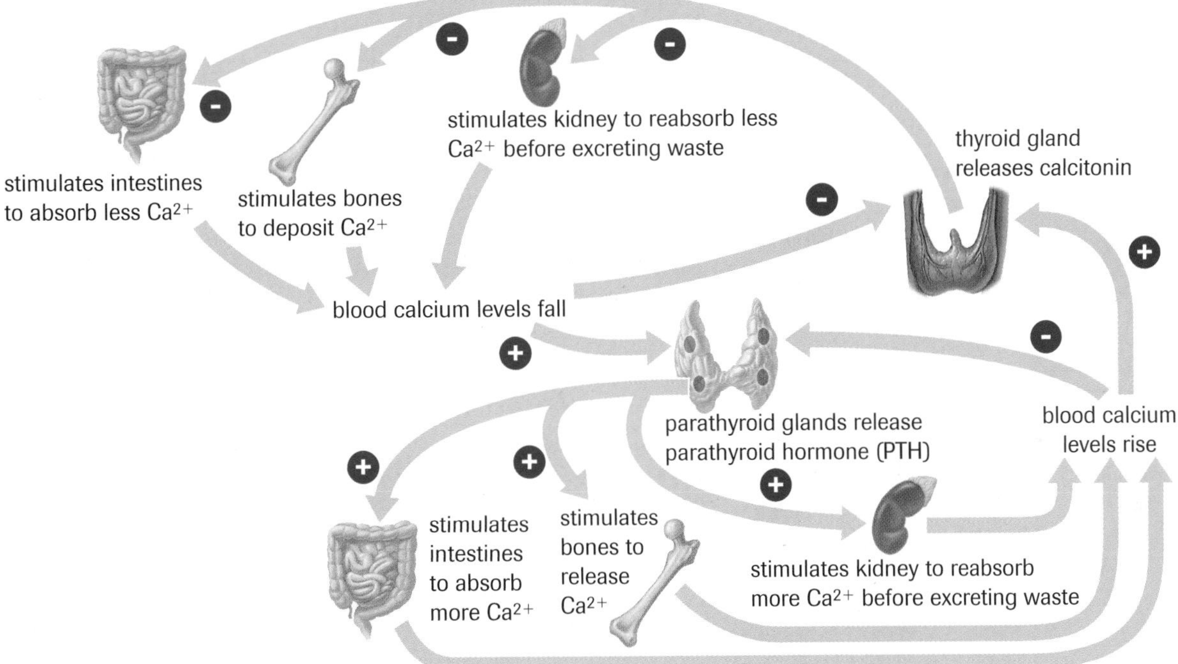

Figure 4
Low levels of blood calcium stimulate release of PTH from the parathyroid glands and inhibits release of calcitonin from the thyroid. PTH causes the kidneys and gut to retain calcium while promoting calcium release from bone. This causes blood calcium levels to rise, which in turn inhibits release of PTH from the parathyroid glands and stimulates release of calcitonin from the thyroid. Calcitonin causes the kidneys and gut to release calcium, while inhibiting calcium release from bone.

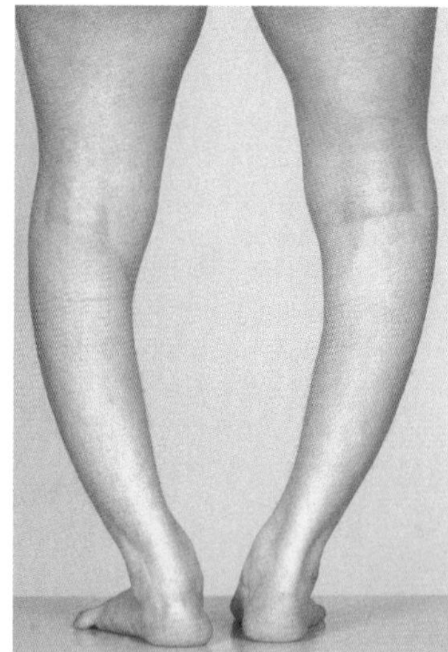

Figure 5
Improper bone formation can result from a diet lacking in fruits and vegetables.

Once calcium levels have risen, release of PTH is inhibited and release of calcitonin is stimulated. This causes the intestines, kidneys, and bones to reduce the amount of calcium they release to the blood, and calcium levels then begin to fall. This part of the feedback mechanism involving PTH and calcitonin ensures the blood calcium levels will not increase beyond the body's needs. Abnormally high levels of PTH or low levels of calcitonin can cause health problems. A strong, rigid skeleton is necessary for support, so prolonged breakdown of bone is dangerous. High calcium levels can cause it to collect in blood vessels or to form hard structures in the kidneys called kidney stones.

PTH also helps activate vitamin D. Low levels of vitamin D can cause a disease called rickets (**Figure 5**). With this disease, too little calcium and phosphorus are absorbed from foods and the bones develop improperly.

Growth Hormone (hGH)

Growth hormone (hGH) is produced by the anterior pituatary gland, and stimulates the elongation of the skeleton. The effects are most evident when the body produces too much (hypersecretion) or too little of it (hyposecretion). Hyposecretion of hGH during childhood can result in dwarfism; hypersecretion during childhood can result in gigantism. Hypersecretion in adulthood causes acromegaly, an abnormal bone growth in the hands, feet, and head. Although hGH affects most of the cells of the body, the effect is most pronounced on cartilage cells and bone cells.

Under the influence of growth hormone, cells of soft tissues and bone begin to grow by increasing the number of cells (hyperplasia) and increasing the size of cells (hypertrophy). Growth hormone increases cell size in muscle cells and connective tissues by promoting protein synthesis while inhibiting protein degradation or breakdown. Proteins in many cells, such as muscle, are in a constant state of breakdown and repair. Amino acid uptake increases, which in turn provides the raw materials for protein synthesis. This may help explain the link between declines in growth hormone production and the aging process. As a person ages, hGH production begins to decline and cellular repair and protein replacement are compromised. As the human body ages, protein is often replaced by fat, causing changes in the body's shape.

Growth hormone also has an important role in maintaining homeostasis. It increases fatty acid levels in the blood by promoting the breakdown of fats. Muscles use the fatty acids instead of glucose as a source of metabolic fuel. By switching fuel sources from glucose to fatty acids, growth hormone causes an increase in blood glucose levels. This is especially important for glucose-dependent tissues, such as the brain. The brain is unable to use fat as an energy source. This metabolic pathway is particularly important in times of prolonged fasting where glucose supplies are limited. Growth hormone increases the use of fat stores and promotes protein synthesis, which decreases the amount of fat stored in the body. This may help explain why quick growth spurts are often accompanied by a loss of body fat.

DID YOU KNOW?

Growth Hormone: Not Just for Growth

Even in adults, growth hormone is the most abundant hormone produced by the anterior pituitary gland. In addition to promoting growth, the hormone helps adjust blood sugar in times of prolonged fasting and enhances the immune system.

SUMMARY Hormones That Affect Metabolism

Table 2 Glands and Hormones Involved in Regulating Metabolism

Gland	Hormone	Effect on metabolism
thyroid	thyroxine (T4) and triiodothyronine (T3)	• regulates the rate at which glucose is oxidized within body cells
thyroid	calcitonin	• lowers calcium levels in the blood
parathyroid glands	parathyroid hormone (PTH)	• raises calcium levels in the blood
anterior pituitary	growth hormone (hGH)	• promotes protein synthesis by increasing the uptake of amino acids by cells • causes a switch in cellular fuels from glucose to fatty acids

Section 15.3 Questions

1. How do the pituitary and hypothalamus interact to regulate thyroxine levels?
2. What is a goiter and why does it create a problem?
3. Symptoms such as weight gain, increased sensitivity to cold, fatigue, and depression can indicate the thyroid gland is not working properly.
   (a) Choose one of the symptoms above and explain how the symptom can be linked to poor thyroid function.
   (b) Explain why eating foods, such as fish, green leafy vegetables, and dairy products, which have higher levels of iodine, may be helpful in preventing thyroid problems.
   (c) Explain why individuals with thyroid problems should avoid foods that block iodine absorption, such as soy and many uncooked vegetables.
4. How does parathyroid hormone (PTH) regulate blood calcium levels?
5. Why would removal of the parathyroid glands lead to tetany?
7. How would hyposecretion of growth hormone affect an individual?
8. The purpose of the parathyroid glands is to regulate the calcium level in our bodies within a very narrow range so that the nervous and muscular systems can function properly.
   (a) A person takes some calcium tablets. Draw a feedback loop showing how PTH regulates that person's calcium levels.
   (b) Hyperparathyroidism occurs when the parathyroids make too much PTH. Explain how this would affect blood calcium levels.
   (c) Explain how would hyperparathyroidism affect a person's bones.
9. Negative feedback control systems influence hormonal levels. The fact that some individuals have higher metabolic rates than others can be explained by the response of the hypothalamus and pituitary to thyroxine. Some feedback systems turn off quickly. Sensitive feedback systems tend to have comparatively lower levels of thyroxine; less sensitive feedback systems tend to have higher levels of thyroxine. One hypothesis attempts to link different metabolic rates with differences in the number of binding sites in the hypothalamus and pituitary. How might the number of binding sites for molecules along cell membranes affect hormonal levels? How would you go about testing the theory?
10. In July 1990, Dr. Daniel Rudman published a study in the prestigious *New England Journal of Medicine* proposing that injections of growth hormone could slow the aging process. Today, antiaging enthusiasts believe that growth hormone could be an antidote to the effects of decades of aging. Although researchers warn that the drug's long-term effects have not been documented and that the drug may not be suitable for everyone, speculation about the potentials of an antiaging drug abounds in both scientific and nonscientific communities. Comment on the social implications of using a drug to slow aging.
11. Bovine somatotropin (BST) is a growth hormone now produced by gene recombination. BST can increase milk production in cows by as much as 20 % by increasing nutrient absorption from the bloodstream into the cow's milk. Should BST be used? Why might some individuals be concerned?

15.4 Hormones Affecting Water and Ion Balance

The body adjusts for increased water intake by increasing urine output. Conversely, it adjusts for increased water loss or decreased water intake by reducing urine output. These homeostatic adjustments involve the nervous system and two different hormones of the endocrine system, antidiuretic hormone (ADH) and aldosterone.

ADH and Water Balance

antidiuretic hormone (ADH) a hormone that causes the kidneys to increase water reabsorption

osmoreceptors sensory receptors in the hypothalamus that detect changes in the osmotic pressure of the blood and surrounding extracellular fluids (ECF)

The main function of **antidiuretic hormone** (**ADH**) is to conserve body water by reducing urine output. As you have learned previously, diuresis is urine formation and so antidiuresis is the stopping of urine formation, hence the name *antidiuretic* hormone.

How does the body know when to conserve water? There are sensory receptors in the hypothalamus called **osmoreceptors**, which detect changes in osmotic pressure in body fluids.

When you decrease water intake or increase water loss—by sweating, for example—blood solutes become more concentrated. This increases the blood's osmotic pressure. Consequently, water moves into the blood, causing the osmoreceptor cells of the hypothalamus to shrink (**Figure 1**). When this happens, the osmoreceptors stimulate the posterior pituitary gland to release ADH, which is carried by the bloodstream to the kidneys. ADH causes the kidneys to reabsorb more water and thus produce a more concentrated urine. Conserving water prevents the osmotic pressure of the blood from increasing any further.

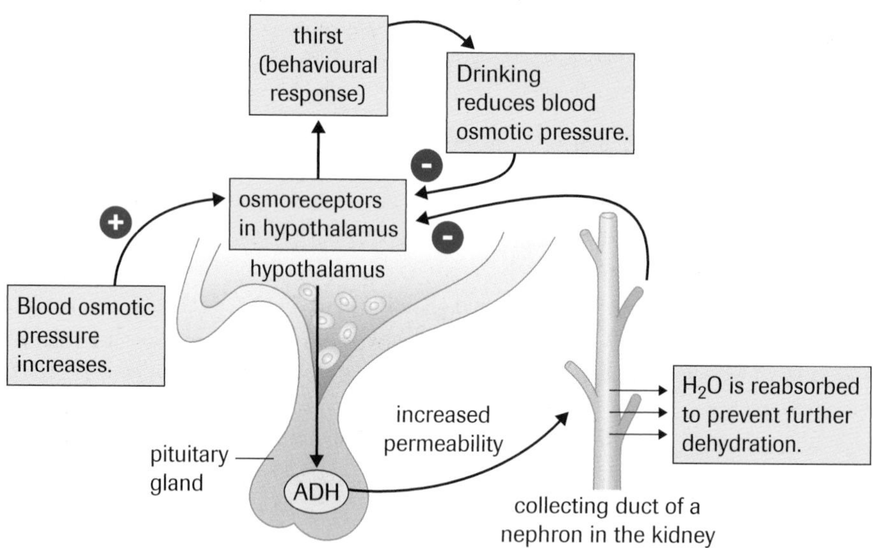

Figure 1
By increasing water reabsorption in the kidneys, ADH helps conserve body water. The osmoreceptors in the hypothalamus initiate the thirst response.

As the osmoreceptors shrink, they also stimulate the sensation of thirst. Drinking water in response to feeling thirsty is a behavioural response rather than a physiological response. As more water is taken in, it is absorbed by the blood and the concentration of solutes in the blood decreases. The greater the volume of water consumed, the lower the osmotic pressure of the blood. As the blood becomes more dilute, fluids move from the blood into the hypothalamus. As a result, the osmoreceptors swell and so they stop stimulating the pituitary gland to release ADH. As ADH levels drop, the tubules in the kidney reabsorb less water. Homeostasis is restored.

DID YOU KNOW ?

Alcohol Affects Fluid Levels

Alcohol consumption decreases the release of ADH. Some of the symptoms experienced the day following excessive alcohol consumption can be attributed to increased water loss through urine and decreased body fluid levels.

ADH and the Nephron

Approximately 85 % of the water filtered into the nephron is reabsorbed in the proximal tubule. Although the proximal tubule is very permeable to water, this permeability does not extend to other segments of the nephron (**Figure 1**, previous page). The remaining 15 % of the water filtered into the nephron will be lost if no ADH is present. ADH makes the upper part of the distal tubule and collecting duct permeable to water. When ADH makes the cell membranes permeable, the high concentration of NaCl in the intercellular spaces creates an osmotic pressure that draws water from the upper section of the distal tubule and collecting duct. As water passes from the nephron to the intercellular spaces and the blood, the urine remaining in the nephron becomes more concentrated. It is important to note that the kidneys control only the last 15 % of the water found in the nephron. By varying water reabsorption, the kidneys regulate the osmotic concentrations of body fluids.

CAREER CONNECTION 

Pharmacist

Monitoring and managing a patient's drug therapy is an essential component of pharmacists' work. They also educate caregivers and health professionals about disease management and drug research related to the health and well-being of individuals under the care of a physician. Specialized courses in biology and chemistry are required to become a pharmacist.

www.science.nelson.com  

Diabetes Insipidus

Diabetes insipidus is the most common disease associated with ADH and its main characteristic is the production of excessive amounts of urine (as much as 16 litres a day). It can be caused by the failure of the posterior pituitary to secrete enough ADH or by the failure of the kidney to respond to ADH. It is not life threatening so long as the person has enough water to drink.

Aldosterone, Blood Pressure and Blood Volume

Conditions that lead to increased fluid loss can decrease blood pressure, reducing the delivery of oxygen and nutrients to tissues. Near the glomerulus is a complex of cells called the **juxtaglomerular apparatus (JGA)**. Blood pressure receptors in the juxtaglomerular apparatus (**Figure 2**, next page) detect changes in blood pressure. When blood pressure is low, specialized cells within the structure release renin, an enzyme that converts angiotensinogen, a plasma protein produced by the liver, into angiotensin.

juxtaglomerular apparatus (JGA) a functional unit near a kidney glomerulus that controls renin release in response to changes in blood pressure

Angiotensin has two important functions. First, it causes constriction of blood vessels. Blood pressure increases when the diameter of blood vessels is reduced. Second, angiotensin stimulates the release of the hormone aldosterone from the adrenal cortex. Aldosterone is then carried in the blood to the kidneys, where it acts on the cells of the distal tubule and collecting duct to increase Na^+ reabsorption. This causes blood volume and blood pressure to increase. Not surprisingly, as Na^+ reabsorption increases, the osmotic pressure increases and more water moves out of the nephron into the blood by osmosis. This pathway is called the renin-angiotensin-aldosterone system (RAAS).

At first glance, it might appear that the role of ADH is the same as the renin-angiotensin-aldosterone system. Both increase water reabsorption. However, ADH responds to an increase in osmotic pressure of the blood. For example, when the body is dehydrated due to lack of water. The renin-angiotensin-aldosterone system responds when the blood volume is reduced but the osmotic pressure of the blood remains the same. For example, when there is a large loss of body fluid, perhaps from severe diarrhea or from a hemorrhage.

Blood Osmolarity and the Role of Antidiuretic Hormone

Listen to a discussion of blood osmolarity, and the homeostatic interactions that occur among the blood, the hypothalamus, and the collecting ducts of the kidneys.

www.science.nelson.com 

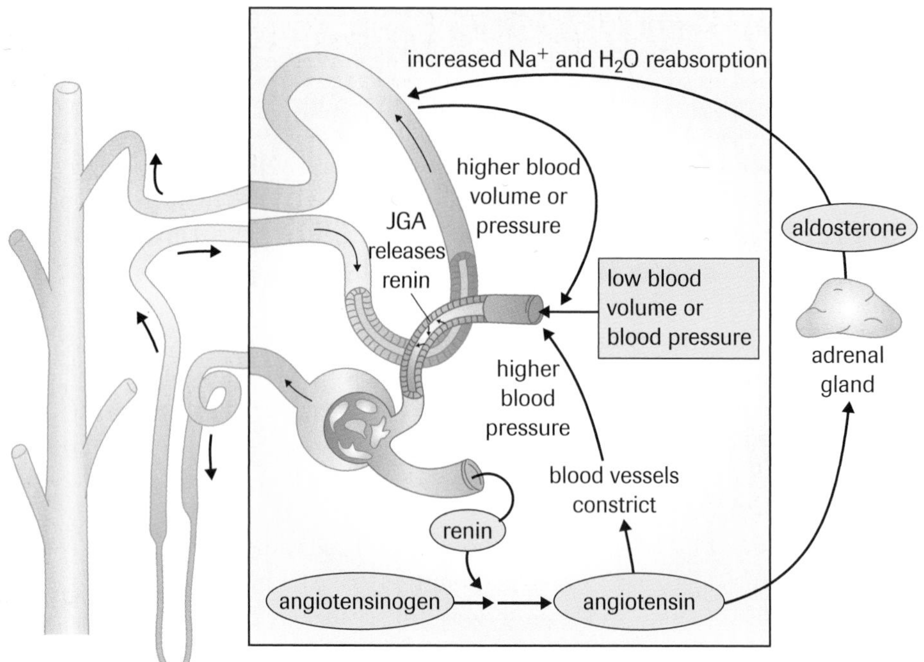

Figure 2
The hormone aldosterone maintains homeostasis by increasing Na^+ and water reabsorption.

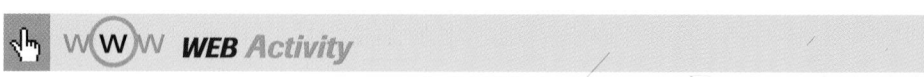

Case Study—Homeostasis and Space Travel

As humans spend more time in space, scientists have found that the microgravity environment changes the ability of the body to maintain homeostasis. Astronauts who spend substantial periods in space are at highest risk of developing hypercationa, a condition that causes kidney stone formation. Aldosterone and ADH work together to adjust urine volume and reabsorption of salts by the kidney. In this activity, you will infer the role of ADH and aldosterone from data on blood and urine composition, and relate it to the changes in homeostasis during space flight.

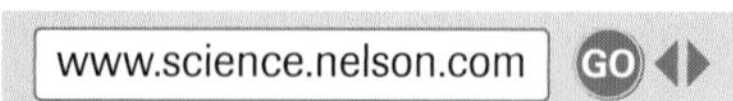

Hormones Affecting Water and Ion Balance

- Osmoreceptors in the hypothalamus stimulate the release of ADH from the posterior pituitary in response to increased osmotic pressure in the blood.
- ADH causes the distal tubules and collecting ducts of the kidneys to reabsorb more water, which makes the blood less concentrated.
- Aldosterone forms part of the renin-angiotensin-aldosterone system, which is activated by low blood pressure or low blood volume.
- Aldosterone causes the distal tubules to reabsorb more Na^+ ions and water, which increases blood volume and blood pressure.

Section 15.4 Questions

1. In **Figure 3**, labels 1 and 2 represent two hormones that directly affect the permeability of the kidney. Identify these hormones and state their functions.

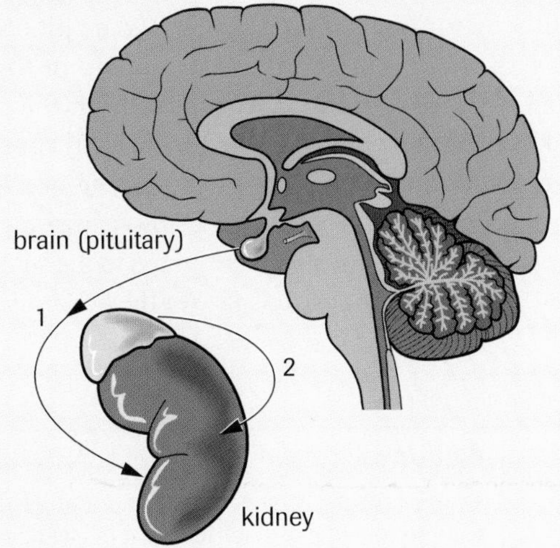

Figure 3

2. Describe the mechanism that regulates the release of ADH.
3. Where is the thirst centre located?
4. Describe the physiological adjustment to increased osmotic pressure in body fluids.
5. Discuss the mechanism by which aldosterone helps to maintain blood pressure.
6. Draw a flow chart that shows why the release of ADH is a negative feedback mechanism.
7. An experiment was performed to determine the effect of a drug, labelled X, on human metabolism. The rate of metabolism can be measured indirectly by monitoring changes in body temperature. Four comparable groups of 50 individuals each were used in the experiment. At the same time each day, all group members were given a dosage of the drug, except for group 4, which was given a placebo that did not contain the drug. Urine output and urea concentrations in urine were monitored one hour after the drug was taken. Each group member was monitored for changes in body temperature and in the volume of secretion from the thyroid gland. The observations are recorded in **Table 1**.
   (a) What controls were used for this experiment?
   (b) Identify the dependent and independent variables for this experiment.
   (c) Using the information provided, does the drug increase metabolic rate? Justify your answer.
   (d) What evidence suggests that drug X exerts a negative feedback response?
   (e) What evidence suggests that ADH and/or aldosterone were released in response to the drug?
   (f) What indirect evidence could you collect that would confirm whether aldosterone was being released?

Table 1 Effects of Different Dosages of Drug X on Metabolism

Group	Dosage of Drug X*	Change in body temp. (°C)	Perspiration	Urea g/100 mL of urine	Urine output mL	Thyroid gland output*
1	1	+0.2	slight increase	1.55	750	0.9
2	10	+0.9	moderate increase	2.01	600	9.8
3	100	+1.2	large increase	2.79	410	97.2
4	placebo	0.0	no change	1.55	810	0.0

* (10^{-6}g/50 kg of body mass)

15.5 Adjustments to Stress

Figure 1
Dr. Hans Selye (1907–1982), the Austrian-born Canadian endocrinologist, was an authority on the link between psychological stress, biochemical changes, and disease.

Dr. Hans Selye (**Figure 1**) was one of the first to identify the human response to long-term stress from a noxious stimulus. According to Selye, a general adaptation syndrome results from exposure to prolonged stress brought on by a disruption of the external and internal environment. When stressful stimulus is identified, both the endocrine system and nervous system make adjustments that enable the body to cope with the problem. The nervous system rapidly adjusts to stress by increasing heart rate and diverting blood to the needed muscles. Although somewhat slower in response, hormones from the endocrine system provide a more sustained response to the stimulus. (See **Figure 5** in Section 15.2, page 482.) **Table 1** summarizes some of the hormonal changes in response to stress.

Table 1 Hormonal Changes in Response to Stress

Hormone	Change	Adjustment
epinephrine	increases	• mobilizes carbohydrate and fat energy stores • increases blood glucose and fatty acids • accelerates heart rate and the activity of the respiratory system
cortisol	increases	• mobilizes energy stores by converting proteins to glucose • elevates blood amino acids, blood glucose, and blood fatty acids
glucagon	increases	• converts glycogen to glucose
insulin	decreases	• decreases the breakdown of glycogen in the liver

Stress hormones provide more blood glucose to cope with the elevated energy requirements brought on by stress. Remember that the primary stimulus for insulin secretion is a rise in blood glucose. If insulin release was not inhibited during a stress response, the hyperglycemia caused by stress would lead to an increased secretion of insulin, which would then lower blood glucose. Consequently, the elevated blood glucose would not be sustained to deal with the continued stress.

In addition to hormones that regulate blood sugar during stress, other hormones regulate blood pressure and blood volume. The nervous system activates the renin–angiotensin–aldosterone pathway in response to reduced blood flow to the kidneys. By increasing Na^+ reabsorption, the kidneys help maintain increased fluid volume. This helps sustain adequate blood pressure during stress. In addition, the stressor activates the hypothalamus, which causes an increased release of antidiurectic hormone (ADH). ADH will further increase water reabsorption from the nephron to help maintain body fluids.

During athletic competition, the accelerated cardiovascular activity provides greater oxygen delivery to the tissues for cellular respiration. Increases in blood sugar and fatty acid levels provide more fuel for metabolic processes. In turn, the greater supply of reactants can provide more ATP for activity.

It is more difficult to adjust to emotional or psychological stress because the increased energy supply is not always used. Although increased nerve activity requires greater energy, the ATP provided by homeostatic adjustment often outstrips demand. Prolonged exposure to high blood glucose, high blood pressure, and an elevated metabolic rate often causes a readjustment of control systems to permit the higher operating range. As shown in **Table 2**, operating with elevated blood sugar, blood pressure, and heart rate creates more problems for the body.

Table 2 Problems Associated with Long-Term Stress

New operating limit	Problem created
higher blood sugar	• alters osmotic balance between blood and extracellular fluids; can lead to increased fluid uptake by the blood and increased blood pressure • increased water loss from nephron
increased blood pressure	• possible rupture of blood vessels due to higher pressure • increased blood clotting
increased heart rate	• can lead to higher blood pressure • possible destruction of heart muscle

Prostaglandins

Prostaglandins are a group of hormones, but unlike other hormones, they do not travel to other sites in the body. They act on the cells that produced them, and virtually all cells in the body produce them. When a tissue is damaged (stressed), the tissue's cells produce prostaglandins in response. Prostaglandins stimulate inflammation at the damage site, increase blood flow, and stimulate platelets to form clots in damaged blood vessels. They also play a role in producing a fever and cause an increase in the perception of pain.

prostaglandins a group of hormones that act on the cells that produce them in response to cell damage; produced by most cells

Interestingly, aspirin is an effective reducer of fever, pain, and inflammation. It does this by blocking enzyme involved in prostaglandin production. Because aspirin reduces prostaglandin production, blood does not clot as easily. Thus aspirin is often prescribed to prevent clotting in people with heart disease. One of the downsides of aspirin is that if a person is injured while taking it, they may bleed more profusely.

Chemically Enhanced Sports Performance

Strenuous exercise places stress on body systems, which compensate by delivering more fuel and oxygen to the tissues. Long before they were used in sport, ancient people documented how different drugs could mirror hormones produced by the body to affect heart rate, breathing rate, and blood pressure. Caffeine, for example, was found to produce many of the same effects as epinephrine (adrenaline), by increasing heart rate, blood pressure, and alertness.

The quest to gain an advantage began in the 1950s when weight lifters began injecting themselves with **anabolic steroids**. Anabolic steroids are designed to mimic many of the muscle-building traits of the sex hormone testosterone. Although still controversial, some have reported that anabolic steroids can provide athletes with greater lean muscle development and increased strength and, therefore, are advantageous for weightlifting and shorter sprints. However, anabolic steroids do not provide increased agility or skill level, nor do they enhance the ability of the cardiovascular system to deliver oxygen. In fact, they would be detrimental to athletes who need to sustain a high level of aerobic activity over a longer duration, such as marathon runners or cyclists. Although some athletes claim that steroids provide faster recovery from injury, and, therefore, allow more rigorous training, these claims have not been conclusively proven by laboratory studies. Whether advantageous or not, these types of drugs have been banned from competitive sports. During the 1988 Olympics, Canadian sprinter Ben Johnson was disqualified and stripped of a gold medal for using Stanozolol, an anabolic steroid.

anabolic steroids substances that are designed to mimic many of the muscle-building traits of the sex hormone testosterone

A number of health risks have been linked to the extended use of large dosages of anabolic steroids (**Figure 2**). Of particular interest to teens is that anabolic steroids prematurely fuse growth plates in the long bones, thereby reducing the height potential of the individual. Psychological effects, such as mood swings and feelings of rage, have also been documented.

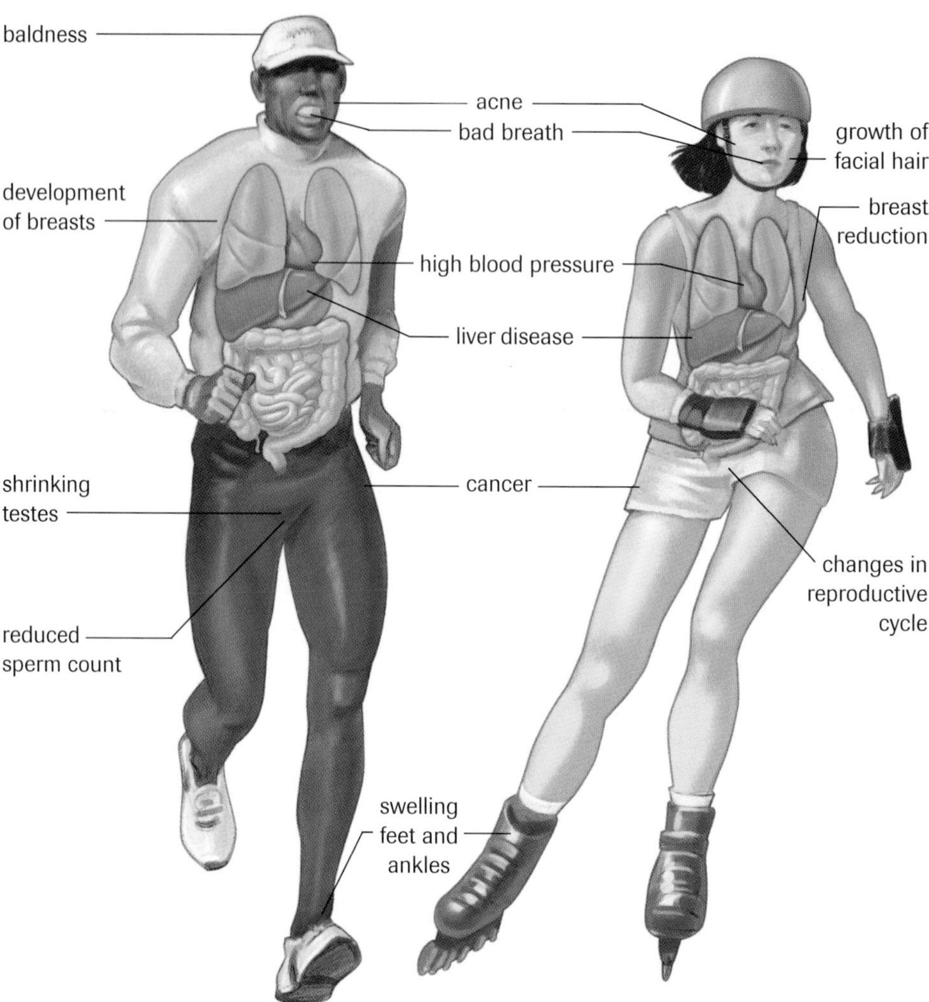

Figure 2
Effects of prolonged anabolic steroid use

Today, athletes have access to a myriad of drugs that do more than just increase strength. Sharpshooters and archers have used beta blockers to slow the heartbeat, which helps to steady their aim and calm jangled nerves. Endurance athletes can gain an advantage by taking erythropoietin (EPO). Human growth hormone decreases fat mass and promotes protein synthesis for muscle development; the enhancement of repair and growth increases strength and permits more vigorous training.

Because the body naturally produces hGH and EPO, they are difficult to detect with standard testing methods. More sophisticated methods must be used to detect small chemical differences between natural and artificial growth hormone. (Artificial growth hormone is synthesized by genetically modified bacteria.) Esters of testosterone are another group of muscle-building drugs that are difficult to detect. The esters slow the metabolism of testosterone by the body, keeping it in the body longer. Normally, testosterone would be metabolized in a few hours. The ester and testosterone raise little suspicion when testing is performed because both occur naturally in the body.

EXPLORE an issue

Protecting Athletes

Issue Checklist

○ Issue ○ Design ● Analysis
● Resolution ● Evidence ● Evaluation

Winning high-profile sporting competitions such as the Tour de France or Olympic events can be worth millions of dollars in endorsements to the winner (in addition to the fame and adoration they receive in their home countries). It is not surprising that athletes will do almost anything to gain an advantage over their competitors.

Drug testing began at the 1968 Olympics, a year after a British cyclist died of heart failure at the Tour de France after taking a stimulant. The International Olympic Committee (IOC) banned the use of anabolic steroids in 1975. But detection methods did not keep pace with masking agents. A sensitive test for steroids was finally developed in 1983. In 1990, the IOC added testosterone and caffeine to its banned substance list.

Today the most prevalent banned substances are synthetic hormones such as erythropoietin (EPO) (mentioned in the Chapter 15 introduction, page 468). A recombinant version of EPO was originally developed to treat renal failure in dialysis patients. However, some athletes now use it to gain a competitive edge. EPO has been linked to deaths of cyclists, cross-country skiers and runners. In 2006, cyclist Floyd Landis was stripped of his title of winner of the Tour de France when tests revealed he had been taking a synthetic form of testosterone.

Statement

Not enough is being done to prevent the use of banned substances in sports.

In your group, research the issue. Search for information in newspapers, periodicals, CD-ROMs, DVDs, and on the Internet.

www.science.nelson.com 

- Prepare a list of points and counterpoints for your group to discuss. You might consider these questions:
  (i) Are some countries complicit in helping athletes hide positive drug tests? Are athletes being sacrificed for national glory?
  (ii) Are organizers of events compromised in their desire to identify users of banned substances by continually pushing for more records?
  (iii) What improvements could be made to help eliminate banned drugs from athletics?
- Develop and reflect on your opinion.
- Communicate your views in an appropriate manner.

SUMMARY Adjustments to Stress

- The endocrine and nervous systems interact to help the body cope with stress.
- Prostaglandins are produced by cells that have been damaged and they produce a variety of physiological effects in the damaged cells.
- Anabolic steroids are one of many chemicals used to enhance athletic performance.

Section 15.5 Questions

1. Both the nervous system and endocrine system respond to stress. Explain the benefits of each system's response.
2. Explain what advantage is gained by elevating blood sugar and blood pressure in times of stress.
3. Why is the secretion of insulin reduced in times of stress?
4. Explain the roles of the adrenal medulla and adrenal cortex in times of stress.
5. What are prostaglandins?
6. You have received a bad wound on your arm. Describe the effects prostaglandins have on the wounded area.
7. What are anabolic steroids? Outline their benefits to an athlete and their dangerous side effects.
8. Explain why a marathon runner would be unlikely to take growth hormone or anabolic steroids.
9. Why would erythropoietin (EPO) give an athlete competing in an endurance event an unfair advantage?
10. Why is it difficult to detect banned drugs like growth hormone and EPO?
11. The International Olympic Committee has banned performance-enhancing drugs. Research the classes of banned drugs. Describe the advantages and side effects of one drug in each class.

www.science.nelson.com 

INVESTIGATION 15.1

Identification of Hyperglycemia

In this investigation, you will use simulated urine samples to determine how urinalysis is used to identify hyperglycemia and diabetes. Before the investigation, record the purpose of the investigation and then predict what colour(s) you expect to observe in the urine samples using Benedict's test and glucose test tape that will indicate diabetes. Outline the criteria you used to make your decision. When you have gathered and recorded the evidence, analyze it and identify any subjects that might have diabetes. Explain any other reasons there may be for a positive test.

Report Checklist

- Purpose
- Problem
- Hypothesis
- Prediction
- Design
- Materials
- Procedure
- Evidence
- Analysis
- Evaluation
- Synthesis

Problem

How is urinalysis used to identify hyperglycemia diabetes?

Materials

- safety goggles
- laboratory apron
- 4 test tubes
- wax pen
- 10 mL graduated cylinder
- Benedict's solution
- medicine dropper
- 4 samples of simulated urine
- test-tube rack
- 400 mL beaker
- beaker tongs
- hot plate
- test-tube clamp
- distilled water
- forceps
- glucose test tape

Benedict's solution is toxic and an irritant. Avoid skin and eye contact. Wash all splashes off your skin and clothing thoroughly. If you get any chemical in your eyes, rinse for at least 15 minutes and inform your teacher.

Procedure

Part 1: Benedict's Test

Benedict's solution identifies reducing sugars. Cupric ions in the solution combine with sugars to form cuprous oxides, which produce colour changes (**Table 1**).

Table 1 Benedict's Test Colour Chart

Colour of solution	Glucose concentration
blue	0.0 %
light green	0.15 %–0.5 %
olive green	0.5 %–1.0 %
yellow-green to yellow	1.0 %–1.5 %
orange	1.5 %-2.0 %
red to red-brown	2.0 %+

1. Label the four test tubes A, B, C, and D. Use a 10 mL graduated cylinder to measure 5 mL of Benedict's solution into each test tube.
2. With a medicine dropper, add 10 drops of urine from sample A to test tube A. Rinse the medicine dropper and repeat for samples B, C, and D.
3. Fill a 400 mL beaker with approximately 300 mL of tap water. Using beaker tongs, position the beaker on a hot plate. The beaker will be used as a hot-water bath. Use the test-tube clamp to place the test tubes in the hot-water bath for 5 min.
4. With the test-tube clamp, remove the samples from the hot-water bath. Record the final colours of the solutions.

Part 2: Glucose Test Tape

The reducing sugar in the urine will react with copper sulfate to reduce cupric ions to cupric oxide. The chemical reaction is indicated by a colour change of the test tape. **Table 2** provides quantitative results.

Table 2 Glucose Test Tape Colour Chart

Colour of solution	Glucose concentration
blue	0.0 %
green	0.25 %–0.5 %
green to green-brown	0.5 %–1.0 %
orange	2.0 %+

5. Clean the four test tubes and place 10 drops of distilled water into each of them.
6. Add five drops of urine to each of the appropriately labelled test tubes. Place the test tubes in a test-tube rack.
7. Use forceps to dip test tape into each of the test tubes. Record the final colours of the test tape.

INVESTIGATION 15.1 *continued*

Evaluation

(a) Describe any difficulties you had in carrying out your investigation.

(b) Explain the advantage of conducting two different tests. Which test was more appropriate? Explain your answer.

(c) Today, people with diabetes test their blood to monitor sugar levels. Explain why blood tests are preferred for people with diabetes. Why weren't blood tests carried out in this investigation?

Synthesis

(d) Why is insulin not taken orally?

(e) Explain why people with diabetes experience the following symptoms: low energy levels, large volumes of urine, the presence of acetone on the breath, and acidosis (blood pH becomes acidic).

(f) Why might the injection of too much insulin be harmful?

(g) Explain how you would help someone who had taken too much insulin.

EXTENSION

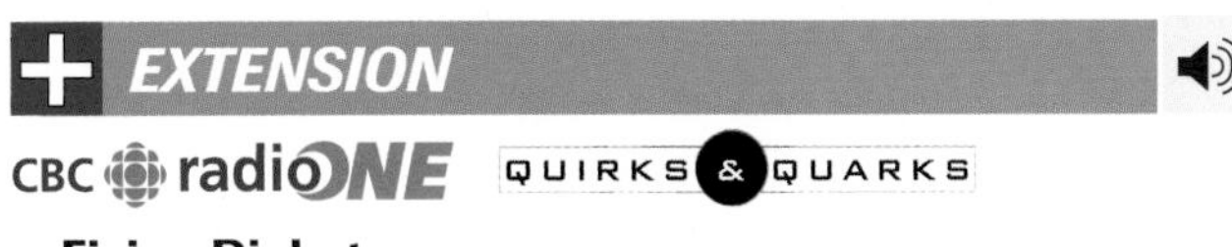

Fixing Diabetes

Dr. Alex Rabinovitch (University of Alberta) has come up with a new solution addressing the main problem of juvenile diabetes—that the insulin-producing cells, called beta cells, have been destroyed. He's found that he can expose a pancreas to certain chemical growth factors and stimulate it to produce more beta cells. This research opens up the possibility that, in the future, a diabetic will be able to stimulate her or his own pancreas to build new beta cells and regain the ability to make insulin.

www.science.nelson.com GO

Chapter 15 SUMMARY

Outcomes

Knowledge

- identify the principal endocrine glands of the human organism (15.1, 15.2, 15.3)
- describe the function of the hormones of the principal endocrine glands (15.1, 15.2, 15.3, 15.4)
- explain the metabolic roles hormones may play in homeostasis (15.2, 15.3, 15.4, 15.5)
- explain how the endocrine system allows human organisms to sense their internal environment and respond appropriately (15.1, 15.2, 15.3, 15.4, 15.5)
- compare the endocrine and nervous control systems and explain how they act together (i.e., stress and the adrenal gland) (15.2, 15.3, 15.5)
- describe, using an example, the physiological consequences of hormone imbalances (15.2, 15.3, 15.4)

STS

- explain that science and technology are developed to meet societal needs and expand human capability (15.1, 15.2, 15.5)
- explain that science and technology have both intended and unintended consequences for humans and the environment (15.1, 15.3, 15.5)

Skills

- ask questions and plan investigations by formulating a hypothesis, from published data, on an environmental factor that can be detected and responded to by humans (15.4)
- conduct investigations and gather and record data and information (15.2, 15.4)
- analyze data and apply models by: inferring the role of ADH and aldosterone in maintenance of water and ions using data on blood and urine composition (15.4); and, inferring the role of insulin in regulation of blood sugar by investigating the presence of glucose in simulated urine and comparing with normal blood glucose levels (15.2)

Key Terms

15.1

homeostasis
dynamic equilibrium
negative feedback
positive feedback
hormones
endocrine hormones
insulin
human growth hormone (hGH)
epinephrine (adrenaline)
pituitary gland
releasing hormone
inhibiting factor

15.2

islets of Langerhans
glucagon
diabetes
adrenal medulla
adrenal cortex
norepinephrine
glucocorticoid
mineralocorticoid
sex hormone
cortisol
adrenocorticotropic hormone (ACTH)
tropic hormone
aldosterone

15.3

thyroid gland
parathyroid glands
thyroxine (T4)
triiodothyronine (T3)
calcitonin
goiter
parathyroid hormone (PTH)

15.4

antidiuretic hormone (ADH)
osmoreceptors

15.5

prostaglandins
anabolic steroids

MAKE a summary

1. Sketch the human endocrine system and show how the system maintains homeostasis in response to stress. Use as many of the key terms as possible.
2. Revisit your answers to the Starting Points questions at the start of the chapter. Would you answer the questions differently now? Why?

Go To

The following components are available on the Nelson Web site. Follow the links for *Nelson Biology Alberta 20–30.*

- an interactive Self Quiz for Chapter 15
- additional Diploma Exam-style Questions
- Illustrated Glossary
- additional IB-related material

There is more information on the Web site wherever you see the Go icon in the chapter.

UNIT 30 A PERFORMANCE TASK

Determining the Effects of Caffeine on Homeostasis

In this Performance Task, you will investigate the effects caffeine has on an invertebrate and how it affects homeostasis. Go to the 30 A Performance Task link on the Nelson web site to complete this task.

www.science.nelson.com GO

Many of these questions are in the style of the Diploma Exam. You will find guidance for writing Diploma Exams in Appendix A5. Science Directing Words used in Diploma Exams are in bold type. Exam study tips and test-taking suggestions are on the Nelson Web site.

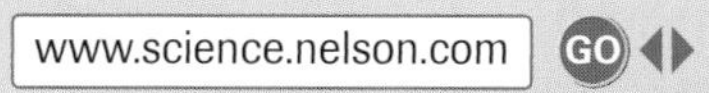

DO NOT WRITE IN THIS TEXTBOOK.

Part 1

1. Which of the following describes a negative feedback reaction?
   A. Glucagon stimulates the release of glucose from the liver, which increases blood glucose.
   B. Insulin stimulates cells to absorb glucose, which inhibits the release of insulin.
   C. The hypothalamus releases TRH, which travels to the pituitary gland initiating the release of TSH, which stimulates the release of thyroxine from the thyroid gland.
   D. Calcitonin is released from the thyroid gland and blood calcium levels decrease.

2. Glucagon is produced in an organ and affects target cells that are in another part of the body. The organ of production and the location of the target cells are, respectively,
   A. the adrenal medulla and the adrenal cortex
   B. the liver and the pancreas
   C. the pituitary and the adrenal medulla
   D. the pancreas and the liver

3. Two hormones that adjust body systems for short-term stress and long-term stress are, respectively,
   A. thyroxine and PTH
   B. estrogen and growth hormone
   C. epinephrine and cortisol
   D. TSH and epinephrine

4. A hypersecretion of growth hormone (acromegaly) in an adult would result in which of the following symptoms?
   A. decreased growth of the long bones, causing dwarfism
   B. increased growth of the long bones, causing gigantism
   C. decreased heart rate and an increased amount of fat tissue
   D. widening of the fingers and toes and broadening of the facial bones

5. A person with diabetes could be identified by which of the following symptoms?
   A. increased blood sugar and decreased urine output
   B. increased blood sugar and increased urine output
   C. decreased blood sugar and decreased urine output
   D. decreased blood sugar and increased urine output

6. A laboratory animal is accidentally given too much insulin and begins convulsing. To quickly return the animal to a normal blood sugar you could
   A. provide sugar in a fruit drink
   B. increase water intake
   C. inject erythropoietin
   D. cool the animal as rapidly as possible

7. In times of stress, under the influence of cortisol, amino acid levels increase in the blood. Why is an increase in the amino acid level in the blood beneficial as a response to stress?
   A. The amino acids are converted into proteins, which are used to repair cells damaged by the stress.
   B. The amino acids are converted to glucose by the liver, raising blood sugar, thereby providing more energy to deal with stress.
   C. The amino acids are converted into proteins, which provide more energy to deal with stress.
   D. The amino acids are converted to glycogen by the liver, lowering blood sugar, which stimulates the release of insulin.

8. Hypersecretion of the thyroid gland would cause a
   A. tendency not to gain weight, warm peripheral body temperature, and high energy level
   B. tendency to gain weight, cold peripheral body temperature, and high energy level
   C. tendency not to gain weight, cold peripheral body temperature, and low energy level
   D. tendency to gain weight, warm peripheral body temperature, and low energy level

9. NR Humans respond to stress by secreting ACTH, which causes an increase in blood sugar levels. In your notebook, place the correct number from **Figure 1** above the appropriate step. (Record all four digits of your answer.)

______	______	______	______
Nerve message signals stress.	Gland secretes ACTH.	Target organ for ACTH.	Organ responds to increased blood sugar.

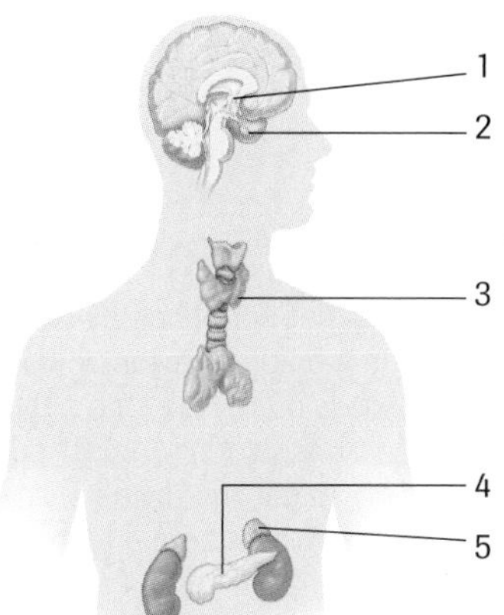

Figure 1

10. The thyroid disorder referred to as goiter is caused by
    A. low levels of TSH, which stimulate thyroid development
    B. low levels of thyroxine, which stimulate thyroid development
    C. decreased thyroxine due to decreased dietary iodine
    D. decreased TSH due to decreased dietary iodine

11. The body responds to a drop in blood pressure by
    A. increasing ADH production and water uptake, and decreasing urine formation
    B. decreasing ADH production and water uptake, and increasing urine formation
    C. increasing Na^+ and water reabsorption, and decreasing urine formation
    D. decreasing Na^+ and water reabsorption, and increasing urine formation

Part 2

12. **List** and **explain** the symptoms experienced by people with diabetes.
13. **Sketch** negative feedback diagrams to **illustrate** how insulin and glucagon regulate blood sugar.
14. With reference to the adrenal glands, **explain** how the nervous system and endocrine system interact in times of stress.
15. **Why** do insulin levels decrease during times of stress?
16. **Explain** the role osmoreceptors play in sensing the body's internal environment.
17. With reference to the importance of negative feedback, provide an example of **why** low levels of iodine in your diet can cause goiters.
18. DE A physician notes that individuals with a tumour on the pancreas secrete unusually high levels of insulin. Unfortunately, insulin in high concentrations causes blood sugar levels to fall below the normal acceptable range. In an attempt to correct the problem, the physician decides to inject the patient with cortisol. Write a unified response that addresses the following aspects of the cortisol treatment.
    - **Why** would the physician give the patient cortisol?
    - **Predict** the problems that might arise from this treatment.
19. A rare virus destroys cells of the anterior lobe of the pituitary. **Predict** how the destruction of the pituitary cells would affect blood sugar. **Explain.**
20. A physician notes that her patient is very active and remains warm on a cold day, even when wearing a light coat. Further discussion reveals that although the patient's daily food intake exceeds that of most people, the patient remains thin. **Why** might the doctor suspect a hormone imbalance? **Identify** which hormone the doctor might suspect.

Use the following information to answer questions 21 to 28.

Caffeine was one of the first performance-enhancing drugs used by athletes. Some people believe that it can increase endurance. Dramatic increases in caffeine levels and high consumption of caffeine have been linked with sleep disorders, impaired fine motor activities, increased fatty acid levels in the blood, and heart attacks. A study was conducted on a group of elite cyclists and a group of high school students to determine whether caffeine provided any marked advantage. Each group pedalled at 80 % maximum capacity for as long as possible. **Table 1** reveals the average amount of time each group was able to pedal after drinking decaffeinated coffee and drinking coffee with caffeine.

Table 1 Cycling Time and Caffeine Consumption in Two Groups

	Average cycling time (min)	
Group	***Decaffeinated coffee (250 mL)***	***Coffee with caffeine (250 mL, 340 mg caffeine)***
elite athletes	82	123
students	41	42

21. DE **Identify** the problem being investigated by the research group.
22. DE **Hypothesize** about the relationship between caffeine consumption and athletic endurance in non-athletes versus elite athletes.
23. DE **Identify** the control for the experiment.
24. DE **Identify** the independent and dependent variables.
25. DE **Infer** conclusions from the evidence in **Table 1**.
26. DE **Why** was neither group told which coffee contained caffeine?
27. DE The procedure does not indicate how much time passed between each exercise test. **Explain** why this is an important factor to know.
28. DE To learn more about how caffeine helps your body adjust to physical stress, you might want to monitor changes in certain hormones during testing. **Identify** hormone levels that you might want to monitor in the blood during the testing and explain what information might be gained by monitoring these hormones.

---

29. **Compare** the control system of a thermostat to the control system that regulates the body's blood sugar levels.
30. A survey by the Harvard School of Business indicated that CEOs are most often above average height. Another study commissioned by a women's magazine showed that men are attracted to taller women. **Describe** how studies such as these could lead to the misuse of recombinant growth hormone.

Many of these questions are in the style of the Diploma Exam. You will find guidance for writing Diploma Exams in Appendix A5. Science Directing Words used in Diploma Exams are in bold type. Exam study tips and test-taking suggestions are on the Nelson Web site.

www.science.nelson.com 

DO NOT WRITE IN THIS TEXTBOOK.

Part 1

1. Use the data in **Table 1**, which compares plasma components (in g/100 mL of plasma) of several patients, and the key below to answer the following question.

Table 1 Plasma Components of Five Individuals

	Urea	Uric acid	Glucose	Amino acids	Proteins
normal person	0.03	0.004	0.10	0.05	8.00
patient 1	0.03	0.004	0.50	0.05	8.00
patient 2	0.03	0.005	1.70	0.05	8.00
patient 3	0.03	0.050	0.10	0.09	8.00
patient 4	0.07	0.004	0.10	0.06	4.00

According to the data provided, which patient(s) might have diabetes mellitus?
A. patient 1
B. patient 2
C. patient 3
D. patient 4

2. Sound is measured in decibels (dB). A normal conversation registers between 60 dB and 80 dB. Street traffic is about 80 dB and a rock concert can exceed 140 dB. Permanent damage occurs at 85 dB and pain is experienced at 120 dB. Hearing loss occurs when
A. ossicles of the middle ear pierce the tympanic membrane
B. violent wave-like motions cause fluids of the inner ear to tear the round window
C. vibrations tear hair cells from the basilar membrane of the cochlea
D. fluids build up in the Eustachian tube causing great pressure on the oval window

3. Identify the pathway in a simple reflex arc.
A. sensory receptor > sensory neuron > CNS > motor neuron
B. sensory neuron > interneuron > motor neuron > muscle or gland
C. interneuron > motor neuron > muscle or gland > motor receptor
D. motor receptor > sensory receptor > CNS > muscle or gland

Use the following information to answer questions 4 and 5.

During a football game, a receiver collides with a linebacker. Both football players collide and both appear to have received serious injuries. Both athletes are X-rayed upon arriving at the hospital. The linebacker is believed to have a fractured skull resulting in extensive damage to the motor cortex of the left frontal lobe of his brain. The receiver has no broken bones but lost feeling in his lower right leg. During the examination, the doctor uses a needle to gently poke the right leg of the receiver, beginning at the foot and working slowly upward on the leg. Further tests revealed that the loss of feeling in the receiver's leg is the result of a tear in the outer neural tissue at one location of the spinal cord.

4. By poking the receiver's leg with a needle, the physician is most likely
A. trying to locate the area of the leg where muscle damage occurred
B. trying to locate the area of the spinal cord where nerve damage occurred
C. trying to locate the area of the brain where nerve damage occurred
D. trying to locate the area of the leg where muscle and nerve damage occurred

5. Indicate what the prognosis for recovery for the linebacker would be if tests continued to yield memory loss and problems with motor coordination weeks after the initial check.
A. Good: grey matter of the brain has myelinated neurons, which have some capacity for repair.
B. Good: white matter of the brain has unmyelinated neurons, which have some capacity for repair.
C. Poor: grey matter of the brain has unmyelinated neurons, which have little capacity for repair.
D. Poor: white matter of the brain has myelinated neurons, which have little capacity for repair.

6. A fighter jet banks steeply to one side as it changes direction, i.e., one wing is lower than the other. In this situation, a pilot can sometimes become briefly disoriented, thinking that "down" is still toward his or her feet, even though the orientation of the aircraft has changed. How is the disorientation corrected?
A. The otoliths provide information on head position and the direction of gravity while the semicircular canals provide information on movement.
B. The cochlea provides information on head position and the direction of gravity while the semicircular canals provide information on movement.
C. The cochlea provides information on head position and the direction of gravity while the otoliths provide information on movement.
D. The otoliths provide information on head position and the direction of gravity while the cochlear canals provide information on movement.

Use **Figure 1** to answer questions 7 and 8.

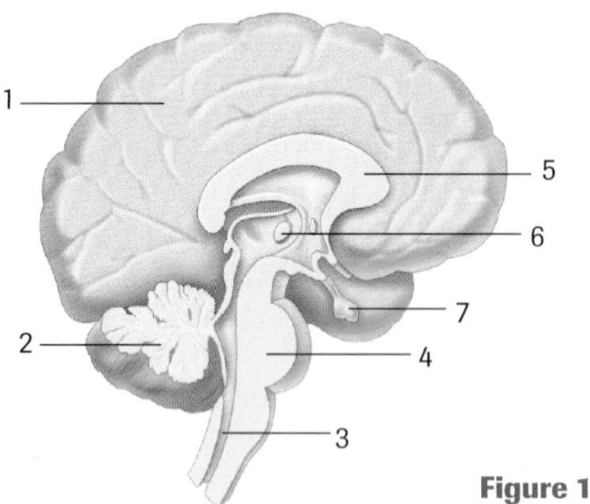

Figure 1

7. Identify the areas shown below by number. (Record all four digits of your answer.)
NR

______	______	______	______
medulla oblongata	cerebellum	corpus callosum	pons

8. The function of the area labelled 5 is to
A. communicate between the right and left hemisphere
B. coordinate sensory and motor function from the cerebellum
C. store sensory information and sequence motor activity
D. coordinate the autonomic nervous system

9. Match each of the descriptions with the appropriate hormone. (Record all four digits of your answer.)
NR
1. Released when blood Ca^+ levels are low, this hormone causes the kidneys and gut to retain calcium while promoting calcium release from the bone.
2. Released into the blood during stressful situations, this pituitary hormone is carried to the adrenal glands where it stimulates the release of glucocorticoids.
3. Anterior pituitary hormone that stimulates the male gonads to release testosterone and female gonads to release estrogen.
4. Posterior pituitary hormone that acts upon the kidneys to increase water reabsorption.

______	______	______	______
ADH	FSH	PTH	ACTH

Part 2

10. Illustrate with a flow chart how the hypothalamus and ADH regulate the water content of blood.

11. Outline in a list the organs of the endocrine system.

12. In the homeostatic process of negative feedback, the secretion of most hormones is regulated by other hormones. Using thyroxine as an example, **sketch** a flow chart to **illustrate** this process of regulation by negative feedback.

13. A person's kidneys fail to respond to ADH. **Identify** the disease he or she suffers from and **describe** the physiological consequences of the disease.

14. Compare excitatory synapses to inhibitory synapses.

15. Explain why two stimuli, applied 0.0001 s apart, would produce only one nerve impulse along the fiber of a specific neuron.

16. Cerebral palsy is a group of disorders that affects body movement and muscle coordination. It is caused by damage to, or malformation of, the brain during development in the womb or in the first few years of life. The effects of cerebral palsy vary widely, from slight awkwardness of movement or hand control to eating difficulties, poor bladder and bowel control, and breathing problems. **Identify** which area(s) of the brain are most likely affected. **Explain** your answer.

17. Describe how the kidney senses changes in blood pressure and how it responds to those changes

18. Describe how the eye adjusts its focus when changing from looking at an object far away to looking at an object close by. Include the following terms in your description: point of focus, retina, ciliary muscle, suspensory ligaments, and lens.

19. Explain in a unified response how sounds are heard. In your explanation, include the following items:
DE
- **Describe** the structures through which the sound waves and nerve impulses travel, beginning with the outer ear and ending with the cerebrum.
- **Describe** the function of each structure.

Use the following information to answer questions 20 to 22.

Prior to the work of Banting and Best, patients with type 1 diabetes mellitus usually died within months of the onset of the disease. Today, patients are treated with insulin injections; however, many of these patients do not escape insulin-related disorders brought on by the fluctuations in blood glucose levels. Changes in blood glucose may damage blood vessels, limiting circulation, which in turn can lead to blindness, kidney failure, and the destruction of muscle and nerve tissue in the hands and feet.

20. Explain why the transplant of islet cells from a donor's pancreas into a diabetic patient is a promising option.
DE

21. Describe two technological challenges presented by islet transplants.
DE

22. Describe one societal issue that researchers must face as islet transplants become more common.
DE

Use the following information to answer questions 23 to 27.

On April 26, 1986, a nuclear accident in Chernobyl caused the release of radioactive wastes into the air. The extent of the problem is still unknown, but the effects on children have been the most extreme. One of the most dangerous radioactive materials released was iodine-131, which was absorbed by the thyroid glands of children. Iodine-131 causes inflammation of the thyroid gland and can lead to cancer.

23. **Describe** some possible symptoms of children who had DE their thyroid glands completely or partially destroyed.

24. **Sketch** a feedback loop that **illustrates** how thyroxine DE levels might be affected.

25. **Explain** why children were given non-radioactive iodine. DE

26. Initially, the government tried to suppress information DE about the nuclear accident. **Describe** what should have been done.

27. Nuclear wastes were carried over the European continent DE with weather. Should surrounding countries be able to demand financial and medical compensation? **Justify** your answer.

Use the following information to answer questions 28 to 32.

A laboratory experiment was conducted to determine the effect of thyroxine on metabolic rate. Four groups of adult male rats were used. All groups were maintained in similar environments, designed to provide maximum physical activity. Each group was provided with adequate supplies of water and one of the following diets:

Diet A: food containing all essential nutrients

Diet B: food containing all essential nutrients and an extract of thyroxine

Diet C: food containing all essential nutrients and a chemical that counteracts the effect of thyroxine

Diet D: food containing all essential nutrients, except iodine

The results of the experiment appear in **Table 3**.

Table 3 Metabolism of Four Rats Fed Different Diets

Group	Average initial mass (g)	Average mass after 2 weeks of treatment (g)	Final average oxygen consumption (mL/kg/min)
I (diet A)	310	312	4.0
II (diet ?)	320	309	10.1
III (diet ?)	318	340	2.7
IV (diet ?)	315	400	2.0

28. **Hypothesize** about the relationship between the variables DE (formulate a hypothesis) for this experiment.

29. **Identify** the dependent and independent variables. DE

30. Which group was most likely used as a control? **Explain** DE your response.

31. Diet B was most likely fed to which group(s)? **Explain** your DE answer.

32. Diet D was most likely fed to which group(s)? **Explain** your DE answer.

Use the following information to answer questions 33 to 36.

Serotonin is a naturally occurring neurotransmitter that has a role in determining mood and emotions. A shortage of serotonin has been linked to phobias, schizophrenia, aggressive behaviour, depression, uncontrolled appetite, and migraine headaches. Several types of drugs, shown in **Table 4**, affect serotonin levels.

Table 4 Effects of Various Drugs on Serotonin Levels

Drug	Effect
Prozac, Paxil, Zoloft	serotonin remains longer in the brain
clozapine	prevents serotonin from binding to the postsynaptic membranes
hallucinogens (LSD, ecstasy)	react directly with the serotonin receptors to produce the same effect as serotonin

33. **Why** is Prozac (fluoxetine hydrochloride) prescribed for DE people with depression?

34. **Identify** which drug should not be taken by someone DE experiencing clinical depression.

35. **Sketch** a diagram showing the effect of LSD or ecstasy on DE serotonin.

36. **Explain** how taking hallucinogens over time could reduce DE serotonin levels.

37. The formation of amyloid plaques in the brains of people with Alzheimer's disease can cause acetylcholine levels to drop. **Explain** how an acetylcholine deficiency could cause memory loss, a common symptom of Alzheimer's disease.

38. Review the focusing questions on page 402. Using the knowledge you have gained from this unit, briefly **outline** a response to each of these questions.

unit

30 B Reproduction and Development

The 100 trillion cells of your body are truly awe-inspiring, when you think that they all started from a single, fertilized egg. They stand as proof of the ability of human cells to grow and reproduce.

Every year, approximately 350,000 babies are born in Canada. With one of the lowest child mortality rates in the world, this woman will likely have a healthy son or daughter. Improvements in diet and a better understanding of environmental risk factors, such as alcohol consumption and second-hand smoke, have reduced the rate of health problems in babies. Healthy women are more likely to have healthy babies. Moderate exercise during pregnancy helps maintain the health of the mother and baby. Exercise promotes muscle tone, strength, and endurance—three qualities that can help the mother adjust to the weight increase during pregnancy, prepare for the physical challenge of labor, and make it easier to get back into shape after the baby is born.

Should problems arise, improvements in diagnostic techniques and emerging procedures, such as the treatment of an embryo in the uterus, have helped to improve the health of mother and baby.

As you progress through the unit, think about these focusing questions:

- How do reproductive systems function to ensure survival of the species?
- What mechanisms are responsible for regulating reproductive systems?
- What are the major processes and events of human embryonic and fetal development?
- How have reproductive technologies affected the functioning of reproductive systems?

UNIT 30 B PERFORMANCE TASK

Society and Reproductive Technology

The speed at which new reproductive technologies emerge can exceed our ability as a society to agree on their possible implications. Reproductive technologies are changing old definitions of motherhood and of parent. In the Performance Task for this unit, you will examine new reproductive technologies and assess their social and ethical implications.

www.science.nelson.com 

GENERAL OUTCOMES

In this unit, you will

- explain how survival of the human species is ensured through reproduction
- explain how human reproduction is regulated by chemical control systems
- explain how cell differentiation and development in the human organism are regulated by a combination of genetic, endocrine, and environmental factors

Unit 30 B
Reproduction and Development

ARE YOU READY?

Prerequisites

Concepts
- cell division
- cell specialization in multicellular organisms
- asexual and sexual reproduction
- chromosomes, genes, and DNA
- inheritance

Skills
- interpret patterns and trends in data, and infer or calculate linear and nonlinear relationships among variables
- use electronic research tools to collect information on a given topic

You can review prerequisite concepts and skills on the Nelson Web site and in the Appendices.

A Unit Pre-Test is also available online.

www.science.nelson.com 

These questions will help you find out what you already know, and what you need to review, before you continue with this unit.

Knowledge

1. Adult humans have developed from a single fertilized egg into a complex organism composed of many types of cells.
   (a) How does one cell grow into a multicellular organism?
   (b) If all the cells in your body came from the same fertilized egg cell, why don't they all look alike?
   (c) Why are there more of some cell types than others?

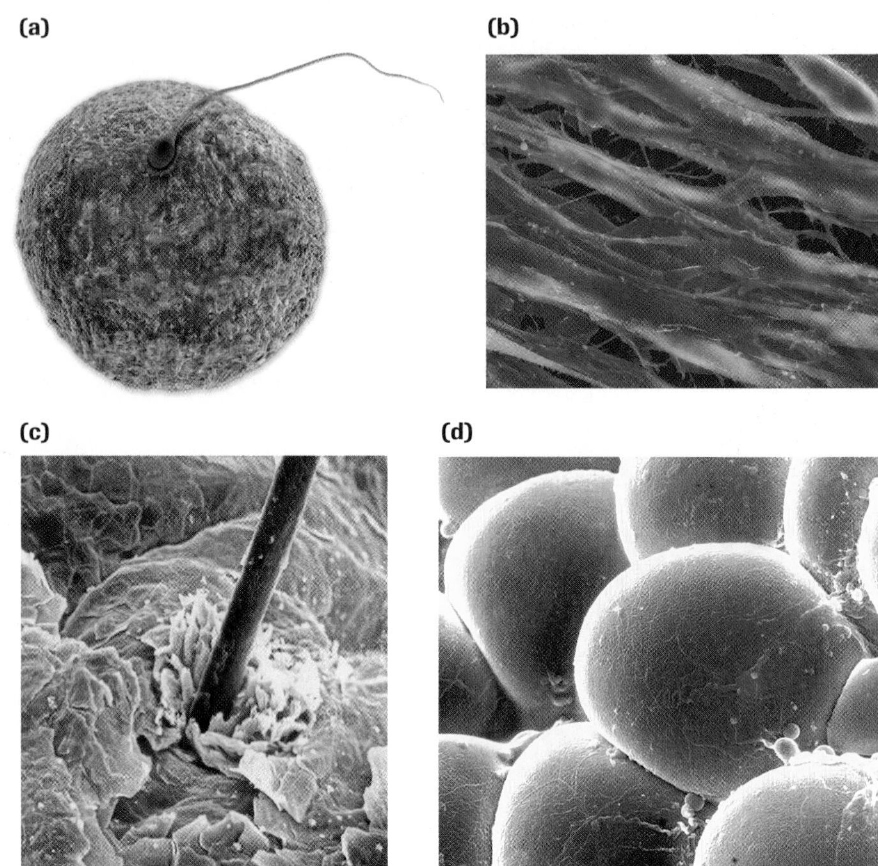

Figure 1
Photomicrographs of **(a)** a fertilized egg cell, **(b)** muscle cells, **(c)** epithelial cells, and **(d)** fat cells

2. A quaking aspen located near Salt Lake City, Utah, may be the world's largest organism, according to Dr. Stewart Rood at the University of Lethbridge. What appears to be a grove of individual aspen trees is actually one organism with a common root system. The single organism covers 43 hectares! The tree-like shoots develop from runners (horizontal roots) that grow above or below the ground.
   (a) What are the advantages of reproducing by runners?
   (b) Do all the trees have the same genetic information since they are one organism? Explain why or why not.
   (c) List three other plant species that reproduce through runners.

3. Over 2000 years ago, the Greek philosopher Aristotle proposed that heredity could be traced to the power of the male's semen. What observation or previous learning would allow you to support or refute this statement?
4. The time that unborn young spend developing in the uterus is called the gestation period. In mammals, the gestation period ranges from 16 days for golden hamsters to 650 days for elephants (**Figure 2**). Identify the advantages and disadvantages of short and longer gestation periods.

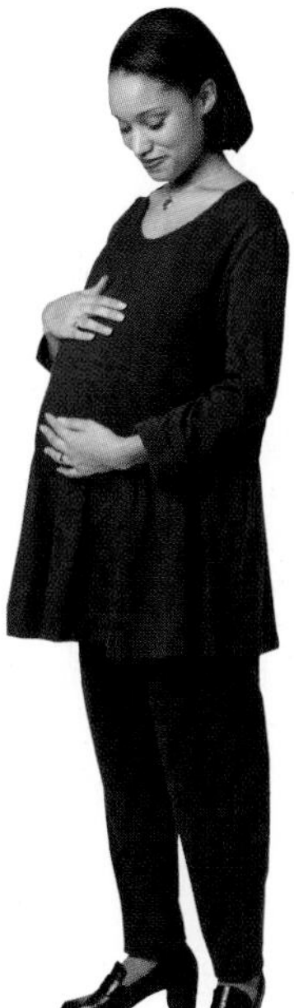

Figure 2
The gestation period in mammals ranges widely.

STS Connections

5. On April 25, 1978, the birth of a young girl, Louise Brown, caused people around the world to stop in amazement. She was the first baby ever conceived outside of the human body. A sperm cell fertilized an egg cell within a glass Petri dish in the laboratory (**Figure 3**). This revolutionary technique heralded the beginning of the new field of reproductive technology.
   (a) Could a woman give birth to a baby who carries none of her genetic information? Explain your answer.
   (b) Is it possible, through reproductive technology, for a 60-year-old woman to have a baby?
   (c) What ethical problems might arise because of research in this field?

Figure 3
In vitro fertilization

chapter

16 Reproduction and Development

In this chapter

- Exploration: Comparing Gametes
- Mini Investigation: Microscopic Examination of the Testes
- Lab Exercise 16.A: Understanding the Regulation of Male Sex Hormones
- Web Activity: Structures of the Female Reproductive System
- Mini Investigation: Microscopic Examination of the Ovary
- Web Activity: Tubal Ligation
- Lab Exercise 16.B: Hormonal Levels during the Menstrual Cycle
- Web Activity: The Visible Embryo
- Investigation 16.1: Observing Embryo Development
- Web Activity: Dr. Keith Bagnall
- Explore an Issue: Fetal Alcohol Spectrum Disorder
- Web Activity: Fetal Rights and FASD
- Web Activity: Creating a Database of Sexually Transmitted Infections
- Case Study: Human Reproductive Technology
- Web Activity: Reproductive Technologies

Reproduction ensures the survival of a species. Sexual reproduction contributes to the survival of a species because the offspring of a sexually reproducing species have different characteristics than their parents or their siblings. Natural selection acts on this diversity since individuals with characteristics that make them well-adapted to their environment have a greater chance of survival and of producing offspring of their own.

The survival of a species is also affected by the number of offspring each individual can produce. This number varies greatly among sexually reproducing species. Female oysters produce an estimated 115 million eggs for each spawning. Each year, female frogs produce hundreds of thousands of eggs for fertilization (**Figure 1**). Human females, on the other hand, have 400 000 egg cells, of which only about 400 mature throughout the reproductive years—from about the age of 12 years to 50 years. According to one source, the greatest number of children born to one woman is 57. The limited capacity of human females to produce sex cells contrasts with that of males. From about age 13 to 80 or 90, the average human male can produce as many as one billion sex cells every day.

STARTING Points

Answer these questions as best you can with your current knowledge. Then, using the concepts and skills you have learned, you will revise your answers at the end of the chapter.

1. What advantage is gained from producing millions of eggs?
2. What mechanism helps ensure survival of a species for animals that produce single young at a single birth?
3. During the summer months, it is rare to find a male aphid. Female aphids reproduce asexually and give birth to other female aphids. In the fall, some females become males and the aphids reproduce sexually.
   (a) What advantage is gained from aphids reproducing in two different ways?
   (b) What advantage is gained from reproducing asexually?
   (c) What advantage is gained from reproducing sexually?
4. Millions of sperm cells are released to fertilize a single egg cell. Why are so many sperm cells produced, if only a single cell fertilizes the egg?

Career Connections:
Diagnostic Medical Sonographer; Midwife; Pediatrician

Figure 1
The production of many varied offspring ensures the survival of a species.

Exploration — Comparing Gametes

Sperm cells and egg cells have different functions in reproduction. Sperm cells travel through the vagina into the uterus and then into the Fallopian tubes to fertilize an egg cell. Once fertilized, the egg cell undergoes multiple divisions, forming trillions of specialized cells of the human body. The structures of the egg and sperm cells provide clues to their function.

Materials: prepared slides of egg and sperm cells, light microscope

- Examine egg and sperm cells using a light microscope.
- Compare the amount of cytoplasm found in the sperm and egg cell.

(a) Estimate the size of the sperm and egg cell.
(b) What advantage is gained from the sperm cell having a dramatically reduced cytoplasm?
(c) What advantage is gained from the egg cell having a great amount of cytoplasm?

16.1 The Male Reproductive System

Recall that natural selection acts on the inherited traits of an organism, and that organisms with traits that are better adapted to their environment will be most likely to survive. (You can review this on pages 150–152 of this textbook.) Sexual reproduction gives rise to offspring that are different from their parents and from each other (with the exception of identical multiple births, such as twins). During sexual reproduction, specialized reproductive cells containing genetic material from two individuals (parents) join together. Since the two individuals both donate genetic material, the offspring will have a different set of inherited traits than either parent. The new set of traits may make the individual more or less adapted to the environment than its parent. When the environment changes, there is more variation for natural selection to act upon in sexually reproducing species. In contrast, during asexual reproduction, a single cell (parent cell) divides to give rise to two cells that have an identical set of inherited traits to each other and to the parent cell.

Humans reproduce by sexual reproduction. The specialized reproductive cells of humans are produced by, unite in, and develop within the organs of the male and female reproductive systems. The male gonads, the **testes** (singular *testis*), produce male sex cells called sperm. The female gonad, the **ovary**, produces eggs. The fusion of a male and female sex cell occurs within the female reproductive system, in a process called **fertilization**, which produces a **zygote**. The zygote divides many times to form an **embryo**, which in turn continues to grow into a **fetus**. In the rest of this section, you will find out about the biology of the male reproductive system.

testes the male gonads, or primary reproductive organs; male sex hormones and sperm are produced in the testes

ovary the female gonad, or reproductive organ; female sex hormones and egg cells are produced in the ovary

fertilization fusion of a male and a female sex cell

zygote the cell resulting from the union of a male and female sex cell

embryo the early stages of an animal's development

fetus the later stages of an unborn offspring's development

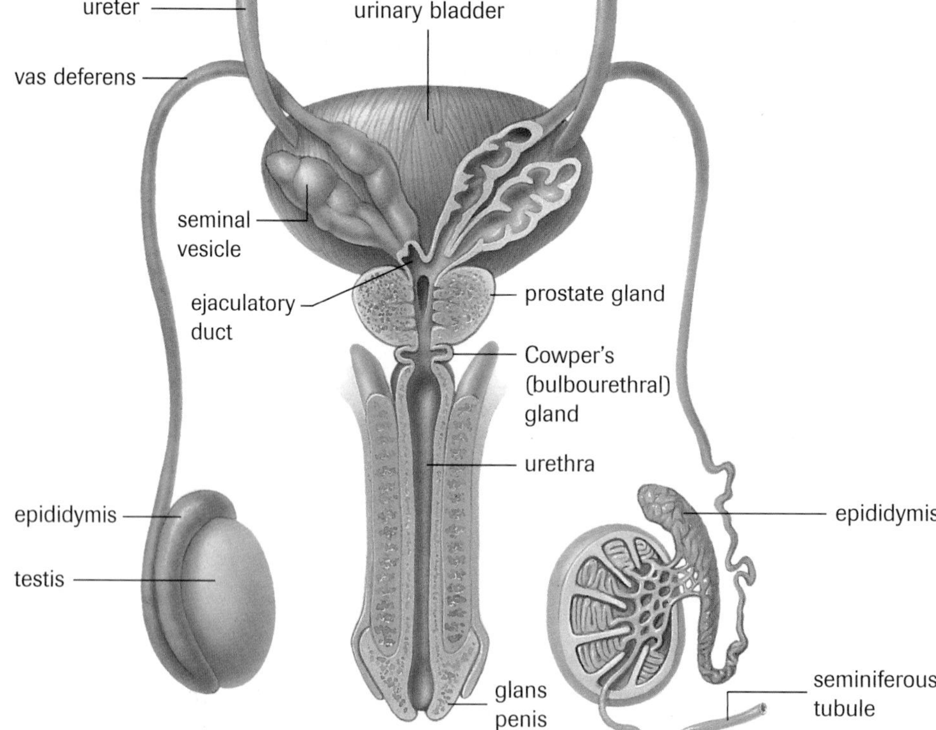

Figure 1

The male reproductive system. The urinary bladder and ureter are not part of the reproductive system.

+ EXTENSION

Cancers of the Prostate

Prostate cancer is one of the most common cancers in males. In this extension activity, you will research how prostate cancer is detected and what treatments are available.

www.science.nelson.com 

Structures of the Male Reproductive System

Figure 1, on the previous page, illustrates the main structures of the male reproductive system in humans. Human male and female sex organs originate in the same area of the body—the abdominal cavity—and are almost indistinguishable until about the third month of embryonic development. At that time, the genes of the sex chromosomes cause differentiation. During the last two months of fetal development, the testes descend through a canal into the **scrotum**, a pouch of skin located below the pelvic region. A thin membrane forms over the canal, thereby preventing the testes from re-entering the abdominal cavity. Occasionally, an injury may cause the rupture of this membrane, producing an inguinal hernia. The hernia can be dangerous because a segment of the small intestine can be forced into the scrotum. The small intestine creates pressure on the testes, and blood flow to either the testes or small intestine may become restricted.

The temperature in the scrotum is a few degrees cooler than that of the abdominal cavity. The cooler temperatures are important, since sperm will not develop at body temperature. Should the testes fail to descend into the scrotum, the male will not be able to produce viable sperm. This makes the male sterile.

A tube called the **vas deferens** (plural *vasa deferentia*) carries sperm from the testis to the **ejaculatory duct**. Any blockage of the vas deferens will prevent the movement of sperm from the testes to the external environment. A surgical procedure, in which the vas deferens from each testicle is cut and tied, called a vasectomy, can be performed on males as a means of birth control (**Figure 2**). The ejaculatory duct propels the movement of sperm and fluids, called **semen**, into the urethra, which also serves as a channel for urine. A sphincter regulates the voiding of urine from the bladder. Both regulatory functions work independently and are never open at the same time. At any given time, the urethra conducts either urine or semen, but never both.

During sexual excitement, the erectile tissue within the penis fills with blood. Stimulation of the parasympathetic nerve causes the arteries leading to the penis to dilate, thereby increasing blood flow. As blood moves into the penis, the sinuses swell, compressing the veins that carry blood away from the penis. Any damage to the parasympathetic nerve can cause impotency, in which the penis fails to become erect. (Other causes, such as hormone imbalance and stress, have also been associated with impotency.)

Male Reproductive System
View this animated side view of the male reproductive system and the roles of the various structures.

www.science.nelson.com 

scrotum the sac that contains the testes

vas deferens tube that conducts sperm toward the urethra

ejaculatory duct a tubule formed at the union of the vasa deferentia and the seminal vesicle ducts and opening into the urethra

semen (seminal fluid) a secretion of the male reproductive organs that is composed of sperm and fluids

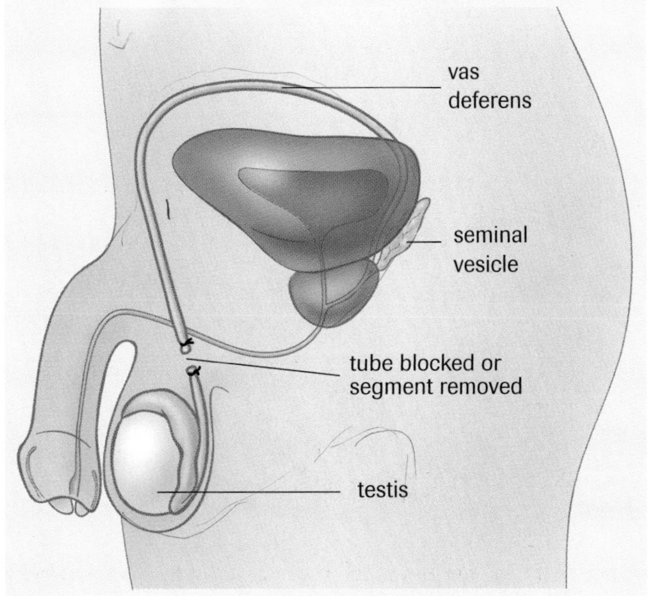

Figure 2
In a vasectomy, the vas deferens are cut, so that sperm can no longer exit the body.

A Male Flower
The word *testis* comes from the Latin, meaning 'witness.' It has been suggested that the word *witness* comes from the idea that testes are witness to virility. The Greek word for testes is *orchis*. The orchid derives its name from the resemblance of its paired bulbous roots to the testes.

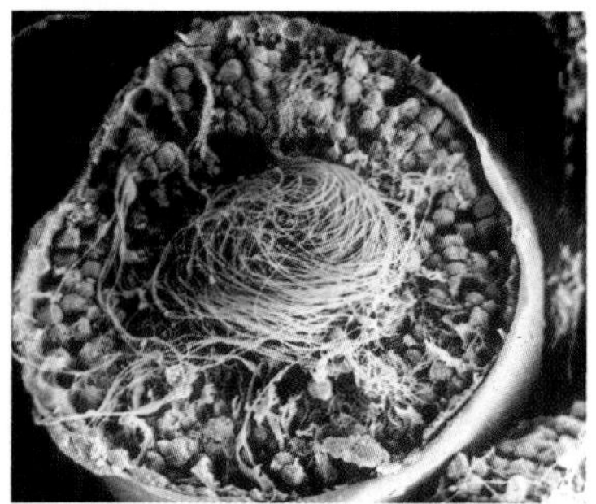

Figure 3
Scanning electron micrograph of a seminiferous tubule in cross-section

> **Practice**
>
> 1. What would happen if the testes failed to descend into the scrotum?
> 2. What is semen and where is it found in the male body? What function does it serve?

Spermatogenesis

The inside of each testis, which is only about 5 cm long, is filled with twisting tubes, called **seminiferous tubules**, that measure approximately 250 m in length (**Figure 3**). Seminiferous tubules are the site of **spermatogenesis**, which is the formation of sperm cells. The seminiferous tubules are lined with sperm-producing cells called **spermatogonia** (Figure 4).

During spermatogenesis, spermatogonia divide to form to **spermacytes**. Spermacytes then differentiate into **spermatids**, which are immature sperm cells. The body cells (**somatic cells**) of humans usually contain 46 chromosomes. Spermatids have half this number (23 chromosomes) and, therefore, half as much genetic material as the spermatogonia. It takes 9 to 10 weeks for the spermatocytes to differentiate into sperm cells. You will learn more about spermatogenesis and its importance in Unit 30 C.

Specialized cells in the seminiferous tubules, called **Sertoli cells**, nourish the developing sperm cells until they are mature. Sertoli cells also provide a barrier between the blood and the seminiferous tubules (the blood-testis barrier). This barrier controls the entry and exit of hormones, nutrients, and other chemicals into the seminiferous tubules, which protects the developing sperm cells. If the barrier is damaged and sperm enter the bloodstream, the body can develop antibodies against its own sperm. This can result in a decreased ability to fertilize egg cells.

Although sperm cells are produced in the testes, they mature in the **epididymis,** a compact, coiled tube attached to the outer edge of the testis. Sperm cells in the epididymis begin swimming motions within four days. It is believed that some defective sperm cells are destroyed by the immune system during their time in the epididymis.

seminiferous tubules coiled ducts found within the testes, where immature sperm cells divide and differentiate

spermatogenesis process by which spermatogonia divide and differentiate into mature sperm cells

spermatogonia sperm-producing cells found in the seminiferous tubules

spermatocyte a cell that arises from division of spermatogonia during spermatogenesis

spermatid an immature sperm cell that arises from division of a spermatocyte

somatic cell any cell in a multicellular organism that is not a reproductive cell

Sertoli cell a cell that provides metabolic and mechanical support to developing sperm cells

epididymis structure located along the posterior border of the testis, consisting of coiled tubules that store sperm cells

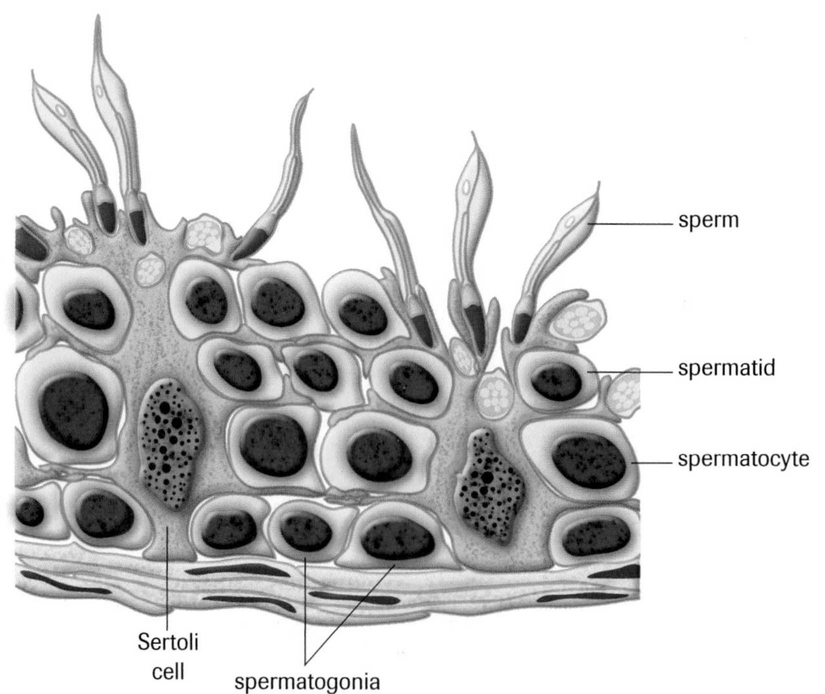

Figure 4
Development of sperm cells inside the seminiferous tubule

In many ways, the mature sperm cell is an example of mastery in engineering design. Built for motion, the sperm cell is streamlined with only a small amount of cytoplasm surrounding the nucleus (**Figure 5**). Although reduced cytoplasm is beneficial for a cell that must move, it also presents a problem. Limited cytoplasm means a limited energy reserve. In mature sperm, the energy-transforming organelles, the mitochondria, are found between the nucleus and the flagellum, the organelle that propels the sperm cell. An entry capsule, called the **acrosome**, caps the head of the sperm cell. Filled with special enzymes that dissolve the gelatinous outer coating surrounding the egg, the acrosome allows the sperm to penetrate the cell layer surrounding the egg.

acrosome the cap found on sperm cells, containing enzymes that permit the sperm cell to move through the outer layers that surround the egg

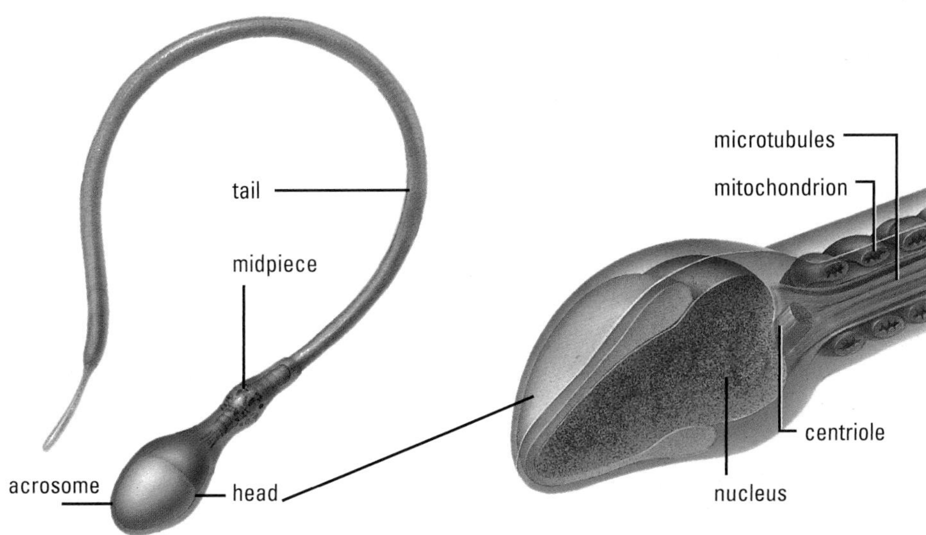

Figure 5
A human sperm cell

Practice

3. What is spermatogenesis?
4. Explain how sperm are formed.

mini Investigation Microscopic Examination of the Testes

Purpose
To view structures within the testes

Materials: lens paper, light microscope, prepared slides of testes (cross-section), pencil

Visit the Nelson Web site to view micrographs of the testes to help you identify the structures on the prepared slides.

www.science.nelson.com 

- Using lens paper, clean the ocular and all the objective lenses of the microscope.
- Rotate the revolving nosepiece so that the low-power objective is in place.
- Position the prepared slide on the stage of the microscope and view the cross-section of the testes under low power.
- Centre the slide on a single seminiferous tubule and rotate the revolving nosepiece to the medium-power objective. Use only the fine adjustment to focus the cells.
- Locate an interstitial cell and a seminiferous tubule.
- Rotate the nosepiece to the high-power objective lens. View the immature sperm cells within the seminiferous tubules.

(a) Estimate the number of seminiferous tubules seen under low-power magnification.
(b) Estimate the diameter of the seminiferous tubule and size of the interstitial cell.
(c) Diagram five different cells within the seminiferous tubules.
(d) Would you expect to find mature sperm cells in the seminiferous tubule? Give your reasons.

Seminal Fluid

Sperm leave the body as part of a fluid, semen, which provides a swimming medium for the flagellated sperm. Ejaculation is the process by which the semen leaves a man's body via the penis. The vasa deferentia, seminal vesicles, ejaculatory duct, and prostate gland contract, forcing the semen to the base of the penis. Strong muscular contractions force the semen into the urethra and out of the penis. Every time a man ejaculates, between 3 and 4 mL of fluid, containing approximately 500 million sperm cells, are released.

seminal fluid the fluid part of semen, which is secreted by three glands

seminal vesicle structure that contributes to the seminal fluid (semen), a secretion that contains fructose and prostaglandins

prostate gland structure that contributes to the seminal fluid (semen), a secretion containing buffers that protect sperm cells from the acidic environment of the vagina

Cowper's (bulbourethral) gland structure that contributes a mucus-rich fluid to the seminal fluid (semen)

The **seminal fluids** (the fluid part of semen) are secreted by three glands along the vasa deferentia and ejaculatory duct. Fluids from the **seminal vesicles** contain fructose and prostaglandins. The fructose provides a source of energy for the sperm cell. Recall that the sperm cell carries little energy reserves. Prostaglandins act as a chemical signal in the female system, triggering the rhythmic contraction of smooth muscle along the reproductive tract. It is believed that the contraction of muscles along the female reproductive pathways assists the movement of sperm cells toward the egg. The **prostate gland** secretes an alkaline buffer that protects sperm cells against the acidic environment of the vagina.

Cowper's (bulbourethral) glands (see **Figure 1** on page 512) secrete mucus-rich fluids prior to ejaculation. The fluids are thought to protect the sperm cells from the acids found in the urethra associated with the passage of urine. The fluid may also assist sperm movement.

Although sperm cells can exist for many weeks in the epididymis, life span is reduced when they come in contact with the various fluids in the semen. At body temperature, sperm cells will live only 24 to 72 hours. When stored at –100 °C, sperm cells have been known to remain viable for many years.

Practice

5. How does seminal fluid protect the sperm?

Hormonal Control of the Male Reproductive System

primary sexual characteristics physical characteristics of an organism that are directly involved in reproduction

Table 1 summarizes the structures and functions of the male reproductive system. These structures are collectively referred to as the **primary sexual characteristics**. Primary sexual characteristics are directly involved in reproduction and are present at birth.

Table 1 The Male Reproductive System

Structure	Function
testes	• produce sperm cells
seminiferous tubules	• produce immature sperm cells
epididymis	• matures and stores sperm cells in coiled tubules
vas deferens	• carries sperm from the epididymis to its junction with the urethra
seminal vesicle	• secretes fructose into the semen to provide energy for the sperm
prostate gland	• secretes an alkaline buffer into the semen to protect the sperm from the acidic environment of the vagina
Cowper's gland	• secretes mucus-rich fluids into the semen that may protect the sperm from acids in the urethra
urethra	• carries semen during ejaculation • carries urine from the bladder to the exterior of the body
penis	• deposits sperm into the female reproductive system during ejaculation • contains the urethra

The maturation and functioning of the male reproductive system is regulated by a number of hormones. As a male reaches puberty, the levels of these hormones change, which initiates the development of secondary sexual characteristics. **Secondary sexual characteristics** are external features, other than the reproductive organs, that differ between mature males and females. Male secondary sexual characteristics are summarized in **Table 2**.

secondary sexual characteristics external features of an organism that are indicative of its gender (male or female), but are not the reproductive organs themselves

Table 2 Secondary Sexual Characteristics of Males

• chest and abdominal hair • more facial hair than women • hair growth in armpits and pubis (crotch) • deeper voice due to enlargement of the larynx • larger, stronger muscles	• fat deposits around the abdomen and waist • coarser skin texture • hands and feet usually larger than females • angle from thigh to ankle forms a straight line

Perhaps the most important male hormone is testosterone. **Testosterone** is the primary male sex hormone. It is produced in the **interstitial cells**, which are found between the seminiferous tubules within the testes. Testosterone stimulates the maturation of the testes and penis and also spermatogenesis. It also promotes the development of facial and body hair; the growth of the larynx, which causes the lowering of the voice; and the strengthening of muscles. In addition, testosterone increases the secretion of body oils and has been linked to the development of acne in males as they reach puberty. Once males adjust to higher levels of testosterone, skin problems decline. The increased oil production can also create body odour. Testosterone levels are also associated with sex drive and more aggressive behaviour.

The hypothalamus and pituitary gland in the brain control the production of sperm and male sex hormones in the testes. The pituitary gland produces and stores the **gonadotropic hormones** (**gonadotropins**) that regulate the functions of the testes. There are two gonadotropins: follicle-stimulating hormone and luteinizing hormone. In males, **follicle-stimulating hormone** (**FSH**) stimulates the production of sperm cells in the seminiferous tubules and **luteinizing hormone** (**LH**) promotes the production of testosterone by the interstitial cells. **Table 3** provides a summary of the male reproductive hormones, their sites of production, and their functions.

testosterone male sex hormone produced by the interstitial cells of the testes

interstitial cells cells found in the testes surrounding the seminiferous tubules that secrete testosterone

gonadotropic hormones (gonadotropins) hormones produced by the pituitary gland that regulate the functions of the testes in males and the ovaries in females

follicle-stimulating hormone (FSH) in males, hormone that increases sperm production

luteinizing hormone (LH) in males, hormone that regulates the production of testosterone

gonadotropin-releasing hormone (GnRH) chemical messenger from the hypothalamus that stimulates secretions of FSH and LH from the pituitary

inhibin a hormone produced by the Sertoli cells that inhibits production of FSH

Table 3 Male Reproductive Hormones

Hormone	Location	Description of Function
testosterone	interstitial cells	• stimulates spermatogenesis • promotes and regulates the development of secondary sexual characteristics • associated with sex drive levels
follicle-stimulating hormone (FSH)	pituitary gland	• stimulates the production of sperm cells in the seminiferous tubules
luteinizing hormone (LH)	pituitary gland	• promotes the production of testosterone by the interstitial cells
gonadotropin-releasing hormone (GnRH)	hypothalamus	• stimulates secretion of FSH and LH

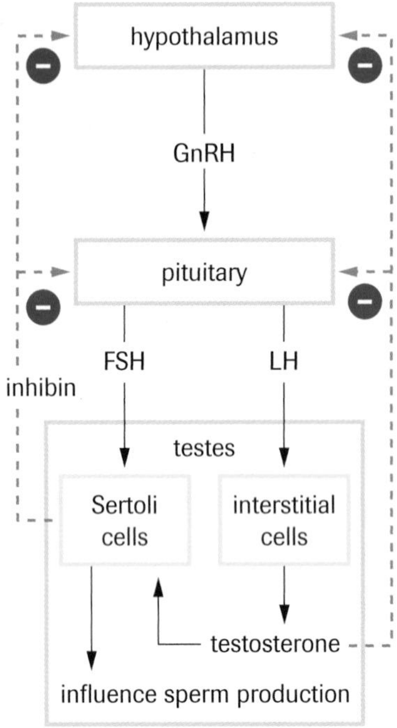

Figure 6
Negative feedback regulation of FSH, LH, and testosterone

Interconnecting negative feedback systems ensure that adequate numbers of sperm cells and constant levels of testosterone are maintained (**Figure 6**). Beginning at puberty, the hypothalamus secretes the **gonadotropin-releasing hormone** (**GnRH**) when testosterone levels are low. The secreted GnRH activates the pituitary gland to secrete and release FSH and LH. FSH acts directly on the sperm-producing cells of the seminiferous tubules, while LH stimulates testosterone production. Testosterone, in turn, stimulates spermatogenesis.

The broken lines on **Figure 6** show the negative feedback loops that maintain sperm counts and steady hormone levels. The feedback loop for sperm production is not well understood. When sperm counts are high, the Sertoli cells of the seminiferous tubules produce a hormone called inhibin. **Inhibin** sends a feedback message to the pituitary that inhibits further production of FSH. It also causes the hypothalamus to reduce its production of GnRH.

LH stimulates the interstitial cells to produce testosterone. A coordinated negative feedback system regulates LH and testosterone levels. High testosterone levels reduce LH production directly by feedback inhibition of LH release from the pituitary and indirectly by feedback inhibition of GnRH release from the hypothalamus. When high levels of testosterone are detected by the hypothalamus, it releases less GnRH, leading to decreased production of LH. Decreased GnRH output, in turn, slows the production and release of LH, which leads to lower testosterone production. Testosterone levels thus remain in check.

LAB EXERCISE 16.A

Understanding the Regulation of Male Sex Hormones

Report Checklist

- ● Purpose
- ○ Problem
- ● Hypothesis
- ○ Prediction
- ● Design
- ○ Materials
- ○ Procedure
- ○ Evidence
- ○ Analysis
- ● Evaluation
- ● Synthesis

An experiment was performed in which the circulatory systems of two male mice (A and B) with compatible blood types were joined (**Figure 7**). The data analysis from the experiment is shown in **Table 4**. (Note that + indicates "found," – indicates "not found.")

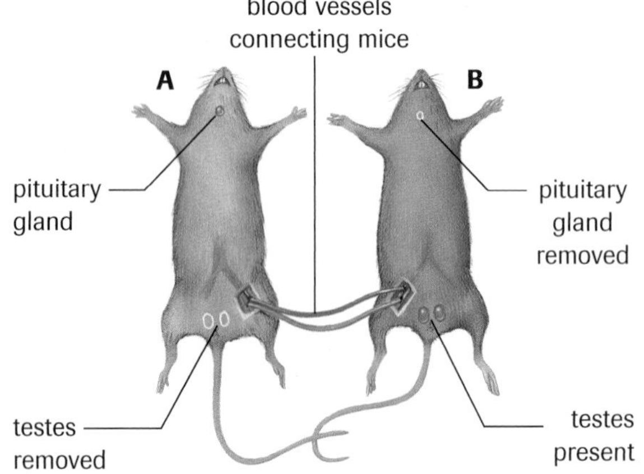

Figure 7
Circulatory systems of two mice are joined.

Table 4 Presence of Hormones and Sperm in Joined Mice

Animal	Testosterone	LH	FSH	Sperm in urethra
A	+	+	+	–
B	+	+	+	+

(a) State the purpose of the experiment

(b) Write a hypothesis for the experiment.

(c) Write a design statement for the experiment. In your statement, identify one manipulated variable and one responding variable.

Evaluation

(d) Why were the circulatory systems joined?

(e) If LH and FSH are produced in the pituitary gland, explain how it is possible to find these hormones in mouse B.

(f) Explain why testosterone is found in both mice.

(g) Why is sperm found in the urethra of mouse B but not in the urethra of mouse A?

Synthesis

(h) In another experiment, the circulatory systems of the two mice were not joined and the data in **Table 5** were collected. Predict which glands and organs are present or absent from each animal. Give reasons for your prediction.

Table 5 Presence of Hormones and Sperm in Two Mice

Animal	Testosterone	LH	FSH	Sperm in urethra
A	–	+	+	–
B	–	–	–	–

SUMMARY *The Male Reproductive System*

- The male reproductive system is composed of testes, seminiferous tubules, interstitial cells, Sertoli cells, epididymides, vasa deferentia, Cowper's glands, seminal vesicles, prostate gland, ejaculatory duct, urethra, and penis.
- The testes produce sperm cells and the male sex hormone, testosterone.
- Seminal fluids provide energy to the sperm and facilitate fertilization.
- The gonadotropic hormones FSH and LH are produced by the pituitary gland in response to GnRH from the hypothalamus.
- Sperm production is stimulated by FSH and testosterone.
- LH stimulates testosterone production in the testes.
- FSH, LH, and testosterone levels are regulated by negative feedback.
- High FSH levels stimulates production of inhibin, which lowers production of FSH by the pituitary and GnRH by the hypothalamus.
- High testosterone levels cause the hypothalamus to release less GnRH which, in turn, decreases production of LH. Decreased LH levels, in turn, leads to lower testosterone production.

Section 16.1 Questions

1. Draw a diagram of the male reproductive system and label the following parts: penis, testis, urethra, seminiferous tubule, Cowper's gland, epididymis, prostate gland, vas deferens, seminal vesicle.
2. Describe the function of the following structures: Sertoli cells, seminiferous tubules, and epididymis.
3. Outline the functions of testosterone.
4. How do gonadotropic hormones regulate spermatogenesis and testosterone production?
5. What are the sources of energy for developing and mature sperm?
6. Using luteinizing hormone (LH) and testosterone as examples, explain how a negative feedback system works.
7. A vasectomy is a surgical procedure that blocks each vas deferens and keeps sperm from reaching the seminal fluid. The sperm are absorbed by the body instead of being ejaculated.
   (a) Would a male who has had a vasectomy produce semen? Explain your answer.
   (b) Would a male who has had a vasectomy continue to produce testosterone? Explain your answer.
   (c) Why might this operation be performed?

16.2 The Female Reproductive System

ovum (*plural* **ova**) egg cell

In many ways, the female reproductive system (**Figure 1**) is more complicated than that of the male. Once sexual maturity is reached, males continue to produce sperm cells at a somewhat constant rate. In contrast, during their reproductive years, females follow a complicated sexual cycle, in which one **ovum** matures approximately every month.

CAREER CONNECTION

Diagnostic Medical Sonographer

Sonographers use ultrasound technology to assess the health of a woman's reproductive organs and to monitor pregnancies. They report their technical findings to physicians. Find out the entrance requirements for a program in medical sonography.

www.science.nelson.com 

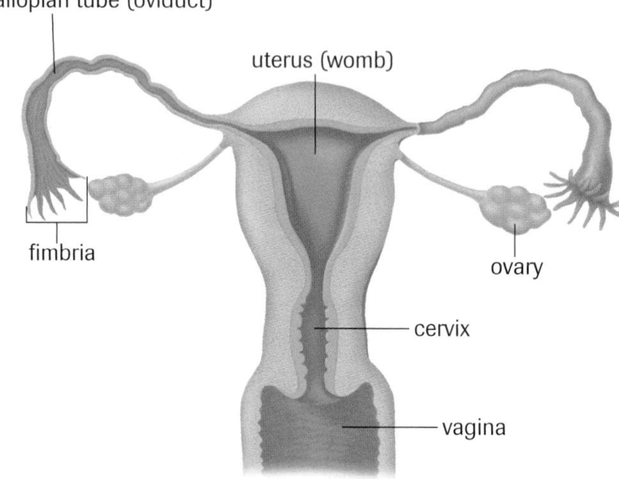

Figure 1
Female reproductive anatomy, frontal view.

As in males, secondary sexual characteristics begin to develop in females during puberty as a result of hormonal stimulation. In females, the development of breasts, widening of the hips, and the growth of hair in the armpits and pubis are linked with puberty (**Table 2**). These changes may occur very slowly and extend over a period of more than a decade, or they may appear rather suddenly and be completed within one or two years. While general social conditions, diet, and climate may affect the development, much of it is also determined by heredity.

Table 2 Secondary Sexual Characteristics in Females

- enlarged breasts
- less facial hair than men
- hair growth in armpits and pubis (crotch)
- wider at the hips than at the shoulders
- fat deposits around buttocks and hips
- more body fat than men
- hands and feet usually smaller and narrower than males
- angle from thigh to ankle is slightly bent

oocyte an immature ovum

During fetal development in the female, paired ovaries (flattened, olive-shaped organs) form in the same abdominal region as the testes in the male. Like the similarly shaped testes, the ovaries descend, but unlike the testes, which come to lie outside of the abdominal cavity, the ovaries remain in the pelvic region. At birth, **oocytes** (immature ova) are already present within the ovary.

The **uterus** or **womb** is the largest organ in the female reproductive system. It is a muscular, hollow organ shaped like an inverted pear. The embryo and fetus develop in the uterus during normal pregnancies. The uterus is composed of two major tissues: a muscular outer lining and a glandular inner lining of the uterus, known as the **endometrium**.

The ovaries are connected to the uterus by two **Fallopian tubes** (**Figure 1**, previous page), named after Gabriello Fallopio, a 16th-century Italian anatomist. A Fallopian tube may also be called an **oviduct**. At the ends of each Fallopian tube are fingerlike projections called **fimbria** (singular, **fibrium**). The uterus is connected to the outer environment by the **vagina**. Sexual intercourse occurs within the vagina, which also serves as the birth canal. The vagina is acidic, creating a hostile environment for microbes that might enter the female reproductive system. A muscular ring, called the **cervix**, separates the vagina from the uterus.

Cancer of the cervix is one of the major forms of cancer in females. Fortunately, early detection by a Pap test greatly improves the chances of curing this form of cancer. Like skin cells and the cells that line your mouth, cervical cells slough off. To collect a sample for a Pap test, a physician simply uses a swab to collect cells from the cervix. These cells are then checked for abnormalities that could indicate cancer.

Note that in females, the reproductive and excretory structures remain distinct. The urethra (the tube through which urine exits the body) of females is not connected to the reproductive organs. In males, the urethra provides a common pathway for sperm and urine to exit the body through the penis. A valve prevents both fluids from being released at the same time. However, the urethra of males is longer than that of females, which may account for the fact that females are more prone to bladder infections.

uterus (womb) the hollow, pear-shaped organ located between the bladder and the anus in females

endometrium the glandular inner lining of the uterus

Fallopian tube (oviduct) one of two tubes that connect the ovaries to the uterus

fibrium (*plural* **fibria**) a fingerlike projection at the end of a Fallopian tube

vagina the muscular canal extending from the cervix to the outer environment; the birth canal

cervix a muscular band that separates the vagina from the uterus

Simulation—Structures of the Female Reproductive System

In this activity, you will view a computer simulation of the structures of the female reproductive system. From the simulation, you will draw a diagram of the female reproductive system and label the following structures: vagina, ovaries, cervix, Fallopian tubes (oviducts), uterus, and endometrium.

www.science.nelson.com 

Oogenesis and Ovulation

The ovum is much larger than the male sex cell, the sperm (**Figure 2**). An ovum is packed with nutrients, so that when it is fertilized it can divide rapidly. Unlike males, who manufacture millions of sperm cells every day, usually only one ovum is produced in human females at a time.

As in sperm development, during its development, an oocyte undergoes a type of cell division that halves the number of chromosomes, from 46 chromosomes to 23. An ovum therefore has half as much genetic material as the original cell from which it developed. (You will learn about types of cell division in Unit 30 C).

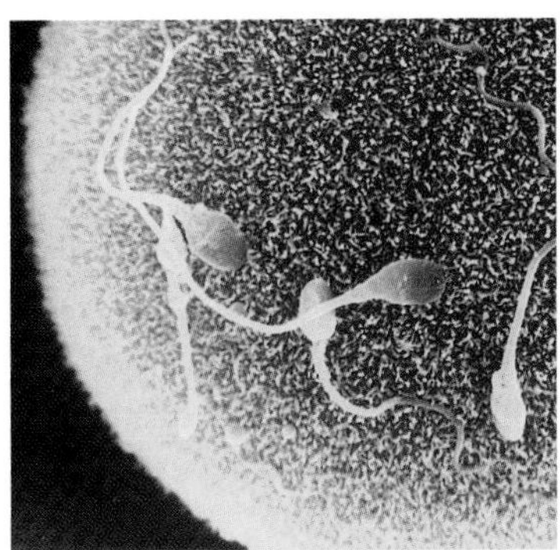

Figure 2
The male sperm cell is dwarfed by the much larger female egg cell. In humans, the egg cell is 100 000 times larger than the sperm cell.

oogenesis the formation and development of mature ova

follicle structure in the ovary that contains the oocyte

granulosa the layer of small cells that forms the wall of a follicle

Oogenesis is the formation of an ovum. In humans, oogenesis occurs in specialized cells in the ovaries, called **follicles** (**Figure 3**). A follicle contains two types of cells: a primary oocyte and cells of the granulosa. The **granulosa** is the layer of cells that forms the follicle wall. These cells provide nutrients for the developing oocytes.

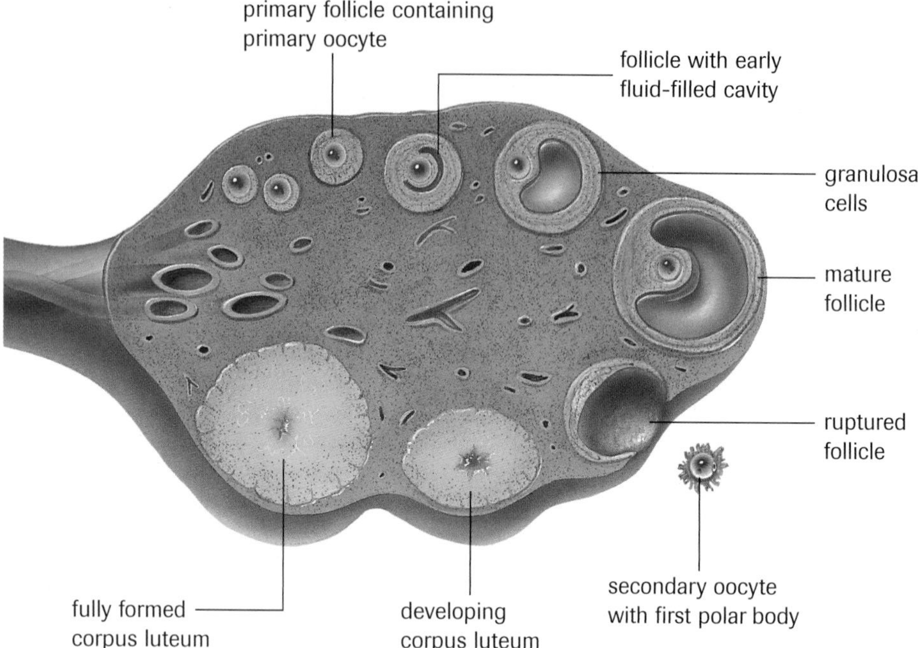

Figure 3
The process of ovulation. Pituitary hormones regulate the events of follicle development, ovulation, and the formation of the corpus luteum.

Oogenesis begins when nutrient follicle cells surrounding the primary oocyte begin to divide. As the primary oocyte undergoes cell division, the majority of cytoplasm and nutrients move to one of the end poles and form a secondary oocyte. The secondary oocyte contains 23 chromosomes. The remaining cell, referred to as the first polar body, receives little cytoplasm and dies. As the follicle cells surrounding the secondary oocyte proliferate, a fluid-filled cavity forms. Eventually, the dominant follicle pushes outward, ballooning the outer wall of the ovary. Constriction of blood vessels weakens the ovarian wall above the follicle, while enzymes weaken the wall of the follicle from the inside. The outer surface of the ovary wall bursts and the secondary oocyte is released. This process is referred to as **ovulation**. Surrounding follicle cells remain within the ovary and are transformed into the **corpus luteum**, which secretes hormones essential for pregnancy. If pregnancy does not occur, the corpus luteum degenerates after about 10 days.

ovulation release of the secondary oocyte from the follicle held within the ovary

corpus luteum a mass of follicle cells that forms within the ovary after ovulation; secretes estrogen and progesterone

Upon its release from the ovary, the secondary oocyte is swept into the funnel-shaped end of the Fallopian tube by the fimbria. The secondary oocyte is moved along the Fallopian tube by cilia where, if healthy sperm are present, it will become fertilized. The secondary oocyte will then undergo another unequal division of cytoplasm and nutrients and develop into the fertilized ovum. The cell that retains most of the cytoplasm and nutrients becomes the ovum, and the other cell becomes the second polar body, which deteriorates. If the secondary oocyte is not fertilized, it will deteriorate within 24 hours and die. When this occurs, the woman will undergo a menstrual cycle.

Practice

1. What is the role of follicles in ovulation?
2. Describe how the corpus luteum forms in the ovary.

▶ mini *Investigation* — *Microscopic Examination of the Ovary*

Purpose
To view structures within the ovaries

Materials: lens paper, light microscope, prepared slides of ovary (cross-section), pencil

Visit the Nelson Web site to view micrographs of the ovary to help you to identify the structures on the prepared slides.

www.science.nelson.com 

- Using lens paper, clean the ocular and all the objective lenses of the microscope.
- Rotate the revolving nosepiece so that the low-power objective is in place.
- Position the prepared slide on the stage of the microscope and view the cross-section of the testes under low power.
- Centre the slide on a follicle and rotate the revolving nosepiece to the medium-power objective. Use only the fine adjustment to focus the cells.

(a) Is the follicle mature or immature?

(b) Diagram the follicle, and label any cell types that are visible, using **Figure 3**, on the previous page, as a guide.

- Locate a second follicle that is at a different stage of development, and examine it under the medium-power objective.

(c) State whether this follicle is mature or immature, and draw and label it.

- Find a mature follicle either on the same slide or another slide.

(d) Draw and label the mature follicle.

- Locate a slide that shows the corpus luteum. Find and view this structure.

(e) Draw and label the corpus luteum.

(f) Organize your diagrams to reflect the process of ovulation. Explain the reasons behind your sequence of diagrams.

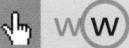

 WWW ***WEB** Activity*

Case Study—Tubal Ligation

Similar to vasectomy in males, tubal ligation is a surgical method of female sterilization. As its name suggests, during tubal ligation, the surgeon cuts and then ties off the Fallopian tubes. **Figure 4** shows the Pomeroy technique for a tubal ligation, which can be reversed. Approximately 60 % of the women who have had the procedure reversed become pregnant.

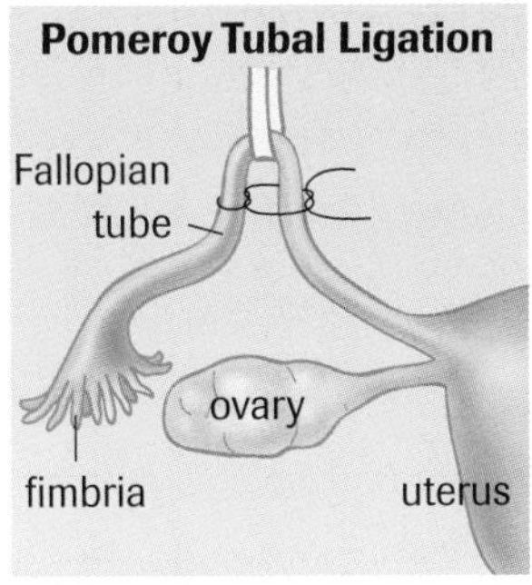

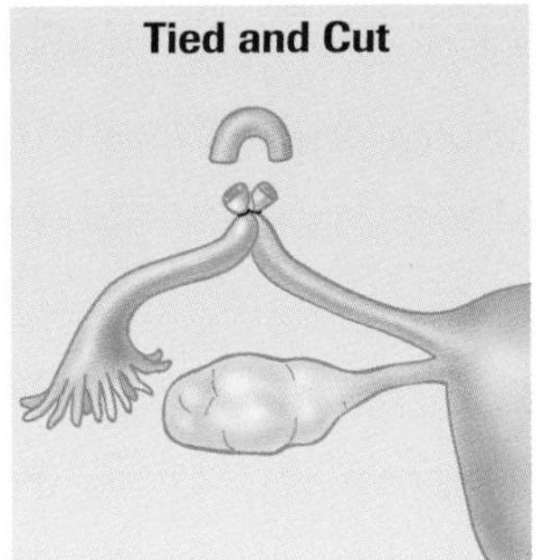

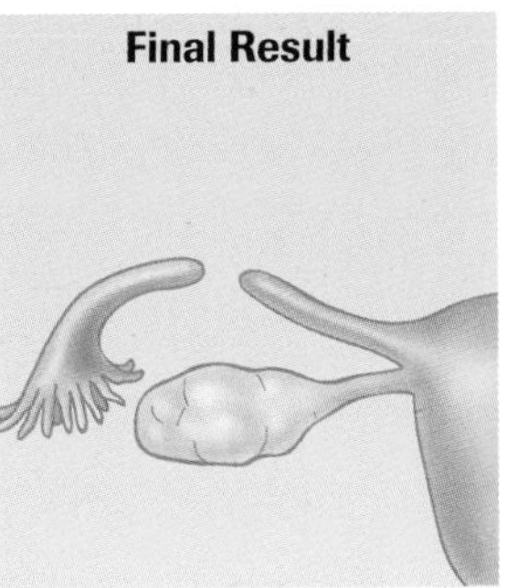

Figure 4
The Pomerory method of tubal ligation is reversible in up to 60 % of cases.

In this Web Activity, you will find out more about the Pomeroy procedure and its reversal. You may also find out about other technologies that can be used to prevent pregnancy.

www.science.nelson.com 

Menstrual Cycle

Along with the development of secondary sexual characteristics, puberty also initiates the **menstrual cycle**, which includes oogenesis, ovulation, and thickening and shedding of the endometrium. The menstrual cycle lasts an average of 28 days (although variation in this cycle is common) and is repeated throughout a woman's reproductive lifetime. The cycle is regulated by changes in the levels of various hormones.

The menstrual cycle can be divided into four distinct phases: flow phase, follicular phase, ovulatory phase, and luteal phase (**Figure 5**). Shedding of the endometrium, or **menstruation**, marks the **flow phase**. This is the only phase of the female reproductive cycle that can be determined externally. For this reason, the flow phase is used to mark the beginning of the menstrual cycle. Approximately five days are required for the uterus to shed the endometrium.

The **follicular phase** is characterized by the development of follicles within the ovary. As follicles develop, the hormone **estrogen** is secreted, increasing the estrogen concentration in the blood. The follicular phase normally takes place between days 6 and 13 of the female menstrual cycle.

During the **ovulatory phase**, the third phase of the female menstrual cycle, the secondary oocyte bursts from the ovary and follicular cells differentiate into the corpus luteum. The development of the corpus luteum marks the beginning of the **luteal phase**.

menstruation (flow phase) the shedding of the endometrium during the menstrual cycle

follicular phase phase marked by development of ovarian follicles before ovulation

estrogen hormone that activates development of female secondary sex characteristics, and increased thickening of the endometrium during the menstrual cycle

ovulatory phase phase in which ovulation occurs

luteal phase phase of the menstrual cycle characterized by the formation of the corpus luteum following ovulation

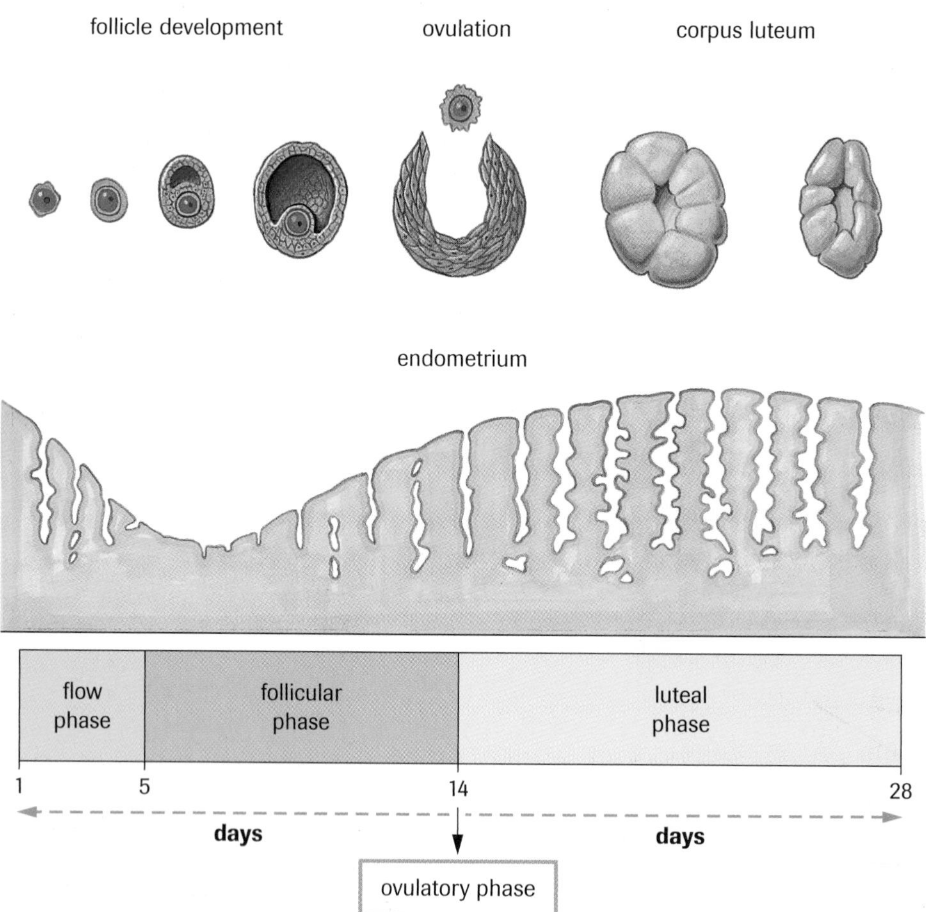

Figure 5
The thickness of the endometrium increases from the beginning of the follicular phase to the end of the luteal phase. The development of blood vessels and glandular tissues helps prepare the uterus for a developing embryo. Should no embryo enter the uterus, menstruation occurs, and the menstrual cycle begins again.

Estrogen levels begin to decline when the oocyte leaves the ovary, but are somewhat restored when the corpus luteum forms. The corpus luteum secretes both estrogen and **progesterone**. Progesterone continues to stimulate the endometrium and prepares the uterus for an embryo. It also inhibits further ovulation, prevents uterine contractions, and firms the cervix to prevent expulsion of the fetus. The luteal phase, which occurs between days 15 and 28, prepares the uterus to receive a fertilized egg. Should fertilization of an ovum not occur, the concentrations of estrogen and progesterone will decrease, thereby causing uterine contractions. These uterine contractions make the endometrium pull away from the uterine wall. The shedding of the endometrium marks the beginning of the next flow phase, and the female menstrual cycle starts all over again. This cycle is summarized in **Table 2**.

progesterone hormone produced primarily by the corpus luteum, that induces changes in the endometrium during the menstrual cycle

Table 2 The Female Menstrual Cycle

Phase	Description of events	Hormone produced	Days
flow	• menstruation		1-5
follicular	• follicles develop in ovaries • endometrium is restored	estrogen produced by follicle cells	6–13
ovulation	• oocyte bursts from ovary		14
luteal	• corpus luteum forms and endometrium thickens	estrogen and progesterone produced by the corpus luteum	15–28

menopause the termination of the female reproductive years

follicle-stimulating hormone (FSH) in females, a gonadotropin that promotes the development of the follicles in the ovary

luteinizing hormone (LH) in females, a gonadotropin that promotes ovulation and the formation of the corpus luteum

Unlike the testes, which replenish sex cells, the female ovaries undergo continual decline after the onset of puberty. Each of the two ovaries contains about 400 000 follicles at puberty. Many follicles develop during each female reproductive cycle, but usually only a single follicle becomes dominant and reaches maturity. The remaining follicles deteriorate and are reabsorbed within the ovary. Between the ages of about 12 and 50 in a woman's life, approximately 400 eggs will mature. By the time a woman reaches **menopause**, when ovulation ceases, few follicles remain. It has been suggested that the higher incidence of genetic defects in children produced by older women can be linked to the age of the follicles. Older follicles are presumed to have a greater chance of genetic damage. Because female sex hormones are produced within the ovary, menopause marks the end of a female's reproductive life and signals a drop in the production of female hormones.

Feedback Control of the Menstrual Cycle

The hypothalamus–pituitary complex regulates the production of estrogen and progesterone, the hormones of the ovary. In females, the gonadotropins **follicle-stimulating hormone (FSH)** and **luteinizing hormone (LH)** regulate the control of hormones produced by the ovaries: estrogen and progesterone. In turn, ovarian hormones, as part of a complex negative feedback mechanism, regulate the gonadotropins.

The onset of female puberty is signalled by the release of GnRH (gonadotropin-releasing hormone) from the hypothalamus (**Figure 6**). GnRH activates the pituitary gland, which is the production and storage site of FSH and LH. During the follicular phase of the menstrual cycle, the blood carries FSH secretions to the ovary, where follicle development is stimulated. The follicles within the ovary secrete estrogen, which initiates the development of the endometrium. As estrogen levels rise, a negative feedback message is sent to the pituitary gland to turn off secretions of FSH. The follicular phase of the menstrual cycle has ended. Simultaneously, the rise in estrogen stimulates the LH-producing cells of the pituitary gland. LH secretion rises dramatically and ovulation occurs.

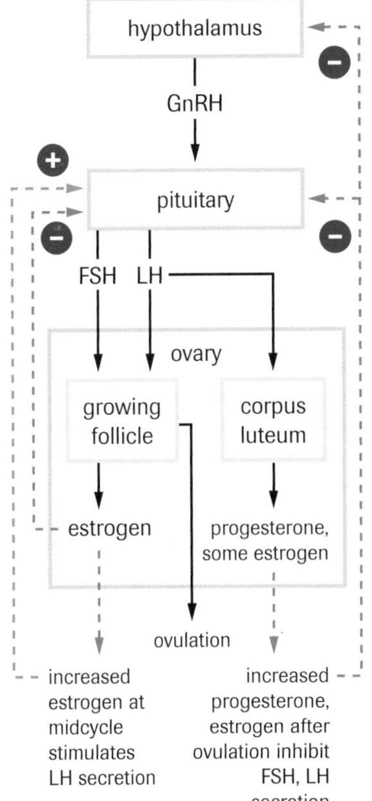

Figure 6
Feedback loop showing the regulation of ovarian hormones

After ovulation, the remaining follicular cells, under the influence of LH, are transformed into a functioning corpus luteum. The luteal phase of the menstrual cycle has begun. Cells of the corpus luteum secrete both estrogen and progesterone. The buildup of estrogen and progesterone will further increase the development of the endometrium. As progesterone and estrogen build up within the body, a second negative feedback mechanism is activated. Progesterone and estrogen work together to inhibit the release of both FSH and LH. Without gonadotropic hormones, the corpus luteum begins to deteriorate, slowing estrogen and progesterone production. The drop in ovarian hormones signals the beginning of menstruation. Some birth control pills (also called oral contraceptives) contain high concentrations of progesterone, which inhibits ovulation and thereby prevents conception.

Hormones involved in the menstrual cycle and their roles are summarized in **Table 3**.

Table 3 Female Reproductive Hormones

Hormone	Location	Description of function
estrogen	follicle cells (ovary)	inhibits growth of facial hair, initiates secondary sexual characteristics, and causes thickening of the endometrium
progesterone	corpus luteum (ovary)	inhibits ovulation, inhibits uterine contractions, firms the cervix, and stimulates the endometrium
follicle-stimulating hormone (FSH)	pituitary	stimulates the development of the follicle cells in the ovary
luteinizing hormone (LH)	pituitary	stimulates ovulation and the formation and maintenance of the corpus luteum

You may recall from the previous section that LH and FSH are also involved in regulation of the male reproductive system. Similarities between male and female systems extend beyond this. Testosterone and estrogen can be produced by either sex. Male characteristics result because the levels of male hormones exceed the levels of estrogen. Males are ensured of maintaining low levels of female hormones by excreting them at an accelerated rate. This may explain why the urine of a stallion contains high levels of estrogen. In humans, the secretions of male hormones will stimulate the development of the male's prostate gland, but injections of estrogen will slow the process. This may explain why cancerous tumours of the prostate can be slowed by injections of estrogen-like compounds.

Practice

3. Outline the functions of estrogen and progesterone.
4. How do gonadotropic hormones regulate the function of ovarian hormones?

DID YOU KNOW ?

Menopause Is a Major Transition

When a middle-aged woman has missed her menstrual period for 12 consecutive months, she has officially reached menopause. By that point, estrogen levels have dropped by as much as 90 % from their lifetime high.

EXTENSION

A Woman's Dilemma: The Benefits and Risks of HRT

Alicia Priest (medical journalist in Victoria), Heather Davies (61-year-old Victoria woman and former nurse), Dr. Christine Derzko (leading authority on HRT and an associate professor of obstetrics and gynaecology at the University of Toronto), Dr. Nanette Wenger (cardiologist at Atlanta's Emory University), and Dr. Jerilyn Prior, (professor of endocrinology at the University of B.C.) discuss the benefits and risks of estrogen and HRT for menopausal women, including recent research results that show the treatment may not be as safe as earlier presumed.

www.science.nelson.com

LAB EXERCISE 16.B

Hormone Levels during the Menstrual Cycle

Report Checklist

- ○ Purpose
- ○ Problem
- ○ Hypothesis
- ○ Prediction
- ○ Design
- ○ Materials
- ○ Procedure
- ○ Evidence
- ● Analysis
- ● Evaluation
- ○ Synthesis

How do hormone levels regulate the female menstrual cycle? Use the following experimental data to analyze hormone levels during the menstrual cycle.

Analysis and Evaluation

1. Gonadotropic hormones regulate ovarian hormones. Study the feedback loop shown in **Figure 7**.

(a) Which of the four hormones (W, X, Y, and Z) are gonadotropic hormones?

(b) Which of the four hormones are ovarian hormones?

(c) Which of the four hormones exert negative feedback effects?

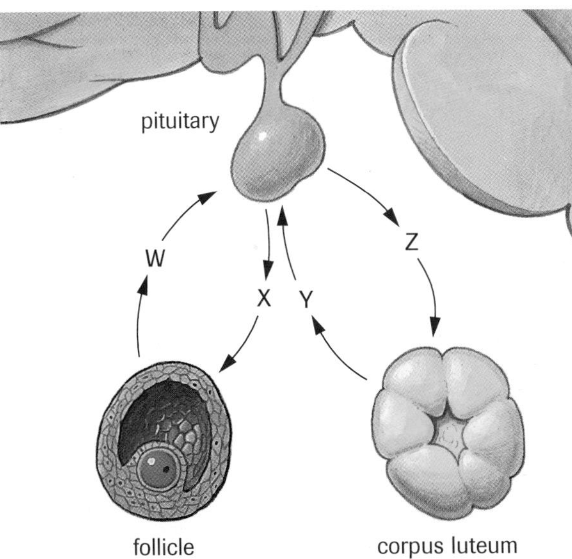

Figure 7
Feedback loop showing the regulation of gonadotropic and ovarian hormones.

2. Body temperatures of two women were monitored during their menstrual cycles. One woman ovulated; the other did not. The results are shown in **Table 4**.

(d) Graph the data in **Table 4**.

(e) Assuming this menstrual cycle represents the average 28-day cycle, label the ovulation day on the graph.

(f) Describe changes in temperature before and during ovulation.

(g) Compare body temperatures with and without a functioning corpus luteum.

Table 4 Temperature Changes in an Ovulating Woman and a Non-Ovulating Woman

	Temperature (°C)	
Days	**Ovulation occurs**	**No ovulation**
5	36.4	36.3
10	36.2	35.7
12	36.0	35.8
14	38.4	36.2
16	37.1	36.1
18	36.6	36.0
20	36.8	36.3
22	37.0	36.3
24	37.1	36.4
28	36.6	36.5

3. **Figure 8** shows changes in the thickness of the endometrium throughout the menstrual cycle.

(h) Identify the events that occur at times X and Z.

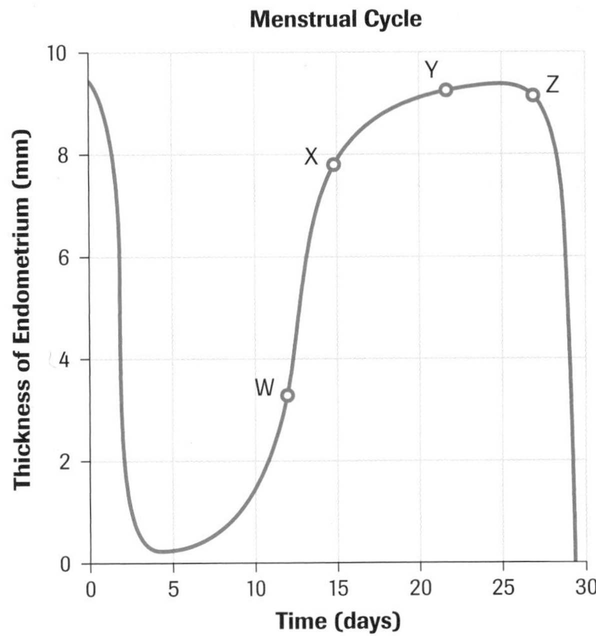

Figure 8
Changes in the thickness of the endometrium during the menstrual cycle

LAB EXERCISE 16.B *continued*

(i) Identify by letter the time at which follicle cells produce estrogen.

(j) Identify by letter the time at which the corpus luteum produces estrogen and progesterone.

4. Levels of gonadotropic hormones monitored throughout the reproductive cycle are shown in **Figure 9**. Levels are recorded in relative units.

(k) How does LH affect estrogen and progesterone?

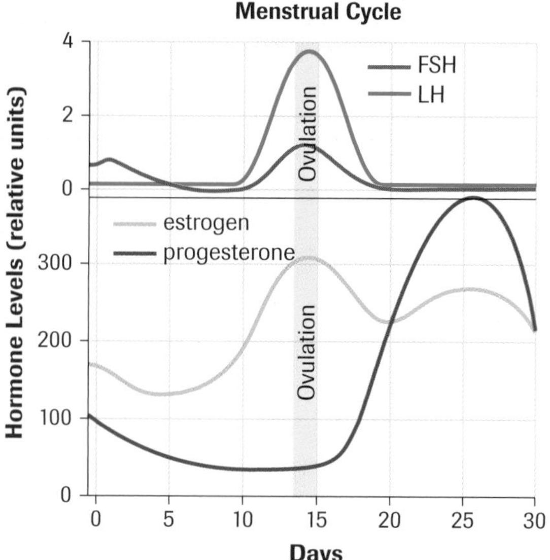

Figure 9
Changes in estrogen and progesterone during the menstrual cycle

SUMMARY The Female Reproductive System

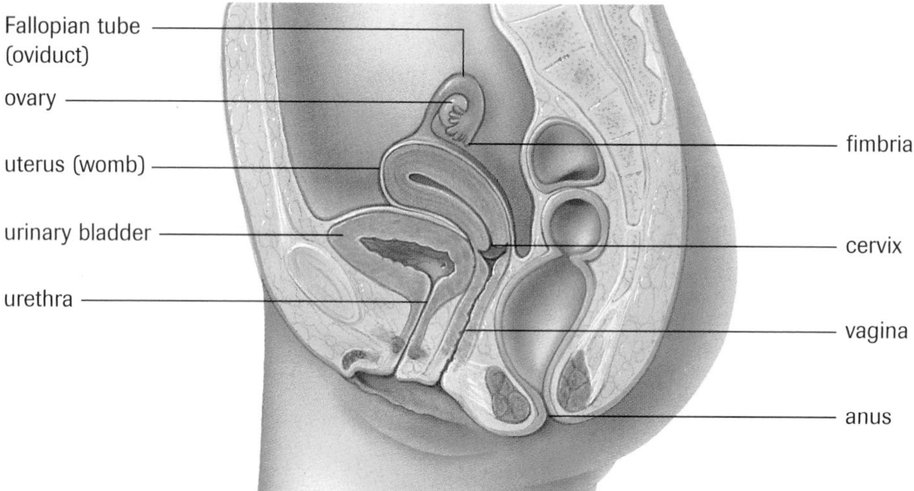

Figure 10
Female reproductive anatomy, side view. Note there are two oviducts and two ovaries. **Table 5** on the next page summarizes the structures and functions of the female reproductive system.

Table 5 The Female Reproductive System

Structure	Function
ovaries	• produce the hormones estrogen and progesterone • site of ovum (egg cell) development and ovulation
Fallopian tubes (oviducts)	• carry the ovum from the ovary to the uterus • usually the site of fertilization
fimbriae	• sweep the ovum into the Fallopian tube following ovulation
uterus (womb)	• pear-shaped organ in which the embryo and fetus develop • involved in menstruation
cervix	• separates the vagina from the uterus • holds the fetus in place during pregnancy • dilates during birth to allow the fetus to leave the uterus
vagina	• extends from the cervix to the external environment • provides a passageway for sperm and menstrual flow • functions as the birth canal

- Oogenesis the process by which an ovum matures within a follicle. Oogenesis is stimulated by FSH (follicle stimulating hormone).
- Ovulation involves the release of the egg from the follicle, and is stimulated by LH (leutenizing hormone).
- Menstruation is the shedding of the endometrium, and marks the beginning of the menstrual cycle.
- During the menstrual cycle, levels of estrogen and progesterone change. Estrogen stimulates thickening of the endometrium. Progesterone inhibits ovulation and uterine contractions, firms the cervix, and stimulates the endometrium.

EXTENSION

The Estrous Cycle

Mammals vary greatly in the detailed functioning of their reproductive systems. Complete this extension activity to compare the human menstrual cycle to the estrous cycle, which occurs in mammals such as dogs, cattle, and bears.

www.science.nelson.com 

Section 16.2 Questions

1. Describe the process of ovulation. Differentiate between primary oocytes, secondary oocytes, and ova.
2. Describe the events associated with the flow phase, follicular phase, and luteal phase of menstruation.
3. With reference to the female reproductive system, provide an example of a negative feedback control system.
4. Predict how low secretions of gonadotropin-releasing hormone (GnRH) from the hypothalamus would affect the female menstrual cycle.
5. What is a Pap smear?
6. Tubal ligation, ties the Fallopian tubes as a method of female sterilization.
   (a) Why would a woman who has undergone this procedure be unable to get pregnant? Explain your answer.
   (b) Would a woman who undergoes a tubal ligation still menstruate?
7. Explain why birth control pills often contain high concentrations of progesterone and estrogen.
8. Explain why only one corpus luteum may be found in the ovaries of a woman who has given birth to triplets.
9. Estrogen plays a crucial role in maintaining bone strength and density. This is why women over age 50 and women who experience premature menopause are at risk for developing osteoporosis, a disease characterized by low bone mass and increased bone fragility. What can be done to minimize this risk? Investigate both hormone therapies and lifestyle factors.

   www.science.nelson.com 

10. Cattle are given various steroid hormones to increase meat production. Recently, some scientists have expressed concern that animal growth stimulators might have an effect on humans. State and justify your opinion on the practice of using hormones in cattle. What potential problems in humans might be associated with such procedures?

16.3 Fertilization, Pregnancy, and Birth

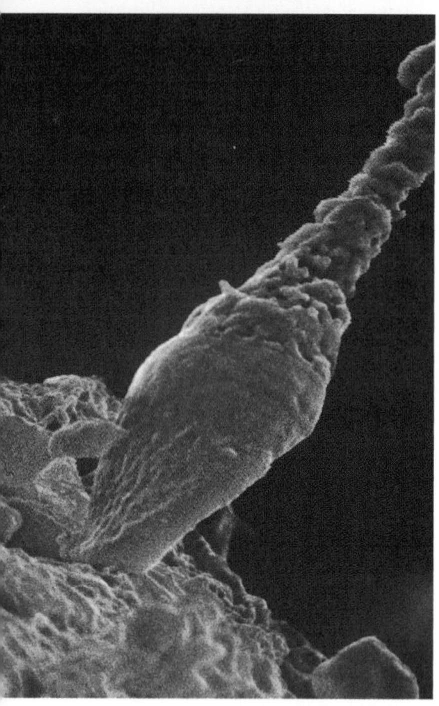

Figure 1
Human sperm cell attached to ovum

Fertilization in humans occurs in a Fallopian tube, and involves the union of a sperm cell with a secondary oocyte. The secondary oocyte then completes its development to become the fertilized ovum (zygote). The zygote receives 23 chromosomes from the sperm cell and 23 chromosomes from the oocyte, and so has 46 chromosomes. Between 150 million and 300 million sperm cells of the 500 million ejaculated during intercourse will travel through the cervix into the uterus. However, only a few hundred actually reach the Fallopian tubes. Although several sperm become attached to the outer edge of the ovulated oocyte, only a single sperm cell fuses with it (**Figure 1**).

The length of time required for the fertilized ovum to travel the 10 to 12 cm Fallopian tube to the uterus is between three and five days. During this time, it undergoes many cell divisions in a process called cleavage. **Cleavage** involves equal divisions of the cells of the zygote without any increase in size (**Figure 2 (a)**). As a result, the cells of the zygote become progressively smaller with each division. By the time it reaches the uterus, in about six days, the zygote has developed into a fluid-filled structure called a blastocyst (**Figure 2 (b)**). The **blastocyst** consists of an outer sphere of cells, from which the extraembryonic structures develop, and an inner cell mass, from which the embryo develops. Once in the uterus, the blastocyst becomes attached to the wall of the endometrium, a process referred to as **implantation**.

cleavage cell division of a zygote, in which the number of cells increases without any change in the size of the zygote

blastocyst an early stage of embryo development

implantation the attachment of the embryo to the endometrium

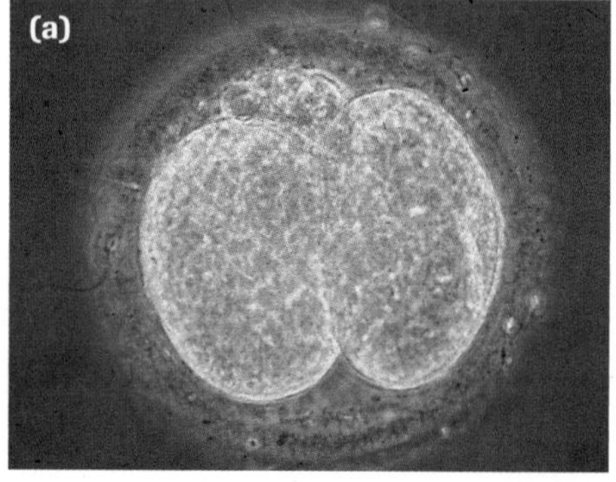

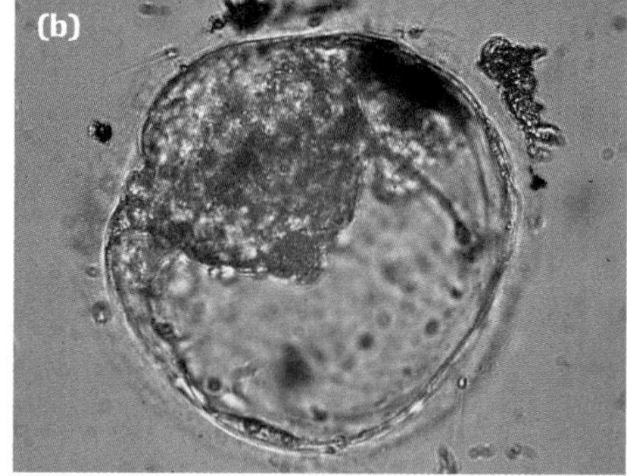

Figure 2
(a) Two-cell stage of a human zygote undergoing cleavage
(b) Blastocyst after 4 to 6 days

Changes in the Female Reproductive System

In humans, four days after fertilization, the zygote becomes an embryo. It will remain an embryo until the end of the eighth week of pregnancy, after which time it is referred to as a fetus. The events of pregnancy, usually take place over about nine months from the woman's last menstrual period. Over this time, a woman's body will change to ensure the pregnancy continues and the embryo/fetus is protected. Some of these changes are shown in **Figure 3** on the next page.

For pregnancy to continue, menstruation cannot occur. Any shedding of the endometrium would mean the dislodging of the embryo from the uterus. However, maintaining the endometrium presents a problem for the hormonal system. To prevent menstruation, progesterone and estrogen levels must be maintained. High levels of these hormones have a negative-feedback effect on the secretion of gonadotropic hormones.

+ EXTENSION

Blocking Polyspermy
What prevents more than one sperm from fertilizing the ovum (polyspermy)? This audio clip outlines the sequence of actions that are associated with preventing polyspermy.

www.science.nelson.com 

LH levels must remain high to sustain the corpus luteum. Should the corpus luteum deteriorate, the levels of estrogen and progesterone would drop, stimulating uterine contractions and the shedding of the endometrium.

EXTENSION

Cleavage and Implantation
This animation shows events that happen in the female reproductive system from fertilization of the egg to formation of the chorion.

www.science.nelson.com GO

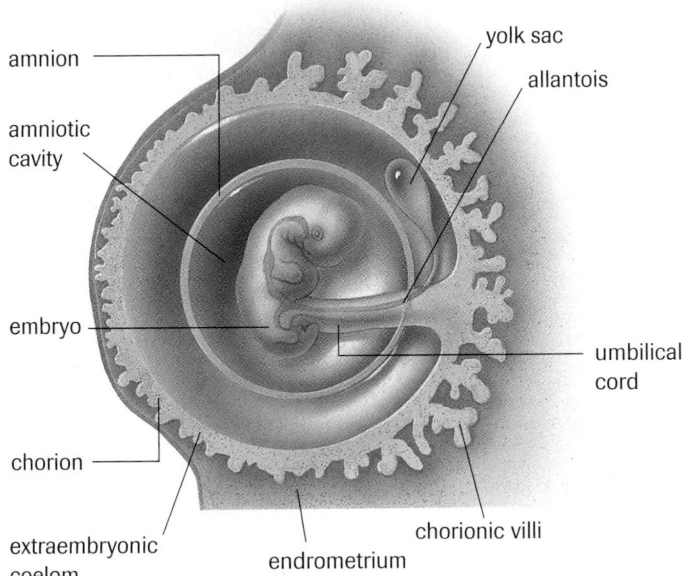

Figure 3
Structures that support the developing embryo at 4 weeks

This problem is avoided by secretion of hormone from the blastocyst itself. The outer layer of the blastocyst gives rise to two structures: the **chorion** and the **amnion**. The chorion produces the hormone **human chorionic gonadotropic hormone (hCG)**, which maintains the corpus luteum for the first three months of pregnancy. The functioning corpus luteum continues producing progesterone and estrogen, which in turn maintain the endometrium. The endometrium and embryo thus remain in the uterus. Pregnancy tests identify hCG levels in the urine of women.

Between the amnion and the embryo or fetus is the **amniotic cavity**, a fluid-filled sac that insulates the embryo, and later the fetus, protecting it from infection, dehydration, impact, and changes in temperature. The **extraembryonic coelom** is a fluid-filled space between the amnion and the chorion. By the second week of pregnancy, the **yolk sac** forms beneath the embryo. The yolk sac is the site of early red blood cell formation and later contributes to the primitive digestive tract.

Cells from the embryo and endometrium combine to form the **placenta**, through which materials are exchanged between the mother and developing embryo. At approximately the fourth month of pregnancy, the placenta begins to produce estrogen and progesterone. High levels of progesterone prevent further ovulation. This means that once a woman is pregnant, she cannot become pregnant again during that pregnancy.

The placenta is richly supplied with blood vessels. Projections called **chorionic villi** ensure that a large number of blood vessels of the fetus are exposed to maternal blood. The **allantois**, provides umbilical blood vessels in the placenta. However, unlike the chorion and amnion, the allantois does not envelop the fetus. The placenta provides an interface for exchange between mother and fetus. Nutrients and oxygen diffuse from the mother's blood into the blood of the developing fetus. Wastes diffuse in the opposite direction, moving from the fetus to the mother. The **umbilical cord** connects the embryo with the placenta (**Figure 4**, next page).

chorion the outer extraembryonic structure of a developing embryo that will contribute to the placenta

amnion a fluid-filled extraembryonic structure

human chorionic gonadotropic hormone (hCG) an embryonic hormone that maintains the corpus luteum

amniotic cavity the fluid-filled cavity surrounding the developing embryo

extraembryonic coelom body cavity between the amnion and the chorion

yolk sac a membranous sac that forms during embryo development of most vertebrates; in humans, it does not contain yolk

placenta the site for the exchange of nutrients and wastes between mother and fetus

chorionic villi vascular projections of the chorion

allantois extraembryonic structure that contributes to the blood vessels of the placenta

umbilical cord structure that connects the fetus to the placenta

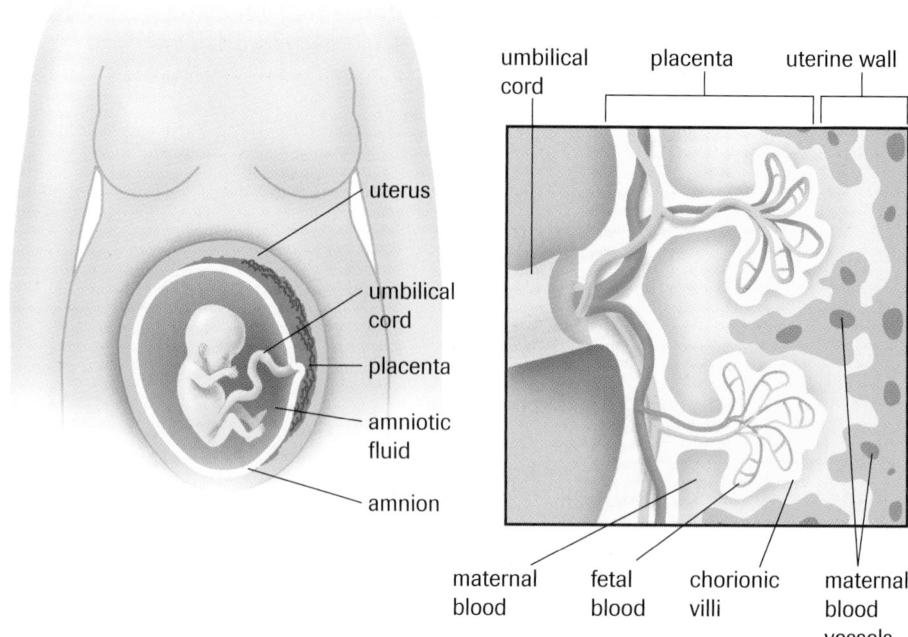

Figure 4 The developing fetus is nourished by the placenta. The rich supply of blood vessels allows for exchange of nutrients, oxygen, and waste between the maternal blood supply and the fetal blood supply.

Practice

1. Using a diagram, differentiate between the allantois and the amnion. What are their functions?

Embryonic and Fetal Development

Morphogenesis is the development of an organism or part of it. Morphogenesis in humans and other multicellular organisms involves two processes: growth (increase in size) and differentiation (cell specialization). In this section, we will explore the morphogenesis that takes place during pregnancy.

first trimester the period during pregnancy from conception until the end of the third month

gastrulation process by which a gastrula is formed

gastrula stage of embryonic development in which the embryo is composed of three layers: ectoderm, mesoderm, and endoderm

The nine months of pregnancy are divided into three trimesters. The **first trimester** extends from fertilization to the end of the third month. By the second week of development, the inner cells of the blastula have reorganized into a flattened disk made up of two layers. **Gastrulation** is the process in which the two-layered structure develops into a three-layered structure called a **gastrula**. Gastrulation is a very important developmental step. Each of these three layers has a particular developmental fate. In other words, each layer will give rise to specific organs and structures in the fetus. These are shown in **Table 1**.

Table 1 Organs and Structures Arising from the Three Gastrula Layers

Gastrula layer	Structures
ectoderm	• skin, hair, finger nails, sweat glands • nervous system, brain, peripheral nerves • lens, retina, cornea • inner ear, cochlea, semicircular canals • teeth, inside lining of mouth
mesoderm	• muscles (skeletal, cardiac, and smooth) • blood vessels and blood • kidneys, reproductive structures • connective tissue, cartilage, bone
endoderm	• liver, pancreas, thyroid, parathyroid • urinary bladder • lining of digestive system • lining of respiratory tract

Gastrulation begins when the disk elongates and forms a narrow line of cells at the midline. Cells migrate inward near this line and differentiate into the three layers of the gastrula. The outer layer is the **ectoderm**, the middle layer is the **mesoderm**, and the inner layer is the **endoderm**.

By the end of the first month, the 1 cm long embryo is 500 times larger than the fertilized egg (**Table 2** on page 534, **Figure 5 (a)**). Many of the important organs and systems are beginning to develop by this point . The four-chambered heart has formed, a large brain is visible, and limb buds with tiny fingers and toes have developed. By the ninth week (**Figure 5 (b)**), the embryo is referred to as a fetus. Arms and legs begin to move and a sucking reflex is evident.

By the beginning of the **second trimester**, the fetus is about 8 cm long and all of its organs have formed, although they are not fully developed. During this trimester, the organs continue to develop and the fetus increases in size. It will move enough to make itself know to the mother and it begins to look more like a human infant (**Figure 5 (c)**). As in other mammals, soft hair begins to cover the entire body. By the sixth month, eyelids and eyelashes form. Most of the cartilage that formed the skeleton has been replaced by bone cells. Should the mother go into labour at the end of the second trimester, there is a chance that the 34 cm, 1000 g fetus will survive.

During the **third trimester,** the baby grows rapidly (**Figure 5 (d)**). Organ systems have been established during the first two trimesters; all that remains is for the body mass to increase and the organs to enlarge and become more developed. At birth, the average human infant is approximately 51 cm long and weighs about 3400 g.

Table 2, on the next page, outlines the major events in human embryo development.

Weeks 3 to 4 of Development

This animation shows early events in organ formation during development of a human embryo.

www.science.nelson.com 

ectoderm the outer layer of cells in an embryo

mesoderm the middle layer of cells in an embryo

endoderm the inner layer of cells in an embryo

second trimester the period during pregnancy from the fourth month to the end of the sixth month

third trimester the period during pregnancy from the seventh month until birth

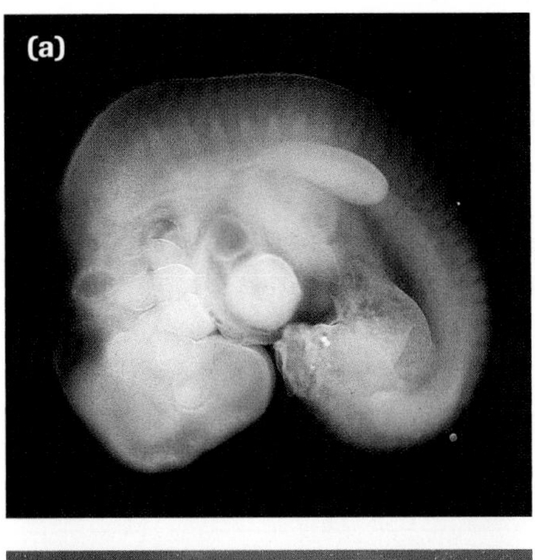

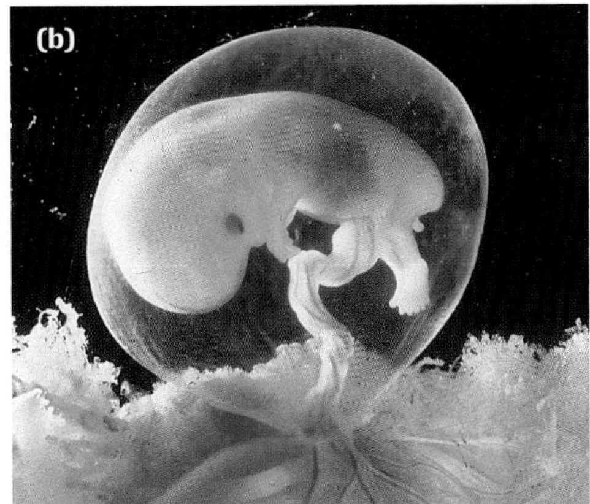

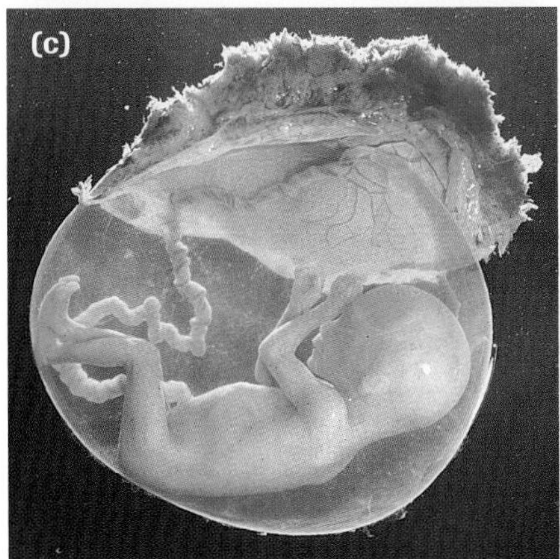

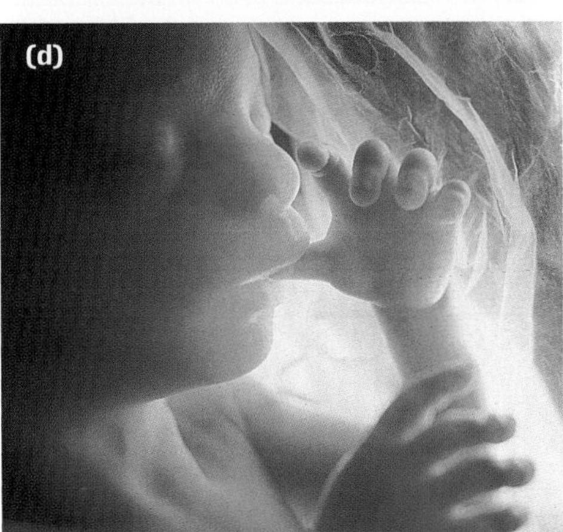

Figure 5
(a) Human embryo at 4 weeks
(b) Fetus at 9 weeks
(c) Fetus at 16 weeks
(d) Fetus at 18 weeks

Table 2 Three Stages of Development

Stage	Characteristics
First Trimester	
0–1.5 weeks	• fertilization and early development • formation of a viable zygote by the union of sperm and ovum; fertilization • implantation normally positioned in the uterus
1.5 weeks	• embryonic development begins • amnion and yolk sac formed
2nd week	• formation of primitive streak and primary germ layers
3rd week	• central nervous system begins to develop • heart development initiated; beating begins
4th week	• about 1 cm long and weighs less than 1 g • early eyes • limb buds of arms and legs
5th week	• nose and lips formation begins • basic architecture of brain and spinal cord established
8th week	• now about the size of a chicken's egg • embryo 2 cm long and weighs about 4 g • hands and feet seen • baby extremely reactive to its environment • male sex hormone (testosterone) produced by testes • masculine development in males; no change in females
9th week	• fetal development begins
12th week	• embryo about the size of a goose egg • placenta well-established and weighs more than the baby • baby approximately 9 cm long and weighs about 60 g
Second Trimester	
14th–16th week	• brain developed to the point that baby can suck, swallow, and make irregular breathing movements
16th week	• 14 cm long and weighs 180 g • complete closure of nasal septum and palate • fetal heart beat heard with amplification • fetal movement is recognized • sex distinguishable now
20th week	• 20 cm long and weighs 300 g • fine hair covering over entire body; probably for protection of skin • fetal heart beat heard: 120-160 beats per minute
Third Trimester	
28th week	• baby can survive outside uterus if lungs capable of breathing • 10 %-20 % survival if born at this time • 35 cm long and weighs 1100 g
32nd week	• maturing: 50 % survival if born at this time • should turn to head down position • 41 cm long, weighs 1680 g • skin red and wrinkly
30th–34th week	• baby the same size as placenta
36th week	• 94 % survival rate if born at this age • 46 cm long, weighs 2500 g • some subcutaneous fat • fingernails now at the tips of the fingers
40th week	• full term: 51 cm long, weighs 3400 g

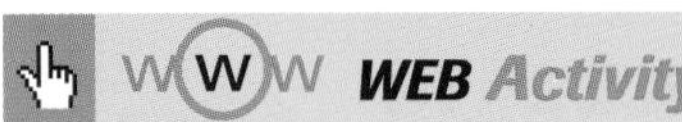

Simulation—The Visible Embryo

A zygote is formed by the union of a sperm cell and an egg cell. In humans, the single fertilized egg cell is transformed into a multicellular embryo by cell division. During embryonic development, cells become specialized and begin to form organs and organ systems.

In this Web Activity, you will examine the changes that occur during embryonic development. Week 1 describes fertilization and cleavage, week 2 implantation, and week 3 the process of gastrulation. Week 4 presents photos and descriptions of folding and tissue formation. Each section includes self quizzes to assist in you in learning more about embryonic development.

www.science.nelson.com 

Human Sex Determination

Sex is determined by the genetic makeup of the fetus. Females have two X chromosomes, while males have a single X and a much smaller Y chromosome. You will find out more about X and Y chromosomes in Unit 30 C. In 1987, geneticists were able to locate the principal gene for sex determination on the Y chromosome. The *SRY* (**S**ex-determining **R**egion of the **Y** chromosome) gene is mainly responsible for determining the male phenotype in humans. It might surprise you to find out that a male fetus does not differ from a female fetus until about the sixth or seventh week of pregnancy. In the presence of the *SRY* gene, the developing gonad becomes a testis. Synthesis of hormones by cells of the testis subsequently directs the development of male characteristics. The testes develop inside the body cavity in the same location as the ovaries and gradually descend. It may appear that the absence of the *SRY* gene causes the development of the female characteristics. However, things may not be quite this simple. Some researchers have speculated that female sex determination might be even more complicated than that of the male.

The balance between male and female is also determined by the hormones circulating in the bloodstream. Women produce some male sex hormones or androgens, along with estrogen. A woman's body will synthesize estrogen from androgens such as testosterone. Similarly, males produce female sex hormones, but in much smaller quantities than females do.

At no time is the hormonal balance between male and female sex hormones more critical than during fetal development. Too much estrogen at the wrong time can transform an organism with male genes into what outwardly appears to be a female. Conversely, an overabundance of androgens or male sex hormones during fetal development can produce the sex organs of a male in the genetic body of a female.

DID YOU KNOW ?

Environmental Estrogens

Many widely used synthetic chemicals and natural plant compounds can alter or interfere with the endocrine system. These so-called environmental estrogens can mimic estrogen and have been associated with health and reproductive problems in wildlife and laboratory animals. In humans, the reproductive tract of males begins to develop between the 7th and 14th week of pregnancy. The appearance of additional estrogen and/or progesterone during this phase can trigger the reversal of gender.

INVESTIGATION 16.1 ***Introduction***

Observing Embryo Development

The transformation of a zygote to an embryo to a fetus is a remarkable process. The zygote undergoes many cell divisions, each of which doubles the number of cells. As the number of cells increases, they also begin to differentiate, eventually forming various tissues and organs. It is very difficult to view these events in humans. However, the early stages of all vertebrates are very similar. In this investigation, you can begin to appreciate what occurs in the development of a human embryo by observing embryo development in frogs.

Report Checklist

○ Purpose	○ Design	● Analysis
● Problem	○ Materials	● Evaluation
○ Hypothesis	○ Procedure	● Synthesis
○ Prediction	● Evidence	

To perform this investigation, turn to page 545. 

Figure 6
Dr. Keith Bagnall

Canadian Achievers—Dr. Keith Bagnall

Dr. Keith Bagnall (**Figure 6**) is a professor in the Division of Anatomy and a member of the Perinatal Research Centre at the University of Alberta. His research interests include the development of the vertebral column, focusing on congenital anomalies, and the development of scoliosis (curvature of the spine) and osteoarthritis.

Dr. Bagnall takes his passion for teaching and learning into high schools and teacher conferences. Among other topics, he explains the crucial steps of fetal development and the negative consequences when an embryo is exposed to chemicals such as nicotine and alcohol. His engaging, interactive presentations have earned him the Distinguished Service Award from the ATA Science Council. Visit the Nelson Web site to learn more about Dr. Bagnall's research contributions.

www.science.nelson.com 

Effects of Environmental Agents on Embryonic Development

The dependency of a newborn on its mother provides a special relationship. However, the dependency prior to birth is even greater. The health and lifestyle decisions of the mother remain with her child for a lifetime.

Proper nutrition prevents many developmental problems. Spina bifida is a relatively common condition that results from a failure of the spinal cord to develop properly. This defect is associated with low levels of folic acid, a member of the B vitamin complex. Because the nervous system is formed in the first month of development (often before a woman knows she is pregnant), some physicians recommend folic acid supplementation for all women of childbearing years.

DID YOU KNOW ?

Teratogenesis

Teratogenesis is a medical term from the Greek, literally meaning 'monster making.'

Lifestyle choices also affect the development of the embryo. Research has demonstrated that women who smoke have smaller babies. This can in part be attributed to the drug nicotine (found in cigarettes) which constricts blood vessels. The reduced blood flow to the placenta means that less oxygen and fewer nutrients are available for growth of the fetus. One study has shown that women who smoke while pregnant have lower levels of vitamin C, even when they consume as much vitamin C as the members of a control group. Smoking may affect the utilization of other nutrients as well.

teratogen any medication, chemical, infectious disease, or environmental agent that might interfere with the normal development of a fetus or embryo

Agents (chemicals and microbes) that are capable of causing developmental abnormalities *in utero* are called **teratogens** (**Table 3**). A number of drugs that can cross the placental membrane have been suspected of adversely affecting fetal development. Most teratogens cause problems early in fetal development. Some organ systems, such as the nervous system, are sensitive to teratogens very early during pregnancy (**Figure 7**, next page).

Practice

2. Outline the events of development during the first, second, and third trimester.
3. Why is an embryo less susceptible to teratogens prior to implantation?

Table 3 Effect of Teratogens on the Developing Embryo

Groups	Agents	Effects on embryo
social drugs	alcohol	Alcohol crosses the placenta to the baby. It can accumulate in the amniotic fluid surrounding the baby before the birth and cause problems such as miscarriage, stillbirth, bleeding during pregnancy, and premature births.
	cigarettes	Carbon monoxide and nicotine reduce the amount of oxygen available in the mother's blood, which can affect the development and size of the baby.
	cocaine	Cocaine increases the heart rate in both the mother and baby, and the supply of oxygen and blood to the baby is reduced, which makes it more likely that the baby will be small and grow slowly. Several cases of bleeding in the brain have been reported in babies whose mothers were dependent on cocaine.
medications	thalidomide	Thalidomide blocks blood vessels that lead to the limbs.
	seizure medication (Dilantin, Tegretol, and valproic acid)	Seizure medication reduces blood flow to the central nervous system.
infectious diseases	rubella	The rubella virus enters the respiratory tract via airborne droplets and spreads to the lymphatic system.
	genital herpes	A pregnant woman who develops genital herpes can pass the virus to her fetus. This produces a higher risk of premature delivery. Newborns rarely become infected with herpes; however, half of those who do become infected either die or suffer neurological damage.

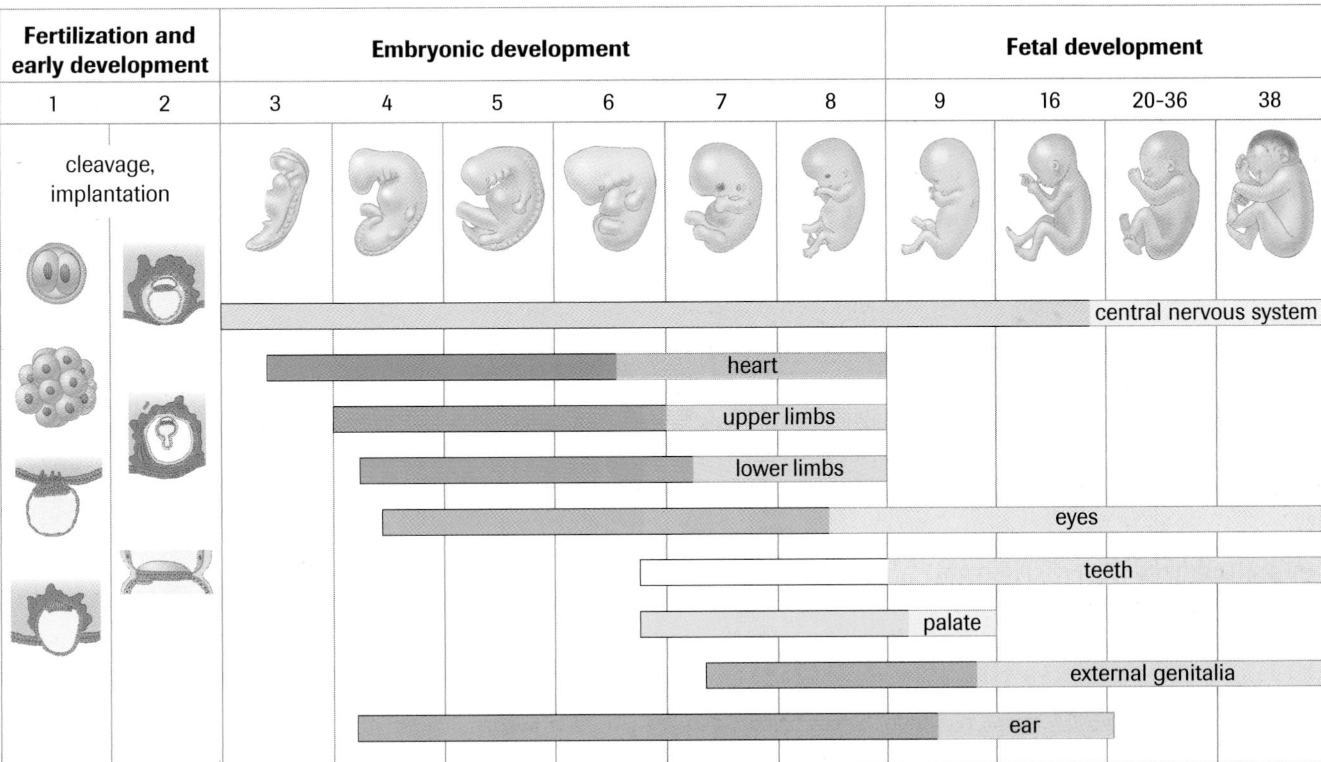

Figure 7
Periods of system and organ development during embryonic and fetal development. Dark areas indicate stages of development that are most sensitive to the effects of teratogens.

EXPLORE an issue

Issue Checklist

● Issue ○ Design ● Analysis
● Resolution ○ Evidence ● Evaluation

Fetal Alcohol Spectrum Disorder

The placenta is a selective barrier that prevents the mother's blood cells from entering the circulatory system of the fetus. Smaller molecules, however, can move across the membrane. Unfortunately, some harmful agents, such as alcohol, are small enough to cross the placenta. When a mother takes in alcohol, it crosses the placenta and enters the blood of the fetus **(Figure 8)**. As the mother drinks, the fetus absorbs alcohol.

The effects on the fetus are the same as those on the mother: alcohol impairs the functioning of the nervous system and it is a depressant. It is also a poisonous substance. Like other poisons, it is broken down by the liver. Unfortunately, the liver of a fetus is not fully developed until the very final stages of pregnancy, and alcohol cannot be broken down quickly. This means that alcohol remains in its most harmful form much longer in the fetus than it does in the mother. Not only can alcohol kill many of the cells of the fetus, but it has also been linked to changing a cell's genetic information.

Fetal alcohol spectrum disorder (FASD) is a host of birth defects associated with excessive alcohol consumption. Dr. Matthew Hicks, who researches FASD at the University of Calgary, indicates that although FASD is preventable, it is one of the most common birth defects in Canada. FASD crosses all cultural and ethnic boundaries, but occurs only in children born to mothers who consumed alcohol during pregnancy. Children with FASD may have physical abnormalities such as a low body weight, slowed development, deformed organs, a poorly formed rib cage, limited joint movement, and missing digits, as well as distinctive facial features such as a small head, thin upper lip, and small jaw bone. Symptoms of FASD can also include abnormalities of the nervous system, which can cause learning disabilities, poor hand and finger coordination, irritability in infancy, and hyperactivity in childhood.

Approximately 60 % to 70 % of women who are alcoholics give birth to babies with FASD. What may be most disturbing is that evidence suggests that the problem may be getting worse. A 1997 study indicated that four times as many pregnant women admitted to "frequent" drinking in 1995 as compared with a similar 1991 poll. Among 1,313 pregnant women, 3.5 % said they drank an average of seven or more drinks a week or had consumed five or more drinks on at least one occasion in the previous month.

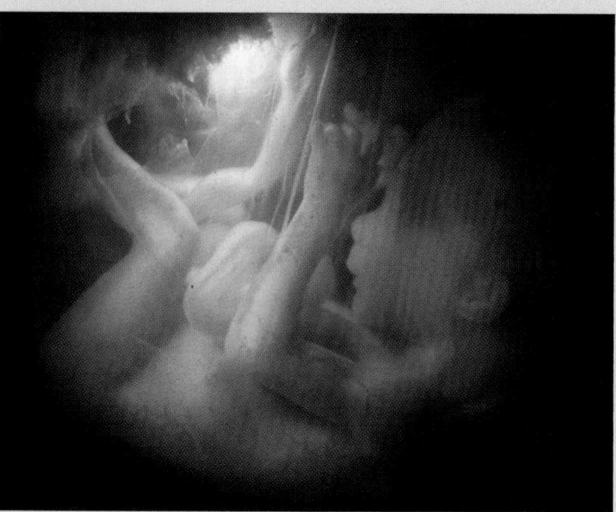

Figure 8
Alcohol passes from the mother's blood across the placenta into the baby.

Understanding the Issue

1. What is FASD?
2. Why are scientists concerned with decreasing the number of women who drink?
3. What are some symptoms of an FASD baby?

Statement

Pregnant women should be required to have blood tests on a regular basis to monitor drinking problems.

- In your group, discuss the statement and the points and counterpoints in **Table 4**. Write down additional points and counterpoints that your group considered.

Table 4 Perspectives on Requiring Pregnant Women to Have Blood Tests

Point	Counterpoint
FASD is the third most common reason for babies being born with mental retardation in Canada and the United States. Alcohol consumption affects mother and baby. Heart defects and defects of the nervous system are most common.	The idea of suspending the rights of pregnant women is unbelievable. All people would hope that mothers would recognize their responsibility, but legislation is not the answer. Changes in attitudes are accomplished best through education.
Despite a growing awareness that avoiding alcohol prevents the disorder, about one-fifth of pregnant women continue to drink even after they learn they are pregnant.	Most birth defects occur in the period between two weeks and three months of development, when the organs are forming. Does this mean that women should be monitored to ensure that they have a well-balanced diet? Many factors have been linked to birth problems by scientific studies.

- Decide whether your group agrees or disagrees with the statement.
- Conduct research for information on FASD and other preventable birth defects.

www.science.nelson.com 

- Prepare to defend your group's position in a class discussion.

 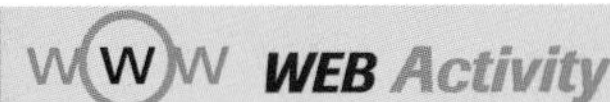

Web Quest—Fetal Rights and FASD

The issue of giving human rights to fetuses is very controversial in Canada and elsewhere. If a fetus were to be given human rights, then pregnant women who behaved in ways that risk the health of a fetus, such as by consuming alcohol, could be held criminally responsible for any damage done as a result. Some people find this unfair to women struggling with addictions. Others think that it unfair that the children of such women may have to struggle throughout their lives with health problems caused by their mothers' addictions. The Canadian government has so far held off deciding whether to give human rights to fetuses. Its stance is that the issue is too complex and that there should be careful consideration of all the potential consequences before such legislation is proposed.

In this Web Quest, you will gather information on this issue as it relates to Fetal Alcohol Spectrum Disorder (FASD), decide where you stand on the issue, and then prepare to defend your viewpoints in a debate. You will consider whether a father of a FASD child can sue the mother, the legal precedents that have already been set in Canada, and what rights a fetus in Canada currently has.

www.science.nelson.com 

CAREER CONNECTION 

Midwife

Midwives care for women and infants through pregnancy, labour, delivery, and after a birth. They also provide information about the changes that occur during pregnancy, the development of the fetus, birthing procedures, and newborn growth and development. Would you enjoy educating men and women about pregnancy and birth?

www.science.nelson.com 

Birth

Approximately 266 days after implantation, uterine contractions signal the beginning of **parturition**, or labour. The cervix thins and begins to dilate (**Figure 9** (**a**), next page). As the amnion is forced into the birth canal, it often bursts, and amniotic fluid lubricates the canal (a process referred to as the breaking of the water) (**Figure 9** (**b**), next page). As the cervix dilates, uterine contractions move the baby through the birth canal (**Figure 9** (**c**) and (**d**), next page). Following the birth of the baby, the placenta is also delivered.

parturition the act of giving birth; labour

Hormones play a vital role in the birthing process. **Relaxin**, a hormone produced by the placenta prior to labour, causes the ligaments within the pelvis to loosen and the cervix to soften, providing a more flexible passageway for the baby during delivery. Although the mechanism is not completely understood, it is believed that a decreased production of progesterone is crucial to the onset of labour. **Oxytocin**, a hormone from the pituitary gland, causes strong uterine contractions. Prostaglandins, which are also believed to trigger strong uterine contractions, appear in the mother's blood prior to labour.

relaxin a hormone produced by the placenta prior to labour; causes the ligaments within the pelvis to loosen

oxytocin a hormone from the pituitary gland; causes strong uterine contractions

Labour can be induced by administering prostaglandins or pitocin, which is a synthetic form of the hormone oxytocin. The medication stimulates uterine contractions.

EXTENSION

Hormones, Labour, and Parturition

Listen to a discussion of the positive feedback cycle that starts the uterine contractions leading to parturition.

www.science.nelson.com GO

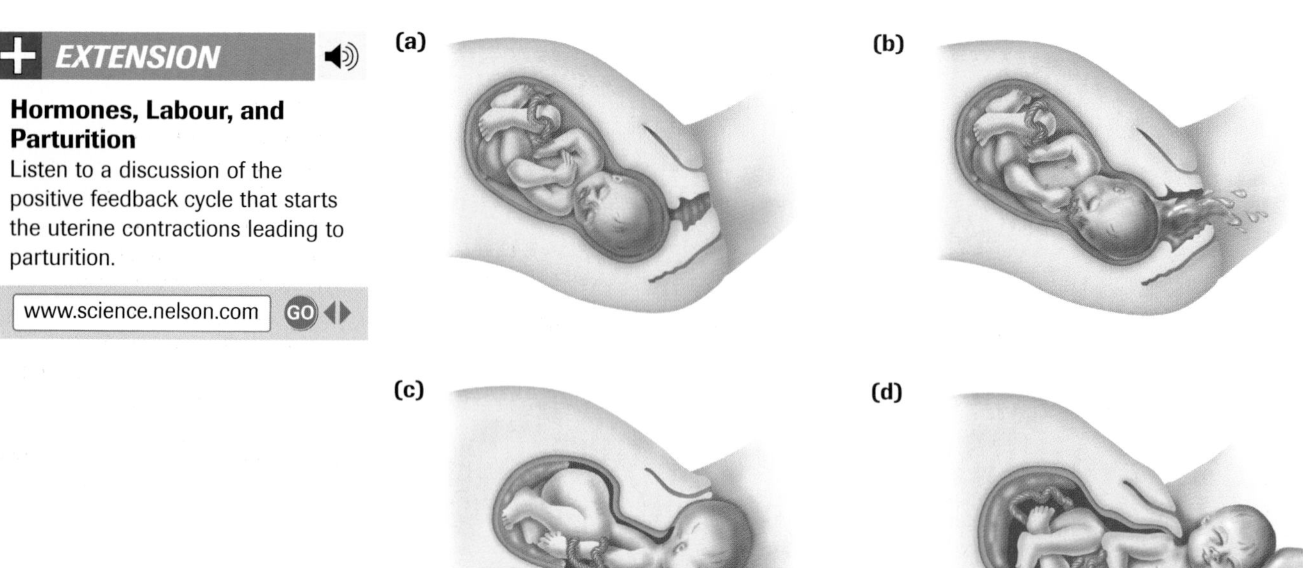

Figure 9
Parturition (labour) begins when **(a)** the cervical opening starts to enlarge. Next **(b)**, the amniotic sac breaks and fluid flows out. Contractions of the uterine muscles push the baby from the uterus **(c)** until it emerges from the birth canal **(d)**.

Lactation

Breast development is stimulated from the onset of puberty by estrogen and progesterone. During pregnancy, elevated levels of estrogen and progesterone prepare the breasts for milk production. Each breast contains about 20 lobes of glandular tissue, each supplied with a tiny duct that carries fluids toward the nipple (**Figure 10**). A hormone called **prolactin**, produced by the pituitary gland, is responsible for stimulating glands within the breast to begin producing fluids. Estrogen stimulates the release of large amounts of prolactin during pregnancy; milk production does not occur before birth, however, because the action of prolactin is inhibited by the high levels of progesterone that are present. The drop in estrogen and progesterone levels after birth results in decreased *amounts* of prolactin, but an increase in prolactin *activity* because the progesterone-induced inhibition is relieved. Prolactin initially causes the production of colostrum, a fluid that closely resembles breast milk. Colostrum contains milk sugar and milk proteins, but lacks the milk fats found in breast milk. A few days after birth, prolactin stimulates the production of milk. Colostrum and mother's milk supply the baby with an important source of antibodies.

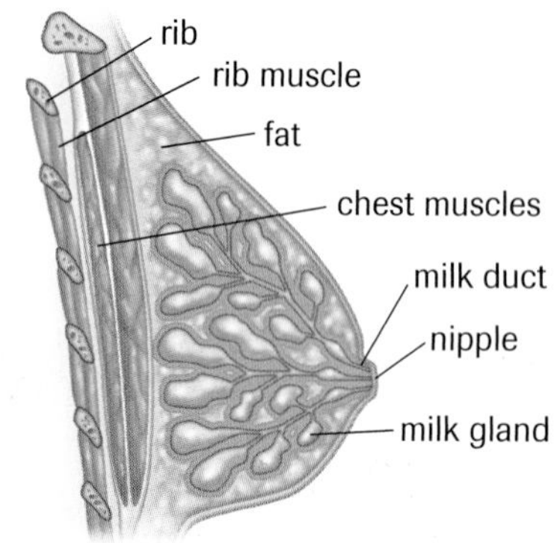

Figure 10
Structure of the human breast

prolactin a hormone produced by the pituitary gland and associated with milk production

Although prolactin increases milk production, the milk does not flow easily. Milk produced in the lobes of glandular tissue must be forced into the ducts that lead to the nipple. The suckling action of the newborn stimulates nerve endings in the areola of the breast. Sensory nerves carry information to the pituitary gland, causing the release of oxytocin. The hormonal reflex is completed as oxytocin is carried by the blood to the breasts and uterus (**Figure 11**). Within the breast, oxytocin causes weak contractions of smooth muscle, forcing milk into the ducts. Within the uterus, oxytocin causes weak contractions of smooth muscle, allowing the uterus to slowly return to its pre-pregnancy size and shape.

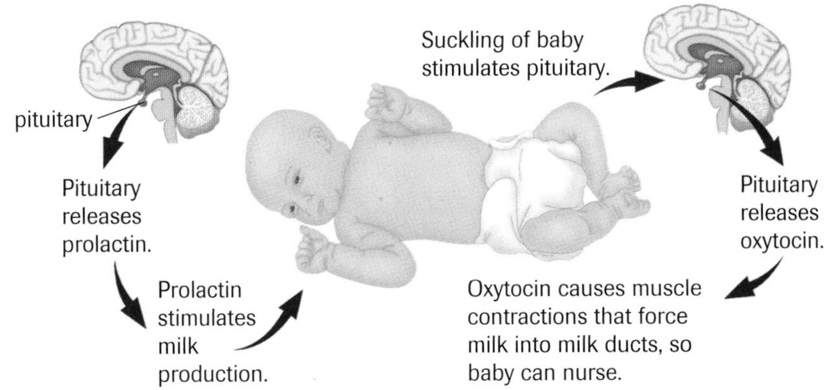

Figure 11
The hormone prolactin stimulates the breast to produce milk. The suckling action of the baby initiates a hormonal reflex involving the hormone oxytocin.

CAREER CONNECTION

Pediatrician
Pediatricians specialize in children's health. They assess the well-being of newborns to adolescents, and may diagnose and treat a wide range of problems, such as infections, congenital abnormalities, or cancer. Would you like to be part of a health care professional team working with children?

www.science.nelson.com 

Although most North American mothers prefer to end breast-feeding once their youngster begins to develop teeth, women in some countries, especially where sources of protein are scarce, often continue to breast-feed for four or five years. Milk production causes a metabolic drain on the mother. At the height of lactation a woman can produce as much as 1.5 L of milk each day. A mother producing that much milk would lose approximately 50 g of fat and up to 100 g of lactose sugar. In addition, a breast-feeding mother would have to replace some 2 to 3 g of calcium phosphate each day. To maintain adequate levels of calcium and phosphate, the parathyroid glands enlarge and bones decalcify. Failure to replace the needed calcium results in a progressive deterioration of the skeleton and teeth.

WWW WEB Activity

Case Study—Creating a Database of Sexually Transmitted Infections

Worldwide, sexually transmitted infections (STIs) find more than 250 million hosts each year. STIs are easily spread through any person-to-person transfer of bodily fluids such as semen, vaginal secretions, or blood. If left untreated, some STIs can cause inflammation and scarring of reproductive passages, leading to infertility. STIs can also result in other serious health problems. The database you will create in this Web Activity will help people find information about STIs.

www.science.nelson.com 

The Face of AIDS
AIDS is a sexually transmitted infection that is still spreading. This video explores how this disease is affecting families in regions of Africa where AIDS continues to spread.

www.science.nelson.com  

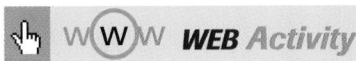

Case Study

Human Reproductive Technology

Reproductive technology gives individuals, who would not otherwise be able to have a baby, a chance at parenthood. Few technologies have raised interest and concern the way that reproductive technology has. Reproductive technology is changing not only the way in which babies are born, but also the laws that decide parenthood and responsibility.

Fertility Drugs

Fertility drugs stimulate the action of pituitary hormones (**Figure 12**). Follicle development within the ovary is enhanced and the release of one or more egg cells becomes more probable. Because fertility drugs increase follicle development within the ovary causing multiple ovulations, the chances of having fraternal twins increases.

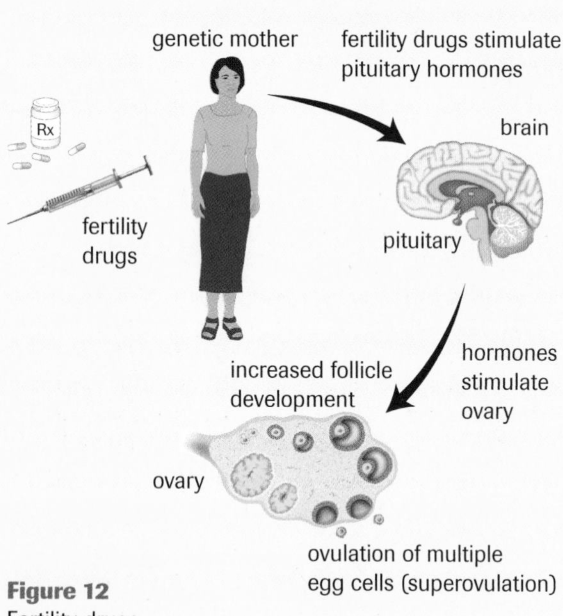

Figure 12
Fertility drugs

Intrauterine Insemination

Sperm cells, either from the woman's partner or from a sperm donor, are transferred into the uterus of the woman following ovulation (**Figure 13**). Most sperm cells normally die before they reach the egg cell and this technique ensures that greater numbers of motile sperm cells reach the egg.

Cytoplasmic Transfer

The cytoplasm from an egg from a younger woman is transferred into the egg cell of an older woman. It is believed that the cytoplasm from the younger woman's egg will reduce the probability of genetic defects following fertilization.

Gamete Intrafallopian Transfer (GIFT)

Sperm and eggs are inserted in the Fallopian tube. The technique is believed to increase the chances of successful fertilization by bringing sperm and egg cells together.

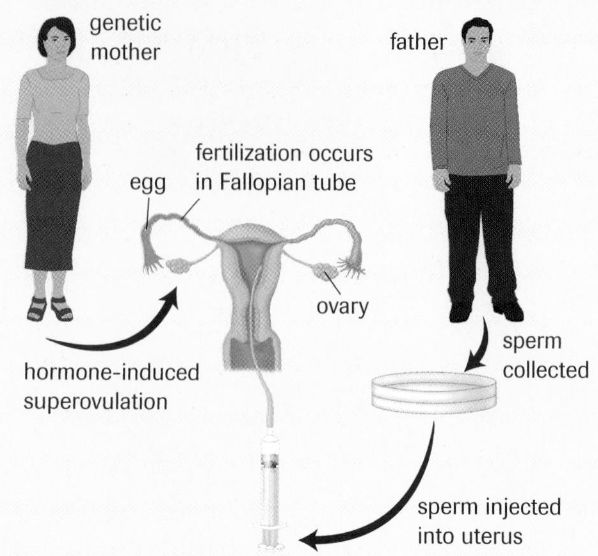

Figure 13
Intrauterine insemination

In Vitro Fertilization

The ovaries are hormonally prepared for ovulation. A device called a laparoscope is inserted into the woman's abdomen (**Figure 14**). An optical device within the instrument enables the physician to locate the ovary. A suction apparatus within the laparoscope allows the extraction of eggs from the ovary. The eggs are placed in a dish and fertilized by the partner's sperm (in vitro literally means 'in glass'). Following a brief incubation period, one or more of the embryos is transferred into the uterus.

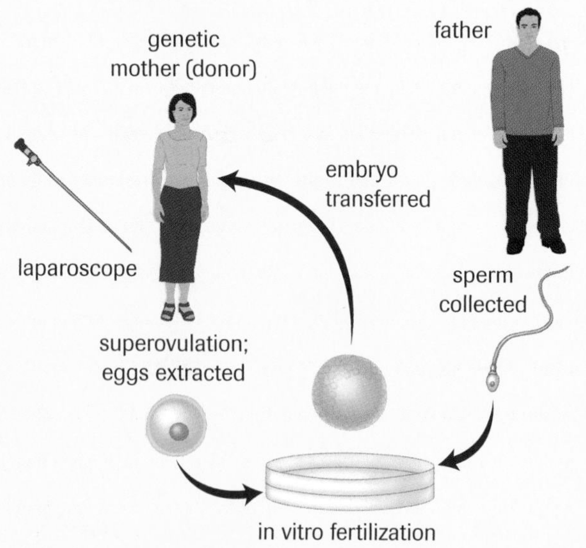

Figure 14
In vitro fertilization

Egg Donations and Egg/Embryo Freezing

Fertility drugs are employed to initiate multiple ovulations. Although a single egg may be fertilized, excess eggs are frozen (**Figure 15**). At a later date, these eggs can be thawed. Some of the eggs could be fertilized and the embryos implanted back into the same mother. Alternatively, unfertilized eggs could be given to another woman who either had no eggs in her ovary or was unable to ovulate.

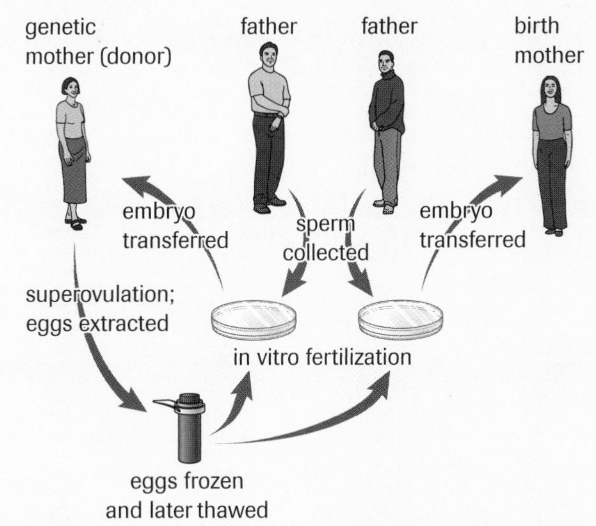

Figure 15
Egg donation and egg/embryo freezing

Embryo Transfer

Combining the technologies of in vitro fertilization and artificial insemination permits another procedure (**Figure 16**). A woman with a defective cervix or uterus may ask another woman (surrogate) to give birth to her genetic child. In this case, the egg from the woman is combined with the sperm of her partner. Fertilization occurs in vitro. The egg is transferred to the surrogate who carries the baby to term and then returns it to the genetic parents. The two technologies raise a fundamental question. Is the mother the one who gives birth or the one who contributes the genetic information?

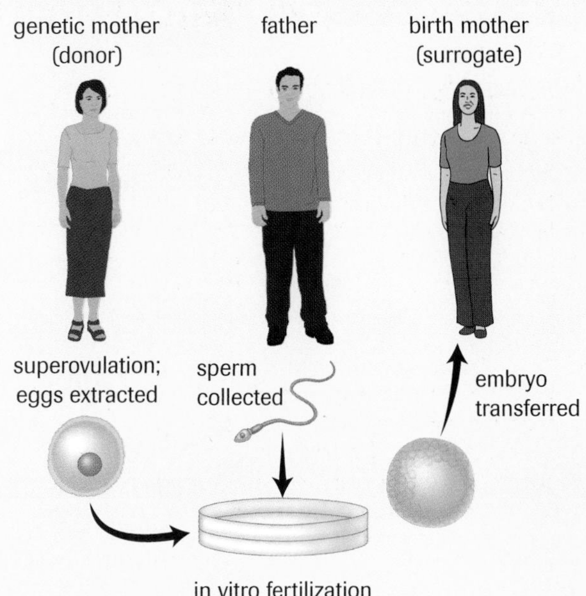

Figure 16
Embryo transfer

Case Study Questions

1. Identify one disadvantage of using fertility drugs.
2. Why might in vitro fertilization be used?
3. If a woman has a cervix that fails to hold the developing fetus in the uterus, then a premature birth can be expected. Despite advancing technology that helps premature babies complete development outside the uterus, the prospects for babies born prior to six months is not good. What reproductive technologies could be employed if a woman wants to be the genetic mother?
4. Explain how a baby could have five different parents if reproductive technology was used.
5 What ethical issues might arise when unused eggs or embryos are donated to parents who cannot produce their own? What should be done with abandoned embryos?

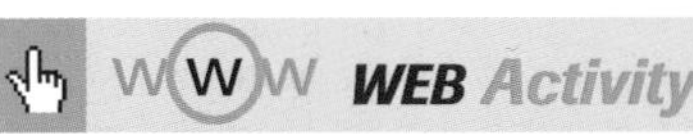

Web Quest—Reproductive Technologies

Reproductive technologies offer hope to couples seeking to have children, but these technologies do not come without a cost. In addition to the financial cost, there are ethical, moral, and legal issues. This Web Quest guides you through the legal, moral, ethical, and general issues surrounding reproductive technologies. To complete the Web Quest, you will carry out research on one reproductive technology and create a multi-media presentation highlighting what you learned.

www.science.nelson.com 

EXTENSION

Mind-Boggling Births

There is a higher risk of having more than one baby per pregnancy when couples use some reproductive technologies. This video discusses problems this can sometimes cause.

www.science.nelson.com 

SUMMARY Fertilization and Pregnancy

- In humans, fertilization and cleavage takes place in the Fallopian tubes. Cleavage is the division of cells in which the cell number increases but the embryo stays the same size.
- When the embryo reaches the uterus, it attaches to the wall of the endometrium.
- The implanted embryo secretes hCG, which maintains the corpus luteum. The corpus luteum secretes progesterone and estrogen to prevent shedding of the endometrium (menstruation).
- Changes in hormone levels in a pregnant woman's body trigger the formation of structures that protect and nurture the developing embryo changes, including the amniotic cavity, the placenta, and the umbilical cord.
- The implanted embryo develops into a gastrula, which has three layers: ectoderm, mesoderm, and endoderm. Each of these layers forms specific structures in the body.
- Pregnancy is divided into three trimesters. Development of the embryo takes place in the first trimester. Development of the fetus takes place over the last two trimesters.
- Birth begins with parturition (labour). During labour, uterine contractions are triggered by the hormone oxytocin. The hormone relaxin loosens the pelvis and softens the cervix.
- Breast development is stimulated by estrogen and progesterone levels during pregnancy. Milk production is stimulated by prolactin. After birth, suckling triggers release of oxytocin, which stimulates release of milk.
- Reproductive technologies can help people with lower fertility to have children.

Section 16.3 Questions

1. What is a blastocyst?
2. Explain how hCG maintains pregnancy during the first three months.
3. After about 20 weeks, human development is less sensitive to teratogens. How does this relate to events in embryo and fetal development?
4. Draw a positive feedback response for the release of oxytocin during labour.
5. Chlamydia is an STI caused by infection with a bacterial pathogen. A person can have chlamydia and have no symptoms. In women, untreated infection can spread into Fallopian tubes and cause permanent damage. By referring to events during fertilization and pregnancy, describe why damage to the Fallopian tubes can make a woman unable to bear children.
6. In Alberta, the number of teenage pregnancies has been described as alarming. Two very different solutions have been proposed by groups to address this concern. Visit the Nelson Web site for research information to assist you in answering the following questions:
   (a) Information on abstinence and support for teens practicing abstinence has been suggested as the best possible solution to the issue. Research why some groups advocate this solution.
   (b) Other groups propose harm reduction strategies that provide teens with information on contraceptives. Survey different methods of contraception and assess the effectiveness of each methodology.
   (c) Construct a chart that compares the advantages provided by abstinence and contraception. Which personal values would make one solution preferable to another?

www.science.nelson.com 

INVESTIGATION 16.1

Observing Embryo Development

Although vertebrates vary greatly as adults, their initial stages of development are surprisingly similar. The stages of development of a human embryo therefore can be appreciated by observing embryo development in other species.

Report Checklist

○ Purpose	○ Design	● Analysis
● Problem	○ Materials	● Evaluation
○ Hypothesis	○ Procedure	○ Synthesis
○ Prediction	● Evidence	

Purpose

To observe structures of developing frog embryos

Materials

microscope slide
tweezers
prepared slides frog embryology set
light microscope

Procedure and Evidence

1. Obtain prepared slides of developing frog embryos and examine them using the low power of the microscope.
2. Use **Figures 1, 2,** and **3** to identify the different structures. Make labelled diagrams of the slides you view.

(a) first cleavage, 2.5 h

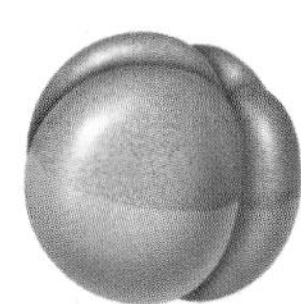

(b) second cleavage, 3.5 h

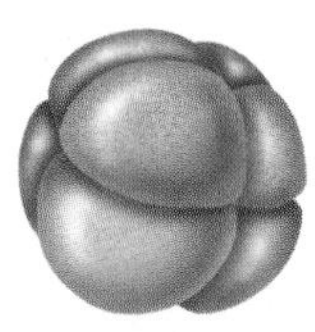

(c) eight-cell stage, 4.5 h

Figure 1
After fertilization, the zygote undergoes a series of divisions that transform it into a tadpole.
(a) The first cleavage divides the egg into two sections.
(b) The next cleavage is perpendicular to the first and divides the egg into four sections.
(c) The next cleavage, dividing the embryo into eight cells, occurs crosswise.

Learning Tip

See Appendix A6 Scientific Drawing for a review of how to make a labelled scientific diagram.

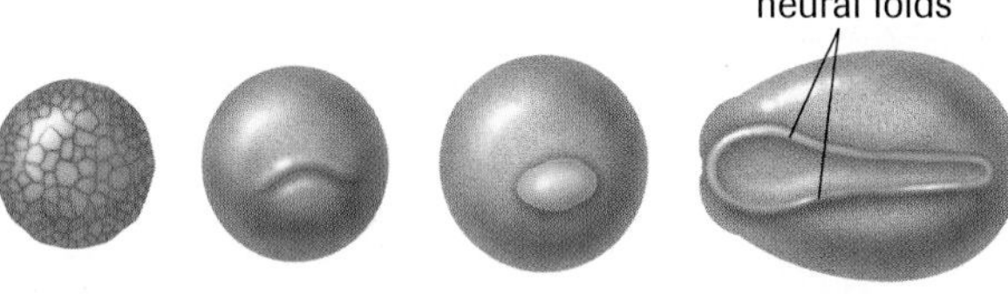

(a) blastula, 12 h **(b)** gastrula, about 20 h **(c)** yolk plug stage, 32 h **(d)** embryo, 48 h

Figure 2
(a) By the 64-cell stage, the embryo forms a hollow ball called a blastula.
(b) At the gastrula stage, the embryo has three primary germ layers: ectoderm, mesoderm, and endoderm.
(c) The yolk plug now protrudes from the inner layer.
(d) The neural folds develop along what will become the back of the embryo. Cells in this area will develop into the spinal cord and brain.

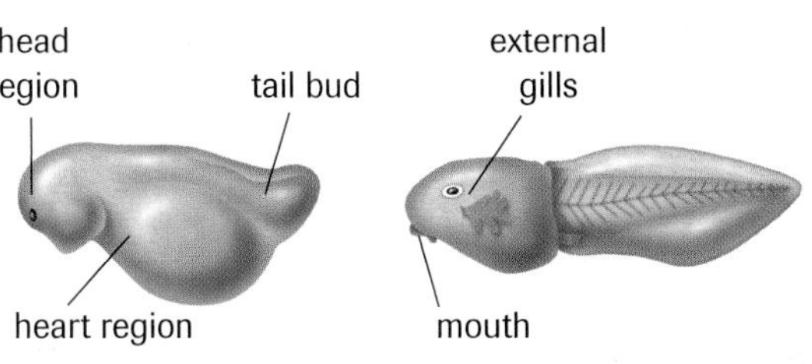

(a) heartbeat, 4 days **(b)** circulation in gills, 6 days

Figure 3
(a) On day 4, beating of the heart is visible.
(b) After 6 days, blood can be seen moving through the developing gills.

Analysis and Evaluation

The early stages of vertebrate development have many similarities. Compare the stages of development of frog embryos that you observed and sketched, to the stages of human development shown in **Table 2** on page 534. Organize your response in a table or other appropriate format. Include both similarities and differences.

SUMMARY

Outcomes

Knowledge

- identify the structures in the female reproductive system and describe their functions, i.e., ovaries, Fallopian tubes, uterus, cervix, vagina, endometrium, fimbrae, allantois (16.2)
- identify the structures in the male reproductive system and describe their functions, i.e., testes, seminiferous tubules, interstitial cells, Sertoli cells, epididymides, vasa (ductus) deferentia, Cowper's glands, seminal vesicles, prostate gland, ejaculatory duct, urethra, penis (16.1)
- distinguish egg and sperm from their supporting structures, i.e., seminiferous tubules, interstitial cells, Sertoli cells, follicle, corpus luteum (16.1, 16.2)
- describe the chromosomal factors and hormonal influences on the formation of the gonads and reproductive organs in the female and male embryo and fetus, i.e., Y chromosome and role of testosterone (16.3)
- explain how sexually transmitted infections can interfere with fertility and reproduction (16.3)
- describe the role of hormones (gonadotropic-releasing hormone (GnRH), FSH, LH, estrogen, progesterone, testosterone, inhibin) in the regulation of primary and secondary sex characteristics in females and males (16.1, 16.2)
- identify the principal reproductive hormones in the female and explain their interactions in the maintenance of the menstrual cycle, i.e., estrogen, progesterone, luteinizing hormone (LH), follicle-stimulating hormone (FSH) (16.2)
- identify the principal reproductive hormones in the male and explain their interactions in the maintenance and functioning of the male reproductive system, i.e., testosterone, luteinizing hormone (LH), follicle-stimulating hormone (FSH) (16.1)
- trace the processes of fertilization, implantation, and extra-embryonic membrane formation; i.e., amnion, chorion, followed by embryo development, placental and fetal development, parturition and lactation, and the control mechanisms of the above events, i.e., progesterone, LH, human chorionic gonadotropin (hCG), oxytocin, prolactin, prostaglandins (16.3)
- describe development from fertilization to parturition in the context of the main physiological events that occur in the development of organ systems during each major stage (trimester), i.e., zygote, blastocyst, gastrulation, general morphogenesis (16.3)
- identify major tissues and organs that arise from morphological development of the ectoderm, mesoderm, and endoderm , i.e., ectoderm: nervous system, epidermis; mesoderm: skeleton, muscles, reproductive structures; endoderm: lining of the digestive and respiratory systems, endocrine glands (16.3)
- describe the influence of environmental factors on embryonic and fetal development of body structures or systems (16.3)
- describe the physiological or mechanical basis of different reproductive technology methods, i.e., conception control, in vitro fertilization, infertility reversal (16.3)

STS

- explain that decisions regarding the use of scientific and technological developments involve a variety of perspectives, including social, cultural, environmental, ethical, and economic considerations (16.3)
- explain how science and technology are influenced and supported by society and have influenced, and been influenced by, historical development and societal needs (16.3)
- explain that science and technology are developed to meet societal needs and expand human capability (16.2, 16.3)

Skills

- ask questions and plan investigations (all)
- conduct investigations and gather and record data and information by: observing the principal features of the human reproductive system using models or computer simulations, and identifying the major structures from drawings (16.1, 16.2); using a microscope to observe prepared slides of ovaries and testes so as to distinguish eggs and sperm from their supporting structures, i.e., follicle, corpus luteum, seminiferous tubules, interstitial cells, Sertoli cells (16.1, 16.2); graphing the changes in estrogen, progesterone, and LH and FSH levels in the blood of a female through a single menstrual cycle (16.2); using models, diagrams, or computer simulations, identifying the follicle and corpus luteum within the ovary (16.2); investigating the effects of environmental factors on embryo and fetal development (16.3)
- analyze data and apply mathematical and conceptual models by: evaluating practical solutions to decreased fertility, i.e., low sperm count, difficulty in egg production, hormonal imbalance (16.3); analyzing blood hormone data and physiological events for a single menstrual cycle, inferring the roles of female sex hormones (16.2); analyzing blood hormone data and physiological events, inferring the roles of male sex hormones (16.1); observing the changes during embryo development, using preserved material such as chicken embryos, prepared slides, models, or computer simulations, and extrapolating these events to the development of a human (16.3); evaluating, from published data, the effectiveness and safety of various reproductive technologies (16.3) and; interpreting hormonal data from published investigations (16.1, 16.2)
- work as members of a team and apply the skills and conventions of science (all)

Key Terms

16.1

testes
ovary
fertilization
zygote
embryo
fetus
scrotum
vas deferens
ejaculatory duct
semen
seminiferous tubules
spermatogenesis
spermatogonia
spermatocyte
spermatid
somatic cell
Sertoli cell
epididymis
acrosome
seminal fluid
seminal vesicle
prostate gland
Cowper's (bulbourethral) gland
primary sexual characteristics
secondary sexual characteristics
testosterone
interstitial cell
gonadotropic hormones
follicle-stimulating hormone (FSH)
luteinizing hormone (LH)
gonadotropin-releasing hormone (GnRH)
inhibin

16.2

ovum
oocyte
uterus (womb)
endometrium
Fallopian tube (oviduct)
fibrium (plural: fibria)
vagina
cervix
oogenesis
follicle
granulosa
ovulation
corpus luteum
menstruation (flow phase)
follicular phase
estrogen
ovulatory phase
luteal phase
progesterone
menopause
follicle-stimulating hormone (FSH)
luteinizing hormone (LH)

16.3

cleavage
blastocyst
implantation
chorion
amnion
human chorionic gonadotropic hormone (hCG)
amniotic cavity
extraembryonic coelom
yolk sac
placenta
chorionic villi
allantois
umbilical cord
first trimester
gastrulation
gastrula
ectoderm
mesoderm
endoderm
second trimester
third trimester
teratogen
parturition
relaxin
oxytocin
prolactin

MAKE a summary

1. Hormones control many events in the reproductive system. Create a table, spreadsheet, or use presentation software to list the hormones involved in each of the following events and summarizes their roles:
   - spermatogenesis
   - the menstrual cycle
   - birth
   - lactation
2. Revisit your answers to the Starting Points questions at the start of the chapter. Would you answer the questions differently now? Why?

Go To

www.science.nelson.com GO

The following components are available on the Nelson Web site. Follow the links for *Nelson Biology Alberta 20–30*.

- an interactive Self Quiz for Chapter 16
- additional Diploma Exam-style Review Questions
- Illustrated Glossary
- additional IB-related material

There is more information on the Web site wherever you see the Go icon in the chapter.

UNIT 30 B PERFORMANCE TASK

Society and Reproductive Technology

In this Performance Task, you will use the knowledge and skills you gained in this Unit to survey how much knowledge the public has, prepare an information display, and/or write a futuristic play related to reproductive technology. Go to the Unit 30 B Performance Task link on the Nelson web site to complete the task.

www.science.nelson.com GO

Many of these questions are in the style of the Diploma Exam. You will find guidance for writing Diploma Exams in Appendix A5. Science Directing Words used in Diploma Exams are in bold type. Exam study tips and test-taking suggestions are on the Nelson Web site.

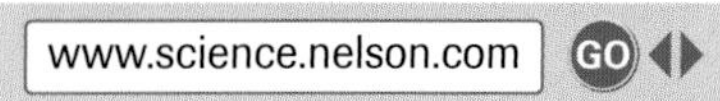

DO NOT WRITE IN THIS TEXTBOOK.

Part 1

1. Using the numbers from **Figure 1**, identify the site of production for each of the listed hormones. (Record all four digits of your answer). NR

_______ GnRH _______ LH _______ Estrogen _______ Testosterone

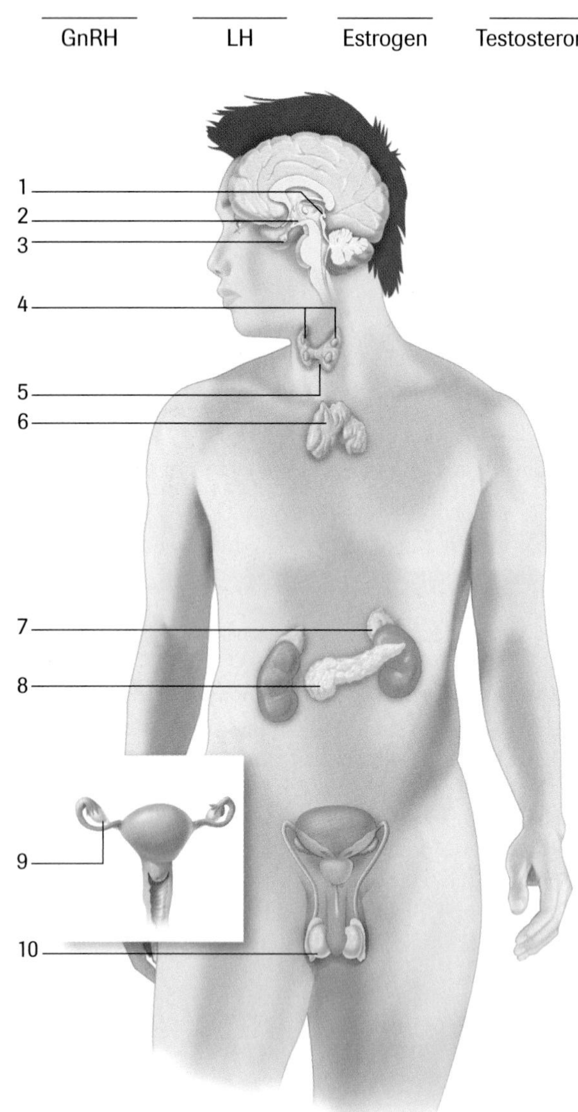

Figure 1

2. Which statement identifies a homeostatic response for LH and testosterone?
   A. If testosterone levels increase, then LH production decreases. If LH levels increase, then testosterone production decreases
   B. If testosterone levels increase, then LH production increases. If LH levels increase, then testosterone production increases
   C. If testosterone levels increase, then LH production decreases. If LH levels increase, then testosterone production increases
   D. If testosterone levels increase, then LH production increases. If LH levels increase, then testosterone production remains constant

3. The hormonal mechanism that regulates sperm production is
   A. LH production increases and sperm production decreases
   B. LH production decreases and sperm production increases
   C. FSH production increases and sperm production increases
   D. FSH production increases and sperm production decreases

4. Which of the following are a function of testosterone in males? (Record all three digits of your answer in lowest-to-highest order.) NR
   1. stimulates spermatogenesis
   2. stimulates the production of sperm cells in the seminiferous tubules
   3. stimulates secretion of FSH and LH
   4. promotes and regulates the development of secondary sexual characteristics
   5. associated with sex drive levels

5. Menstruation begins when
   A. there are no longer any eggs remaining in the ovary
   B. estrogen levels rise and progesterone levels begin to decline
   C. FSH and LH secretions decrease and the corpus luteum deteriorates
   D. progesterone levels increase and positive feedback to the pituitary increases the LH secretions

6. In females, LH is a gonadotropin that
   A. promotes the development of the follicle in the ovary
   B. inhibits the development of the endometrium in the uterus
   C. promotes ovulation and formation of the corpus luteum in the ovary
   D. inhibits the release of progesterone from the follicle cells in the ovary

7. In the female reproductive system, the roles of estrogen and progesterone, respectively, are to
- A. initiate ovulation and promote the growth of the endometrium
- B. initiate ovulation and stimulate the development of the follicles in the ovary
- C. stimulate the development of secondary female characteristics and the development of the corpus luteum
- D. stimulate the development of secondary female characteristics and promote the growth of the endometrium

8. The function of the female menstrual cycle is to
- A. produce mature ova and provide a nutrient-rich environment for a zygote
- B. prevent invading microbes from taking up residence in the uterus and to ensure ovulation
- C. create an environment suitable for the survival of sperm cells and enable fertilization
- D. maintain constant levels of estrogen and progesterone, which help develop a mature endometrium

9. In humans, the stage of development in which the major organs begin to differentiate is the
- A. zygote
- B. fetus
- C. embryo
- D. blastocyst

10. NR Place the following in the order in which they occur during embryo and fetal development. (Record all four digits of your answer.)
1. Cleavage occurs.
2. The ecotoderm, mesoderm, and endoderm are formed.
3. The blastula is formed.
4. Gastrulation occurs.

11. The extraembryonic structure responsible for secreting hCG is the
- A. amnion
- B. chorion
- C. allantois
- D. placenta

Use the following information to answer questions 12 and 13.

Figure 2 shows structures in a pregnant woman that support the developing embryo at 4 weeks.

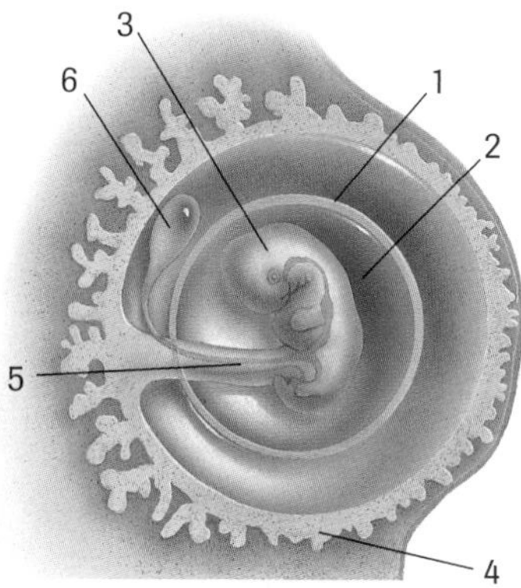

Figure 2

12. NR Identify the correct number that identifies structures shown in **Figure 2**. (Record all four digits of your answer.)

___	___	___	___
embryo	umbilical cord	amnion	chorion

13. Identify the statement that correctly matches the number of the label on Figure 2, the name of the structure, and its function.
- A. Structure 6 is the yolk sac, which is for early red blood cell formation.
- B. Structure 2 is the amnionic cavity, which is for diffusion of nutrients from mother.
- C. Structure 5 is the allantois, which is the site of estrogen and progesterone production.
- D. Structure 1 is the placenta, which is the site of nutrient and waste exchange between mother and embryo.

---

14. NR The following statements describe steps that occur during in vitro fertilization. Reorder them in the sequence in which these steps would be performed. (Record all four digits of your answer.)
1. Eggs are extracted.
2. Eggs are fertilized by sperm.
3. Embryo is transferred to the uterus.
4. Embryos are incubated to about the four-cell stage.

Part 2

15. **Predict** the consequences if the testes fail to descend from the abdominal cavity during embryo development.

16. Using **Figure 3**, **explain** how testosterone levels are maintained at constant levels.

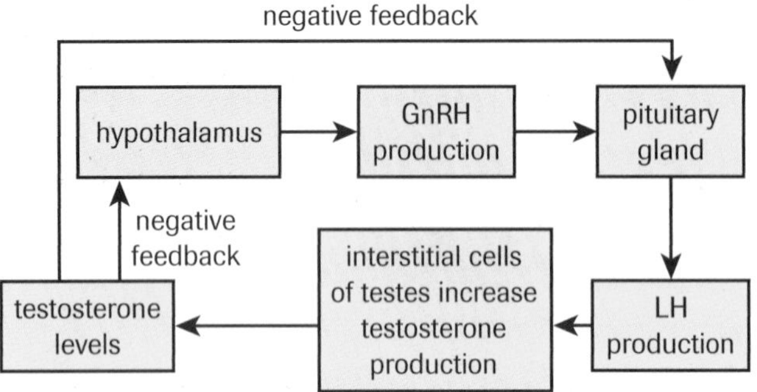

Figure 3

Use the following information to answer questions 17 and 18.

Anabolic steroids have improved the performance levels of athletes. They stimulate certain tissues (muscles in particular) to develop. They are either synthetic or natural versions of testosterone.

17. **Explain** why anabolic steroids often cause lower sperm count? DE

18. **Why** do anabolic steroids commonly lower levels of testosterone? DE

19. Some research has shown that males go through hormonal changes, called andropause, similar to menopause. In small groups, conduct research on this topic. Divide your group into two teams and assign teams to either support or refute the existence of male andropause. Can the group as a whole come to an agreement? In an appropriate way of your choosing, **outline** your group's stance and the information you collected that supports it.

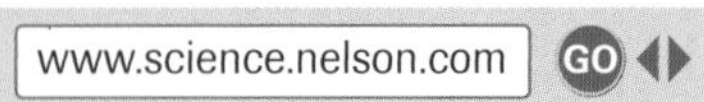

20. **Sketch** a diagram of the female reproductive system. Label the sites of ovulation, fertilization, and implantation.

21. Contraceptive pills contain synthetic estrogen and progesterone.
    (a) **How** do contraceptive pills prevent pregnancy?
    (b) **Why** aren't contraceptive pills taken for the entire 28-day menstrual cycle?

Use the following information to answer questions 22 and 23.

Figure 4 shows estrogen and progesterone levels during a menstrual cycle.

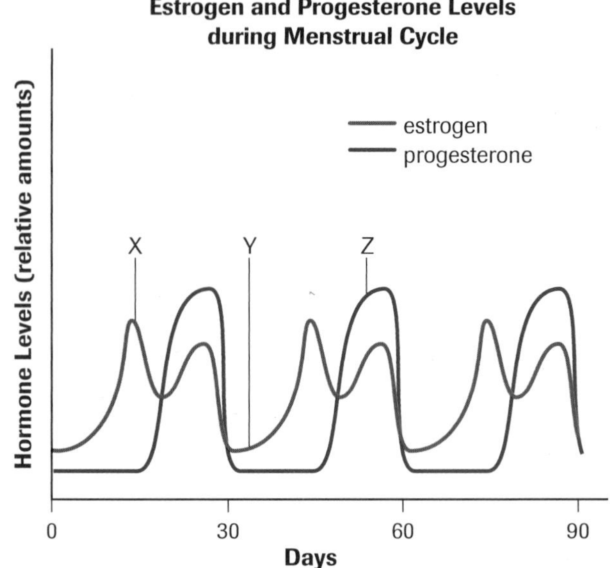

Figure 4

22. **Identify** the day (*X*, *Y*, or *Z*) on which ovulation would occur. **Explain** your answer. DE

23. **Identify** the day (*X*, *Y*, or *Z*) on which you expect to find a functioning corpus luteum. **Explain** your answer. DE

24. **Design** an experiment to show how female gonadotropic hormones are regulated by ovarian hormones.

25. **Compare** the functions of follicle-stimulating hormone (FSH) and luteinizing hormone (LH) in both males and females by completing **Table 1**.

Table 1 Functions of FSH and LH in Males and Females

Hormone	Male	Females
follicle-stimulating hormone (FSH)		
luteinizing hormone (LH)		

26. Using changes in hormonal levels, write a unified response to **explain** the following observations as a woman approaches menopause: DE
    - thin endometrium
    - no ovulation
    - low levels of LH

27. During pregnancy, menstruation is inhibited. **Explain** the hormonal mechanism that maintains the endometrium.

28. **Figure 5** shows hormone levels during the 40 weeks of pregnancy. **Explain** the changes in hCG, estrogen, and progesterone levels during pregnancy.

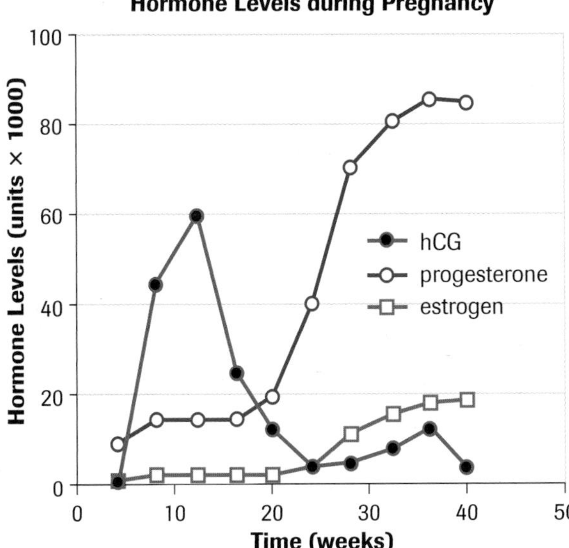

Figure 5

29. Imagine a situation in which a woman's ovaries are removed during the eighth month of pregnancy. **How** will removal of the ovaries affect the fetus? **Explain** your answer.

30. **Describe** the effects of biological parents taking drugs and alcohol on the conception and development of their fetus.

31. Sometimes labour must be induced in order to avoid complications.
    (a) **Identify** a hormone that could be used to aid and induce labour.
    (b) **Explain** why this hormone would be used.

32. How many corpus lutei would be found in the ovaries of a woman who has just given birth to identical twins? Would this number be different if the twins were fraternal? **Explain** why.

33. DE A couple is unable to have a baby. A number of different factors can reduce the reproductive potential of the male. In a unified response, **explain** why each of the factors could reduce reproductive success.
    - blocked vas deferens
    - reduced levels of testosterone
    - testes fail to descend into the scrotum

Use the information in **Figure 6** to answer questions 34 to 36.

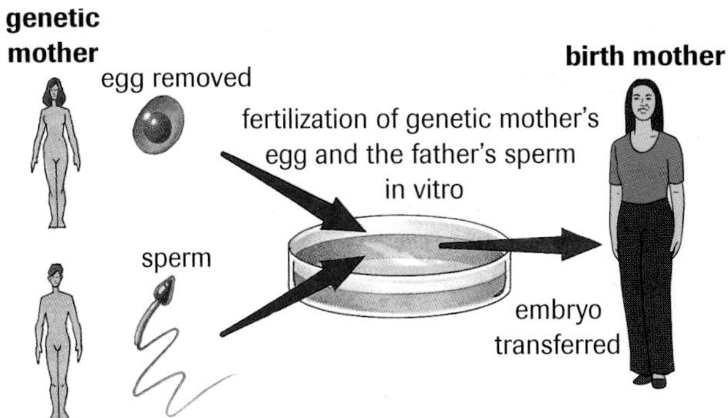

Figure 6

34. DE **Identify** the reproductive technology shown in **Figure 6**.

35. DE **Describe** the reproductive problem that this technology would be used to solve.

36. DE **Describe** any legal or ethical issues that might arise from this technology.

37. Do all human have the right to reproduce? Should someone lose the right to reproduce because they have a history of alcohol or drug abuse? Write a unified response to these two questions that includes the following considerations:
    - Who determines if an individual should not be allowed to reproduce?
    - What special circumstances would cause the "right to reproduce" to be questioned?
    - **Why** are legislators reluctant to enter into these discussions?

38. Review the focusing questions on page 506. Using the knowledge you have gained from this unit, briefly outline a response to each of these questions.

unit

30 C

Cell Division, Genetics, and Molecular Biology

Cancer is a broad group of diseases associated with the uncontrolled, unregulated growth of cells. Much more active than normal cells, cancer cells divide at rates that far exceed those of the parent cells from which they arose. Cancer cells also do not mature into specific cell types, as do normal cells. Cancer cells cannot carry out some of the functions of normal cells, which in turn can seriously affect a patient's health.

Cancer research aims at understanding how cells become cancer cells, and how they differ from normal cells. A research team at the University of Alberta, led by Dr. Mark Glover, is making significant contributions to our knowledge of one form of breast cancer. People at risk of developing this form of breast cancer have a mutation in a particular gene, which in turn directs the production of a mutant protein. Dr. Glover's group created the first three-dimensional model of the part of this protein that is involved in cancer development. This knowledge may lead to a method to screen patients for this type of cancer early on.

As you progress through the unit, think about these focusing questions:

- What cellular processes allow for reproduction and growth of an organism?
- What regulates the transmission of genetic information from one generation to the next?
- How is DNA responsible for the production of proteins?

UNIT 30 C PERFORMANCE TASK

Investigating Human Traits

Genetics allows us to understand and predict the inheritance of traits. This kind of information can be very important for traits that cause health problems, such as cancer. How can human genetic traits be investigated? What do the patterns of inheritance of some common traits tell us about the genes that determine those traits? At the end of this unit, you may apply your skills and knowledge to complete this Performance Task.

www.science.nelson.com 

GENERAL OUTCOMES

In this unit, you will

- describe the processes of mitosis and meiosis
- explain the basic rules and processes associated with the transmission of genetic characteristics
- explain classical genetics at a molecular level

Unit 30 C ARE YOU READY?

Cell Division, Genetics, and Molecular Biology

These questions will help you find out what you already know, and what you need to review, before you continue with this unit.

Prerequisites

Concepts

- DNA, genes, chromosomes
- sexual reproduction
- asexual reproduction
- adaptations and variations
- traits
- nature versus nurture

Skills

- relate biological diversity to genetic diversity
- probability

You can review prerequisite concepts and skills on the Nelson Web site and in the Appendices.

A Unit Pre-Test is also available online.

www.science.nelson.com 

Knowledge

1. Identify the cell structures shown in **Figure 1** and explain the importance or function of each.

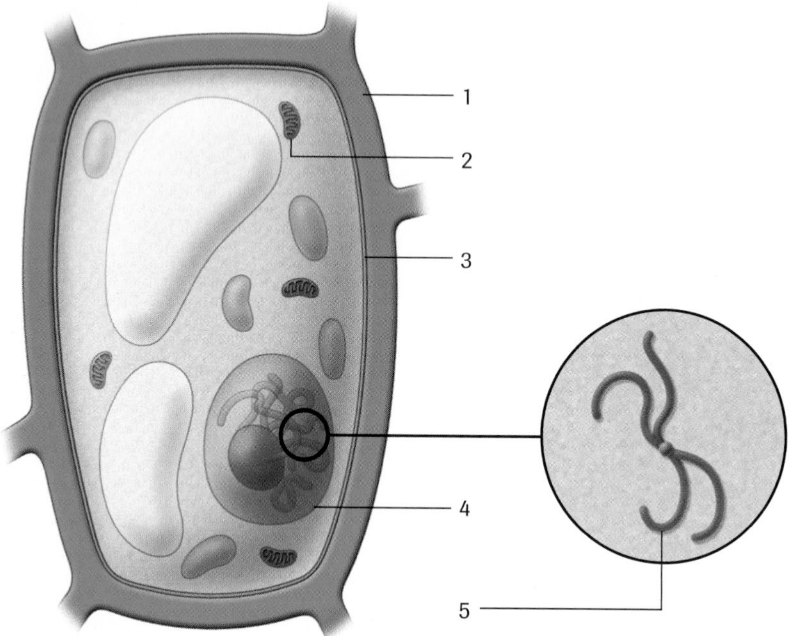

Figure 1

2. (a) Organize the following structures from largest to smallest: organ, chromosome, organism, nucleus, tissue, DNA molecule, cell, gene.
   (b) Copy **Figure 2**. Use the listed structures in (a) as labels for your diagram.

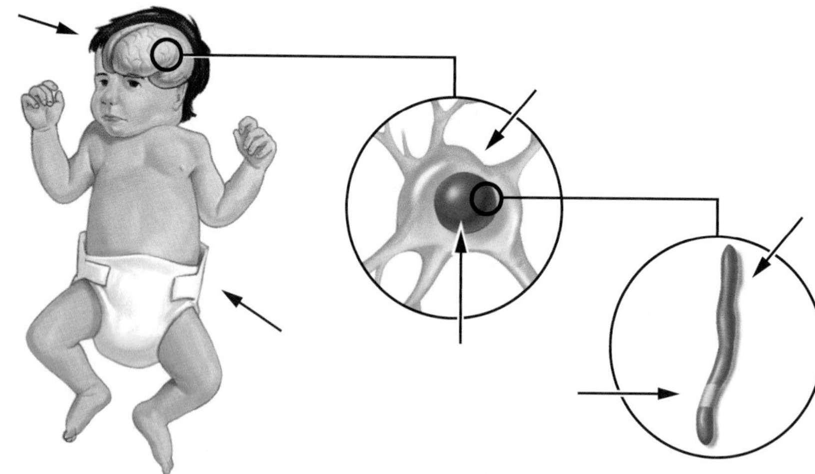

Figure 2

3. If a human muscle cell contains 46 chromosomes, indicate the number of chromosomes that you would expect to find in the cells shown in **Figures 3**, **4**, **5**, and **6**, on the next page.

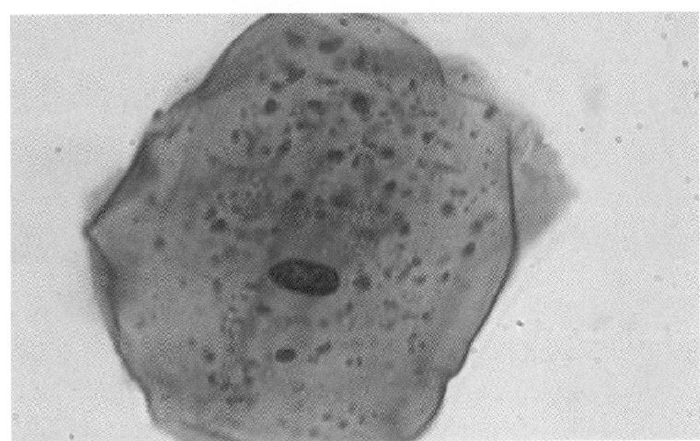

Figure 3
Skin cell, 450×

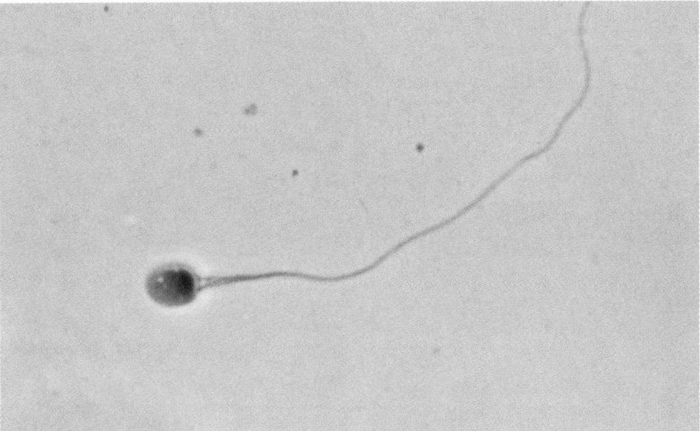

Figure 4
Sperm cell, 1000×

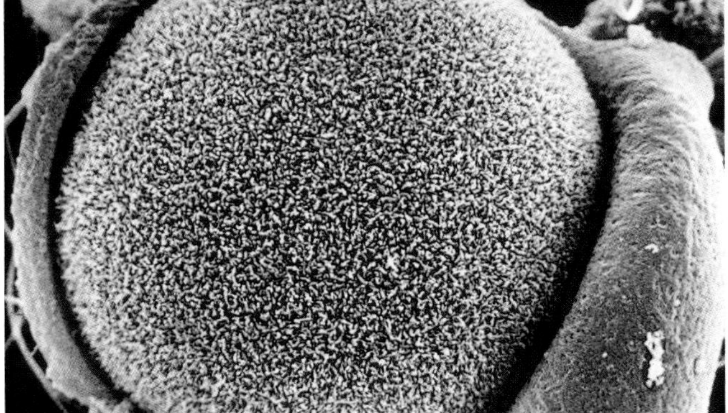

Figure 5
Unfertilized egg cell, 2000×

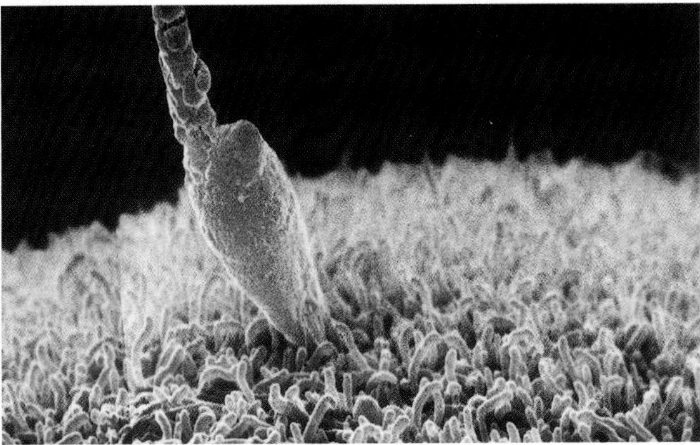

Figure 6
Egg cell being fertilized by sperm cell, 5000×

4. Provide examples of hereditary traits that are
   (a) determined by genes
   (b) influenced by the environment

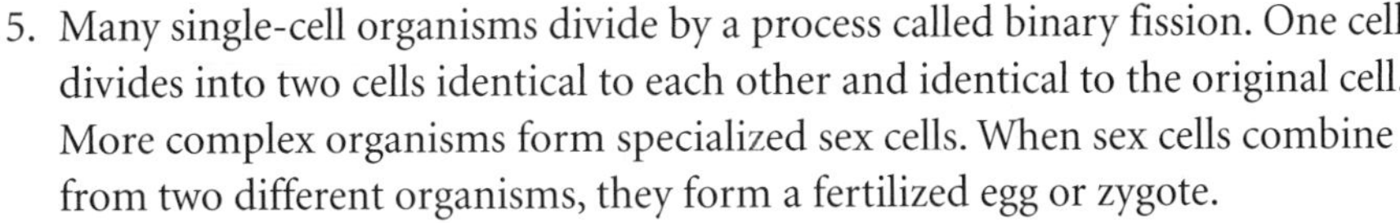

5. Many single-cell organisms divide by a process called binary fission. One cell divides into two cells identical to each other and identical to the original cell. More complex organisms form specialized sex cells. When sex cells combine from two different organisms, they form a fertilized egg or zygote.
   (a) Identify one advantage of binary fission as a means of reproduction.
   (b) Identify and explain an advantage of reproduction by the union of sex cells from different individuals.

6. Explain why the duplication of genetic material is essential prior to division.

Skills

7. **Table 1** shows the events in a typical cell cycle. Draw and label a circle graph to represent the data.

8. A couple are expecting their third child. After the birth of two boys, they reason that the next child will be a girl.
   (a) Determine the probability of having three boys in a row.
   (b) Determine the probability that the next child will be a girl.

Table 1 Events in the Cell Cycle

Event	Time (h)
rapid growth	15
growth and DNA replication	20
preparation for division	10
mitosis	5

chapter

17 Cell Division

In this chapter

- Exploration: Observing *Daphnia*
- Investigation 17.1: Frequency of Cell Division
- Mini Investigation: Cloning from a Plant Cutting
- Explore an Issue: The Ethics of Stem Cell Research
- Web Activity: Stem Cell Cord Blood
- Investigation 17.2: Identification of a Cancer Cell
- Mini Investigation: Gamete Formation in Grasshoppers
- Investigation 17.3: Comparing Mitosis and Meiosis
- Web Activity: Comparing Life Cycles of Plants
- Web Activity: Dr. Renée Martin
- Web Activity: Modelling Mitosis and Meiosis

All life depends on the ability to grow and reproduce. Both these processes involve cell division. Organisms that reproduce asexually produce offspring that are identical to the parents. Sexually reproducing organisms exchange genetic information, so that the offspring have a unique combination of traits. The genetic material determines the proteins that make up cells, which ultimately give rise to physical traits.

Daphnia (**Figure 1**, next page) is a truly remarkable animal. Females can produce offspring without a mate since they can produce eggs that require no fertilization. Upon development, these eggs become females, which in turn produce females, all of which are identical to each other and to the parent. Then, in response to some environmental cue, *Daphnia* begin producing eggs that develop as either males or females. The males and females produce sex cells. Sexual reproduction occurs when the sperm cells fertilize the egg cells, producing many offspring with a variety of traits. Asexual reproduction occurs when food is plentiful, while sexual reproduction is triggered during times of environmental stress.

All of the cells in *Daphnia* arise from one single cell. To develop into the complex organism in **Figure 1**, that single cell must divide many times. In this chapter, you will explore the events that occur during cell division in order to produce cells of the body and specialized cells involved in reproduction.

STARTING Points

Answer these questions as best you can with your current knowledge. Then, using the concepts and skills you have learned, you will revise your answers at the end of the chapter.

1. Make a list of the advantages of being multicellular.
2. Suggest possible advantages of reproducing
   (a) asexually
   (b) sexually
3. If 22 chromosomes are found in the muscle cell of a mouse, predict the number of chromosomes found in each cell of the following types:
   (a) brain cell
   (b) sperm cell
   (c) fertilized egg cell
   Explain your predictions.

Career Connection: Geneticist

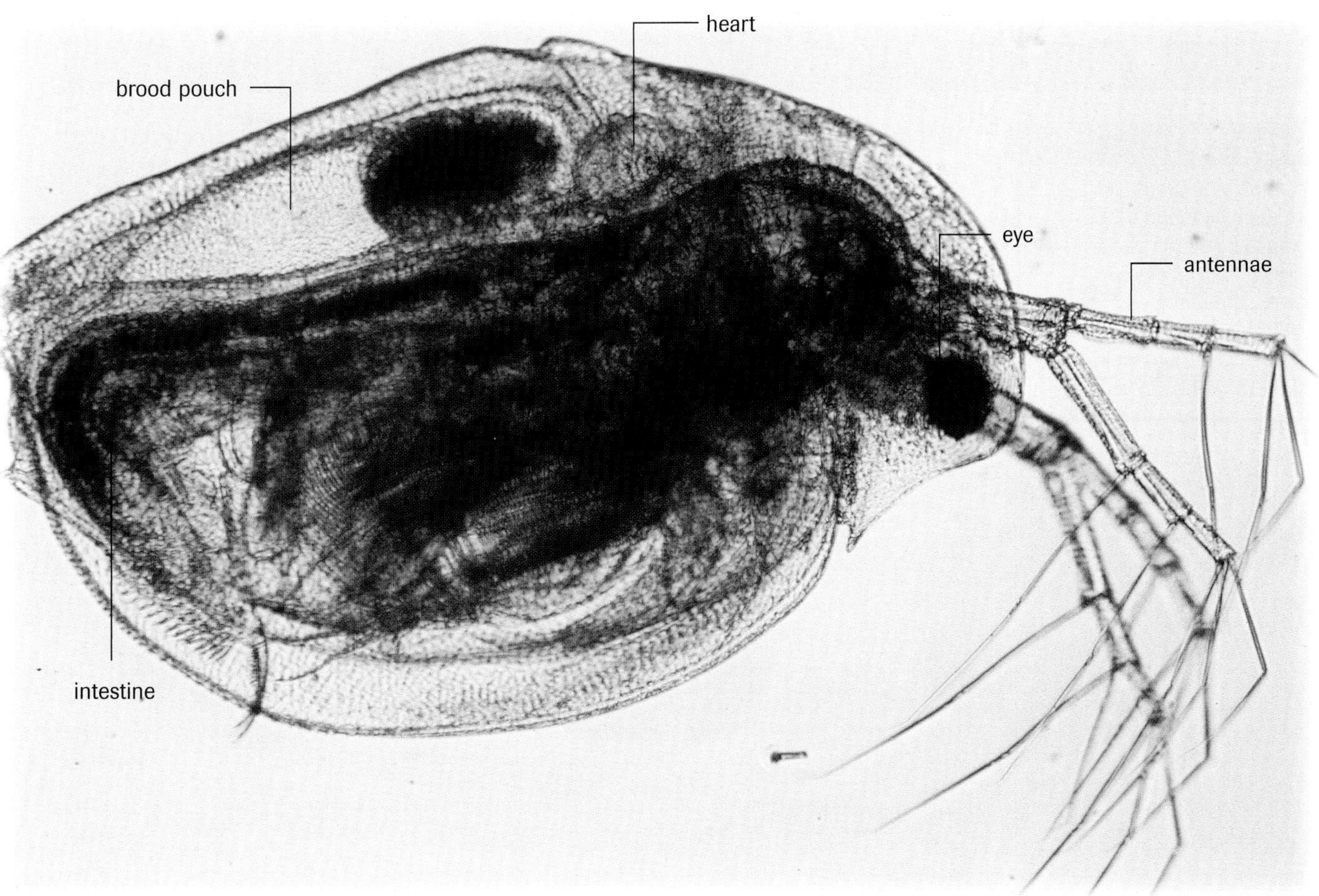

Figure 1
Daphnia is also known as a water flea, but it is a crustacean, not an insect.

Exploration Observing Daphnia

Materials: prepared slide of *Daphnia*, concave depression slide, glycerin, cover slip, *Daphnia* culture, medicine dropper, microscope, ice cubes, cotton swab

- If available, look at a prepared slide of *Daphnia*. Take note of the *Daphnia*'s general appearance and the location of certain features (e.g., eyes, antennae, heart) so that you will be able to identify them more easily in the *Daphnia* culture.
- Remove the prepared slide. Obtain the other materials. Using a cotton swab, smear some glycerin into the depression on the slide. Then, using a medicine dropper, place a small drop of *Daphnia* culture onto the glycerin. Prepare a wet mount by adding a cover slip. Examine the slide under low-power magnification. Pay attention to the movement and heart rate of the organism.
- Place the slide on an ice cube for 3 min, then dry the bottom of the slide with a paper towel and observe once again under low-power magnification.

(a) Why did you smear glycerin on the slide?
(b) Why did you put the slide on an ice cube?
(c) Make and label a scientific drawing of a *Daphnia*.
(d) Do you think that *Daphnia* are composed of many cells? Describe any features that you observe that demonstrate this fact.
(e) Try viewing the *Daphnia* under medium power. (*Hint:* You may have to adjust the diaphragm.) Draw what you see.

17.1 The Cell Cycle

Learning Tip

DNA, the cell's hereditary information, is found in the chromosomes of a cell. In eukaryotic cells (cells with a nucleus), the chromosomes are found in the nucleus. Review this information in Section 6.5 of this book.

All the estimated 100 trillion cells that make up your body arose from a single fertilized egg. As with the frog egg shown in **Figure 1**, this fertilized egg cell underwent a series of divisions that increased the number of cells, thus increasing the size and complexity of your body until eventually you reached your current size. Cell division also maintains a fully grown individual. All multi-cellular eukaryotic organisms grow in size and maintain the cells of their body (the somatic cells) by a sequence of events called the **cell cycle**.

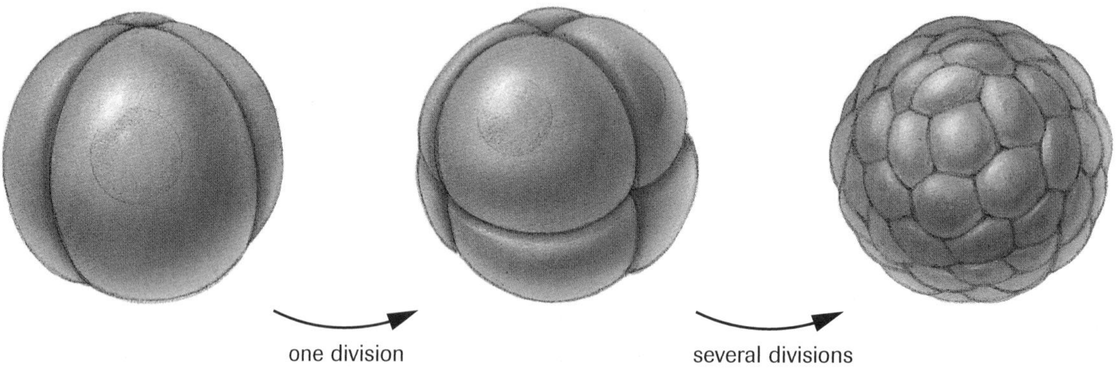

Figure 1
Early stages of cell division of a fertilized frog egg

cell cycle the sequence of stages through which a cell passes from one cell division to the next

mitosis (M) a type of cell division in which a daughter cell receives the same number of chromosomes as the parent cell

cytokinesis the division of cytoplasm

interphase the time interval between nuclear divisions when a cell increases in mass, roughly doubles the cytoplasmic components, and duplicates its chromosomes

The cell cycle is often described as taking place in phases (**Figure 2**, next page). However, the cycle is a continuous process and does not pause after each phase. During the division phase (**mitosis**, or **M**), the components of the cytoplasm and the components of the nucleus of the parent cell are divided to give rise to two identical daughter cells by two processes, mitosis and cytokinesis. Mitosis ensures the equal distribution of the nuclear contents. This process includes the duplication of chromosomes, so that each daughter cell ends up with the same number of chromosomes as the parent cell. **Cytokinesis** divides the cytoplasm and its constituent organelles of the parent cell roughly equally between the daughter cells.

For most cells, the nuclear division that occurs during mitosis marks only a small part of their cycle. The stage between division phases, called **interphase**, is marked by a period of rapid growth (gap 1, or G1), the duplication of chromosomes (synthesis, or S), another period of growth (gap 2, or G2), and preparation for further divisions. Cells carry out their particular functions during interphase.

Chromosome Structure

Before looking at the details of mitosis, you will need to know something about the structure of chromosomes. In animals such as humans, the DNA is divided among a number of chromosomes. Chromosomes contain both DNA and a number of proteins.

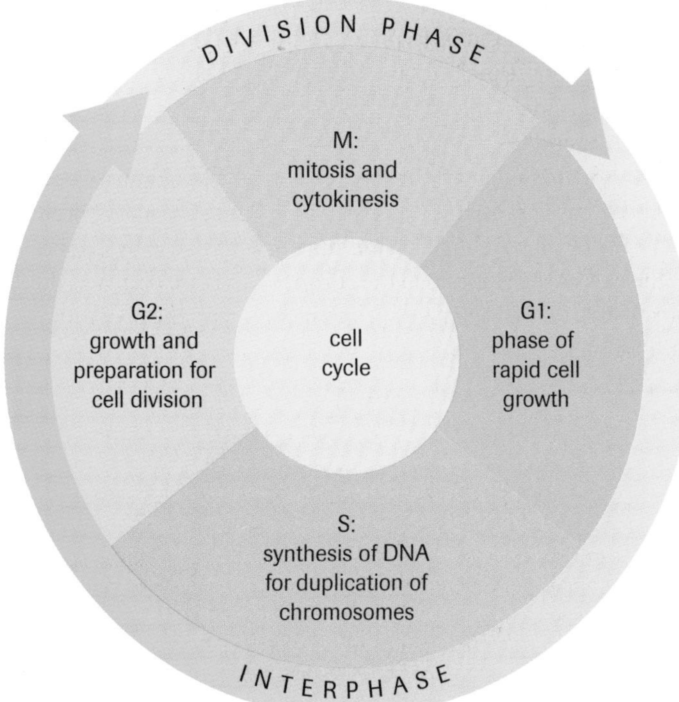

Figure 2
The cell cycle. The circle represents the entire life cycle of the cell, which can be divided into two major phases: interphase and the division phase. Most cells spend the majority of their time in interphase.

This combination of DNA and proteins is called **chromatin**. As the cell moves through the cell cycle, chromosomes may be either uncondensed or condensed. Uncondensed chromosomes are long, thin strands that cannot be seen under a light microscope. A condensed chromosome can be seen under a light microscope and may resemble the diagram in **Figure 3**. Condensed chromosomes may be either unduplicated or duplicated. In a duplicated chromosome, the original chromosome and its duplicate are attached to each other by a structure called the **centromere**. While attached to one another, the two chromosome duplicates are called **sister chromatids**. Since sister chromatids contain identical genetic information, the pair, attached at the centromere, is still considered to be one chromosome.

chromatin the complex of DNA and protein that make up chromosomes

centromere the structure that holds chromatids together

sister chromatids a chromosome and its duplicate, attached to one another by a centromere until separated during mitosis

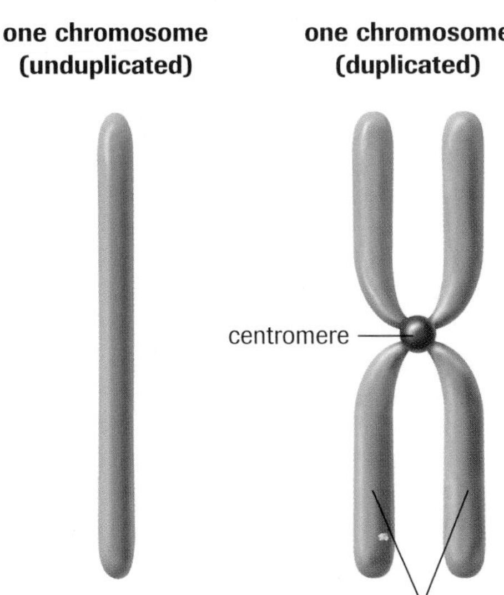

Figure 3
An unduplicated and a duplicated chromosome

Interphase

Cells spend most of their lives in interphase. In this phase of the cell cycle, cells are not actively dividing. Interphase includes the G1, S, and G2 phases of the cell cycle. Cells in interphase grow and undergo the various metabolic processes needed for their functioning during G1, S, and G2.

Chromosomes are uncondensed throughout interphase (**Figure 4**). During G1, cells undergo a period of rapid growth, and the chromosomes are unduplicated. During the S phase, cells begin to prepare for division during interphase by duplicating its chromosomes. At the end of the S phase, all the chromosomes are therefore duplicated chromosomes. During G2, the cell again grows and it completes the preparations for division (mitosis, or the M phase).

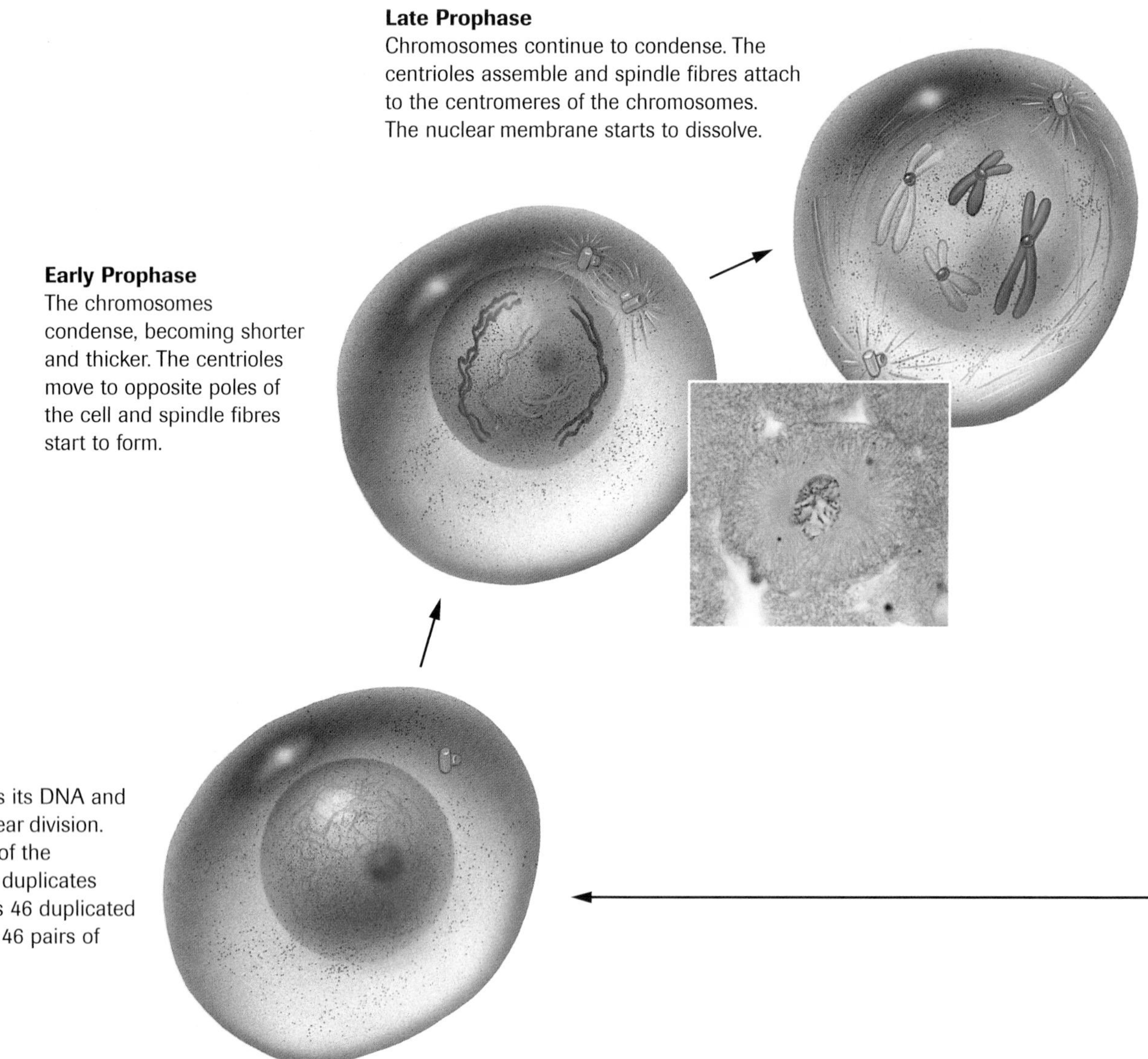

Late Prophase
Chromosomes continue to condense. The centrioles assemble and spindle fibres attach to the centromeres of the chromosomes. The nuclear membrane starts to dissolve.
Early Prophase
The chromosomes condense, becoming shorter and thicker. The centrioles move to opposite poles of the cell and spindle fibres start to form.
Interphase
The cell replicates its DNA and prepares for nuclear division. In humans, each of the 46 chromosomes duplicates itself. The result is 46 duplicated chromosomes, or 46 pairs of chromatids.

Figure 4
Interphase and mitosis in an animal cell. Interphase includes the G1, S, and G2 phases of the cell cycle. Mitosis and cytokinesis occur during the M phase.

The Stages of Mitosis

Prophase

Prophase is the first phase of mitosis. The chromosomes in the nucleus become visible under a microscope as they shorten and thicken (**Figure 4**). In animal cells, a small body in the cytoplasm separates and its parts move to opposite poles of the cell as the chromosomes become visible. These tiny structures, called **centrioles**, provide attachment for the **spindle fibres**, which serve as guide wires for the attachment and movement of the chromosomes during cell division. Collectively, the centrioles and spindle fibres make up the spindle apparatus. Most plant cells do not have centrioles, but spindle fibres still form and serve a similar purpose. The centromere joining the two chromatids helps anchor the chromosomes to the spindle fibres. When viewed under a microscope during prophase, the nuclear membrane appears to fade; in effect, it is dissolving to allow the separation of chromosomes and cell organelles.

centriole small protein body found in the cytoplasm of animal cells that provides attachment for spindle fibres during cell division

spindle fibre protein structure that guides chromosomes during cell division

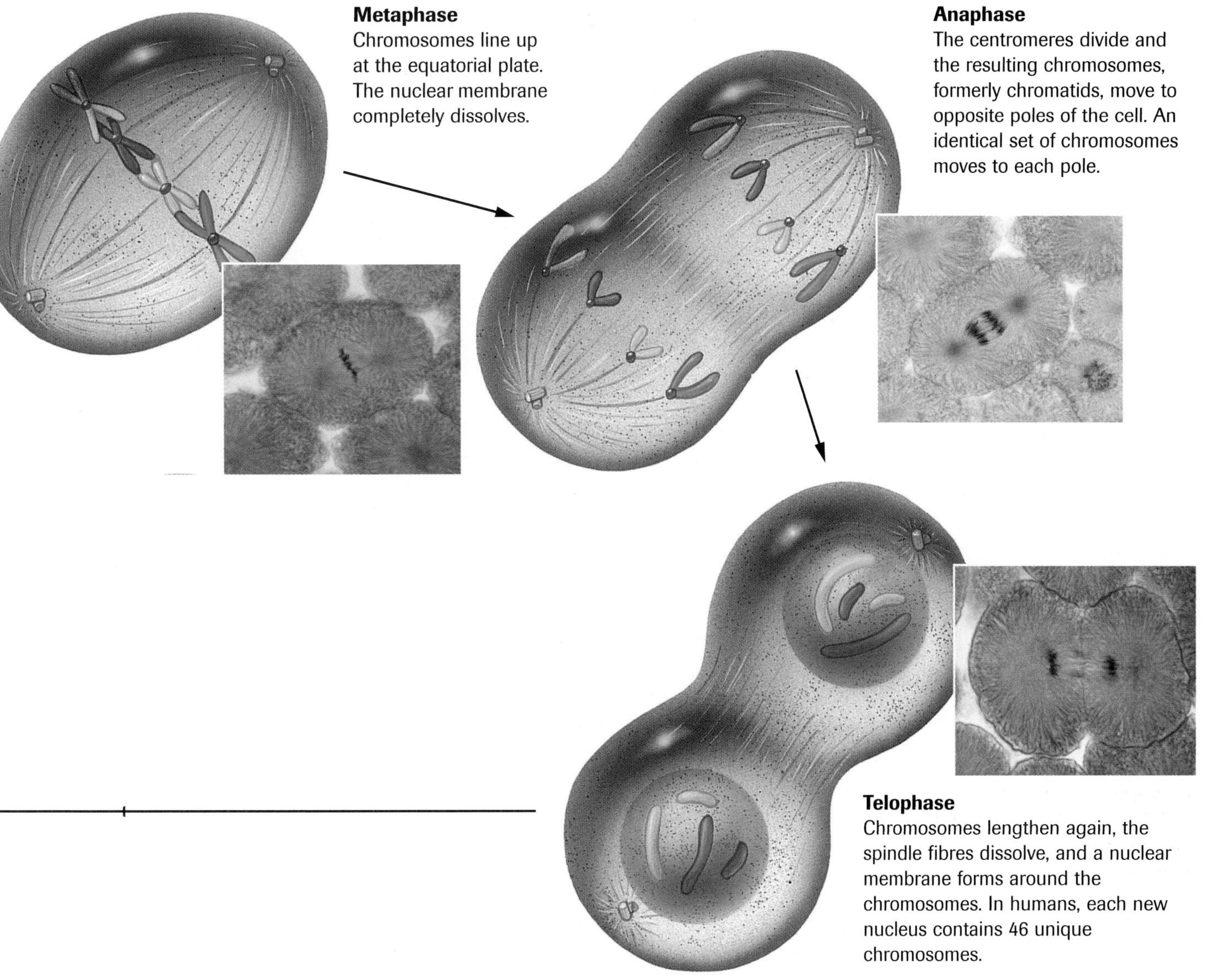
Metaphase
Chromosomes line up at the equatorial plate. The nuclear membrane completely dissolves.
Anaphase
The centromeres divide and the resulting chromosomes, formerly chromatids, move to opposite poles of the cell. An identical set of chromosomes moves to each pole.
Telophase
Chromosomes lengthen again, the spindle fibres dissolve, and a nuclear membrane forms around the chromosomes. In humans, each new nucleus contains 46 unique chromosomes.

Mitosis and Cell Division in Plants and Animals
This audio clip highlights the observable differences between plant and animal cell mitosis and cytokinesis.

www.science.nelson.com 

Metaphase

The second phase of mitosis is metaphase. Chromosomes composed of sister chromatids move toward the centre of the cell. This centre area is called the equatorial plate, because, like the equator of Earth, it is midway between the poles of the cell. The chromosomes appear as dark, thick filamentous structures that are attached to the spindle fibres. Even though they are most visible at this stage, it is still very difficult to count the number of chromosomes in most cells because the chromosomes are entangled. Chromatids can become intertwined during metaphase.

Anaphase

Anaphase is the third phase of mitosis. The centromeres divide and the sister chromatids, now referred to as chromosomes, move to opposite poles of the cell. If mitosis proceeds correctly, the same number and type of chromosomes will be found at each pole. Occasionally, segments of the chromatids will break apart, and may reattach, in anaphase.

Telophase

The last phase of mitosis is telophase. The chromosomes reach the opposite poles of the cell and begin to lengthen. The spindle fibres dissolve and a nuclear membrane forms around each mass of chromatin. Telophase is followed by cytokinesis, the division of the cytoplasm.

Cytokinesis

Once the chromosomes have moved to opposite poles, the cytoplasm begins to divide. Cytokinesis appears to be quite distinct from nuclear division. In an animal cell, a furrow develops, pinching off the cell into two parts. This is the end of cell division. In plant cells, the separation is accomplished by a cell plate that forms between the two chromatin masses. The cell plate will develop into a new cell wall, eventually sealing off the contents of the new cells from each other.

Practice

1. List the stages of mitosis. Briefly describe what occurs in each stage. To help in your description, sketch the sequence of events that occurs in an animal cell. Include labels for different structures.
2. A cell with 10 chromosomes undergoes mitosis. Indicate how many chromosomes would be expected in each of the daughter cells.

Situation A | **Situation B**

Cells are grown in culture.

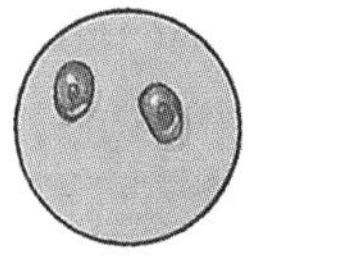

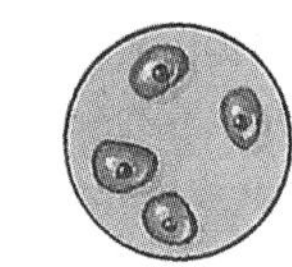

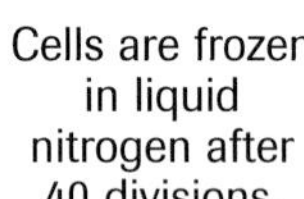

Cells are frozen in liquid nitrogen after 20 divisions. | Cells are frozen in liquid nitrogen after 40 divisions.

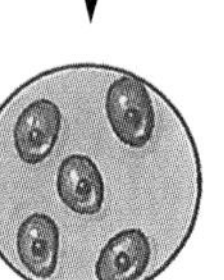

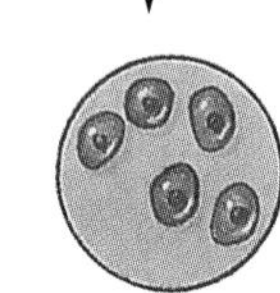

After cells thaw, they divide 30 more times. | After cells thaw, they divide 10 more times.

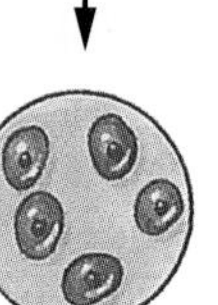

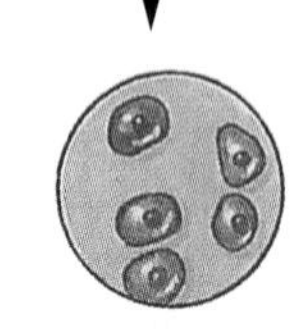

Total: 50 cell divisions

Figure 5
Cell division appears to be controlled by a biological clock.

A Cell Clock

How old can cells become? If cells continue to undergo mitosis, could an organism stay eternally young and live forever? Research on cultured cells (cells grown in a nutrient medium) indicates that a biological clock may regulate the number of cell divisions available to cells. When immature heart cells maintained in tissue culture were frozen, they revealed an internal memory of the number of cell divisions they had undergone. If a cell had undergone twenty divisions before freezing, the cell completed another thirty divisions once it thawed, then died. When a cell was frozen after ten divisions, it completed another forty divisions after thawing and then died. Cells always completed a total of fifty divisions no matter how long the freezing or at what stage the cell division was suspended (**Figure 5**).

Not all cells of the body have the same ability to undergo mitosis. Age is one reason cells stop dividing. However, division is usually stopped by cell specialization. Relatively unspecialized cells, such as skin cells and the cells that line the digestive tract, reproduce more often than do the more specialized muscle cells, nerve cells, and secretory cells. Only two cell types in the human body divide endlessly: the sperm-producing cells, called spermatogonia, and the cells of a cancerous tumour. Males are capable of producing as many as one billion sperm cells a day from the onset of puberty well into old age. However, once the sperm cells are formed, they lose the ability to divide further. Cancer cells divide at such an accelerated rate that the genes cannot regulate the proliferation and cannot direct the cells toward specialization.

It would appear that the more specialized a cell is, the less able it is to undergo mitosis. The fertilized egg cell is not a specialized cell; differentiation begins to occur only after its third division, which results in eight cells. Interestingly, it is at the point where differentiation begins that the biological clock within the cell is turned on.

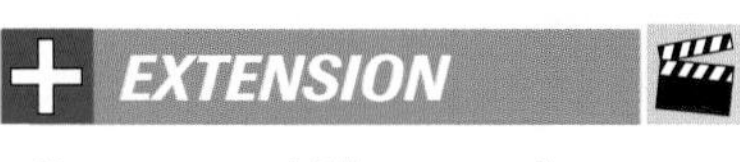

Cancer and Metastasis

Cells that divide uncontrollably can become cancer. This animation shows how cancer cells can spread from one part of the body to another.

www.science.nelson.com 

INVESTIGATION 17.1 *Introduction*

Frequency of Cell Division

Report Checklist

● Purpose	○ Design	● Analysis
○ Problem	○ Materials	● Evaluation
○ Hypothesis	○ Procedure	● Synthesis
○ Prediction	● Evidence	

In this activity, you will view and compare cells from onion cells and from a whitefish blastula in various stages of mitosis. Because slides are used, the cell divisions you will be viewing are frozen in time. Therefore, it will not be possible for you to watch a single cell progress through the stages of mitosis. Based on your observations, you will determine the frequency of cell division and construct a clock representing the division cycle, given the time taken to complete one cycle of mitosis. In a table, you will record the number of cells in each stage of mitosis.

To perform this investigation, turn to page 587. 

SUMMARY *The Cell Cycle*

- Cell division produces new cells for cell growth and for the replacement of worn-out cells in the body.
- Cell division involves a series of steps that produce two genetically identical daughter cells. Two divisions occur during cell division: nuclear division (mitosis) and cytoplasmic division (cytokinesis).
- During interphase, genetic material is replicated.
- Cells seem able to divide only a finite number of times.
- Cells lose the ability to divide as they specialize.

Section 17.1 Questions

1. During interphase, what event must occur for the cell to be capable of undergoing future divisions?
2. Using a dictionary, look up the meaning of the prefixes used in the stages of mitosis: *pro-*, *meta-*, *ana-*, and *telo-*. Why would they be used in the naming of the phases of mitosis?
3. Compare and contrast the structure of the daughter cells with that of the original parent cell.
4. Describe the structure and explain the function of the spindle fibres.
5. What is the significance of cytokinesis? Speculate what would happen if cytokinesis did not occur.
6. When a cell has reached its maximum size, what two alternatives does it have? When does the cell carry out one alternative over the other?
7. What would happen if you ingested a drug that prevented mitosis? What if it only prevented spindle fibre formation?
8. A cell from a tissue culture has 38 chromosomes. After mitosis and cytokinesis, one daughter cell has 39 chromosomes and the other has 37. What might have occurred to cause the abnormal chromosome numbers?
9. Suppose that during mitosis, both sister chromatids moved to the same pole, resulting in daughter cells with a different number of chromosomes than the parent cell. How might this abnormality affect cell structure, cell function, or both?
10. Explain the concept of the cell clock.
11. Suggest reasons why skin cells, blood cells, and the cells that line the digestive tract reproduce more often than other types of cells such as muscle cells. If some of these cells were to become cancerous, how might a chemical therapy to stop those cells from reproducing work?
12. (a) Describe the differences between the two cell cycles in **Figure 6**.
    (b) Which cell cycle do you believe would represent a cell of an embryo and which would represent an unspecialized cell in an adult? Give your reasons.
13. List areas of the body where you think cell division is most rapid. Also, indicate the comparative level of specialization of the cells in each area. Explain your predictions.
14. It is believed that weed killers like 2,4-D and 2,4,5-T may work by stimulating cell division. Why would the stimulation of cell division make these chemicals effective weed killers?
15. At one time, blood was transfused only from younger individuals to the elderly. It was believed that younger blood would provide the elderly with more energy. Do older people actually have older blood cells? Support your answer.
16. X-rays and other forms of radiation break chromosomes apart. Physicians and dentists will not X-ray pregnant women. Even women who are not pregnant wear a lead apron when being X-rayed near the reproductive organs. The apron blocks the passage of X-rays. Why is it undesirable to X-ray the reproductive organs? Why is it especially undesirable to X-ray pregnant women?
17. Scientists have developed techniques aimed at getting highly-specialized cells to act as if they are immature cells that have not yet become specialized. Why would scientists want to be able to get a mature nerve cell to respond like a cell that hasn't undergone specialization?

Cell Cycle for Cell A: 36 h

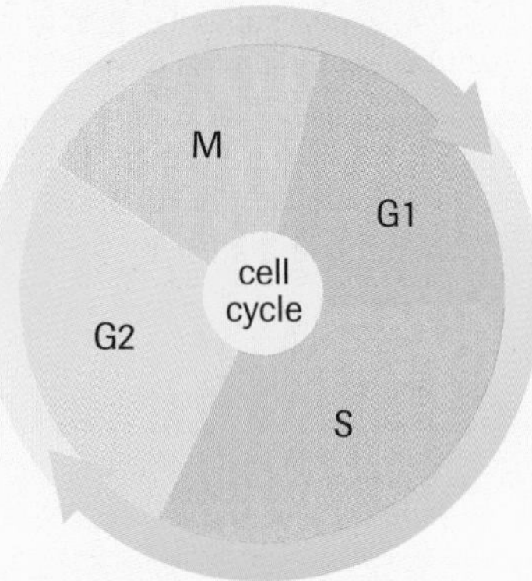

Cell Cycle for Cell B: 25 h

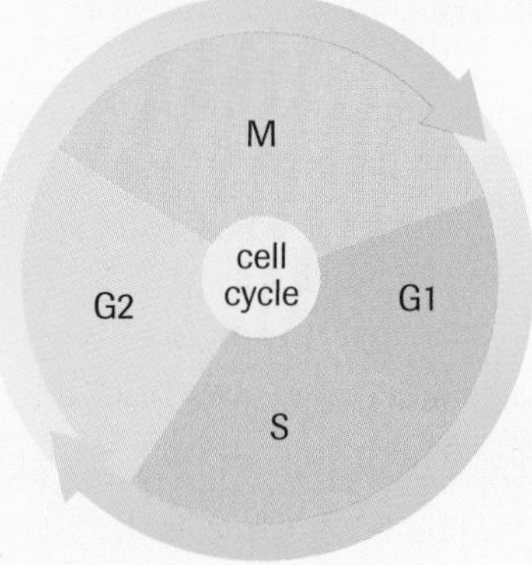

Figure 6

Applications of the Cell Cycle 17.2

Scientists continue to study the cell cycle and to gain a deeper understanding of the mechanisms and the role of the process. As more is learned about the cell cycle, we have been able to apply this knowledge to many human needs. There are various perspectives on the costs and benefits of these new technologies, and when they are appropriate to use.

Cloning

Cloning is the process of forming identical offspring from a single cell or tissue in the parent organ. A clone originates from a single parent cell, and both the clone and parent have identical (or nearly identical) nuclear DNA. Although some clones show accidental changes in genetic information, cloning does not result in the variation of traits that would occur with the combination of male and female sex cells. Cloning is therefore considered a form of asexual reproduction. In fact, clones occur naturally. Some species, such as hydra (**Figure 1 (a)**) reproduce by undergoing mitosis to produce buds with identical DNA to the larger parent cell. The smaller plantlets on a runner of a strawberry plant are identical clones of the larger parent plant (**Figure 1 (b)**). In animals, offspring with an identical genetic makeup are sometimes produced when a single fertilized egg undergoes mitosis and the resulting early embryo (called a zygote) then splits in two (**Figure 1 (c)**). This results in identical twins. They are also called monozygotic twins, since they formed from a single zygote. Fraternal twins are formed when two different eggs are fertilized separately. They are also known as dizygotic twins. Fraternal twins, therefore, are no more genetically similar than are non-twin siblings (**Figure 1 (d)**).

DID YOU KNOW ?

Multiple Births

It has been estimated that 1 in 85 births will produce twins, 1 in 7500 will produce triplets, 1 in 650 000 will produce quadruplets, and 1 in 57 000 000 will produce quintuplets.

(a)

(b)

(c)

(d)

Figure 1

(a) Hydra reproduce asexually by budding. The buds break off to form separate, genetically identical organisms.

(b) The strawberry plant can reproduce asexually by forming genetically identical plantlets on runners.

(c) Identical twins originate from a single fertilized egg that undergoes mitosis to produce an early embryo which then splits into two, producing two genetically identical individuals.

(d) Development of fraternal twins does not involve the splitting of a fertilized egg. Instead, fraternal twins develop from two independent fertilization events, such as occurs when a mother has two eggs in her uterus that are fertilized by two different sperm cells. Each fertilized egg then develops independently.

mini Investigation Cloning from a Plant Cutting

In some plants, asexual reproduction is accomplished naturally when a portion of the plant, such as a stem or leaf, breaks off and develops roots at the base of the broken portion. It is possible for the broken part to become a new plant. This activity is an example of artificial propagation.

Materials: coleus plant, scissors, goggles, gloves, fungicide, flower pot, potting soil, apron

The fungicide is poisonous. Review the MSDS before beginning this investigation. Any spills on the skin, in the eyes, or on clothing should be washed immediately with cold water. Report any spills to your teacher.

- Perform the following steps as shown in **Figure 2**.
  1. Using scissors, carefully cut off the tips of three coleus stems. Cut on an angle. Include several leaves on each stem.
  2. Remove a few leaves from the bottom. Put on splash goggles, and wear gloves and/or use tongs to immerse the stem in fungicide.
  3. Plant the cuttings in soil.
- Record each cutting's initial height and number of leaves. Take these measurements every week for two months.
- Describe the new plants each time.

(a) What evidence suggests that coleus can regenerate parts of the plant that were lost?

(b) Without removing the plant from the pot, how can you demonstrate that the roots from the cutting are growing?

Figure 2

Plant Cloning Technology

In 1958, Fredrick Stewart created great excitement in the scientific world when he revealed that he had produced a plant from a single carrot cell (**Figure 3**). Today, this technique

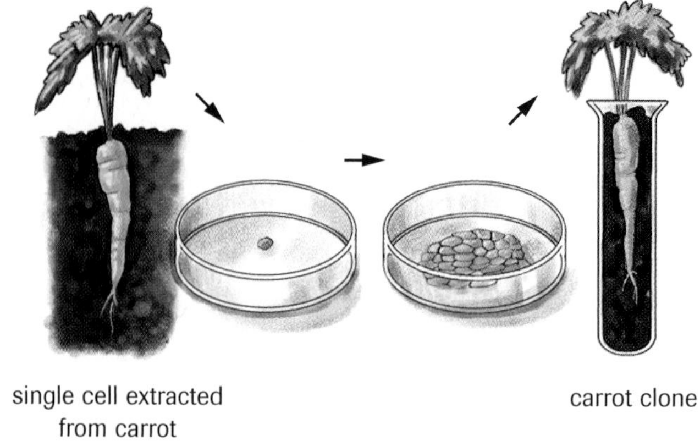

Figure 3
Fredrick Stewart was able to grow a clone from a single cell of a carrot plant. This allowed production of many identical individuals from a sexually reproducing species. This was the first application of knowledge of mitosis in generating clones.

is commonly called cloning. Many commercially important plant species, including orchids, are now produced from clones. Unlike plants that arise from sexual reproduction, cloned plants are identical to their parents. This allows production of strains of plants with predictable characteristics. Not all plant species can be cloned, however. Carrots, ferns, tobacco, petunias, and lettuce respond well to cloning, but the grass and legume families do not. Scientists continue to investigate these differences.

Each cell in the cloned plant contains the complete complement of chromosomes from the parent. As the new plant develops, it undergoes mitosis to increase in size. Some cells then specialize (differentiate) and form roots, stems, or leaves, until a complete plant is formed.

enucleated the condition where a cell does not contain a nucleus

Animal Cloning Technology

While plant cloning experiments were being conducted, Robert Briggs and Thomas King were busy investigating nuclear transplants in frogs. Working with the common grass frog, the scientists extracted the nucleus from an unfertilized egg cell by inserting a fine glass tube, or micropipette, into the cytoplasm and sucking out the nucleus (**Figure 4**). A cell without a nucleus is referred to as **enucleated**.

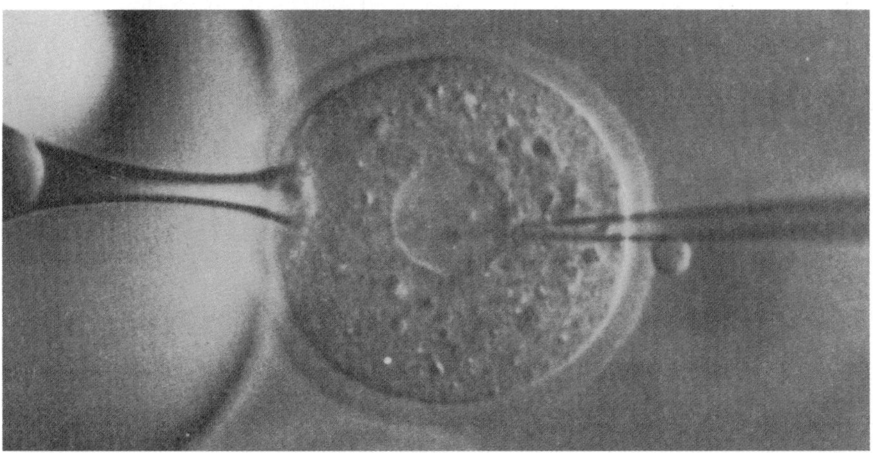

Figure 4
A small glass tube, called a micropipette, is used to remove the nucleus from a cell and later introduce a new nucleus.

Next, the nucleus of a cell from a frog embryo in the blastula stage of development was removed and inserted into the enucleated cell (**Figure 5**). The egg cell with the transplanted nucleus began to divide much like any normal fertilized egg cell. In later trials, the cell with the transplanted nucleus occasionally grew into an adult frog. The adult frogs displayed the characteristics from the transplanted nucleus. Careful analysis proved that the adults were clones of the frog that donated the nucleus.

However, different results were obtained when the nucleus was taken from cells at later stages of development. For example, the nucleus from cells in a later stage, called the gastrula stage, did not bring the enucleated egg from the single-cell stage to the adult. If mitosis occurred at all, it did not progress as far as it did in eggs that received a blastula nucleus. The difference is that the nucleus of a cell in the gastrula stage of development, unlike a cell in the earlier blastula stage, has specialized. As cells begin to specialize, they become less able to undergo mitosis.

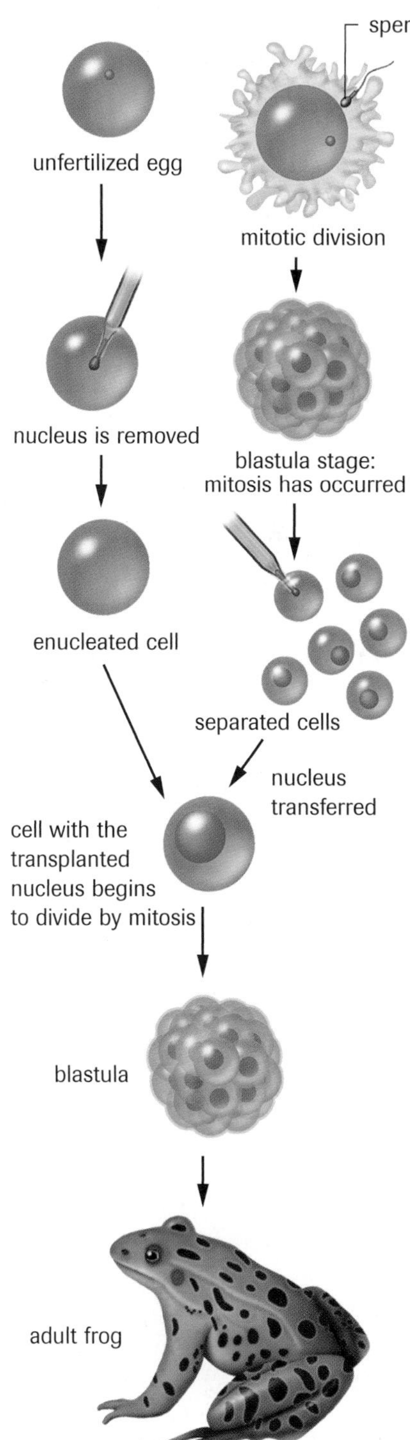

Figure 5
Cloning a common grass frog using embryo splitting

Cloning from adult mammalian cells has proved even more difficult, since they tend to be highly specialized. Until recently, the only way to get clones was by splitting off cells from a developing embryo (**Figure 6**). However, cells beyond the eight-cell stage of development seem to be unable to stimulate cell division.

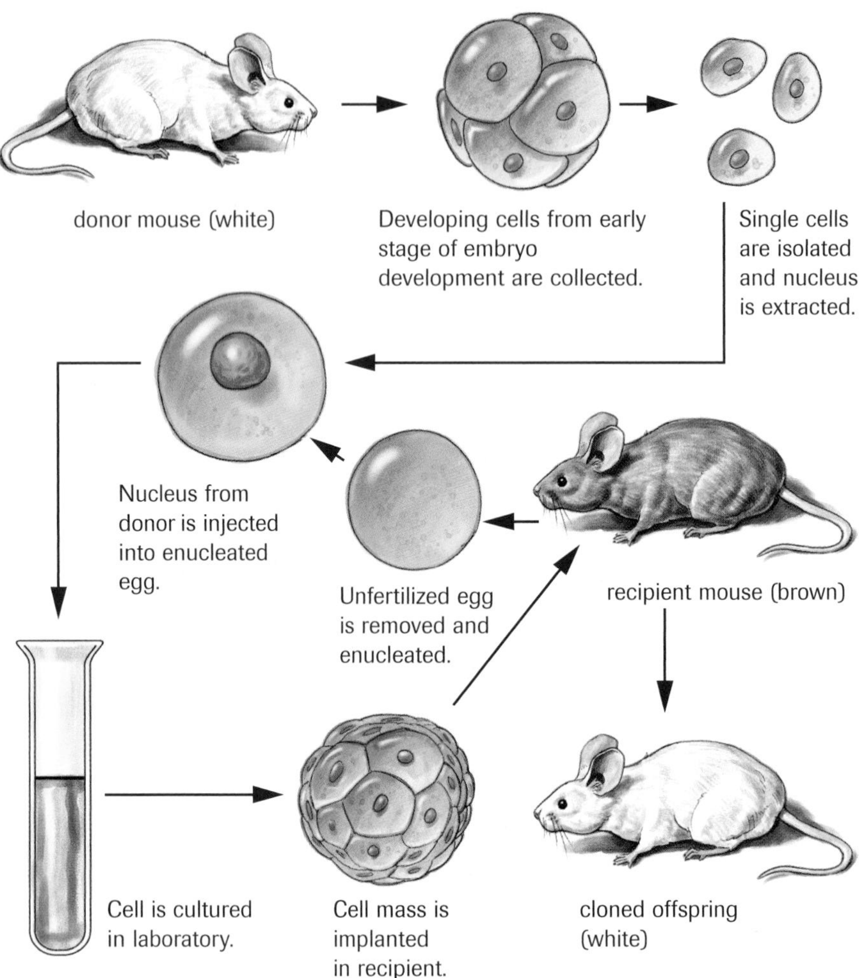

donor mouse (white)
Developing cells from early stage of embryo development are collected.
Single cells are isolated and nucleus is extracted.
Nucleus from donor is injected into enucleated egg.
Unfertilized egg is removed and enucleated.
recipient mouse (brown)
Cell is cultured in laboratory.
Cell mass is implanted in recipient.
cloned offspring (white)

Figure 6
Cloning a mammal using embryo splitting

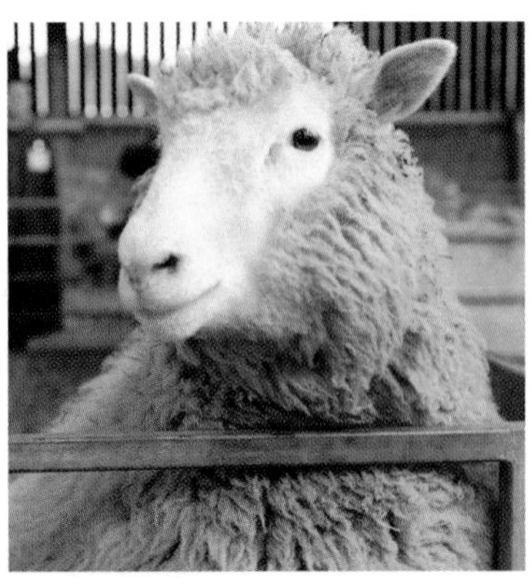

Figure 7
Dolly could claim three different sheep as mothers. The genetic mother died before Dolly was born.

The long-held scientific belief that adult cells cannot be used to clone animals was disproved with the appearance of a sheep named Dolly. Dr. Ian Wilmut, of the Rosalind Institute in Scotland, extracted the nucleus from an udder cell of an adult Finn Dorsett sheep and placed the nucleus into the enucleated egg cell from a Poll Dorsett sheep. The egg was allowed to develop in a Petri dish until an early embryo stage was reached. Then this embryo was placed into the womb of a third sheep, a Scottish Blackface. Her genetic information was shown to be identical to that of the Finn Dorsett adult; Dolly was a clone (**Figure 7**).

Medical experimentation and research could potentially benefit from the availability of cloned animals. For example, experiments on the effectiveness of a drug are often difficult to interpret because of the genetic variation among the individuals tested. If all the test subjects were genetically identical, clearer results could be obtained. In agriculture, the strongest livestock could be cloned, decreasing farmers' losses due to disease, and thereby increasing yield. However, many people have moral and ethical problems with this technology and worry about the impact on society .

Practice

1. List the steps involved in cloning animals from nuclei taken from the blastula stage of development.
2. Why are identical twins often called "nature's clones"?
3. Do all the cells of your body divide at the same rate? Explain.
4. What is an enucleated cell?

EXTENSION

Stem Cells

What are they, and how do we find a balance between hope for cures and respect for life?

www.science.nelson.com 

EXPLORE an issue

The Ethics of Stem Cell Research

Issue Checklist

- Issue
- Resolution
- Design
- Evidence
- Analysis
- Evaluation

A **stem cell** is a cell from which any other type of cell can arise (stem). Upon receiving the appropriate signals, stem cells differentiate into specialized cells with a particular function, such as heart muscle cells. Since a stem cell has not differentiated, it can undergo many cell divisions. Fertilized eggs and early embryos are composed entirely of stem cells. Plants retain many stem cells throughout life, in the growing tips of roots and shoots. Some adult animals also retain many stem cells, such as in salamanders that can grow a lost tail. In contrast, the adult human body has very few stem cells. Stem cells are found in the adult human body in bone marrow, fat, blood, and even in hair follicles. The richest source of non-embryonic stem cells is umbilical cord blood.

Stem cells have the potential of having enormous medical benefits. Since stem cells can potentially give rise to any other type of cell, they may be able to help people whose cells are not able to function properly. For example, stem cells could be used to replace faulty insulin-producing cells in the pancreas of diabetics or faulty neurotransmitter-producing cells in the brains of people with Parkinson disease.

Some people do not agree with the use of stem cells on ethical grounds. Scientists still do not fully understand how a single, unspecialized cell becomes a complex organism with many specialized cells. Some people worry that scientists may use human embryos to answer these questions. Others believe that any cell that can potentially give rise to a human being should not be used for research or therapy.

- In small groups, conduct background research on this rapidly changing field of research using newspapers, periodicals, CD-ROMs, and the Internet. Outline how the issue is changing and any new issues that are emerging. Prepare a bibliography and make notes as you work.

  www.science.nelson.com 

- Based on your background research, describe one ethical issue related to the use of stem cells in research or therapy.
- For the issue you have stated, write a statement that describes one viewpoint. For example, you might state, "Withholding a potential cure because it uses stem cells is unethical, because it causes people with a medical condition to suffer."
- Decide whether you agree or disagree with the statement. If necessary, conduct additional research to find evidence to support or refute your viewpoint.
- Write a position paper. Be prepared to defend your group's position to your classmates.

WEB Activity

Web Quest—Stem Cell Cord Blood

Research into stem cell cord blood has provided major steps forward in scientific understanding. It is becoming commonplace for parents to save the blood from their newborn's umbilical cord and to bank it in case of future medical needs. The issue is no longer whether or not banking the cord blood is acceptable, but rather the argument between the use of private or public stem cell cord blood banks. This Web Quest asks you to develop a supported position on this issue and create a presentation that can be given to your class.

www.science.nelson.com 

EXTENSION

Stem Cells Update

A new technique for creating stem cells may ease ethical concerns.

www.science.nelson.com 

Mitosis and Telomeres

telomere the cap at the end of a chromosome

Telomeres are caps at the ends of chromosomes (**Figure 8**). Scientists have determined that telomeres reduce in length each time a cell goes through the cell cycle and divides. Telomeres might have a role in cell aging and in the behaviour of cancer cells.

In 1984, Carol Greider and Elizabeth Blackburn set out to find the enzyme that affected the length of the telomere. Not only did they find the enzyme, but they also discovered much about how it works. Dr. Blackburn demonstrated a connection between telomerase and aging. Yeast cells that lack the enzyme telomerase undergo telomere shortening and eventually die. Other researchers working in Scotland found that as human cells age, telomere length shortens. The length of the chromosomes of a 70-year-old human is much shorter than that of a child. As we saw in Section 17.1, normal cells pass through the cell cycle only a finite number times. Once a cell can no longer undergo mitosis, cell death occurs. Telomeres length serves as a molecular "clock" for cellular aging.

What impact does telomere length have on cloning technology? The answer is not yet clear. Since Dolly was cloned from the cells of a six-year-old sheep, she began life with shorter telomeres than would a non-cloned sheep. Dolly developed arthritis at an early age and died of lung disease in February of 2003 at only six years of age—half the normal life expectancy of a sheep. These events may be linked to telomere length. However, some cloned animals appear to have longer telomeres, as if they were younger.

In the human body, cells generally undergo mitosis only 50 to 100 times during their lifespan. Cancer cells, however, never seem to lose their ability to divide, and their telomere length is also maintained. Telomerase is also not present in most normal cells. A group working at McMaster University under the direction of Calvin Harley was the first to show that telomerase is reactivated in human cancer cells. This allows cancer cells to maintain telomere length and, therefore, their ability to divide (**Figure 9**). Dr. Harley is now working with a pharmaceutical company to develop a drug that can block telomerase action. They hope that decreasing telomerase activity will slow cell division of the cancer cells, but have little impact on normal cells.

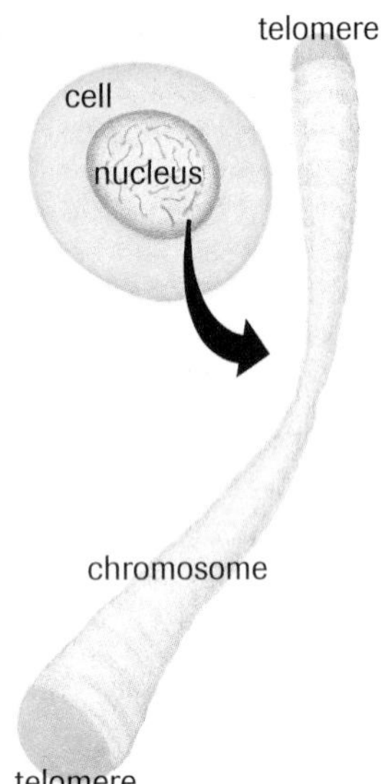

Figure 8
Telomeres are end caps of chromosomes. An enzyme, called telomerase, acts on the telomere causing changes in length.

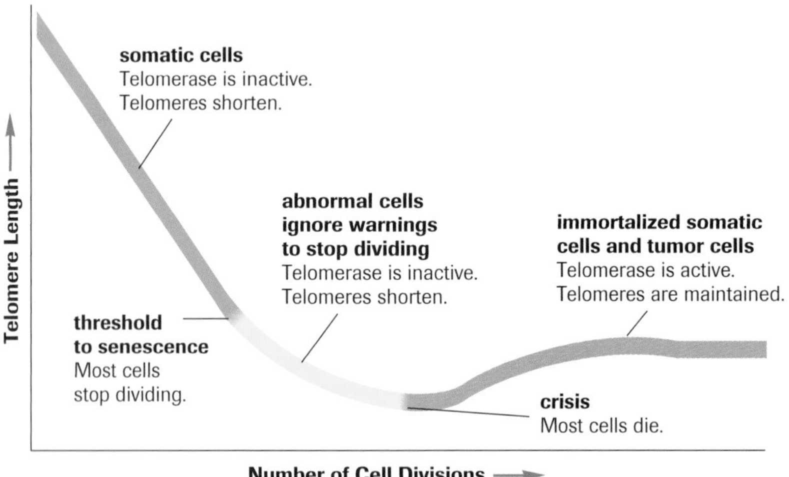

Figure 9
The activity of telomerase in normal cells (turquoise line) decreases as the cell ages. Eventually, the cells reach the point where damage to the chromosomes will result if the telomeres become any shorter. At this point, normal cells stop dividing and die. Abnormal cells continue to divide (yellow line). Cancer cells (brown line) reactivate telomerase and so are able to continue mitosis.

INVESTIGATION 17.2 *Introduction*

Identification of a Cancer Cell

Cancer cells have unique features that can be used to distinguish them from non-cancerous cells. These differences can be used by medical professionals as a means of detecting cancer, often in earlier, easy-to-treat stages by technologies such as X-rays, infrared photography, and cell biopsies. Some of these differences can be viewed using a light microscope. What are these differences? Do they relate to the ability of these cells to continue undergoing mitosis?

Report Checklist

○ Purpose	● Design	● Analysis
● Problem	○ Materials	● Evaluation
○ Hypothesis	○ Procedure	● Synthesis
○ Prediction	● Evidence	

In this investigation, you will examine stained slides of cancerous and non-cancerous cells under a light microscope to observe some differences between these cell types.

To perform this investigation, turn to page 589.

SUMMARY *Applications of the Cell Cycle*

- Cloning is the process of forming identical offspring from a single cell or tissue.
- Cloning permits the production of offspring with characteristics identical to those of the parent.
- Some plants and animals naturally clone themselves (reproduce asexually).
- Technologies have been developed to clone both plants and animals. Further development of cloning technology relies on increased understanding of cell processes such as mitosis.

Section 17.2 Questions

1. Describe how nuclear transplants are used to clone frogs.
2. Dolly was not the first cloned animal, nor was she the first mammal clone. What made her cloning so special?
3. Explain why male animals would no longer be needed if cloning became the accepted method of reproduction.
4. If the nucleus is extracted from an adult animal cell and placed into an enucleated egg, how would it be possible to distinguish the cloned individual from the original?
5. Make a list of benefits and potential problems associated with cloning farm animals.
6. Speculate on the potential benefits and problems associated with cloning humans.
7. Research the nature versus nurture debate and the evidence provided by studies of twins. Find out about some psychological conditions that have both a genetic and an environmental component. What are the advantages and disadvantages of each approach? Think about the social, moral, and ethical implications of each viewpoint.

www.science.nelson.com 

17.3 Meiosis

meiosis two-stage cell division in which the chromosome number of the parental cell is reduced by half

haploid refers to the number of chromosomes in a gamete

diploid refers to twice the number of chromosomes in a gamete

homologous chromosomes paired chromosomes similar in shape, size, gene arrangement, and gene information

Meiosis is the type of cell division involved in the formation of sex cells, or gametes. In humans, this takes place in the testes and ovaries. Meiosis involves two stages of cell division that have some similarities to the phases in mitosis. In mitosis, the chromosome number of the daughter cells is the same as in the parent cell. In meiosis, the chromosome number of the daughter cells is half that of the parent cell. A human cell containing 46 chromosomes will undergo meiosis and produce gametes that have 23 chromosomes. Each gamete will contain both the same number and the same kind of chromosomes. The number of chromosomes in a gamete is called the **haploid** chromosome number, or n; the number of chromosomes in all other cells having a nucleus is twice the haploid number and is called the **diploid** number, or $2n$. In humans, the haploid chromosome number is 23 and the diploid chromosome number is 46.

Offspring carry genetic information from each of the parents. This explains why you might have your father's eyes but your mother's hair. Although you may look more like one parent than another, you receive genetic information from each parent. For example, your father gives you a chromosome with genes that code for eye colour, but so does your mother. Each of the 23 chromosomes that you receive from your biological father is matched by 23 chromosomes from your biological mother, so that each parent gives you half of your genetic information. The paired chromosomes are called **homologous chromosomes** because they are similar in shape, size, and gene arrangement (**Figure 1**). The genes in homologous chromosomes deal with the same traits. Each cell in your body, except the sex cells, contains 23 pairs of homologous chromosomes, or 46 chromosomes in total. The 23rd pair of chromosomes, which determine sex in mammals, are called the X and Y chromosomes and are only partially homologous. Males receive an X and a Y chromosome and females receive two X chromosomes. You will learn more about these chromosomes later in this chapter and in Chapter 22.

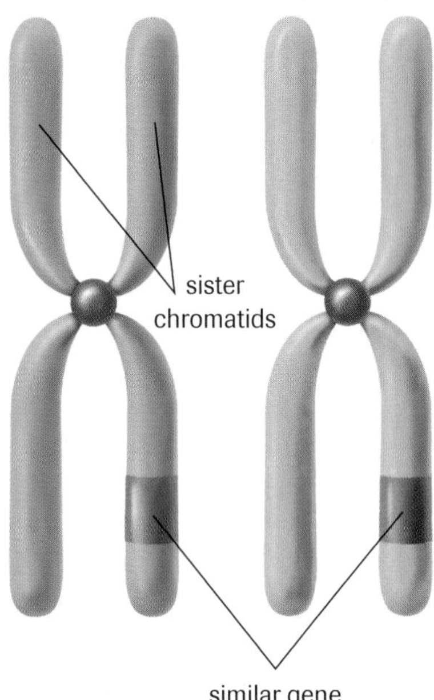

Figure 1
Homologous chromosomes

During fertilization, a haploid ($n = 23$) sperm cell unites with a haploid ($n = 23$) egg cell to produce a diploid ($2n = 46$) zygote. The fusion of male and female gametes restores the diploid chromosome number in the zygote. The zygote will begin dividing by mitosis and will eventually become a multicellular human baby.

Stages of Meiosis

Meiosis involves two nuclear divisions that produce four haploid cells. Meiosis I is often called reduction division because the diploid, or $2n$, chromosome number is reduced to the haploid, or n, chromosome number. The second phase, meiosis II, is marked by a separation of the two chromatids. The phases used to describe the events of mitosis can also be used to describe meiosis. As with mitosis, DNA synthesis occurs prior to the cell division phase.

Meiosis I

tetrad a pair of homologous chromosomes, each with two chromatids

synapsis the pairing of homologous chromosomes

crossing over the exchange of genetic material between two homologous chromosomes

During prophase I, the nuclear membrane begins to dissolve, the centriole splits and its parts move to opposite poles within the cell, and spindle fibres are formed. The chromosomes come together in homologous pairs. Each chromosome of the pair is a homologue and is composed of a pair of sister chromatids. The whole structure is then referred to as a **tetrad** because each pair is composed of four chromatids.

This process is referred to as **synapsis**. As the chromosomes synapse, the chromatids often intertwine. Sometimes the intertwined chromatids from different homologues break and exchange segments in a process called **crossing over** (**Figure 2**, next page). Crossing over permits the exchange of genetic material between homologous pairs of chromosomes.

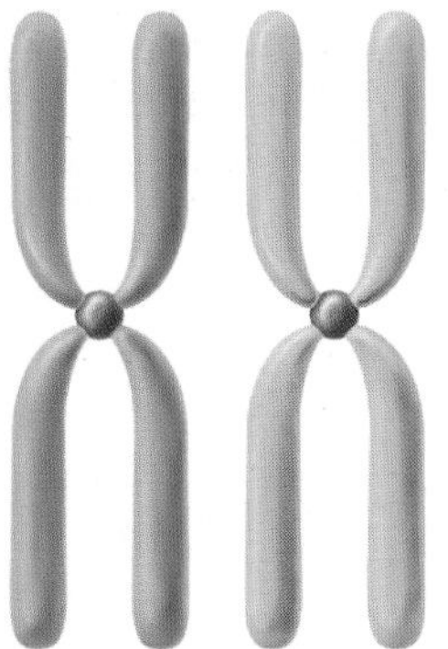

homologous chromosome pair

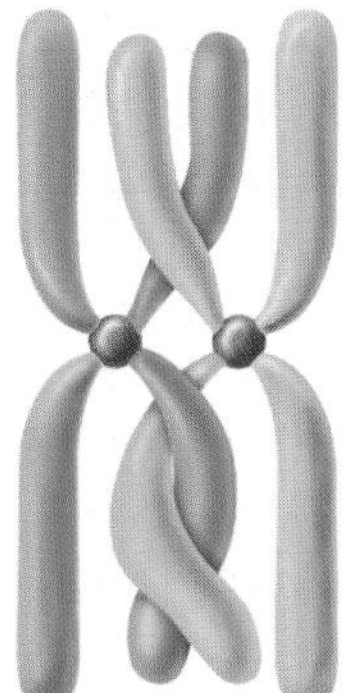

As the chromosomes move closer together, synapsis occurs.

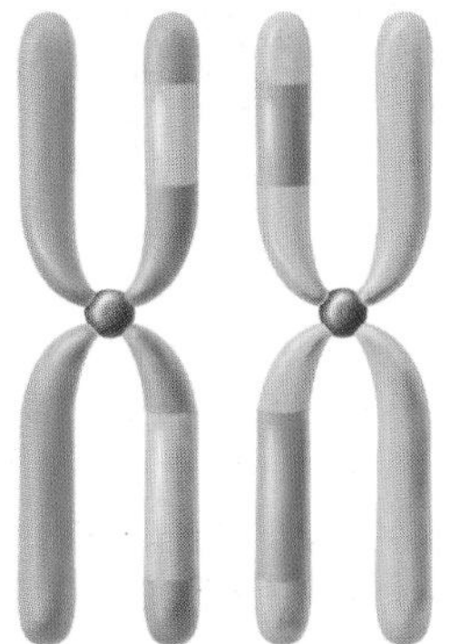

Chromatids break, and genetic information is exchanged.

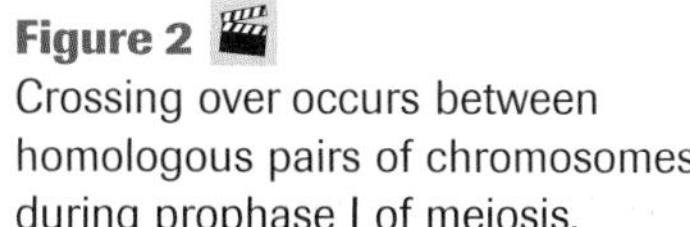

Figure 2
Crossing over occurs between homologous pairs of chromosomes during prophase I of meiosis.

Metaphase I follows prophase I (**Figure 3**). The homologous chromosomes attach themselves to the spindle fibres and line up along the equatorial plate.

During anaphase I, the homologous chromosomes move toward opposite poles. The process is known as segregation. At this point of meiosis, reduction division occurs. One member of each homologous pair will be found in each of the new cells. Each chromosome consists of two sister chromatids.

During telophase I, a membrane begins to form around each nucleus. However, unlike in mitosis, the chromosomes in the two nuclei are not identical because each of the daughter nuclei contains one member of the homologous chromosome pair. Although homologous chromosomes are similar, they are not identical. They carry genes for the same traits (for example, eye colour), but those genes may differ (for example, coding for brown eyes or coding for blue eyes). The cells are now ready to begin the second stage of meiosis.

Crossing Over
This audio clip will discuss the timing of crossing over and the benefit that a species derives from this process.

www.science.nelson.com

prophase I
The replicated chromosomes condense. Homologous chromosomes come together in synapsis and crossing over occurs. Chromosomes attach to the spindle.

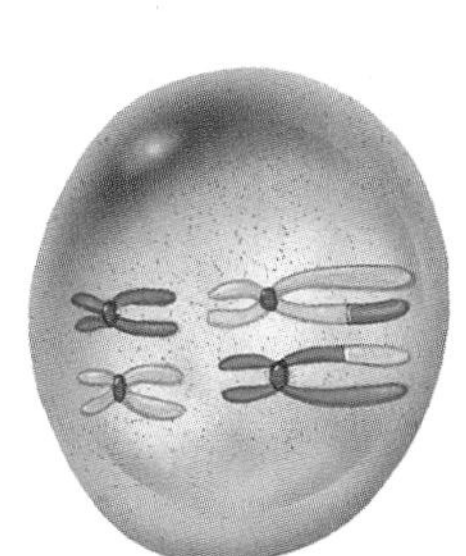

metaphase I
Chromosomes line up at the equatorial plate.

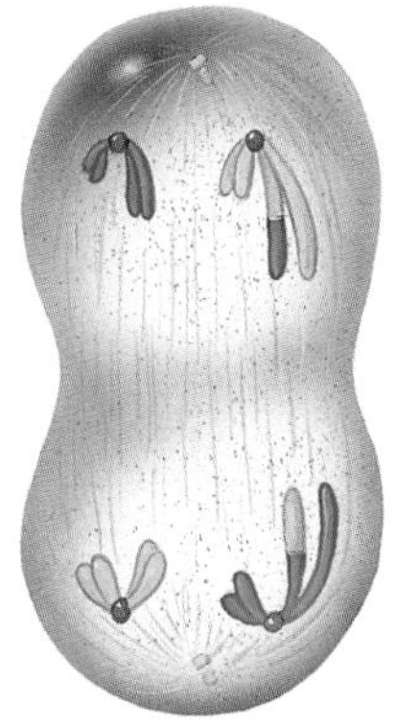

anaphase I
Each chromosome separates from its homologue. They move to opposite poles of the cell.

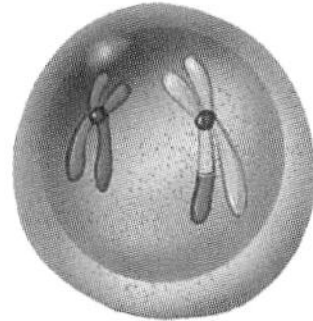

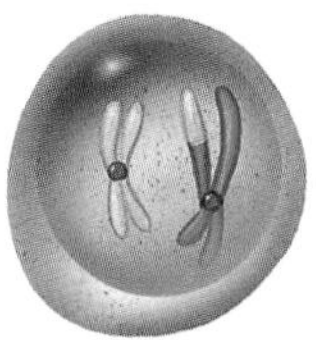

telophase I
The nucleus completes its division. The chromosomes are still composed of sister chromatids. The cytoplasm divides after telophase.

Figure 3
During meiosis I, homologous chromosomes are segregated.

Meiosis II

Meiosis II occurs at approximately the same time in each of the haploid daughter cells. However, for simplicity, consider the events in only one of the cells. (In **Figure 4**, both cells from meiosis I are shown). During meiosis II, pairs of chromatids will separate and move to opposite poles. Note that, unlike with mitosis and meiosis I, there is no replication of chromosomes prior to meiosis II.

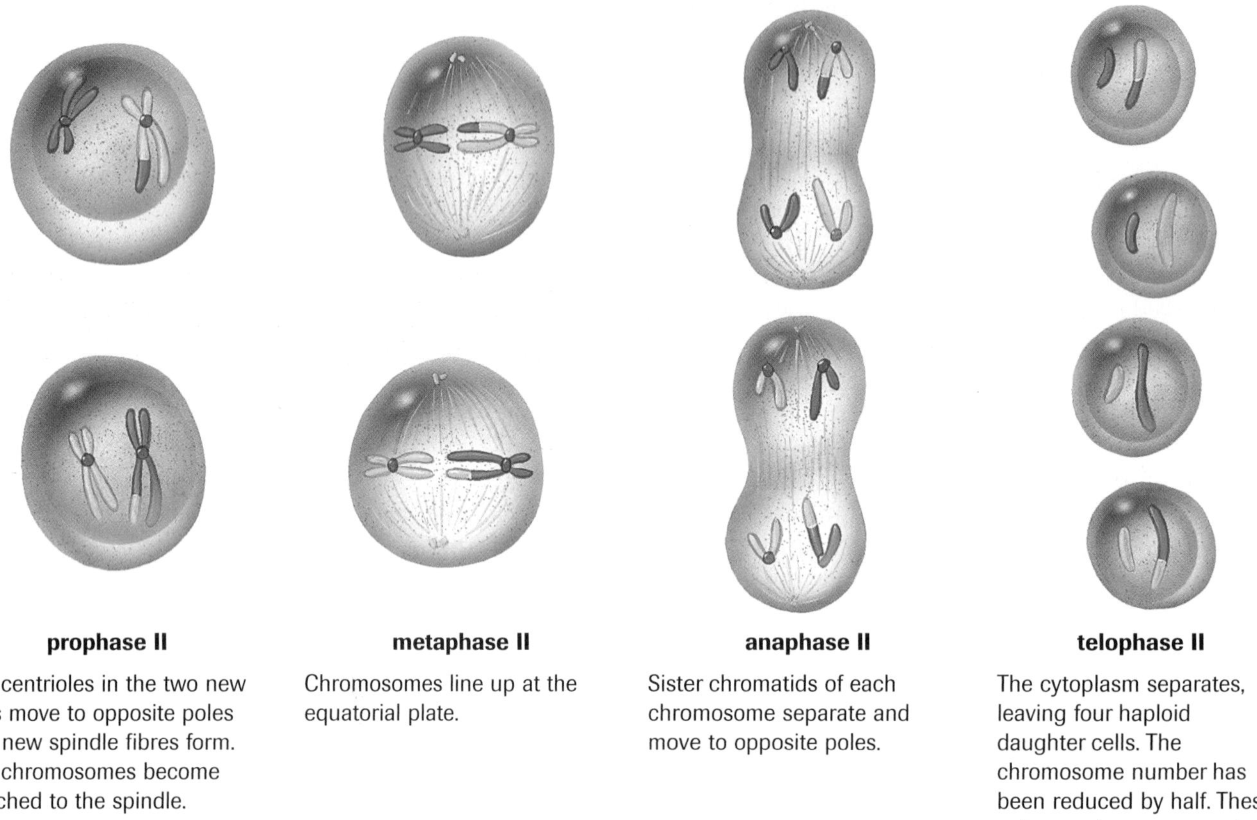

prophase II

The centrioles in the two new cells move to opposite poles and new spindle fibres form. The chromosomes become attached to the spindle.

metaphase II

Chromosomes line up at the equatorial plate.

anaphase II

Sister chromatids of each chromosome separate and move to opposite poles.

telophase II

The cytoplasm separates, leaving four haploid daughter cells. The chromosome number has been reduced by half. These cells may become gametes.

Figure 4
During meiosis II, sister chromatids separate.

Prophase II signals the beginning of the second meiotic division. During this stage, the nuclear membrane dissolves and the spindle fibres begin to form.

Metaphase II follows prophase II. It is signalled by the arrangement of the chromosomes, each with two chromatids, along the equatorial plate. The chromatids remain pinned together by the centromere.

Anaphase II can be identified by the breaking of the attachment between the two chromatids and by their movement to the opposite poles. This stage ends when the nuclear membrane begins to form around the chromatids, now referred to as chromosomes.

The cell then enters its final stage of meiosis: telophase II. During this stage, the second nuclear division is completed and then the second division of cytoplasm occurs. Four haploid daughter cells are produced from each meiotic division.

Practice

1. Define meiosis. Describe the main stages in the process. Sketch the sequence of stages to help you in your description. Label your diagrams appropriately.
2. How are haploid cells different from diploid cells in humans?
3. What is a tetrad?
4. What are homologous chromosomes?
5. Do homologous chromosomes have the same number of genes? Explain.
6. Do homologous chromosomes have identical genes? Explain.

mini *Investigation* — Gamete Formation in Grasshoppers

Obtain prepared slides of grasshopper (**Figure 5**) testes and identify cells undergoing meiosis. Make a few sample diagrams of cells at various stages of cell division.

(a) Label the chromosomes.

(b) Are you able to count the chromosome number? Explain why or why not.

(c) Explain and compare what happens in prophase, metaphase, and anaphase of meiosis I and II.

(d) How do cells undergoing meiosis II differ from cells undergoing meiosis I?

Figure 5

Comparing Mitosis and Meiosis

Single-celled eukaryotic species undergo asexual reproduction by mitosis, followed by cytokinesis. In multicellular eukaryotic species, somatic cells undergo these same processes in order to grow and repair tissue. In contrast, meiosis occurs only in the sex cells of multicellular eukaryotic species, in order to produce the gametes needed for sexual reproduction.

The most significant difference between mitosis and meiosis is the end result (**Figure 6**). Mitosis results in two daughter cells that are identical to each other. The daughter cells have the same genetic information and carry the same number of chromosomes as the

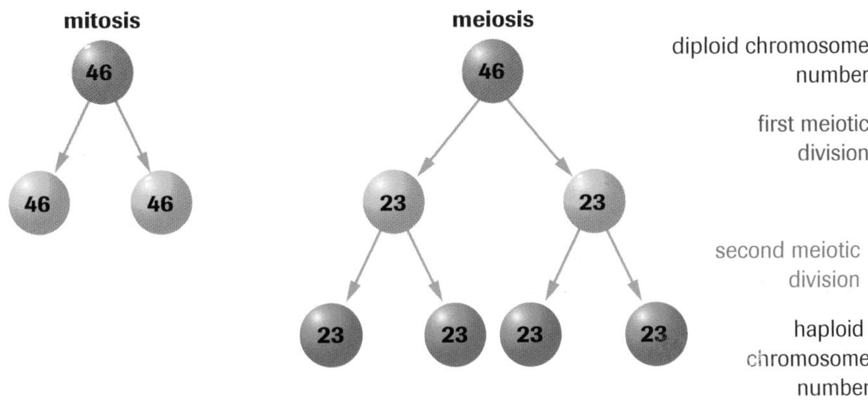

Figure 6
Comparison of mitosis and meiosis in humans. Mitosis produces two diploid cells from one diploid cell. Meiosis produces four haploid cells from one diploid cell.

parent cell. In contrast, meiosis results in four daughter cells that are different from each other and from the parent cell. The daughter cells have different genetic information from each other and from the parent cell and carry half the number of chromosomes as the parent cell.

Figure 7 and **Figure 8** (next page) summarize the similarities and differences between mitosis and meiosis. As you examine **Figures 7** and **8**, make note of the chromosome number of the cell or cells, whether the chromosome number is haploid or diploid, and during which stage the chromosome number changes.

Meiosis, combined with fertilization, explains the variation in traits that is observed in species that reproduce sexually. The variation occurs through three mechanisms. First, crossing over during prophase I exchanges genes on the chromosomes. Second, during metaphase I, the paternal and maternal chromosomes are randomly assorted. Although homologues always go to opposite poles, a pole could receive all the maternal chromosomes, all the paternal ones, or some combination. Lastly, during fertilization, different combinations of chromosomes and genes occur when two gametes unite.

prophase I

The replicated chromosomes condense. Homologous chromosomes come together in synapsis and crossing over occurs. Chromosomes attach to the spindle.

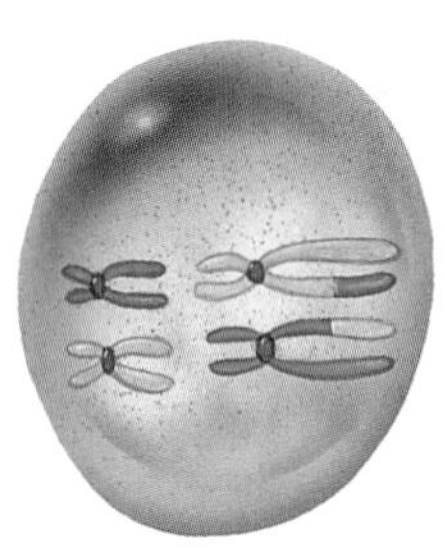

metaphase I

Homologous chromosomes line up at the equatorial plate.

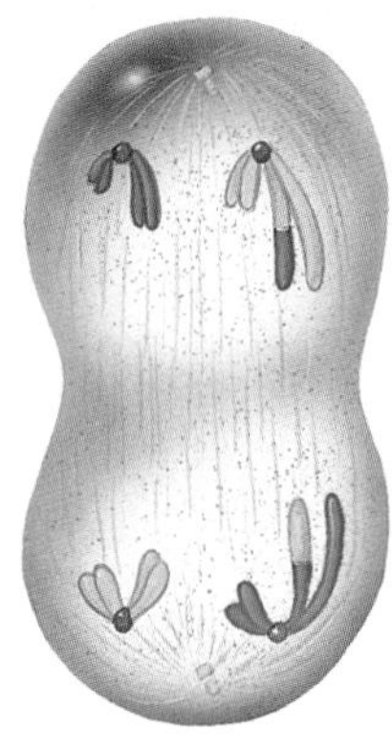

anaphase I

Each chromosome separates from its homologue. They move to opposite poles of the cell.

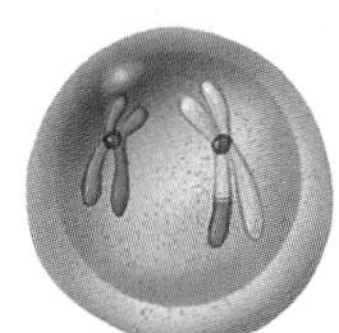

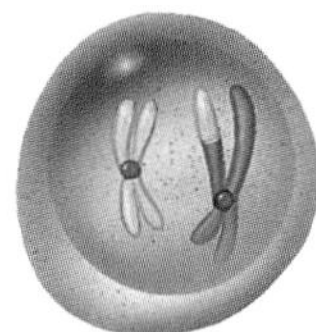

telophase I

The nucleus completes its division. The chromosomes are still composed of sister chromatids. The cytoplasm divides after telophase.

Figure 7
Stages of meiosis I. During meiosis I, crossing over occurs and homologous pairs separate. These events do not occur during mitosis.

INVESTIGATION 17.3 *Introduction*

Comparing Mitosis and Meiosis

Scientists often use models to help them to understand complex processes. To understand the consequences of mitosis and meiosis, you must have a clear view of the similarities and differences between these two modes of cell division. In this investigation, you construct and use models to investigate these essential processes.

To perform this investigation, turn to page 590. 

Report Checklist

- ● Purpose
- ● Problem
- ○ Hypothesis
- ○ Prediction
- ○ Design
- ○ Materials
- ○ Procedure
- ○ Evidence
- ● Analysis
- ● Evaluation
- ○ Synthesis

(a) Mitosis

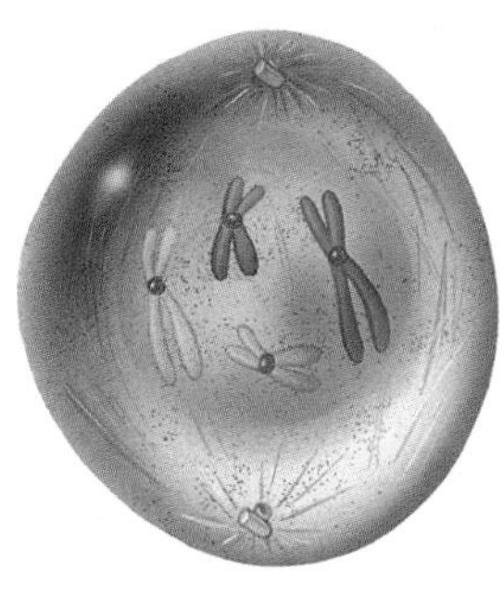

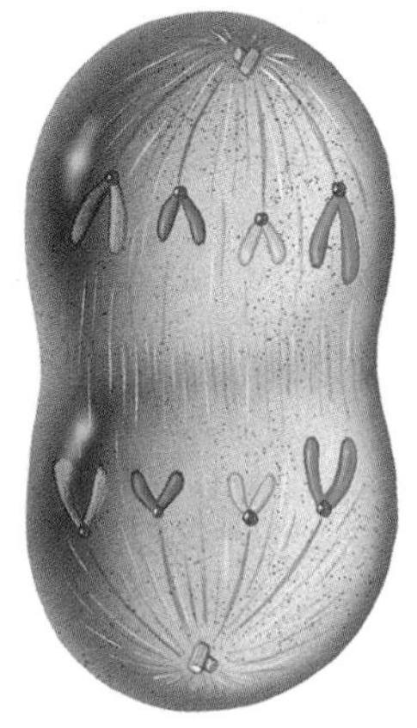

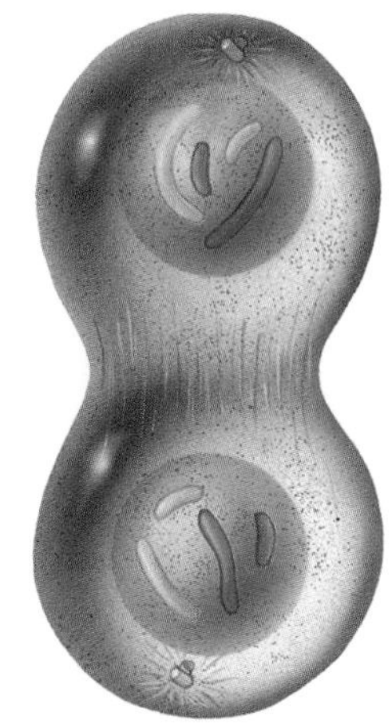

prophase

The chromosomes condense, becoming shorter and thicker. The centrioles assemble and spindle fibres attach to the centromeres of the chromosomes. The nuclear membrane starts to dissolve.

metaphase

Chromosomes line up at the equatorial plate. The nuclear membrane completely dissolves.

anaphase

The centromeres divide and the resulting chromosomes, formerly chromatids, move to opposite poles of the cell. An identical set of chromosomes moves to each pole.

telophase

Chromosomes lengthen again, the spindle fibres dissolve, and a nuclear membrane forms around the chromosomes.

(b) Meiosis II

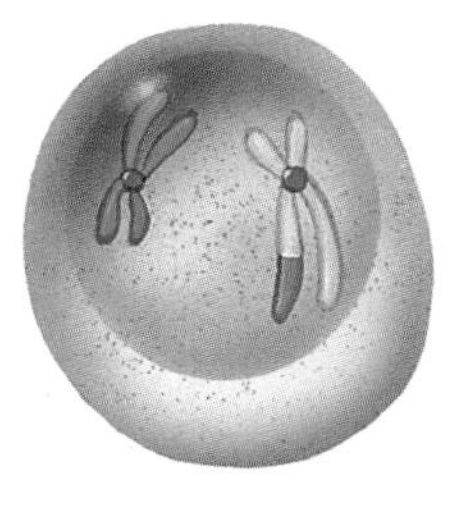

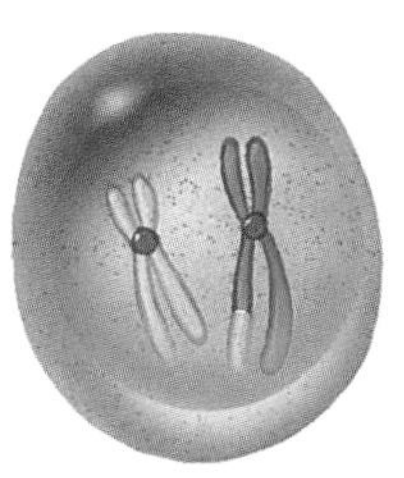

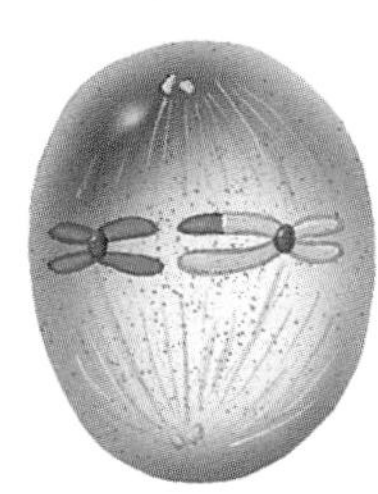

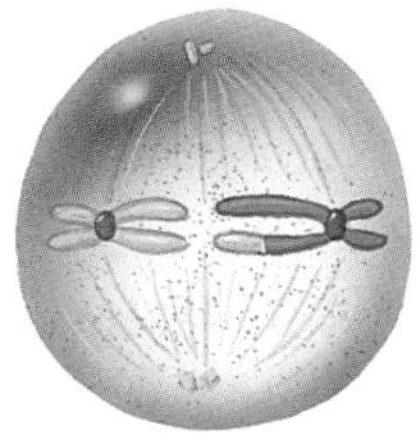

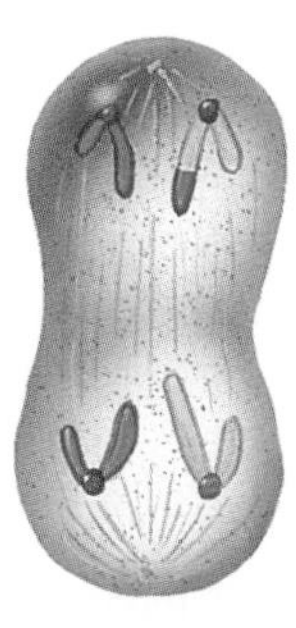

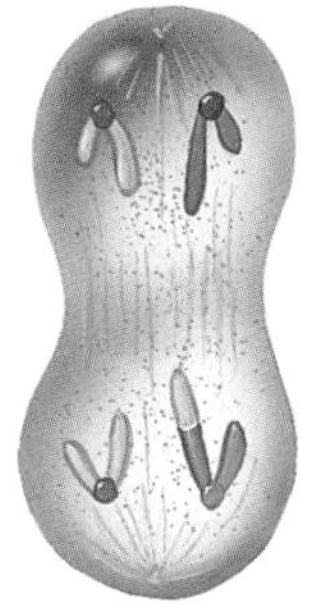

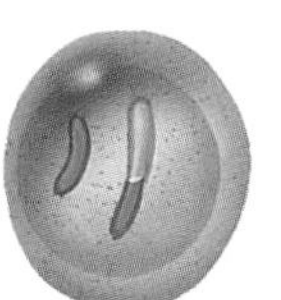

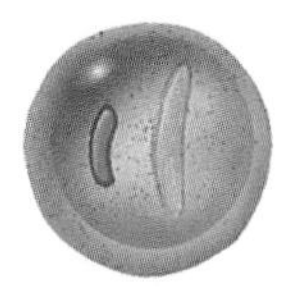

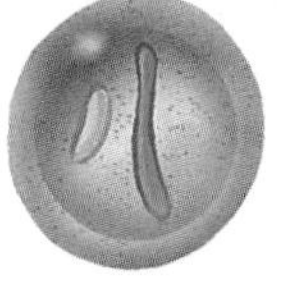

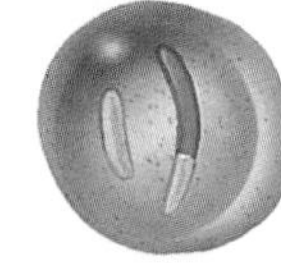

prophase II

The centrioles in the two new cells move to opposite poles and new spindle fibres form. The chromosomes become attached to the spindle.

metaphase II

Chromosomes line up at the equatorial plate.

anaphase II

Sister chromatids of each chromosome separate and move to opposite poles.

telophase II

The cytoplasm separates, leaving four haploid daughter cells. The chromosome number has been reduced by half. These cells may become gametes.

Figure 8

Comparison of the stages in **(a)** mitosis and **(b)** meiosis II. In mitosis, homologous chromosomes are separated, giving rise to genetically identical sister cells. In meiosis II, the sister chromatids in the products of meiosis I separate as the cells divide again. This gives rise to four genetically different sex cells.

Practice

7. Copy and complete **Table 1**. Compare the chromosome number in the organisms before, during, and as a result of meiosis. Indicate whether the chromosome number is haploid or diploid.

Table 1 Chromosome Number in Cells of Four Organisms

	Human	Cat	Shrimp	Bean
Before meiosis				
chromosome number (haploid or diploid?)	46	?	?	?
number of pairs of homologous chromosomes	23	?	127	?
After meiosis I				
chromosome number (haploid or diploid?)	23	19	?	?
After meiosis II				
chromosome number (haploid or diploid?)	23	?	?	11
number of pairs of homologous chromosomes	0	?	?	?

Development of Male and Female Gametes

gametogenesis the formation of gametes (sex cells) in animals

ootid an unfertilized ovum

The formation of sex cells during meiosis is referred to as **gametogenesis**. Although human male and female gametes both follow the general process of meiosis, some differences do exist. The cytoplasm of the female gametes does not divide equally after each nuclear division. As shown in **Figure 9**, one of the daughter cells, called the **ootid**, receives most of the cytoplasm. The other cells, the polar bodies, die, and the nutrients are absorbed by the body of the organism. Only one ovum (egg cell) is produced from meiosis. In contrast, with sperm cells, there is an equal division of cytoplasm. Sperm cells have much less cytoplasm than egg cells. Sperm cells are specially designed for movement: they are streamlined and cannot carry excess weight. Egg cells use the nutri-

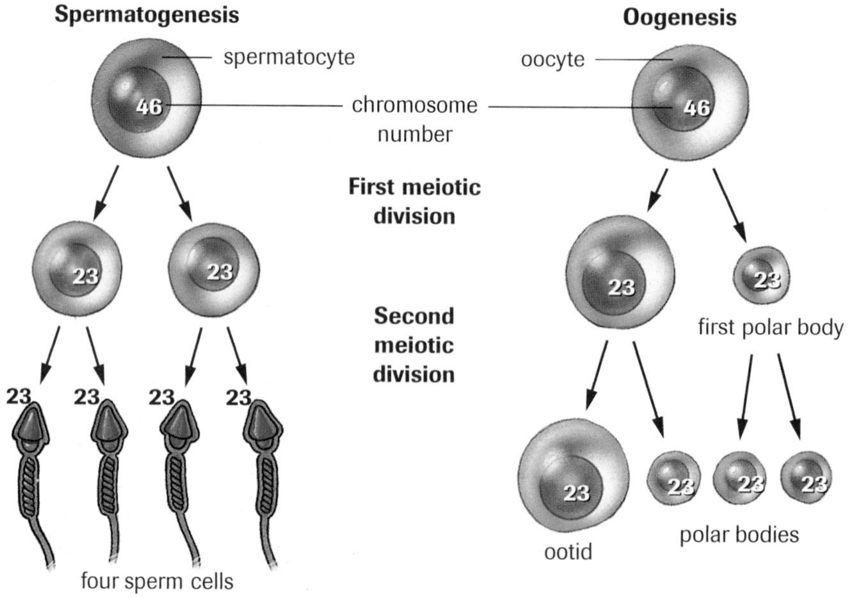

Figure 9
Generalized diagram of sperm and egg cell formation in humans

ents and organelles carried within the cytoplasm to fuel future cell divisions in the event that the egg cell becomes fertilized.

Human males make many more sex cells than females. The diploid spermatocytes—the cells that give rise to sperm cells—are capable of many mitotic divisions before meiosis ever begins. Males can produce one billion sperm cells every day. At birth, human females have about two million primary oocytes in their ovaries. Primary oocytes have already entered meiosis I, but they will remain suspended in prophase I until the female reaches reproductive age, or puberty. Starting at the first menstrual cycle, meiosis will resume in one oocyte at a time, once a month.

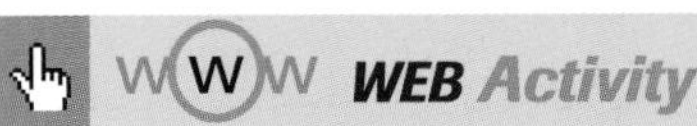

WEB Activity

Case Study—Comparing Life Cycles of Plants

In this Web-based Case Study, you will observe and compare the life cycles of different plants. By examining the reproductive life cycles of plants you will gain a greater understanding of how reproductive diversity contributes to the evolution of complex organisms.

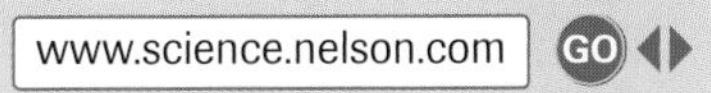

Cell Division and Life Cycles

Organisms that undergo asexual reproduction produce offspring by mitosis. In this type of life cycle, cells divide by mitosis and give rise to daughter cells with the same chromosome number as the parent cell. There is no change in chromosome number. Examples of organisms that reproduce asexually are bacteria and yeasts.

In contrast, the chromosome number changes during the life cycle of a species that undergoes sexual reproduction. Examples of sexually reproducing species include flowering plants and birds. Two events in sexual reproduction change chromosome number: meiosis and fertilization. The gametes are formed by meiosis; these cells have half the chromosome number as the somatic cells. During fertilization, two gametes join to form a zygote, and the chromosome number is restored to that of the somatic cells.

There are variations in these two main types of the life cycles. **Figure 10**,on the next page shows a common life cycle found in flowering plants. In flowering plants, pollen contains the male sex cells, and the female egg cells are stored within the flower. The gametes contain a haploid chromosome number ($1n$). At fertilization, a diploid zygote ($2n$) is formed. The zygote undergoes mitosis to produce seeds, which then undergoes further mitosis to produce the adult $2n$ plant, called the sporophyte. Specialized cells in the mature $2n$ plant undergo meiosis to produce haploid ($1n$) spores. The spores then undergo mitosis to produce a mature, multicellular gametophyte. In most flowering plants, the gametophyte is too small to see without magnification. Since mitosis does not change chromosome number, the gametophyte is also haploid ($1n$). Specialized cells in the gametophyte develop into gametes, and the cycle begins again. Many familiar plants are sporophytes, such as the pine trees in a boreal forest. In other plant species, such as ferns, it is the gametophyte that is the larger, dominant form.

Figure 11,on the next page shows a common life cycle for animals, such as humans. In this life cycle, the gametes (sperm cells and egg cells) are haploid ($1n$) and single-celled. During fertilization, the gametes fuse and form a diploid ($2n$) zygote. This zygote undergoes mitosis to form the multi-cellular diploid adult body. Specialized cells in the adult body (in humans, cells in the testes and ovaries) undergo meiosis to produce gametes. Up to this point, the life cycles of plants in **Figure 10** and of animals in **Figure 11** are the same. However, the gametes of most animals do not undergo mitosis to form a multi-cellular gametophyte. Instead, the haploid stage remains single celled. When these haploid gametes unite, fertilization occurs and the life cycle begins again.

+ EXTENSION

Reproductive Strategies for Survival (Non-Human)

The different species on our planet have a remarkable variety of strategies to ensure their survival. Review some of these reproductive strategies by completing this extension activity.

www.science.nelson.com 

DID YOU KNOW?

Two Styles of Life Cycle

Some species undergo both sexual and asexual life cycles. For example, the spider plant can reproduce by seeds (sexual reproduction) or by runners (asexual reproduction). Aphid females reproduce asexually when the environment is stable, and sexually when the environment changes. Similarly, the male drones in a honey bee colony are produced by asexual reproduction, but the female workers and the queens are products of sexual reproduction.

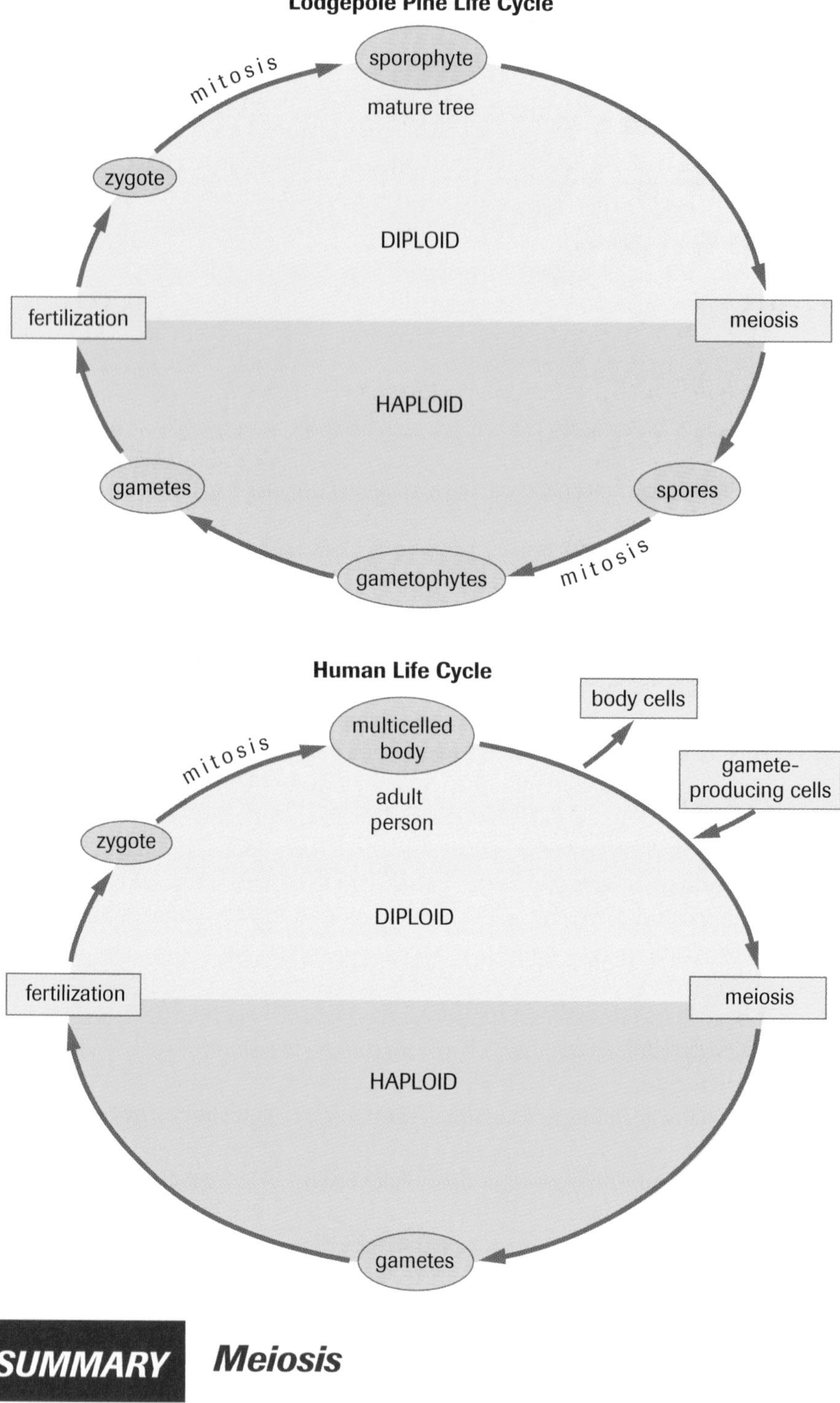

Figure 10
Lodgepole pine life cycle. The diploid cells formed at fertilization undergo mitosis to form the multicelled *sporophyte (the tree).* The haploid stage starts when meiosis produces spores. These undergo mitosis to form a multicellular gametophyte, which is contained in the cones.

Figure 11
Human life cycle. The diploid cells formed at fertilization undergo mitosis to form the multicelled body. The haploid stage is the single-celled gametes.

SUMMARY *Meiosis*

- Meiosis involves the formation of sex cells or gametes. All gametes produced by meiosis have haploid chromosome numbers.
- Cells undergoing meiosis pass through two divisions.
- Homologous chromosomes are similar in shape, size, gene arrangement, and gene information.
- Crossing over is the exchange of genetic material between homologous chromosomes that occurs during meiosis.

Section 17.3 Questions

1. How does the first meiotic division differ from the second meiotic division?
2. Explain why synapsis may lead to the exchange of genetic information.
3. Construct a table to compare meiosis with mitosis. How does meiosis differ from mitosis?
4. A muscle cell of a mouse contains 22 chromosomes. Based on this information, how many chromosomes are there in the following types of mouse cells?
   (a) daughter muscle cell formed from mitosis
   (b) egg cell
   (c) fertilized egg cell
5. Compare the mechanisms of gametogenesis in males and females.
6. When meiosis occurs in females, the cytoplasm is not divided equally among the resulting four cells. Explain why.
7. Compare the life cycles of plants and animals.
8. **Figure 12** shows sperm cell production following meiosis.
   (a) Which cells do not contain homologous pairs?
   (b) If the chromosome number for cell A is 12, indicate the chromosome number for cell C.

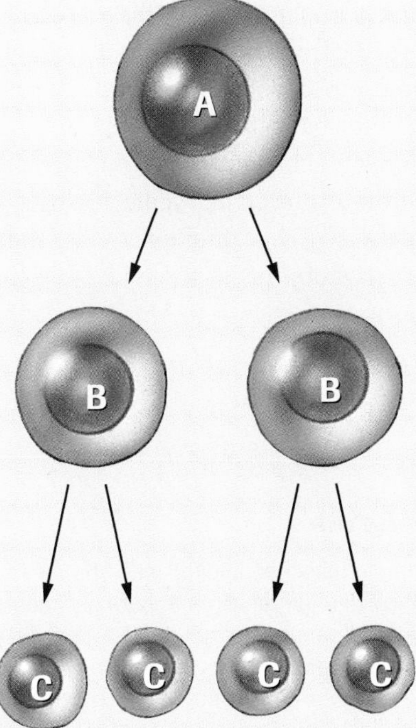

Figure 12
Sperm cell production in humans

9. Use **Figure 13** to answer the questions below.
   (a) Which process(es) identify mitosis? Explain your answer.
   (b) Which process(es) identify meiosis? Explain your answer.

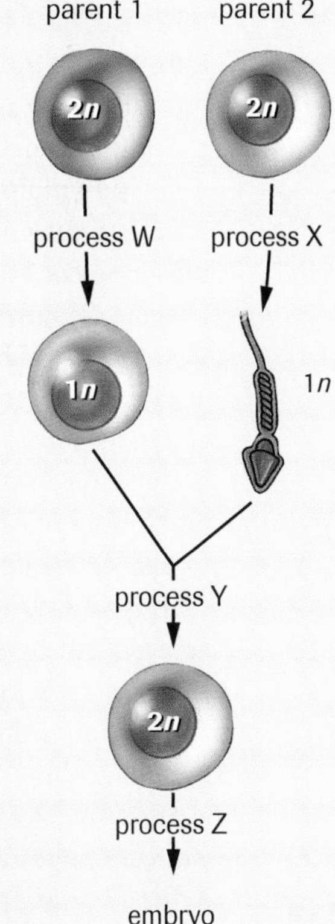

Figure 13
The processes and number of sets of chromosomes involved in the production of an embryo in humans

10. King Henry VIII of England had some of his wives executed for not producing sons. Indicate why a little knowledge of meiosis might have been important for Henry's wives.
11. A microscopic water animal called *Daphnia* can be reproduced from an unfertilized egg. This form of reproduction is asexual because male gametes are not required. Indicate the sex of the offspring produced. Explain your answer.

17.4 Abnormal Meiosis

nondisjunction the failure of a pair of homologous chromosomes to separate properly during meiosis

Meiosis, like most processes of the body, is not immune to mistakes. **Nondisjunction** occurs when two homologous chromosomes fail to separate during meiosis or mitosis. The result is that one of the daughter cells will have too many chromosomes, while the other will have too few. Cells that lack genetic information, or have too much information, will not function properly. Nondisjunction can also occur in any cell during mitosis, but the effects are most devastating during the formation of sex cells in meiosis.

polyploidy a condition in which an organism has more than two complete sets of chromosomes

Some organisms have more than two complete chromosome sets. This condition is called **polyploidy**. Polyploid organisms may have three chromosome sets (triploidy or $3n$), four chromosome sets (tetraploidy or $4n$), and rarely, even more than four chromosome sets. Polyploidy can result when a diploid ($2n$) egg cell is fertilized by a haploid ($1n$) sperm, giving rise to a $3n$ cell. Nondisjunction of all chromosomes within the egg cell produces a diploid sex cell, which then becomes triploid upon fertilization. Tetraploid organisms are most often produced by the failure of the $2n$ zygote to divide after replicating its chromosomes. Following normal mitosis a $4n$ embryo is formed. Polyploidy is common in plants. Wheat, oats, tobacco, and potatoes are agriculturally important polyploid species. Plant geneticists may use chemicals that create errors in meiosis and mitosis to create new polyploid plants.

trisomy the condition in which there are three homologous chromosomes in place of a homologous pair

monosomy the condition in which there is a single chromosome in place of a homologous pair

In humans, nondisjunction produces gametes with 22 and 24 chromosomes. The gamete with 24 chromosomes has both chromosomes from one of the homologous pairs. If that gamete joins with a normal gamete of 23 chromosomes from the opposite sex, a zygote containing 47, rather than 46, chromosomes will be produced. The zygote will then have three chromosomes in place of the normal pair. This condition is referred to as **trisomy**. However, if the sex cell containing 22 chromosomes joins with a normal gamete, the resulting zygote will have 45 chromosomes. The zygote will have only one of the chromosomes rather than the homologous pair. This condition is called **monosomy**. Once the cells of the trisomic or monosomic zygotes begin to divide, each cell of the body will contain more or fewer than 46 chromosomes.

Figure 1
Dr. Renée Martin

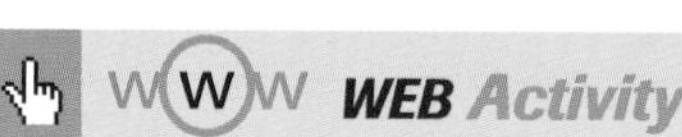

WEB Activity

Canadian Achievers—Dr. Renée Martin

Pregnancy loss, birth defects, and mental retardation have been linked with chromosome abnormalities in sperm and eggs, but much of the scientific research to date has focused on abnormalities in the egg. Dr. Renée Martin, a medical geneticist from the University of Calgary, is recognized for her research on chromosomal abnormalities in human sperm cells. A research centre at the university has been named after her. Dr. Martin's research indicates that 10 % of sperm in normal men have a chromosomal abnormality, but men who have undergone radiotherapy have much higher frequencies of abnormal sperm. One of the most important questions to be answered is whether or not any of these abnormal sperm cells actually fertilize an egg. Dr. Martin's research will provide valuable information on birth defects and miscarriages. Visit the Nelson Web site to learn more about Dr. Martin's research contributions.

www.science.nelson.com 

Nondisjunction Disorders

Nondisjunction is associated with many different human genetic disorders. For example, Down syndrome is a trisomic condition. Down syndrome is also called trisomy 21 because it usually results from three copies of chromosome 21. People with Down syndrome (**Figure 2**) can be identified by several common traits, regardless of race: a round, full face; enlarged and creased tongue; short height; and a large forehead. Down syndrome is generally associated with mental retardation, although people with this condition retain a wide range of mental abilities. The risk of having a baby with Down syndrome increases with the age of the mother. About 1 in 600 babies is born with Down syndrome.

Turner syndrome occurs when sex chromosomes undergo nondisjunction. This monosomic disorder produces a female with a single X chromosome. In the egg cell, both homologous X chromosomes move to the same pole during meiosis I (**Figure 3**). When the egg with no X chromosome is fertilized by a normal sperm cell with an X chromosome, a zygote with 45 chromosomes is produced. Individuals with Turner syndrome appear female, but do not usually develop sexually and tend to be short and have thick, widened necks. About 1 in every 3000 female babies is a Turner syndrome baby. Most Turner syndrome fetuses are miscarried before the 20th week of pregnancy.

Klinefelter syndrome is caused by nondisjunction in either the sperm or egg (**Figure 3**). The child inherits two X chromosomes—characteristic of females—and a single Y chromosome—characteristic of males. The child appears to be a male at birth; however, as he enters sexual maturity, he begins producing high levels of female sex hormones. Males with Klinefelter syndrome are sterile. It has been estimated that Klinefelter syndrome occurs, on average, in 1 of every 500 male babies.

Figure 2
People with Down syndrome have a wide range of abilities.

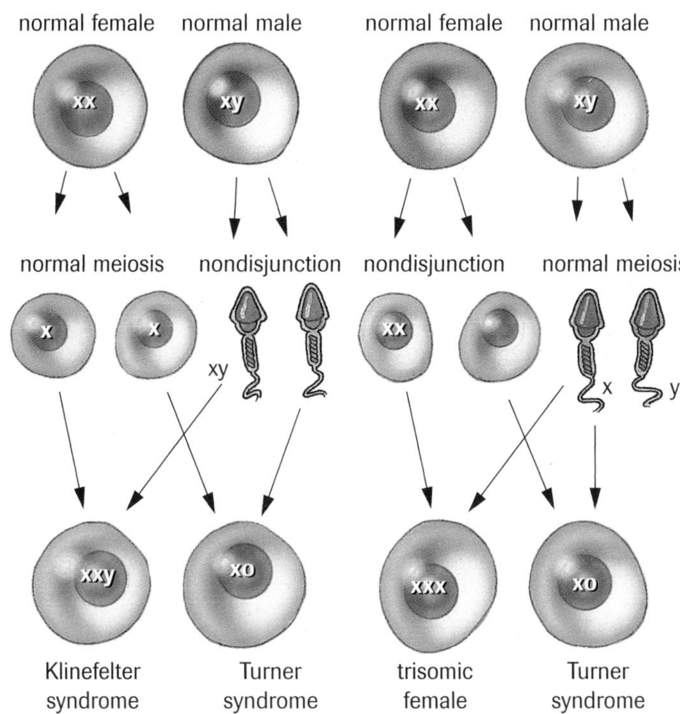

Figure 3
Nondisjunction disorders in humans

CAREER CONNECTION 

Geneticist

Geneticists are professionals with specialized education, training, and experience in genetics. Those with expertise in medical genetics may help families understand birth defects and how diseases are inherited. They may counsel people who carry genes that increase their risk of developing disease, such as some forms of cancer.

www.science.nelson.com 

Karyotype Charts

karyotype chart a picture of chromosomes arranged in homologous pairs

Karyotype Preparation
This animation depicts the steps involved in preparing a karyotype chart. You can also see representative karyotypes from individuals with nondisjunction disorders.

www.science.nelson.com 

One tool for detecting the results of abnormal meiosis is a chart of the chromosomes called a karyotype. Technicians obtain a **karyotype chart** by mixing a small sample of tissue with a solution that stimulates mitotic division. A different solution is added which stops division at metaphase. Since chromosomes are in their most condensed form during metaphase—their size, length, and centromere location are most discernible—it is the best phase in which to obtain a karyotype. The metaphase cells are placed onto a slide and then stained, so that distinctive bands appear. A photograph of the chromosomes is taken. The image is enlarged, and each chromosome is cut out and paired up with its homologue. Homologous chromosomes are similar in size, length, centromere location, and banding pattern. Finally, all the pairs are aligned at their centromeres in decreasing size order. The sex chromosomes are always placed last.

Figure 4 shows karyotypes of a normal male and of a female with Down syndrome. In about 95 % of cases, a child with Down syndrome has an extra chromosome in chromosome number 21. This trisomic disorder is produced by nondisjunction; the person has too much genetic information. Compare the chromosomes of a male shown in **Figure 4 (a)**, with the chromosomes of a female who has Down syndrome, shown in **Figure 4 (b)**. Notice how the chromosomes are arranged in pairs.

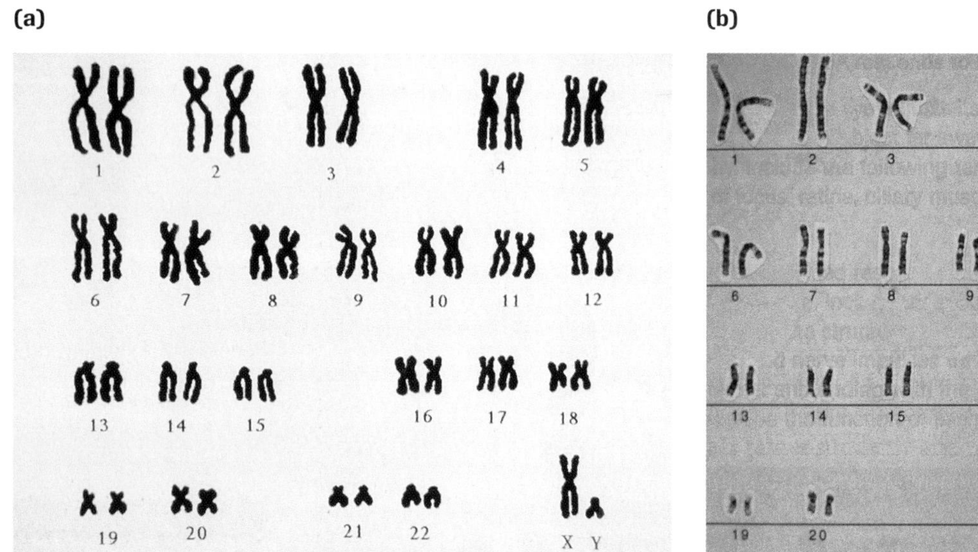

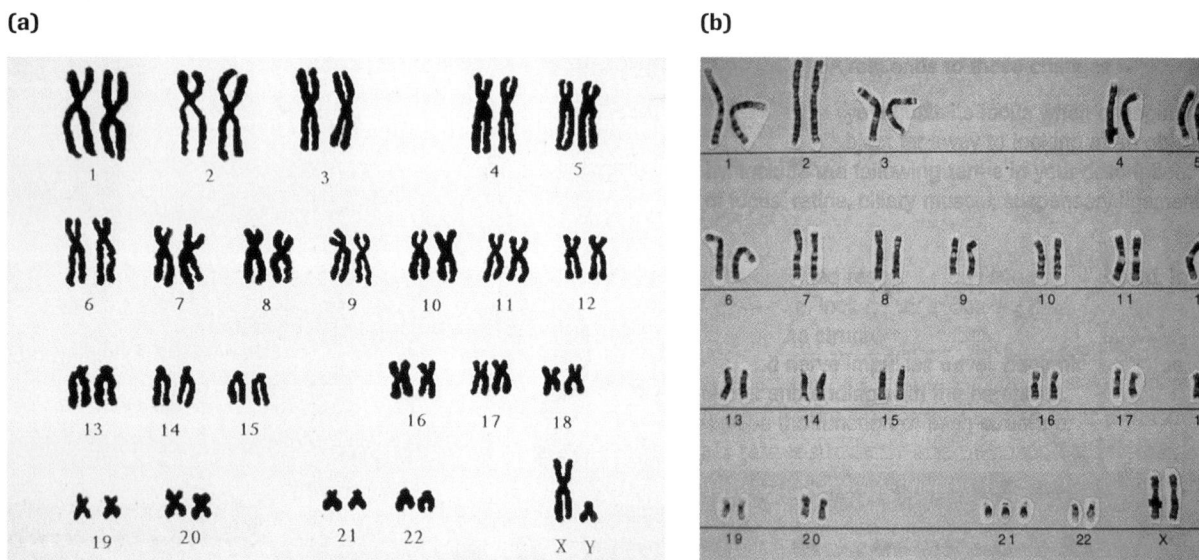

Figure 4
(a) Karyotype chart of a male with 46 chromosomes. Notice that the chromosome pair number 23 is not homologous. Males contain an X and a Y chromosome. They act as a homologous pair in meisois, but they are not similar in size and shape as are the other chromosome pairs.
(b) Karyotype of a female with Down syndrome. Note the trisomy of number 21. Down syndrome affects both males and females.

SAMPLE exercise 1

Figure 5 shows the incomplete karyotype chart of a human. Notice that several chromosomes are missing. Identify where chromosomes a to f (**Figure 6**) should be in this karyotype chart.

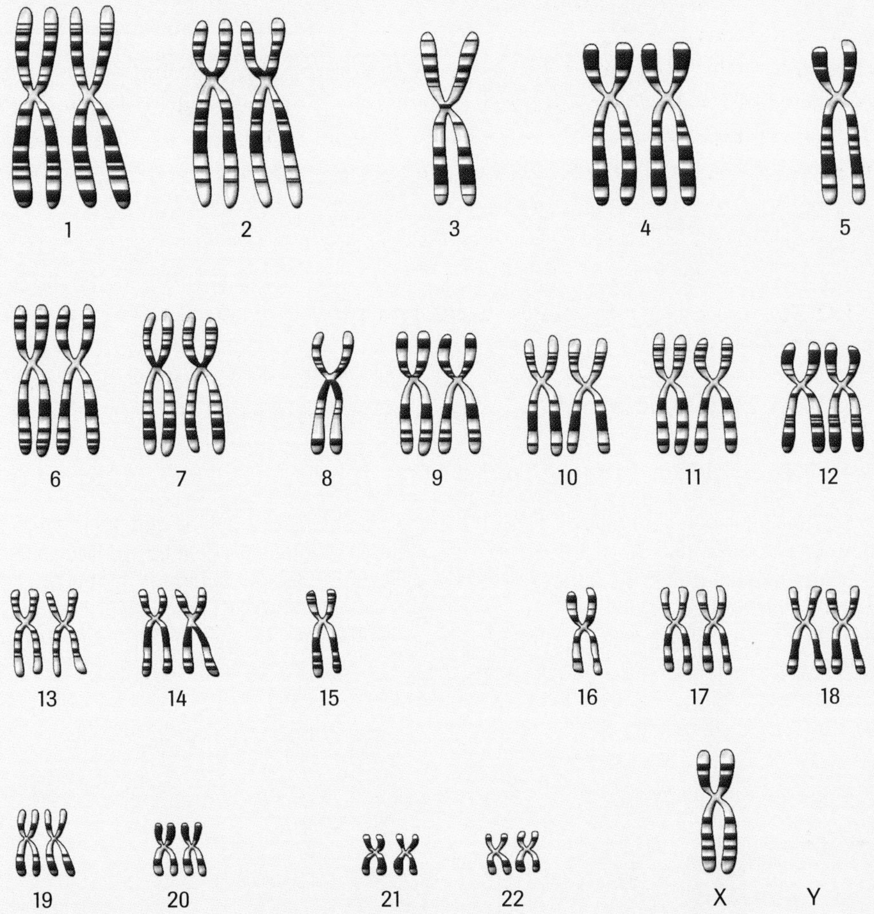

1 2 3 4 5

6 7 8 9 10 11 12

13 14 15 16 17 18

19 20 21 22 X Y

Figure 5

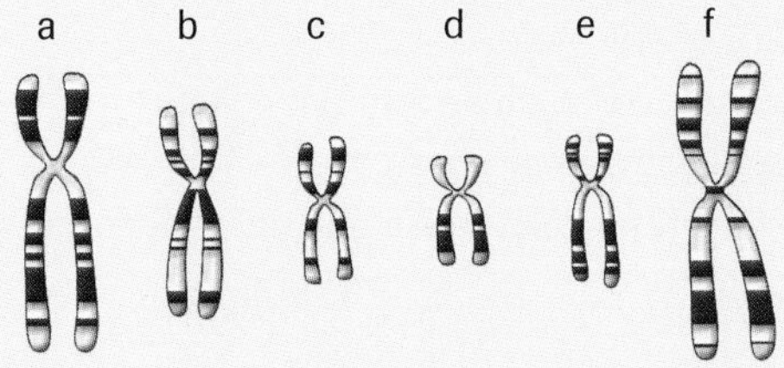

a b c d e f

Figure 6

Solution

1. Start by scanning the karyotype chart to see which pairs are missing a chromosome. Pairs 3, 5, 8, 15, and 16 need a partner.
2. Match the most obvious chromosomes first: the longest, shortest, or most distinctively banded chromosomes.
3. For chromosome matches that are not as obvious, look carefully at the banding pattern and location of the centromere.

DID YOU KNOW ?

Amniocentesis

A diagnostic technique known as amniocentesis can be used to test for nondisjunction and other genetic disorders in developing fetuses. During this procedure, a fine needle is inserted into the amniotic sac that surrounds the fetus, and about 10 mL of the amniotic fluid in which the fetus is bathed is withdrawn. This fluid contains fetal cells that can be used to produce a karyotype chart, as well as chemicals that may signal specific disorders.

www.science.nelson.com 

Learning Tip

You can also construct a karyotype chart using a copy of the chromosome images. For the Sample Exercise and Practice question 1, copy **Figures 5**, **6** and **7**. Then, cut out the chromosome images in **Figures 6** and **7**, and position them on **Figure 5** according to their size, shape, and banding patterns.

4. Always pay attention to the X and Y chromosomes. In **Figure 5**, on the previous page, the missing chromosome might be X or Y. If it is Y, it will have to be found through elimination since it will not match X.

a, 5 b, 8 c, 16 d, Y e, 15 f, 3

Practice

1. This person has either Down syndrome or Klinefelter syndrome. Identify the placement of chromosome g (**Figure 7**) to identify which of these two disorders the patient has.

g

Figure 7

EXTENSION

Karyotyping

There are a number of human genetic disorders that involve nondisjunction. In this Virtual Biology Lab, you will construct karyotype charts and use them to predict genetic disorders, in much the same way as a genetic counsellor might.

www.science.nelson.com 

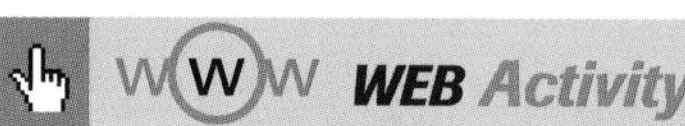

Web Quest—Modelling Mitosis and Meiosis

Cellular division is one of the most critical processes an organism regularly undergoes. Unfortunately, errors during cellular division can result in a number of genetic syndromes such as Down syndrome, Turner syndrome, Klinefelter syndrome, and XYY syndrome. In this Web Quest, you will explore normal and abnormal cellular division. You will use the knowledge that you gathered to create an animation or presentation that shows exactly how abnormal cellular divisions occur.

www.science.nelson.com 

SUMMARY Abnormal Meiosis

- Nondisjunction occurs when two homologous chromosomes move to the same pole during meiosis. In humans, this produces gametes with 22 and 24 chromosomes.
  - Trisomy: a zygote containing 47 chromosomes; causes human genetic disorders such as Down syndrome and Klinefelter syndrome
  - Monosomy: a zygote containing 45 chromosomes; causes Turner syndrome
- A karyotype chart is a picture of chromosomes arranged in homologous pairs in descending order by size, with the sex chromosomes placed last.

Section 17.4 Questions

1. What is nondisjunction?
2. Differentiate between monosomy and trisomy.
3. What is Down syndrome?
4. What is a karyotype?
5. What is Turner syndrome?
6. Use a diagram to illustrate how nondisjunction in meiosis I ($2n = 4$) differs from nondisjunction in meiosis II.

INVESTIGATION 17.1

Frequency of Cell Division

Report Checklist

- ● Purpose
- ● Problem
- ○ Hypothesis
- ○ Prediction
- ○ Design
- ○ Materials
- ○ Procedure
- ● Evidence
- ● Analysis
- ● Evaluation
- ● Synthesis

In this activity, you will view and compare cells from onion cells and from a whitefish blastula in various stages of mitosis. Because slides are used, the cell divisions you will be viewing are frozen in time. Therefore, it will not be possible for you to watch a single cell progress through the stages of mitosis. Based on your observations, you will determine the frequency of cell division and construct a clock representing the division cycle, given the time taken to complete one cycle of mitosis. In a table, you will record the number of cells in each stage of mitosis.

Materials

microscope
lens paper
prepared slides of onion root tip
prepared slides of whitefish blastula

Procedure

Part 1: Observing Dividing Cells

1. Obtain an onion root tip slide and place it on the stage of your microscope. View the slide under low-power magnification. Focus using the coarse-adjustment knob.
2. Centre the root tip in the field of view and then rotate the nosepiece to the medium-power objective lens. Focus the image using the fine-adjustment knob. Observe the cells near the root cap. This area is referred to as the meristematic region of the root.
3. Move the slide to view the cells away from the root tip. These are the mature cells of the root. Record the differences between the cells of the meristematic area and the mature cells of the root. Draw a diagram to help you (**Figure 1**).
4. Return the slide to the meristematic area and centre the root tip. Rotate the nosepiece to the high-power objective lens. Use the fine adjustment to focus the image.
5. Locate and observe cells in each of the phases of mitosis. It will be necessary to move the slide to find each of the four phases. Use **Figure 1** as a guide. Draw, label, and title each of the phases of mitosis. It is important to draw only the structures that you can actually see under the microscope.

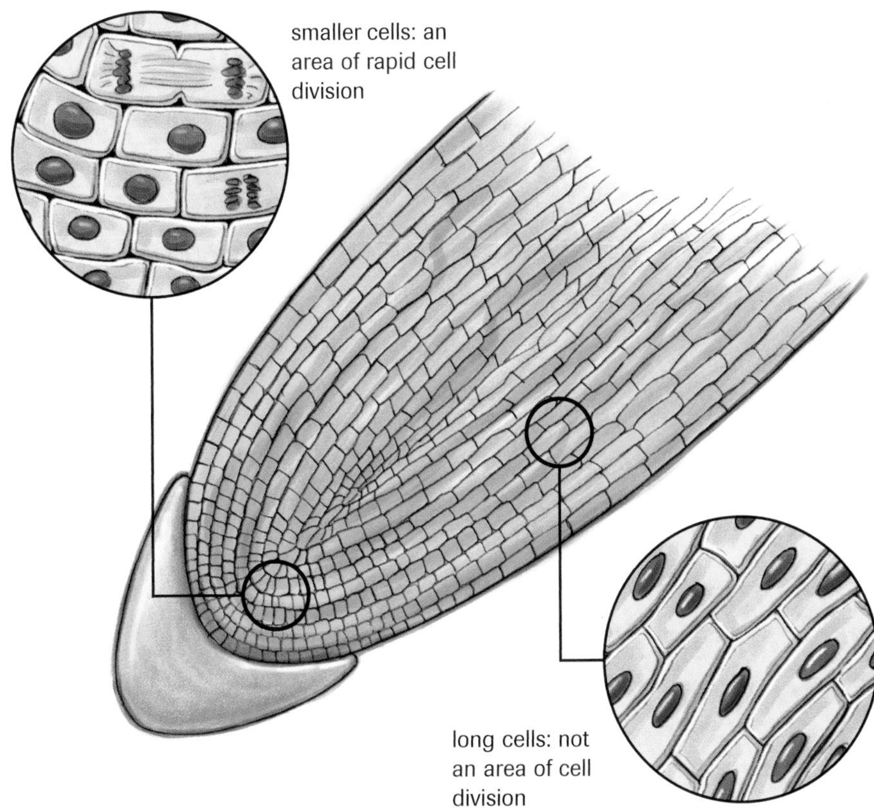

Figure 1
Meristematic region of the onion root tip where the cells are actively growing and dividing

6. Return your microscope to the low-power objective lens and remove the slide of the onion. Place the slide of the whitefish blastula on the stage. Focus with the coarse-adjustment knob. Repeat the procedure that you followed for the onion cells and, in the whitefish blastula, locate dividing cells under high-power magnification. Note how different the animal cells are compared to the plant cells.

Part 2: Determining the Frequency of Cell Division

7. Count 20 adjacent whitefish blastula cells and record whether the cells are in interphase or division phase. Record the number of cells in interphase and the number of cells that are actively dividing.
8. Repeat the same procedure for the meristematic region of the plant root.

Part 3: Creating a Cell-Division Clock

9. Under high-power magnification, locate 50 onion root cells that are dividing. Do not include cells that are between divisions. Identify the phase of mitosis each cell is in. Record the number of cells in each phase.
10. Repeat the procedure for the cells of the whitefish blastula.

Analysis and Evaluation

Part 1: Observing Dividing Cells

(a) How do the cells of the meristematic area differ from the mature cells of the root?

(b) Why were plant root tip cells and animal blastula cells used for viewing cell division?

(c) Explain why the cells that you viewed under the microscope do not continue to divide.

(d) Compare and contrast cell division in plant and animal cells. Use a Venn diagram to organize your ideas.

Part 2: Determining the Frequency of Cell Division

(e) For both the plant and animal cells, calculate the percentage of cells that are dividing. Use the following formula:

$$\frac{\text{Number of cells dividing}}{\text{Total number of cells counted}} \times 100 = \_\_\_ \text{ \% dividing}$$

(f) For both plant and animal cells, create a circle graph showing the percentage of cells in division phase and the percentage of cells in interphase. Label the diagrams appropriately. Compare the graphs. How are they different? How are they the same?

Part 3: Creating a Cell-Division Clock

(g) For both plant and animal cells, calculate the percentage of cells that are in each of these four phases: prophase, metaphase, anaphase, and telophase.

(h) For each cell type, construct a circle graph showing the percentage of cells in each phase of mitosis. Include labels and titles.

(i) If it takes 16 h to complete one cycle of mitosis for whitefish and 12 h for onions, determine the time spent in each phase. Include this information in your circle graphs.

Synthesis

(j) The number of animal cells in each phase of mitosis was recorded in **Table 1**. If the time taken to complete one cycle of mitosis was 15 h, create a cell-division clock to represent the data.

Table 1 Number of Cells in Different Phases of Mitosis

Mitotic phase	Number of cells in phase
prophase	15
metaphase	20
anaphase	10
telophase	5

INVESTIGATION 17.2

Report Checklist		
○ Purpose	● Design	● Analysis
● Problem	○ Materials	● Evaluation
○ Hypothesis	○ Procedure	● Synthesis
○ Prediction	● Evidence	

Identification of a Cancer Cell

Purpose

To identify cancerous cells and to recognize the differences between cancerous and non-cancerous cells

Materials

light microscope
lens paper
prepared slide of squamous cell carcinoma

Procedure

1. Clean the microscope lenses with lens paper. Rotate the revolving nosepiece to the low-power objective lens. Place the slide of the carcinoma on the stage of the microscope and bring the image into focus using the coarse-adjustment knob.
2. Locate the dermal and epidermal layers. Draw a line diagram showing the position of the epidermal and dermal cell layers. Determine and record whether the cells of the epidermis are invading the dermis.
3. Rotate the revolving nosepiece to the medium-power objective lens. Locate a cancerous cell. **Figure 1** is an example of cancerous cells. Use the fine-adjustment knob to bring the image into focus. Observe how cells of the carcinomas have a much larger nucleus. They appear pink in colour and often have an irregular shape.

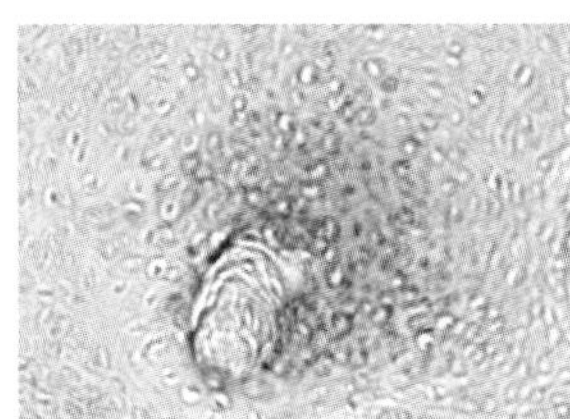

Figure 1

4. Rotate the nosepiece to high-power magnification, and bring the image into focus using the fine-adjustment knob.
5. Estimate and record the size of the cell, in micrometres (μm).
6. Estimate and record the size of the nucleus of the same cell, in micrometres (μm).
7. Rotate the revolving nosepiece to the medium-power objective lens and locate a normal cell. Rotate the nosepiece to the high-power objective lens, and bring it into focus with the fine-adjustment knob. **Figure 2** is an example of normal cells.

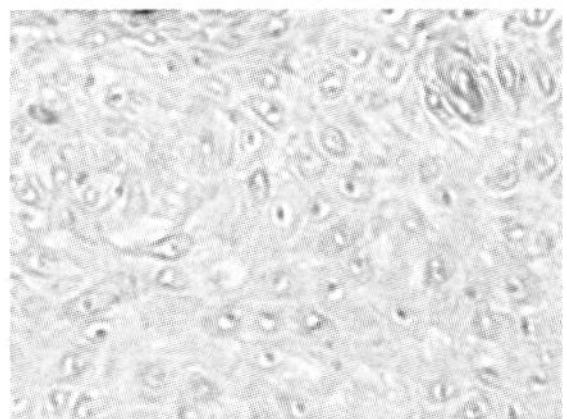

Figure 2

8. Repeat steps 5 and 6 for the normal cell.

Analysis

(a) Using the formula below, determine the nucleus-to-cytoplasm ratio for the cancerous cell and for the normal cell.

Evaluation

(b) Compare the cancerous and normal cells in a table similar to **Table 1**.

Table 1

Cell type	Cell size	Nuclear shape	Nuclear size	Nucleus-to-cytoplasm ratio
normal cell				
cancerous cell				

INVESTIGATION 17.2 *continued*

Synthesis

(c) Cancerous cells are often characterized by a large nucleus. Based on what you know about cancer and cell division, provide an explanation for the enlarged nucleus.

(d) Why are malignant (cancerous) tumors a greater threat to life than benign tumors?

(e) Provide a hypothesis that explains why the skin is so susceptible to cancer.

(f) A scientist finds a group of irregularly shaped cells in an organism. The cells demonstrate little differentiation, but the nuclei in some of the cells stain darker than others.
   (i) Based on these findings, would it be logical to conclude that the organism has cancer? Justify your answer.
   (ii) What additional tests might be required to prove or disprove the hypothesis that the cells are cancerous?

INVESTIGATION 17.3

Comparing Mitosis and Meiosis

Report Checklist

- ● Purpose
- ○ Problem
- ○ Hypothesis
- ○ Prediction
- ○ Design
- ○ Materials
- ○ Procedure
- ○ Evidence
- ● Analysis
- ● Evaluation
- ○ Synthesis

In this investigation, you will model and compare the events of mitosis and meiosis. In this model, you will create homologous chromosomes that have the same size and shape, but different colours. This will show that they are similar but not identical.

Materials

red modelling clay
blue modelling clay
green modelling clay
plastic knife
sheets of paper
pencil

Procedure

For each step, make a coloured sketch of your model with appropriate labels. Include brief descriptions of your steps and make sure to use the same step numbers as given.

Part I: Mitosis

1. Take some red clay and roll it between your hands to create a piece 10 cm long and about as thick as your finger. Make another piece about 5 cm long.
2. Repeat step 1 with the blue clay.
3. Make an identical copy of each piece of clay. Then attach the identical pieces with a green ball of clay (**Figure 1**).
4. Draw a line down the length of a sheet of paper. Line up the four chromosomes along the line (**Figure 2**).

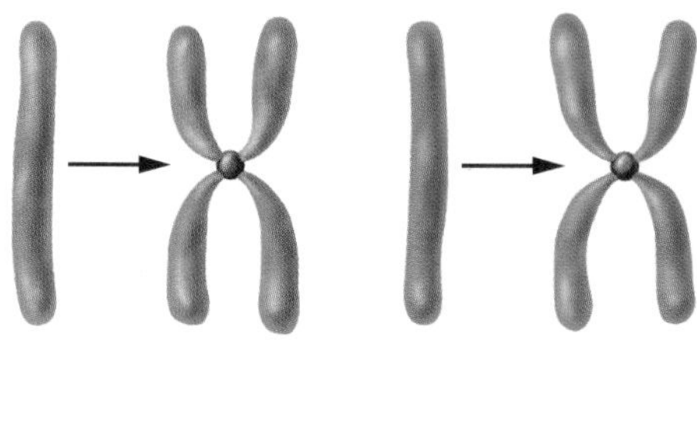

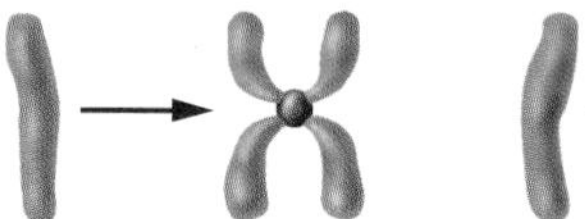

Figure 1

5. Remove the green balls and move each of the single pieces of clay to opposite ends of the paper (**Figure 3**, next page).
6. Before every mitotic division, each chromosome is duplicated during interphase. Make an identical copy of each piece of clay as before (**Figure 4**, next page).

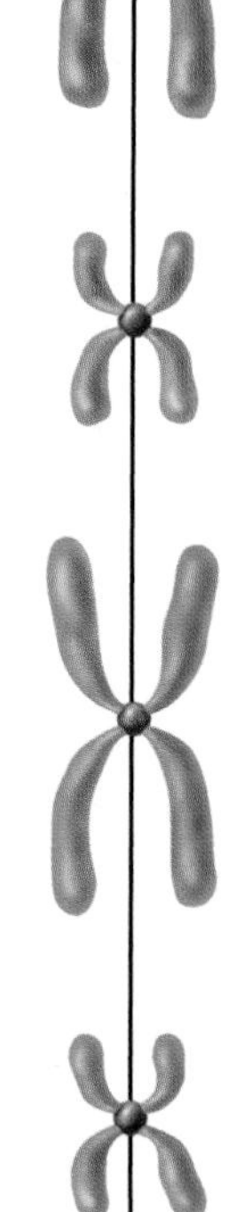

Figure 2

Part II: Meiosis

7. Follow steps 1 to 3 from part 1.

INVESTIGATION 17.3 *continued*

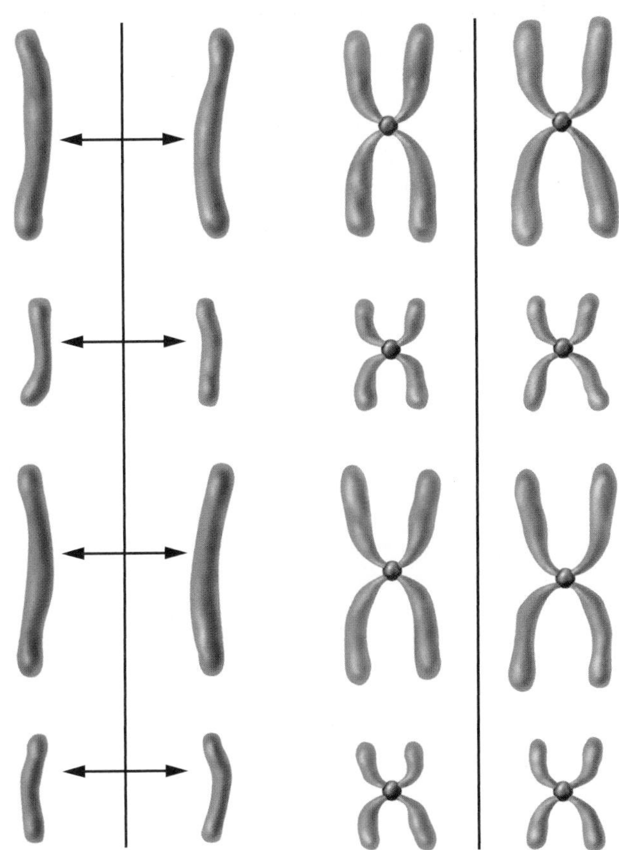

Figure 3

Figure 4

8. Demonstrate crossing over. Break off a piece of clay from one chromosome and attach it to the other chromosome (**Figure 5**). Repeat a few times if you like.
9. To simulate metaphase I, place the chromosomes on either side of the equatorial plate, represented by a line drawn on a piece of paper (**Figure 6**).
10. Choose one of the haploid daughter cells and line the chromosomes up along the equatorial plate. Remove the centromere and move chromosomes to opposite poles (**Figure 7**).

Analysis and Evaluation

Part I: Mitosis

(a) In step 3, what process did you model?

(b) What do the red and blue pieces of clay represent? What do the green balls of clay represent?

(c) In step 4, what is the diploid chromosome number of the cell?

(d) What phase of mitosis does the model represent?

(e) In step 5, what structure do the single pieces of clay represent after separation?

(f) What phase of mitosis does the model represent?

(g) In step 6, how many chromosomes are in each of the daughter cells?

(h) Compare the daughter cells with the parent cell.

Part II: Meiosis

(i) In steps 1 to 3, on what basis are chromosomes considered to be homologous?

(j) What is the diploid chromosome number?

(k) In step 8, what must happen before the homologous chromosomes can cross over?

(l) In which phase does crossing over occur?

(m) What happens during crossing over?

(n) In step 9, how does metaphase I of meiosis differ from metaphase of mitosis?

(o) What is the haploid chromosome number?

(p) In step 10, compare the resulting daughter cells of mitosis and meiosis.

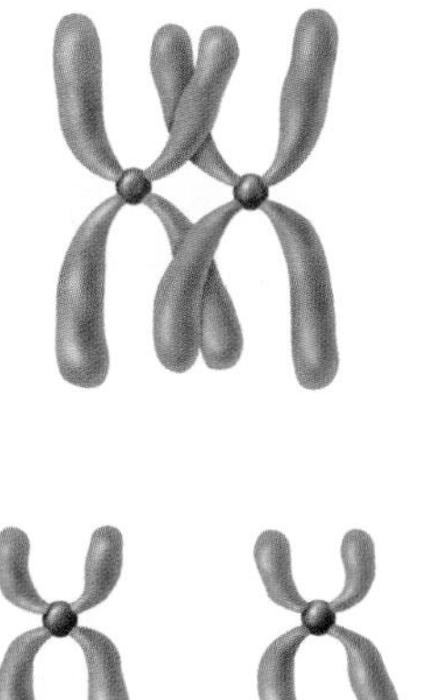

Figure 5

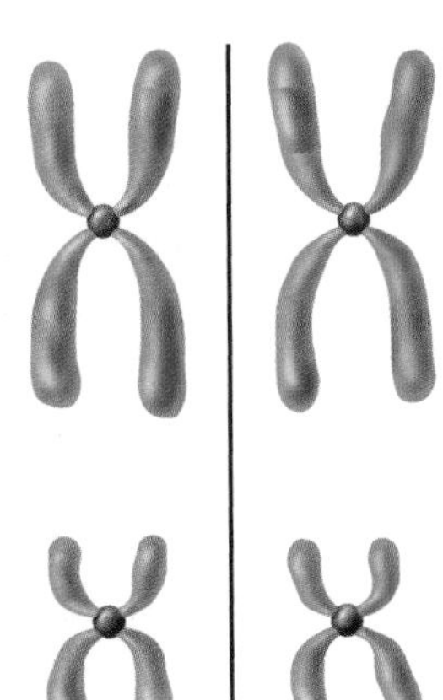

Figure 6

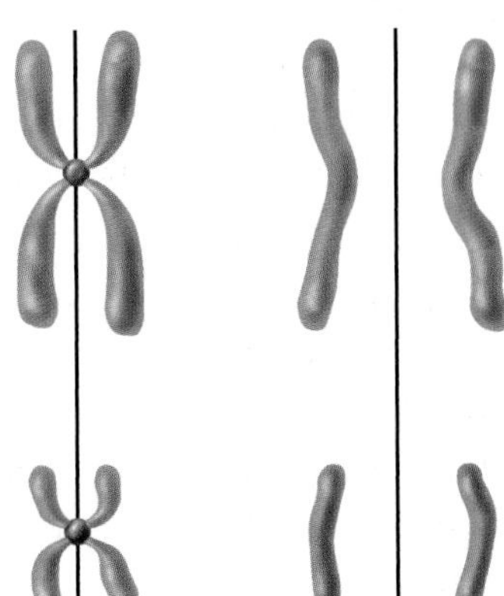

Figure 7

Chapter 17 SUMMARY

Outcomes

Knowledge

- define and explain the significance of chromosome number in somatic and sex cells (i.e., haploidy, diploidy and polyploidy) (17.3, 17.4)
- explain cell cycle events (i.e., interphase, including G1, S, and G2 phases, chromosomal behaviour in mitosis and cytokinesis) (17.1)
- describe spermatogenesis and oogenesis and the reduction of chromosomal number in meiosis (17.3)
- compare the processes of mitosis and meiosis (17.3)
- describe the processes of crossing over and nondisjunction in terms of stages, replication, and resultant chromosome numbers and evaluate their significance to variation in organism inheritance and development (17.4)
- compare the formation of fraternal and identical offspring in a single birthing event (17.1)
- describe the diversity of reproductive strategies by incorporating the principles of mitosis and meiosis when comparing the alternation of generations in a range of organisms (17.3)

STS

- explain that science and technology are developed to meet societal needs and expand human capability (17.2, 17.4)

Skills

- ask questions and plan investigations of questions, ideas, problems, and issues (all)
- gather and record data and information by performing a simulation to demonstrate the behaviour of chromosomes during mitosis (17.1); use a microscope and prepared slides of onion root tip cells to identify the stages of a cell cycle, and calculate the duration of each stage; research and compare a range of reproductive strategies in organisms and present them in charts, tables, or diagrams (17.3)
- analyze data and apply mathematical and conceptual models by preparing and interpreting models of human karyotypes (17.4)
- work as members of a team and apply the skills and conventions of science (all)

Key Terms

17.1

somatic cell
cell cycle
mitosis
cytokinesis
interphase
chromatin
centromere
sister chromatids
centriole
spindle fibre

17.2

enucleated
stem cell
telomere

17.3

meiosis
haploid
diploid
homologous chromosomes
tetrad
synapsis
crossing over
gametogenesis
ootid
polar body
oocyte

17.4

nondisjunction
polyploidy
trisomy
monosomy
karyotype chart

MAKE a summary

1. Sketch the processes of meiosis and mitosis and show the differences between them. Label the sketch with as many of the key terms as possible. Check other sketches and use appropriate designs to make your sketch more clear.
2. Revisit your answers to the Starting Points questions at the start of the chapter. Would you answer the questions differently now? Why?

Go To

The following components are available on the Nelson Web site. Follow the links for *Nelson Biology Alberta 20–30.*

- an interactive Self Quiz for Chapter 17
- additional Diploma Exam-style Review Questions
- Illustrated Glossary
- additional IB-related material

There is more information on the Web site wherever you see the Go icon in the chapter.

EXTENSION

A Cure for Aging

Dr. Siegfried Hekimi, (professor of biology at McGill University), Dr. Michael West, (Chief Executive Officer of Advanced Cell Technology in Worcester Massachusetts), Dr. Cynthia Kenyon, (biochemistry and biophysics professor from the University of California, San Francisco), and Dr. Marc Tatar (Brown University in Rhode Island) all discuss the causes of aging and their research into slowing the aging process.

www.science.nelson.com 

▸ Chapter 17 REVIEW

Many of these questions are in the style of the Diploma Exam. You will find guidance for writing Diploma Exams in Appendix A5. Science Directing Words used in Diploma Exams are in bold type. Exam study tips and test-taking suggestions are on the Nelson Web site.

www.science.nelson.com 

DO NOT WRITE IN THIS TEXTBOOK.

Part 1

1. Select the diagram that represents metaphase.
   A. Figure 1 (a)
   B. Figure 1 (b)
   C. Figure 1 (c)
   D. Figure 1 (d)

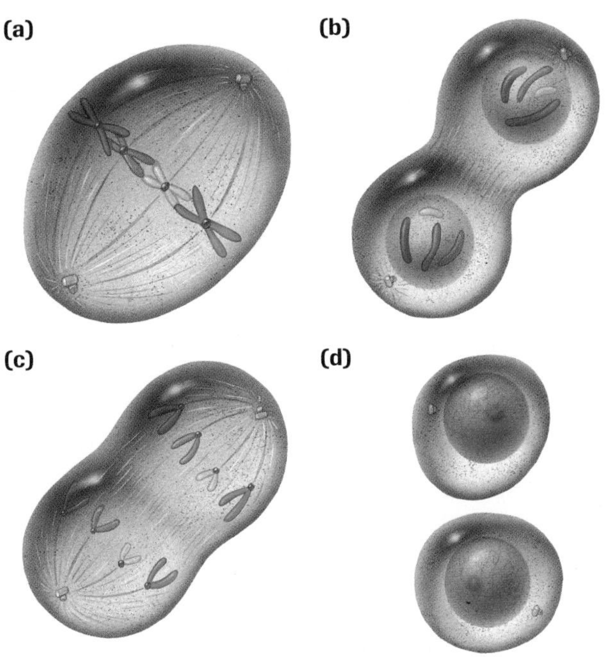

Figure 1

2. The following descriptions explain events in the various stages of a cell cycle. Arrange the description in the correct sequence of events. (Record all four digits of your answer.) NR
   1. Chromatids separate and move to opposite poles.
   2. Chromosomal alignment occurs in the equatorial plate.
   3. Chromosomes become longer and thinner.
   4. Chromosomes shorten and thicken.

Use the following information to answer questions 3 to 6.

A student observed three different areas in the mitotic region in an onion root tip. She counted the number of cells that were at each stage of the cell cycle at the time the root was killed and mounted on the slide. Her results are presented in **Table 1**.

Table 1 Number of Cells in Different Stages of Division

	Number of cells			
Phase	***Area 1***	***Area 2***	***Area 3***	***Total***
interphase	99	79	88	
prophase	12	14	16	
metaphase	6	4	5	
anaphase	0	2	2	4
telophase	2	3	4	9

3. According to the data in **Table 1**, the duration of the phases of the cell cycle, from the longest to the shortest, is
   A. prophase, metaphase, anaphase, telophase, interphase
   B. interphase, prophase, metaphase, telophase, anaphase
   C. interphase, prophase, metaphase, anaphase, telophase
   D. not possible to list, since the number of cells and not the duration was observed

4. Calculate the percentage of cells in prophase. (Record your answer as a value rounded to one decimal place.) NR

5. If the total time for the completion of one cell cycle is 660 min, determine the time required to complete metaphase. (Record all four digits of your answer.) NR

6. Calculate the percentage of cells undergoing mitosis. (Record your answer as a value rounded to one decimal place.) NR

7. A researcher studied the growth rate of a malignant cell in mice. Every two days, he counted the number of cells in a 1 mm^2 area, over a period of two months. Select the graph in **Figure 2**, on the next page, that represents the data collected.
   A. Figure 2 (a)
   B. Figure 2 (b)
   C. Figure 2 (c)
   D. Figure 2 (d)

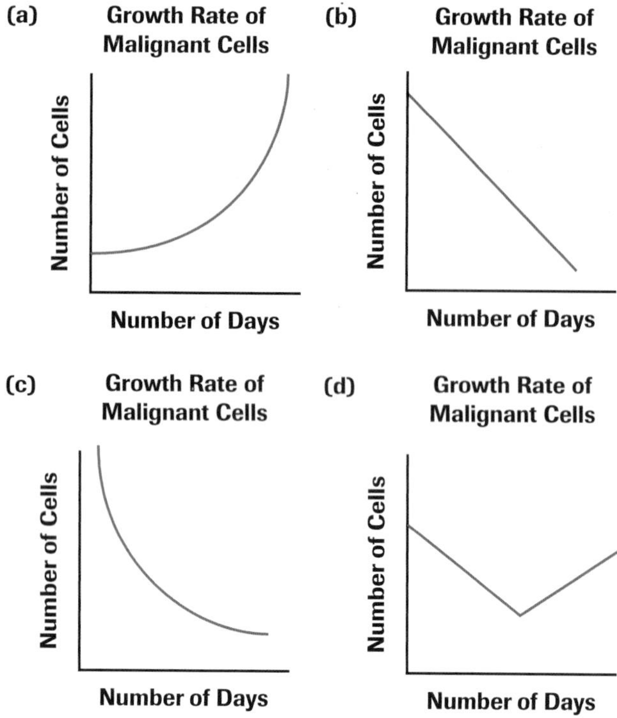

Figure 2

Use the following information to answer questions 8 to 10.

Figure 3 shows the early events in fertilization of a human egg and sperm, and development of the embryo. The numbers refer to the number of chromosomes.

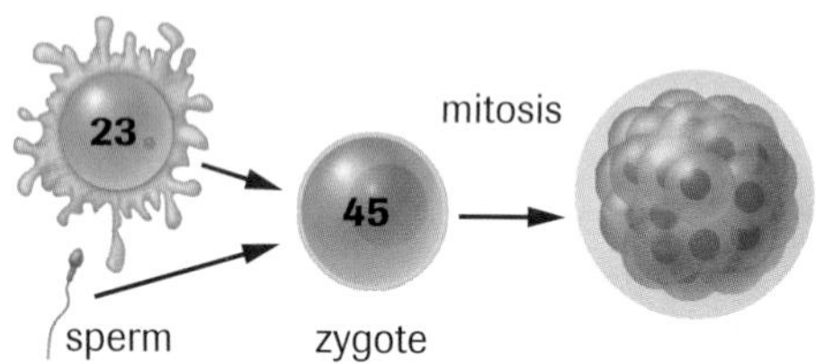

Figure 3

8. Select the number of chromosomes that were in the sperm cell.
   A. 20
   B. 22
   C. 23
   D. 45

9. Select the number of homologous pairs of chromosomes that would be in the zygote if it were female.
   A. 21
   B. 22
   C. 23
   D. 24

10. Select the number of chromosomes that would be in each blastula cell, following mitosis.
    A. 20
    B. 22
    C. 23
    D. 45

11. Indicate which of the following cells would be capable of meiosis:
    A. brain cells
    B. fat cells
    C. cells of a zygote
    D. sperm-producing cells of the testes

Part 2

12. **Figure 4** shows plant and animal cells during cell division.
    (a) **Identify** each cell as either a plant or an animal cell. **Justify** your answer.
    (b) **Identify** the phases of cell division.

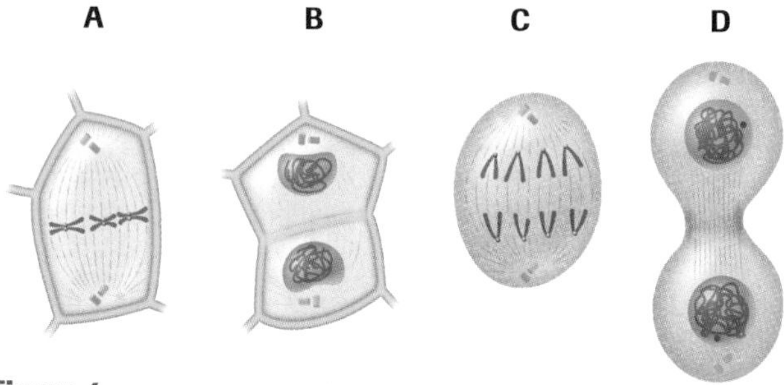

Figure 4

13. **Explain** why a better understanding of the mechanism of cell division may enable scientists to regenerate limbs.

14. **Explain** why the formation of calluses on the hands provides evidence that cell division can be stimulated by cell damage.

15. **Explain** how it is possible to produce a trisomic XXX female.

16. **Sketch** a diagram that shows the kind of nondisjunction that would cause a male and female each with an abnormal number of chromosomes to produce an XYY offspring.

17. If nondisjunction disorders could be eliminated by screening sperm and egg cells, sperm and egg banks could all but eliminate many genetic disorders. **Describe** the social, moral, and ethical implications to society of the systematic elimination of genetic disorders in humans.

Use the following information to answer questions 18 and 19.

Table 2 shows data collected from two different fields of view while examining hamster embryo cells. The number of cells found in each of the cell phases was recorded. It took 660 min to complete one cycle from interphase to interphase.

Table 2

Cell phase	Area 1	Area 2	Total cell count	Time spent in phase
interphase	91	70	?	?
prophase	10	14	?	?
metaphase	2	1	?	?
anaphase	2	1	?	?
telophase	4	4	?	?

18. Copy **Table 2** into your notebook, **determine** the missing DE values, and complete the table. To calculate the time spent in interphase, for example, you would use the following equation:

$$\frac{\text{Number of cells in interphase}}{\text{Total number of cells counted}} = \frac{\text{Time spent in phase}}{\text{Total time of cycle (660 min)}}$$

19. Using the data provided, **sketch** a circle graph showing DE the amount of time spent in each phase of the cell cycle.

20. **Identify** one advantage of using a cutting instead of using seeds to grow a new plant.

Use the following information to answer questions 21 to 25.

Fruit flies normally have eight chromosomes. Flies with fewer chromosomes die before maturity. **Figure 5** shows the process of meiosis in three fruit flies.

21. **Identify** the parent in which nondisjunction takes place. DE

22. **Identify** how many chromosomes would be in zygotes D, DE E, and F.

23. **Describe** what is happening during process X. DE

24. **Identify** which zygote would most likely be healthy. DE

25. **Identify** by name the conditions that the other zygotes DE have.

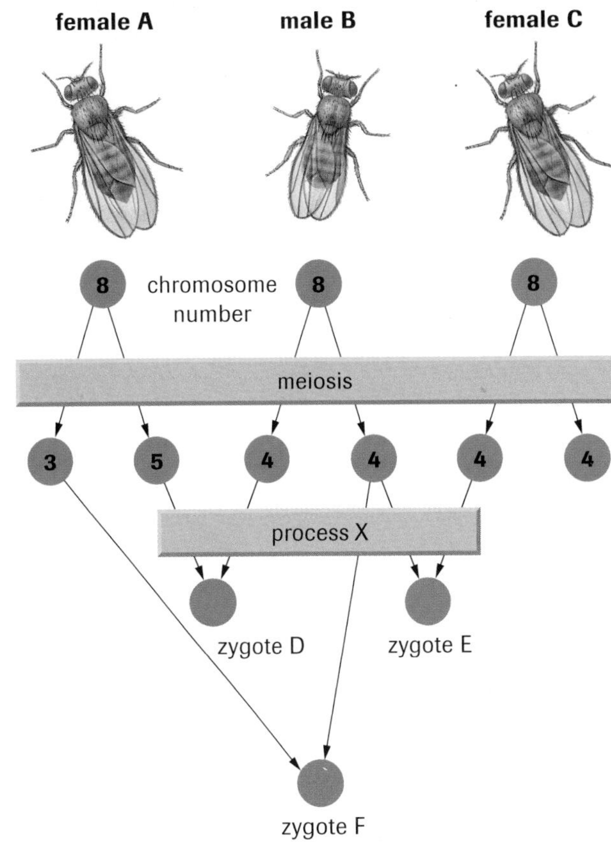

Figure 5

26. Twins can be either identical or fraternal. Write a unified DE response that includes the following aspects of twins:

- Copy **Table 3** in your notebook. **Identify** with a check mark (✓) the statements that you believe are always, or almost always, true for fraternal twins and for identical twins.
- **Justify** each choice.

Table 3

Descriptor	Fraternal twins	Identical twins
They have the same blood type.	?	?
They are the same sex.	?	?
They like the same hockey team.	?	?
They have the same mass.	?	?
They have the same hair colour.	?	?
They know what the other one is thinking.	?	?

chapter

18 The Basis of Heredity

In this chapter

- Exploration: Similarities and Differences
- Mini Investigation: Cross-Pollination
- Web Activity: Creating a Personal Profile
- Explore an Issue: Genetic Screening
- Web Activity: Pedigree Analysis
- Investigation 18.1: How Do Environmental Factors Affect Gene Expression?
- Case Study: A Mystery of Blood Types
- Investigation 18.2: Genetics of Corn
- Explore an Issue: Drought-Tolerant and Salt-Tolerant Plants

Have you ever been able to identify a person as a member of a particular family by certain physical traits? Some traits, such as curly hair or a prominent nose, can be traced through a family's lineage. Heredity is the transmission of biological traits from parents to offspring. When the members of different generations all share a particular trait, this is evidence that the trait is inherited. Genetics is the study of inheritance of biological traits.

Biological traits are determined by genes, which are specific segments of DNA. During reproduction, genes of the parent or parents are transmitted to the next generation. Long before we knew of genes and DNA, humans were able to use knowledge of transmission of biological traits to their advantage. Domesticated animals, such as cows and dogs, were produced by choosing parents having traits that were desired in the offspring. Crop plants were also developed by selecting parents with desirable traits.

Every person inherits one of about eight million possible combinations of his or her parents' chromosomes. Your set of genes and your traits are therefore all your own. Even twins who are genetically identical may not share all the same traits.

What patterns can be found in the transmission of genetic traits? How do these relate to the transmission of genes? In this chapter, you will explore patterns of inheritance of biological traits and explain how these patterns arise.

STARTING Points

Answer these questions as best you can with your current knowledge. Then, using the concepts and skills you have learned, you will revise your answers at the end of the chapter.

1. Is it possible for two parents with black hair to have a child with red hair? Why or why not?
2. Sometimes, when breeders cross two individuals with valuable traits, the offspring do not show the same traits. Suggest a reason why this may be so.
3. A team of researchers at the University of Alberta studied sets of identical twins to see if driving a truck or other heavy machinery was related to back pain. Each set of twins included one individual who drove for a living and another who did not. They found that the amount of back pain experienced by a truck-driving twin was the same as for the non-driving twin.
   (a) Why was it important to study identical twins?
   (b) Could the study have used fraternal twins instead? Why or why not?

Career Connections: Veterinarian; Agrologist

Figure 1
Bobby Hull and Brett Hull starred in the National Hockey League and were the first father and son to win the Hart Trophy.

Figure 2
The father of former prime minister Paul Martin was also a federal politician.

Figure 3
Keifer and Donald Sutherland have successful acting careers.

Exploration — Similarities and Differences

Look at the people shown in **Figure 1**, **Figure 2**, and **Figure 3**. Identify any traits, such as eye colour, eye shape, face shape, and nose length and width, that show a family resemblance. Consider the information in the captions.

- Organize the traits in a chart or table.
- Identify the traits that you think are inherited.

(a) Describe the criteria you used to decide that a trait was inherited.

(b) Brett Hull is one of the NHL's all-time goal scorers. Do you think Brett inherited the ability to score goals from his father, Bobby Hull (**Figure 1**), or is this a skill he learned? Give reasons for your answer.

18.1 Gregor Mendel—Pioneer of Genetics

Figure 1
Gregor Mendel (1822–1884) was an Austrian monk whose experiments with garden peas laid the foundation for the science of genetics.

Humans have long understood that certain characteristics were passed down from generation to generation. Stone tablets crafted by the Babylonians 6000 years ago show pedigrees of successive generations of champion horses. However, the first real understanding of inheritance would not come until the work of an Austrian monk, Gregor Mendel, in the mid-19th century (**Figure 1**). Mendel tracked and recorded the transmission of seven visible traits through several generations of the garden pea. To keep track of the different generations, he called the first cross the parental generation, or P generation. The offspring of this cross he called the first filial generation, or the F_1 generation. The next generations were the F_2 generation, the F_3 generation, and so on.

Why did Mendel work with the garden pea? First, he observed that garden peas have a number of characteristics that are expressed in one of only two alternative forms. This made it easier to see which form was inherited.

The second reason is related to how this species reproduces. Garden peas usually reproduce through self-pollination. During pollination, the pollen produced by the anthers of the stamens attaches to the pistil. The pistil consists of the stigma, style, and ovary (**Figure 2**). The ovary contains an egg cell or female sex cell (gamete). Sperm cells (the male gametes) in the pollen grains fertilize the egg cell, and seeds are produced. In self-pollination, the pollen grains and the pistil are from the same plant: in cross-pollination, the pollen grains and the pistil are from different plants. The garden peas that Mendel worked with were "pure" varieties with known traits that came from a long line of self-pollinated pea plants. The traits of each variety had, therefore, been present in all individuals of that variety over many generations.

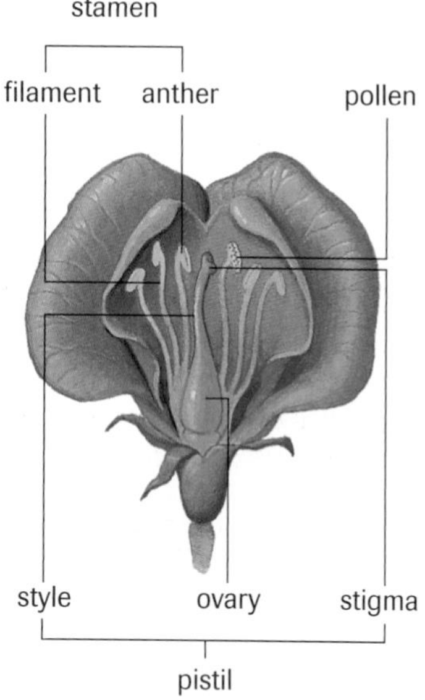

Figure 2
The structure of a flower

The Principle of Dominance

When Mendel used pollen from a pea plant with round seeds to fertilize a pea plant with wrinkled seeds, he found that all the offspring (the **progeny**) in the F_1 generation had round seeds. Did this mean that the pollen determines the shape of a seed? Mendel tested this by using pollen from a plant with wrinkled seeds to fertilize a plant with round seeds. Once again, all the progeny had round seeds. Round-seed shape was always the **dominant trait**, regardless of parentage. Mendel called the other wrinkled-seed shape the **recessive trait**. Mendel repeated the experiment for other traits. One trait was always dominant and the other recessive.

Mendel reasoned that each trait must be determined by something he called "factors." Today, we know these factors are genes. Mendel also realized that there can be alternate forms of a gene, which give rise to alternate forms of a trait. We now call the alternate form of a gene an **allele**. For example, the gene for seed colour has two alleles, one that determines green-seed colour and one that determines yellow. Alleles that determine dominant traits are dominant alleles. Alleles that determine recessive traits are recessive alleles. A dominant allele is indicated by an uppercase italic letter, such as *R* for round seeds. The recessive allele is designated by the lowercase italic letter, such as *r* for wrinkled seeds.

progeny new individuals that result from reproduction; offspring

dominant trait a characteristic that is expressed when one or both alleles in an individual are the dominant form

Mendel's Principle of Segregation

Mendel next let the F_1 plants self-fertilize, to observe the pattern of transmission of traits in the F_2 generation. When he had crossed pure round-seed plants with pure wrinkled-seed plants, 100 % of the F_1 generation had round seeds. Mendel was astonished to find that 75 % of the F_2 generation had round seeds and 25 % had wrinkled seeds. That is, for seed shape, the ratio was 3:1 round to wrinkled. He performed crosses to follow other traits and found the F_1 generations all had the same 3:1 ratio of dominant to recessive trait.

To explain these ratios, Mendel reasoned that each plant must carry two copies (alleles) of each gene that can be the same or different. An individual with round seeds must carry at least one dominant allele (*R*), but individuals with wrinkled seeds must always carry two copies of the recessive allele (*rr*).

When both alleles of a gene pair are the same, an individual is said to be **homozygous** for that trait. When the alleles of a gene pair are different, an individual is **heterozygous** for that trait. The complement of genes of an organism is called its **genotype**, and the physical expression of the genotype is the **phenotype**.

Mendel also correctly concluded that the two copies of a gene in a gene pair undergo **segregation** during the formation of the sex cells. Each mature gamete contains only one member of a gene pair. When an individual is homozygous for a gene, all of its gametes carry the same allele. When an individual is heterozygous for a gene, each gamete could receive either allele. **Figure 3 (a)** shows the results of a cross between two homozygous peas. At fertilization, the new individual receives one copy of the gene from the female parent and one from the male parent. All members of the F_1 generation, therefore, are heterozygous. When the F_1 generation was allowed to self-pollinate, three different genotypes were produced, which determined the two phenotypes that Mendel observed (**Figure 3 (b)**).

recessive trait a characteristic that is expressed only when both alleles in an individual are the recessive form

allele one of alternative forms of a gene

homozygous having identical alleles for the same gene

heterozygous having different alleles for the same gene

genotype the genetic complement of an organism

phenotype the observable characteristics of an organism

segregation the separation of alleles during meiosis

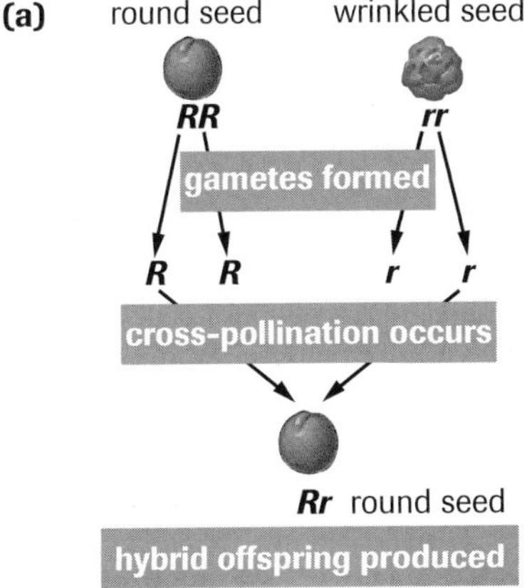

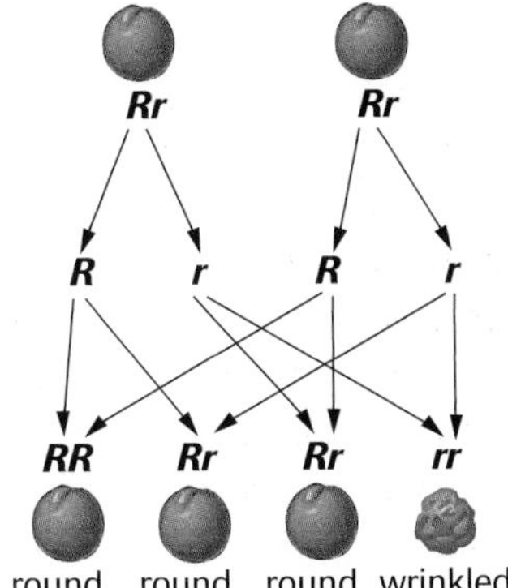

Figure 3
(a) When a pea plant homozygous for round seeds is cross-pollinated with a pea plant homozygous for wrinkled seeds, the offspring are all heterozygous.
(b) The F_2 progeny from a cross of two heterozygous pea plants with round seeds will have three possible genotypes *RR*, *Rr*, and *rr*).

+ EXTENSION

Genetic Terms

This animation gives a visual review of some of the terms used in studying genetics.

www.science.nelson.com GO

mini Investigation Cross-Pollination

Materials: two plants of the same species that have different colours of flowers, small scissors, paint brush, plastic bags, potting soil, water, small pots

- On the plant you want to be the seed-parent, select a flower that is not yet open. Using **Figure 4** as a guide, remove the anthers from the flower.
- Using the paint brush, transfer pollen from the pollen-parent to the stigma of the seed-parent flower from which you removed the anthers.

(a) Predict the flower colour of the offspring of your cross-pollinated plant. Give reasons for your prediction.

(b) Why were the anthers removed from the plant that received the pollen?

(c) Why was a plastic bag placed over the flower?

- If there is time, collect and grow seeds from the flower you pollinated. Cover the pollinated flower with a plastic bag. Once the flower has produced seeds, plant the seeds in moist soil. Place the plant in sunlight (or under a bright light) and keep it watered until it produces flowers.

(d) Was your prediction correct?

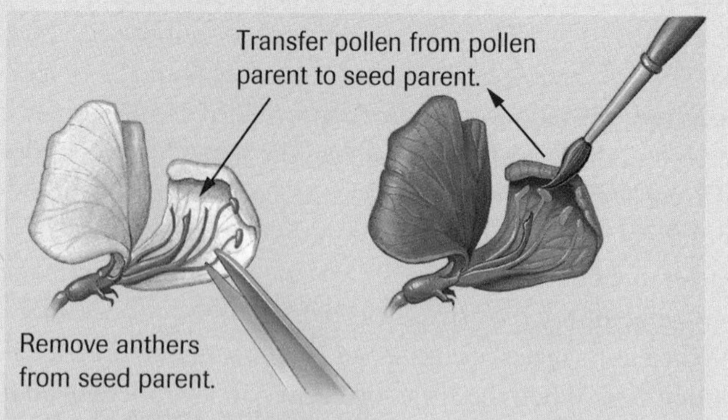
Transfer pollen from pollen parent to seed parent.
Remove anthers from seed parent.

Figure 4
Pollen is transferred from the donor plant to the pistil of the recipient, which has had its stamens removed to prevent self-pollination.

SUMMARY Gregor Mendel—Pioneer of Genetics

- Inherited traits are controlled by factors—genes—that occur in pairs. Each member of a pair of genes is called an allele.
- One factor, or allele, masks the expression of another. This is known as the principle of dominance.
- A pair of factors, or alleles, separates from one another (segregate) during the formation of sex cells. This is often referred to as the law of segregation.

Section 18.1 Questions

1. Why were the pea plants selected by Mendel ideally suited for studying the transmission of traits?
2. Explain why, under normal circumstances, an individual can carry only two alleles of a gene.
3. Use an example that helps differentiate between the terms genotype and phenotype.
4. Black fur colour is dominant to yellow in Labrador retrievers.
   (a) Explain how the genotype of a homozygous black dog differs from that of a heterozygous black dog.
   (b) Could the heterozygous black dog have the same genotype as a yellow-haired dog? Explain.
5. A pea plant with round seeds is cross-pollinated with a pea plant that has wrinkled seeds. The plant with round seeds is heterozygous. Indicate each of the following:
   (a) the genotypes of the parents
   (b) the gametes produced by the parent with round seeds
   (c) the gametes produced by the parent with wrinkled seeds
   (d) the possible genotype(s) and the phenotype(s) of the F_1 generation

Probability and Inheritance of Single Traits 18.2

For every cross, Mendel kept track of the number of offspring that inherited the dominant trait and recessive trait. Based on mathematical analysis of these numbers, Mendel also concluded that each gamete produced by a heterozygous individual has an equal chance of getting either allele of a gene pair. Recall that when Mendel allowed peas that were heterozygous for the seed shape allele to self-pollinate, 75 % of the F_2 generation had the round-seed phenotype and 25 % had the wrinkled-seed phenotype. In other words, the **phenotypic ratio** of offspring with the dominant trait to offspring with the recessive trait was 3 to 1. To get this ratio, each sex cell must have had an equal probability of getting the *R* allele as the *r* allele during the process of segregation.

phenotypic ratio the ratio of offspring with a dominant trait to the alternative, recessive trait

Punnett square a chart used to determine the predicted outcome of a genetic cross

genotypic ratio the ratio of offspring with each possible allele combination from a particular cross

The probability of an outcome is a measure of the likelihood that the outcome will occur. Probability may be expressed as a fraction, a decimal, or a percentage. Probability (P) can be determined using the following formula:

$$P = \frac{\text{number of ways that a given outcome can occur}}{\text{total number of possible outcomes}}$$

For example, you might calculate the probability of getting heads when you toss a coin. There is only one way of tossing heads, so the numerator is 1. Since there are two possible outcomes in total, the denominator is 2. Therefore, the probability P of tossing heads is $\frac{1}{2}$, or 0.5, or 50 %.

A **Punnett square** is a chart that can help us to predict the phenotypes of the progeny of a cross between parents of known genotypes, or to deduce the genotypes of parents from the observed phenotypic ratio of their progeny. Punnett squares also allow us to determine the expected ratio of the genotypes (**genotypic ratio**) and the phenotypes for a cross, and to state the probability of that particular genotype or phenotype will occur in the progeny of a cross.

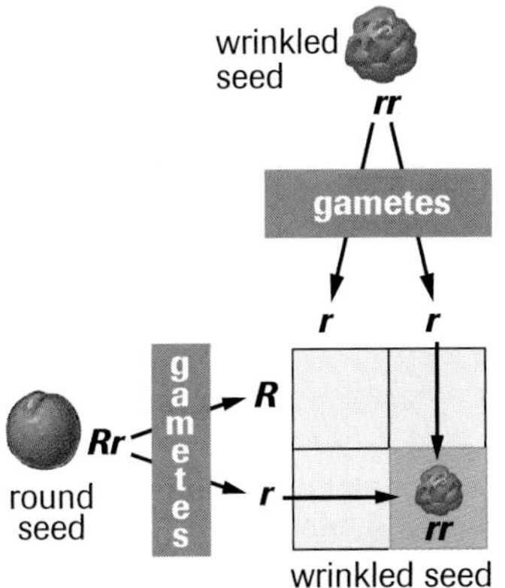

Figure 1 The partially completed Punnett square for a cross between a pea plant with genotype *rr* and a pea plant with genotype *Rr*. The genotype *rr* in one cell of the Punnett square is one of four possible combinations of the parental alleles.

SAMPLE exercise 1

A breeder crosses a pea plant with wrinkled seeds and a pea plant with round seeds. She knows that the plant with round seeds is heterozygous for the gene for seed shape. The allele for round seeds (*R*) is dominant over the allele for wrinkled seeds (*r*). Determine the expected genotypic ratio and phenotypic ratio of the progeny.

Solution

Since *r* is the recessive allele, the genotype of the plant with wrinkled seeds must be *rr*. Since the plant with round seeds is heterozygous, its genotype must be *Rr*. The symbols for the alleles in the gametes are written across the top and along the left side of the Punnett square (**Figure 1**). Each cell is then filled in by entering one allele from the top of the square and a second allele from the side of the square.

Figure 2 shows a completed Punnett square for a cross between a heterozygous round-seed pea plant and a wrinkled-seed pea plant. Two of the four cells show the genotype *Rr* and two show *rr*. The expected genotypic ratio in the progeny of *Rr* to *rr* is, therefore, 1:1. Offspring with genotype *Rr* will have round seeds, and those with genotype *rr* will have wrinkled seeds.

Therefore, the phenotypic ratio is 1:1 ($\frac{1}{2}$ round and $\frac{1}{2}$ wrinkled).

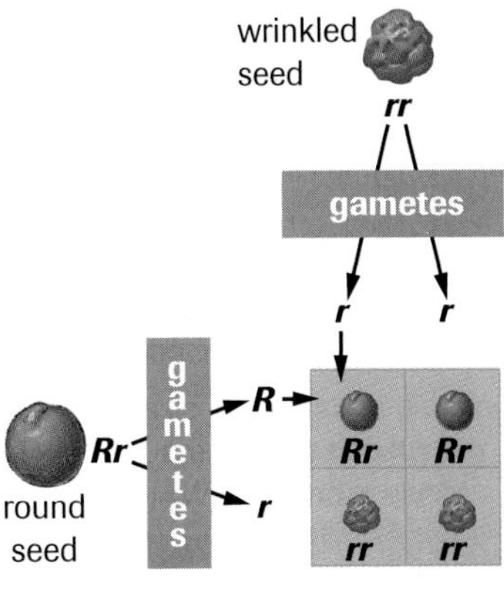

Figure 2

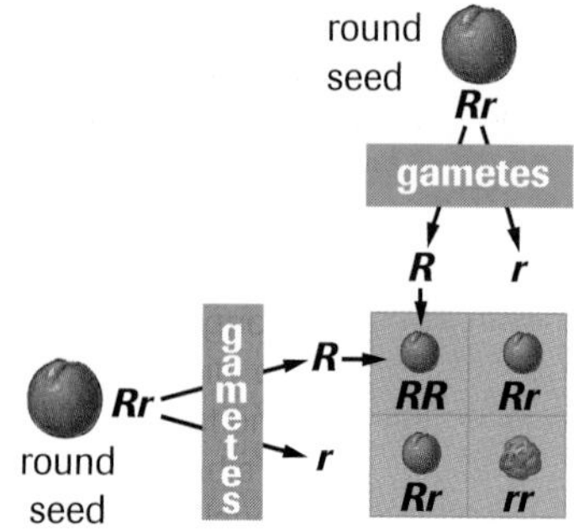

Figure 3
A Punnett square showing the results of a cross between two heterozygous plants with round seeds

SAMPLE exercise 2

For the cross shown in **Figure 3**, what is the probability that an offspring will have a phenotype of wrinkled seeds? Express the answer as a percent.

Solution

Since the allele for wrinkled seeds, *r*, is recessive, only offspring with a genotype *rr* will have wrinkled seeds. From the Punnett square, 1 of every 4 offspring are expected to have this genotype, so the probability that an offspring will have wrinkled seeds is 25 %.

Practice

1. What is the phenotypic ratio of the cross in the Punnett square shown in **Figure 4**?

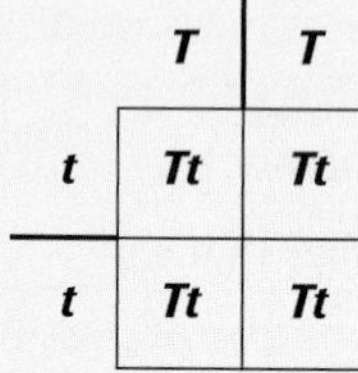

Figure 4
Punnett square of a monohybrid cross between a homozygous tall pea and a homozygous short pea

2. Using a Punnett square, determine the expected phenotypic ratio and genotypic ratio for the progeny of a cross between a pea plant that is homozygous for the white allele (*r*) for flower colour and a pea plant that is homozygous for the red allele (*R*).

F_2 Ratios
This animation shows some of the results of Mendel's crosses, which you can then convert to phenotypic ratios. How close are the observed phenotypic ratios to the predicted phenotypic ratio?

www.science.nelson.com 

Case Study—Creating a Personal Profile

Some human genes determine visible traits that show an inheritance pattern that is similar to that of Mendel's garden peas. As a result, you can predict a person's genotype for these traits just by observing him or her. In this activity, you will use a list of some common dominant and recessive traits, and use this information to create a profile of your own phenotype and potential genotype.

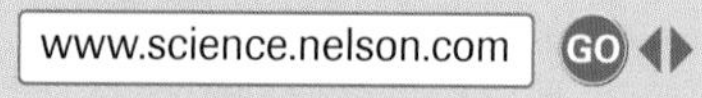

Genetics
In this Virtual Biology Laboratory, you can assess data and perform simulated crosses to explain the inheritance of shell colour in glyptodonts, an extinct relative of the armadillo.

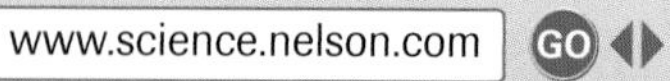

Test Crosses

Wool producers often prefer sheep with white wool, since black wool tends to be brittle and difficult to dye. Black sheep can be avoided by breeding only homozygous white rams. However, the allele for white wool (*W*) is dominant over the allele for black wool (*w*), so white rams can be heterozygous. How could a wool producer be sure that a white ram is homozygous?

A **test cross** is the cross of an individual of unknown genotype to an individual with a recessive genotype. The phenotypes of the F_1 generation of a test cross reveal whether an individual with a dominant trait (such as a white ram) is homozygous or heterozygous for the dominant allele. If a white ram is crossed with a black ewe and the observed phenotypic ratio is 1:1 black to white, then the genotype of the ram must be *Ww* (**Figure 5**). If all the offspring are white, then the genotype of the white ram must be *WW*.

Test crosses are the simplest way of determining the genotype of an individual. Sometimes, however, the parents are not available to test cross. When only information about the phenotypes of the offspring of a cross is available, the genotypes and phenotypes of the parents can be found by working backwards through a Punnett square.

test cross the cross of an individual of unknown genotype to an individual that is fully recessive

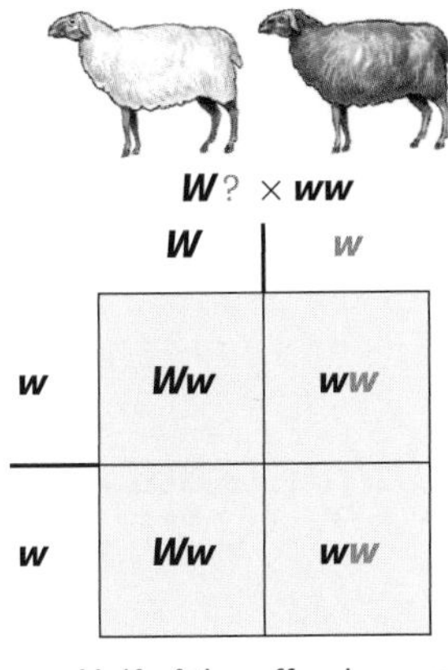

Half of the offspring are black and half are white.

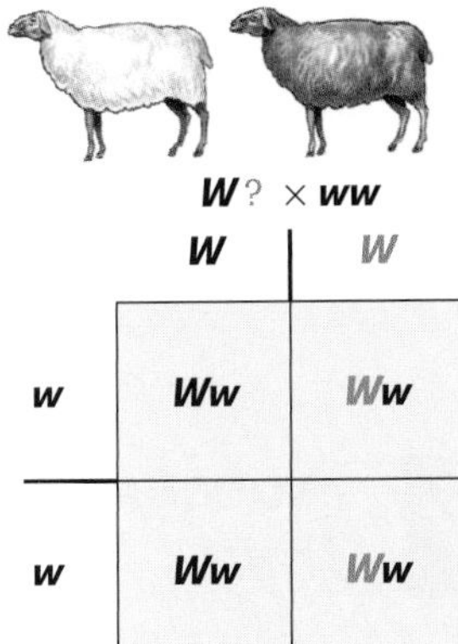

All of the offspring are white.

Figure 5
A test cross is a way of determining if an individual with the dominant trait is heterozygous or homozygous.

SAMPLE exercise 3

A horticulture worker has seeds from a particular cross, but has no information about the genotype or the phenotype of the parents. He plants and grows the offspring, and records the traits of each offspring (**Table 1**). What was the genotype and phenotype of the parent plants?

Table 1

Offspring phenotype	Numbers
round-seed peas	5472
wrinkled-seed peas	1850

Solution

Determine the observed phenotypic ratio of the progeny, rounding off if needed.

$$\frac{\text{round}}{\text{wrinkled}} = \frac{5472}{1850} \simeq \frac{3}{1}$$

List the possible genotypes for each phenotype, as shown in **Table 2**.

Table 2

Phenotype	Genotype
round-seed peas	*RR* or *Rr*
wrinkled-seed peas	*rr*

+ EXTENSION 

Factors that Contribute to Genetic Variation
In this audio clip, you will hear about the underlying mechanisms that create genetic variation in the offspring of sexually reproducing individuals.

www.science.nelson.com 

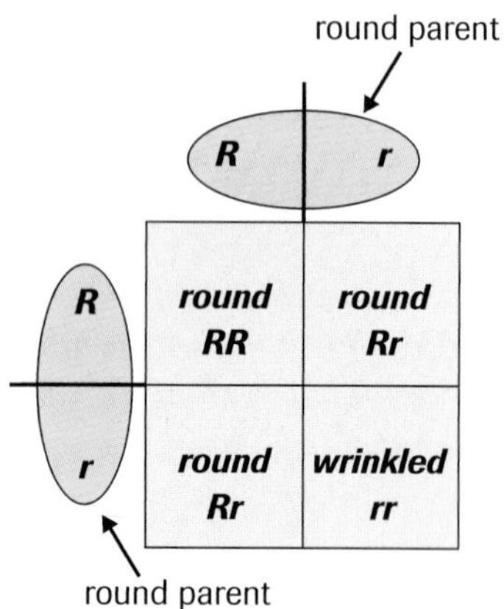

Figure 6
The observed phenotypic ratio is the same as the ratio predicted by the Punnett square.

A 3:1 phenotypic ratio occurs when two heterozygous individuals are crossed, so we know that the parents must be heterozygous. Since only $\frac{1}{4}$ of the progeny had wrinkled seeds, this is the recessive phenotype and must be determined by two copies of the recessive allele. The parents were heterozygous, so their genotype was *Rr*. Check the answer using a Punnett square **(Figure 6)**.

Practice

3. A fish breeder has a red male cichlid of unknown parentage. Red colour is dominant to yellow in the fish. He must know whether the fish is heterozygous for these colours. Suggest a way the fish breeder might find out the genotype of his red male. Use a Punnett square to explain your answer.
4. A neighbour gives a home gardener some seeds that he collected last year from his red carnations. The gardener plants 50 of the seeds and is surprised to find 12 of the plants have white flowers. Assuming that all the seeds came from one cross, what was the genotype of the parents?

SUMMARY Probability and Inheritance of Single Traits

- By using a Punnett square, the expected phenotypic ratio and genotypic ratio of the offspring of a cross can be determined.
- Probability, $P = \dfrac{\text{number of ways that a given outcome can occur}}{\text{total number of possible outcomes}}$

  Probability values can be used to predict the likelihood that a particular phenotype will appear in a cross.
- A test cross is the cross of an individual of unknown genotype to an individual with a fully recessive genotype.

Section 18.2 Questions

1. In Dalmatian dogs, the spotted condition is dominant to non-spotted.
   (a) Using a Punnett square, show the cross between two heterozygous parents.
   (b) A spotted female Dalmatian dog has six puppies sired by an unknown male. From their appearance, the owner concludes that the male was a Dalmatian. Three of the pups are spotted and three are not. What is the genotype and phenotype of the puppies' father?
2. For Mexican hairless dogs, the hairless trait is dominant to hairy. A litter of eight pups is found; six are hairless and two are hairy. What are the genotypes of their parents?
3. Test crosses are valuable tools for plant and animal breeders.
   (a) Provide two practical examples of why a cattle rancher might use a test cross.
   (b) Why are most test crosses performed using bulls rather than cows?

Pedigree Charts 18.3

Pedigree analysis is another tool for solving genetic problems. This approach is especially useful when it is not possible to perform crosses using specific individuals or to generate large numbers of progeny, such as for humans. A **pedigree chart** is like a family tree in which the inheritance of a trait can be traced from parents to offspring.

pedigree chart a chart used to record the transmission of a particular trait or traits over several generations

A pedigree chart shows the family relationship among individuals. Symbols identify the gender of each individual and whether an individual had the trait of interest. Pedigree charts may also show when an individual is known to be homozygous or heterozygous for a trait. The top of **Figure 1** shows some commonly used symbols. The pedigree chart in the lower part of **Figure 1** shows the transmission of an inherited disease among members of a family. Genetic counsellors may use pedigree charts in their work.

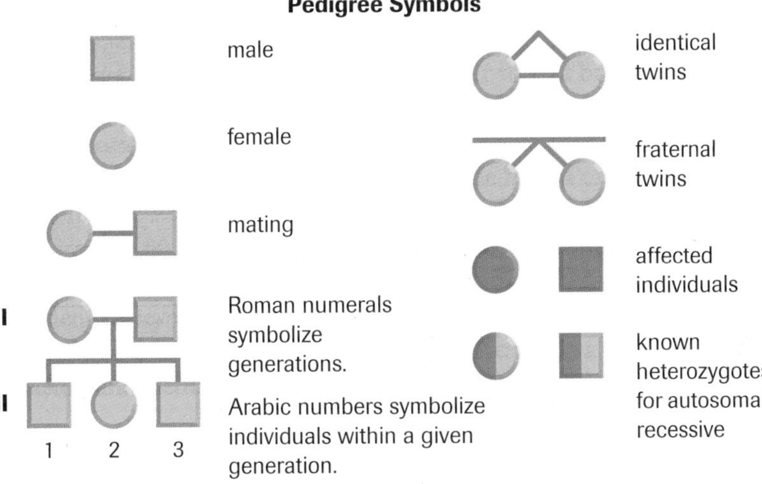

Birth order within each group of offspring is drawn left to right, oldest to youngest.

Sample Pedigree

I 1 2

II 1 2 3 4 5

III 1 2 3

Figure 1

Squares represent males and circles represent females. A slash through a symbol indicates that person is deceased. Vertical lines connect parents to offspring, horizontal lines connect mates and connect siblings. Individuals affected by the inherited disease are identified by the darker-coloured symbols. Symbols having two different colours identify individuals heterozygous for the disease.

Practice

1. People with albinism do not produce normal pigment levels. Albinism is a recessive trait. Use the pedigree chart in **Figure 2** to answer the following questions. Use an uppercase "A" to represent the dominant allele, and a lowercase "a" for the recessive allele.
   (a) How many children do the parents A and B have?
   (b) Indicate the genotypes of the parents.
   (c) Give the genotypes of M and N.

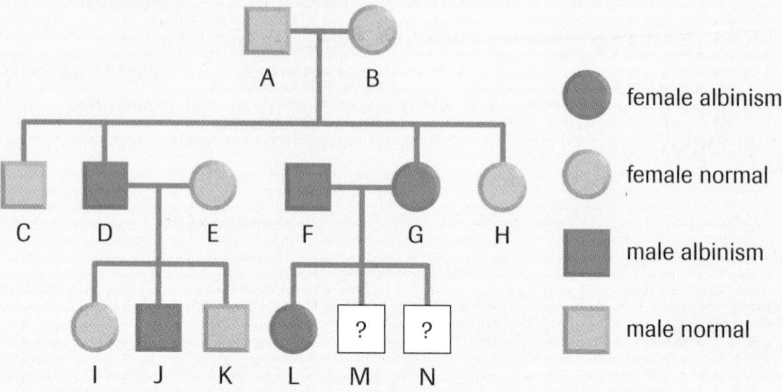

Figure 2

EXPLORE an issue

Genetic Screening

Due to advances in technology, it is now possible to get information about the genotype of any person relatively easily. Genetic screening may be carried out before birth (prenatal screening) or any time after birth. The most common reason for parents to want prenatal genetic screening is because they are at increased risk of passing a genetic disease to their child.

Thalassemia is one genetic disease for which prenatal genetic screening may be performed. Thalassemia is a disease of the blood, which affects a person's ability to produce enough red blood cells. Only people with two copies of a mutant allele of a particular a gene will have the disease. Genetic screening for thalassemia is performed only on those people with a family history of the disease. Prenatal screening can identify the presence of the thalassemia allele before the child is born.

Persons at risk of Huntington disease may request either pre- or post-natal screening. Huntington disease is a neurological disorder caused by a dominant allele. Huntington is characterized by rapid deterioration of nerve control, which causes a range of symptoms, including involuntary movements, slurred speech, loss of memory, and depression. Huntington disease is fatal. There is no cure and available treatments have little effect on symptoms. Symptoms of Huntington disease begin gradually, usually in middle age, when most people have already had children. Genetic screening allows people to know whether they have inherited the disease before any symptoms develop, so they may know whether they are at risk of passing it on to their children.

Issue Checklist

- ● Issue
- ● Resolution
- ○ Design
- ● Evidence
- ● Analysis
- ● Evaluation

Understanding the Issue

- Working in a group, conduct research and find out more about genetic screening.

www.science.nelson.com 

1. Define genetic screening. Describe some technologies used in genetic screening.
2. What are some advantages of genetic screening? Provide an example.
3. What are some physical dangers associated with genetic screening methods? Provide an example.

Take a Stand

Consider this position statement: Genetic screening should be compulsory for any person with a family history of a genetic disease.

With your group members, create a list of different stakeholders in this issue. Based on your research, determine points that support and refute the position statement from the perspective of each stakeholder. Then, decide whether your group agrees or disagrees with the position statement. Present your position to the class. Prepare to defend your group's position in a class discussion.

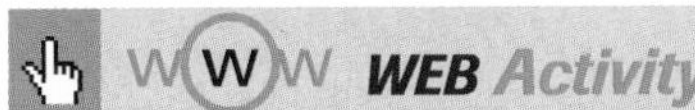

Simulation—Pedigree Analysis

Complete the interactive Pedigree Analysis Tutorial in this Virtual Biology Laboratory. You can also use pedigree analysis to examine the inheritance of several genetic diseases in humans, and to act as a "genetic counsellor" in some hypothetical case studies.

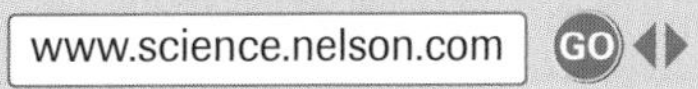

SUMMARY *Pedigree Charts*

- A pedigree chart traces the inheritance of a trait from parents to offspring through several generations.
- Pedigree charts are useful in cases when it is not possible to perform and follow specific crosses, such as in human genetic studies.

Section 18.3 Questions

1. A woman begins to show symptoms of Huntington disease. Her father had Huntington disease, but her mother never developed the disorder. Neither her husband nor anyone in his immediate family have any symptoms.
   (a) What is the genotype of the woman with Huntington disease?
   (b) What is the probable genotype of the woman's husband?
   (c) If the woman has six children, how many are likely to develop Huntington disease?
2. Phenylketonuria (PKU) is a genetic disorder caused by a dominant allele. Individuals with PKU are unable to metabolize a naturally occurring amino acid, phenylalanine. If phenylalanine accumulates, it inhibits the development of the nervous system, leading to mental retardation. The symptoms of PKU are not usually evident at birth, but can develop quickly if the child is not placed on a special diet. The pedigree in **Figure 3** shows the inheritance of the defective PKU allele in a family.
   (a) How many generations are shown by the pedigree?
   (b) How many children were born to the parents of the first generation?

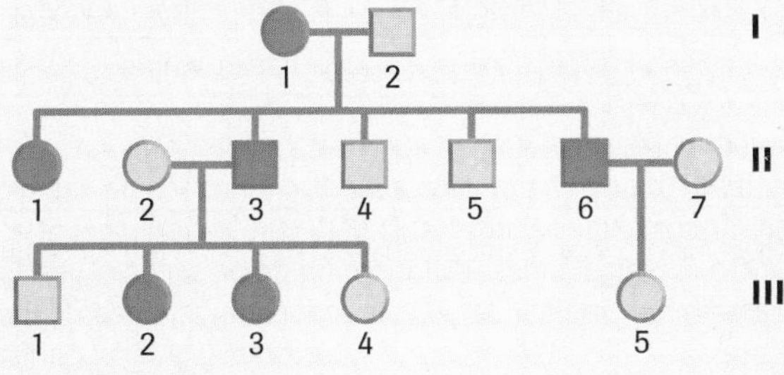

Figure 3

   (c) What is the genotype of individuals 1 and 2, generation I?
   (d) How is it possible that in generation II, some of the children showed symptoms of PKU, while others did not? (Hint: Use a Punnett square to help with your explanation.)
   (e) For individuals 6 and 7, in generation II, a child without PKU symptoms was born. Does this mean that they can never have a child with PKU? Explain your answer.
3. Research the inheritance of one of the traits in **Table 1** in a family that you know. Get information from at least three generations of the family. Use the information you collect to make a pedigree chart.

Table 1

Trait	Dominant	Recessive
freckles	present	absent
dimples	present	absent
earlobe	suspended	attached
hairline	pointed on forehead	straight across forehead
chin dimple	present	absent

4. (a) How or where might genetic screening be used for purposes other than genetic counselling?
   (b) What laws, if any, do you think are likely to arise regarding the use of genetic screening? Why?

www.science.nelson.com GO

18.4 Other Patterns of Inheritance

pleiotropic gene a gene that affects more than one characteristic

Pleiotropic Effects of Marfan Syndrome
Marfan Syndrome is caused by a mutation in a single gene. This animation shows you how this one gene affects four different organ systems.

www.science.nelson.com 

wild type the most common allele of a gene with multiple alleles

mutant any allele of a gene other than the wild type allele

(a)

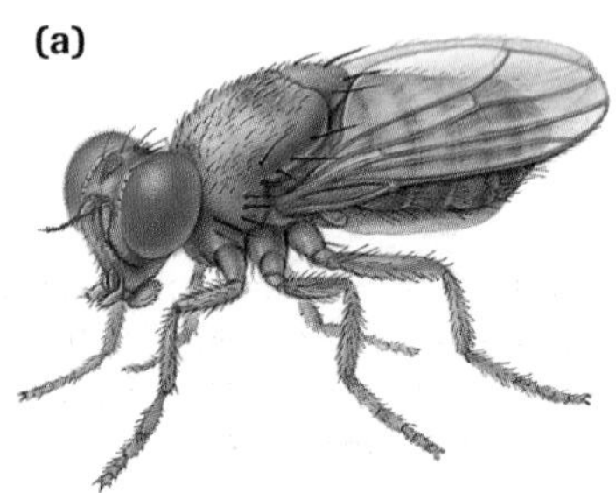

(b)

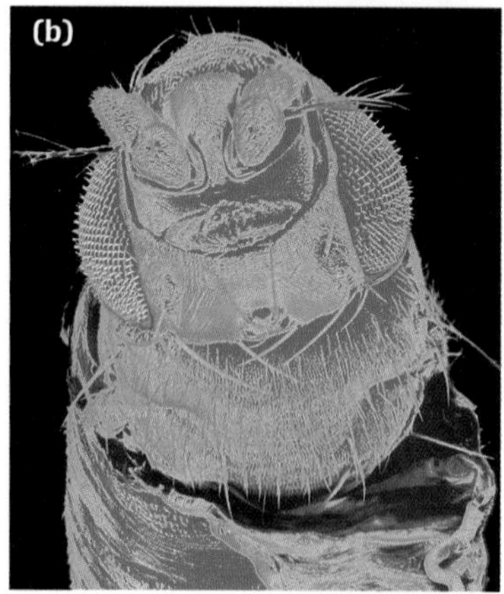

Figure 1
(a) *Drosophila melanogaster*, the fruit fly, is widely used for genetic studies.
(b) Wild type, or red, is the most common eye colour. It is dominant over all the other alleles for eye colour.

The traits that Mendel studied showed little variability. Each had only two alleles, one that was clearly dominant and one clearly recessive. However, many inherited traits show more variability than just two alternate forms. These types of traits will not be inherited in the predicted 3:1 phenotypic ratio of a trait with one dominant allele and one recessive allele.

Pleiotropic Genes

Some genes, called **pleiotropic genes**, affect many different characteristics. Sickle-cell anemia, a blood disorder, is caused by a pleiotropic gene. Normal hemoglobin (the pigment that carries oxygen in the blood) is produced by the allele *HbA*. Sickle cell anemia occurs in individuals who have two copies of the mutated allele, *HbS*. This mutation produces abnormally shaped hemoglobin molecules that interlock with one another. The new arrangement of molecules changes the shape of the red blood cells, which become bent into a sickle shape. The sickle-shaped red blood cells cannot pass through the capillaries, and so cannot deliver oxygen to the cells. People with sickle-cell anemia can suffer from fatigue and weakness, an enlarged spleen, rheumatism, and pneumonia. Patients often show signs of heart, kidney, lung, and muscle damage.

Multiple Alleles

When traits are determined by more than two (multiple) alleles, the most commonly seen trait is called the **wild type**, and the allele that determines it is the wild-type allele. Non-wild-type traits are said to be **mutant**, and the alleles that determine them are mutant alleles. In most cases of multiple alleles, there is a hierarchy of dominance.

Members of the species *Drosophila melanogaster*, the fruit fly (**Figure 1**), can have any one of four eye colours. Red eye colour is the wild type, but the eyes may also be apricot, honey, or white. The *Drosophila* species as a whole has more than two alleles for eye colour but, since fruit flies are diploid, each individual carries only two genes for eye colour.

The dominance hierarchy and symbols for eye colour in *Drosophila* are shown in **Table 1**. When there are multiple alleles for the same gene, upper case letters and superscript numbers are used to express the dominance relationships between the different alleles. For simplicity, the capital letter *E* is used for the eye colour gene and superscript numbers to indicate the position of each allele in the dominance hierarchy.

Table 1 Dominance Hierarchy and Symbols for Eye Colour in *Drosophila*

Phenotype	Allele symbol	Possible genotype(s)	Dominant over
wild type	E^1	E^1E^1, E^1E^2, E^1E^3, E^1E^4	apricot, honey, white
apricot	E^2	E^2E^2, E^2E^3, E^2E^4	honey, white
honey	E^3	E^3E^3, E^3E^4	white
white	E^4	E^4E^4	

SAMPLE exercise 1

What will be the phenotypic ratio of the offspring from the mating of the following *Drosophila* individuals?

E^1E^4 (wild-type eye colour) × E^2E^3 (apricot eye colour)

Solution

The problem can be solved by using a Punnett square. The first parent is heterozygous, and so will produce gametes with the E^1 allele and the E^4 allele. The other parent is also heterozygous, and will produce gametes with the E^2 allele and the E^3 allele. The Punnett square for this cross is, therefore, as shown in **Figure 2**.

Using the dominance hierarchy in **Table 1**, the phenotypic ratio of the F_1 offspring will produce two wild-type eye colour (genotypes E^1E^2 and E^1E^3) to one apricot eye colour (genotype E^2E^4) to one honey eye colour (genotype E^3E^4).

Practice

1. A student working with *Drosophila* makes the following cross:

   E^1E^2 (wild-type eye colour) × E^2E^4 (apricot eye colour)

   What will be the phenotypic ratio of the offspring?

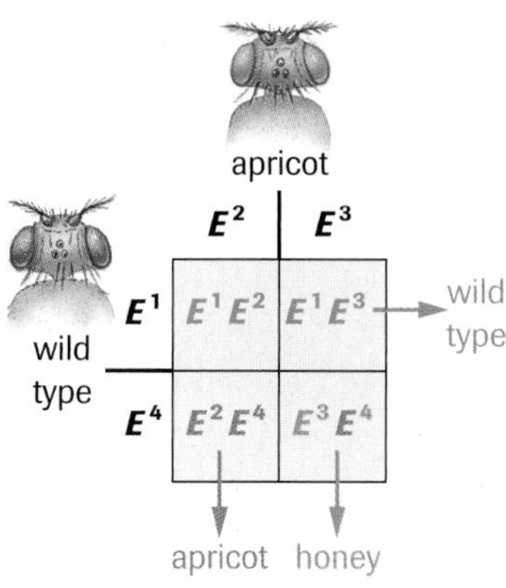

Figure 2
A cross between a fruit fly with wild-type eye colour and one with apricot-coloured eyes

Incomplete Dominance

When two alleles are equally dominant, they interact to produce a new phenotype—this form of interaction between alleles is known as **incomplete dominance**. When an individual is heterozygous for two alleles that show incomplete dominance, both alleles are equally expressed, but at half the level that would occur were the individual homozygous for either allele. The phenotype of a heterozygous individual is, therefore, intermediate between its homozygous parents. For example, when a homozygous red snapdragon is crossed with a homozygous white snapdragon, all of the F_1 generation have pink flowers. If members of the F_1 generation are crossed, the F_2 generation has a surprising phenotypic ratio of one red to two pink to one white (1:2:1). The Punnett square in **Figure 3** shows the genotypes behind this ratio.

incomplete dominance the expression of both forms of an allele in a heterozygous individual in the cells of an organism, producing an intermediate phenotype

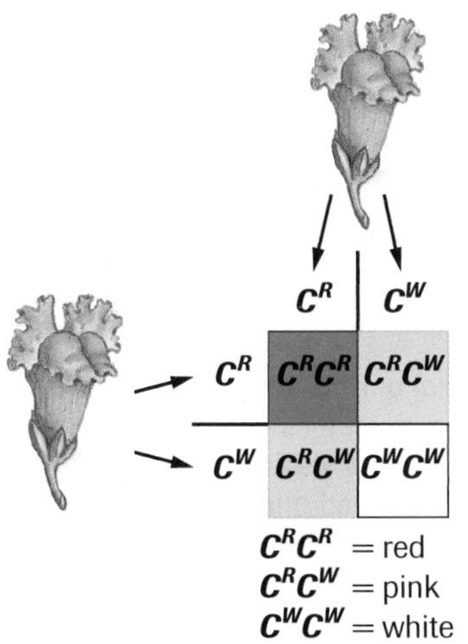

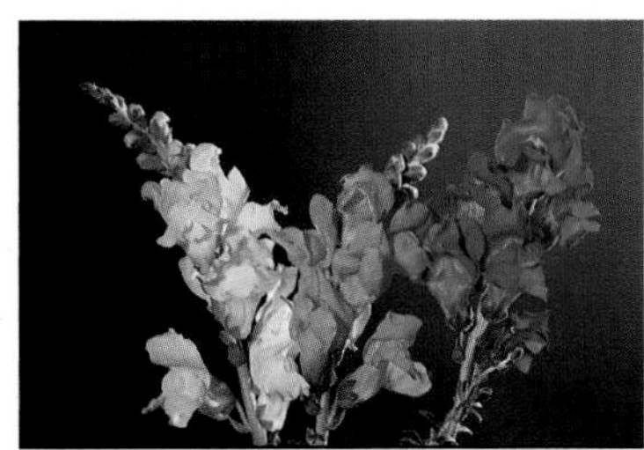

Figure 3
Colour in snapdragons is an example of incomplete dominance. When homozygous red-flowered snapdragons are crossed with homozygous white-flowered snapdragons, the F_1 generation all have pink flowers. When a cross is made between two F_1 individuals, the F_2 generation has a phenotypic ratio of one red to two pink to one white.

codominance the expression of both forms of an allele in a heterozygous individual in different cells of the same organism

Codominance

Another form of allele interaction is **codominance**. When two alleles show codominance, both alleles are fully expressed in a heterozygous individual, but not in the same cells. Coat colour in shorthorn cattle shows codominance (**Figure 4**). Red coats are composed of all red hairs, and white coats are all white hairs. When a red shorthorn is crossed with a white shorthorn, any calves produced will have roan-coloured coats, which is intermediate between the red and the white coat colour. However, each hair is not the intermediate roan colour. Instead, a roan coat has a mixture of white hairs and red hairs.

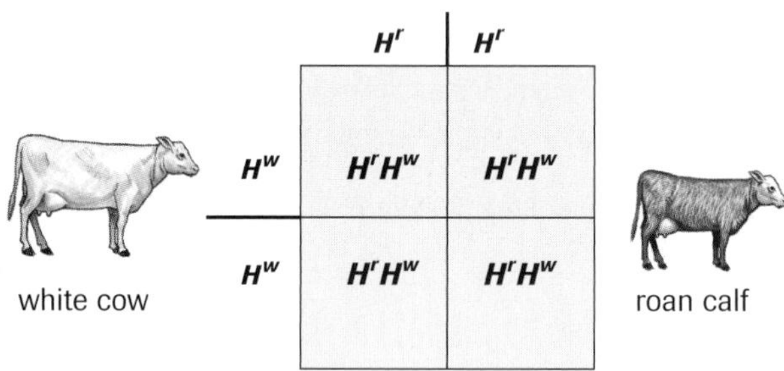

	H^r	H^r
H^w	H^rH^w	H^rH^w
H^w	H^rH^w	H^rH^w

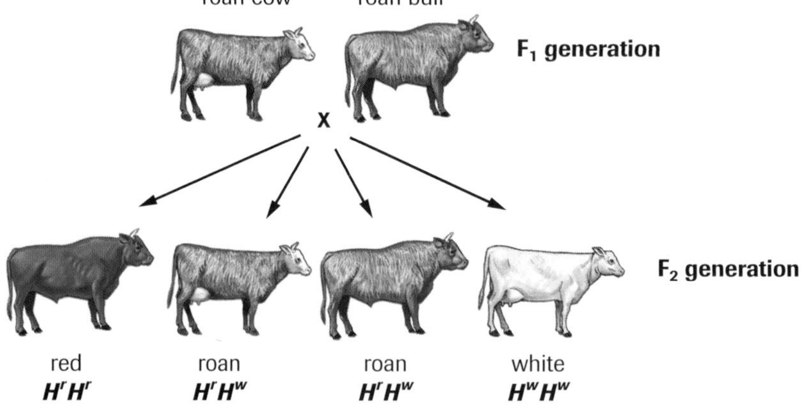

Figure 4
In codominance, either one of two different alleles is expressed. In shorthorn cattle, the coats of roan animals have intermingled red and white hair.

CAREER CONNECTION

Veterinarian
Veterinarians provide health care services that include the diagnosis and treatment of injured and sick animals. They give advice about the breeding of animals and perform genetic procedures and embryo transfers. Veterinarians work long hours and are dedicated animal health specialists. Learn more about their duties.

www.science.nelson.com 

Environment and Phenotype

Sometimes, variation of a trait is determined by the interaction of the genotype with the environment. The environment can have a profound effect on phenotype. Himalayan rabbits have black fur when they are raised at low temperatures, but white fur when raised at high temperatures. In some cases, different parts of the same organism can have different traits when exposed to different environments. Leaves of the water buttercup, *Ranunculus aquatilis*, that develop above the surface of the water are broad, lobed, and flat, while those that develop below the water are thin and finely divided. However, the leaves all have identical genetic information.

EXTENSION

Coat Colour in the Himalayan Rabbit
View this animation of how coat colour in this species is affected by temperature.

www.science.nelson.com 

INVESTIGATION 18.1 *Introduction*

How Do Environmental Factors Affect Gene Expression?

Design and carry out an investigation of the effect of an environmental factor on the phenotype of genetically identical plants.

To perform this investigation, turn to page 620.

Report Checklist

- ● Purpose
- ● Problem
- ● Hypothesis
- ● Prediction
- ● Design
- ● Materials
- ● Procedure
- ● Evidence
- ● Analysis
- ● Evaluation
- ○ Synthesis

Case Study

A Mystery of Blood Types

Humans have four blood types; A, B, AB, and O. The alleles for blood types A and B are codominant but dominant to O (**Table 2**). We also each have one of two forms of rhesus factor–the positive form (Rh+) or the negative form (Rh−). The allele for the Rh+ form is dominant to the Rh− allele. Blood types can identify individuals and family members.

Table 2 Human Blood Types

Phenotypes	Genotypes
Type A	I^AI^A, I^Ai
Type B	I^BI^B, I^Bi
Type AB	I^AI^B
Type O	ii

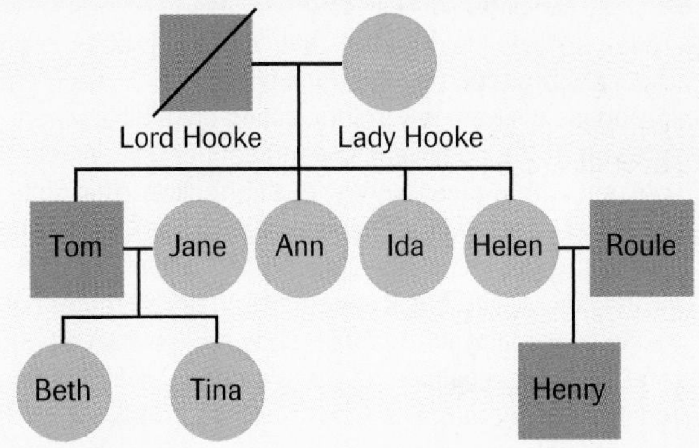

Figure 6
The family tree of the members of Lord Hooke's family who were in the castle

Evidence

In Black Mourning Castle, a scream echoed from the den of Lord Hooke. When the maid peered through the door, a freckled arm reached for her neck. She bolted and telephoned the police. Inspector Holmes arrived to find the dead body of Lord Hooke. Apparently, the lord had been strangled. The inspector noted blood on a letter opener, even though Lord Hooke did not have any cuts. This blood was type O, Rh−. Inspector Holmes took blood samples from the family members shown in **Figure 6**.

The inspector gathered the information shown in **Table 3**. The gene for freckles is dominant to the gene for no freckles. Some family members were wearing long-sleeved shirts, so the inspector could not determine whether freckles were present.

The inspector then announced, "Lady Hooke had been unfaithful to her husband. One of the heirs to the fortune was not Lord Hooke's child. The murder was committed to preserve a share of the fortune!"

Table 3 Traits of the Hooke Family

Family	Blood type	Rh factor	Freckles
Lord Hooke	AB	+	no
Lady Hooke	A	+	no
Helen	A	+	no
Roule	O	+	no
Henry	refused blood test		?
Ida	A	-	?
Ann	B	+	?
Tom	O	-	no
Jane	A	+	?
Beth	O	-	?
Tina	A	+	yes

Case Study Questions

1. Who was the murderer? What was the murderer's probable blood type?
2. Describe how you obtained your answer.
3. How did the inspector eliminate the other family members?

SUMMARY Other Patterns of Inheritance

- Some genes have more than two alleles, and can determine more than two forms of a trait. Multiple alleles may display a dominance hierarchy.
- Alleles that show incomplete dominance are equally dominant. An individual who is heterozygous for alleles that show incomplete dominance will have an intermediate phenotype.
- Codominant alleles are both expressed in a heterozygous individual.

Section 18.4 Questions

1. Multiple alleles control the coat colour of rabbits. A grey colour is produced by the dominant allele C. The C^{ch} allele produces a silver-grey colour, called chinchilla, when present in the homozygous condition, $C^{ch}C^{ch}$. When C^{ch} is present with a recessive gene, a light silver-grey colour is produced. The allele C^{h} is recessive to both the full-colour allele and the chinchilla allele. The C^{h} allele produces a white colour with black extremities. This coloration pattern is called Himalayan. An allele C^{a} is recessive to all genes. The C^{a} allele results in a lack of pigment, called albino. The dominance hierarchy is $C>C^{ch}>C^{h}>C^{a}$. **Table 4** provides the possible genotypes and phenotypes for coat colour in rabbits. Notice that four genotypes are possible for full-colour but only one for albino.

Table 4 Coat Colour in Himalayan Rabbits

Phenotypes	Genotypes
full colour	CC, CC^{ch}, CC^{h}, CC^{a}
chinchilla	$C^{ch}C^{ch}$
light grey	$C^{ch}C^{h}$, $C^{ch}C^{a}$
Himalayan	$C^{h}C^{h}$, $C^{h}C^{a}$
albino	$C^{a}C^{a}$

   (a) Indicate the genotypes and phenotypes of the F_1 generation from the mating of a heterozygous Himalayan-coat rabbit with an albino-coat rabbit.
   (b) The mating of a full-colour rabbit with a light-grey rabbit produces two full-colour offspring, one light-grey offspring, and one albino offspring. Indicate the genotypes of the parents.
   (c) A chinchilla rabbit is mated with a light-grey rabbit. The breeder knows that the light-grey rabbit had an albino mother. Indicate the genotypes and phenotypes of the F_1 generation from this mating.
   (d) A test cross is performed with a light-grey rabbit, and the following offspring are noted: five Himalayan rabbits and five light-grey rabbits. Indicate the genotype of the light-grey rabbit.
2. A horse that is homozygous for the allele C^{r} will have a chestnut, or reddish, coat. A horse that is homozygous for the allele C^{m} will have a very pale cream coat, called cremello. Palomino coat colour is determined by the interaction of both the chestnut and the cremello allele. Indicate the expected genotypic ratio and phenotypic ratio of the F_1 progeny of a palomino horse with a cremello horse.
3. Two pea plants are cross-pollinated. Using a Punnett square and probability analysis, you predict that $\frac{3}{4}$ of the offspring will be tall. However, less than $\frac{1}{4}$ grow to be tall. What other factors can affect phenotype? How much trust should be put on probability calculations?

Dihybrid Crosses and Polygenic Traits 18.5

A **dihybrid cross** is a cross that involves individuals with two independent traits that are present in alternate forms. Mendel performed dihybrid crosses with his garden peas to see if traits were inherited independently or with one another. He first crossed plants that were pure-breeding (homozygous) for two dominant traits with plants that were homozygous for two recessive traits, as shown in **Figure 1**. Each parent is homozygous for two traits, seed shape and seed colour. All the members of the F_1 offspring are heterozygous for the seed-colour gene and for the seed-shape gene. Since all the F_1 progeny had yellow, round seeds, Mendel's principle of dominance applies to this dihybrid cross.

dihybrid cross a genetic cross involving two genes, each of which has more than one allele

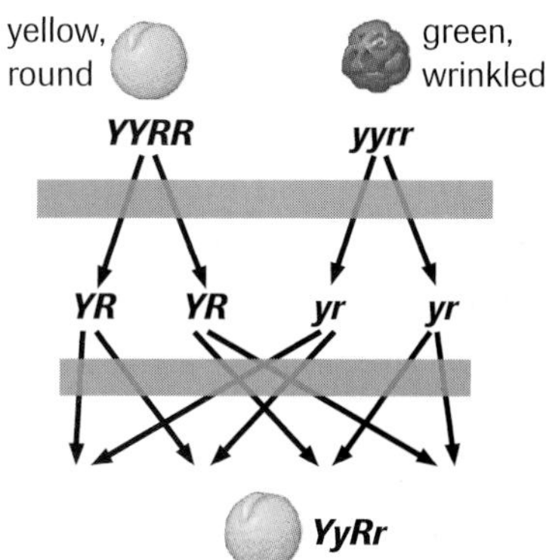

Figure 1
A dihybrid cross between a pea plant that is homozygous for yellow seed colour (*YY*) and round seed shape (*RR*) with a plant that is homozygous for green seed colour (*yy*) and wrinkled seed shape (*rr*).

Evidence of Independent Assortment

Mendel explained the result shown in **Figure 1** by postulating that each gene was inherited independently. Today, this is referred to as Mendel's second law or the law of *independent assortment*. This law states that genes that are located on different chromosomes assort independently.

To create a Punnett square for a dihybrid cross, we include one allele for both of the genes in the possible gametes. The Punnett square in **Figure 2** shows the expected genotypes and phenotypes for Mendel's dihybrid cross when we assume that the genes for seed shape and seed colour are inherited independently. One parent will produce gametes with alleles *yR* and the other will produce gametes with alleles *Yr*. The predicted phenotype of the F_1 generation is the same as Mendel observed.

Figure 3 shows the behaviour of two separate chromosomes, one that carries the gene for seed shape and another that carries the gene for seed colour. (Pea plants actually have more than two chromosomes.) As the homologous chromosomes move to opposite poles during meiosis, each gamete receives two chromosomes, one carrying the seed-shape gene and one carrying the seed-colour gene. According to the law of segregation, the alleles of both these genes will segregate during meiosis. Therefore, the allele for yellow seeds segregates from the allele for round seeds, and the allele for wrinkled seeds segregates from the allele for round seeds.

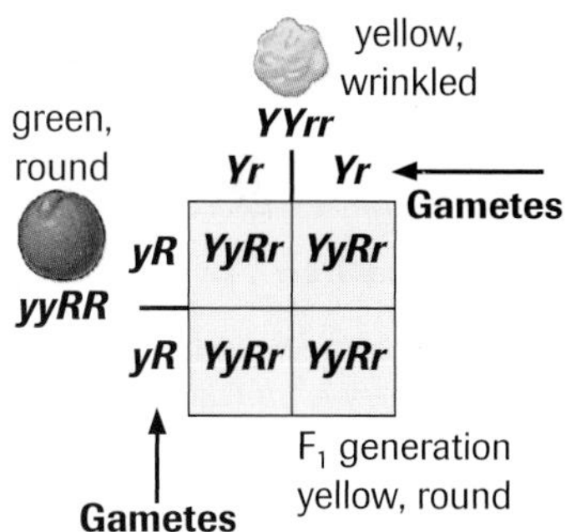

Figure 2
All gametes produced by a pea plant homozygous for yellow seed colour (*YY*) and wrinkled seed shape (*rr*) will have the alleles *Yr*. Similarly, all gametes produced by a pea plant homozygous for green seed colour (*yy*) and round seed shape (*RR*) will have the alleles *yR*. Since all the offspring have yellow, round seeds, the genotype of all the F_1 generation must be *YyRr*. This would not be possible if the genes for seed shape and seed colour were inherited together.

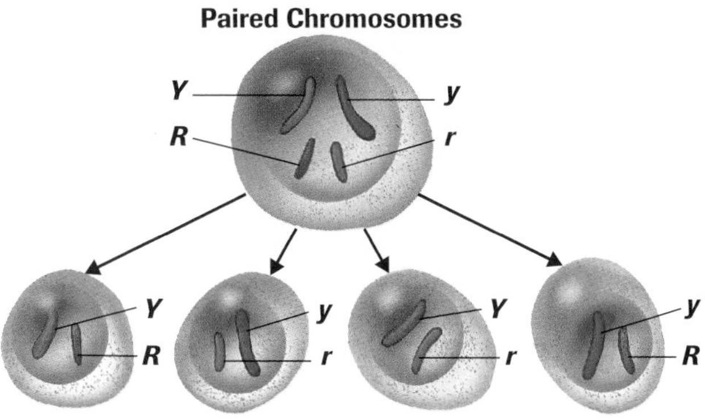

Figure 3
Segregation of alleles and independent assortment of chromosomes during meiosis gives rise to four possible combinations of alleles in the gametes of a plant of genotype *YyRr*.

Mendel then produced an F_2 generation by allowing the F_1 progeny to self-fertilize. He recorded the phenotypes of all the F_2 progeny and then calculated the ratio of each phenotype he observed. The F_2 generation had the following phenotypic ratios: $\frac{9}{16}$ yellow, round seeds; $\frac{3}{16}$ green, round seeds; $\frac{3}{16}$ yellow, wrinkled seeds; and $\frac{1}{16}$ green, wrinkled seeds.

Figure 4 shows the expected genotypes from this cross when we assume that independent assortment occurred. The parents would produce four types of gametes. The genotypes in nine of the 16 cells would determine yellow, round seeds (*YYRR*, *YyRR*, *YYRr*, and *YyRr*); three of the 16 cells would determine green, round seeds (*yyRR* and *yyRr*); three more cells would determine yellow, wrinkled seeds (*YYrr* and *Yyrr*); and one cell would determine green, wrinkled seeds (*yyrr*). Since the predicted phenotypic ratio is the same as the ratio that Mendel observed, this cross also provides evidence for independent assortment.

Gametes	*YR*	*yR*	*Yr*	*yr*
YR	*YYRR*	*YyRR*	*YYRr*	*YyRr*
yR	*YyRR*	*yyRR*	*YyRr*	*yyRr*
Yr	*YYRr*	*YyRr*	*YYrr*	*Yyrr*
yr	*YyRr*	*yyRr*	*Yyrr*	*yyrr*

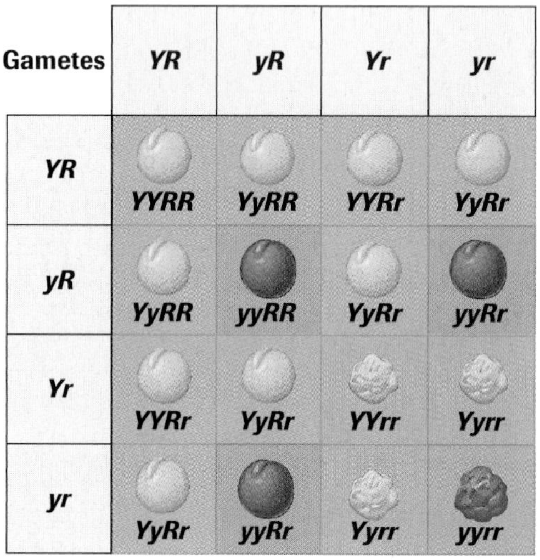

Figure 4
From the Punnett square analysis, self-fertilization of the F_1 generation will result in an F_2 generation with a 9:3:3:1 ratio. This ratio can only result if segregation of alleles and independent assortment of chromosomes occurs.

INVESTIGATION 18.2 *Introduction*

Genetics of Corn

Use Punnett squares and phenotypic ratios to analyze the inheritance of two traits in corn.

Report Checklist

- ○ Purpose
- ○ Problem
- ○ Hypothesis
- ○ Prediction
- ● Design
- ○ Materials
- ○ Procedure
- ● Evidence
- ● Analysis
- ● Evaluation
- ● Synthesis

To perform this investigation, turn to page 620.

Probability and Dihybrid Crosses

We can determine the probability of particular phenotypes and genotypes in the progeny of dihybrid crosses in much the same way as for monohybrid crosses. Probability values can be used to predict the chances of getting a particular genotype or phenotype in an offspring, or to tell us whether two genes are likely to be located on different chromosomes. In dihybrid crosses, however, we are interested in finding out the probability that two outcomes will occur at the same time. Recall that probability (P) is given by

$$P = \frac{\text{number of ways that a given outcome can occur}}{\text{total number of possible outcomes}}$$

SAMPLE exercise 1

In humans, free ear lobes are determined by the dominant allele *E*, and attached ear lobes by the recessive allele *e*. The dominant allele *W* determines a widow's peak hairline and the recessive allele *w* determines a straight hairline (**Figure 5**). The genes for these two traits are located on different chromosomes. Suppose a man with the genotype *EeWw* and a woman with the genotype *EeWw* are expecting a child. What is the probability that the child will have a straight hairline and attached ear lobes?

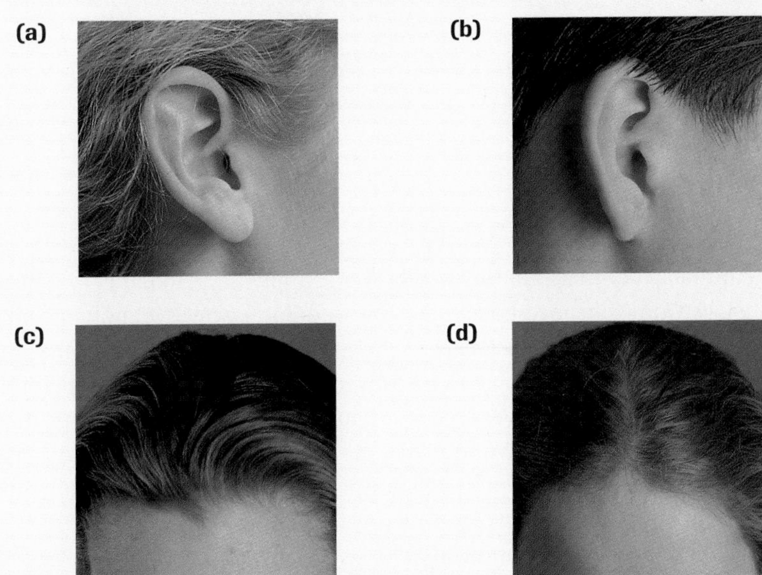

Figure 5
In humans, both ear lobe shape and hairline shape are inherited. The free ear lobe in **(a)** is dominant to the attached ear lobe in **(b)**, and the widow's peak in **(c)** is dominant to a straight hairline in **(d)**.

Solution

To have attached ear lobes and a straight hairline, the child must have the genotype *eeww*. Since the two genes are on separate chromosomes, the gene for ear shape and hairline shape will assort independently. The outcome that the child will receive two *e* alleles is, therefore, independent of the outcome that the child will receive two *w* alleles.

First, determine the probability of each of these outcomes separately, using a separate Punnett square for each gene. From **Figure 6 (a)**, we see the probability that the child will have attached ear lobes is one in four ($\frac{1}{4}$). From **Figure 6 (b)**, we see the probability that the child will have a straight hairline is also one in four ($\frac{1}{4}$).

(a)

	$\frac{1}{2}$ *E*	$\frac{1}{2}$ *e*
$\frac{1}{2}$ *E*	$\frac{1}{4}$ *EE*	$\frac{1}{4}$ *Ee*
$\frac{1}{2}$ *e*	$\frac{1}{4}$ *Ee*	$\frac{1}{4}$ *ee*

(b)

	$\frac{1}{2}$ *W*	$\frac{1}{2}$ *w*
$\frac{1}{2}$ *W*	$\frac{1}{4}$ *WW*	$\frac{1}{4}$ *Ww*
$\frac{1}{2}$ *w*	$\frac{1}{4}$ *Ww*	$\frac{1}{4}$ *ww*

Figure 6
Punnett squares showing monohybrid crosses between heterozygous parents for **(a)** free ear lobes and **(b)** for a widow's peak

Learning Tip

When thinking about probability, keep the following two rules in mind:

- When outcomes are independent, the probability of one outcome is not affected by the result of any other outcomes. For example, if you toss two heads in a row, the probability of tossing heads a third time is still 1 out of 2.
- The probability of independent events occurring together is equal to the *product* of those events occurring separately. The chances of tossing heads once is $\frac{1}{2}$, the probability of tossing heads twice in a row is $\frac{1}{2} \times \frac{1}{2} = \frac{1}{4}$, and the probability of tossing heads three times in a row is $\frac{1}{2} \times \frac{1}{2} \times \frac{1}{2} = \frac{1}{8}$.

+ EXTENSION

Probability—The Sum and Product Rules

This audio clip will explore the use of the sum and product rules of probability.

www.science.nelson.com

CAREER CONNECTION

Agrologist
Agrologists are plant, crop, and food production specialists. New breeds of plants and animals are of great interest to these scientists. They work with grain farmers and livestock producers on research projects designed to overcome challenges and realize economic opportunities in agriculture. Learn how agrologists specialize in many fields.

www.science.nelson.com 

Now, multiply these probabilities to calculate the probabilities of each event occurring in a dihybrid cross—that is, for the combination of traits. Therefore, the probability that the child will have the genotype *eeww* is $\frac{1}{4} \times \frac{1}{4} = \frac{1}{16}$.

Practice

1. Calculate the probability that the couple will have a child with
   (a) a widow's peak and free ear lobes
   (b) a straight hairline and free ear lobes
   (c) a widow's peak and attached ear lobes

Selective Breeding

selective breeding the crossing of desired traits from plants or animals to produce offspring with both characteristics

The plants and animals that make up the world's food supply have, in large part, been developed artificially from wild ancestors. **Selective breeding** involves identifying individuals with desirable traits and using them as parents for the next generation. Over time, the desirable traits became more and more common. For example, North American Aboriginal farmers used selective breeding to develop many useful crop plants, long before the arrival of Europeans. Many crops that are important to Canadian agriculture were developed by selective breeding, including rust-resistant wheat; sweet, full-kernel corn; and canola, which germinates and grows rapidly in colder climates.

inbreeding the process whereby breeding stock is drawn from a limited number of individuals possessing desirable phenotypes

You are probably familiar with the term "purebreds." Many dogs and horses are considered to be purebreds, or thoroughbreds. Genotypes of these animals are closely regulated by a process called **inbreeding,** in which similar phenotypes are selected for breeding. The desirable traits vary from breed to breed. For example, Irish setters are bred for their long, narrow facial structure and long, wispy hair, but dalmations are bred for broader faces and short hair with spots. The bull terrier (pit bull) was originally bred for fighting. Quick reflexes and strong jaws were chosen as desirable phenotypes. Some geneticists have complained that inbreeding has caused problems for the general public as well as for the breed itself.

DID YOU KNOW?

Aboriginal Crop Plants
For centuries, Aboriginal peoples bred many crop plants besides corn, which they ultimately introduced to European settlers. These include beans, tomatoes, potatoes, peanuts, peppers, cocoa, squash, pumpkins, sunflowers, long-fibre cotton, rubber, and quinine.

New varieties of plants and animals can be developed by hybridization. This process is the opposite to that of inbreeding. Rather than breed plants or animals with similar traits, the hybridization technique attempts to blend desirable but different traits. Corn has been hybridized extensively, beginning with the work of Aboriginal peoples thousands of years ago. The hybrids tend to be more vigorous than either parent. **Figure 7**, on the next page, shows the most common method used. Two homozygous plants, A and B, are crossed to produce an AB hybrid. Two other homozygous plants, C and D, are crossed to produce a CD hybrid. Hybrids AB and CD are then crossed to produce hybrid ABCD. This hybrid will have desired traits from plants A, B, C, and D, and will be more vigorous.

Polygenic Traits

polygenic trait inherited characteristics that are determined by more than one gene

In dihybrid crosses, two genes determine two separate traits. However, sometimes a single trait is determined by more than one gene. Many of your characteristics are determined by several pairs of independent genes. Skin colour, eye color, and height are but a few of your characteristics that are **polygenic traits**. Polygenic traits have much more variability in a population than those determined by a single gene. Each of the genes can have multiple alleles, show incomplete dominance or co-dominance, and can be affected by the environment.

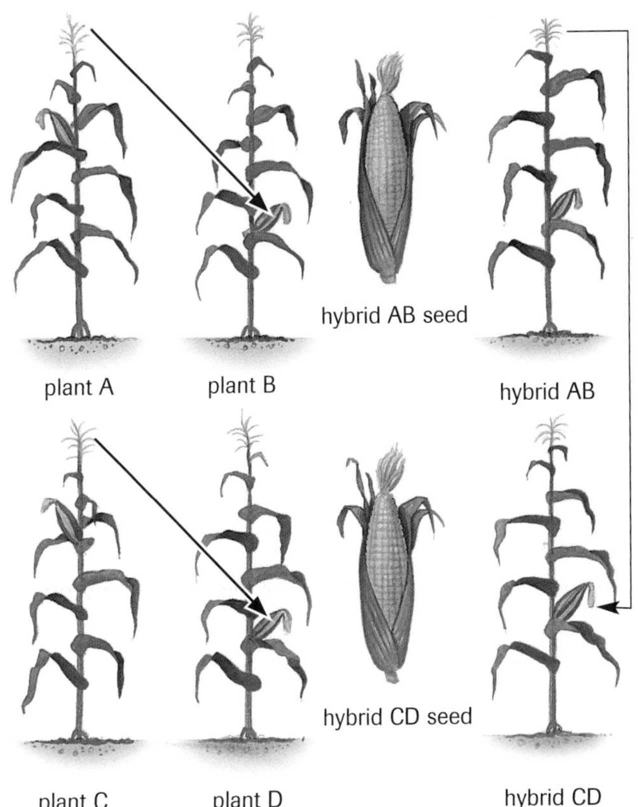

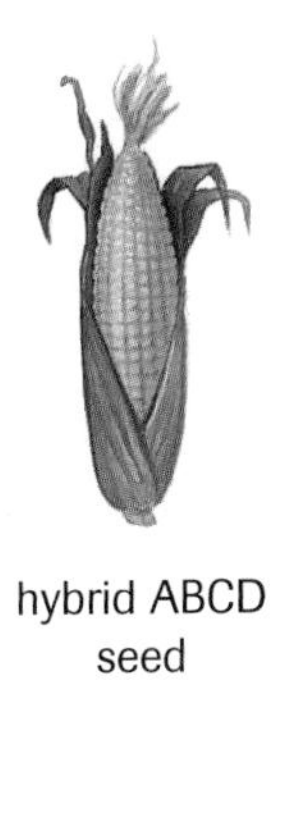

Figure 7
Hybridization can be used to produce a more vigorous strain of corn.

Coat Colour in Labrador Retrievers

Coat colour variations in this breed of dog is determined by two interacting genes. Choose a genotype for each gene and observe the phenotype.

www.science.nelson.com

epistatic gene a gene that masks the expression of another gene or genes

Examples of polygenic traits in humans include skin colour, height, and intelligence. In other animals and plants, many desirable traits, such as milk production in cows or yield in canola, are also determined by more than one gene pair. This makes breeding for these traits very difficult.

In some cases, two different genotypes interact to produce a phenotype that neither is capable of producing by itself. In other cases, one of the genes will interfere with the expression of the other, masking its effect. Genes that interfere with the expression of other genes are said to be **epistatic.**

Observed phenotypic ratios of polygenic traits vary significantly from the phenotypic ratios predicted by Punnett square analysis of non-interacting genes. Coat colour in dogs provides an example of epistatic genes. As shown in the Punnet square in **Figure 8**, the allele *B* produces black coat-colour, while the recessive allele *b* produces brown coat-colour. However, a second gene also affects coat-colour. The allele *W* of this second gene prevents the formation of pigment, thereby preventing colour. The recessive allele *w* does not prevent colour. The genotype *wwBb* would be black, but the genotype *WwBb* would appear white. The *W* allele masks the effect of the *B* colour gene. In humans, the gene responsible for albinism is epistatic. This gene interferes with the expression of genes that determine pigment formation in the skin, hair, and eyes.

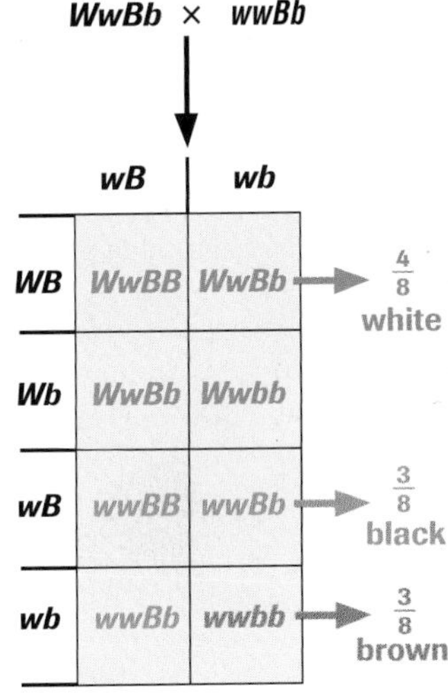

Figure 8
Punnett square of a cross between a white dog (*WwBb*) and a black dog (*wwBb*)

 EXPLORE an issue

Issue Checklist

○ Issue	○ Design	● Analysis
● Resolution	● Evidence	● Evaluation

Drought-Tolerant and Salt-Tolerant Plants

Unwise agricultural practices have dramatically reduced the productivity of the world's agricultural land. By one estimate, the reduction in crop yields since 1940 is the same as if all the land in India and China had produced no crops at all. In addition, land equivalent to the area of Hungary has become so degraded that it is unable to produce any viable crop at all. Much of the problem is linked to poor irrigation techniques (**Figure 9**). When water, rich in minerals, floods the land, evaporation carries away water but leaves the minerals. Eventually, the mineral salts accumulate within the soil, creating an environment difficult for plants to survive.

Proposed Solutions from Genetics

Traditionally, plant breeders have used selective breeding to create new varieties with desirable traits. Today, molecular biologists have developed gene insertion techniques that provide breeders with a more precise tool. Using gene splicing, desired traits from one species can be introduced into a non-related species.

In 2001, articles in scientific journals reported the production of genetically modified (GM) tomatoes that can grow in soils with high salt levels. Researchers inserted a gene that enhanced the ability of cells in the tomato plants to transport excess salts into fluid storage sacs (vacuoles). The GM tomatoes can grow in soils 50 times more saline than non-GM tomatoes. The salts accumulate in the leaves, so the tomato fruit does not have a salty taste. The development of other plants capable of living in saline solutions will allow farmers to reclaim marginal land.

In related research, geneticists are looking at developing drought-tolerant plants. Several genes have been identified that enable plants to cope with arid conditions. The Rockefeller Foundation committed $50 million to support the effort to improve drought resistance for GM maize and rice.

However, as with any technology, GM drought-tolerant and salt-tolerant plants could have undesirable consequences. Some of these concerns are outlined below.

Environmental Concerns: Every year, some of the best farmland in the world is converted to urban land. This expansion of cities into farmland also reduces food production. Producing GM drought-tolerant and salt-tolerant plants that can grow on marginal land does nothing to resolve the issue of urban expansion.

GM drought-tolerant and salt-tolerant plants could lead to the conversion of deserts and saltwater marshes into agricultural land, disrupting the natural balance within these ecosystems. These ecosystems provide habitat for many species, and saltwater marshes also help filter and clean water systems.

Food Production Concerns: At present, 5 billion people inhabit Earth, and the population is projected to increase to nearly 10 billion within 50 years. Only 3.7 billion ha (hectares) of the world's 13.1 billion ha of land can be used for crop production. According to the United Nations Food and

Figure 9
Irrigation allows plants to grow in arid lands.

Agricultural committee, over the next 50 years, the amount of arable land on Earth per person will decline from 0.24 ha to about 0.12 ha, which will not be enough to feed many of the poor. Although GM crops may not be the entire answer, they may allow an increase in food production, and so deserve further study.

Geneticists' Concerns: Some geneticists worry about the consequences if GM crops hybridize with non-GM species. Traditional methods of crop breeding involve selecting particular individuals with desirable traits from within a population, thereby altering gene frequencies within a population of a single species. Newer technologies allow genes to be transferred between entirely different species. It is difficult to predict how these transferred genes will interact in a naturally reproducing population. For example, would a gene that increases drought tolerance also make a plant more susceptible to disease?

- Evaluate each of the concerns expressed.

(a) What assumptions lie at the basis of these divergent opinions?

(b) What additional information would be useful to make an informed decision about whether or not GM crops should be pursued?

- Working in a group, discuss the different viewpoints presented above.
- Still in your group, conduct additional research on the issue of developing GM drought-tolerant and salt-tolerant plants. When research is complete, discuss the question below until you reach a consensus.

(c) Should GM crops, resistant to drought and salinity, be funded? Do they provide at least a partial solution?

- Be prepared to debate the issue as a class. Express your opinion and provide a rationale for your view.

www.science.nelson.com 

SUMMARY Dihybrid Crosses

- The phenotypic ratios that Mendel observed in his dihybrid crosses provide evidence for independent assortment of chromosomes.
- The probability of inheritance of the two traits together is the same as the product of the probability of inheritance of both traits separately.

Section 18.5 Questions

1. In guinea pigs, black coat colour (*B*) is dominant to white (*b*), and short hair length (*S*) is dominant to long (*s*). Indicate the genotypes and phenotypes from the following crosses:
   (a) A guinea pig that is homozygous for black and heterozygous for short hair crossed with a white, long-haired guinea pig.
   (b) A guinea pig that is heterozygous for black and for short hair crossed with a white, long-haired guinea pig.
   (c) A guinea pig that is homozygous for black and for long hair crossed with a guinea pig that is heterozygous for black and for short hair.
2. Black coat colour (*B*) in cocker spaniels is dominant to white coat colour (*b*). Solid coat pattern (*S*) is dominant to spotted pattern (*s*). The gene for pattern arrangement is located on a different chromosome than the one for colour, and the pattern gene segregates independently of the colour gene. A male that is black with a solid pattern mates with three females. The mating with female A, which is white and solid, produces four pups: two black, solid, and two white, solid. The mating with female B, which is black and solid, produces a single pup, which is white, spotted. The mating with female C, which is white and spotted, produces four pups: one white, solid; one white, spotted; one black, solid; one black, spotted. Indicate the genotypes of the parents.
3. For human blood, the alleles for types A and B are codominant, but both are dominant over the type O allele. The Rh factor is separate from the ABO blood group and is located on a separate chromosome. The Rh+ allele is dominant to Rh−. Indicate the possible phenotypes of a child of a woman with type O, Rh− and a man with type A, Rh+.
4. Skin colour in humans is determined by more than one gene pair, whereas Rh factor in blood is controlled by one gene pair. Which would show more variability in the human population? Why?

INVESTIGATION 18.1

How Do Environmental Factors Affect Gene Expression?

Report Checklist

- ● Purpose
- ● Problem
- ● Hypothesis
- ● Prediction
- ● Design
- ● Materials
- ● Procedure
- ● Evidence
- ● Analysis
- ● Evaluation
- ○ Synthesis

Many environmental factors can affect the phenotype of a plant. Traits such as growth rate, colour, leaf size, and leaf shape can be affected by environmental factors such as light intensity, hours of darkness, wavelength of radiation, and air temperature. In this investigation, you will design an experiment to explore how one environmental factor of your choice affects the phenotype of a plant.

You can find more information about designing an experiment in Appendix A1. Have your teacher check the procedure before beginning the experiment. Then, write a lab report, following the guidelines in Appendix A3.

INVESTIGATION 18.2

Genetics of Corn

Report Checklist

- ○ Purpose
- ○ Problem
- ○ Hypothesis
- ○ Prediction
- ● Design
- ○ Materials
- ○ Procedure
- ● Evidence
- ● Analysis
- ● Evaluation
- ● Synthesis

Corn is one of the world's most important food crops. It has been subject to selective breeding techniques and hybridization for many years, which have resulted in vigorous, high-yielding varieties. Nearly all corn grown today is hybrid corn. Some varieties of corn are chosen for their sweet flavour while the mixed coloration of other, inedible varieties makes them popular decorations during the autumn months.

Purpose

To determine the genotypes of parents by examining phenotypes of corn for two different and independent traits.

Problem

To determine the probable genotypes of the parents of the sample corn ears.

Materials

dihybrid corn ears (sample A, sample B)

Procedure

1. Obtain a sample A corn ear from your instructor (**Figure 1**). The kernels display two different traits that are located on different chromosomes.

Figure 1

(a) Indicate the two different traits.

(b) Predict the dominant phenotypes.

(c) Predict the recessive phenotypes.

INVESTIGATION 18.2 *continued*

2. Assume that the ear of corn is from the F_2 generation. The original parents were pure breeding homozygous for each of the characteristics. Assign the letters *P* and *p* to the alleles for colour, and *S* and *s* to the alleles for shape. Use the symbols *PPss* × *ppSS* for the parent generation.

(d) Indicate the phenotype of the *PPss* parent.

(e) Indicate the phenotype of the *ppSS* parent.

3. Count 100 of the kernels in sequence, and record the actual phenotypes in a table similar to **Table 1**.

Table 1 Phenotypes of the F_2 Generation

Phenotype	Number	Ratio
dominant genes for colour and shape		
dominant gene for colour, but recessive for shape		
recessive gene for colour, but dominant gene for shape		
recessive genes for colour and shape		

4. Obtain sample B. Assume that this ear was produced from a test cross. Count 100 kernels in sequence and record your results.

Analysis and Evaluation

(f) Indicate the expected genotypes and phenotypes of the F_1 generation resulting from a cross between the original parents *PPss* × *ppSS*.

(g) Use a Punnett square to show the expected genotypes and the phenotypic ratio of the F_2 generation. Compare your results with what you obtained in question 3. What factors might account for discrepancies?

(h) Assuming that sample B was produced from a test cross, indicate the phenotypic ratio of the F_1 generation.

(i) Indicate the phenotype of the unknown parent.

Synthesis

(j) Why are test crosses important to plant breeders?

(k) A dihybrid cross can produce 16 different combinations of alleles. Explain why 100 seeds were counted rather than only 16.

(l) A dominant allele *Su*, called starchy, produces smooth kernels of corn. The recessive allele *su*, called sweet, produces wrinkled kernels of corn. The dominant allele *P* produces purple kernels, while the recessive *p* allele produces yellow kernels. A corn plant with starchy, yellow kernels is cross-pollinated with a corn plant with sweet, purple kernels. One hundred kernels from the hybrid are counted, and the following results are obtained: 52 starchy, yellow kernels and 48 starchy, purple kernels. What are the genotypes of the parents and the F_1 generation?

(m) The wild ancestor of corn grew only in Central America. From this ancestor, Aboriginal peoples used selective breeding to develop different types of corn. Today, scientists continue to use technology and selective breeding methods to develop varieties of corn that can grow in a wide range of environmental conditions. As a result, corn is now grown in many places where its ancestor would not be able to survive. What are some risks associated with growing a species in a foreign environment?

+ EXTENSION

Comb Shape in Chickens

Two genes interact to produce comb shape in chickens. Change the genotype and see what happens to the phenotype .

www.science.nelson.com 

Outcomes

Knowledge

- describe the evidence for dominance, segregation, and the independent assortment of genes on different chromosomes, as investigated by Mendel (18.1, 18.2)
- compare ratios and probabilities of genotypes and phenotypes for dominant/recessive alleles, multiple alleles, and incompletely dominant or codominant alleles, epistatic, and pleiotropic alleles (18.2, 18.3, 18.4, 18.5)
- explain the relationship between variability and the number of genes controlling a trait (18.3)

STS

- explain that decisions regarding the application of scientific and technological development involve a variety of perspectives (18.3)

Skills

- ask questions and plan investigations by designing a plan for collecting data to demonstrate human inheritance (18.2)
- conduct investigations and gather and record data by performing an experiment to demonstrate inheritance of a trait controlled by a single pair of genes (18.5), and by designing and performing an experiment to demonstrate that an environmental factor can cause a change in the expression of genetic information in an organism (18.4)
- analyze data and apply mathematical and conceptual models by predicting, quantitatively, the probability of inheritance from monohybrid and dihybrid (18.2, 18.4); using Punnett squares to interpret patterns and trends associated with monohybrid and dihybrid patterns of inheritance (18.2, 18.4); performing, recording, and explaining predicted phenotypic ratios versus actual counts in genetic crosses to show a relationship between chance and genetic results (18.2, 18.4, 18.5); and drawing and interpreting pedigree charts from data on human single-allele and multiple-allele inheritance patterns (18.3, 18.4)
- work as members of a team and apply the skills and conventions of science (all)

Key Terms

18.1

progeny
dominant trait
recessive trait
allele
homozygous
heterozygous
genotype
phenotype
segregation

18.2

phenotypic ratio
Punnett square
genotypic ratio
test cross

18.3

pedigree chart

18.4

pleiotropic gene
wild type
mutant
incomplete dominance
codominance

18.5

dihybrid cross
selective breeding
inbreeding
polygenic trait
epistatic gene

MAKE a summary

1. Create a concept map that shows the principles of inheritance of traits. Label the sketch with as many of the key terms as possible.
2. Revisit your answers to the Starting Points questions at the start of the chapter. Would you answer the questions differently now? Why?

Go To

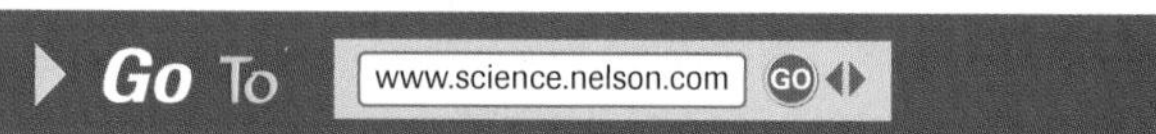

The following components are available on the Nelson Web site. Follow the links for *Nelson Biology Alberta 20–30.*

- an interactive Self Quiz for Chapter 18
- additional Diploma Exam-style Review Questions
- Illustrated Glossary
- additional IB-related material

There is more information on the Web site wherever you see the Go icon in the chapter.

EXTENSION

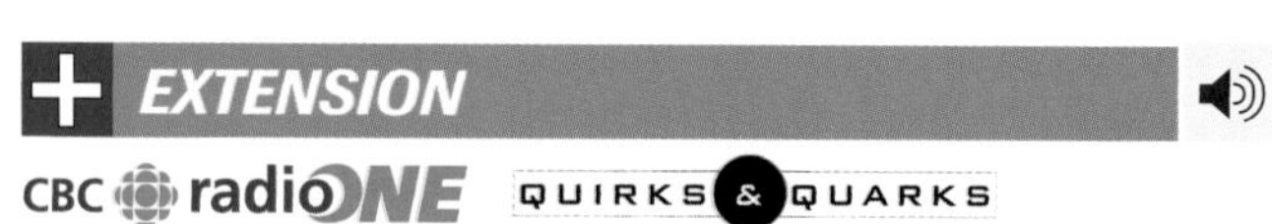

Spawning Trouble

Dr. Daniel Heath, (University of Windsor) has discovered that the eggs of captive-bred salmon are getting smaller each year. The lack of selective pressure on the eggs in a hatchery may be the cause, since more small fish are surviving than would be if the eggs developed in the wild. Dr. Heath is concerned this will lead to health problems in the wild population, and if this may also be a general problem with captive breeding programs for other animals, including endangered species.

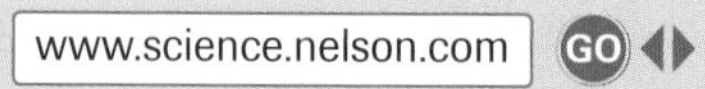

Many of these questions are in the style of the Diploma Exam. You will find guidance for writing Diploma Exams in Appendix A5. Science Directing Words used in Diploma Exams are in bold type. Exam study tips and test-taking suggestions are on the Nelson Web site.

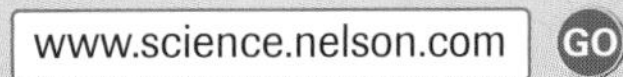

DO NOT WRITE IN THIS TEXTBOOK.

Part 1

Use the following information to answer questions 1 and 2.

Long stems are dominant over short stems for pea plants. A heterozygous long-stem plant is crossed with a short-stem plant.

1. Determine and identify the genotypic ratio of the F_1 progeny from the cross.
   A. 50 % *Ss* and 50 % *ss*
   B. 75 % *SS* and 25 % *Ss*
   C. 75 % *Ss* and 25 % *ss*
   D. 100 % *Ss*

2. Determine and identify the phenotypic ratios of the F_1 progeny of the cross.
   A. 75 % long stem and 25 % short stem
   B. 50 % long stem and 50 % short stem
   C. 75 % short stem and 25 % long stem
   D. 100 % long stem

Use the following information to answer questions 3 to 5.

The pedigree chart in **Figure 1** shows the transmission of blood types in a family.

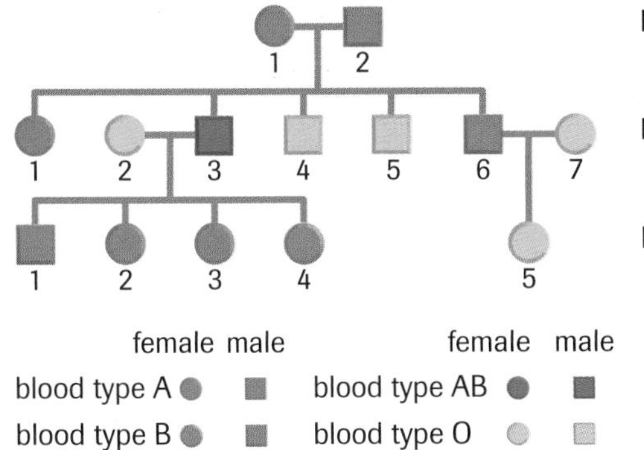

Figure 1

3. Indicate the genotypes for individuals 1 and 2, generation I.
   A. I^Ai and I^Bi
   B. I^AI^A and I^BI^B
   C. I^Ai and I^BI^B
   D. I^AI^B and I^Bi

4. NR Predict the chance of parents 1 and 2 from generation I having a child with blood type AB. (Record your answer in decimal form.)

5. NR If individuals 6 and 7 had another child, calculate the probability that the child would have blood type O. (Record your answer in decimal form.)

Use the following information to answer questions 6 and 7.

In cattle, the polled trait (hornless) is dominant to the horned condition. A single bull mates with three different cows and produces offspring as shown in **Figure 2**.

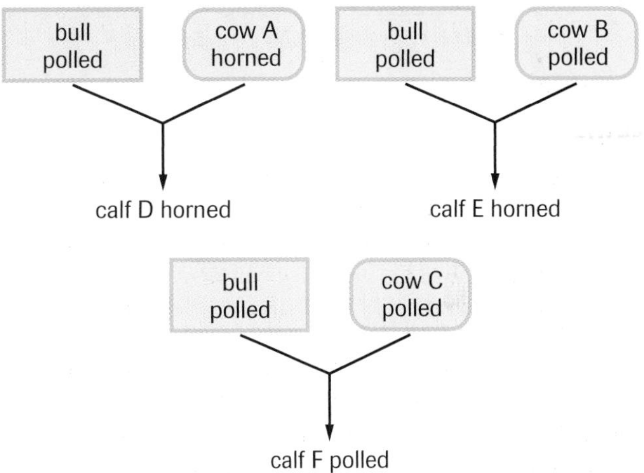

Figure 2

6. Identify the respective genotypes for the bull, cow A, and cow B.
   A. bull = *Pp*, cow A = *pp*, cow B = *Pp*
   B. bull = *PP*, cow A = *pp*, cow B = *Pp*
   C. bull = *Pp*, cow A = *pp*, cow B = *pp*
   D. bull = *PP*, cow A = *Pp*, cow B = *Pp*

7. Identify which of the cattle could have two possible genotypes.
   A. cow C and calf F
   B. cow B and calf E
   C. cow A and calf D
   D. bull and calf D

Part 2

8. **Explain** the advantages and limitations of using blood typing by the courts to prove paternity.

9. Cystic fibrosis is regulated by a recessive allele, *c*. **Explain** how two parents without this condition can produce a child with cystic fibrosis.

10. In horses, the trotter trait is dominant to the pacer trait. A male, described as a trotter, mates with three different females. Each female produces a foal. The first female, a pacer, gives birth to a foal that is a pacer. The second female, also a pacer, gives birth to a foal that is a trotter. The third female, a trotter, gives birth to a foal that is a pacer. **Determine** the genotypes of the male, all three females, and the three foals sired.

11. For ABO blood groups in humans, the A and B genes are codominant, but both A and B are dominant over type O.
    (a) **Identify** the possible blood types in the children of a man with blood type O and a woman with blood type AB.
    (b) Could a woman with blood type AB ever produce a child with blood type AB? Could she ever have a child with blood type O? **Explain** your answer.

12. Some cats have six toes, a condition determined by a dominant allele. **Sketch** a pedigree chart showing the mating of a male cat with six toes to a normal female. Assume the following:
    - The male cat with six toes had a normal mother.
    - The cats produce six offspring (four females and two males). Two of the female offspring and one of the male offspring have six toes.
    - One of the six-toed female offspring mates with a six-toed male from different parents. Four female offspring are produced, and three of them have six toes.

13. In shorthorn cattle, the mating of a red bull and a white cow produces a calf that is described as roan. Roan animals have intermingled red and white hair. After many matings between roan bulls and roan cows, the following phenotypic ratio was observed in the offspring: one red, two roan, one white. Does this ratio indicate codominance or multiple alleles? **Explain** your answer.

Use the following information to answer questions 14 to 16.

Thalassemia is a serious human genetic disorder which causes severe anemia. The homozygous condition (T^mT^m) leads to severe anemia. People with thalassemia die before sexual maturity. The heterozygous condition (T^mT^n) causes a less serious form of anemia. The genotype T^nT^n causes no symptoms of the disease.

14. DE **Predict** all the possible genotypes of the offspring of a male with the genotype T^mT^n and a woman of the same genotype.

15. DE **Predict** all the possible phenotypes of the offspring of a man with the genotype T^mT^n and a woman of the same genotype.

16. DE Would it ever be possible for offspring to be produced from two individuals with the genotypes T^mT^m and T^mT^n respectively? **Explain** your answer.

Use the following information to answer questions 17 and 18.

Baldness is an autosomal trait, but it is influenced by sex. Baldness (*HB*) is dominant in males but recessive in females. The normal gene (*Hn*) is dominant in females, but recessive in males.

17. DE **Explain** how a bald offspring can be produced from the mating of a normal female and a normal male.

18. DE Could normal parents ever produce a bald girl? **Explain** your answer.

19. The ability to curl your tongue up on the sides (*T*) is dominant to not being able to roll your tongue (*t*).
    (a) A woman who can roll her tongue marries a man who cannot. Their first child has his father's phenotype. **Predict** the genotypes of the mother, father, and child.
    (b) **Determine** the probability that their second child will not be able to roll her or his tongue.

20. Phenylketonuria (PKU) is an inherited disease caused by the lack of the enzyme needed to metabolize the amino acid phenylalanine. If untreated, PKU builds up in the brain and causes mental retardation. PKU is determined by a recessive allele. A woman and her husband are both carriers of PKU. **Determine** the probability of
    (a) their first child having PKU.
    (b) both of their first two children having PKU.

21. DE Amniocentesis is a common prenatal procedure, used to obtain cells to test for genetic abnormalities such as cystic fibrosis. The test is usually carried out in the 15th to 18th week of pregnancy when a woman has an increased risk of having children with genetic abnormalities. A woman with cystic fibrosis in her family history (**Figure 3**, next page) is carrying a child. Her husband's lineage also is linked to cystic fibrosis. Cystic fibrosis is caused by a recessive allele found on chromosome 7. Write a unified response addressing the following aspects of performing amniocentesis in the case of father K and mother O.
    - Like all procedures that enter the body, some risk, although small, is associated with amniocentesis. On the basis of the information provided, would you recommend an amniocentesis be done for mother O and father K? **Explain** your reasons.
    - Would you recommend the procedure if father K had married mother O's cousin, woman J? **Explain** your reasons.
    - Should amniocentesis be performed even if there is no strong evidence suggesting genetic problems? **Explain** your reasons.
    - Should this pedigree be made public? **Identify** both pros and cons before coming to a conclusion.

Father K's Family Tree

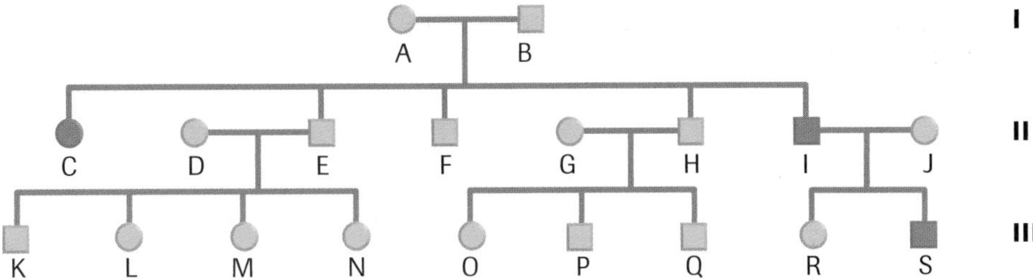

Mother O's Family Tree

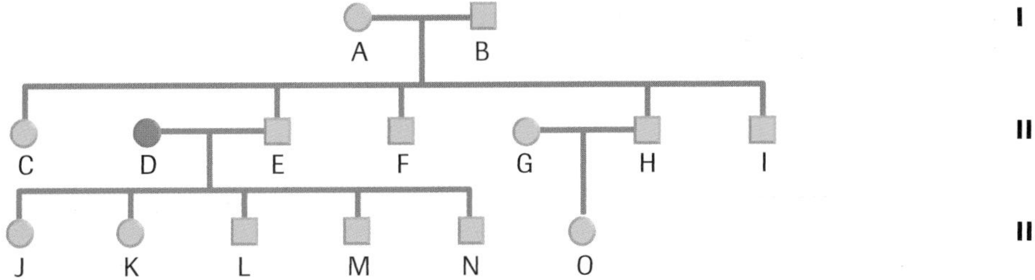

Figure 3

22. In Canada, it is illegal to marry your immediate relatives. Using the principles of genetics, **explain** why inbreeding of humans is discouraged.

Use the following information to answer questions 23 to 26.

When paper impregnated with the bitter chemical phenylthiocarbamide (PTC) is placed on the tongue, about 70 % of people can taste the chemical. The ability to taste PTC is determined by a dominant taster allele (*T*). Those who cannot taste PTC are homozygous for the recessive alleles (*t*). A second gene on another chromosome determines skin pigmentation. Allele (*A*) is dominant, and determines normal pigmentation. People who are homozygous for the recessive allele (*a*) will be albino. A normally pigmented woman who cannot taste PTC has a father who is an albino and a PTC taster. She marries a normally pigmented man who is homozygous for the dominant (A) allele for pigmentation. The man can taste PTC, but his mother cannot.

23. **Predict** all the possible genotypes for these two traits for children by this couple. DE

24. **Determine** the probability that a child from this couple will not be able to taste PTC. DE

25. **Determine** the probability that a child from this couple will be albino? DE

26. **Determine** the probability that a child from this couple will be able to taste PTC and be albino. DE

Use the following information to answer questions 27 to 29.

In a specific variety of soybeans, the allele for seeds containing a high oil-content (*H*) is dominant to the allele for low oil-content (*h*). A gene located on another chromosome determines the number of seeds in a pod. Through crossing experiments, it was determined that the allele that determines four seeds per pod (*E*) is dominant to the allele that determines two seeds per pod (*ee*). A plant breeder crosses two soybean plants of this variety, both of which have high oil-content and four seeds per pod. The phenotypes of the F_1 generation and their ratios are shown in **Table 1**.

Table 1 Phenotypes of the F_1 Generation

Phenotype	Ratio
high oil-content–four seeds per pod	9
high oil-content–two seeds per pod	3
low oil-content–four seeds per pod	3
low oil-content–two seeds per pod	1

27. **Predict** the genotypes of the parent plants. DE

28. The plant breeder crosses two individuals from the F_1 generation that have high oil-content and four seeds per pod. If all the members of the F_2 generation all have high oil-content and four seeds per pod, **predict** the genotypes of the two F_1 parent plants chosen by the breeder. DE

29. The breeder wants to confirm the genotype of the two F_1 parent plants using a cross. What genotype should the plant she crosses the F_1 parent plants have? **Explain.** DE

Beyond Mendel

In this chapter

Early scientists believed that hereditary traits were located in the blood. The term "pure bloodline," which is still used today by animal breeders (**Figure 1**), is a reminder of this misconception, as is the French term Métis conferred by European fur traders on peoples of mixed Aboriginal and European "blood." Today we know that inherited traits are determined by genes, which are located along the thread-like chromosomes found in the nucleus of each cell.

The field of genetics changed quickly once scientists began to describe the location and the chemical makeup of chromosomes. Genes can now be identified and selected, and sometimes even altered. One of the most dramatic examples of changing inherited traits is the production of mice that are smarter than mice are naturally. This genetically modified strain was dubbed Doogie, after a television character who was a teenage genius.

The modification and insertion of a single gene, *NR2B*, into a chromosome of the mice improves the functioning of nerve receptors that play a key role in memory and learning. The laboratory-bred Doogie mice learn faster and remember more than normal mice. For example, scientists found that when a new and an old object were introduced into the cage with the Doogie mice, they spent most of their time exploring the new object. This indicated that they recognized and remembered the old object. Normal mice spent equal time with the new and old objects. The Doogie mice generated great excitement, because humans possess a corresponding gene.

STARTING Points

Answer these questions as best you can with your current knowledge. Then, using the concepts and skills you have learned, you will revise your answers at the end of the chapter.

1. In what part of the cell would you find genes?
2. Can you distinguish males from females by looking at their genetic material?
3. Explain how a better understanding of chromosome structure could lead to a more complete understanding of gene function.
4. Why might some people be opposed to making mice smarter?
5. Why might the research with mice prove important for people with Alzheimer's disease?

Figure 1
Animal breeders produce varieties of a species with a specific set of traits, such as these Appaloosa horses. The value of an individual animal is often determined by its bloodline, a term that dates back to early misconceptions about heredity.

Exploration Inherited Traits

Some physical characteristics are controlled by a single gene that can be expressed in one of two ways. Try the tests below to see what phenotype you express.

- Fold your arms in front of your body.
  (a) Which arm is on top?
- Change arm position so that the other arm is on top.
  (b) Describe how it feels.
- Interlock your fingers.
  (c) Are the fingers from your left hand or your right hand on top?
- Place a strip of PTC paper on your tongue.
  (d) Could you taste the paper?
- Gather and compile the class data for all three tests.
  (e) For each test, which trait occurred most frequently in your class?
  (f) Do traits determined by dominant genes always occur with the highest frequency? Explain your answer.

19.1 Chromosomes and Genetics

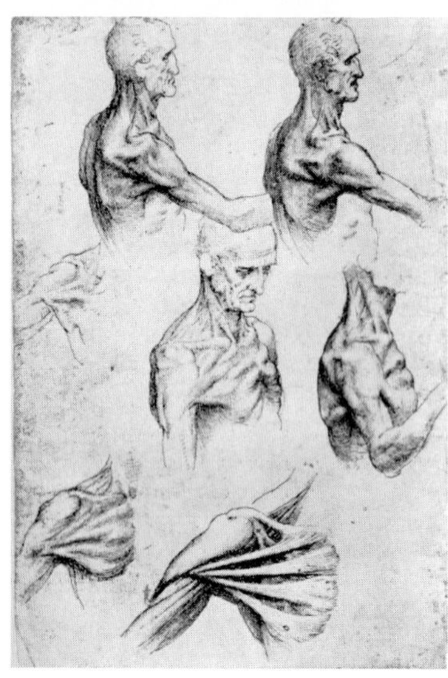

Figure 1
The artist Leonardo da Vinci became interested in anatomy and dissection because of his desire to paint the human form better.

During the Middle Ages (500–1300 CE), curious individuals would sneak into caves to dissect corpses. Despite strict laws prohibiting such behaviour, the inquiring minds of early physicians and scientists compelled them to conduct their investigations. Generations of artists sketched different parts of the body (**Figure 1**), creating a guide to anatomy in the process. As a composite structure of organs began to appear, theories about function arose. The principle that structure gives clues about function also applies to genetics. However, the early geneticists had to wait for the emergence of the light microscope before investigations into genetic structure could seriously progress. The study of genes is closely connected with technology. The light microscope, the electron microscope, X-ray diffraction, and gel electrophoresis have provided a more complete picture of the mechanisms of gene action.

The discovery of the nucleus in 1831 was an important step toward understanding the structure and function of cells and the genes they contain. By 1865, the year in which Mendel published his papers, biologists knew that the egg and sperm unite to form a zygote, and it was generally accepted that factors from the egg and sperm were blended in developing the characteristics of the offspring. Even though Mendel knew nothing about meiosis or the structure or location of the hereditary material, he was able to develop theories about inheritance that adequately explain how traits are passed on from generation to generation.

At about the same time that Mendel was conducting his experiments with garden peas, new techniques in lens grinding were providing better microscopes. The improved technology helped a new branch of biology, cytology, to flourish. Cytology is the study of cell formation, structure, and function. Aided by these technological innovations, in 1882, Walter Fleming described the separation of threads within the nucleus during cell division. He called the process mitosis. In the same year, Edouard van Benden noticed that the sperm and egg cells of roundworms had two chromosomes, but the fertilized eggs had four chromosomes. By 1887, August Weisman offered the theory that a special division took place in sex cells. By explaining the reduction division now known as meiosis, Weisman added an important piece to the puzzle of heredity and provided a framework in which Mendel's work could be understood. When scientists rediscovered Mendel's experiments in 1900, the true significance of his work became apparent.

Chromosomal Theory

Learning Tip

Recall that homologous chromosomes occur in pairs and are similar in size, shape, and gene information and arrangement.

In 1902, American biologist Walter S. Sutton and German biologist Theodor Boveri independently observed that chromosomes came in pairs that segregated during meiosis. The chromosomes then formed new pairs when the egg and sperm united. The concept of paired, or homologous, chromosomes supported Mendel's explanation of inheritance based on paired factors. Today, these factors are referred to as the alleles of a gene. One factor, or allele, for each gene comes from each sex cell.

The union of two different alleles in offspring and the formation of new combinations of alleles in succeeding generations could be explained and supported by cellular evidence. The behaviour of chromosomes during gamete formation could help explain Mendel's law of segregation and law of independent assortment.

Sutton and Boveri knew that the expression of a trait, such as eye colour, was not tied to only the male or only the female sex cell. Some structures in both the sperm cell and the egg cell must determine heredity. Sutton and Boveri deduced that Mendel's factors (alleles) must be located on the chromosomes. The fact that humans have 46 chromosomes (44 **autosomes** and 2 sex chromosomes), but thousands of different traits, led Sutton to hypothesize that each chromosome carries genes. Genes that are on the same chromosome are said to be **linked genes**.

autosome a chromosome not involved in sex determination

linked genes genes that are located on the same chromosome

The chromosomal theory of inheritance can be summarized as follows:

- Chromosomes carry genes, the units of heredity.
- Paired chromosomes segregate during meiosis. Each sex cell or gamete has half the number of chromosomes found in the somatic cells. This explains why each gamete has only one of each of the paired alleles.

As you saw in the previous chapter, chromosomes assort independently during meiosis. Each gamete receives one member from each pair of chromosomes, and each chromosome pair has no influence on the movement of any other chromosome pair. This explains why in a dihybrid cross an F_1 parent, *AaBb*, produces four types of gametes: *AB*, *aB*, *Ab*, *ab*. Each gamete appears with equal frequency due to segregation and independent assortment. Each chromosome contains many different alleles and each gene occupies a specific locus or position on a particular chromosome.

Morgan's Experiments and Sex-Linked Traits

The American Thomas Hunt Morgan was among the first of many geneticists who used the tiny fruit fly, *Drosophila melanogaster*, to study the principles of inheritance. There are several reasons why the fruit fly is an ideal subject for study. First, the fruit fly reproduces rapidly. Offspring are capable of mating shortly after leaving the egg, and females produce over 100 eggs after each mating. Female *Drosophila* can reproduce for the first time when they are only 10 to 15 days old, so it is possible to study many generations in a short period of time. Since genetics is based on probability, the large number of offspring is ideal. A second benefit arises from *Drosophila*'s small size. Many individuals can be housed in a single culture tube. A small, solid nutrient at the bottom of the test tube can maintain an entire community. The third and most important quality of *Drosophila* is that males can easily be distinguished from females. Males are smaller and have a rounded abdomen with a dark-coloured posterior segment while the larger females have a pointed abdomen with a pattern of dark bands.

Figure 2
In *Drosophila*, the allele that codes for white eyes (male fly, top photo) is recessive to the allele that codes for red eyes (female fly, bottom photo).

While examining the eye colour of a large number of *Drosophila*, Morgan noted the appearance of a white-eyed male among many red-eyed offspring (**Figure 2**). He concluded that the white-eyed trait must be a mutation. Morgan was interested in tracing the inheritance of the allele coding for white eyes, so he mated the white-eyed male with a red-eyed female. All members of the F_1 generation had red eyes. Normal Mendelian genetics indicated that the allele for red eyes was dominant. Most researchers might have stopped at that point, but Morgan did not. Pursuing further crosses and possibilities, he decided to mate two hybrids from the F_1 generation. An F_2 generation produced $\frac{3}{4}$ red eyes and $\frac{1}{4}$ white eyes, a ratio that could again be explained by Mendelian genetics. But further examination revealed that all the females had red eyes. Only the males had white eyes. Half of the males had red eyes and half had white eyes. Did this mean that the white-eyed phenotype only appears in males? Why could males express the white-eyed trait but not females? How did the pattern of inheritance differ between males and females? To find an answer, Morgan turned to cytology.

Previous researchers had stained and microscopically examined the eight chromosomes from the cells of the salivary glands of *Drosophila*. They found that females have four homologous pairs and males have only three homologous pairs. The fourth pair, which determines sex, is only partially homologous. Males were found to have one

CAREER CONNECTION

Entomologist
Entomologists study the life cycle of insects and conduct research into evolution and biodiversity. The science of entomology has made a significant contribution to understanding genetics and gene mapping. Would you like to work with fruit flies or arthropods, such as spiders and mites? Explore this field of study.

www.science.nelson.com 

X chromosome paired with a small, hook-shaped Y chromosome. Females have two paired X chromosomes (**Figure 3**). Since the X and Y chromosomes are not completely homologous (although they act as homologous pairs during meiosis), it was concluded that they contain different genes.

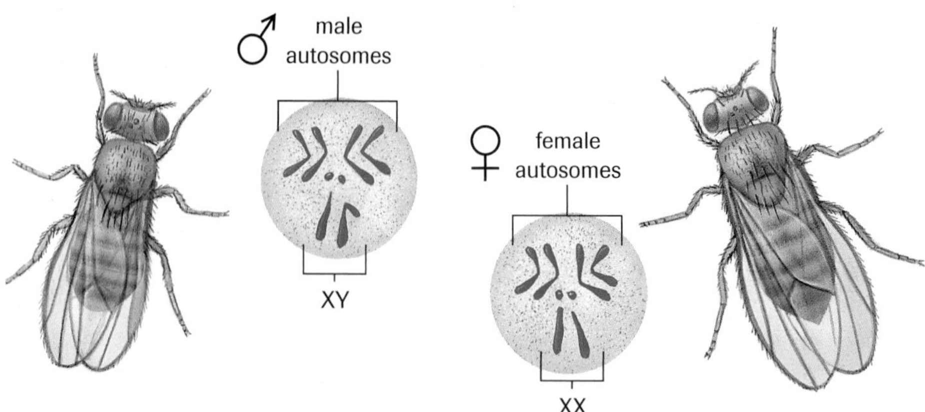

Figure 3
Drosophila contain three pairs of autosomes and a single pair of sex chromosomes.

Morgan explained the results of his experiments by concluding that the Y chromosome does not carry the gene to determine eye colour. We now know that the gene for eye colour in *Drosophila* is located on the part of the X chromosome that does not match the Y chromosome. Therefore, Morgan's conclusion was correct. The Y chromosome does not carry an allele for the eye-colour gene. Traits determined by genes located on sex chromosomes are called **sex-linked traits**.

sex-linked trait trait that is determined by genes located on the sex chromosomes

The initial problem can now be re-examined. The pure-breeding, red-eyed female can be indicated by the genotype X^RX^R and the white-eyed male by the genotype X^rY. The symbol X^R indicates that the allele for red eye is dominant and is located on the X chromosome. There is no symbol for eye colour on the Y chromosome because it does not contain an allele for the trait. A Punnett square, as shown in **Figure 4**, can be used to

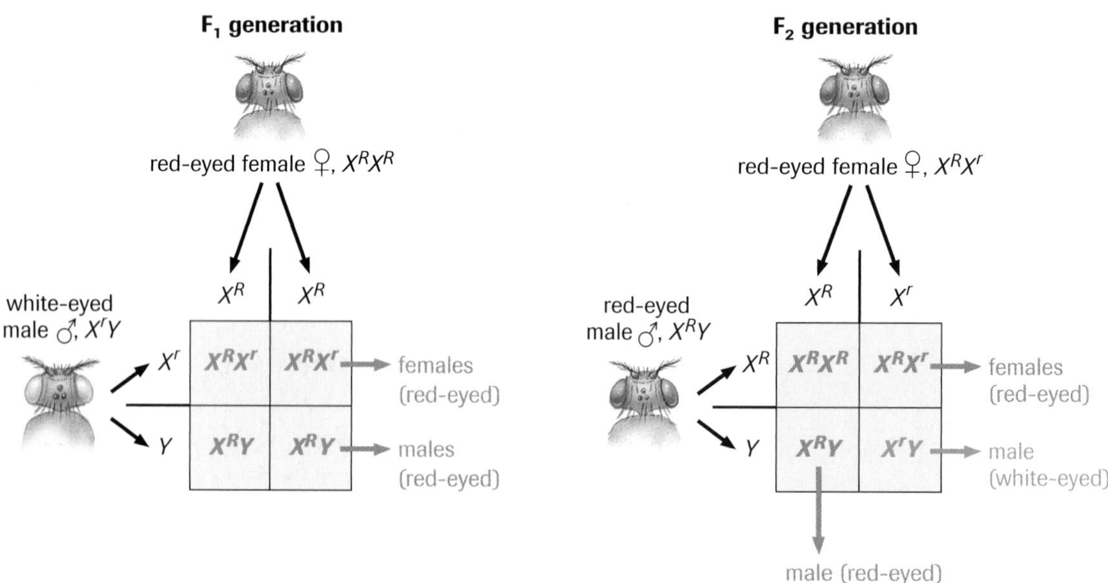

Figure 4
Punnett squares showing F_1 and F_2 generations for a cross between a homozygous red-eyed female and a white-eyed male.

determine the genotypes and the phenotypes of the offspring. All members of the F_1 generation have red eyes. The females have the genotype X^RX^r, and the males have the genotype X^RY.

The F_2 generation is determined by a cross between a male and female from the F_1 generation. Upon examination of the F_1 and F_2 generations, the question arises whether the males inherit the trait for eye colour from the mother or father. The male offspring always inherit a sex-linked trait from the mother. The father supplies the Y chromosome, which makes the offspring male.

The F_2 male *Drosophila* are X^RY and X^rY. The females are either homozygous red for eye colour, X^RX^R, or heterozygous red for eye colour, X^RX^r (**Table 1**). Although Morgan did not find any white-eyed females from his initial cross, some white-eyed females do occur in nature. For this to happen, a female with at least one allele for white eyes must be crossed with a white-eyed male. Notice that females have three possible genotypes, but males have only two. Males cannot be homozygous for an X-linked gene because they have only one X chromosome. The Y chromosome has less than 100 genes.

Recall that humans have 46 chromosomes. Females have 23 pairs of homologous chromosomes: 22 autosomes, and two X sex chromosomes. Males have 22 pairs of homologous chromosomes, and one X sex chromosome and one Y sex chromosome (**Figure 5**). It has been estimated that the human X chromosome carries between 100 and 200 different genes. The Y chromosome has less than 100 genes.

Sex-linked genes are also found in humans. For example, a recessive allele located on the X chromosome determines red–green colour-blindness. More males are colour-blind than females because females require two recessive alleles to exhibit colour-blindness. Since males have only one X chromosome, they require only one recessive allele to be colour-blind. Other sex-linked traits that affect males primarily include hemophilia, hereditary near-sightedness (myopia), and night-blindness.

This explains why **recessive lethal** X-linked disorders in humans, such as infantile spinal muscular atrophy, occur more frequently in males. This could also explain why the number of females reaching the age of 10 and beyond is greater than the number of males. Males die at birth or before the age of 10 from recessive lethal X-linked disorders.

Table 1 Possible Genotypes for *Drosophila*

Females	Males
X^RX^R	X^rY
X^RX^r	X^RY
X^rX^r	

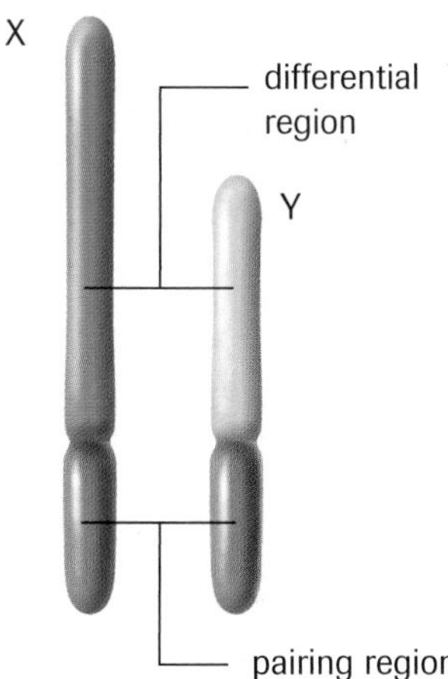

Figure 5
Sex chromosomes. Sections of the X and Y chromosomes are homologous; however, few genes are common to both chromosomes.

Barr Bodies

The difference between male and female autosomal (non-sex) cells lies within the X and Y chromosomes. Dr. Murray Barr, working at the University of Western Ontario in London, recognized a dark spot in some of the somatic cells of female mammals during the interphase of meiosis. This spot proved to be the sex chromatin, which results when one of the X chromosomes in females randomly becomes inactive in each cell. This dark spot is now called a **Barr body** in honour of its discoverer. This discovery revealed that not all female cells are identical; some cells have one X chromosome inactive, while some have the other. This means that some cells may express a certain trait while others express its alternate form, even though all cells are genetically identical. For example, if a human female is heterozygous for the skin disorder *anhidrotic ectodermal dysplasia*, she will have patches of skin that contain sweat glands and patches that do not. This mosaic of expression is typical of X chromosome activation and inactivation. In normal skin, the X chromosome with the recessive allele is inactivated and sweat glands are produced. In the afflicted skin patches, the X chromosome with the recessive allele is activated and no sweat glands are produced.

recessive lethal a trait that, when both recessive alleles are present, results in death or severe malformation of the offspring. Usually, recessive traits occur more frequently in males.

Barr body a small, dark spot of chromatin located in the nucleus of a female mammalian cell

Barr Body Formation
Listen to a discussion of the formation of Barr bodies and mosaic phenotypes in females.

www.science.nelson.com 

LAB EXERCISE 19.A

Report Checklist

- ○ Purpose
- ○ Problem
- ○ Hypothesis
- ○ Prediction
- ○ Design
- ○ Materials
- ○ Procedure
- ○ Evidence
- ● Analysis
- ○ Evaluation
- ○ Synthesis

Tracing the Hemophilia Gene

A pedigree chart provides a means of tracing the inheritance of a particular trait from parents through successive generations of offspring. Hemophilia A is a blood-clotting disorder that occurs in about one in 7000 males. The disorder is associated with a recessive gene located on the X chromosome, normally represented as X^h. Normal blood clotting is controlled by a dominant gene, X^H. The fact that a female must inherit one of the mutated alleles from her mother and another of the mutated alleles from her father helps explain why this disorder is very rare in females. Males, on the other hand, only need to inherit one recessive allele to express the disorder.

Purpose

To use pedigree charts to trace the hemophilia gene from Queen Victoria

Evidence

See **Figure 6**.

Analysis

1. Study the pedigree chart of Queen Victoria and Prince Albert (**Figure 6**). Note the legend at top right.

(a) Who was Queen Victoria's father?

(b) How many children did Queen Victoria and Prince Albert have?

2. Locate Alice of Hesse and Leopold, Duke of Albany, on the pedigree chart.

(c) Using the legend, provide the genotypes of both Alice of Hesse and Leopold.

3. Locate the royal family of Russia on the pedigree chart by finding Alexandra. Alexandra, a descendant of Queen Victoria, married Nikolas II, Czar of Russia. Nikolas and Alexandra had four girls (only Anastasia is labelled), and one son, Alexis.

(d) Explain why Alexis was the only child with hemophilia.

(e) Is it possible for a female to be hemophilic? If not, explain why not. If so, identify a male and female from the pedigree chart who would be capable of producing a hemophilic, female offspring.

(f) On the basis of probability, calculate the number of Victoria's and Albert's children who would be carriers of the hemophilic trait.

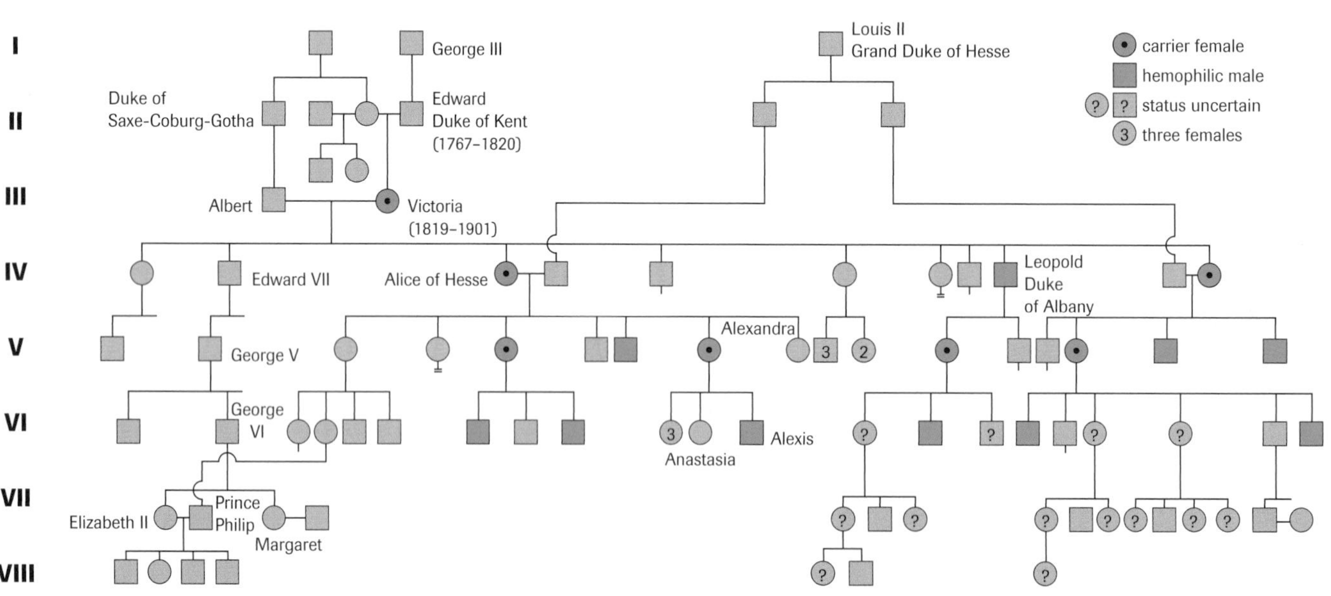

Figure 6

EXPLORE an issue

Report Checklist

- Issue
- Resolution
- Design
- Evidence
- Analysis
- Evaluation

Genetic Screening

Screening for inherited diseases can be carried out by various methods, including detailed pedigrees and biochemical testing for known disorders. Prenatal ("before birth") diagnosis can determine the presence of many genetic conditions in the unborn fetus. Amniocentesis involves the extraction of a small sample of fluid from the amnion, the membranous sac around the fetus. Chorionic villi sampling (CVS) involves withdrawing cells from the chorion, a fluid-filled membranous sac that surrounds the amnion. CVS can yield results earlier than amniocentesis, as early as in the ninth week of pregnancy.

Before the development of a process that permitted the extraction of insulin from animals, the children of parents who passed on two copies of the recessive allele for diabetes died at a young age. Today, genetic screening can tell potential parents if they carry this allele (**Figure 7**). Huntington disease is a neurological disorder caused by a dominant allele that only begins to express itself later in life. The disease is characterized by the rapid deterioration of nerve control, eventually leading to death. Early detection of this disease by genetic screening is possible.

By having knowledge of a genetic disorder prior to birth, parents will have the opportunity to be better prepared to cope with any additional challenges the disorder may bring. Some parents may choose to terminate a pregnancy based on the results of genetic screening. This use of genetic screening is controversial.

- In small groups, research the issue of using genetic screening to detect inherited conditions. Find other ways of dealing with genetic disorders instead of genetic screening. You may wish to focus your research on one of the conditions described above.
- List the points and counterpoints against genetic screening uncovered by your group. After considering each of these, and any alternative means of dealing with genetic disorders that you found, write a statement that outlines your group's position on this issue.
- Prepare to defend your group's position in a class discussion.

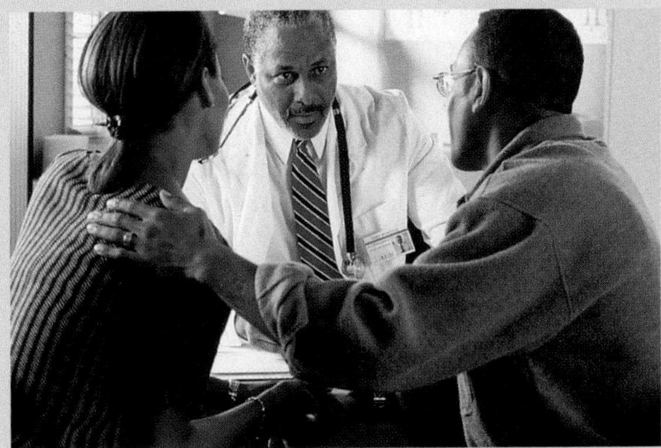

Figure 7
A genetic counsellor helps a couple to assess their risks of having children with inherited diseases.

EXTENSION

The Pros and Cons of Genetic Screening

This audio clip discusses some of the advantages and disadvantages associated with genetic screening practices in humans.

www.science.nelson.com 

WEB Activity

Simulation—Amniocentesis

Amniocentesis involves removing cells from the amniotic fluid, without damaging the fetus. Watch this animated simulation of amniocentesis to see how the cells are gathered and how they are used.

www.science.nelson.com 

INVESTIGATION 19.1 *Introduction*

Sex-Linked Traits

In this activity, you will cross *Drosophila* that carry genes for sex-linked traits, using virtual fruit fly software. To determine if a trait is sex-linked, you will perform two sets of crosses. In the first set of crosses, you will confirm that a trait is sex-linked using males and females with and without a trait. How will you set up the crosses to get the data you will need? In the second set of crosses, you will determine the phenotypic ratios in offspring of the F_1 generation and observe the frequency of one trait in the male and in the female offspring. What ratio would you expect for a sex-linked trait?

Report Checklist

- ● Purpose
- ○ Problem
- ● Hypothesis
- ● Prediction
- ● Design
- ○ Materials
- ○ Procedure
- ● Evidence
- ● Analysis
- ● Evaluation
- ○ Synthesis

To perform this investigation, turn to page 652. 

SUMMARY Chromosomes and Genetics

- The chromosomal theory of inheritance:
  - Chromosomes carry genes, the units of heredity.
  - Each chromosome contains many different genes.
  - Paired chromosomes segregate during meiosis. Each sex cell or gamete has half the number of chromosomes found in a somatic cell.
  - Chromosomes assort independently during meiosis. This means that each gamete receives one member from each pair of chromosomes, and that each chromosome pair has no influence on the movement of any other chromosome pair.
- Females have two X chromosomes. Males have one X and one Y chromosome.
- Sex-linked traits are controlled by genes located on the sex chromosomes. A recessive trait located on the X chromosome is more likely to express itself in males than in females, since males need only one copy of the recessive allele while females need two.
- Female somatic cells can be identified by Barr bodies, which are actually dormant X chromosomes.

Section 19.1 Questions

1. Describe how the work of Walter S. Sutton and Theodor Boveri advanced our understanding of genetics.
2. How do sex cells differ from somatic cells?
3. Describe how Thomas Morgan's work with *Drosophila* advanced the study of genetics.
4. Identify two different sex-linked traits in humans.
5. What are Barr bodies?
6. A recessive sex-linked allele *(h)* located on the X chromosome increases blood-clotting time, causing hemophilia.
   (a) With the aid of a Punnett square, explain how a hemophilic offspring can be born to two normal parents.
   (b) Can any of the female offspring develop hemophilia? Explain.
7. In humans, the recessive allele that causes a form of red–green colour-blindness *(c)* is found on the X chromosome.
   (a) Identify the F_1 generation from a colour-blind father and a mother who is homozygous for colour vision.
   (b) Identify the F_1 generation from a father who has colour vision and a mother who is heterozygous for colour vision.
   (c) Use a Punnett square to identify parents that could produce a daughter who is colour-blind.

Gene Linkage and Crossover 19.2

It is often said that great science occurs when good questions are asked. Like Mendel, Morgan asked great questions when he observed a few unexpected gene combinations when he performed some dihybrid crosses with *Drosophila*. Morgan had found a number of obvious mutations in *Drosophila*. He had noted a number of genes in *Drosophila* that had different alleles that were easy to observe, which he used in many genetic experiments. When he carried out dihybrid crosses of *Drosophila*, Morgan observed that in some of the crosses, almost all the offspring had the same combination of traits as did the parents. Morgan's hypothesis to explain these observations, which he tested with further experiments, gave further support to the theory that the genes are located on chromosomes.

Morgan first crossed *Drosophila* homozygous for wild-type body-colour (*AA*) and straight wings (*BB*) with *Drosophila* homozygous for black body-colour (*aa*) and curved wings (*bb*). The resulting F_1 generation was therefore heterozygous for both traits (*AaBb*). When members of the F_1 generation mated among themselves, the F_2 generation showed far less variability than expected. Since this was a dihybrid cross, Morgan had predicted that the F_2 generation would have a 9:3:3:1 phenotypic ratio, as was observed in the work of Mendel. Instead, nearly all the individuals with wild-type body-colour had straight wings and nearly all those with black body-colour had curved wings.

Why did the observed ratios differ so much from the predicted ratio? From these observations, Morgan concluded that the two genes must not have undergone independent segregation. For this to be true, both genes would have to be located on the same chromosome. In other words, the genes for body colour and wing shape must be linked genes.

Figure 1 illustrates what would happen to the alleles in this cross during meiosis, if Morgan's hypothesis was correct and the genes for body colour and wing shape were linked genes.

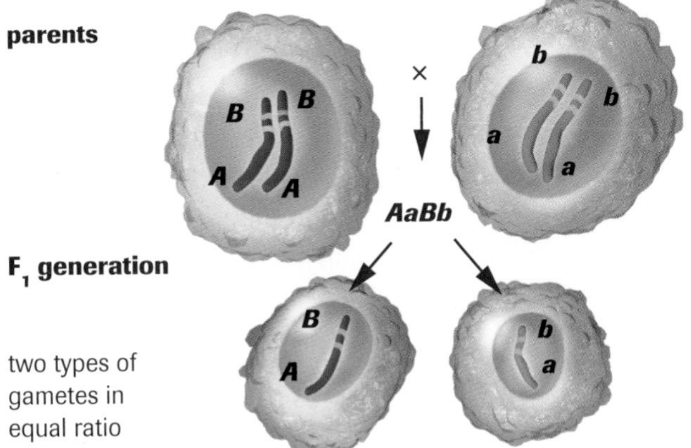

Figure 1
During meiosis, homologous chromosomes (represented as green and red chromosomes) move to opposite poles. One gamete carries the *AB* alleles and the other carries the *ab* alleles.

When two gametes from this cross unite, the new individual is heterozygous for both traits (*AaBb*). Remember that one parent carried the dominant alleles of the two linked genes (*A* is linked to *B*) and the other parent carried the recessive alleles (*a* is linked to *b*). Morgan, therefore, predicted that the F_2 generation would have a 3:1 phenotypic ratio (three flies with wild-type body-colour and straight wings to every one with black body-colour and curved wings), as shown in **Figure 2**, on the next page.

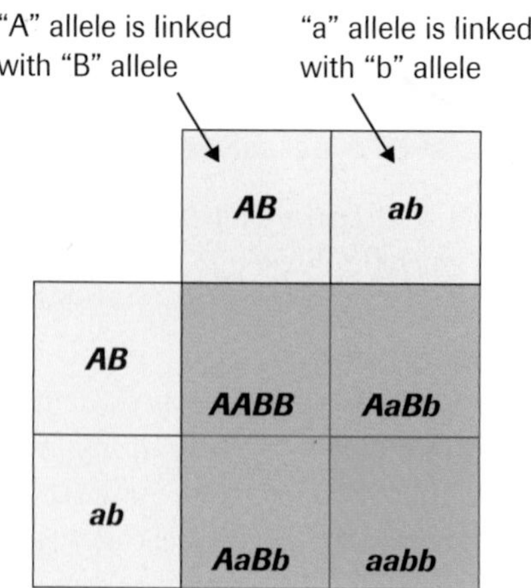

Figure 2
Punnett square analysis, assuming that all the gametes carry the same alleles as the parent. The expected phenotypic ratio is three wild-type body-colour, straight wings to one black body-colour, curved wings.

Morgan was able to find a number of linked genes. Some of these are shown in **Table 1**.

Table 1 Linked Genes Identified by Morgan's Research on *Drosophila*

Trait	Dominant/Recessive	Location
wingless *(wg)*	recessive lethal (all wingless offspring are born dead)	chromosome 2
curly wings *(Cy)*	dominant	chromosome 2
purple eyes *(pr)*	recessive nonlethal	chromosome 2
stubble bristles *(Sb)*	dominant	chromosome 3
ebony body *(e)*	recessive nonlethal	chromosome 3
miniature wings *(m)*	sex-linked recessive	chromosome 4
cut wings *(ct)*	sex-linked recessive	chromosome 4
white eyes *(w)*	sex-linked recessive	chromosome 4
vermillion eyes *(v)*	sex-linked recessive	chromosome 4

Crossing Over

Mendel had explained most of his observations by hypothesizing that the two genes were both on the same chromosome. By the Punnett square analysis shown in **Figure 2**, only two different phenotypes are predicted for these linked genes. This was not what Morgan observed. In a small number of flies from the dihybrid cross, the offspring had a different combination of traits than the parents. **Table 2** shows the numbers of the different phenotypes and their predicted genotypes. Where did the new allele combinations come from? Where did the new combinations of the two traits come from?

Table 2 Observed Progeny (F_2) of *AaBb* × *AaBb* F_1 Parents

Phenotype	Number	Possible genotype
wild-type body-colour, straight wings	290	*AABB* or *AaBb*
black body-colour, curved wings	92	*Aabb*
wild-type body-colour, curved wings	9	*AAbb* or *Aabb* indicated recombinations
black body-colour, straight wings	9	*AaBB* or *aaBb* indicated recombinations

Recall that chromosomes sometimes undergo crossing over during meiosis. During crossing over, a segment of DNA on one homologous chromosome is exchanged with the corresponding segment on the other homologous chromosome (**Figure 3**), recombining the set of genes on the chromosomes. Crossing over occurs in meiosis, during synapsis. Through crossing over, the gene combinations on a single chromosome can be altered as it is passed from generation to generation. In this cross, gametes with the gene combination *Ab* and *aB* would not occur without crossing over.

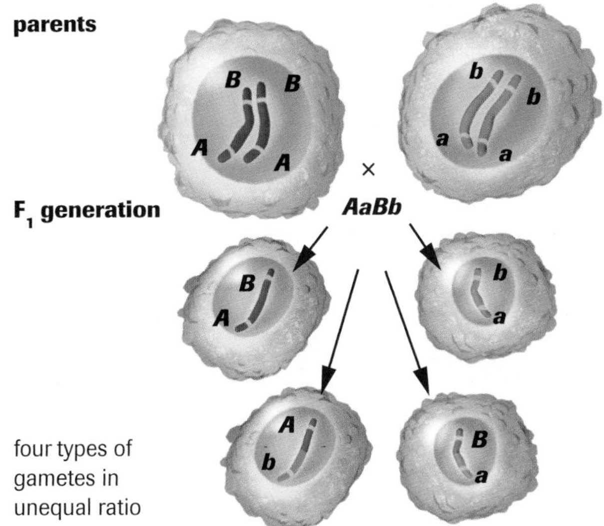

Figure 3
Consider the green chromosome to have been inherited from the father and the red from the mother. In the gametes, a chromosome that has undergone crossing has sections that are maternal (coming from the mother) and sections that are paternal (coming from the father). When the maternal and paternal homologous chromosomes carry different alleles, they may exchange alleles.

Mapping Chromosomes

As other traits in *Drosophila* were studied, it became clear that there were groups of linked genes. These **linkage groups** corresponded to different chromosomes. Furthermore, particular genes were always found at the same location (**locus**) on the chromosome. If this were not true, crossing over would not result in the exact exchange of alleles.

linkage group a group of linked genes on a chromosome

locus (plural, **loci**) a specific location along a chromosome where a particular gene is found

Morgan's experiments also showed that the frequency of crossovers between any two genes in a linkage group was always the same. The frequency of crossing over between any two genes can be stated as a percent:

$$\text{crossover percentage} = \frac{\text{number of recombinations}}{\text{total number of offspring}} \times 100\ \%$$

The crossover percentage in the offspring shown in **Table 2**, on the previous page, is

$$\text{crossover percentage} = \frac{18}{400} \times 100\ \%$$
$$= 4.5\ \%$$

The percentage of crossovers is related to the actual physical distance of the two genes on the chromosome. Genes located farther away from one another cross over at higher frequencies than genes located close together. Two genes with a crossover percentage of 1 % are much closer to one another than two genes with a crossover percentage of 12 %. Armed with this knowledge, geneticists were able to build a map of the chromosomes of *Drosophila* (**Figure 4**, next page).

When genes are in the correct order on a chromosome map, the map distances between the different genes is additive. This fact allows us to place genes in their proper order, based on the percentage crossover values between the different genes.

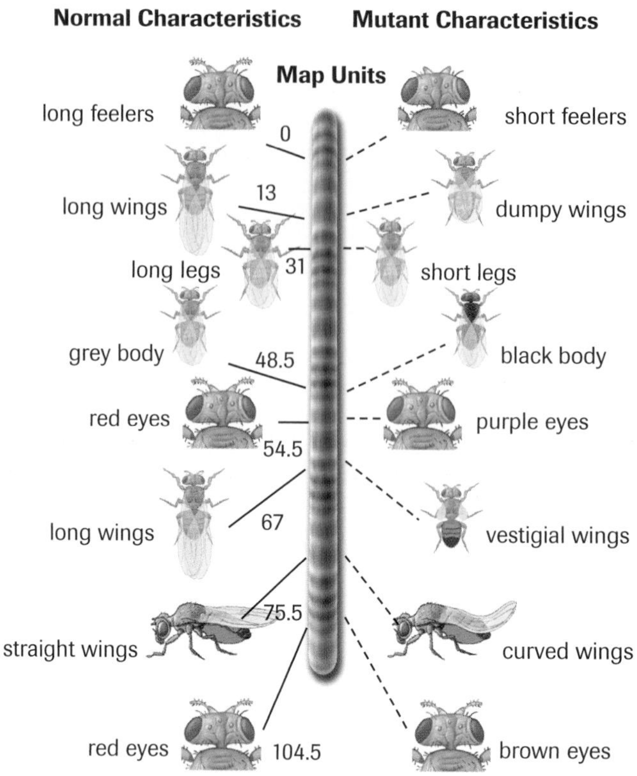

Figure 4
Gene mapping of chromosome 2 for *Drosophila melanogaster*. Note that many genes are located on one chromosome.

SAMPLE exercise 1

From crosses between different *Drosophila*, a geneticist finds that the crossover frequency between gene *A* and gene *B* is 12 %, the crossover frequency between gene *B* and gene *C* is 7 %, and between gene *A* and gene *C* is 5 %. What is the order and relative distances of these three genes on the chromosome?

Solution

If gene A were in the middle, then the sum of the distances between B and A and A and C must equal the distance between B and C. These distances are not equal, so A is not in the middle **(Figure 5)**.

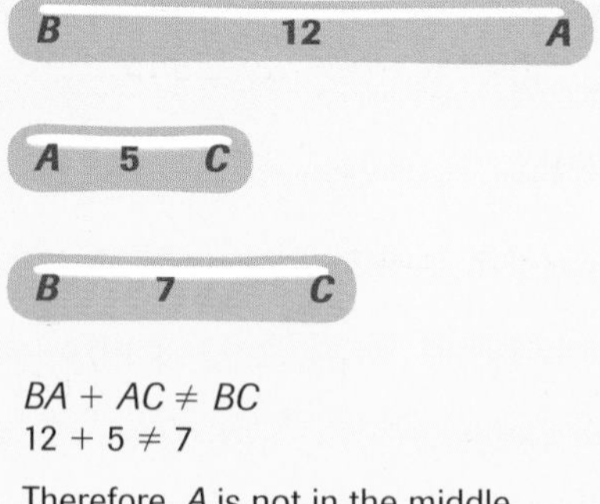

$BA + AC \neq BC$
$12 + 5 \neq 7$

Therefore, *A* is not in the middle.

Figure 5

If gene B were in the middle, then the sum of the distances between A and B and between B and C must equal the distance between A and C. These distances are not equal, so B is not in the middle (**Figure 6**, next page).

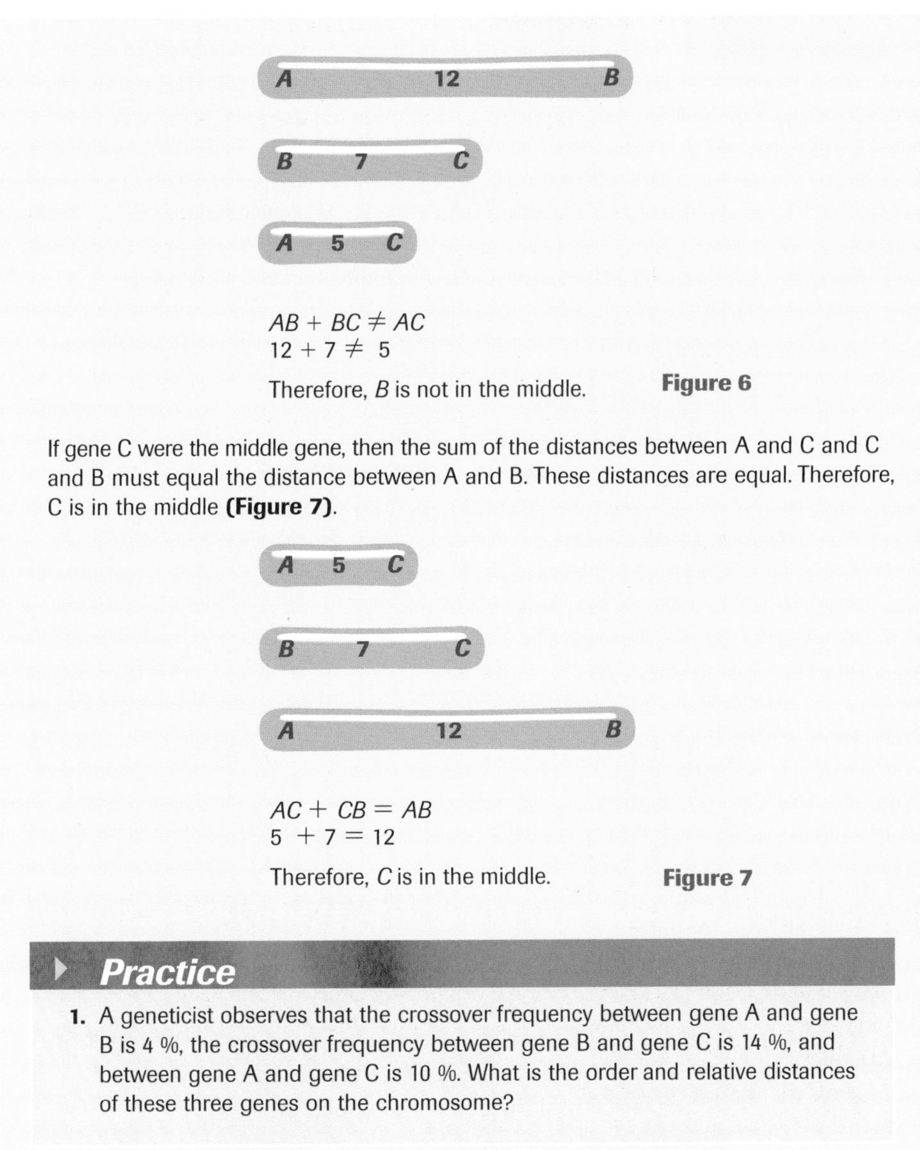

$AB + BC \neq AC$

$12 + 7 \neq 5$

Therefore, *B* is not in the middle.

Figure 6

If gene C were the middle gene, then the sum of the distances between A and C and C and B must equal the distance between A and B. These distances are equal. Therefore, C is in the middle **(Figure 7)**.

$AC + CB = AB$

$5 + 7 = 12$

Therefore, *C* is in the middle.

Figure 7

Practice

1. A geneticist observes that the crossover frequency between gene A and gene B is 4 %, the crossover frequency between gene B and gene C is 14 %, and between gene A and gene C is 10 %. What is the order and relative distances of these three genes on the chromosome?

LAB EXERCISE 19.B

Report Checklist

○ Purpose	○ Design	● Analysis
○ Problem	○ Materials	○ Evaluation
○ Hypothesis	○ Procedure	○ Synthesis
○ Prediction	● Evidence	

Mapping Chromosomes

A. H. Sturtevant, a student who worked with Thomas Morgan, hypothesized that

- genes are located in a linear series along a chromosome, much like beads on a string,
- genes that are closer together will be separated less frequently than those that are far apart,
- and that crossover frequencies can be used to construct gene maps.

Sturtevant's work with *Drosophila* helped establish techniques for chromosome maps.

Procedure

1. Examine the picture of a chromosome (**Figure 8**, next page). Crossing over takes place when breaks occur in the chromatids of homologous chromosomes during meiosis. The chromatids break and join with the chromatids of homologous chromosomes. This causes an exchange of alleles between chromosomes.

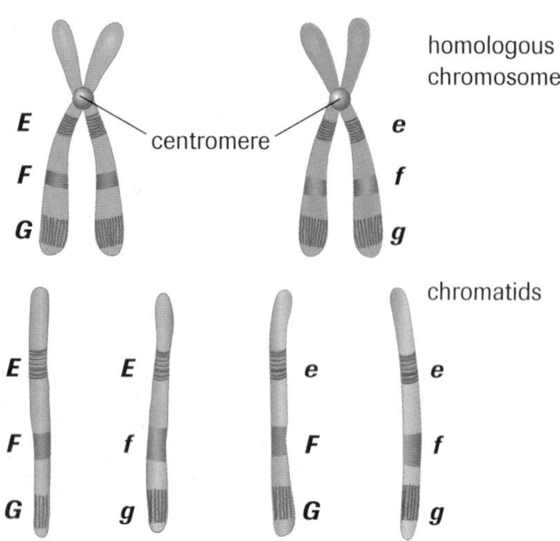

Figure 8
Crossing over

(a) Circle the areas of the chromatids that show crossing over.

(b) Using the diagram above, which genes appear farthest apart? (Choose from *EF*, *FG*, or *EG*.)

(c) Which alleles have been exchanged?

2. In 1913, Sturtevant used crossover frequencies of *Drosophila* to construct chromosome maps. To determine map distances, he arbitrarily assigned one recombination for every 100 fertilized eggs. For example, genes that had a crossover frequency of 15 % were said to be 15 units apart. Genes that had a 5 % recombination rate were much closer. These genes are 5 units apart.

(d) Using the data in **Table 3**, determine the distance between genes *E* and *F*.

Table 3

Cross	Offspring	Frequency (%)
EF × *ef*	*EF* + *ef* (from parent)	94
	Ef + *eF* (recombination)	6

(e) Would the distance between genes *e* and *f* be identical?

3. Use the data in **Table 4** to construct a complete gene map.

(f) What is the distance between genes *E* and *G*?

(g) What is the distance between genes *F* and *G*?

Table 4

Cross	Offspring	Frequency (%)
EF × *ef*	*EF* + *ef* (from parent)	94
	Ef + *eF* (recombination)	6
EG × *eg*	*EG* + *eg* (from parent)	90
	Eg + *eG* (recombination)	10
FG × *fg*	*FG* + *fg* (from parent)	96
	Fg + *fG* (recombination)	4

Analysis

(h) What mathematical evidence indicates that gene *F* must be found between genes *E* and *G*?

(i) Draw the gene map to scale. (Use 1 cm to represent 1 unit.)

(j) For a series of breeding experiments, a linkage group composed of genes *W*, *X*, *Y*, and *Z* was found to show the gene combinations in **Table 5**. (All recombinations are expressed per 100 fertilized eggs.)

Table 5

Genes	*W*	*X*	*Y*	*Z*
W	-	5	7	8
X	5	-	2	3
Y	7	2	-	1
Z	8	3	1	-

Construct a gene map. Show the relative positions of each of the genes along the chromosome and indicate distances in map units.

(k) For a series of breeding experiments, a linkage group composed of genes *A*, *B*, *C*, and *D* was found to show the gene combinations in **Table 6**. (All recombinations are expressed per 100 fertilized eggs.) Construct a gene map. Show the relative positions of each of the genes along the chromosome and indicate distances in map units.

Table 6

Genes	*A*	*B*	*C*	*D*
A	-	12	15	4
B	12	-	3	8
C	15	3	-	11
D	4	8	11	-

Using Marker Genes

Earlier in the chapter, you learned that genes located on the same chromosome are usually inherited together. **Marker genes** can be used to follow the inheritance of a linked trait. Marker genes give rise to an easily identifiable phenotype and are used to trace the inheritance of other genes that are difficult to identify. The marker gene must be located on the same chromosome and, ideally, at a very small distance from the gene being traced.

marker gene a gene that confers an easily identifiable phenotype and is used to trace the inheritance of other genes that are difficult to identify; it must be located on the same chromosome, and ideally, at a very small distance from the gene being followed

Dr. Ram Mehta, president of PBR Laboratories in Edmonton, uses gene markers to identify possible gene mutations in yeast. The yeast cells are treated with agents that might alter the genetic structure of the yeast, such as various chemicals, or environmental agents such as radiation. Since the chemical structure of DNA in human chromosomes and yeast chromosomes is the same, the yeast provides a model that helps scientists to predict how any given agent may affect human chromosomes.

Normally, yeast colonies are an off-white colour. This colour is determined by a dominant gene. Pink or red colonies indicate that a mutation in this normal, dominant gene has taken place (**Figure 9**). The red and pink colour is determined by one of two marker genes that are located along different sections of the chromosome. The marker genes are expressed only when the normal, dominant gene for colour has been inactivated by a mutation. Colonies will show both pink and red colour only when crossing over has occurred. Crossing over indicates that the agent being tested broke apart the yeast chromosome containing the marker genes. Mutation rates can be calculated from the frequency with which pink or red colonies appear.

Figure 9
Mutated yeast colonies

SUMMARY *Gene Linkage and Crossover*

- Linked genes do not segregate independently because they are situated on the same chromosome. Linked genes can undergo recombination due to crossing over.
- Crossing over occurs more frequently between genes located relatively far apart than for those located relatively close together.
- Genetic linkage maps can be created by sorting genes according to the percentage crossover values.

Section 19.2 Questions

1. Why does gene linkage limit the variability of an organism?
2. Does crossing over increase or decrease the variability of an organism? Explain.
3. Create a chromosome map for each set of three genes from the given information.
   (a) The crossover frequency between gene A and gene B is 23 %, the crossover frequency between gene B and gene C is 11 %, and between gene A and gene C is 12 %.
   (b) The crossover frequency between gene X and gene Z is 8.5 %, the crossover frequency between gene Y and gene Z is 2.25 %, and between gene Y and gene X is 6.25 %.

19.3 DNA Is the Hereditary Material

Figure 1
DNA contains the information that ensures that pea plants produce seeds that grow into other pea plants.

continuity of life a succession of offspring that share structural similarities with those of their parents

The nucleus of every cell in your body contains deoxyribonucleic acid, or DNA. DNA is found in the cells of all organisms, from mushrooms to trees, from sponges to mammals. Scientists' fascination with DNA arises from the fact that it is the only molecule known that is capable of replicating itself. Sugar molecules, protein molecules, and fat molecules cannot build duplicates of themselves. DNA can duplicate itself, thereby permitting cell division.

Sometimes referred to as the language of life, the genetic code is contained in 46 separate chromosomes in your body. Characteristics such as your hair colour, skin colour, and nose length are all coded within the chemical messages of DNA. Packed within the DNA are all the instructions that make you unique. Unless you are an identical twin, your DNA code is distinctively one of a kind.

DNA contains instructions that ensure **continuity of life**, which we observe as similar structural traits between members of different generations. Pea plants produce seeds that grow into other pea plants because the DNA holds the chemical messages for the roots, stems, leaves, and seed pods of a pea (**Figure 1**). In a similar way, guinea pigs give birth to other guinea pigs, and humans procreate with other humans. However, you have learned that not all offspring are identical to their parents. The uniqueness of descendants can be explained by new combinations of genes and by mutations. In order to understand how genes affect the expression of an organism's traits, you will have to learn how DNA regulates the production of protein. Proteins are the structural components of cells. DNA, therefore, not only provides continuity of life, but also accounts for the diversity of life forms.

Finding the Material of Heredity

In 1869, twenty-five-year-old Swiss biochemist Friedrich Miescher extracted a viscous white substance from white blood cells deposited on the bandages of wounded soldiers. He named this slightly acidic, phosphorus and nitrogen-rich material nuclein because he found it within the nuclei of these cells. With further work, Miescher found that nuclein was comprised of both an acidic portion, which he called nucleic acid, and an alkaline portion. The alkaline portion was later determined to be protein. Several decades later, Miescher's single nucleic acid was shown to actually be two nucleic acids, one of which was renamed ribonucleic acid (RNA) and the other, deoxyribonucleic acid (DNA). Ongoing research gradually revealed the structure, function, and importance of the remarkable and complex DNA molecule and showed it to be the source of hereditary information. This knowledge in turn triggered revolutions in the biological sciences.

Early work aimed at finding the material of heredity focused on proteins as the most probable source. In 1943, Danish biologist Joachim Hammerling demonstrated that the nucleus was likely to be the region in which the hereditary material of the cell would be found. He was able to do this as a result of research involving the large single-celled green alga *Acetabularia.* This organism grows to an average length of 5 cm and has three distinct regions known as the cap, the stalk, and the foot.

Hammerling's experiments first involved cutting the cap off of some cells and the foot, which contains the nucleus, off of others. The cells whose caps were removed were able to regenerate new caps, but the cells whose feet had been removed were not able to regenerate new ones (**Figure 2**, next page). As a result, Hammerling hypothesized that the hereditary information was contained in the foot and, more specifically, the

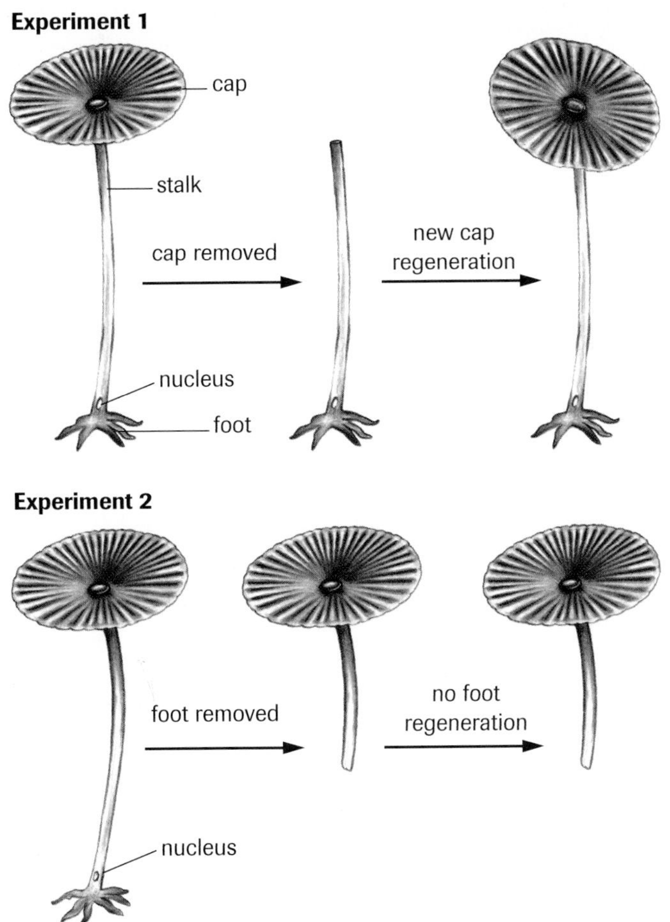

Figure 2
Hammerling's experiment strongly suggested that the hereditary material is located in the nucleus.

DID YOU KNOW?

One Man's Castle Is Another Man's Lab

Friedrich Miescher's discovery took place in the vaults of an old castle that had been converted to a laboratory. You can hear Miescher describe the process he used to isolate nuclein in an animation found by accessing the Nelson Web site.

www.science.nelson.com 

nucleus. To further test his hypothesis, he conducted additional experiments in which he transplanted stalks from a species of *Acetabularia* with a flowerlike cap onto the foot of another species with a disk-shaped cap. The caps that eventually developed on the transplanted stalks were all disk-shaped. Hammerling concluded that the instructions needed to build these new caps were very likely in the nucleus in the foot of the cell and not elsewhere.

Hammerling's results encouraged scientists to concentrate their search for the material of hereditary material on the nucleus and its contents. Proteins and DNA are present in the nucleus in large quantities, but DNA was initially thought to be too simple a material to account for the great variety seen in cells and cell processes, while proteins were already known to play a significant role in metabolic functions. However, work by British biologist Frederick Griffith on *Streptococcus pneumoniae*, in 1928, laid the foundation for later research. Canadian-born scientists Oswald Avery and Colin MacLeod, along with their American teammate Maclyn McCarty, built upon this work over a 14-year period culminating in 1944, and came to the conclusion that DNA was indeed the molecular material of heredity.

DID YOU KNOW?

DNA's Homes

DNA does not just reside in the nucleus. A small amount of DNA is also found in chloroplasts and mitochondria. The size of the genome varies depending on the species. Plants tend to have a larger mitochondrial genome compared with that of animals.

LAB EXERCISE 19.C

Evidence of Hereditary Material

Report Checklist		
○ Purpose	○ Design	● Analysis
○ Problem	○ Materials	● Evaluation
○ Hypothesis	○ Procedure	● Synthesis
○ Prediction	○ Evidence	

In the 1920s, Frederick Griffith, an English medical officer, started experimenting with *Streptococcus pneumoniae*. This bacterium, which causes pneumonia, exists in two forms. One form is surrounded by a polysaccharide coating called a capsule and is known as the S form because it forms smooth colonies on a culture dish. The second harmless form has no coating and is known as the R form because it forms rough colonies on a culture dish (**Figure 3**).

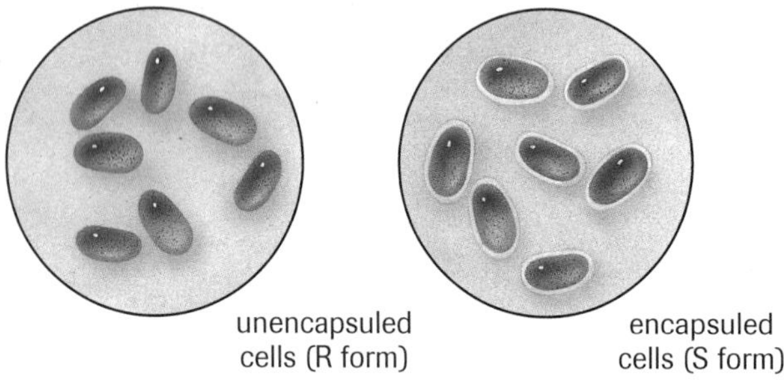

Figure 3
A representation of the two forms of *S. pneumoniae*

The following is an abbreviated summary of Griffith's procedures and results:

Procedure

1. Mouse A was injected with encapsulated cells (S form), while mouse B was injected with unencapsulated cells (R form).
2. Encapsulated (S-form) pneumococcal cells were heated, killed, and then injected into mouse C (**Figure 4**).
3. The heated encapsulated (S-form) cells were mixed with unencapsulated (R-form) cells. The mixture was grown on a special growth medium. Cells from the culture medium were injected into mouse D (**Figure 4**).

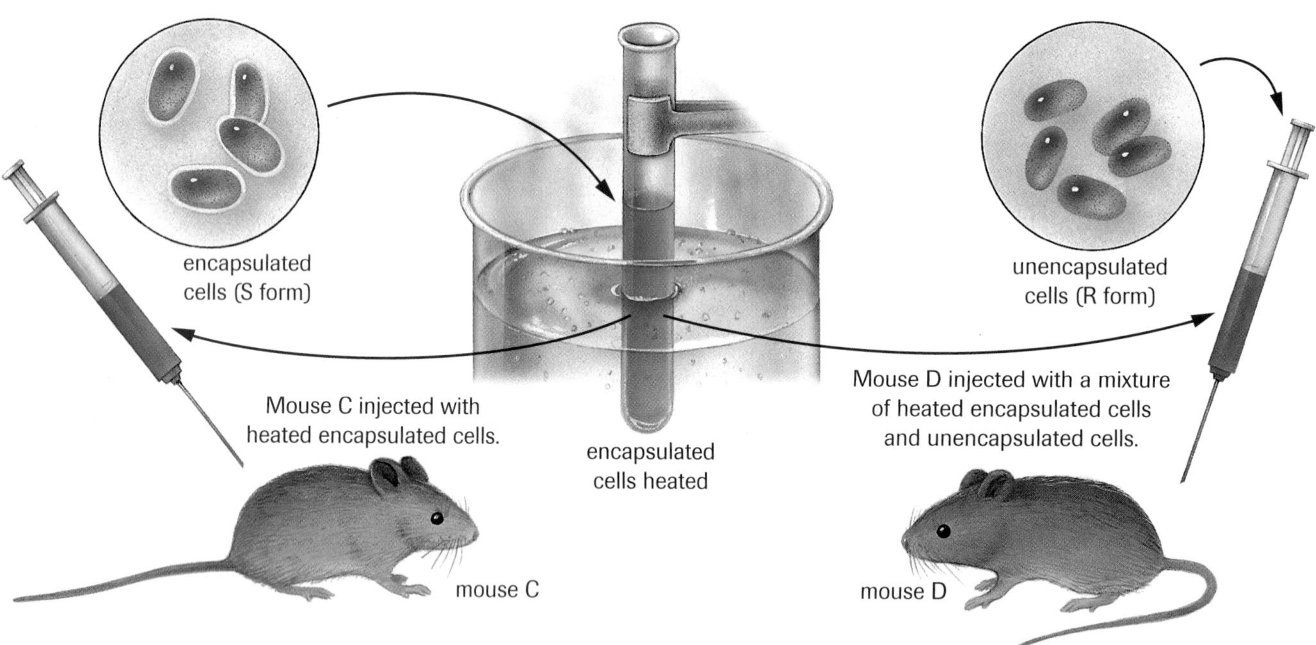

Figure 4
A visual outline of the procedure

LAB EXERCISE 19.C *continued*

Evidence

- Mouse A contracted pneumonia and died, while mouse B continued to live. Mouse B was sacrificed, and an autopsy was conducted on both mice. The autopsies revealed living S cells in mouse A's tissues and living R cells in mouse B's tissues.
- Mouse C continued to live. Mouse C was sacrificed and the autopsy revealed that no living S cells were found in the animal's tissues.
- Mouse D died. An autopsy indicated that the mouse had died of pneumonia; encapsulated (S-form) bacteria and unencapsulated (R-form) bacteria were isolated from the mouse.

Analysis and Evaluation

(a) What conclusions can you derive from the experimental results with mouse A and mouse B?

(b) Why might a scientist decide to repeat step 1 of this experimental procedure on other mice?

(c) What is the significance of the result with mouse C?

(d) Predict what would have happened to the mouse if the unencapsulated (R-form) cells had been heated and then injected. What would this step have represented in the experimental protocol?

(e) Would you have predicted that mouse D would die? Explain why or why not.

(f) A microscopic examination of the dead and live cell mixture (step 3) revealed cells with and without capsules. What influence did the heat-destroyed cells have on the unencapsulated cells?

(g) Griffith hypothesized that a chemical in the dead, heat-treated, encapsulated cells (step 3) must have altered the living unencapsulated cells and he dubbed this chemical phenomenon *transformation*. In 1944, Oswald Avery, Maclyn McCarty, and Colin MacLeod conducted experiments in test tubes with *Streptococcus pneumoniae* that led them to conclude that DNA is the *transforming principle*, as they called it, and not proteins, as was widely believed. In their experiments, what must have happened to the DNA when the cells divided?

Synthesis

(h) To discover the identity of the transforming principle, Avery and his associates ruptured heat-killed, encapsulated cells to release their contents. RNA, DNA, protein, and purified polysaccharide coats were isolated and were tested for transforming activity. Avery and his associates found that only R cells mixed with purified DNA isolated from dead S cells were transformed to S cells. When R cells were mixed with purified RNA, with the polysaccharide coat, or with protein extracted from dead S cells, only R cell colonies were isolated. Do these results support their hypothesis? Explain.

(i) Predict the experimental results of the following protocols. Support your prediction with a hypotheses.

- Polysaccharide-digesting enzymes are used to digest the encapsulated polysaccharide coat of the heated S form of the bacteria. The treated bacteria are then placed with unencapsulated pneumonia cells, which are then injected into a mouse.
- Heated encapsulated bacteria are treated with DNAase, a DNA-digesting enzyme. The treated bacteria are then mixed with unencapsulated pneumonia cells, which are injected into a mouse.
- All proteins are extracted from the heated encapsulated bacteria. The treated bacteria are then mixed with unencapsulated pneumonia cells, which are injected into a mouse.

(j) Based on the information provided, suggest improvements to the experimental protocols.

Figure 5
Dr. Oswald Avery

Figure 6
Dr. Colin MacLeod

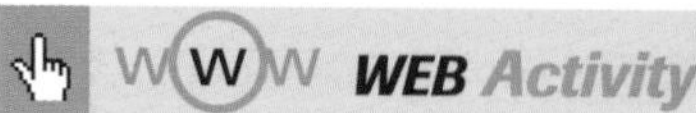

Canadian Achievers—Avery and MacLeod

Canadian-born scientists Dr. Oswald Avery and Dr. Colin MacLeod spent their early years as scientists in Nova Scotia, where they were born. They met in New York, where, together with American scientist Maclyn McCarty, they painstakingly isolated components of pneumococci (*Streptococcus pneumoniae*) for over a decade before identifying DNA as the transforming principle. You can find more information on this classic experiment in an animation by accessing the Nelson science Web site.

www.science.nelson.com 

Confirming the Chemical of Heredity

Frederick Griffith's work in the 1920s began because he was trying to develop a vaccine against pneumonia caused by *Streptococcus pneumoniae*. However, his unexpected experimental observations, followed by the work of Avery, McCarty, and MacLeod, led scientists to begin questioning the initial assumption within the scientific community that the material of heredity was protein. What was now needed was experimental evidence that would clearly and conclusively indicate that DNA was indeed the material of heredity. This evidence was to come some six years after the work of Avery's team as the result of an innovative experiment.

Alfred D. Hershey and Martha Chase

It was not until 1952 that DNA was accepted as the hereditary material. That year, American scientists Alfred Hershey and Martha Chase conducted experiments using a virus (**bacteriophage** T2) that infects a bacterial host (**Figure 7**). Bacteriophages (commonly called phages) consist of two components: DNA and a protein coat. A bacteriophage infects a bacterial cell by attaching to the outer surface of the cell and injecting its hereditary information into it. This leads to the production of thousands of new viruses, which then burst out of the cell, resulting in its death. The results of Hershey and Chase's experiments showed that only the DNA from the bacteriophage, and not the protein coat, enters the bacteria to direct the synthesis of new viral DNA and new viral protein coats.

bacteriophage a virus that infects bacteria

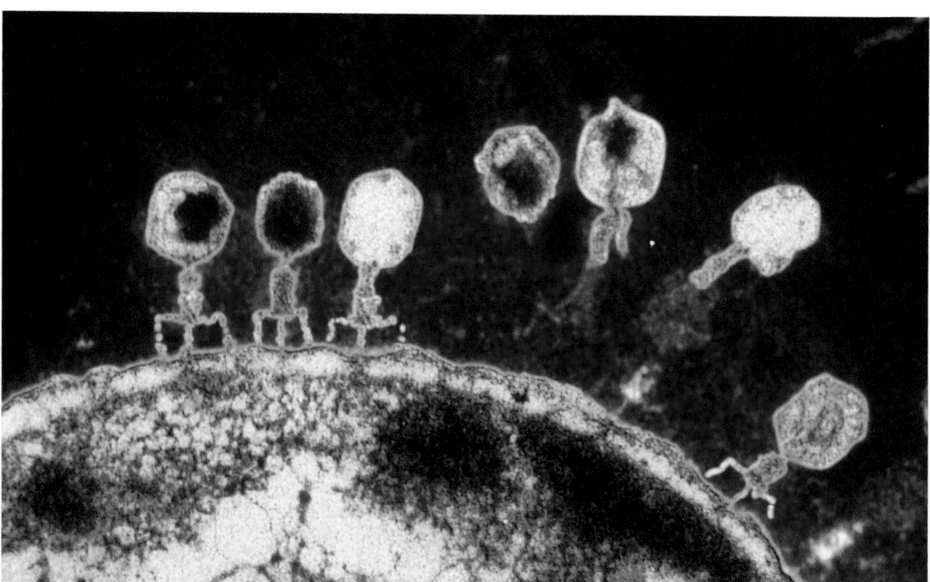

Figure 7
Micrograph of a bacteriophage injecting its DNA into a bacterial cell

Proteins contain sulfur but no phosphorus, whereas DNA contains phosphorus but no sulfur. Therefore, to track the location of DNA and proteins, Hershey and Chase tagged the viral proteins with an **isotope** of sulfur, ^{35}S, and the viral DNA with an isotope of phosphorus, ^{32}P. ^{35}S and ^{32}P are **radioisotopes** of sulfur and phosphorus, respectively. They are easy to track in an experiment because radioisotopes are unstable and the radiation that they emit as they decay can be measured.

isotope one of two or more atoms of the same element containing the same number of protons but a different number of neutrons

radioisotope an unstable isotope that decays spontaneously by emitting radiation

Each type of tagged bacteriophage was allowed to infect a separate batch of bacterial host cells and to multiply. The bacterial cells were put into a blender to remove the protein coats of the viruses from the surfaces of the bacteria. The mixtures were then subjected to centrifugation to isolate the individual components (bacteria as a pellet and viral particles in the liquid). The bacterial cells that were exposed to viruses containing radioactively labelled DNA contained ^{32}P. The bacterial cells that were exposed to viruses whose protein coats were radioactively tagged with ^{35}S did not contain any radioactivity; instead, the radioactive ^{35}S was found in the culture medium (**Figure 8**). These experiments illustrate that phosphorus-rich DNA was injected into the bacterial cells. In addition, Hershey and Chase found that the bacteriophages in both experiments reproduced and destroyed the bacterial cells that they had infected. This observation further supported the claim that DNA entering the host bacterial cell carries all the genetic information. Hershey and Chase's experiments ended the debate. DNA was accepted as the hereditary material.

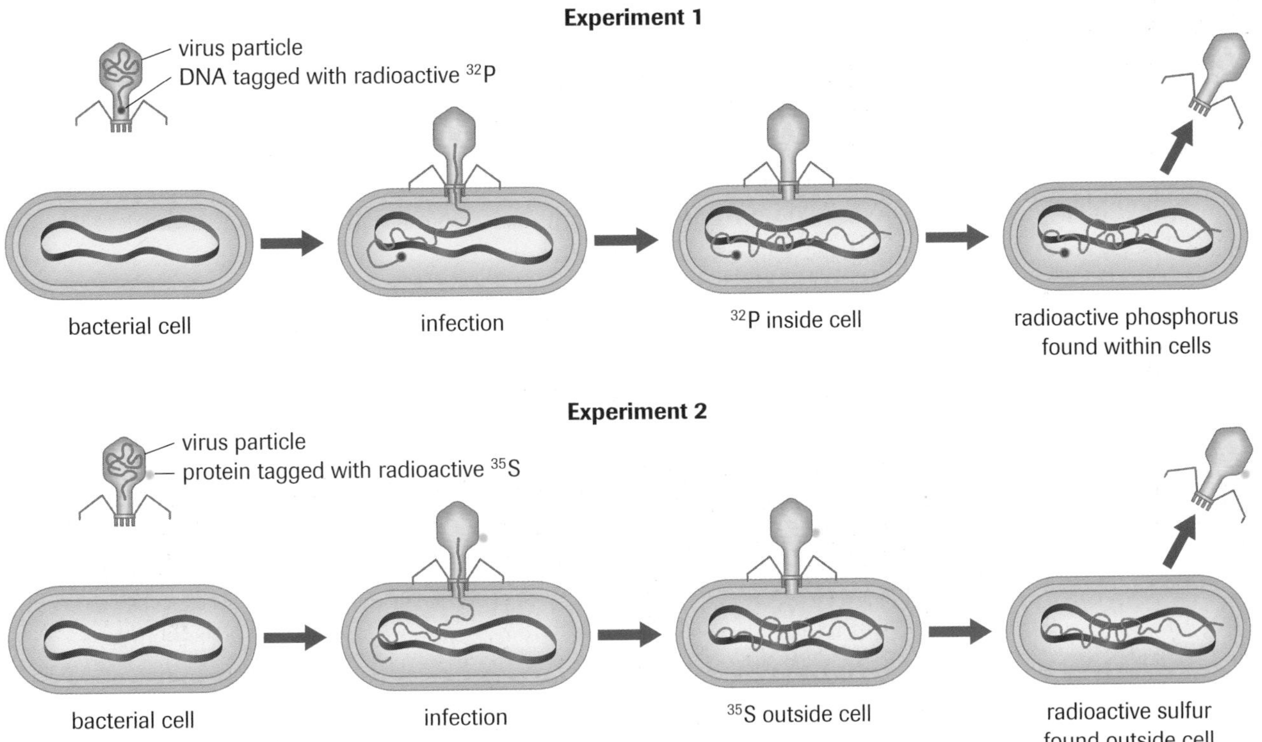

Figure 8
Hershey and Chase's experiment conclusively showed that DNA was the hereditary material.

Figure 9
Francis Crick and James Watson were awarded the Nobel Prize for Physiology or Medicine in 1962 for deducing the structure of DNA.

The Race to Reveal the Structure

When scientists confirmed that DNA was the material of heredity, their focus shifted to understanding how it works. Part of that understanding would come from knowing its structure since, as in other subjects, structure in biology provides many clues about function. In the race to be the first to discover the structure of DNA, scientists around the world employed emerging technologies to help them gain new insights into this mysterious "molecule of life." In the end, the honour would go James Watson and Francis Crick (**Figure 9**).

James Watson was considered a child prodigy when he entered the University of Chicago at the age of 15. He began studying ornithology, but eventually turned his attention to genetics and molecular biology. In 1951, he began studies at England's Cambridge University, where he met Francis Crick, a physicist who had served with the British army during World War II. Each would bring to bear his experience from a different area of science to interpret and synthesize the experimental data that were rapidly mounting.

One source of important data came from the Cambridge laboratory of Maurice Wilkins, where researcher Rosalind Franklin used a technique called X-ray diffraction to help determine the structure of the DNA molecule. Another source of data involved the comparison of the chemical structure of DNA molecules in different organisms. By this time it had long been known that DNA is comprised of chains of molecules called **nucleotides**. The nucleotides consist of a 5-carbon cyclic ring structure called a **deoxyribose sugar** (**Figure 10**) having one of four **nitrogenous bases** attached to its 1′ carbon and a **phosphate group** attached to it 5′ carbon (**Figure 11**). The carbons in the sugar are identified by the numbers one to five and a prime (′) symbol to distinguish them from the carbons in the nitrogenous base. The four nitrogenous bases are adenine (A), guanine (G), thymine (T), and cytosine (C). Adenine and guanine are double-ringed structures classed as purines, while thymine and cytosine are single-ringed structures classed as pyrimidines. The only difference in the nucleotides is in their bases.

nucleotide a molecule having a five-carbon sugar with a nitrogenous base attached to its 1′ carbon and a phosphate group attached to its 5′ carbon

deoxyribose sugar a sugar molecule containing five carbons that has lost the –OH (hydroxyl group) on its 2′ position

nitrogenous base an alkaline, cyclic molecule containing nitrogen

phosphate group a group of four oxygen atoms surrounding a central phosphorus atom found in the backbone of DNA

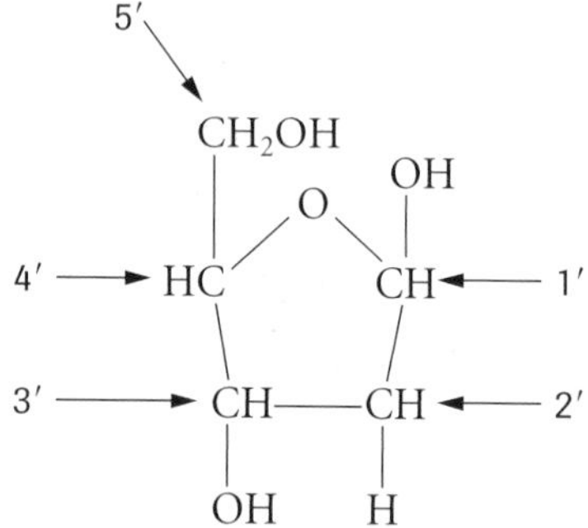

Figure 10
A deoxyribose sugar with numbered carbons

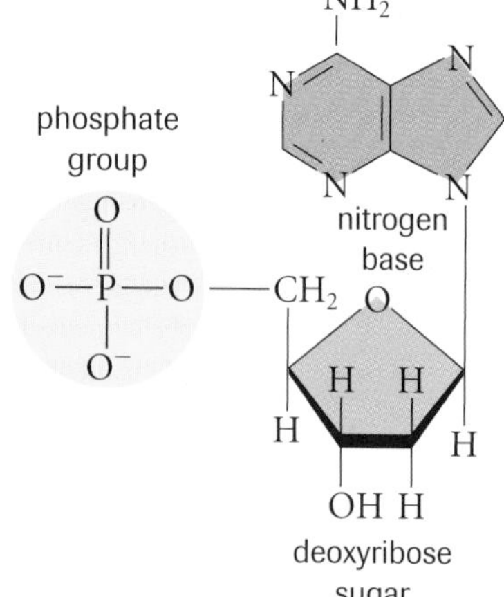

Figure 11
A DNA nucleotide is comprised of a deoxyribose sugar, a nitrogenous base, which in this case is adenine, and a phosphate group.

Biochemist Erwin Chargaff's evidence was crucial to helping Watson and Crick construct an accurate model of DNA. His observations determined that, for the DNA of any given species, the amount of adenine was always equal to the amount of thymine and the amount of guanine was always equal to the amount of cytosine. This relationship between the bases was consistent across all the species that he investigated. Although one species might have a different amount of adenine compared to another species, for example, the amount of thymine in each species was always equal to the amount of adenine.

Just as crucial was the X-ray photograph taken by Rosalind Franklin, which indicated that DNA was a helix that was likely double-stranded, that the distance between the strands was constant, and that the helix completed a full turn once every ten base pairs (**Figure 12**). Given this new data, Watson and Crick were able construct a three-dimensional scale model of DNA that portrayed the relationship between the bases as well as all of the nucleotide chemical bond angles and spacing of atoms consistent with the observations of other researchers. They presented their model to the scientific community in 1953, and in 1962 were awarded the Nobel Prize along with Maurice Wilkins. Because she had died prior to 1962 and the Nobel Prize is awarded only to living recipients, Rosalind Franklin was not included despite the acknowledgement of the significant importance of her photograph to the model proposed by Watson and Crick.

The Watson and Crick model of DNA structure is essentially the same one used by scientists today. Scientists already knew that molecules of DNA were made up of sugars (deoxyribose), phosphate, and four different nitrogen bases: adenine, guanine, cytosine, and thymine. What scientists did not know was the way in which these bases were arranged.

Learning Tip

Chargaff's Rules

The proportion of A always equals that of T (A = T).
The proportion of G always equals that of C (G = C).
A + G = T + C

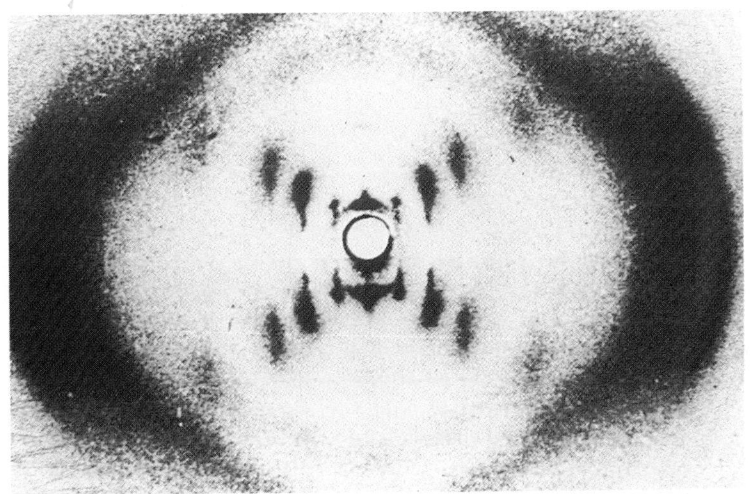

Figure 12
Rosalind Franklin's X-ray diffraction pattern of DNA revealed that it had a helical structure.

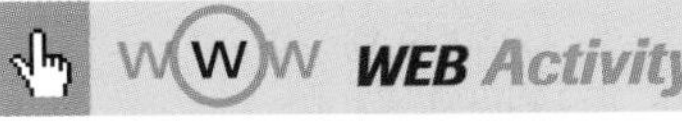

Simulation—Elementary, My Dear Crick

Erwin Chargaff visited Watson and Crick in Cambridge in 1952. Crick's lack of knowledge with respect to nitrogenous bases did not impress Chargaff. By the following year, Watson and Crick had constructed their model of DNA. Enjoy Watson and Crick's deductive process in an animation found by accessing the Nelson Web site.

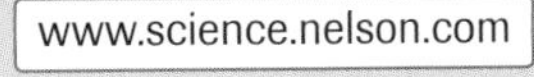

Figure 13
Rosalind Franklin's X-ray crystallography was crucial to the determination of the structure of DNA.

Politics and Science

Watson and Crick might not have been credited as the co-discoverers of DNA were it not for politics. The X-ray diffraction technique developed in England had been used by Maurice Wilkins and Rosalind Franklin (**Figure 13**) to view the DNA molecule. At that time, the American scientist Linus Pauling, a leading investigator in the field, was refused a visa to England to study the X-ray photographs. Pauling, along with others, had been identified by then U.S. Senator Joseph McCarthy as a communist sympathizer for his support of the anti-nuclear movement. Many scientists today believe that the United States passport office may have unknowingly determined the winners in the race for the discovery of the double-helix model of DNA.

The McCarthy era of the early 1950s is considered by many historians as a time of paranoia and repression. Many creative people had their careers stifled or destroyed because of their perceived association with communism. In most cases the charges were unfounded. It is perhaps ironic that, in 1962, Linus Pauling was awarded a Nobel Prize, this time for his dedication to world peace.

INVESTIGATION 19.2 *Introduction*

Isolation and Quantification of DNA

Report Checklist

- ● Purpose
- ○ Problem
- ○ Hypothesis
- ○ Prediction
- ● Design
- ○ Materials
- ○ Procedure
- ● Evidence
- ● Analysis
- ● Evaluation
- ○ Synthesis

In this activity, you will extract DNA from both beef liver and onion cells in Parts 1 and 2. If your school has the necessary reagents and equipment, you will then have the option of testing for the presence of DNA in Part 3 and of determining its concentration using a spectrophotometer in Part 4. You will need to gather evidence and analyze and evaluate the results that you observe, and to then explain those results in writing. Heed all cautions and wear safety equipment as instructed.

To perform this investigation, turn to page 653. 

EXPLORE an issue

Competition and Collaboration Advance Science

Issue Checklist

- ○ Issue
- ● Resolution
- ○ Design
- ● Evidence
- ● Analysis
- ● Evaluation

Scientists have been described as intelligent, ambitious, and sometimes competitive. Yet, for science to progress, many individuals must work together in a collaborative, communicative atmosphere. Current science demands two conflicting ideologies: competition and collaboration. A fine balance is not necessarily struck between the two. Other factors that come into play are economics, politics, market demand, profit, and patriotism in times of war.

Statement

Competition is the key driving force of science, followed by collaboration.

- Form groups to research this issue. Prepare a position paper in point form that supports or disputes this statement, using a specific example. Some scientists and case studies that may be used include Robert Oppenheimer's and Phillip Morrison's role in the Manhattan Project; the perception of Linus Pauling as a communist and the denial of a visa for him to visit Watson and Crick in Cambridge; Craig Venter and Eric Lander leading opposing research teams in the Human Genome Project; and Fritz Haber's role in the production of deadly gases during World War I.
- Search for information in periodicals, on CD-ROMS, and on the Internet.

www.science.nelson.com 

- As a group, present your supported view in a class discussion.

SUMMARY DNA is the Hereditary Material

Year	Scientist	Experimental results
late 1860s	Friedrich Miescher	• isolated nonprotein substance from nucleus of cells; named this substance nuclein
1928	Frederick Griffith	• experimented using mice and two different strains of pneumococcus bacteria (virulent and nonvirulent); observed that when heat-treated virulent pneumococcus was mixed with nonvirulent pneumococcus and was injected into healthy mice, death resulted • discovered the process of transformation
1943	Joachim Hammerling	• experimented using green alga *Acetabularia;* observed that regeneration of new appendages was driven by the nucleus-containing "foot" of the alga • hypothesized that hereditary information is stored in the nucleus
1944	Oswald Avery, Maclyn McCarty, and Colin MacLeod	• demonstrated that DNA was the transforming principle of pneumococcus bacteria
1949	Erwin Chargaff	• discovered that in the DNA of numerous organisms the amount of adenine is equal to the amount of thymine, and the amount of guanine is equal to that of cytosine
1952	Alfred Hershey and Martha Chase	• used radioactively labelled viruses, infected bacterial cells; observed that the infected bacterial cells contained radioactivity originating from DNA of the virus, suggesting that DNA is hereditary material
1953	Rosalind Franklin	• produced an X-ray diffraction pattern of DNA that suggested it was in the shape of a double helix
1953	James Watson and Francis Crick	• deduced the structure of DNA using information from the work of Chargaff, Franklin, and Maurice Wilkins

Section 19.3 Questions

1. Describe how the experiments of Joachim Hammerling; Frederick Griffith; Oswald Avery, Maclyn McCarty, and Colin MacLeod; and Alfred Hershey and Martha Chase strengthened the hypothesis that DNA is the hereditary material.
2. Explain why Hammerling's experiment cannot be used as conclusive scientific evidence that DNA is the hereditary material.
3. Hammerling chose *Acetabularia* as a model organism for his experiment. Identify some of the characteristics of this green alga that rendered it an ideal organism. Scientists use model organisms in many of their experiments. Identify social, economic, and physical characteristics that would make an organism highly suitable for experimental research. Explain why humans do not make ideal research subjects.
4. Explain why it is important to study both the historic experiments that revealed genetic principles and the principles themselves. Support your reasons, using examples.
5. It can be argued that the repetition of experiments is a waste of time, money, and other valuable resources. Provide arguments that support and dispute this statement. Use examples from the experiments of Griffith and of Avery, McCarty, and MacLeod to strengthen your arguments.

INVESTIGATION 19.1

Sex-Linked Traits

In this activity, you will cross *Drosophila* (**Figure 1**) that carry genes for sex-linked traits using virtual fruit fly software. To determine if a trait is sex-linked, you will perform two sets of crosses: A and B.

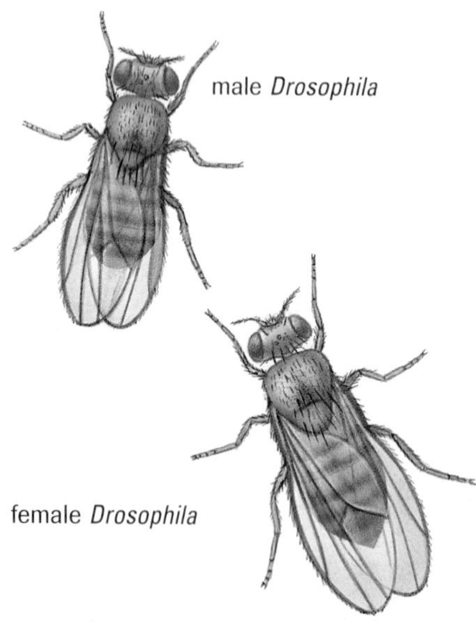

Figure 1
Drosophila males are smaller and have a rounded abdomen while the larger females have a pointed abdomen.

Familiarize yourself with the software before starting this activity. Start with the tutorial. Note that the labelling of traits in the software is different from the conventions used in this textbook. Be sure you understand what each label in the software correlates to in the textbook.

For cross A, these conditions must be met if the trait is sex-linked:

- In the F_1 generation, female offspring inherit the trait of the male parent and male offspring inherit the trait of the female parent.
- In the F_2 generation, there is a 1:1 phenotypic ratio for the traits in both males and females.

For cross B, you will confirm that the trait is sex-linked. You will cross parents with traits that are opposite to the traits of the parents in cross A. By examining the phenotypic ratios in offspring of the F_1 generation, you can observe the greater frequency of one trait in either the male or the female offspring.

Report Checklist

● Purpose	○ Design	● Analysis
○ Problem	○ Materials	● Evaluation
● Hypothesis	○ Procedure	○ Synthesis
● Prediction	● Evidence	

Problems

If white eye colour in *Drosophila* is a sex-linked recessive trait, what are the phenotypic ratios of the F_1 generation when a homozygous red-eyed female and a white-eyed male are crossed?

What other traits are sex-linked in *Drosophila*? Are they recessive or dominant?

Materials

virtual fruit fly simulation software
computers

Procedure

1. Log onto the software. Remember that each parent is homozygous for the trait chosen.
2. Select 1000 offspring.
3. For crosses A and B, follow these algorithms:
   A: P: white-eyed female × red-eyed male
   F_1: red-eyed female × red-eyed male
   F_2: red-eyed female × white-eyed male
   B: P: homozygous red-eyed female × white-eyed male
   F_1: red-eyed female × red-eyed male
4. For cross A, create a Punnett square to show the expected phenotypic ratio of offspring in each generation. Also, be sure to indicate the genotype of each phenotype.
5. After cross A, count the flies and the number of offspring (out of 1000) of each sex and with each trait. Record the information in a table beside the corresponding Punnett square.
6. When you have finished cross A, create a new parental generation.
7. Carry out cross B. Follow steps 4 to 6.
8. Determine if other traits are sex-linked. Follow the same procedure as in step 3, using new traits. Indicate which traits you are examining.

INVESTIGATION 19.1 *continued*

Analysis

(a) In one or two paragraphs, describe the results of crosses A and B. Is white eye colour in *Drosophila* sex-linked? If so, which sex does this trait appear in more frequently? Explain.

(b) In one or two paragraphs, describe the results with the other traits you examined. Is the trait sex-linked? If so, which sex does this trait appear in more frequently? Is the trait recessive or dominant? Explain.

Evaluation

(c) List and briefly explain any technical difficulties you had using the software.

(d) What improvements would you suggest to enhance the usefulness of the software?

(e) What are the advantages of using software to carry out this investigation compared to conducting it with actual *Drosophila*?

INVESTIGATION 19.2

Isolation and Quantification of DNA

In Parts 1 and 2 of this investigation, you will isolate DNA from onion cells and beef liver. Part 3 verifies the presence of DNA in your extraction using a biological analysis and Part 4 quantifies the amount of DNA using spectrophotometry. Parts 3 and 4 are optional depending on whether your school has the necessary reagents.

Report Checklist

- ● Purpose
- ○ Problem
- ○ Hypothesis
- ○ Prediction
- ● Design
- ○ Materials
- ○ Procedure
- ● Evidence
- ● Analysis
- ● Evaluation
- ○ Synthesis

Problem

How much DNA can be extracted from plant and animal cells using simple laboratory methods?

Materials

- safety goggles
- rubber gloves
- fresh beef liver
- scissors
- mortar and pestle
- 0.9 % (w/v) solution of sodium chloride (NaCl)
- three 10 mL graduated cylinders
- sand (very fine, washed)
- cheesecloth
- two 50 mL beakers, or two large test tubes
- 10 % (w/v) solution of sodium dodecyl sulfate (SDS)
- 95 % ethanol (chilled)
- 50 mL graduated cylinder
- glass rod
- four medium test tubes
- 4 % (w/v) solution of sodium chloride (NaCl)
- onion
- blender (optional)
- hot-water bath
- boiling chips
- ice-water bath
- meat tenderizer solution (3 g/50 mL of solution)
- diphenylamine solution
- 25 mL graduated cylinder
- Pasteur pipette, or plastic graduated eyedropper
- distilled water
- DNA standard solution
- test-tube rack
- spectrophotometer
- cuvette
- facial tissue

Procedure

DNA extraction is the first step in many biotechnological procedures. Cell walls and cell membranes must be disrupted to isolate DNA. In addition, lipids, proteins, and sugars must be separated from nucleic acid. In the following procedure, heat, detergents, salts, and cleaving enzymes are used to minimize contamination from nonnucleic acid molecules and to maximize purification.

Part 1: Extraction of DNA from Beef Liver

The ethanol solution is toxic and flammable. Keep it away from all sources of heat.

1. Obtain a 10 g to 15 g sample of beef liver and place it in the mortar.
2. Using scissors, cut the liver into small pieces.

3. Add 10 mL of 0.9 % NaCl solution to the diced liver. Use a 10 mL graduated cylinder to measure out the NaCl. Add a pinch of sand into the mixture to act as an abrasive, and grind the tissue thoroughly for approximately 5 min.
4. Strain the liver cell suspension through several layers of cheesecloth to eliminate any unpulverized liver. Collect the filtrate into a 50 mL beaker.
5. Add 3 mL of 10 % SDS solution. If a centrifuge is available, spin the suspension, and remove and save the supernatant. If a centrifuge is not available, mix the suspension thoroughly for 30 s and proceed to step 6.
6. Gently layer twice the volume (approximately 25 mL) of cold 95 % ethanol on the supernatant as that of the total volume of the cell suspension–SDS mixture. Use a 50 mL graduated cylinder to measure out the ethanol.
7. Using the glass rod, stir gently and slowly. A white, mucuslike substance will appear at the interface between the solutions. This substance is the DNA–nucleoprotein complex. After the complex has formed, twirl the stirring rod slowly and collect it onto the rod. Record your observations.
8. Place the isolated DNA–nucleoprotein complex into a test tube containing 3 mL of 4 % NaCl solution for later use. Use a 10 mL graduated cylinder to measure the 4 % NaCl solution. Pour the waste alcohol into the waste alcohol container designated by your teacher.

Part 2: Extraction of DNA from Onion

Onion is used because of its low starch content, which allows for a higher purity DNA extraction.

9. Repeat steps 1 to 5 using finely chopped onion. Instead of hand chopping the onion, a blender could be substituted, which gives optimum results.
10. Stir the mixture and let it sit for 15 min in a 60 °C water bath containing boiling chips. (Any longer and the DNA starts to break down.)
11. Cool the mixture in an ice-water bath for 5 min, stirring frequently.
12. Add half the volume of meat tenderizer solution as is present in your filtrate and swirl to mix.
13. Repeat steps 6 to 8.

Part 3: Testing for the Presence of DNA

The presence of DNA may be detected qualitatively with the reagent diphenylamine. Diphenylamine reacts with the purine nucleotides in DNA, producing a characteristic blue colour.

Diphenylamine solution contains glacial acetic acid. Be very careful not to spill any of the solution on yourself or on any surface. Inform your teacher immediately if any spills occur. Wear safety goggles and rubber gloves when handling this solution.

14. Stir the DNA from the onion and beef liver with their respective glass rods to resuspend them into the 4 % NaCl solution.
15. Dispense 15 mL of diphenylamine solution into a 25 mL graduated cylinder. The teacher will direct you to the stock diphenylamine solution, which will have been set up in a burette.
16. Transfer 5 mL of the solution to a 10 mL graduated cylinder with a Pasteur pipette or with a plastic graduated eyedropper.
17. Add 5 mL of diphenylamine solution to the DNA suspension obtained from the onion and from the beef liver.
18. Repeat step 16 and add 5 mL of diphenylamine solution to a test tube containing 3 mL of distilled water (the blank).
19. Repeat step 16 and add 5 mL of diphenylamine solution to a test tube containing 3 mL of DNA standard (the standard).
20. Place all of the test tubes in a boiling water bath (containing boiling chips) for 10 min and record the colour changes. Record your observations.
21. Remove the test tubes from the hot-water bath and place into a test-tube rack. Allow the tubes to cool before proceeding.

INVESTIGATION 19.2 *continued*

Part 4: Quantitative Determination of DNA Concentration Using Spectrophotometry

The principle underlying a spectrophotometric method of analysis involves the interaction of electromagnetic (EM) radiation (light) with matter. When EM radiation strikes an atom, energy in the form of light is absorbed. The remainder of the energy passes through the sample and can be detected. The more molecules that are present, the more energy will be absorbed, resulting in a higher absorbance reading. Since the relationship is direct, we can determine the concentration of an unknown by comparing it with a known. In this case, the unknown is the concentration of DNA in your samples and the known is the DNA standard.

22. Set the spectrophotometer to a wavelength of 600 nm. (See the video *Spec 20* on the Nelson Web site.)

23. Fill a dry cuvette with the solution that consists of the distilled water and the diphenylamine. This will serve as a blank.
24. Wipe off any fingerprints from the outside of the cuvette by holding the cuvette at the very top and using a facial tissue. Place the blank into the spectrophotometer and set the absorbance to 0.00. (See the video *Spec 20* on the Nelson Web site.)

www.science.nelson.com GO

25. Pour the blank solution back into its original test tube and place it in a test-tube rack.
26. Rinse the cuvette with a tiny amount of standard DNA solution (DNA standard and diphenylamine from step 19). Wipe off any fingerprints in the manner described in step 24.
27. Place the DNA standard solution into the spectrophotometer, then record the absorbance. (See the video *Spec 20* on the Nelson Web site.)

www.science.nelson.com GO

28. Pour the DNA standard solution into its original test tube and save in case of error.
29. Repeat steps 26 to 28 with the beef liver extract solution and with the onion extract solution.

Analysis

(a) Propose reasons that the onion cells required heating and the liver cells did not.

(b) DNA was spooled out using a glass rod. How do you account for the "stickiness" of DNA to glass?

(c) Describe the DNA you extracted. If DNA is a rigid structure, why do the DNA strands appear flexible? What features of DNA's structure account for its stiffness? If DNA is rigid, how does it coil tightly into a small space?

(d) Comment on the purity of the DNA extracted.

(e) Compare the amount of DNA extracted from the onion versus that from the liver. Which source of DNA provided more of the molecule? Account for this observation, given your knowledge of cell structure and given differences in the procedure.

(f) What was the purpose of the standard DNA solution? What was the purpose of the blank?

(g) Did the spectrophotometric results correlate with the qualitative observations obtained from the diphenylamine test? Comment.

(h) Calculate the amount of DNA extracted from each source using your standard as a guide.

(i) The liver and onion were chopped very finely. Provide reasoning for this step. If the step was omitted, what effect would this omission have on the results?

(j) SDS is a detergent. Describe how detergents work and explain the role of SDS in the protocol.

(k) How does NaCl contribute to maximum DNA extraction? (Hint: Think about DNA's chemical constituents.) Keep in mind that NaCl is a salt that ionizes in solution.

(l) What is the purpose of adding cold ethanol to each extraction? How does this phenomenon work?

(m) In the extraction of DNA from onion, you added a meat tenderizer solution. The meat tenderizer solution contains an enzyme called papain. What role does papain play in the extraction?

(n) Identify three properties of DNA that are demonstrated by this investigation.

Evaluation

(o) Suggest possible sources of error in this procedure and describe their effect on the results.

Chapter 19 SUMMARY

Outcomes

Knowledge

- summarize the historical events that led to the discovery of the structure of the DNA molecule, as demonstrated by Franklin, Watson, and Crick (19.3)
- explain the limitations of variability due to gene linkage and the influence of crossing over on assortment of genes on the same chromosome (19.2)
- explain the relationship between variability and the number of genes controlling a trait (19.2)
- compare the pattern of inheritance produced by genes on the sex chromosomes to that of genes on autosomes, as investigated by Morgan and others (19.1)

STS

- explain that decisions regarding the application of scientific and technological development involve a variety of perspectives including social, cultural, environmental, ethical, and economic considerations (19.2, 19.3)

Skills

- ask questions and plan investigations (19.2, 19.3)
- conduct investigations and gather and record data and information (19.1, 19.2)
- analyze data and apply mathematical and conceptual models by analyzing crossover data for a single pair of chromosomes to create a chromosome map showing gene arrangement and relative distance (19.2)
- work as members of a team and apply the skills and conventions of science (all)

Key Terms

19.1

autosome
linked genes
sex-linked trait
recessive lethal
Barr body

19.2

linkage group
locus (loci)
marker gene

19.3

continuity of life
bacteriophage
isotope
radioisotope
nucleotide
deoxyribose sugar
nitrogenous base
phosphate group

MAKE a summary

1. Create a poster of a human genome that shows the principles of sex-linked genes and helps show the relationship between genes and chromosomes. Label the sketch with as many of the key terms as possible. Check other posters and use appropriate ideas to make your poster clear.
2. Revisit your answers to the Starting Points questions at the beginning of the chapter. Would you answer the questions differently now? Why?

Go To

The following components are available on the Nelson Web site. Follow the links for *Nelson Biology Alberta 20–30*.

- an interactive Self Quiz for Chapter 19
- additional Diploma Exam-style Review Questions
- Illustrated Glossary
- additional IB-related material

There is more information on the Web site wherever you see the Go icon in the chapter.

EXTENSION

Beyond the Genome

Dr. Victor Ambros (professor of genetics at Dartmouth Medical School), Dr. Katherine Wilson (associate professor of cell biology at Johns Hopkins Medical School), and Dr. Wolf Reik, (Babraham Institute in Cambridge, England) discuss their research on how our cells really work, including how genes "know" to turn on at the right times.

www.science.nelson.com GO

Chapter 19 REVIEW

Many of these questions are in the style of the Diploma Exam. You will find guidance for writing Diploma Exams in Appendix A5. Science Directing Words used in Diploma Exams are in bold type. Exam study tips and test-taking suggestions are on the Nelson Web site.

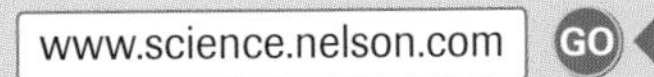

DO NOT WRITE IN THIS TEXTBOOK.

Part 1

1. In performing experiments with fruit flies, *Drosophila melanogaster*, Thomas Morgan discovered that white eye colour is recessive to red eye colour. When females with white eyes were crossed with males with red eyes, Morgan discovered the females all had red eyes and the males all had white eyes. Select the answer that explains this outcome.
   A. Male offspring inherit the white allele from the mother, which in males becomes dominant. Female offspring inherit the red allele from the father, which is dominant over the white allele they inherit from the mother.
   B. Male offspring inherit the white allele from the mother and a Y chromosome from the father that does not carry a gene for eye colour. Female offspring inherit the red allele from the father, which is dominant over the white allele they inherit from the mother.
   C. Male offspring inherit the red allele from the mother, which is recessive in males. Female offspring inherit the red allele from the father and no allele for eye colour from the mother.
   D. Male offspring inherit the red allele from the father and a Y chromosome from the mother that carries an allele for white eye colour. Female offspring inherit the red allele from the mother, which is dominant over the white allele they inherit from the father.

Use the following information to answer questions 2 to 4.

In the pedigree chart shown in **Figure 1**, females are represented by circles and males by squares, while light shading indicates normal phenotype and dark shading indicates Duchenne muscular dystrophy.

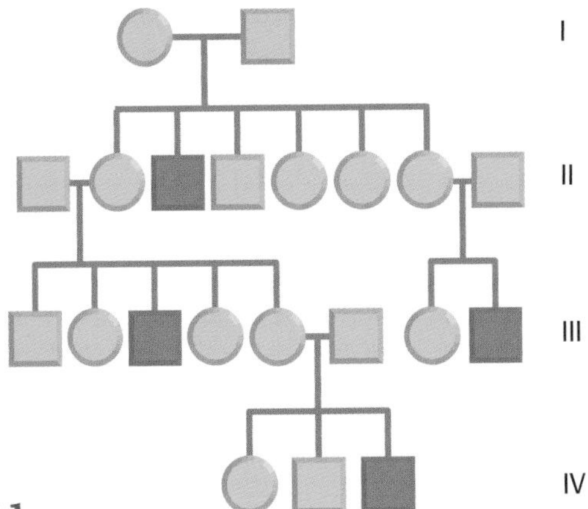

Figure 1

2. Identify the statement that correctly describes how Duchenne muscular dystrophy is inherited.
   A. Duchenne muscular dystrophy is a dominant allele located on an autosome.
   B. Duchenne muscular dystrophy is a recessive allele located on an autosome.
   C. Duchenne muscular dystrophy is a dominant allele located on a sex chromosome.
   D. Duchenne muscular dystrophy is a recessive allele located on a sex chromosome.

3. Identify the statement that is true for generation II.
   A. 50 % of the males inherited the disorder from an allele carried by their mother.
   B. 25 % of the males inherited the disorder from an allele carried by their mother.
   C. 50 % of the females inherited the disorder from an allele carried by their father.
   D. 100 % of the females inherited the allele carried by their mother but did not develop the disorder.

4. Identify the answer that is correct for generations I and III.
   A. In generation I, the mother carries the recessive allele and is heterozygous. In generation III, males and females inherit the Duchenne allele from their mothers.
   B. In generation I, the father carries the recessive allele and is heterozygous. In generation III, females and males inherit the Duchenne allele from their fathers.
   C. In generation I, the mother carries the recessive allele and is homozygous. In generation III, only males inherit the Duchenne allele from their mothers.
   D. In generation I, the father carries the recessive allele and is homozygous. In generation III, females and males inherit the Duchenne allele from their fathers.

---

5. Brown spotting on the teeth is a sex-linked trait in humans. A father with brown spotting passes the trait along to all his daughters but not to his sons. The mother does not have brown spotting on her teeth. This indicates that the brown spotting gene is
   A. dominant and located on the X chromosome
   B. recessive and located on the X chromosome
   C. dominant and located on the Y chromosome
   D. recessive and located on the Y chromosome

6. The recombination frequency among genes found on the same chromosomes depends on
   A. which genes are dominant and which genes are recessive
   B. the number of genes along the chromosome
   C. the size of the chromosome
   D. the distance between the genes

7. Ocular albinism in humans is characterized by a lack of pigment in the iris of the eyes. This X-linked trait often results in blindness for those afflicted. A woman who carries this trait marries a normal man. Identify the chance of ocular albinism in a child from this couple.
   A. 100 % chance of normal female offspring and a 100 % chance of normal male offspring
   B. 50 % chance of female offspring with ocular albinism, 50 % chance of normal female offspring, and 100 % chance of normal male offspring
   C. 100 % chance of normal female offspring, 50 % chance of male offspring with ocular albinism, and 50 % chance of normal male offspring
   D. 50 % chance of female offspring with ocular albinism, 50 % chance of normal female offspring, 50 % chance of male offspring with ocular albinism, and 50 % chance of normal male offspring

8. The allele *R* produces rose combs in chickens. Another allele *P*, located on a different chromosome, produces pea combs. The absence of the dominant rose comb and pea comb alleles (*rrpp*) produces birds with single combs. When the dominant *R* allele and the dominant *P* allele are both present, they interact to produce a walnut comb (*R_P_*). Identify the phenotypes of the parents and the expected phenotypic ratios of the F_1 generation from a cross of chickens with the genotype *RrPp* × *rrPp*.
   A. The parental phenotypes are walnut comb and pea comb. The expected F_1 phenotypic ratio from the cross is 3 walnut:3 pea:1 rose:1 single.
   B. The parental phenotypes are walnut comb and pea comb. The expected F_1 phenotypic ratio from the cross is 4 walnut:4 rose.
   C. The parental phenotypes are rose comb and pea comb. The expected F_1 phenotypic ratio from the cross is 3 walnut:2 rose:2 pea:1 single.
   D. The parental phenotypes are pea comb and single comb. The expected F_1 phenotypic ratio from the cross is 4 rose:4 pea.

Use the following information to answer questions 9 and 10.

The chromosome map in **Figure 2** shows the portion of a chromosome that carries genes for scalloped wings, bar eyes, and garnet eyes—all mutant traits in *Drosophila melanogaster*. It was drawn using data from several test crosses.

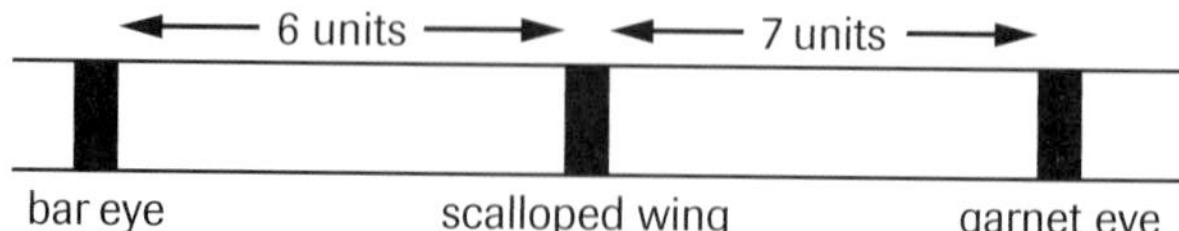

Figure 2

9. NR Determine the frequency of crossover between scalloped wings and garnet eyes, as a percent. (Record all four digits of your answer.)

10. NR Determine the frequency of crossover between bar eyes and garnet eyes, as a percent. (Record all four digits of your answer.)

Part 2

11. **Describe** Erwin Chargaff's contribution to the determination of DNA structure.

12. **Explain** how the development of the chromosome theory is linked with the development of the light microscope.

13. **Describe** the contributions made by Walter Sutton, Theodor Boveri, and Thomas Morgan in the development of the modern-day chromosome theory of genetics.

14. The gene for wild-type eye colour is dominant and sex-linked in *Drosophila melanogaster*. White eyes are recessive. The mating of a male with wild-type eye colour with a female of the same phenotype produces offspring that are $\frac{3}{4}$ wild-type eye colour and $\frac{1}{4}$ white-eyed. **Predict** the genotypes of the P_1 and F_1 generations.

15. The autosomal recessive allele *tra* transforms a female *Drosophila melanogaster* into a phenotypic male when it occurs in the homozygous condition. The transformed females are sterile. The *tra* gene has no effect on the phenotype of XY males. Using Punnett squares, **predict** the genotypes and phenotypes of individuals in the F_1 and F_2 generations from the following cross: XX, + /*tra* crossed with XY, *tra*/*tra*. (Note the + indicates the normal dominant gene.)

16. Edward Lambert, an Englishman, was born in 1717. Lambert had a skin disorder that was characterized by very thick skin, which was shed periodically. The hairs on his skin were very course and quill-like, giving him the name "porcupine man." Lambert had six sons, all of whom exhibited the same traits. The trait never appeared in his daughters. In fact, the trait has never been recorded in females. **Hypothesize** the nature of the inheritance of the "porcupine trait" that would explain these observations.

Use the following information to answer questions 17 to 20.

Figure 3 is a pedigree chart of a family in which some members have hemophilia.

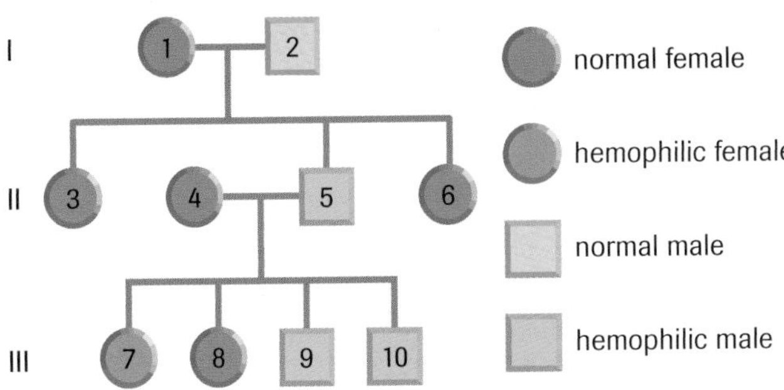

Figure 3

17. **Predict** the phenotypes of the P_1 generation. DE

18. If parents 1 and 2 were to have a fourth child, **determine** the probability that the child would have hemophilia. DE

19. If parents 1 and 2 were to have a second male, **determine** the probability that the boy would have hemophilia. DE

20. **Predict** the genotypes of parents 4 and 5. DE

21. A science student **hypothesizes** that dominant genes occur with greater frequency in human populations than recessive genes occur. Either support or refute the student's hypothesis, using the information that you have gathered in this chapter to **justify** your decision.

Use the following information to answer questions 22 to 24.

In 1911, Thomas Morgan collected the gene crossover frequencies shown in **Table 1** while studying *Drosophila melanogaster*. The loci for four different genes that code for wing shape are located on the same chromosome. Bar-shaped wings are indicated by the *B* allele, carnation wings by the *C* allele, fused veins on wings by the *FV* allele, and scalloped wings by the *S* allele.

Table 1

Gene combinations	Recombination frequency
FV/B	2.5 %
FV/C	3.0 %
B/C	5.5 %
B/S	5.5 %
FV/S	8.0 %
C/S	11.0 %

22. Use the crossover frequencies to **sketch** a gene map. DE

23. **Identify** which genes are farthest apart. **Determine** their distance. **Illustrate** your answer by way of a diagram. DE

24. From the data provided in **Table 1**, **conclude** in a written statement the relative position of the *FV*, *C*, and *B* alleles. DE

chapter

20 Molecular Genetics

▶ In this chapter

- Exploration: Similarities and Differences
- Mini Investigation: Building a DNA Model
- Web Activity: DNA Replication
- Lab Exercise 20.A: Synthesis of a Protein
- Investigation 20.1: Protein Synthesis and Inactivation of Antibiotics
- Web Activity: Electrophoresis
- Web Activity: Researchers in Human Genetic Disorders
- Mini Investigation: Examining the Human Genome
- Investigation 20.2: Restriction Enzyme Digestion of Bacteriophage DNA
- Web Activity: Transformation of Eukaryotes
- Case Study: Gene Mutations and Cancer
- Lab Exercise 20.B: Looking for SINEs of Evolution

By the mid-1950s, scientists had determined that chromosomes contained DNA and that DNA was the genetic material (**Figure 1**). Building on the work of other scientists, Watson and Crick deduced the structure of this complex molecule. This knowledge laid the basis for the field of molecular biology, which aims to understand the inheritance of traits at the level of interactions between molecules in the cell.

A primary goal of molecular genetics is to understand how DNA determines the phenotype of an organism. What happens to DNA during duplication of chromosomes in mitosis? How does the structure of DNA relate to its function? How does one molecule, identical in every somatic cell of an organism, determine the characteristics of the many different types of cells that are found in that organism?

Today, questions such as these continue to drive research in the fields of biology, biotechnology, biochemistry, and medicine. We now know the sequence of all the nucleotides that make up the genome of many organisms, including that of our own species, *Homo sapiens*. This information has given scientists new ways to study the relationships between species and the mechanisms of evolution. It also allows law enforcement agencies to identify individuals with incredible accuracy from minute quantities of DNA.

Using genetic technologies, scientists can move genes from one species to another. In fields such as agriculture, corporations have patented the genomes of these organisms in order to profit from the advantages they offer over conventional organisms. Similar manipulation of human cells may one day lead to treatments for previously untreatable debilitating diseases. The research and application of these technologies raises many social, ethical, and legal issues that society has yet to fully resolve.

STARTING Points

Answer these questions as best you can with your current knowledge. Then, using the concepts and skills you have learned, you will revise your answers at the end of the chapter.

1. Differentiate between DNA and proteins. What cellular roles do they play?
2. Describe the physical and chemical characteristics of DNA.
3. What is the significance of DNA replication in your body?
4. Write a short overview, in paragraph form, of the process of DNA replication.

Career Connections:
Biological Technician; Biotechnologist

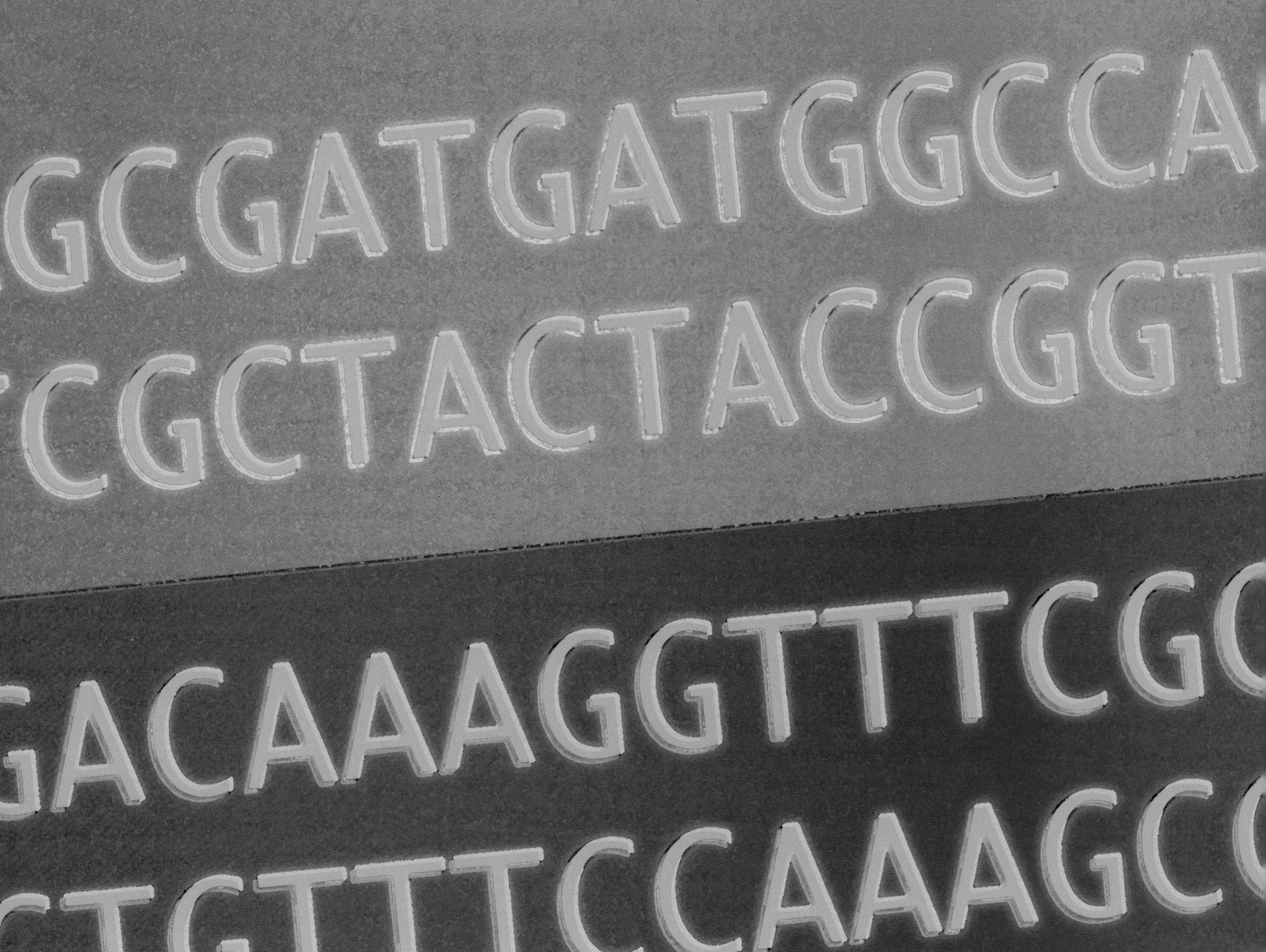

Figure 1
DNA sequences are represented by the letters A, T, C, and G.

▸ Exploration — *Similarities and Differences*

All organisms, no matter how simple they may seem to us, require DNA in each cell to encode the instructions necessary to live and reproduce. The total DNA of an organism is referred to as its genome. In bacteria, the genomic DNA is circular, accounts for 2 % to 3 % of the cell's mass, and occupies about 10 % of its volume. In this activity, you will make a model of an *Escherichia coli* cell that will be 10 000 times bigger than actual size. You will also gain an appreciation for how compactly DNA is packed within a cell.

Materials: 2 cm gelatin capsule, 10 m of white thread, 10 m of coloured thread

- Try to construct the bacterium by placing the long lengths of thread inside the gelatin capsule. Good luck! It's not easy!

(a) Why does it take two lengths of thread to represent the chromosome?

(b) Is the thread that you tried to place in the capsule too thick to represent the actual thickness of the DNA? (What percentage of bacterial cell volume does your thread fill, and what is the actual volume that the DNA occupies in the bacteria?)

(c) If the human genome is 1000 times bigger than the *E. coli* genome, how many metres of thread would it take to represent the human genome?

(d) What size container would you need to hold the thread representing the human genome?

20.1 DNA Structure and Replication

CAREER CONNECTION

Biological Technician

Biological technicians may work in the field, in the laboratory, or both. They perform routine analysis and technical duties to support the work of scientists and engineers working in fields that include molecular biology. What educational background is required to enter this field?

www.science.nelson.com 

According to the model proposed by Watson and Crick, DNA consists of two strands of nucleotides. Each nucleotide contains a deoxyribose sugar, a phosphate group, and a nitrogenous base, all covalently bonded to each other. Each strand of DNA has a backbone of sugar and phosphate groups (**Figure 1**). The nitrogenous bases stick out from the backbone of each DNA strand.

Watson and Crick's model also indicates that the two strands of DNA form a structure that resembles a twisted ladder. The base pairs are the rungs of the ladder and the sugar–phosphate backbones are the struts. This structure is called a double helix (see **Figure 1**). Each DNA strand in the double helix twists in a clockwise direction.

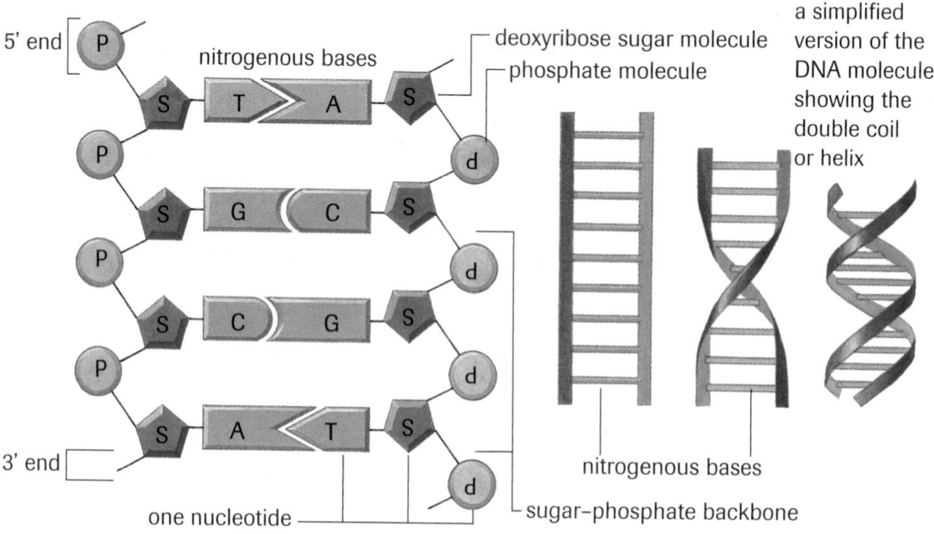

Figure 1
A simplified diagram of the structure of DNA

In the DNA molecule, the bases of one DNA strand are paired with bases in the other strand. A purine is always paired with a pyrimidine. Adenine (a purine) is always paired with thymine (a pyrimidine), and guanine (a purine) is always paired with cytosine (a pyrimidine). This type of pairing is termed **complementary base pairing**. Hydrogen bonds, between the complementary bases (A-T and G-C) on opposite strands, hold the double helix together (**Figure 2**). Although a single hydrogen bond is very weak, large numbers of hydrogen bonds are collectively strong, so the DNA molecule is very stable.

complementary base pairing pairing of the nitrogenous base of one strand of DNA with the nitrogenous base of another strand

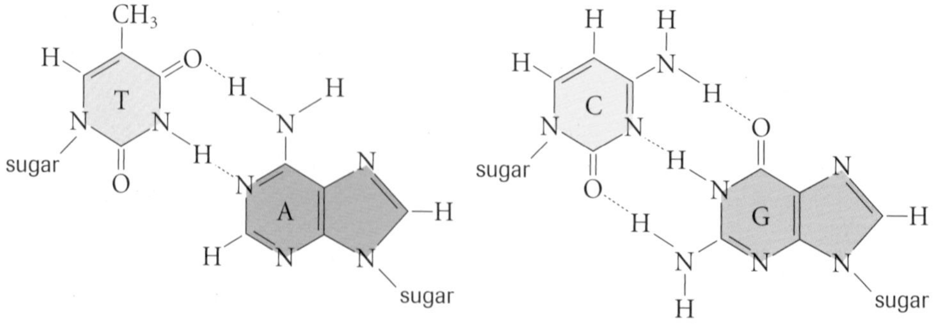

Figure 2
Adenine forms two hydrogen bonds with thymine, while guanine forms three hydrogen bonds with cytosine.

The sequence of bases on any one strand of DNA can vary greatly between species, but its opposite strand will always have the complementary sequence of bases. For example, the sequences of the strands below are complementary:

5′–ATGCCGTTA–3′
3′–TACGGCAAT–5′

antiparallel parallel but running in opposite directions; the 5′ end of one strand of DNA aligns with the 3′ end of the other strand in a double helix

The two strands of nucleotides are **antiparallel**. They run parallel but in opposite directions to one another. One strand will have a 5′ carbon and phosphate group at one end and a 3′ carbon and the hydroxyl group of a deoxyribose sugar at its other end. Its antiparallel strand will have a 3′ carbon and the hydroxyl group of a deoxyribose sugar at the first end and a 5′ carbon and phosphate group at its other end (**Figure 1**, previous page).

The direction of the strand is important when enzymes interact with DNA, either to copy the DNA prior to cell division or to "read" genes in order to make proteins. Enzymes can read or copy DNA in only one direction. The sequence of only one DNA strand is given when sequences are written out since the complementary strand is easily deduced according to the rules of complementary base pairing.

Learning Tip

The rules of complementary DNA base pairing are
- A to T
- G to C

When you know the sequence on one strand, you also know the sequence on the complementary strand.

Practice

1. Define the following terms: nucleotide, complementary base pairing, and antiparallel.
2. In a DNA molecule, a purine pairs with a pyrimidine. If this is the case, then why can't A–C and G–T pairs form? (*Hint:* Look closely at the bonds between the base pairs in **Figure 2** on the previous page.)
3. The following is a segment taken from a strand of DNA: 5′-ATGCCTTA-3′. Write out the complementary strand for this segment. Be sure to show directionality.

mini *Investigation* — *Building a DNA Model*

What would a section of a DNA molecule look like if you could see one close up? You can find out by building your own model of the double helix. For this activity, you need to select materials that will allow you to model the following features:

- the sugar–phosphate backbone
- the anti-parallel strands
- the four different nitrogenous bases
- the bonds between complementary base pairs that hold the two strands together

Your model should show a minimum of 12 base pairs. It should be free-standing and approximately 15 cm tall by 6 cm wide. Include a legend with your model that clearly identifies each part of the DNA strand.

DNA Replication

In Chapter 17, you saw that mitosis involves the duplication of chromosomes. For mitosis to occur, DNA must copy itself and be equally divided between the daughter cells. To have all the correct genetic information, the DNA in each daughter cell must be an exact copy of the DNA in the parent cell. **DNA replication** is the process by which a cell makes an exact copy of its DNA. The main stages of DNA replication are the same in both prokaryotic cells (without a membrane-bound nucleus) and eukaryotic cells (with a membrane-bound nucleus).

DNA replication is semiconservative. **Semiconservative replication** involves separating the two parent strands and using them to synthesize two new strands (**Figure 3**, next page). The hydrogen bonds between complementary bases break, allowing the DNA helix to unzip. Each single DNA strand acts as a **template** to build the complementary strand. Finally, any errors are repaired, resulting in two identical DNA molecules, one for each daughter cell.

DNA replication the process whereby DNA makes exact copies of itself

semiconservative replication process of replication in which each DNA molecule is composed of one parent strand and one newly synthesized strand

template a single-stranded DNA sequence that acts as the guiding pattern for producing a complementary DNA strand

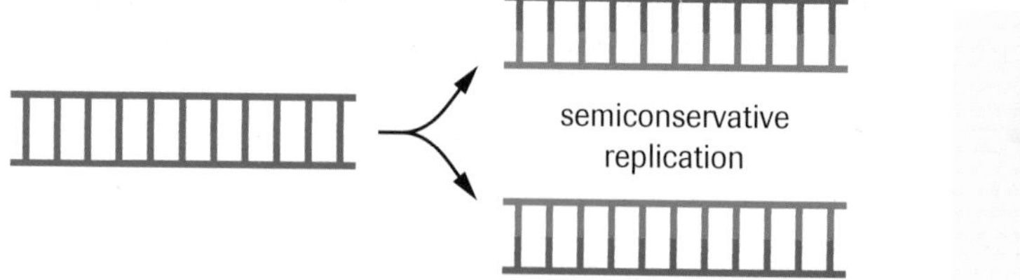

Figure 3
DNA replicates semiconservatively. Each daughter molecule receives one strand from the parent molecule plus one newly synthesized strand.

Separating the DNA Strands

DNA helicase the enzyme that unwinds double-helical DNA by disrupting hydrogen bonds

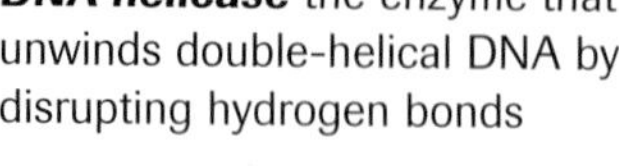

The two strands of the DNA helix cannot simply pull apart because they are tightly held together by the hydrogen bonds between bases and by the twists of the helix. The enzyme **DNA helicase** unwinds the helix by breaking the hydrogen bonds between the complementary bases. As this happens, the bonds between bases tend to reform. To prevent this, proteins bind to the separated DNA strands, helping to hold them apart. The two strands are now separated along part of the DNA molecule and are the template strands for the next step in replication. The point at which the two template strands are separating is called the replication fork. One template strand runs in the 3′ to 5′ direction in relation to the replication fork, while the other runs in the 5′ to 3′ direction (**Figure 4**).

DID YOU KNOW?

DNA Polymerases

There are several DNA polymerases in a cell, all with their own role. Each has a unique name, created by adding a roman numeral after "DNA polymerase." The main DNA polymerase involved in DNA replication is DNA polymerase III. It adds the 5′ phosphate group of a free nucleotide to the 3′ carbon of the sugar in the last nucleotide.

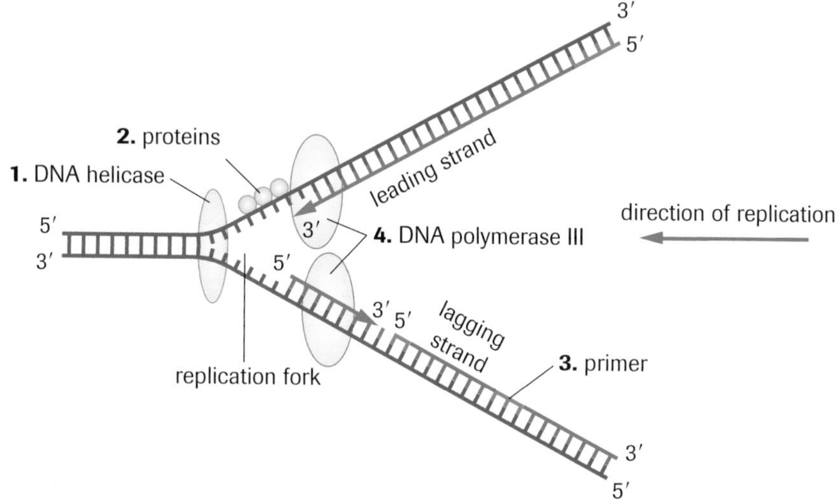

Figure 4
1. DNA helicase opens the double helix. 2. Proteins bind to the DNA to keep the two strands separate. 3. RNA primers are attached to the template strands. 4. DNA polymerase synthesizes the new DNA strands. The leading strand is synthesized continuously, and the lagging strand is synthesized in short fragments. DNA polymerase III adds complementary nucleotides in the 5′ to 3′ direction, using single-stranded primers as starting points. One nucleotide is attached to the next by bonding the phosphate on the 5′ end of the new nucleotide to the hydroxyl group on the 3′ end of the last nucleotide.

Building the Complementary Strands

DNA polymerase III the enzyme that synthesizes complementary strands of DNA during DNA replication

The next stage of DNA replication synthesizes two new DNA strands on the template strands through complementary base pairing. The new strands are synthesized by an enzyme called **DNA polymerase III**. This DNA polymerase builds a new strand by linking together free nucleotides that have bases complementary to the bases in the template. A short piece of single-stranded ribonucleic acid, called a primer, is attached to the template strand. This gives DNA polymerase III a starting point to begin synthesizing the new DNA strand. DNA polymerase III adds nucleotides to a growing strand in *only one direction*—the 5′ to 3′ direction. The phosphate group at the 5′ end of a free nucleotide is connected to the hydroxyl group on the 3′ carbon of the sugar on the last nucleotide in the strand. As a result, one of the new strands will be synthesized continuously as DNA polymerase III moves in the 5′ to 3′ direction toward the replication fork. This strand is called the **leading strand**.

The other new strand, the **lagging strand**, is synthesized in short fragments. This allows the lagging strand to be synthesized in the 5′ to 3′ direction. RNA primers are required. To complete the replication of the DNA, the primers are cut out from the lagging strand and are replaced by DNA nucleotides by a different enzyme called **DNA polymerase I**.

Another enzyme, **DNA ligase**, links the sugar–phosphate backbone of the DNA fragments together (**Figure 5**).

leading strand the new strand of DNA that is synthesized towards the replication fork and continuously during DNA replication

lagging strand the new strand of DNA that is synthesized away from the replication fork and in short fragments, which are later joined together

DNA polymerase I an enzyme that removes RNA primers and replaces them with the appropriate nucleotides during DNA replication

DNA ligase an enzyme that joins DNA fragments together

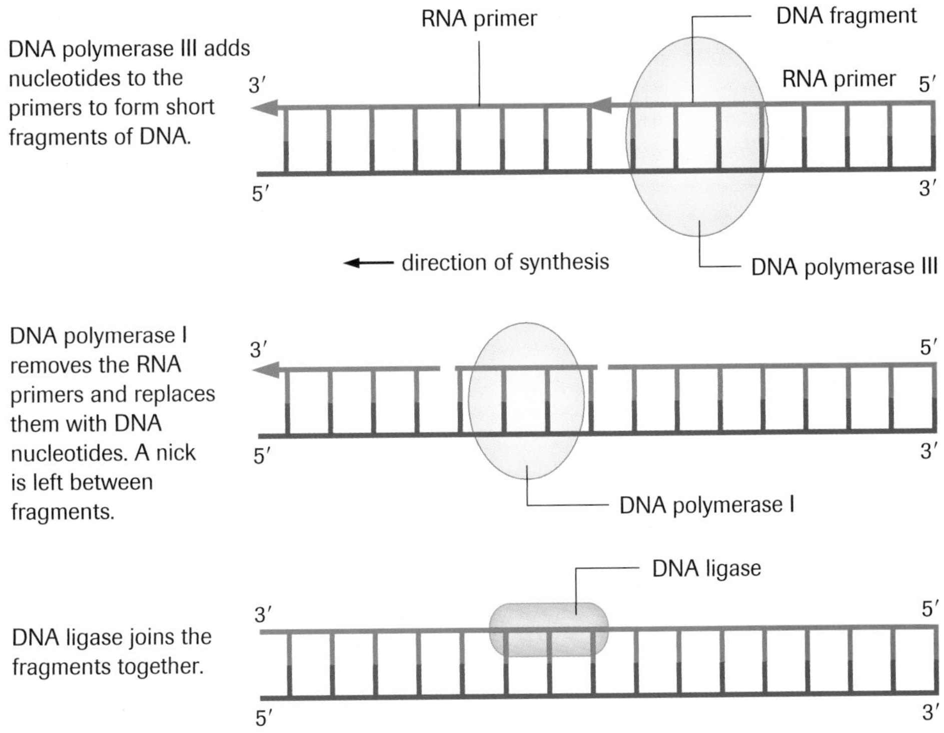

Figure 5
Building the lagging strand

DNA Repair

As complementary strands of DNA are synthesized, both DNA polymerase I and III act as quality control checkers by proofreading the newly synthesized strands. When a mistake occurs, the DNA polymerases backtrack to the incorrect nucleotide, cut it out, and then continue adding nucleotides to the complementary strand. The repair must be made immediately to avoid the mistake from being copied in later replications. Other DNA repair mechanisms can correct any errors that were missed during proofreading.

DID YOU KNOW?

Okazaki Fragments

The short fragments that are synthesized to form the lagging strand during DNA replication are called Okazaki fragments. They were named after Reiji Okazaki, who first described them in the 1960s.

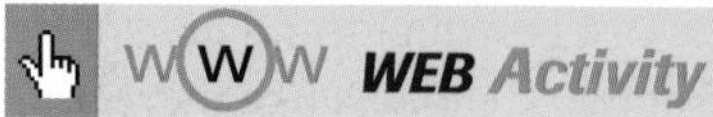

Simulation—DNA Replication

The *Escherichia coli* genome consists of 4.7 million nucleotide pairs. This entire genome is replicated in 40 min. Proofreading by DNA polymerase I and polymerase III maintains the error rate at roughly one error per 1000 cells duplicated! View a complete animation of DNA replication by accessing the Nelson Web site.

www.science.nelson.com 

SUMMARY DNA Structure and Replication

Separating the Strands

- DNA helicase unzips the double helix by breaking the hydrogen bonds between the complementary bases in the two strands of the parent DNA molecule.
- Proteins attach to the newly exposed DNA strands, preventing the hydrogen bonds from re-forming and keeping the strands apart.

Building the Complementary Strands

- DNA polymerase III adds complementary nucleotides to the growing strands, using the exposed strands of the parent DNA molecule as a template.
- The leading strand is formed continuously.
- The lagging strand is formed in short fragments, starting from an RNA primer.
- DNA polymerase I cuts out the RNA primers and replaces them with the appropriate DNA nucleotides.
- DNA ligase joins the fragments together to form a complete DNA strand.

DNA Repair

- DNA polymerase enzymes cut out incorrectly paired nucleotides and add the correct nucleotides in a process called proofreading.

Section 20.1 Questions

1. Summarize the key physical and chemical properties of DNA.
2. Differentiate between a purine and a pyrimidine.
3. Copy **Table 1** into your notebook, fill in the missing information, and supply an appropriate title.

Table 1

Enzyme	Function
DNA helicase	
DNA polymerase I	
DNA polymerase III	
DNA ligase	

4. A molecule of DNA was analyzed and found to contain 20 % thymine. Calculate the percentage of adenine, guanine, and cytosine in this molecule.
5. Define a replication fork.
6. In a double helix, there is a complete turn every 3.4 nm, or 10 nucleotides. Assume that the DNA molecule in a particular chromosome is 75 mm long. Calculate the number of nucleotide pairs in this molecule.
7. Copy **Table 2** into your notebook and complete the missing information. Explain how you determined the missing values.

Table 2

Nucleotide	Sample A	Sample B	Sample C
adenine	10 %		20 %
guanine	40 %	15 %	
thymine		35 %	20 %
cytosine			

Gene Expression 20.2

As you learned in previous chapters, specific segments of DNA on a chromosome are called genes. Genes determine the inherited characteristics, or traits, of an organism. Every somatic (body) cell in an organism contains identical copies of DNA, and each of these DNA copies is a genetic blueprint for the organism. Once scientists knew the structure of DNA and how it replicated, they used this knowledge to further investigate another question: How do the genes in DNA determine an inherited trait?

The way the information in a gene is converted into a specific characteristic or trait through the production of a polypeptide is called **gene expression**. Recall that a polypeptide is a chain of amino acids and that proteins are made up of polypeptides. Proteins form many structures in an organism, such as skin and muscle, and they also form all of the enzymes in a cell. *The products of all genes are polypeptides.*

gene expression conversion of a gene into a specific trait through the production of a particular polypeptide

A second type of nucleic acid is involved in converting the instructions in a gene into a polypeptide chain. **Ribonucleic acid** (**RNA**) is a polymer of nucleotides similar to DNA. There are three main structural differences between RNA and DNA. First, the sugar in RNA has an extra hydroxyl group and is called ribose rather than deoxyribose (**Figure 1**). Second, instead of the base thymine found in DNA, RNA contains the base uracil. Like thymine, uracil can form complementary base pairs with adenine (**Figure 2**). Third, RNA is single-stranded and not double-stranded like DNA. There are three types of RNA that are needed to convert genes into proteins: messenger RNA (mRNA), transfer RNA (tRNA), and ribosomal RNA (rRNA).

ribonucleic acid (RNA) a nucleic acid consisting of nucleotides comprised of the sugar ribose and nitrogenous bases

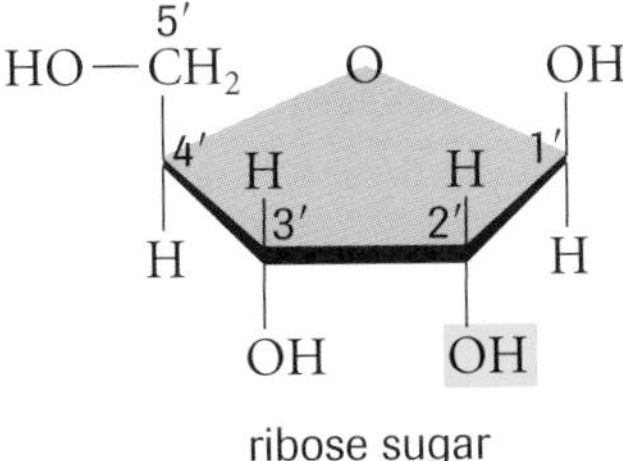

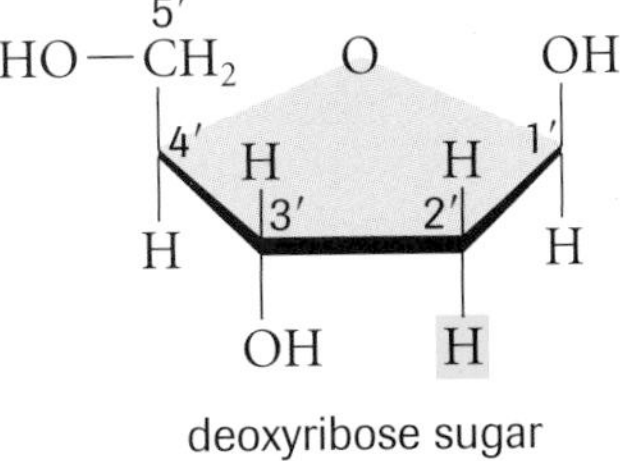

Figure 1
A ribose sugar possesses an –OH group (hydroxyl) on the 2′ carbon. The deoxyribose sugar is missing the –OH group on the 2′ carbon. The *deoxy* part of the name deoxyribose indicates a "loss of oxygen" at position 2.

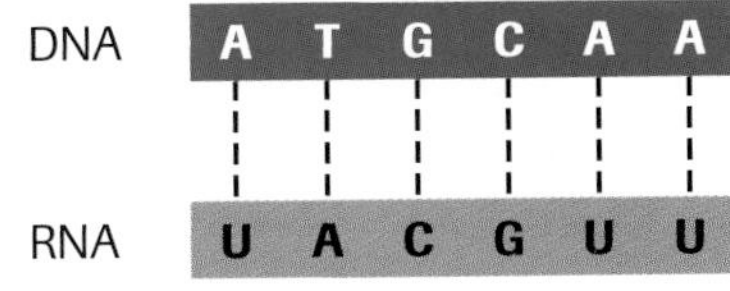

Figure 2
Base pairing of RNA with DNA during transcription. Notice that thymine does not exist in RNA but is substituted with uracil.

The Central Dogma

There are two main stages of gene expression, transcription and translation. In **transcription**, the genetic information is converted from a DNA sequence into **messenger RNA** (**mRNA**). In all cells, the mRNA carries the genetic information from the chromosome to the site of protein synthesis. In eukaryotic cells, which contain a nucleus, the mRNA carries the genetic information from the nucleus to the cytoplasm as it passes through the pores in the nuclear envelope.

transcription the process of converting DNA into messenger RNA

messenger RNA (mRNA) the product of transcription of a gene; mRNA is translated by ribosomes into protein

The second stage of gene expression is **translation**. During translation, the genetic information carried by the mRNA is used to synthesize a polypeptide chain.

translation the process of synthesizing a specific polypeptide as coded for by messenger RNA

The two-step process of transferring genetic information from DNA to RNA and then from RNA to protein is known as the central dogma of molecular genetics (**Figure 3**, next page). We will explore transcription and translation in more detail in this section. You

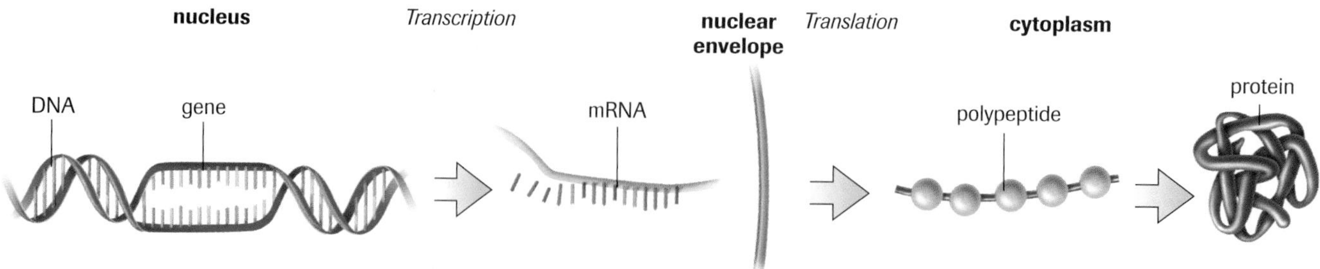

Figure 3
The central dogma of molecular genetics

will see that the sequence of nucleotides in a gene determines the sequence of amino acids in a polypeptide.

Transcription

During transcription, the DNA sequence of a gene is copied (transcribed) into the sequence of a single-stranded mRNA molecule.

Transcription is divided into three processes: initiation, elongation, and termination. During initiation, an enzyme called **RNA polymerase** binds to the DNA at a specific site near the beginning of the gene. During elongation, RNA polymerase uses the DNA as a template to build the mRNA molecule. During termination, the RNA polymerase passes the end of the gene and comes to a stop. The mRNA is then released from the template strand of DNA.

RNA polymerase enzyme that transcribes DNA

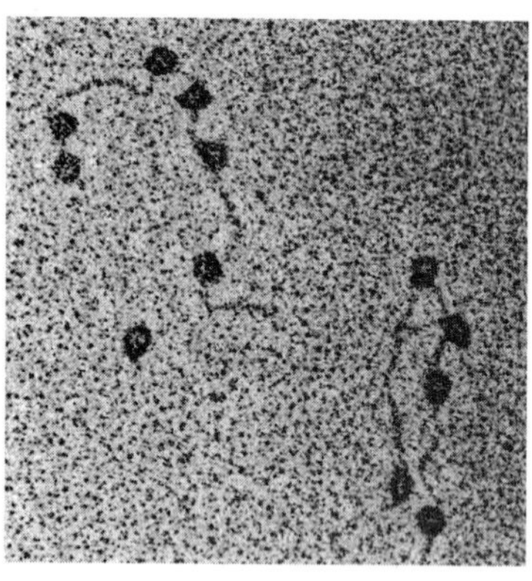

Figure 4
The RNA polymerase (dark circles) binds to the DNA strand and initiates transcription. Transcription occurs simultaneously at numerous locations along the DNA.

Initiation

Transcription starts when the RNA polymerase enzyme binds to the segment of DNA to be transcribed and opens the double helix. **Figure 4** shows an electron micrograph of this process. The RNA polymerase binds to the DNA molecule in front of the gene to be transcribed in a region called the **promoter**. In most genes, the promoter sequence contains a string of adenine and thymine bases that serves as the recognition site for RNA polymerase. The promoter indicates which DNA strand should be transcribed and where the RNA polymerase should start transcribing the DNA. Since the binding site of RNA polymerase only recognizes the promoter region, it can only bind in front of a gene.

promoter sequence of DNA that binds RNA polymerase in front of a gene

Elongation

Once the RNA polymerase binds to the promoter and opens the double helix, it starts building the single-stranded mRNA in the 5′ to 3′ direction. The promoter is not transcribed. The process of elongation of the mRNA molecule is similar to DNA replication. However, RNA polymerase does not require a primer and it copies only one of the DNA strands. The transcribed DNA strand is called the **template strand**. The mRNA sequence is complementary to the DNA template strand except that it contains the base uracil in place of thymine.

template strand the strand of DNA that the RNA polymerase uses as a guide to build complementary mRNA

Termination

Synthesis of the mRNA continues until RNA polymerase reaches the end of the gene. RNA polymerase recognizes the end of the gene when it comes to a stop signal called a **termination sequence**. Transcription stops and the newly synthesized mRNA disconnects from the DNA template strand. RNA polymerase is then free to bind to another promoter region and transcribe another gene. **Figure 5**, on the next page, summarizes the steps in transcription.

termination sequence sequence of bases at the end of a gene that signals the RNA polymerase to stop transcribing

(a) Initiation RNA polymerase binds to DNA at a promoter.	RNA polymerase DNA promoter
(b) DNA double helix is unwound, exposing the template strand.	template strand
(c) Elongation mRNA is synthesized using one strand of DNA as a template. mRNA is synthesized in the 5′ to 3′ direction.	mRNA
(d) As elongation proceeds, RNA polymerase moves along DNA, synthesizing mRNA. DNA that has already been transcribed rewinds into a double helix.	DNA has rewound direction of transcription 5′ mRNA
(e) RNA polymerase reaches the termination sequence at end of gene.	5′ 3′
(f) Termination Transcription stops. mRNA and RNA polymerase are released.	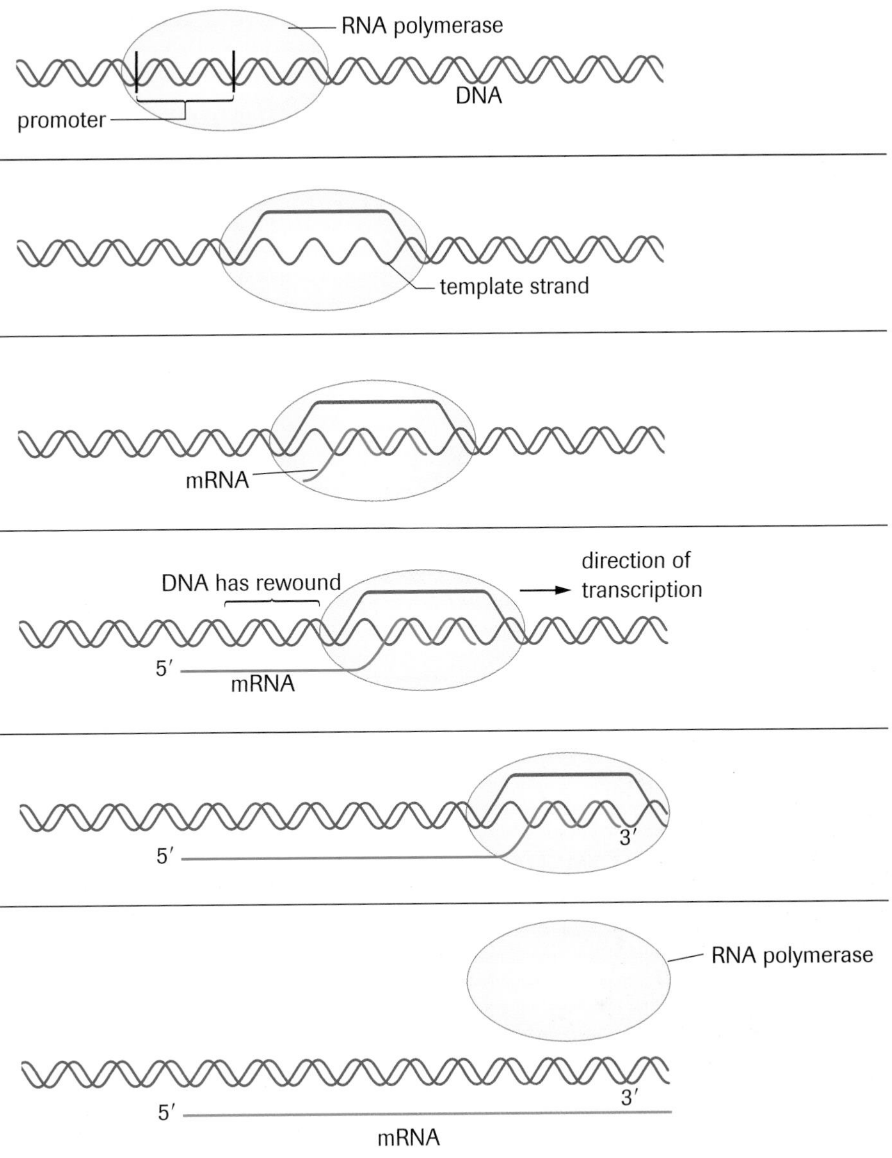 RNA polymerase 3′ 5′ mRNA

Figure 5
A summary of the process of transcription

Practice

1. A short fragment of a particular gene includes the following sequence of nucleotides:

   TACTACGGT

   Write out the corresponding mRNA transcript.

2. A short fragment of another gene includes the following sequence of nucleotides:

   ACCATAATATTACCGACCT TCG

   (a) Explain the purpose of the promoter region in transcription.

   (b) Copy the sequence into your notebook and circle the promoter region. Explain the rationale for your selection.

EXTENSION

Regulation of Transcription

This audio clip discusses the regulatory factors that control when and how much mRNA is transcribed from a given gene.

www.science.nelson.com GO

Translation

The second part of the central dogma of molecular biology (**Figure 3**, page 668) is the translation of the genetic information carried by mRNA into a chain of amino acids to form a polypeptide. Therefore, the process of translation involves protein synthesis, and it depends on the remarkable nature of the genetic code.

Only 20 amino acids are found in proteins. The DNA in a gene codes for these 20 amino acids by combinations of the four nitrogenous bases. During translation, the DNA code is read in groups of three nucleotides, called a **codon**. Each codon calls for a specific amino acid to be placed in the growing polypeptide chain. Codons can consist of any combination of the four nitrogenous bases, so there are 64 ($4^3 = 64$) possible different codons for the 20 different amino acids. The groups of three bases in both DNA and mRNA are both called codons, so it is important to clarify which code is being presented when writing out a genetic sequence. The remainder of this description will use mRNA codons. **Table 1** shows the mRNA codons. One of these codons (AUG) is the **start codon**, where translation begins. It also codes for the insertion of the amino acid methionine, so all polypeptide chains initially start with the methionine, but it may later be edited out. Three other codons (UAA, UAG, and UGA) do not code for amino acids and are called the **stop codons** because they cause protein synthesis to stop. The other 60 codons code for one of the 20 amino acids. Some amino acids have more than one codon; for example, both serine and leucine each have 6 different codons. **Table 2**, on the next page, lists the abbreviations for the amino acids to help you look them up in **Table 1**.

codon sequence of three bases in DNA or complementary mRNA that serves as a code for a particular amino acid

start codon specific codon (AUG) that signals the start of translation

stop codon specific codon that signals the end of translation

Like transcription, translation can be divided into the same three stages: initiation, elongation, and termination.

Table 1 Codons and Their Amino Acids

	2nd (middle) Base of a Codon				
1st Base	**U**	**C**	**A**	**G**	**3rd Base**
U	UUU Phe UUC Phe UUA Leu UUG Leu	UCU Ser UCC Ser UCA Ser UCG Ser	UAU Tyr UAC Tyr UAA STOP UAG STOP	UGU Cys UGC Cys UGA STOP UGG Trp	U C A S
C	CUU Leu CUC Leu CUA Leu CUG Leu	CCU Pro CCC Pro CCA Pro CCG Pro	CAU His CAC His CAA Gln CAG Gln	CGU Arg CGC Arg CGA Arg CGG Arg	U C A S
A	AUU Ile AUC Ile AUA Ile **AUG Met**	ACU Thr ACC Thr ACA Thr ACG Thr	AAU Asn AAC Asn AAA Lys AAG Lys	AGU Ser AGC Ser AGA Arg AGG Arg	U C A S
G	GUU Val GUC Val GUA Val GUG Val	GCU Ala GCC Ala GCA Ala GCG Ala	GAU Asp GAC Asp GAA Glu GAG Glu	GGU Gly GGC Gly GGA Gly GGG Gly	U C A S

EXTENSION

Why Three Nucleotides per Codon?

Why are there always three nucleotides in a codon? Why not two or four? Listen to this audio clip to find out the reason behind the triplet code found in DNA and mRNA sequences.

www.science.nelson.com 

Initiation

ribosome an organelle composed of RNA and protein and located in the cytoplasm that carries out protein synthesis

Initiation of translation occurs when a **ribosome** recognizes a specific sequence on the mRNA and binds to that site. In eukaryotes, the ribosome consists of two subunits, a large subunit and a small subunit (**Figure 6**, next page). The two subunits bind to the mRNA, clamping it between them. The ribosome then moves along the mRNA in the 5′ to 3′ direction, adding a new amino acid to the growing polypeptide chain each time it

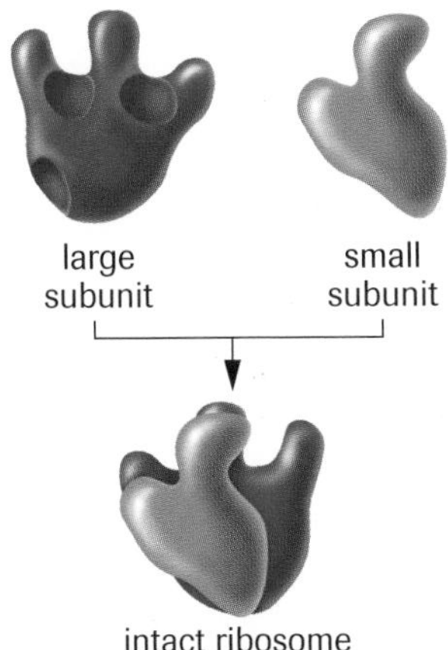

Figure 6
Ribosomes consist of a large subunit and a small subunit.

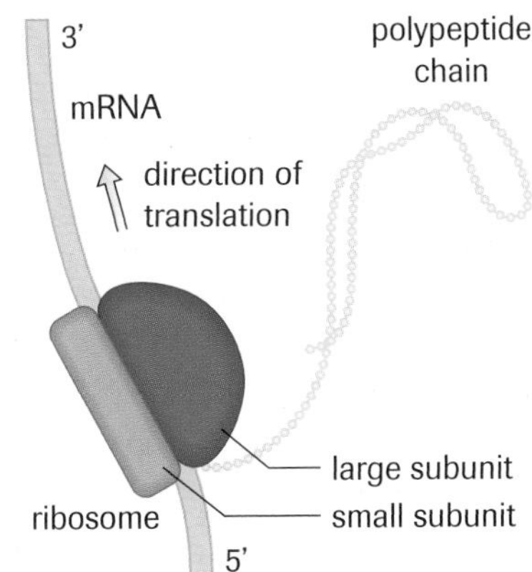

Figure 7
The large and small subunit of a ribosome work together to translate a strand of mRNA into a polypeptide. The polypeptide grows as the ribosome moves farther along the mRNA strand.

reads a codon (**Figure 7**). Ribosomes synthesize different proteins by associating with different mRNAs and reading their coding sequences.

A ribosome must begin reading the coding sequence at the correct place in the mRNA, or it will misread all the codons. The first codon that it recognizes is the start codon AUG. Binding to the start codon ensures that the ribosome translates the genetic code using the reading frame of the mRNA molecule. It is critical that the mRNA be positioned in the ribosome in its reading frame so that the genetic code is translated into the correct sequence of amino acids.

Once the ribosome has bound the mRNA, how does it get the amino acids that correspond to the codon? This job falls to a second type of RNA molecule known as **transfer RNA** (**tRNA**). At one end of the tRNA there is a sequence of three bases, the **anticodon**, that is complementary to the codon of the mRNA. The opposite end carries the corresponding amino acid (**Figure 8**, next page). For example, if the mRNA has the codon UAU, the complementary base sequence of the anticodon is AUA, and the tRNA would carry the amino acid tyrosine. Check **Table 1** to find the mRNA codon and prove to yourself that it calls for tyrosine. Every tRNA carries only one specific amino acid, which means that at least 20 different tRNAs are required. Recall that there are 64 possible codons. In reality, anywhere from 20 to 64 types of tRNA molecules are available, depending on the organism.

Table 2 Amino Acids and Their Abbreviations

Amino acid	Three-letter abbreviation
alanine	Ala
arginine	Arg
asparagine	Asn
aspartic acid	Asp
cysteine	Cys
glutamic acid	Glu
glutamine	Gln
glycine	Gly
histidine	His
isoleucine	Ile
leucine	Leu
lysine	Lys
methionine	Met
phenylalanine	Phe
proline	Pro
serine	Ser
threonine	Thr
tryptophan	Trp
tyrosine	Tyr
valine	Val

transfer RNA (tRNA) the form of RNA that delivers amino acids to a ribosome during translation

anticodon group of three complementary bases on tRNA that recognizes and pairs with a codon on the mRNA

Practice

3. Transcribe the following sequence of DNA into mRNA.
   TACGGATTTCTCCGCAAATTAGGG
4. Translate the following mRNA sequence into an amino acid sequence.
   5′-AUGCCCUCUAUUCCGGGAAGAUAG-3′
5. How many nucleotides are necessary in the DNA to code for the following sequence of amino acids?
   Leu-Tyr-Arg-Trp-Ser

DID YOU KNOW?

RNA Polymerase I, II, III

There are three forms of the RNA polymerase in eukaryotes: RNA polymerase I transcribes ribosomal RNA; RNA polymerase II transcribes mRNA; and RNA polymerase III transcribes tRNA and other short genes that are about 100 base pairs in length.

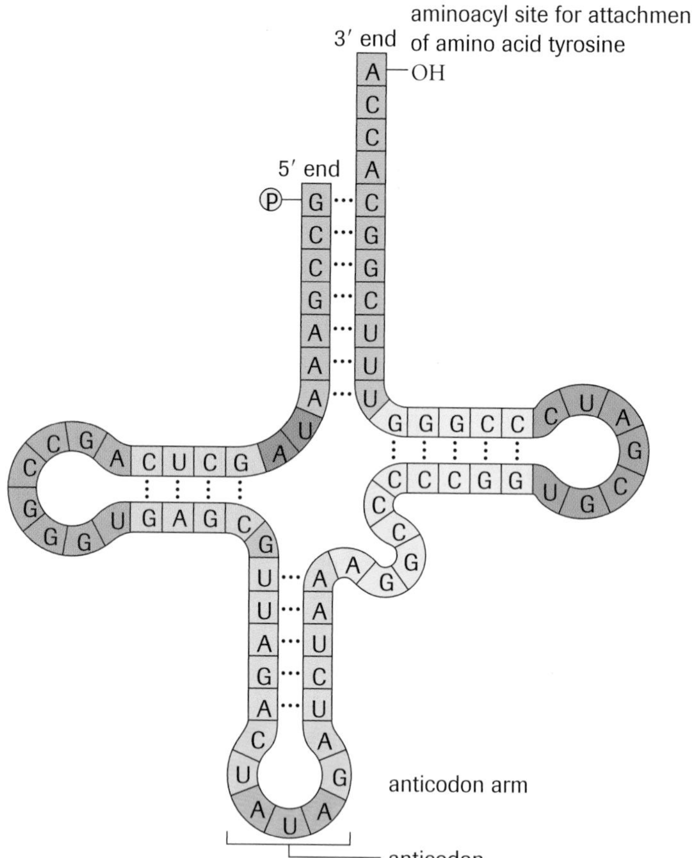

Figure 8

The tRNA molecule has a cloverleaf structure. The molecule folds to form this structure because of hydrogen bonding. The anticodon is located on the anticodon arm and the amino acid is covalently bound to the adenine nucleotide at the 3′ end (aminoacyl). In this case, the amino acid that would be added is tyrosine because the anticodon is AUA.

Elongation

The first codon that is recognized by the ribosome is the start codon AUG. The AUG codon also codes for methionine, so every protein initially starts with the amino acid methionine. The ribosome has two sites for tRNA to attach: the A (aminoacyl) site and the P (peptidyl) site. The tRNA with the anticodon complementary to the start codon enters the P site, as shown in **Figure 9 (a)**. The next tRNA carrying the required amino acid enters the A site, as shown in **Figure 9 (b)**. In **Figure 9 (c)**, a peptide bond has formed between the methionine and the second amino acid, alanine. The ribosome has shifted over one codon so that the second tRNA is now in the P site. This action has released the methionine-carrying tRNA from the ribosome and allowed a third tRNA to enter the empty A site. The process is similar to a tickertape running through a ticker-tape machine, except that the ribosome "machine" moves along the mRNA "tickertape." The tRNAs that have been released are recycled in the cell cytoplasm by adding new amino acids to them. The process continues until the entire code of the mRNA has been translated and the ribosome reaches a stop codon, as shown in **Figures 9 (d)** and **(e)**.

From DNA to Protein

The discovery of the relationship between DNA, mRNA, ribosomes, tRNA, and protein was the result of numerous scientists working on separate pieces of the puzzle. Watch an online animation of their studies.

www.science.nelson.com 

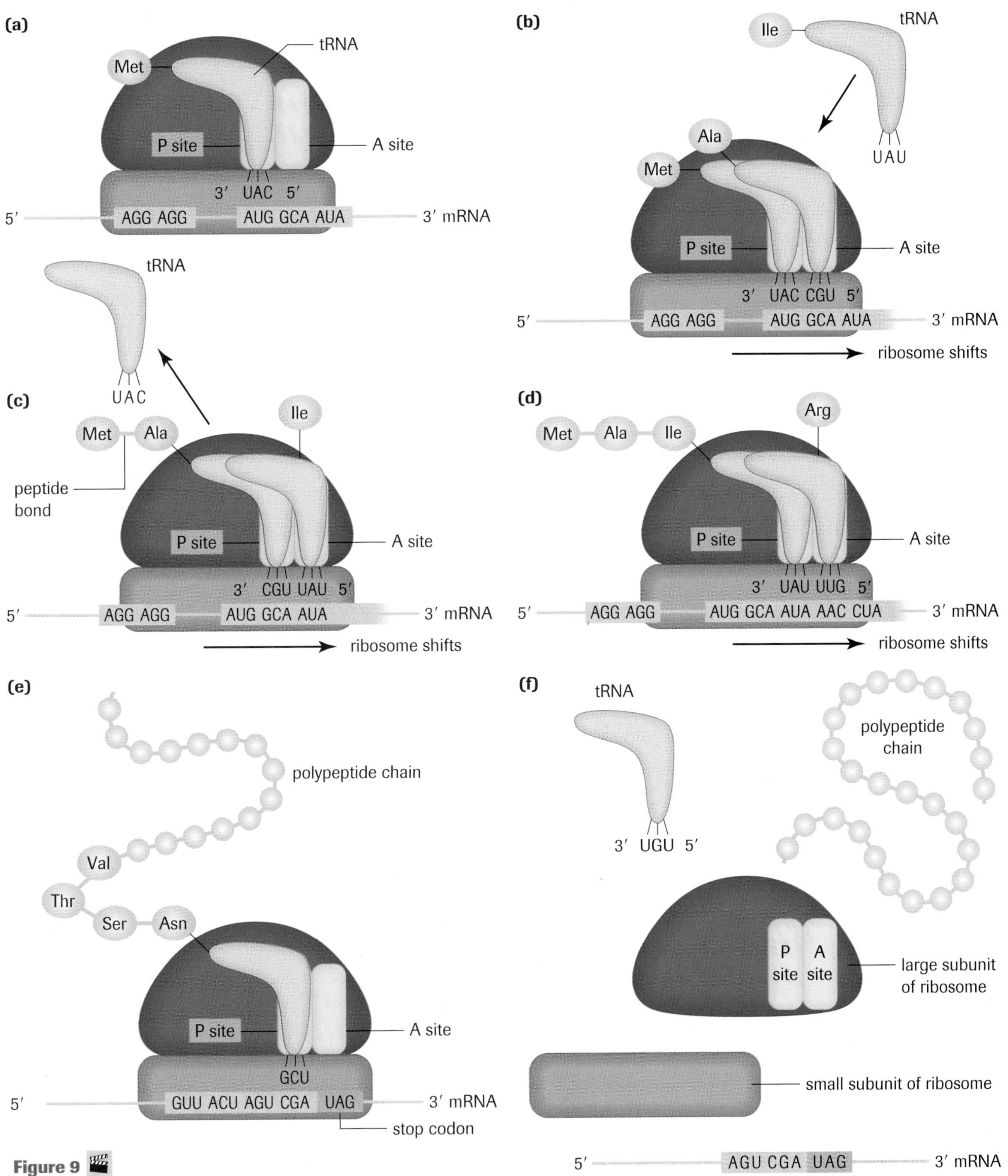

Figure 9
Protein synthesis
(a) The first tRNA that is brought into the P site carries methionine because the start codon is AUG.
(b) The second tRNA enters the A site.
(c) A peptide bond forms between methionine and alanine. The ribosome shifts one codon over and the next tRNA brings in the appropriate amino acid into the A site.
(d) The ribosome moves the mRNA and another amino acid is added to the chain.
(e) The process is repeated until the ribosome reaches a stop codon for which no tRNA exists.
(f) A release-factor protein helps break apart the ribosome–mRNA complex, releasing the polypeptide chain.

Termination

Eventually, the ribosome reaches one of the three stop codons: UGA, UAG, or UAA. Since these three codons do not code for an amino acid, there are no corresponding tRNAs. A protein known as a release factor recognizes that the ribosome has stalled and helps release the polypeptide chain from the ribosome. As shown in **Figure 9 (f)**, on the previous page, the two subunits of the ribosome now fall off the mRNA and translation stops.

LAB EXERCISE 20.A

Report Checklist

- ○ Purpose
- ○ Problem
- ○ Hypothesis
- ○ Prediction
- ○ Design
- ○ Materials
- ○ Procedure
- ○ Evidence
- ● Analysis
- ○ Evaluation
- ○ Synthesis

Synthesis of a Protein

In this activity, you are provided with a DNA nucleotide sequence that codes for a hypothetical protein. The code is given in three fragments. This DNA code is from a eukaryotic cell so in the mRNA transcript there are extra codons called introns. Eukaryotic cells cut these sequences out of the mRNA before it leaves the nucleus, so the codons are transcribed but are not translated.

In this exercise, you will transcribe the three pieces of DNA code into mRNA and identify the beginning fragment, the middle fragment, and the end fragment. In addition, you will remove the intron segment and translate the mRNA into the protein.

Procedure

1. Copy each of the following sequences onto a separate piece of paper. (*Hint:* Turn your paper so you can write the sequence out along the horizontal length of the paper. Leave room below each sequence to write your mRNA sequence directly below.)

   Sequence A
   CTCGCGCCGAAACTTCCCTCCTAAACGTTCAAC
   CGGTTCTTAATCCGCCGCCAGGGCCCC

   Sequence B
   CGTAACAACTTGTTACAACATGGTCATAAACGTCA
   GATGGTCAATCTCTTAATGACT

   Sequence C
   TACAAACATGTAAACACACCCTCAGTGGACCAA
   CTCCGCAACATAAACCAAACACCG

2. Divide the sequences into triplets (codons) by putting a slash between each group of three bases.
3. Transcribe the DNA into mRNA.
4. Identify the middle, end, and beginning sequence. Use your knowledge of start and stop codons to help you figure it out. (*Hint:* You will need to examine the codons that start and end a fragment.)
5. Remove codons 24 to 51, including codon 51. These codons are the intron, or extra codons, found in this DNA segment.
6. Translate the mRNA into protein using the genetic code.

Analysis

(a) Which fragment was the beginning fragment? How do you know?

(b) Which fragment was the end fragment? How do you know?

(c) Codons 24 to 51 represent an intron. If the introns were not cut out of the mRNA before it leaves the nucleus and attaches to a ribosome, what would happen to the protein structure? Is it likely that this protein would still perform the same function? Explain your answer.

(d) How many amino acids does this protein contain?

(e) Is this genetic sequence eukaryotic or prokaryotic? How do you know?

(f) If you worked backward, starting with the amino acid sequence of the protein, would you obtain the same DNA nucleotide sequence? Why or why not?

(g) Provide the anticodon sequence that would build this protein.

INVESTIGATION 20.1 *Introduction*

Protein Synthesis and Inactivation of Antibiotics

Each protein has a specific function. Its presence or absence in a cell may make the difference between life and death. Bacteria that carry an ampicillin-resistance gene produce a protein that inactivates the antibiotic ampicillin. What happens when they are grown on ampicillin-rich media? This investigation allows you to observe the effects of the presence and function of a specific gene.

Report Checklist

● Purpose	● Design	● Analysis
○ Problem	○ Materials	● Evaluation
● Hypothesis	○ Procedure	● Synthesis
● Prediction	● Evidence	

To perform this investigation, turn to page 695.

SUMMARY *Gene Expression*

Table 3 Summary of Transcription

Initiation
• Initiation of transcription starts when the RNA polymerase binds to the promoter region of the gene to be transcribed. • The DNA is unwound and the double helix is disrupted.
Elongation
• A complementary messenger RNA (mRNA) molecule is synthesized in the 5′ to 3′ direction, using one strand of DNA as a template. • Adenine (A) bases in the DNA are paired with uracil (U) in the mRNA. • Transcription continues until the RNA polymerase reaches a termination sequence.
Termination
• When the RNA polymerase comes to a termination sequence, it falls off the DNA molecule. • The mRNA separates from the DNA.

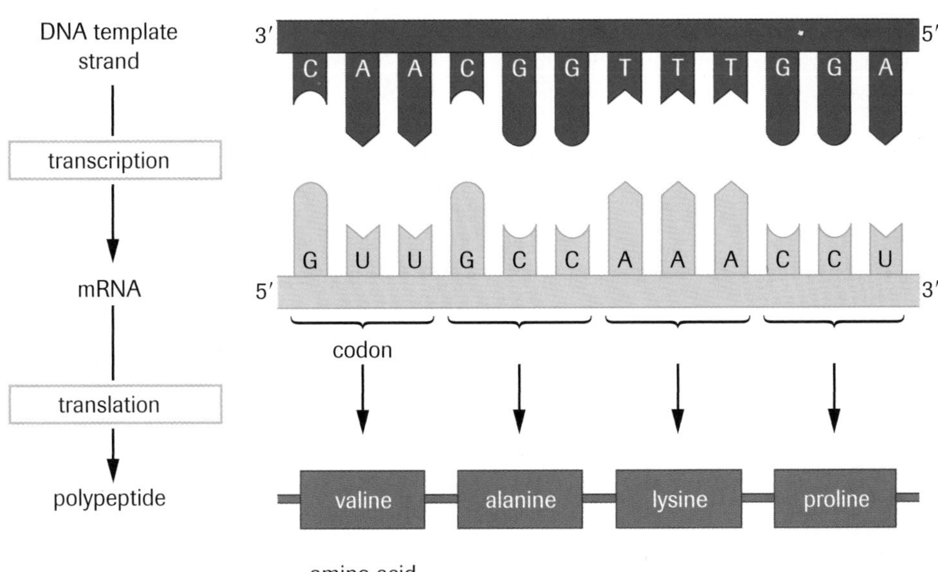

Figure 10
An overview of gene expression

Table 4 Summary of Translation

Initiation
• Ribosome subunits (large and small) bind to the mRNA transcript, sandwiching the mRNA between them. • The ribosome moves along the mRNA, reading the codons. • Translation begins when the ribosome reaches the start codon, AUG.
Elongation
• Through the genetic code, each codon specifies a particular one of the 20 amino acids that make up polypeptides. • Transfer RNA (tRNA) molecules have an anticodon that is complementary to the codon in the mRNA. The tRNA carries the amino acid specified by the codon. • The ribosome contains two sites, the A (aminoacyl) site and the P (peptidyl) site. • When the start codon is in the P site, the first tRNA delivers methionine. Since the start codon codes for methionine, all polypeptides initially start with this amino acid. • The second codon of the mRNA is exposed at the same time in the A site. When the tRNA delivers the second amino acid, a peptide bond is formed between the two amino acids. • The ribosome shifts over one codon. The tRNA that delivered the methionine is released from the P site. • When the ribosome shifts, the tRNA containing the growing polypeptide moves to the P site. A third amino acid, specified by the third codon, is brought in to the A site by the next tRNA. A peptide bond is formed between the second and third amino acid. • Amino acids continue to be added to the polypeptide until a stop codon is read in the A site.
Termination
• The stop codons are UAG, UGA, and UAA. At this point the ribosome stalls. • A protein known as the release factor recognizes that the ribosome has stalled and causes the ribosome subunits to disassemble, releasing the mRNA and newly formed polypeptide.

Section 20.2 Questions

1. State the central dogma of molecular genetics.
2. Describe the role of the following molecules in gene expression: ribosomes, mRNA, tRNA.
3. The genetic code is read in groups of three nucleotides called codons. Explain why reading the code in pairs of nucleotides is not sufficient.
4. The following is the sequence of a fragment of DNA:

   GGATCAGGTCCATAC

   Transcribe this sequence into mRNA.
5. Using the genetic code, decipher the following mRNA sequence:

   5′ - AUGGGACAUUAUUUUGCCCGUUGUGGU - 3′
6. The amino acid sequence for a certain peptide is Leu–Tyr–Arg–Trp–Ser. How many nucleotides are necessary in the DNA to code for this peptide?
7. Identify which step in transcription would be affected and predict what would happen in each situation:
   (a) The termination sequence of a gene is removed.
   (b) RNA polymerase fails to recognize the promoter.
8. Construct a table to compare the processes of replication and transcription. Remember to consider both similarities and differences.
9. Distinguish between the following terms:
   (a) P site and A site
   (b) codon and anticodon
   (c) start and stop codon
   (d) DNA and RNA
10. Identify which of the following selections correctly lists the anticodons for the amino acids threonine, alanine, and proline:
   A. ACU GCU CCA
   B. ACT GCT CCA
   C. TGA CGA GGT
   D. UGA CGA GGU
11. Errors are occasionally made during the process of transcription. Explain why these errors do not always result in an incorrect sequence of amino acids. Describe at least two examples to illustrate your answer.

DNA and Biotechnology 20.3

Carpenters require tools such as hammers, screwdrivers, and saws, and surgeons require scalpels, forceps, and stitching needles. The tools of the molecular biologist are living biological organisms or biological molecules. Using these tools, scientists can treat specific DNA sequences as modules and move them from one DNA molecule to another, forming **recombinant DNA**. Research in exploring and using this type of biotechnology has led to exciting new advances in biological, agricultural, and medical technology. Biotechnology research has also found ways to introduce specific DNA sequences into a living cell. For example, the gene that encodes insulin has been introduced into bacterial cells so that they become living factories producing this vital hormone. The introduction and expression of foreign DNA in an organism is called **genetic transformation**. In this section, you will explore some of the key tools used by molecular geneticists in producing recombinant DNA and genetically transformed organisms.

recombinant DNA fragment of DNA composed of sequences originating from at least two different sources

genetic transformation introduction and expression of foreign DNA in a living organism

DNA Sequencing

Before a DNA sequence can be used to make recombinant DNA or to transform an organism, the scientist or technician must first identify and isolate a piece of DNA containing that sequence. One of the tools used to do this is DNA sequencing. DNA sequencing determines the exact sequence of base pairs for a particular DNA fragment or molecule. In 1975, the first DNA sequencing techniques were simultaneously developed by Frederick Sanger and his colleagues and by Alan Maxim and Walter Gilbert. Sanger's technique relied on first replicating short segments of DNA that terminate due to a chain-terminating nucleotide. Four separate reaction tubes are run, each with a chain-terminating nucleotide incorporating a different base (i.e., A, T, G, and C). The various lengths of DNA segments are then separated by loading and running the contents of the tubes on a sequencing gel (**Figure 1**). Because the end nucleotide of each segment is chain-terminating, its base is already known. Consequently, the sequence can be read directly from the gel in ascending order (shortest to longest segments). The sequence of the strand is written along the edge of the gel diagram, starting from the bottom where the shortest strands have travelled. This method is comparatively slow and can only sequence short fragments of DNA.

DNA can also be sequenced in a test tube using isolated segments of DNA. This technique depends on a primer, DNA polymerase, and the four DNA nucleotides, each of which is labelled with a specific dye. The complementary strand is built from these dye-labelled nucleotides. The nucleotides in the synthesized strand can then be identified by their colours, allowing the original strand sequence to be deduced according to the rules of complementary base pairing.

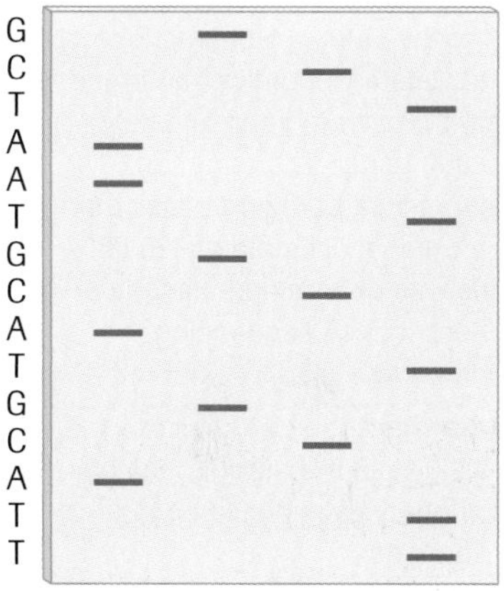

Figure 1
A sequencing gel is a matrix containing many small spaces. The DNA fragments are charged and will move towards one pole of an electric field. Smaller DNA fragments move through the spaces more quickly than larger fragments and are found at the bottom of the gel. The larger fragments will remain towards the top of the gel. The resulting ladder of fragments can be read, giving the sequence of the initial DNA fragment.

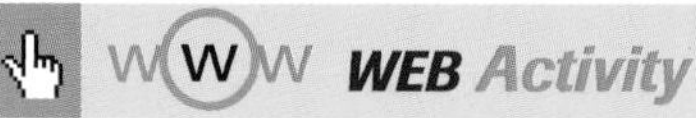

Simulation—Electrophoresis

Electrophoresis is an important tool in molecular biology. In addition to nucleic acids, it is also used to separate proteins from a mixture. Electrophoresis of nucleic acids and proteins depend on the similar factors. In this Virtual Biology Lab, you will perform polyacrylamide gel electrophoresis (PAGE) to identify proteins involved in the biochemistry of shell colour in an extinct organism.

www.science.nelson.com GO

Figure 2
Dr. Judith Hall

Canadian Achievers—Researchers in Human Genetic Disorders

Advances in biotechnology have led a greater understanding of many human genetic disorders. These advances have involved many research teams working together, either directly or by publishing their work in peer-reviewed articles. The following list shows some Canadians who are among the researchers making important contributions:

- Dr. Michael Hayden, University of British Columbia: Huntington disease
- Dr. Lap-Chee Tsui, Hospital for Sick Children, Toronto: cystic fibrosis
- Dr. Judith Hall, University of British Columbia: cystic fibrosis
- Dr. Christine Bear, University of Toronto: cystic fibrosis
- Dr. Ron Warton, Hospital for Sick Children, Toronto: Duchenne muscular dystrophy

Go to the Nelson Web site to find more information on the work of these people. After you have completed reading this material, write a short paragraph that describes your view on the importance of genetic research. Defend your position.

www.science.nelson.com 

DID YOU KNOW ?

Genome Facts

On February 15, 2001, scientists from the Human Genome Project and Celera Genomics confirmed that there were approximately 30 000 genes in the human genome—a number far less than the original estimate of 120 000. This was determined using two different DNA sequencing techniques.

Other Facts

- 99.9 % of the nitrogenous base sequences is the same in all humans.
- Only 5 % of the genes contains the instructions for producing functional proteins; the remaining 95 % does not have any known function.
- A worm has approximately 18 000 genes; a yeast cell has about 6000.

The Human Genome Project

In a series of meetings held in the mid-1980s, plans were developed to begin the process of producing maps of the entire genetic makeup of a human being. The international project began in the United States in October 1990 with James Watson, of Nobel Prize fame, as one of the first directors. The human genome consists of approximately 30 000 genes, with the 23 pairs of chromosomes containing an estimated 3 billion pairs of nucleotides. Constructing the genome map involved using mapping techniques (similar to those you read about in Chapter 19) and DNA sequencing technology. When the project began, only about 4500 genes had been identified and sequenced. The collaborative efforts of many scientists from numerous countries and rapid improvements in sequencing techniques helped complete the gene map by June 2000 (**Table 1**).

Table 1 Milestones in Genome Mapping

Milestone	Date
human chromosome 22 completed (the first chromosome to be mapped)	December 1999
Drosophila genome completed	March 2000
human chromosomes 5, 16, 19 mapped	April 2000
human chromosome 21 completely mapped	May 2000
human genome completely mapped	June 2000

A DNA sequencing technique based on the one developed by Sanger was the most common method used in the project. In this technique, pieces of DNA are replicated and changed so that the fragments, each ending with one of the four nucleotides, can be detected by a laser. Automated equipment can then determine the exact number of nucleotides in the chain. A computer is used to combine the huge amount of data and reconstruct the original DNA sequence.

Prior to the Human Genome Project, the genes for hereditary disorders such as cystic fibrosis, muscular dystrophy, and Huntington disease had been identified. The aim of the project is to add to this list so that new drugs and genetic therapies can be developed to

▶ mini *Investigation* *Examining the Human Genome*

In this activity, you will go to an online map of the human genome. On the map, you will find diagrams containing information about every chromosome in the genome. The magenta and green regions on the diagrams reflect the unique patterns of light and dark bands seen on human chromosomes that have been stained for viewing through a light microscope. The red region represents the centromere or constricted portion of the chromosome. On other chromosome diagrams, you will see yellow regions that mark chromosomal areas that vary in staining intensity. The chromatin in these areas is condensed and sometimes known as heterochromatin, meaning "different colour." Some diagrams have yellow regions overlaid by thin horizontal magenta lines. This colour pattern indicates variable regions called stalks that connect very small chromosome arms (satellites) to the chromosome.

www.science.nelson.com 

Go to the Nelson Web site, and follow the link for Mini Investigation: Examining the Human Genome. On the genome map, click on each chromosome diagram to discover the traits and disorders located on that chromosome. For example, **Figure 3** shows traits and disorders that are found on chromosome 20.

Touch each chromosome pair to find the number of genes mapped on that chromosome.

Use the information you find to answer the questions below.

(a) Which chromosome pair contains the greatest number of genes?

(b) Which chromosome contains the fewest genes?

(c) Estimate the size of the human genome. Show how you calculated your estimate.

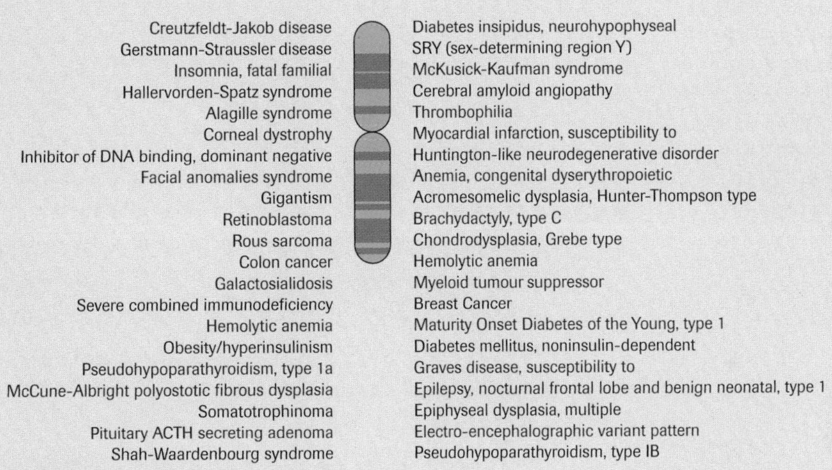

Creutzfeldt-Jakob disease
Gerstmann-Straussler disease
Insomnia, fatal familial
Hallervorden-Spatz syndrome
Alagille syndrome
Corneal dystrophy
Inhibitor of DNA binding, dominant negative
Facial anomalies syndrome
Gigantism
Retinoblastoma
Rous sarcoma
Colon cancer
Galactosialidosis
Severe combined immunodeficiency
Hemolytic anemia
Obesity/hyperinsulinism
Pseudohypoparathyroidism, type 1a
McCune-Albright polyostotic fibrous dysplasia
Somatotrophinoma
Pituitary ACTH secreting adenoma
Shah-Waardenbourg syndrome

Diabetes insipidus, neurohypophyseal
SRY (sex-determining region Y)
McKusick-Kaufman syndrome
Cerebral amyloid angiopathy
Thrombophilia
Myocardial infarction, susceptibility to
Huntington-like neurodegenerative disorder
Anemia, congenital dyserythropoietic
Acromesomelic dysplasia, Hunter-Thompson type
Brachydactyly, type C
Chondrodysplasia, Grebe type
Hemolytic anemia
Myeloid tumour suppressor
Breast Cancer
Maturity Onset Diabetes of the Young, type 1
Diabetes mellitus, noninsulin-dependent
Graves disease, susceptibility to
Epilepsy, nocturnal frontal lobe and benign neonatal, type 1
Epiphyseal dysplasia, multiple
Electro-encephalographic variant pattern
Pseudohypoparathyroidism, type IB

Figure 3
Although chromosome 20 is one of the smallest chromosomes, it has a great number of genes.

combat genetic disorders. The project also may open a Pandora's box of ethical questions, legal dilemmas, and societal problems. Who will own or control the information obtained and how will we prevent potential misuse of the data?

Enzymes and Recombinant DNA

As you have seen in this section, DNA sequencing is one way to identify specific segments of DNA. Another way is by creating genetic linkage maps, as you saw in Chapter 18. Once a particular segment of DNA has been identified, molecular biologists may use enzymes to isolate that segment or modify it. The DNA fragment may then be used to create recombinant DNA or be transferred to another organism. We will review some of the most commonly used enzymes.

CAREER **CONNECTION** 

Biotechnologist

Biotechnologists are involved in improving and developing processes and products used in agriculture, health care, and the chemical industry. A biotechnologist needs specialized knowledge of biochemistry, microbiology, and molecular genetics. Find out more about opportunities in this field.

www.science.nelson.com 

Restriction Endonucleases

Restriction endonucleases, otherwise known as restriction enzymes, are like molecular scissors that can cut double-stranded DNA at a specific base-pair sequence. Each type of restriction enzyme recognizes a particular sequence of nucleotides that is known as its **recognition site**. Molecular biologists use these enzymes to cut DNA in a predictable and precise way. Most recognition sites are four to eight base pairs long and are usually characterized by a complementary **palindromic** sequence (**Table 2**). For example, look at the restriction enzyme *Eco*RI. This sequence is palindromic because both strands have the same base sequence when read in the 5′ to 3′ direction.

restriction endonuclease an enzyme that cuts double-stranded DNA into fragments at a specific sequence; also known as a restriction enzyme

recognition site a specific sequence within double-stranded DNA that a restriction endonuclease recognizes and cuts

palindromic reading the same backwards and forwards

Table 2 Restriction Enzymes and Their Recognition Sites

Microorganism of origin	Enzyme	Recognition site	After restriction enzyme digestion
Escherichia coli	*Eco*RI	5′-GAATTC-3′ 3′-CTTAAG-5′	5′-G AATTC-3′ 3′-CTTAA G-5′
Serratia marcescens	*Sma*I	5′-CCCGGG-3′ 3′-GGGCCC-5′	5′-GGG CCC-3′ 3′-CCC GGG-5′
Arthrobacter luteus	*Alu*I	5′-AGCT-3′ 3′-TCGA-5′	5′-AG CT-3′ 3′-TC GA-5′
Streptomyces albus	*Sal*I	5′-GTCGAC-3′ 3′-CAGCTG-5′	5′-G TCGAC-3′ 3′-CAGCT G-5′
Haemophilus parainfluenzae	*Hin*dIII	5′-AAGCTT-3′ 3′-TTCGAA-5′	5′-A AGCTT-3′ 3′-TTCGA A-5′

DID YOU KNOW ?

Maps and Libraries

Restriction endonucleases are also used to create genetic maps and libraries. Go to the Nelson Web site for information on these applications.

www.science.nelson.com 

Figure 4 shows the action of the restriction enzyme *Eco*RI. *Eco*RI scans a DNA molecule and stops when it is able to bind to its recognition site. Once bound to the site, it cuts the bond between the guanine and adenine nucleotides on each strand. At the end of each cleavage site, one strand is longer than the other and has exposed nucleotides that lack complementary bases. The overhangs produced by the exposed DNA nucleotides are called **sticky ends.** *Eco*RI always cuts between the guanine and the adenine nucleotide on each strand. Since A and G are at opposite ends of the recognition site on each of the complementary strands, the result is the overhang, or sticky end, at each cleavage site.

sticky ends fragment ends of a DNA molecule with short single-stranded overhangs, resulting from cleavage by a restriction enzyme

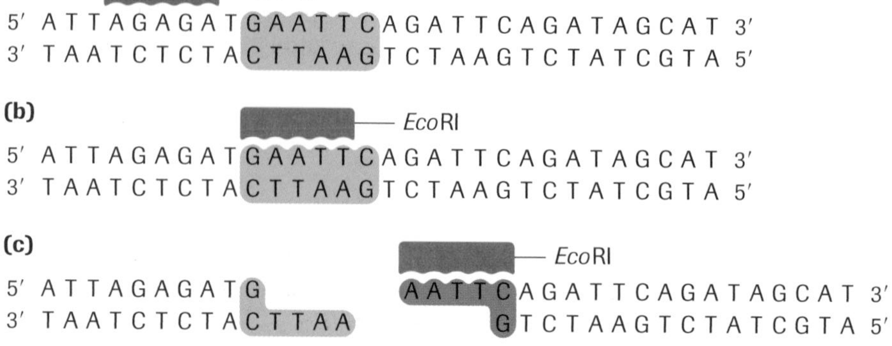

Figure 4
Cleavage of DNA sequence using restriction enzyme *Eco*RI.
(a) *Eco*RI scans the DNA molecule.
(b) *Eco*RI binds to the recognition site.
(c) *Eco*RI cuts between the guanine and adenine nucleotides, producing two fragments with complementary ends.

Not all restriction endonucleases produce sticky ends. For example, the restriction endonuclease *Sma*I produces **blunt ends**, which means that the ends of the DNA fragments are fully base paired (**Table 2**). Since *Sma*I cuts between the cytosine and guanine nucleotides and since these nucleotides are directly opposite each other in their complementary strands, the result is a blunt cut without sticky ends.

blunt ends fragment ends of a DNA molecule that are fully base paired, resulting from cleavage by a restriction enzyme

Restriction endonucleases that produce sticky ends are a generally more useful tool to molecular biologists than those that produce blunt ends. Sticky-end fragments can be joined more easily through complementary base pairing to other sticky-end fragments that were produced by the same restriction endonuclease. However, this is not always possible. To create recombinant DNA, molecular biologists choose restriction enzymes that will not cut in the middle of the DNA sequence of interest. For example, if the goal is to create recombinant DNA containing a particular gene, you would avoid using a restriction enzyme that cuts within the sequence of that gene.

Restriction enzymes are named according to the bacteria they come from. Generally speaking, the first letter is the initial of the genus name of the organism. The second and third letters are usually the initial letters of the species name. The fourth letter indicates the strain, while the numerals indicate the order of discovery of that particular enzyme from that strain of bacteria.

Learning Tip

Restriction enzymes are named according to specific rules. For example, the restriction enzyme *Bam*HI is named as follows:

- *B* represents the genus *Bacillus.*
- *am* represents the species *amyloliquefaciens.*
- *H* represents the strain.
- *I* means that it was the first endonuclease isolated from this strain.

Practice

1. The following sequence of DNA was digested with the restriction endonuclease *Sma*I:

   5′-AATTCGCCCGGGATATTACGGATTATGCATTATCCGCCCGGGATATTTTAGCA-3′

   3′-TTAAGCGGGCCCTATAATGCCTAATACGTAATAGGCGGGCCCTATAAAATCGT-5′

   *Sma*I recognizes the sequence CCCGGG and cuts between the C and the G.

   (a) Copy this sequence into your notebook and clearly identify the location of the cuts on it.

   (b) How many fragments will be produced if *Sma*I digests this sequence?

   (c) What type of ends does *Sma*I produce?

2. *Hin*dIII recognizes the sequence AAGCTT and cleaves between the two A's. What type of end is produced by cleavage with *Hin*dIII?
3. Explain why restriction endonucleases are considered to be molecular tools.
4. Copy the following sequence of DNA into your notebook. Write out the complementary strand. Clearly identify the palindromic sequences by circling them.

   GCGCTAAGGATAGCATTCGAATTCCCAATTAGGATCCTTTAAAGCTTATCC

DID YOU KNOW?

The First Restriction Enzyme

The first restriction endonuclease, *Hin*dIII, was identified in 1970 by Hamilton Smith at John Hopkins University. Smith received the Nobel Prize in 1978 for his discovery. Since then, more than 2500 restriction endonucleases have been identified.

Methylases

Methylases are enzymes that can modify a restriction enzyme recognition site by adding a methyl ($-CH_3$) group to one of the bases in the site (**Figure 5**). Methylases are important tools in recombinant DNA technology. They protect a gene fragment from being cut in an undesired location.

methylase an enzyme that adds a methyl group to one of the nucleotides found in a restriction endonuclease recognition site

Like restriction enzymes, methylases were first identified in bacterial cells. Methylases are used by a bacterium to protect its DNA from digestion by its own restriction enzymes. In bacteria, restriction enzymes provide a crude type of immune system. In fact, the term *restriction* comes from early observations that these enzymes appeared to restrict the infection of *E. coli* cells by viruses known as bacteriophages. The restriction enzymes bind to recognition sites in the viral DNA and cut it, making it useless. Eukaryotic cells also contain methylases. However, in eukaryotes methylation usually occurs in order to inactivate specific genes.

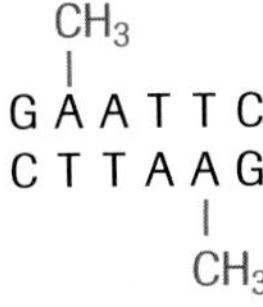

Figure 5
At a methylated *Eco*RI site, *Eco*RI restriction enzyme is no longer able to cut.

DNA Ligase

To create recombinant DNA, pieces of DNA from two sources must be joined together. Using restriction enzymes and methylases, molecular geneticists can engineer fragments of DNA that contain the specific nucleotide sequences they want. These segments of DNA are then joined together by DNA ligase. If two fragments have been generated using the same restriction enzyme, they will be attracted to each other at their complementary sticky ends. Hydrogen bonds will form between the complementary base pairs. DNA ligase then joins the strands of DNA together (**Figure 6**).

DID YOU KNOW ?

Eukaryotic Methylation

Methylases in eukaryotes are connected with the control of transcription. In addition, approximately 2 % of mammalian ribosomal RNA is methylated after it is transcribed.

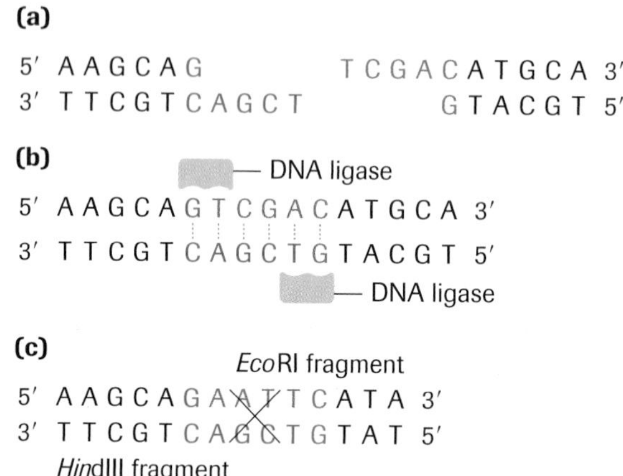

Figure 6
DNA ligase is able to join complementary sticky ends produced by the same restriction enzyme via a condensation reaction.
(a) Complementary sticky ends produced by *Hin*dIII
(b) Hydrogen bonds form between complementary bases. DNA ligase creates bonds between nucleotides in the DNA backbones.
(c) If fragments are not complementary, then hydrogen bonds will not form.

Taq DNA Polymerase and the Polymerase Chain Reaction

polymerase chain reaction (PCR) a technique for amplifying a DNA sequence by repeated cycles of strand separation and replication

In 1985, American scientist Kary Mullis invented a biotechnology technique called the **polymerase chain reaction (PCR)**. PCR allows scientists to make billions of copies of pieces of DNA from extremely small quantities of DNA. The reaction depends on the special property of *Taq* polymerase. In nature, *Taq* DNA polymerase is found in the bacterium *Thermos aquaticus*, which lives at extremely high temperatures. Like all the DNA polymerases, *Taq* DNA polymerase synthesizes DNA during replication. As you have learned previously, enzymes have an optimum temperature range in which they function. One adaptation that allows *Thermos aquaticus* to survive at high temperatures is that its DNA polymerase is stable at much higher temperatures than DNA polymerases from other organisms. Mullis used the heat-stable property of *Taq* polymerase in his PCR technique.

To prepare for PCR, the following materials are placed together in a small tube: *Taq* polymerase, the DNA to be copied, a large quantity of the four deoxynucleotides (A, T, G, and C), and short primers. The tube is then inserted into a PCR machine. PCR involves four simple steps (**Figure 7**).

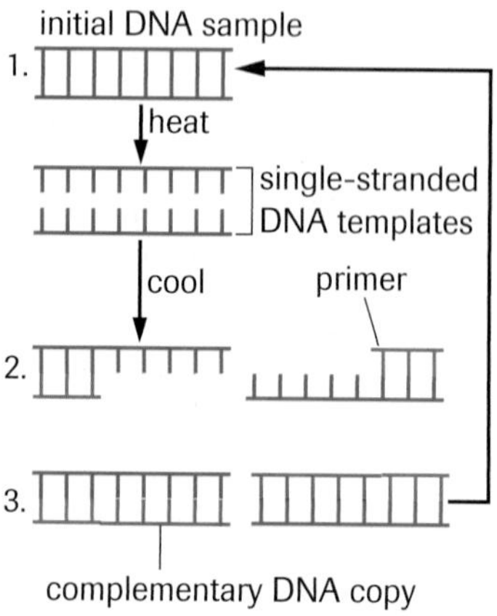

initial DNA sample
1.
heat
single-stranded DNA templates
cool
primer
2.
3.
4.
complementary DNA copy

Figure 7
Steps in the PCR
1. The mixture is heated to a temperature high enough to break the hydrogen bonds in the double helix of the DNA and separate the strands. This forms single-stranded DNA templates.
2. The mixture is cooled, and the primers form hydrogen bonds with the DNA templates.
3. *Taq* polymerase synthesizes a new stand of DNA from the DNA template by complementary base pairing, starting at each primer.
4. The cycle of heating and cooling is repeated many times.

Each PCR cycle doubles the number of DNA molecules. After just 10 cycles there are 2^{10} (over two million) copies of the DNA template. Since scientists can use PCR to synthesize many identical copies from a very small sample of DNA, this technology has led to many advances in medicine, evolutionary biology, genetic engineering, and forensic science. Mullis was awarded the Nobel Prize in Chemistry in 1993 for his invention.

INVESTIGATION 20.2 *Introduction*

Restriction Enzyme Digestion of Bacteriophage DNA

Using restriction enzymes and electrophoresis, molecular biologists are able to excise and isolate target sequences from DNA. How would the banding patterns compare if the same fragment of DNA were digested with different restriction enzymes? In this investigation, you will conduct electrophoresis of bacteriophage DNA that has been digested with restriction enzymes.

Report Checklist

- ● Purpose
- ○ Problem
- ● Hypothesis
- ● Prediction
- ● Design
- ○ Materials
- ○ Procedure
- ● Evidence
- ● Analysis
- ● Evaluation
- ○ Synthesis

To perform this investigation, turn to page 696. 

Transformation

So far, you have seen that mapping and sequencing can be used to identify the relative position and nucleotide sequence of genes in a DNA molecule. Using various enzymes, scientists can isolate DNA fragments containing a gene or genes. Multiple copies of the fragment can be prepared using PCR. The DNA fragment may also be joined (annealed) to other DNA fragments.

In genetics, transformation is any process by which foreign DNA is incorporated into the genome of a cell. A **vector** is the delivery system used to move the foreign DNA into a cell. The specific vector used for transformation is chosen based on the size and sequence of the foreign DNA fragment, the characteristics of the cells to be transformed, and the goal of the transformation. The goal of most genetic transformation is to express the gene product(s), and so change the traits of the organism that receives the foreign DNA. An organism with foreign DNA in its genome is said to be **transgenic**.

vector a vehicle by which foreign DNA may be introduced into a cell

transgenic a cell or an organism that is transformed by DNA from another species

plasmid a small double-stranded circular DNA molecule found in some bacteria

Transformation of Bacteria

Bacteria are the most common organisms that are transformed by molecular biologists. Transgenic bacteria may be used to study gene expression or gene function, to create and maintain a stock of a particular DNA fragment, or to synthesize a useful gene product. For example, transgenic bacteria have been engineered to produce human growth hormone, used in the treatment of pituitary dwarfism.

The first stage of transformation for any organism is to identify and isolate the DNA fragment that is to be transferred. The DNA fragment is then introduced into the vector. **Plasmids** are small, circular, double-stranded DNA molecules that occur naturally in the cytoplasm of many bacteria (**Figure 8**). Plasmids are commonly used as vectors for bacterial transformation. A plasmid contains genes, and it is replicated and expressed independently of the large bacterial chromosome. There can be many copies of a plasmid in a single bacteria cell and, under certain conditions, plasmids can pass through the cell membrane.

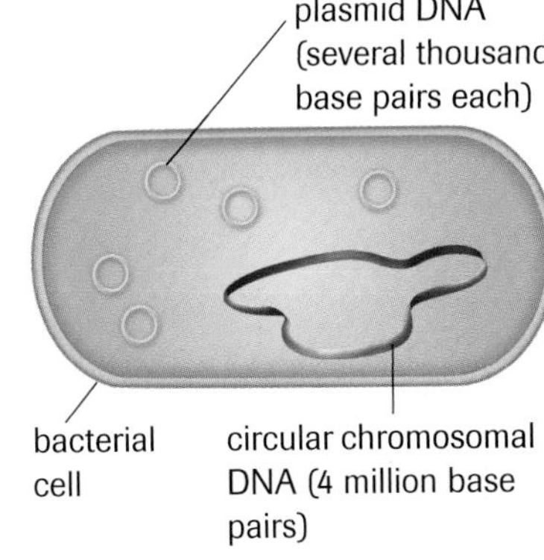

Figure 8
Chromosomal and plasmid DNA coexist in many bacteria.

Figure 9, on the next page, is a diagram of the basic steps in producing transgenic bacteria. First, both the plasmid vector and the DNA containing the desired sequence are cut by the same restriction enzyme(s). In this example, both DNA molecules are cut by *Eco*RI, generating sticky ends. The cut plasmid and DNA fragment are then mixed together and incubated with DNA ligase. This produces recombinant plasmids that

EXTENSION 

cDNA

One way to make copies of a particular gene is to use an enzyme called reverse transcriptase. This enzyme synthesizes DNA from mRNA. The resulting molecule is called copy DNA or cDNA. The cDNA can then be transferred into a vector or a cell.

www.science.nelson.com GO

contain the foreign DNA fragment. The bacterial cells are then treated to open pores in the cell membrane, which allows them to take up the recombinant plasmid. Once a bacterium has been transformed, it makes many copies of the recombinant plasmid, each of which includes a copy of the foreign DNA. This is often called gene cloning since the bacterium produces many identical copies (clones) of the original DNA fragment.

However, not all the bacterial cells will take up the recombinant plasmid. How can a scientist or technician distinguish between bacteria with a plasmid and those without? Plasmids used for transformation experiments often carry genes for antibiotic resistance, which can then be used to select for transformed bacteria. By growing the bacteria in medium that contains the antibiotic, any cells that do not contain a plasmid are killed off. Individual bacteria cells are then grown into colonies so that the plasmid DNA can be isolated from the cells and checked to make sure it contains the desired foreign DNA sequences.

For this transformation procedure to be successful, the plasmid DNA must have only one recognition site for the restriction enzyme that is used, or else it would be cut into a number of useless pieces. Naturally occurring plasmids do not always have a single appropriate restriction enzyme site, so scientists have engineered plasmids especially for transformation. Most of these engineered plasmids contain a **multiple-cloning site**, which is a single region that contains unique recognition sites for an assortment of restriction enzymes. The recognition sites are positioned very close together and are not found anywhere else on the plasmid's DNA sequence.

multiple-cloning site a region in a vector that is engineered to contain the recognition site of a number of restriction enzymes

Vectors other than plasmids may also be used to transform bacteria, including viruses and small inert particles that are literally fired into the cells.

DID YOU KNOW ?

Plasmids: Beneficial Guests

Japanese scientists were the first to discover plasmids that carry genes for multiple drug resistance. The bacterium *Shigella*, which causes dysentery, developed resistance to as many as four antibiotics, including tetracycline, streptomycin, chloramphenicol, and the sulfonamides. The multidrug resistance was due to a plasmid within the bacterium that carried genes for resistance and could be passed naturally from bacterium to bacterium.

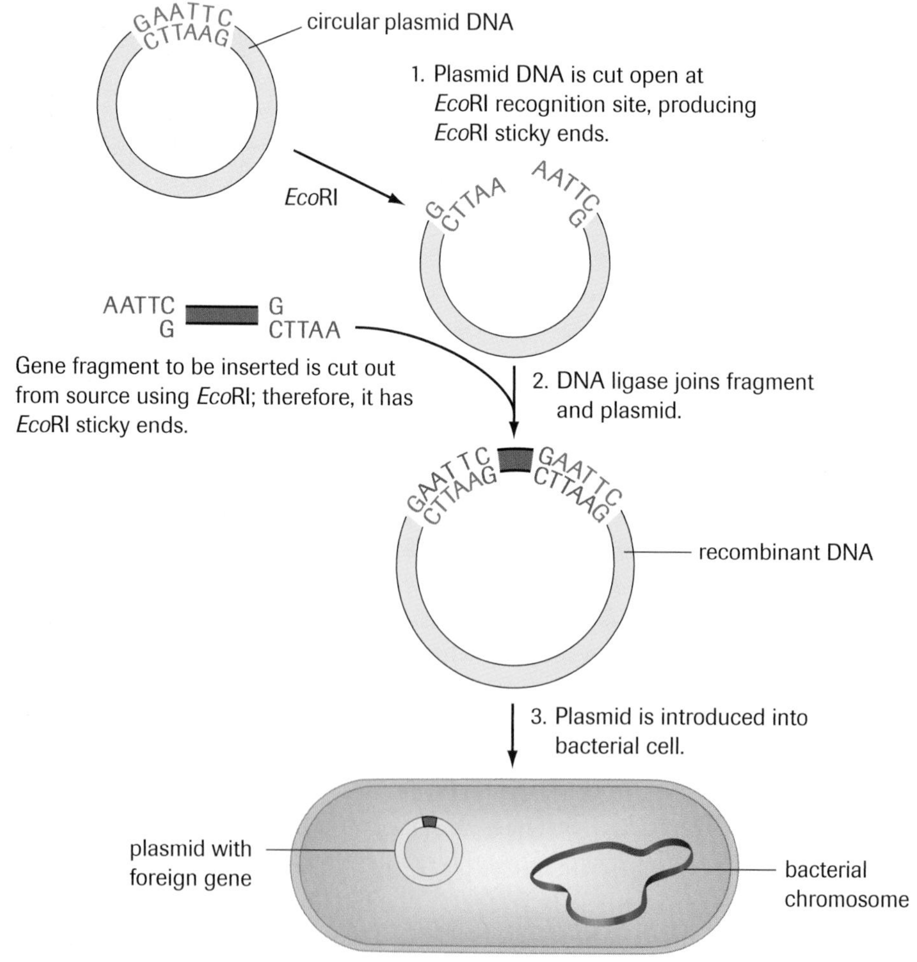

Figure 9
A foreign gene is introduced into a plasmid. The plasmid is now an example of recombinant DNA, which can be introduced into a bacterial cell to produce numerous copies of the gene.

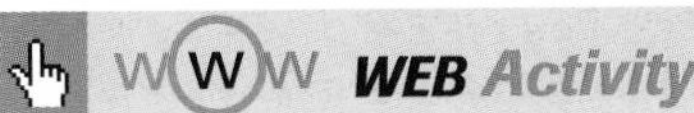

Case Study—Transformation of Eukaryotes

The first transgenic animal and the first transgenic plant were both produced in 1982. The animal was a mouse that contained the gene for growth hormone from a rat. The plant was a tobacco plant that contained a gene from a bacterial cell. The introduced gene produced an antibiotic in the plant's cells that protected the plant from bacterial infection. Since then, many transgenic animals and plants have been produced.

Producing transgenic eukaryotes is a lot more complex than the transformation of bacteria, and new techniques are still being developed. In this activity, you will find out about one technique used to create transgenic eukaryotes.

SUMMARY *DNA and Biotechnology*

Table 3 Key Tools of Molecular Biology

Tool	Use	Example
restriction endonuclease	bacterial enzyme that cuts DNA sequences at a specific recognition site	*Bam*HI recognition site: 5′-GGATCC-3′ 3′-CCTAGG-5′ DNA sequence before cleavage: 5′-TCAGCGGATCCCAT-3′ 3′-AGTCGCCTAGGGTA-5′ DNA sequence after cleavage with *Bam*HI: 5′-TCAGCG GATCCCAT-3′ 3′-AGTCGCCTAG GGTA-5′
methylase	enzyme that adds a methyl group to recognition sites to protect DNA from cleavage by restriction enzyme	*Bam*HI methylase adds methyl group ($-CH_3$) to second guanine nucleotide in the recognition site: 5′-GGATCC-3′ 3′-CCTAGG-5′ DNA sequence no longer cleaved by *Bam*HI methyl group changes recognition site
DNA ligase	enzyme that joins DNA fragments by creating bonds between nucleotides in the DNA backbone	DNA fragments before subjection to DNA ligase: 5′-ATAGTG-3′ 5′-AATTCGG-3′ 3′-TATCACTTAA-5′ 3′-GCC-5′ DNA fragments after subjection to DNA ligase: 5′-ATAGTGAATTCGG-3′ 3′-TATCACTTAAGCC-5′ two fragments are joined
plasmid	small circular DNA that has the ability to enter and replicate in bacterial cells and, therefore, can be used as a vector to introduce new genes into a bacterial cell	plasmid containing multiple-cloning site, ampicillin-resistance gene, and other restriction enzyme sites multiple-cloning site *Hin*dIII *Sma*I *amp*[r] *Bam*HI

Section 20.3 Questions

1. Define *restriction endonuclease* and *methylase.*
2. Restriction endonucleases are found in many species of bacteria.
   (a) Describe their role and function in a bacterial cell.
   (b) How does the role of restriction endonucleases in nature differ from the role of restriction endonucleases in the laboratory setting?
3. Distinguish between blunt ends and sticky ends.
4. Define *recognition site.* Using examples to support your answer, depict the palindromic nature of recognition sites.
5. Restriction enzymes cut at recognition sites that are usually six to eight base pairs in length. Provide reasons why a 2-base-pair recognition site would be too short to be useful and a 14-base-pair recognition site may be too long to be useful in the field of genetic engineering.
6. Sketch a diagram that summarizes the process of polymerase chain reaction (PCR). Clearly label the important features.
7. Explain why the Human Genome Project's initial years were spent developing techniques that would sequence larger DNA strands efficiently. (*Hint:* The human genome contains approximately three billion base pairs.)
8. As a scientist working for a pharmaceutical company, you are asked to engineer bacteria that will produce human growth hormone. The objective is commercial production in order to treat individuals who are deficient in this hormone. Describe the steps you would take in order to produce this hormone.
9. Transformation technology is used in agriculture to create genetically modified organisms (GMOs) that contain useful traits. This is a controversial technology, however. Some people think that GMOs pose unacceptable environmental or health risks. The Government of Canada has set regulations that must be met for approval of GMOs. Using the Internet and other resources, research the regulations that have been put into place. Do you feel these guidelines are adequate? What modification would you make to these guidelines if you could? Explain the implications of the guidelines that have been set.

www.science.nelson.com 

Extension

10. In order to create recombinant DNA containing the desired sequences, scientists have developed a number of procedures to find and isolate DNA, and to confirm whether a transgenic organism contains the foreign DNA. Go to the Nelson Web site to find out how the techniques of electrophoresis, Southern blotting, and Northern blotting work and when they are used. Then, summarize the information in a chart or another appropriate format.

www.science.nelson.com 

11. PCR can be used to create a DNA "fingerprint" that can identify an individual. This technique has been applied to forensics. In some well-known cases, such as that of Guy Paul Morin, PCR has been used to overturn convictions made before the technology was available. In June 2000, the Government of Canada passed the DNA Identification Act, which gave the Royal Canadian Mounted Police the right to create and maintain a database of DNA fingerprints. Conduct research on the use of PCR to identify individuals. Then, use this information to prepare a convincing argument for or against the requirement that anyone accused of a serious crime must supply police with a DNA sample.

www.science.nelson.com 

Mutations and Genetic Variation 20.4

Mutations are changes in the sequence of the DNA molecule and are the source of new genetic variation that may be acted on by natural selection. A beneficial mutation gives an organism a selective advantage and tends to become more common over time, leading to new evolutionary changes. A harmful mutation reduces an individual's fitness and tends to be selected against. Harmful mutations occur at low rates in a species. Some mutations are neutral, having neither a benefit nor a cost, and are not acted on by natural selection.

Learning Tip

Review how mutations contribute to the variability of species and how natural selection acts on mutations in Chapter 6 of this book.

As scientists gained more knowledge about the nature of DNA and the genetic code, they were able to more fully understand mutations. **Point mutations** are changes in a single base pair of a DNA sequence. They may or may not change the sequence of amino acids. **Gene mutations** change the amino acids specified by the DNA sequence, and they often involve more than a single base pair. **Figure 1** summarizes the DNA changes that occur in some common types of mutation.

point mutation a mutation at a specific base pair

gene mutation a mutation that changes the coding for amino acids

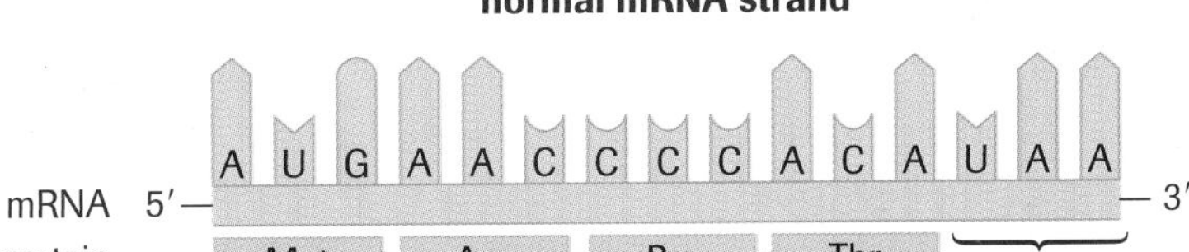

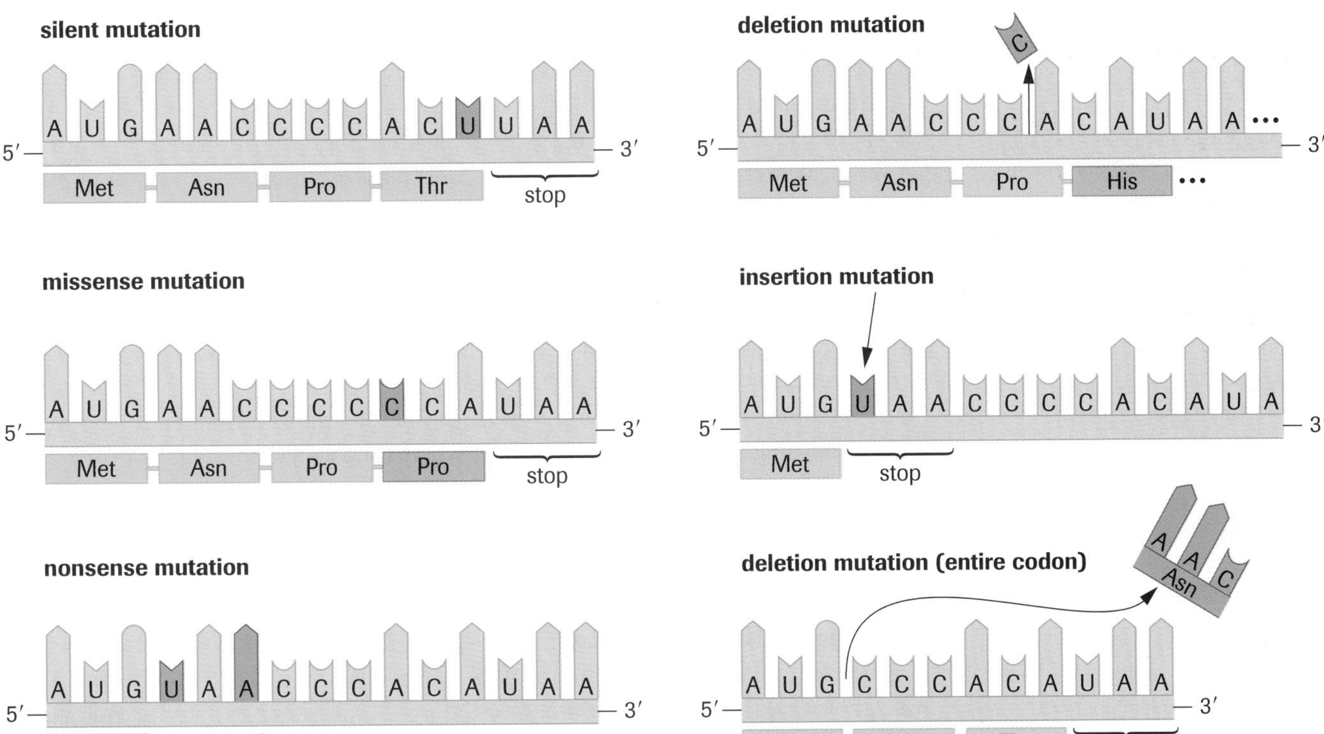

Figure 1
A summary of different types of mutations that may occur in a DNA sequence, affecting the transcribed RNA sequence.

silent mutation a mutation that does not result in a change in the amino acid coded for

One type of point mutation, called a **silent mutation**, has no effect on the operation of the cell. In the silent mutation example in **Figure 1**, the codon for threonine has changed from ACA to ACU. However, this mutation does not change the amino acid because both these codons code for threonine. Most silent mutations occur in the non-coding regions, so they do not affect protein structure.

missense mutation a mutation that results in the single substitution of one amino acid in the polypeptide

nonsense mutation a mutation that converts a codon for an amino acid into a stop codon

A **missense mutation** arises when a change in the base sequence of DNA alters a codon, leading to a different amino acid being placed in the polypeptide. Sickle cell anemia is the result of a missense mutation. Another type of point mutation is a nonsense mutation. A **nonsense mutation** occurs when a change in the DNA sequence causes a stop codon to replace a codon specifying an amino acid. During translation, only the part of the protein that precedes the stop codon is produced, and the fragment may be digested by cell proteases. Nonsense mutations are often lethal to the cell. Missense and nonsense mutations arise from the substitution of one base pair for another.

deletion the elimination of a base pair or group of base pairs from a DNA sequence

An example of a gene mutation is a **deletion**, which occurs when one or more nucleotides are removed from the DNA sequence. In the deletion mutation example in **Figure 1**, on the previous page, a cytosine nucleotide has been deleted. This changes the third codon from CCC to CCA, but the amino acid does not change because both CCC and CCA code for proline. However, the deletion also causes a change in the fourth codon, from ACA to CAU. This does affect the amino acid, changing it from threonine to histidine. Such shifts in the reading frame usually result in significant changes to the protein.

insertion the placement of an extra nucleotide in a DNA sequence

frameshift mutation a mutation that causes the reading frame of codons to change

Another way that a shift in the reading frame can occur is by the **insertion** of a nucleotide. Since the DNA sequence is read in triplets of nucleotides, inserting an extra nucleotide will cause different amino acids to be translated, similar to a deletion mutation. When a mutation changes the reading frame, it is called a **frameshift mutation**. Insertions and deletions can both cause frameshift mutations. A deletion or insertion of two nucleotides will also result in a shift of the reading frame; however, a deletion or insertion of three nucleotides does not have this effect. Instead, the insertion or deletion of three nucleotides results in the addition or removal of one amino acid.

translocation the transfer of a fragment of DNA from one site in the genome to another location

Another category of mutations involves large segments of DNA and is seen at the chromosomal level. **Translocation** is the relocation of groups of base pairs from one part of the genome to another. Usually translocations occur between two nonhomologous chromosomes. A segment of one chromosome breaks and releases a fragment, while the same event takes place on another chromosome. The two fragments exchange places, sometimes disrupting the normal structure of genes. When unrelated gene sequences come together and are transcribed and translated, the result is a fusion protein with a completely altered function, if any. Some types of leukemia are associated with translocations and their respective fusion proteins.

inversion the reversal of a segment of DNA within a chromosome

Finally, an **inversion** is a section of a chrosome that has reversed its orientation in the chromosome (has turned itself around). There is no gain or loss of genetic material, but, depending on where the inversion occurs, a gene may be disrupted.

spontaneous mutation a mutation occurring as a result of errors made in DNA replication

mutagenic agent an agent that can cause a mutation

induced mutation a mutation caused by a chemical agent or radiation

Causes of Genetic Mutations

Some mutations are simply caused by error of the genetic machinery and are known as **spontaneous mutations**. For example, DNA polymerase I occasionally misses a base or two, which results in a point mutation. Mutations may also arise from exposure to **mutagenic agents**. These are **induced mutations**. Some examples of mutagenic agents include ultraviolet (UV) radiation, cosmic rays, X-rays, and certain chemicals.

Case Study

Gene Mutations and Cancer

Cancer is considered a genetic disease because it is always associated with a mutation in the genetic sequence. However, many different things can alter DNA, including viruses and various environmental factors (**Figure 2**).

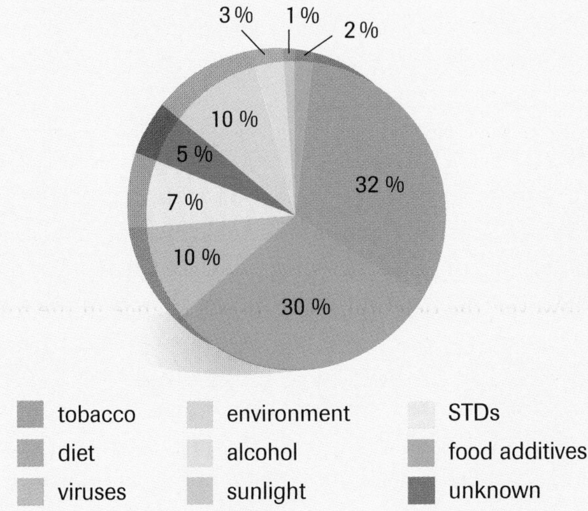

Figure 2
Estimates of risk factors for cancer calculated in percentages. Lifestyle choices related to diet and smoking can be linked with over 60 % of cancer cases.

Viruses inject foreign genetic information into cells, disrupting the DNA that codes for cell division. Some viruses that are linked to sexually transmitted diseases are known to cause cancer. For example, women who have human papillomavirus (HPV) have a greater incidence of cancer. Environmental factors have been linked to other types of cancer. Skin cancer, for example, has been linked with ultraviolet radiation from the Sun. Exposure to harmful chemicals in our environment can also cause cancer. A number of cancer-causing substances can be found in cigarettes.

Whatever the initial cause, scientists agree that all cancers are related to mutations. Usually, it takes more than one mutation to trigger a malignant growth. This is why cancer usually occurs more frequently in older people.

Two lines of evidence indicate that cancer results from mutations. First, cancer cells often display nitrogen base substitution, or the movement of genetic material from one part of the chromosome to another. Second, many known mutagens are also known to cause cancer. X-rays, ultraviolet radiation, and mutagenic chemicals can induce cancer.

In 1982, molecular biologists were able to provide additional evidence to support the hypothesis that cancer could be traced to genetic mutations. Segments of chromosomes extracted from cancerous mice were used to transform normal mouse cells (growing in tissue culture) into cancerous cells. The cancer-causing genes, called oncogenes, seemed to turn on cell division. In their noncancerous state, oncogenes are usually referred to as proto-oncogenes. Proto-oncogenes may remain inactive or may perform some useful function until they are triggered to become active oncogenes. Evidence suggests that activation occurs in a number of steps, so a single "hit" (mutation) does not immediately result in cancerous cell divisions.

Further studies indicate that cancer-causing oncogenes are present in normal strands of DNA. But if oncogenes are found in normal cells, why do normal cells not become cancerous? One current theory that has gained acceptance from the scientific community suggests that the cancer gene has been transposed (moved) to another gene site. Such transpositions may have been brought about by environmental factors or mutagenic chemicals or other agents.

Genes that direct the assembly of amino acids into proteins are referred to as structural genes. Genes called regulator genes act like a switch to turn "off" segments of the DNA molecule, so that a gene is active only when and where its gene product is needed. In very simple terms, when a mutagen causes the oncogene to become separated from its regulator gene, the cell may then be unable to turn the gene "off" (**Figure 3**). This causes the cell to continue to divide at an accelerated rate.

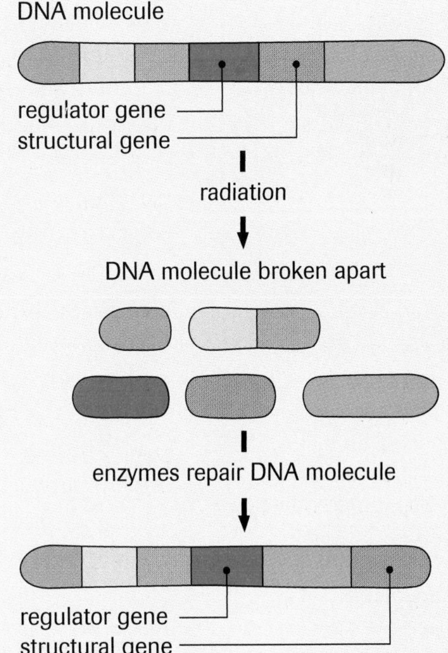

Figure 3
Mutagenic agents may cause the separation of the regulator and structural genes. If the structural gene codes for a protein involved in controlling cell division, this separation can lead to cancer.

The most common oncogene, *ras,* is found in 50 % of colon cancers and 30 % of lung cancers. Present in normal cells, *ras* makes a protein that acts as an "on" switch for cell division. *Ras* ensures that cells divide to replace damaged or dead cells. After a sufficient number of cells have been produced, the *ras* gene should be turned off. But the cancer-causing oncogene produces a protein that blocks the "off" switch. With the switch left on, cell division goes on continuously.

Case Study Questions

1. Why do many scientists believe that certain viruses cause cancer?
2. How does sunlight cause cancer?
3. List three environmental carcinogens and suggest a possible source for each.
4. Distinguish between oncogenes and proto-oncogenes.
5. Explain how oncogenes are activated.
6. What is the *ras* gene?

Inferring Relationships from DNA Sequences

At one time, scientists could compare and classify species based only on their morphology and behaviour. For example, Charles Darwin found evidence for the theory of evolution by comparing anatomical features of different species (see Chapter 6). Today, biologists can compare the genetic makeup of different species for evidence of relationships among them.

phylogeny proposed evolutionary history of a species or group of organisms

Phylogeny is the proposed evolutionary history of a group of organisms, or of a species. Overall, species that are closely related will share very similar DNA sequences, while those that are more distantly related will have more genetic differences. For example, you might expect that the sequence of DNA in a house cat's genome would have more similarities to that of a lion than to a sparrow. As we have seen, the DNA of any organism can mutate. Natural selection acts on beneficial and harmful mutations in a population, changing the relative proportions of these mutations that are passed on from generation to generation. The genomes of two species with a recent common ancestor would have had less time and opportunity for mutations to accumulate and be selected, and so we can predict that they would show fewer differences.

Learning Tip

Lab Exercise 5.A in Chapter 5 shows an example of how differences in genomic DNA sequences provide evidence for the relationships among various species.

Mutations do not occur only in genomic DNA. Nuclear DNA is often quite a large genome, so for some research it is more efficient for scientists to examine the changes in the smaller genomes of mitochondria or chloroplasts. In particular, mitochondrial DNA (mtDNA) can be used to trace inheritance through the maternal line in mammals, as the egg is the only source of the mitochondria that are passed on to new offspring.

Mitochondrial DNA has also provided some fascinating clues about the evolutionary history of modern humans. Two theories are proposed to explain the current distribution of humans around the world. One proposes that modern humans, *Homo sapiens,* evolved simultaneously in different regions of the world from an earlier species, *Homo erectus.* This theory is called the multiregional model and proposes that the different ethnic groups observed worldwide today would have begun their evolution to *Homo sapiens* between one and two million years ago. According to this model, the groups interbred to some degree, and so didn't form into different species. The second theory, called the monogenesis model, proposes that *Homo* species moved out of Africa twice: first as *Homo erectus,* and second as *Homo sapiens* between 100 000 and 200 000 years ago, and that modern ethnic groups are all descendants of the second migration.

DID YOU KNOW?

The Romanovs

Mitochondrial DNA was used to identify the suspected remains of the imperial Romanov family in Russia, who were murdered by the Bolsheviks in 1918. To do so, mitochondrial DNA from Prince Philip of England, a close relative of the former Tsarina Alexandra through his maternal side, was compared to mitochondrial DNA recovered from the remains, resulting in positive identification and the resolution of an 80-year-old mystery.

Mitochondrial DNA analyses for a variety of individuals, representing the ethnic groups found around the world, seem to support the monogenesis model. The greatest variety of mtDNA mutations exist in African ethnic groups, which is consistent with the theory that mutations accumulate over time and that the population that has existed the longest will demonstrate the largest accumulation of mutations. Additionally, the mtDNA from ethnic groups on continents other than Africa were traced back to Africa rather than to each other.

Interspersed Elements

Other DNA analyses focus on intervening sequences inserted into DNA. For example, **SINEs** (short **in**terspersed **e**lements) and **LINEs** (long **in**terspersed **e**lements) are often associated with the genes of retroviruses within the genome and are thought to have been inserted by those viruses. SINEs and LINEs are often located in areas of the DNA that appear to be noncoding regions. That is, the DNA in these areas does not code for one of the known gene products of that species. Although the function of the DNA in these regions is not known, it is inherited; therefore, changes to these DNA sequences, such as insertions, are passed to succeeding generations.

If two species have the same SINE or LINE located at precisely the same position in their DNA, it can be assumed that the insertion occurred only once in a common ancestor. SINEs and LINEs make ideal markers for tracing evolutionary pathways. They are easy to find and identify, even if they undergo small mutational changes, because they are relatively large and recognizable segments of DNA often hundreds of base pairs in length. The possibility of a mutation reverting to an older form is extremely remote, as the chances of a SINE or LINE being inserted in exactly the same location in two different species is highly unlikely.

SINEs repeated DNA sequences 300 base pairs long that alternate with lengths of DNA sequences found in the genomes of higher organisms

LINEs repeated DNA sequences 5000 to 7000 base pairs long that alternate with lengths of DNA sequences found in the genomes of higher organisms

LAB EXERCISE 20.B

Looking for SINEs of Evolution

Report Checklist

○ Purpose	○ Design	● Analysis
○ Problem	○ Materials	● Evaluation
○ Hypothesis	○ Procedure	● Synthesis
○ Prediction	○ Evidence	

In this activity, you will use DNA sequences to predict and chart phylogenetic relationships among species.

Suppose you find a pattern in the noncoding SINE DNA of two different species, and do not find that pattern in other species. Evolution can explain the situation by saying that the two species recently had a common ancestor, and that both species inherited this pattern from their ancestor. The predicted family tree is shown in **Figure 4**.

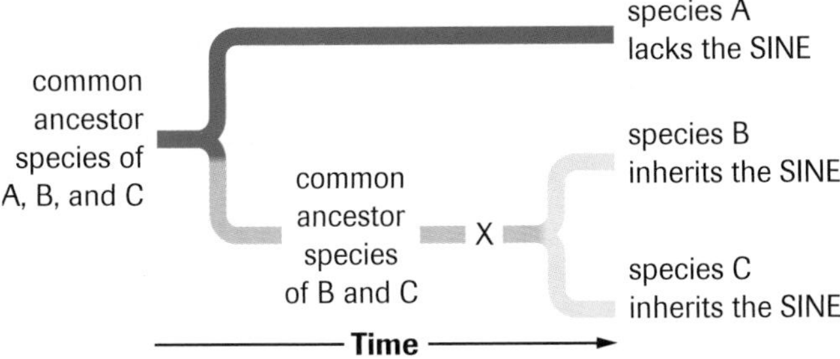

Figure 4
X indicates the time when the SINE became inserted into the genome. Since the SINE insertion occurs only once, at time X, the size and precise location of the SINE will be identical in species B and C.

Part I: Looking for a SINE

Procedure I

1. Examine the hypothetical DNA code from four different species (**Figure 5**). These species have large sections of DNA that appear to be homologous. These homologous sequences have been aligned vertically so that similarities and differences can be easily seen and colours are used to highlight those nucleotides that are not matches (**Figure 6**).

Species W	AGATAGCGCGTAAAAAG
Species X	AAATAGCGCGTAAATAG
Species Y	AAATAGTTAAAGTTACGCATAAATAC
Species Z	AGATAGCGCGTAAATGG

Figure 5
Sequenced DNA fragments from four distantly related species

Species W-	AGATAG.........CGCGTAAAAAG
Species X-	AAATAG.........CGCGTAAATAG
Species Y-	AAATAGTTAAAGTTACGCATAAATAC
Species Z-	AGATAG.........CGCGTAAATGG

Figure 6
DNA sequences from **Figure 5** aligned for comparison. Note that spaces appear in the sequences only to facilitate comparisons.

The single nucleotide differences have most likely resulted from point mutations, while the nine-nucleotide segment in species Y is probably the result of an insertion. (Note that this is much more likely than the alternative possibility—that each of the other species experienced an identical deletion event in its past.) The type of pattern observed in species Y often results from a SINE or LINE insertion.

2. Copy the DNA sequences in **Figure 7** into your notebook. Align the homologous sections vertically.
3. Use a highlighter to colour all positions that have the same nucleotide in all four species.
4. Use a different colour to highlight the SINE insertion.

Analysis and Evaluation I

(a) Identify any nucleotide differences in the SINE sequences. Explain how these differences might have occurred.

(b) Identify whether mutations that occur within the SINE are likely to be harmful, beneficial, or neutral. Explain.

(c) Based on the data alone, construct a chart similar to **Table 1** showing the phylogenetic relationship of these species.

Part II: Evolution Displayed by SINEs and LINEs

Procedure II

5. Study the data in **Table 1**. DNA sequencing was used to document the presence or absence of interspersed elements A through I in five mammals. Camels are included as the outgroup.

Table 1 Molecular Evidence for the Evolution of Whales*

Group	SINE or LINE								
	A	B	C	D	E	F	G	H	I
cow	+	+	–	–	–	–	+	–	+
pig	–	–	–	+	+	–	–	–	+
whale	–	+	+	–	–	–	+	+	+
deer	+	+	–	–	–	–	+	–	+
hippopotamus	–	+	+	–	–	+	+	+	+
camel	–	–	–	–	–	–	–	–	–

\+ indicates presence of element - indicates absence of element
* Data modified from Nikaido 1999

6. Use the data to construct a chart showing the phylogenetic relationships between these mammals. Clearly indicate the relative positions at which each insertion most likely occurred.

Analysis and Evaluation II

(d) Are whales more closely related to cows or hippopotamuses? Explain your rationale.

(e) Identify which insertion happened first: A or B? Explain your reasoning.

Synthesis

(f) Explain whether pigs and camels are more closely related than hippopotamuses and camels.

(g) What must be true about the genomes of all whale species (i.e., which SINEs must they all contain)? Explain your rationale.

(h) A researcher interested in the evolution of whales wants to know whether orcas are more closely related to white-sided dolphins or to pilot whales. Describe a way to answer this question.

```
Species P  ...AAATTGCTTCGTATTTTCGAATTGCCCCGCTAAAGCGCTTTAGC.......
Species Q  ...AACTTGCTTCGTATTAAGCTGTTGCGTAAAGTTAGTACGAATTGCCCCGGTGAAGCGCTTTAGC......
Species R  ...AATTTGCTTCGTTTTTTCGAATTGCCCCGCTAAAGCGCTTTAGC.......
Species S  ...AACTTGCTACGTATTAAGCCGTTGCGTAAAGTTAGGACGAATCGCCACGGTGACGCGCTTGAGC......
```

Figure 7
Homologous DNA sequences from four species

SUMMARY *Mutations and Genetic Variation*

Table 2 Types of Mutations

Category	Type	Result
point mutation	**substitution** AAG CCC GGC AAA AAG ACC GGC AAA	**missense mutation** only one amino acid substituted
	deletion AAG CCC GGC AAA AAC CCG GCA AA ↑	**frameshift mutation** can result in many different amino acids substituted or a stop codon read (nonsense mutation)
	insertion AAG CCC GGC AAA AAG ACC GGG CAA A	
chromosomal	**translocation** chromosome 1 5′ AAATTCG GCACCA 3′ chromosome 2 5′ TAGCCC AAGCGAG 3′ ↓ chromosome 1 5′ TAGCCC GCACCA 3′ chromosome 2 5′ AAATTCG AGCGAG 3′	inactivation of gene if translocation or inversion is within a coding segment
	inversion normal chromosome 5′ AATTGGCCATA ATATGAA AAGCCC 3′ 3′ TTAACCGGTAT TATACTT TTCGGG 5′ ↓ after inversion 5′ AATTGGCCATA TTCATAT AAGCCC 3′ 3′ TTAACCGGTAT AAGTATA TTCGGG 5′	

- In mammals, mitochondrial DNA can be used to trace inheritance through the maternal lineage.
- Comparisons of DNA sequences can provide detailed phylogenetic relationships by revealing the specific changes in the genetic makeup of species and populations.
- SINEs and LINEs provide excellent inheritable markers for tracing the evolution of species' lineages.

Section 20.4 Questions

1. Clearly define the following terms and give an example of each: *mutation, frameshift mutation, point mutation, nonsense mutation, missense mutation.*
2. Explain why mutations, such as insertions or deletions, are often much more harmful than nitrogen-base substitutions.
3. Which of two types of mutations, nonsense or missense, would be more harmful to an organism? Explain your answer using your knowledge of protein synthesis.
4. Identify three factors that can produce gene mutations.
5. Identify the type of mutation that has occurred in the strands below. Describe the effect on the protein. The original strand is

   AUG UUU UUG CCU UAU CAU CGU

   Determine whether or not the following mutations would be harmful to an organism. Translate the mRNA sequence into protein to help you decide. The mutation is indicated in red.

   (a) AUG UUU UUG CCU UAU CAU CGU
   AUG UUU UUG CCU UAC CAU CGU

   (b) AUG UUU UUG CCU UAU CAU CGU
   AUG UUU UUG CCU UAA CAU CGU

   (c) AUG UUU UUG CCU UAU CAU CGU
   AUG UUU CUU GCC UUA UCA UCG U

   (d) AUG UUU UUG CCU UAU CAU CGU
   AUG UUU UUG CCU AUC AUC GU

   (e) AUG UUU UUG CCU UAU CAU CGU
   UGC UAC UAU UCC GUU UUU GUA
6. Which of the following amino acid changes can result from a single base-pair substitution?
   (a) arg to leu
   (b) cys to glu
   (c) ser to thr
   (d) ile to ser
7. Explain why a food dye that has been identified as a chemical mutagen poses greater dangers for a developing fetus than for an adult.
8. List three changes that can be made to your personal lifestyle that would reduce the odds of a mutation taking place.
9. Explain how mutations may be of benefit to an organism, and describe how these beneficial mutations are maintained in a species. Identify the biological process that influences which mutations stay in a population over time.
10. Both mitochondria and chloroplasts contain their own genomes, which are separate from the nuclear genome. The DNA in mitochondria and chloroplasts have been used as evidence for the endosymbiotic theory of the evolution of eukaryotic organisms. This theory was developed by the American scientist Dr. Lynn Margulis. According to this theory, mitochondria and chloroplast arose from bacteria and algae cells that became engulfed by another cell with which they had a symbiotic relationship. Over time, the bacteria and algae became a part of the other cell. Evidence of this theory can be found by comparing the DNA of mitochondria with bacteria, and of chloroplasts with algae. Go to the Nelson Web site to learn more about the theory of endosymbiosis, and summarize the DNA evidence that supports it.

    www.science.nelson.com GO

Extension

11. The mutation that causes sickle cell anemia involves the substitution of the amino acid valine for the amino acid glutamic acid. Research the structure of valine and glutamic acid and, with your knowledge of chemistry, hypothesize why this substitution results in a large conformational change for the hemoglobin protein. List other amino acids that could have been substituted instead of valine that may not have caused such serious side effects. List amino acids that are similar to glutamic acid that would probably cause similar side effects.

INVESTIGATION 20.1

Protein Synthesis and Inactivation of Antibiotics

In this investigation, you will examine the effects of ampicillin on two types of bacteria. *E. coli* MM294/pAmp contains a gene insert that directs the synthesis of a protein that inactivates ampicillin, whereas *E. coli* MM294 does not. Ampicillin inhibits bacterial growth by interfering with cell wall biosynthesis. Based on your knowledge of protein synthesis, make a prediction about the survival of *E. coli* MM294/pAmp and *E. coli* MM294 on ampicillin-rich media.

Report Checklist

- ● Purpose
- ○ Problem
- ● Hypothesis
- ● Prediction
- ● Design
- ○ Materials
- ○ Procedure
- ● Evidence
- ● Analysis
- ● Evaluation
- ● Synthesis

Problem

What effect does the presence of an ampicillin-resistance gene in a bacterium have on its growth on ampicillin-rich media?

Materials

apron	masking tape
safety goggles	permanent marker
gloves	inoculating loop
10 % bleach	Bunsen burner
2 LB agar plates	MM294 culture
2 LB + ampicillin (LB/amp) plates	MM294/pAMP culture
	37 °C incubator

Wear safety goggles at all times.

Wear gloves when performing the experiment. Disposable latex gloves are best avoided since allergic reactions to latex have been widely reported. Disposable polyethylene, PVC, or neoprene gloves are recommended.

Wipe down all surfaces with 10 % bleach before and after the laboratory exercise.

All resulting cultures must be immersed in 10 % bleach before disposal to ensure sterilization.

Do not leave a lit Bunsen burner unattended. Refer to Appendix C2 for a review of the safe use of a Bunsen burner.

Wash your hands thoroughly at the end of the laboratory.

Procedure

1. Put on your safety goggles and gloves, and wipe down your bench with a 10 % bleach solution.
2. Obtain two LB plates and two LB/amp plates from your teacher.
3. Label the bottom of each plate with your name and the date, using a permanent marker.
4. Label both of the LB plates "− amp" for the *E. coli* MM294 cells. Label both of the LB/amp plates "+ amp" for the *E. coli* MM294/pAMP cells.
5. Hold your inoculating loop like a pencil and sterilize it in the nonluminous flame of the Bunsen burner until it becomes red hot. Cool the sterilized loop by touching it to the edge of the agar on one of the LB plates.
6. Using the sterilized loop, pick up one colony of *E. coli* MM294 from a start culture plate. Glide the inoculating loop across an LB agar plate, making sure not to gouge the agar (**Figure 1**).

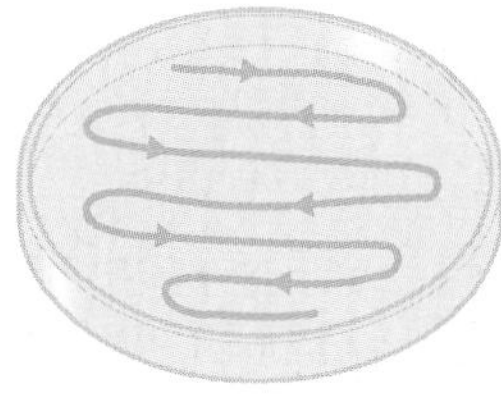

Figure 1
Pattern of streaking on an agar plate

7. Resterilize your loop as directed in step 5.
8. Repeat step 6 with *E. coli* MM294 streaked on an LB/amp plate.
9. Resterilize your loop as directed in step 5.
10. Repeat step 6 with *E. coli* MM294/pAmp streaked on the other LB plate.
11. Resterilize your loop as directed in step 5.
12. Repeat step 6 with *E. coli* MM294/pAmp streaked on the other LB/amp plate.
13. Sterilize and cool your inoculating loop.
14. Place all four streaked plates in a stack and tape them together. Seal the edges of your plates with masking tape.
15. Place the streaked plates upside down in the incubator. Alternatively, if you do not have an incubator, place the plates in a warm part of the room for a couple of days.

INVESTIGATION 20.1 *continued*

16. Disinfect your laboratory bench using the bleach solution.
17. Wash your hands thoroughly with soap and water.

Analysis

(a) After sufficient time has elapsed, remove your plates from the incubator and note any changes.

Never open the plates, as any bacterial colonies within are a potential source of contamination. If condensation has accumulated on one side of a plate, try looking through its bottom to observe the colonies you may have cultured. Once the experiment has been completed, flood plates with bleach to kill the bacterial colonies that have been cultured. Alternatively, place plates in an autoclave before they are disposed.

Evaluation

(b) Compare your results to your prediction. Explain any possible causes for variation.

(c) What evidence is there to indicate that protein was synthesized by the bacteria?

(d) Why was it important to streak out both types of bacteria on both types of plates?

(e) This experiment contains both positive and negative controls. Identify them. What information do the controls provide in this experiment?

(f) Why was it important to cool the inoculating loop before obtaining a bacterial colony from a stock plate?

(g) Why was it important to resterilize the inoculating loop between transfers of bacteria?

(h) Suggest possible sources of error in this procedure and indicate their effect on the results.

Synthesis

(i) *E. coli* strains containing the genetic sequence pAmp are resistant to ampicillin. Research how the ampicillin can be deactivated by β-lactamase, the protein coded for by the ampicillin-resistance gene.

(j) Predict what would happen if there was an error in the genetic sequence that codes for β-lactamase.

INVESTIGATION 20.2

Restriction Enzyme Digestion of Bacteriophage DNA

In this investigation, bacteriophage lambda DNA will be digested using the restriction endonucleases *Eco*RI, *Hin*dIII, and *Bam*HI. The fragments produced will be separated using gel electrophoresis. Fragment sizes will be calculated from an analysis of the agarose gel. Bacteriophage lambda DNA is obtained from a virus that infects bacterial cells and is 48 514 base pairs in length.

Before you begin, predict the number and size of the DNA fragments you will obtain, using the restriction enzyme site map shown in **Figure 1** on the next page.

Problem

How do the patterns of DNA fragments compare when a piece of DNA is digested using different restriction endonucleases?

Report Checklist

- ● Purpose
- ○ Problem
- ● Hypothesis
- ● Prediction
- ● Design
- ○ Materials
- ○ Procedure
- ● Evidence
- ● Analysis
- ● Evaluation
- ○ Synthesis

Materials

safety goggles
gloves
70 % ethanol solution (or 10 % bleach)
4 1.5 mL Eppendorf tubes
waterproof pen for labelling
masking tape
polystyrene cup
freezer
crushed ice
20 μL of 0.5 μg/μL lambda DNA
5 μL 10× restriction buffer
1.0–20 μL micropipette with tips
2 μL each of *Bam*HI, *Eco*RI, and *Hin*dIII restriction endonucleases

INVESTIGATION 20.2 *continued*

microcentrifuge (optional)
37 °C water bath
thermometer
1 g agarose
paper boat
electronic balance
500 mL Erlenmeyer flask
250 mL graduated cylinder
microwave or hot plate
flask tongs or oven mitts
gel casting tray and gel electrophoresis box
1L 1× TBE buffer
5 μL loading dye
power supply (45 V)
plastic wrap
25–30 mL 0.025 % methylene blue, or enough to cover the gel in the staining tray
light box or overhead projector
acetate sheet

Wear safety goggles at all times.

Wear gloves when performing the experiment.

Wipe down all surfaces with 70 % ethanol, or 10 % bleach, before and after the laboratory exercise.

Do not use ethanol near a heat source.

Wash your hands thoroughly at the end of the laboratory.

Procedure

Day 1: Restriction Enzyme Digestion

1. Put on your safety goggles and gloves, and wipe down your bench with a 70 % ethanol solution (or 10 % bleach).

Ethanol is highly flammable. Make sure that any flame on your desk or near it is turned off before use.

2. Label four 1.5 mL Eppendorf tubes "*Bam*HI," "*Eco*RI," "*Hin*dIII," and "control." Place the tubes in a polystyrene cup containing crushed ice. **Table 1** outlines the amount of reagents to add to each tube. To keep track of each tube's contents, copy the table into your notebook and check off each reagent as you add it to the tube.

Table 1 Reagents to Add to Tubes

Tube	DNA (μL)	10× buffer (μL)	Water (μL)	*Bam*HI (μL)	*Eco*RI (μL)	*Hin*dIII (μL)
***Bam*HI**	4	1	4	1	–	–
***Eco*RI**	4	1	4	–	1	–
***Hin*dIII**	4	1	4	–	–	1
control	4	1	5	–	–	–

3. Read down each column, adding the same reagent to all appropriate tubes. Use a fresh tip on the micropipette for each reagent. Add the 4 μL of DNA to each tube first, followed by the 10× reaction buffer, and then the water. *Make sure you add the enzyme last.* Dispense all the contents close to the bottom of the Eppendorf tubes. Ensure that the pipette tip is touching the side of the tubes when dispensing the contents. *Keep everything on ice at all times.*
4. Close the Eppendorf tube tops. Place the tubes in the microcentrifuge, close it, and spin at maximum speed for approximately 3 s. If you do not have access to a microcentrifuge, then just tap the tubes on a soft pad or thick paper towel on the bench, pooling the contents to the bottom.

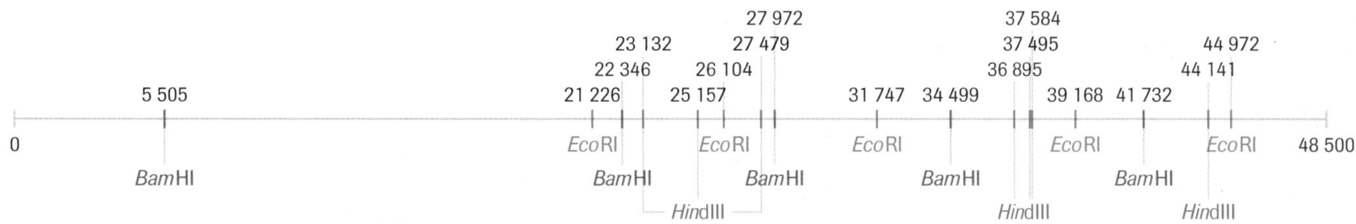

Figure 1
Restriction enzyme map of bacteriophage lambda DNA

When using the microcentrifuge:

- **Do not open the centrifuge until it stops completely.**
- **If the centrifuge tubes are smaller than the metal holder or holes, use the proper adaptor to accommodate them.**
- **Do not unplug the centrifuge by pulling on the cord. Pull the plug.**

5. Place the tubes in a 37 °C water bath for a minimum of 45 min. Use a thermometer to check the temperature of the water.
6. Once the digestion is complete, place the tubes in the polystyrene cup and put the cup in a freezer until your next class. Make sure you have labelled your cup with your name.

Day 2: Gel Electrophoresis

7. Measure 0.96 g of agarose powder in a paper boat on an electronic balance and transfer to a 500 mL Erlenmeyer flask.
8. Use a graduated cylinder to add 125 mL of 1× TBE buffer and swirl to mix.
9. Heat the flask on a hot plate or in a microwave until the solution is completely clear. Handle carefully, using tongs or oven mitts. Make sure you wear goggles and a lab coat.

If the agarose gets too hot it may bubble over. Be sure to observe your Erlenmeyer flask throughout the heating process. If the agarose solution starts to bubble up the neck of the flask, remove it immediately from the heat source using an oven mitt or tongs. Handle all hot glassware with caution.

10. Prepare the gel casting tray. Depending on your gel electrophoresis unit, you may have to tape the gel casting tray. Ensure that the plastic comb is inserted properly.
11. Once the flask with agarose solution is cool enough to handle with bare hands, pour the mixture into the gel casting tray. The comb teeth should be immersed in about 6 mm of agarose. The gel should cover only about one-third of the height of the comb teeth. Use a micropipette tip to remove bubbles from the gel as soon as it is poured.
12. Allow the agarose to set for a minimum of 20 min. The gel will become cloudy as it solidifies.
13. Once the gel has set (you may test this by gently touching the lower righthand corner with your finger), flood the gel with 1× TBE running buffer and then pull out the comb gently without ripping any of the wells.
14. Orient the tray containing the gel in the gel electrophoresis box so that the wells made by the comb are at the end with the positive electrode.
15. Add 1× TBE buffer to the gel electrophoresis box until the buffer is approximately 5 mm above the gel. Place the gel electrophoresis box to the side.
16. Add 1 μL of loading dye to each of the Eppendorf tubes. Microfuge for 3 s.
17. Micropipette the full contents of one Eppendorf tube into a well on the gel. Do the same for each tube. Be sure to record the order in which you dispense the tubes. Steady the micropipette over each well using both hands.
18. Close the gel box and connect it to the power supply. If you are using a gel box that you made, set the voltage to 45 V dc and turn it on. Electrophorese for 12 h. Alternatively, if you have a stronger power supply or a store-bought electrophoresis unit, electrophorese at 110 V for 2.5 h.

When using the power supply:

- **Be sure the grounding pin in the power supply is not broken.**
- **Pull the plug, not the cord, when unplugging the power source.**
- **Do not let the wire leads connected to the electric power supply or batteries touch each other.**

19. Unplug the power supply and carefully remove the gel. Wrap the gel in plastic wrap and place it in the refrigerator for a maximum of one day.

Day 3: Staining the Gel

20. Unwrap the gel and place it in the staining tray.
21. Flood the gel with 0.025 % methylene blue solution. Let the gel sit in the solution for at least 20 to 25 min. Pour off the water and replace it with fresh water. Repeat this process three more times. Keep an eye on the intensity of the DNA bands. If you destain for too long, you may lose the smaller fragments.

INVESTIGATION 20.2 *continued*

If you do not destain for long enough, the whole gel remains blue and the fragments cannot be differentiated.

22. Place the destained gel on a light box or on an overhead projector.
23. Obtain a blank acetate sheet or plastic wrap and place it over the gel. Trace the pattern of bands onto the wrap or sheet. Be sure to draw a line where the bottom of each well starts.

Evidence

(a) Carefully measure the distance in millimetres that each band migrated from the well origin. Copy **Table 2** into your notebook and use it to record the distances.

Analysis

(b) Using the *Hin*dIII digestion as a marker, plot the distance travelled (x-axis) versus the fragment base-pair size (y-axis) on semilogarithmic paper. Please note that the 23 130-base-pair fragment and the 27 491-base-pair fragment do not resolve, but instead travel as one band. Therefore, take an average of their size for graphing purposes.

(c) Using interpolation, determine the fragment size of the bands produced by digestion with *Bam*HI and *Eco*RI. Enter your calculated base-pair fragment sizes into your table.

(d) Compare the calculated base-pair fragments to the actual base-pair fragments. Use the restriction enzyme map of bacteriophage lambda (**Figure 1**) to determine the size of the actual band fragments for each enzyme. Calculate the percentage error.

Evaluation

(e) What was the purpose of each tube? of the control?

(f) Why do the smaller bands migrate faster than the larger bands?

(g) Some bands that are close in size migrate together. What measures may be taken to resolve bands close in size?

(h) What purpose does the 1× running buffer serve?

(i) Why must the gel be made using 1× TBE buffer?

(j) During electrophoresis, bubbles are produced at the anode and at the cathode. Explain why bubbles appear.

(k) Why must loading dye be added to the samples before they are loaded into the wells of the gel?

(l) Notice on your gel that the larger fragments are stained darker than the smaller fragments. Explain why this is the case.

(m) Suggest possible sources of error in this procedure. Indicate the effects of these sources of error on the results.

Table 2 Distance Travelled by Each Band From the Well Origin

***Hin*dIII**		***Eco*RI**			***Bam*HI**		
Actual fragment size	***Distance travelled (mm)***	***Actual fragment size***	***Distance travelled (mm)***	***Calculated fragment size***	***Actual fragment size***	***Distance travelled (mm)***	***Calculated fragment size***
27 491							
23 130							
9 416							
6 557							
4 361							
2 322							
2 027							

Chapter 20 SUMMARY

Outcomes

Knowledge

- describe, in general, how genetic information is contained in the sequence of bases in DNA molecules in chromosomes; how the DNA molecules replicate themselves; and how the genetic information is transcribed into sequences of bases in RNA molecules and is finally translated into sequences of amino acids in proteins (20.1, 20.2)
- explain, in general, how restriction enzymes cut DNA molecules into smaller fragments and how ligases reassemble them (20.3)
- explain, in general, how cells may be transformed by inserting new DNA sequences into their genomes (20.3)
- explain how a random change (mutation) in the sequence of bases results in abnormalities or provides a source of genetic variability (20.4)
- explain how sequences of nucleic acids contained in the nucleus, mitochondria, and chloroplasts gives evidence for the relationships among organisms of different species by examining similarities and differences in base sequences (20.4)

STS

- explain that science and technology have both intended and unintended consequences for humans and the environment (20.3, 20.4)
- explain that scientific research and technological development help achieve a sustainable society, economy, and environment (20.3, 20.4)

Skills

- ask questions and plan investigations (20.4)
- conduct investigations and gather and record data and information (20.2, 20.3, 20.4)
- analyze data and apply mathematical and conceptual models to develop and assess possible solutions (20.2, 20.4)
- work as members of a team and apply the skills and conventions of science (all)

Key Terms

20.1

complementary base pairing
antiparallel
DNA replication
semiconservative replication
template
DNA helicase
DNA polymerase III
leading strand
lagging strand
DNA polymerase I
DNA ligase

20.2

gene expression
ribonucleic acid (RNA)
transcription
messenger RNA (mRNA)
translation
RNA polymerase
promoter
template strand
termination sequence
codon
start codon
stop codon
ribosome
transfer RNA (tRNA)
anticodon

20.3

recombinant DNA
genetic transformation
restriction endonuclease
recognition site
palindromic
sticky ends
blunt ends
methylase
polymerase chain reaction (PCR)
vector
transgenic
plasmid
multiple-cloning site

20.4

point mutation
gene mutation
silent mutation
missense mutation
nonsense mutation
deletion
insertion
frameshift mutation
translocation
inversion
spontaneous mutation
mutagenic agent
induced mutation
phylogeny
SINEs
LINEs

MAKE a summary

1. Starting with the title "The Human Genome," produce a flowchart that illustrates the flow of information from gene to protein. Include as many key concepts as possible.
2. Revisit your answers to the Starting Points questions at the beginning of the chapter. Would you answer the questions differently now? Why?

Go To

The following components are available on the Nelson Web site. Follow the links for *Nelson Biology Alberta 20–30.*

- an interactive Self Quiz for Chapter 20
- additional Diploma Exam-style Review Questions
- Illustrated Glossary
- additional IB-related material

There is more information on the Web site wherever you see the Go icon in the chapter.

EXTENSION

DNA Motors

Dr. Vanessa Auld, Quirks and Quarks genetics columnist explains the details behind the discovery by a group of American and Czech researchers of proteins that act like small motors inside the nucleus of the cell. This discovery is changing our understanding of how DNA is used to manufacture the proteins and chemicals the cell uses to sustain life.

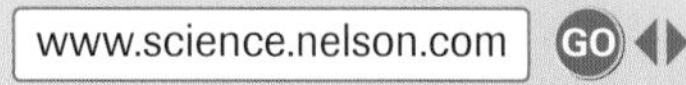

EXTENSION

Cracking the Code of Life

In this video, follow corporate and academic scientists as they race to capture one of the biggest prizes in scientific history: the complete, letter-by-letter sequence of genetic information that defines human life–the human genome.

EXTENSION

Artificial Life

Scientists can now synthesize strands of DNA with any nucleotide sequence they want. Does this mean that they can create artificial life from these blueprints? Some scientists believe the answer is yes, and that it isn't that far away!

EXTENSION

Golden Rice or Frankenfood?

Vitamin A deficiency is a leading cause of preventable blindness. Scientists have developed a genetically-modified rice that contains β-carotene, the precursor to vitamin A. Some see this new rice as an important contribution to world health, but others warn that genetically modified foods could have hidden dangers. What do you think?

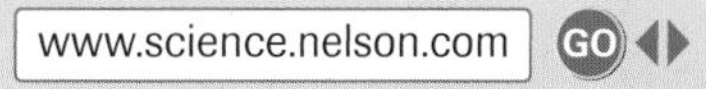

UNIT 30 C PERFORMANCE TASK

Investigating Human Traits

In this Performance Task, you will use the skills you gained in this Unit to design and carry out a correlational study on human traits to determine if they are autosomal or sex-linked. Go to the Unit 30 C Performance Task link on the Nelson web site to complete the task.

www.science.nelson.com

Many of these questions are in the style of the Diploma Exam. You will find guidance for writing Diploma Exams in Appendix A5. Science Directing Words used in Diploma Exams are in bold type. Exam study tips and test-taking suggestions are on the Nelson Web site.

DO NOT WRITE IN THIS TEXTBOOK.

Part 1

Use the following information to answer questions 1 to 3.

The cause of cystic fibrosis has been identified as a variety of mutations to the *CFTR* gene on chromosome 7. The most common of these involves the loss of three nucleotides, which in turn results in the loss of a phenylalanine at amino acid position 508.

1. Identify the DNA sequence that would result in phenylalanine being placed in a polypeptide chain.
   A. UUG
   B. AAC
   C. UUU
   D. TTT

2. Identify the term that best describes the mutation that causes the loss of phenylalanine.
   A. silent mutation
   B. insertion mutation
   C. deletion mutation
   D. missense mutation

3. NR Gene therapy trials to correct this defect in the *CFTR* gene have been conducted by doctors in several centres. The following is a list of some genetic technologies that might be used in this work:

1. restriction endonucelases
2. mtDNA
3. polymerase chain reaction
4. DNA ligase
5. viruses
6. bacterial plasmids
7. gene sequencing

Identify the technologies that would most likely be used to isolate the gene for a therapy trial. (Record all four digits of your answer in the order in which the technologies would be used.)

4. Identify the enzyme that is correctly matched with its function.
   A. DNA polymerase I: synthesis of the continuous matching strand
   B. DNA helicase: synthesis of messenger RNA
   C. DNA polymerase III: cuts out the primer and replaces it with DNA nucleotides
   D. DNA ligase: links adjacent nucleotides together by covalent bond

5. Select the response that correctly identifies the complementary DNA strand for this strand:
5′-TACTTTGGCCCAGAG-3′
   A. 3′-AUGAAACCGGGUCUC-5′
   B. 3′-UACUUUGGCCCAGA-5′
   C. 3′-ATGAAACCGGGTCTC-5′
   D. 5′-ATGAAACCGGGTCTC-3′

Use the following information to answer questions 6 and 7.

1. Amino acids are brought to the ribosome and linked together in the correct order.
2. A copy of the gene is taken to the ribosome.
3. RNA polymerase attaches to the promoter site.
4. The two subunits of the ribosome attach to the RNA strand.
5. DNA polymerase III makes a matching strand using complementary base pairs.
6. Release factor binds to the A site and the ribosome releases the amino acid chain.
7. The two original strands serve as templates for the synthesis of new matching stands.
8. The lagging strand is synthesized in short fragments.
9. The two strands are unwound and the hydrogen bonds are broken.

6. NR Identify the steps described above that correspond to the process of replication. (Record all four digits of your answer in the order the steps would occur in the cell.)

7. NR Match these terms to the selection above that best describes them. (Record all four digits of your answer.)

______	______	______	______
initiation of transcription	termination of translation	elongation of amino acid chain	initiation of translation

Part 2

8. Use a diagram to **illustrate** how the two DNA strands in a double helix run antiparallel. Make sure you label your diagram.
9. **How** does the fact that DNA replicates semiconservatively decrease the possibility of errors made during DNA replication? **Describe** another mechanism that minimizes DNA replication error.
10. Numerous enzymes are involved in DNA replication. **Outline** the role that the following enzymes play: DNA ligase, DNA gyrase, DNA helicase, DNA polymerase I, and DNA polymerase III.
11. What is the complementary strand of AATTGCATA?
12. DNA polymerase III can only extend an existing DNA strand in the 5′ to 3′ direction. **Describe** the mechanisms in place that compensate for DNA polymerase III's inability to intitiate a strand and for its stringent directionality.
13. One strand of a DNA molecule contains the nucleotide proportions 15 % adenine (A), 30 % thymine (T), 20 % guanine (G), and 35 % cytosine (C). **Predict** the proportions of the four base pairs in the double-stranded form of this DNA.
14. **Describe** the function of mRNA and tRNA in protein synthesis.
15. **Distinguish** between transcription and translation. Use a table to organize your answer.
16. The following is a sequence of DNA for a hypothetical peptide:
    5′- AAGTACAGCAT - 3′
    3′- TTCATGTCGTA - 5′
    Translate this sequence into protein using the genetic code.
17. Every codon consists of a triplet of base pairs. **Explain** why amino acids cannot be coded with just two base pairs.
18. **Describe** how the structure of mRNA is similar to DNA. **How** does mRNA differ from DNA?
19. DE Cutting a piece of DNA with a restriction enzyme can give DNA fragments with sticky ends or with blunt ends, depending on the restriction enzyme that is used. Write a unified response addressing the following aspects of cutting DNA with a restriction enzyme:
    - **Distinguish** between sticky ends and blunt ends.
    - **Describe** how a DNA fragment with a sticky ends could be produced.
    - **Describe** how a DNA fragment with blunt ends could be produced.
    - **Illustrate** your descriptions with diagrams.
20. The DNA fragment CGTCATCGATCATGCAGCTC contains a restriction enzyme recognition site. **Identify** the site.
21. **Explain** how the presence of an antibiotic-resistance marker gene in a plasmid can be used to determine whether a transformation protocol has been successful.
22. Recently, the Human Genome Project (HGP) was completed. The HGP has provided us with a complete sequence of the human genome. Despite this great advancement, we are far away from realizing the numerous medical treatments that will eventually be made available because of, or as a result of, the project. Scientists are now working on the Human Proteome Project, which involves linking genes to both functional and dysfunctional proteins. **Explain** why there would be limited progress in medical research if scientists were restricted to working only with DNA sequences and not with proteins.
23. DE *Pseudomonas syringae* is a bacterium found in raindrops and most ice crystals. These bacteria act as nuclei for ice crystal formation, catalyzing ice formation at temperatures approaching 0 °C. It does so by producing an ice-nucleation protein in the outer membrane of its cells. Researchers have been able to cleave the gene for this protein from its genome, thereby preventing the bacteria from forming ice crystals. When the genetically engineered "ice-minus" bacteria are sprayed on tomato plants, frost damage is reduced. The presence of the ice-minus bacteria can extend growing seasons, thus increasing crop yields, especially in cold climates. However, environmental groups have raised serious concerns about releasing genetically engineered bacteria into the environment. Write a unified response addressing the following aspects of the use of ice-minus bacteria:
    - **Predict** whether the new microbes could gain a selective advantage over the naturally occurring species?
    - **Describe** what might happen if the genetically engineered microbes mutate?
    - Do you think that genetically engineered microbes should be introduced into the environment? **Justify** your opinion.

Use the following information to answer questions 24 to 26.

Huntington disease is an inherited disorder that manifests itself in abnormal body movements and memory loss that degenerates into dementia and cognitive decline. This disorder is caused by a codon repeat in the Huntington protein gene on chromosome 4. In the normal form of this gene there are fewer than 40 repeats of the codon CAG. More repeats result in the eventual onset of the disease and severity seems to increase with the number of repeats.

24. **Identify** the amino acid specified by the CAG codon.
DE

25. **Explain** what increased inclusions of the CAG codon in the Huntington gene might do to the protein structure of the Huntington protein.
DE

26. **Describe** the steps a lab would take to diagnose the number of CAG repeats on the Huntington gene of an individual. **Identify** the specific technologies and **describe** how they would be used in this analysis.
DE

Use the following information to answer questions 27 and 28.

The first recombinant DNA organisms were bacteria that were altered for commercial purposes to produce a protein product when grown in culture. These recombinant organisms caused little public concern, as they were perceived to be contained within a laboratory or factory. However, subsequent genetic engineering projects have included the release of engineered organisms into the environment. Agricultural transgenic products being grown today include golden rice, insect-resistant maize and cotton, and herbicide-resistant canola and corn, to name a few.

27. **Identify** and **describe** the technologies used to create these recombinant organisms.

28. **Explain** the concerns of those who oppose the use of these organisms, and the benefits touted by their proponents.

Use the following information to answer questions 29 to 32.

A company, Gene Tree, offers kits that can be used to test whether an individual has DNA sequences found most often in the Aboriginal peoples. The tests are compared to known genetic markers in mitochondrial DNA (mtDNA), Y chromosome DNA, and nuclear DNA that are unique to the Aboriginal peoples of North America. Testing to establish the ethnic background of individuals may raise concerns about the use of this information. Historically, there have been political, legal, and moral issues around attempts to identify an individual's ethnicity as distinct from those of others.

29. **Identify** the technique listed above that would best determine paternal inheritance of Aboriginal ancestry. **Explain** your selection.

30. **Sketch** a diagram of meiosis that shows the formation of a human egg. Label the important features and clearly label the ploidy of the key stages. Describe how mtDNA is inherited during the formation of the human zygote, and identify which parent would be contributing the genetic markers for Aboriginal ancestry if they were identified in mtDNA.

31. **Identify** and **describe** two DNA technologies that would be used to carry out these tests.

32. **Identify** two advantages and two disadvantages to both society and individuals that might arise from using DNA technology to trace ethnic patterns of inheritance.

Many of these questions are in the style of the Diploma Exam. You will find guidance for writing Diploma Exams in Appendix A5. Science Directing Words used in Diploma Exams are in bold type. Exam study tips and test-taking suggestions are on the Nelson Web site.

DO NOT WRITE IN THIS TEXTBOOK.

Part 1

1. Indicate the correct order, beginning with prophase, of the following events of cell division.
NR
1. Nuclear membrane begins to dissolve.
2. Chromatids move to opposite poles.
3. Chromosomes align along the equatorial plate.
4. Chromosomes reach opposite poles and begin to lengthen.

2. A fertilized mosquito egg has six chromosomes. During mitosis, the egg cell undergoes multiple divisions. Which row shows the correct number of chromosomes found in telophase and interphase?

	Number of chromosomes	
Row	**Telophase**	**Interphase**
A.	3	3
B.	3	6
C.	6	3
D.	6	6

Use the following information to answer questions 3 and 4.

Figure 1 shows four phases of cell division in a plant cell.

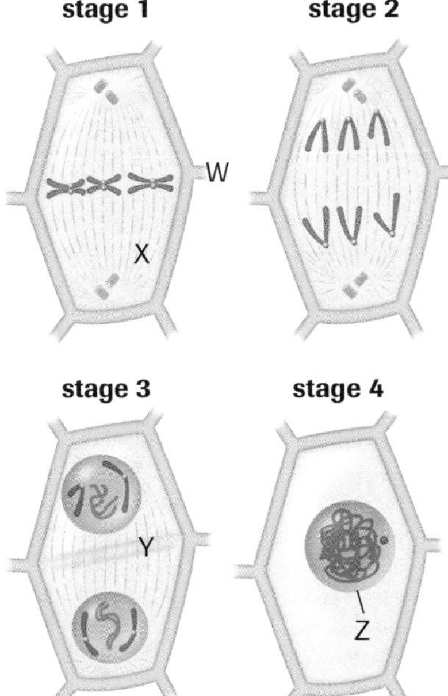

Figure 1

3. Identify the phases of cell division in **Figure 1**.

______ prophase ______ metaphase ______ anaphase ______ telophase

4. The correct labels for the structure identified by letters in **Figure 1** are
A. W = centriole, X = centromere, Y = cytoplasm, Z = nucleolus
B. W = centromere, X = spindle fibre, Y = division plate, Z = nuclear membrane
C. W = chromatid, X = centromere, Y = nuclear membrane, Z = nucleolus
D. W = chromosome, X = spindle fibre, Y = chromatin, Z = nuclear membrane

Use the following information to answer questions 5 to 7.

A corn plant with white seeds, a large cob, and small leaves is crossed with a corn plant with yellow seeds, a large cob, and large leaves. All of the F_1 offspring have yellow seeds, large cobs, and large leaves.

5. Identify the row that correctly gives the dominant traits, according to this data.

Row	**Seed colour**	**Cob type**	**Leaf size**
A.	white	large	small
B.	white	small	large
C.	yellow	small	small
D.	yellow	large	large

6. Identify the row that correctly gives the expected traits of the offspring, if a plant from the F_1 generation were cloned.

Row	**Seed colour**	**Cob type**	**Leaf size**
A.	white	large	small
B.	white	small	large
C.	yellow	small	small
D.	yellow	large	large

7. If a plant from the F_1 generation were crossed with a corn plant with white seeds, identify the colour seeds you would expect to see in the F_2 generation.
A. 100 % of individuals would have white seeds
B. 75 % of individuals would have yellow seeds and 25 % white seeds
C. 50 % of individuals would have white seeds and 50 % yellow seeds
D. 100 % of individuals would have yellow seeds

8. Correctly match the cell number in **Figure 2** with the condition. (Record all four digits of your answer.)
NR

________	________	________	________
Turner's syndrome	trisonomic female	will not survive	trisonomic male

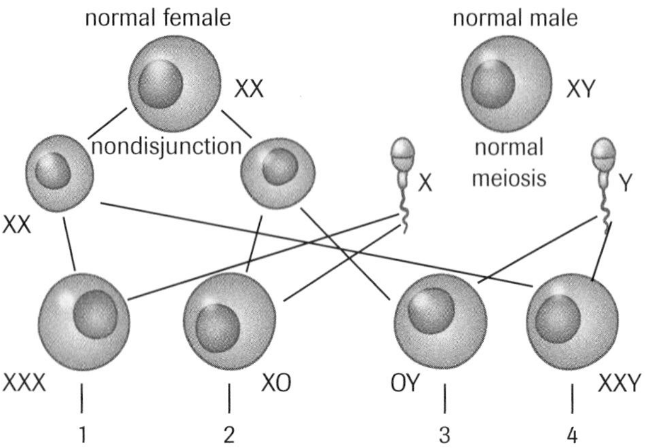

Figure 2

Use the following information to answer questions 9 and 10.

Thalassemia is a serious human genetic disorder that causes severe anemia. People with thalassemia die before sexual maturity. There are over 90 different mutations that can lead to thalassemia. One of the mutations changes the codon TAC to TAA.

9. Identify the row that best describes the type of mutation and its consequence to the structure of the protein.

Row	Mutation	Consequence
A.	insertion	causes a shift to the reading frame and results in an entirely different amino acid sequence
B.	deletion	causes a shift to the reading frame and results in an entirely different amino acid sequence
C.	substitution	causes a different amino acid at one location
D.	inversion	causes different amino acids for the sequence inverted as reading frame is reversed

10. Select the statement that best describes the codons given in the description of thalassemia.

A. These are mRNA codons as they contain the base uracil.

B. These are mRNA codons as they contain the base thyamine.

C. These are DNA codons as they contain the base uracil.

D. These are DNA codons as they contain the base thymine.

Use the following information to answer questions 11 and 12.

1. Initiation commences when the RNA polymerase binds to the promoter region of the gene to be transcribed.
2. The ribosome continues to move along the mRNA, reading the code in triplets known as codons.
3. When the ribosome moves over, the tRNA containing the growing peptide is shifted over to the P site. A third amino acid, specified by the third codon, is brought into the A site by the next tRNA. A peptide bond is formed between the second and third amino acid.
4. A complementary RNA strand is synthesized in the direction of 5′ to 3′, using one strand of DNA as a template. This step is known as elongation. The complement of adenine in RNA is uracil.
5. New amino acids are added to the chain in the process of elongation, which continues until a stop codon is read in the A site. The stop codons are UAG, UGA, and UAA. At this point, the ribosome stalls.
6. Once the termination sequence is reached by the RNA polymerase, the process ceases. The mRNA is separated from the DNA and the RNA polymerase falls off the DNA molecule.
7. When the start codon is in the P site, a tRNA delivers the amino acid methionine. The tRNA recognizes the codon because of the complementary anticodon.

11. Identify the statements that describe the process of transcription. (Record all three digits of your answer in the order in which they would occur in the cell.)
NR

12. Identify the statements that describe the process of translation. (Record all four digits of your answer in the order in which they would occur in the cell.)
NR

Use the following information to answer questions 13 to 15.

Genetic inheritance of risk for certain types of breast cancer has long been inferred from its incidence in family clusters. Mutations in either the *BRCA*1 or *BRCA*2 genes accounts for 2 % to 3 % of breast cancers and 9 % of ovarian cancers. People who are identified as having a mutation in either of these genes have a 60 % to 85 % lifetime risk of getting breast cancer and a 15 % to 40 % lifetime risk of getting ovarian cancer. The gene *BRCA*1 is located on chromosome 17 and codes for approximately 1800 amino acids, while the gene *BRCA*2 is located on chromosome 13 and codes for approximately 3400 amino acids.

13. Select the statement that is supported by these data.
   A. Mutations in the *BRCA*1 and *BRCA*2 genes are inherited in an autosomal recessive pattern.
   B. Mutations in the *BRCA*1 and *BRCA*2 genes always cause breast cancer and sometimes cause ovarian cancer.
   C. Mutations in the *BRCA*1 and *BRCA*2 genes cause cancer when influenced by environmental factors.
   D. Mutations in the *BRCA*1 and *BRCA*2 genes always cause ovarian cancer and sometimes cause breast cancer.

14. NR Determine the minimum number of base pairs a *BRCA*2 gene would contain to code for a complete protein. (Record all four digits of your answer.)

15. Identify which of the following statements about *BRCA*1 and *BRCA*2 gene mutations is incorrect:
   A. A woman's risk for genetically linked breast cancer is only elevated if the maternal branch of her family had a history of breast cancer.
   B. Mutations in the *BRCA* genes also increase the risk of ovarian cancer.
   C. Women without mutations in the *BRCA* genes may still be at high risk of getting breast cancer.
   D. A woman's lifetime risk of genetically linked breast cancer is elevated if there is a family history of breast cancer in either branch of her family.

Part 2

16. Genetic testing to identify mutations of the *BRCA*1 and *BRCA*2 genes can be accomplished by gene cloning. **Explain** why a patient might or might not want to have such genetic tests done.

Use the following information to answer questions 17 to 19.

A student observed fertilized eggs of two different species, whitefish and frog, undergoing mitosis. The number of cells in each stage of the cell cycle, at the time the egg masses were prepared and mounted on a slide, were counted. These numbers are presented in **Table 1**.

Table 1 Number of Cells in Specific Stages of the Cell Cycle

Cell cycle stage	Whitefish	Frog
interphase	81	88
prophase	10	6
metaphase	5	5
anaphase	1	0
telophase	3	1

17. DE **Determine** the total time for which cells were in each phase, for both whitefish and frog cells.

18. DE **Identify** the phase of the cell cycle that took the longest time to complete, for both whitefish and frog cells.

19. DE **Sketch** the cell cycle for the fertilized whitefish and frog eggs.

Use the following information to answer questions 20 to 22.

Cancer cells can divide at rates that far exceed those of normal cells. Some drugs used to treat cancer block the action of enzymes that are essential for chromosomal duplication.

20. DE **Why** would these drugs be useful in treating cancer?

21. DE **Predict** the phase of the cell cycle that would likely be affected by these drugs.

22. DE **Predict** the phase of mitosis that might be affected.

23. Approximately 25 plant species make up about 90 % of the human diet. Some scientists have speculated that global warming will reduce plant diversity, making us even more dependent on these species. Our ability to maintain our food supply under these conditions would require advances in genetic engineering, selective breeding, and cloning of plants. **Describe** ways in which these technologies might be used to increase crop production.

Use the following information to answer questions 24 to 27.

Figure 2 is a flowchart showing the stages of meiosis for spermatogenesis.

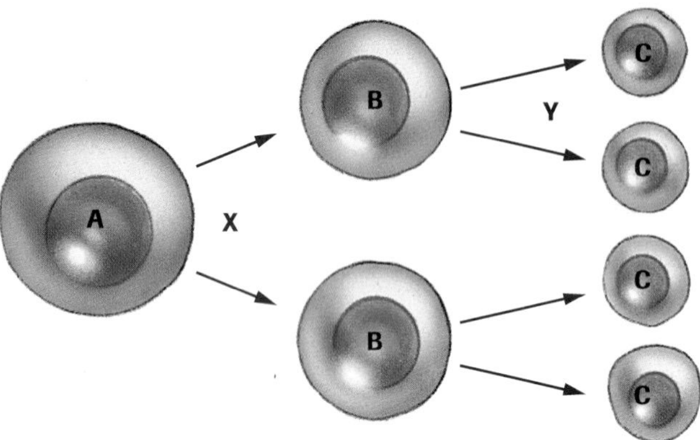

Figure 2

24. **Identify** the stage of meiosis indicated by the labels X and Y on **Figure 2**.
DE

25. **Describe** the events at each stage of meiosis shown on the flowchart in **Figure 2**.
DE

26. **Identify** which cells in **Figure 2** would have haploid chromosomes?
DE

27. Cell A in **Figure 2** contains 44 chromosomes. **Infer** the number of chromosomes that cell C contains.
DE

Use the following information to answer questions 28 to 30.

A normal human sperm cell fertilizes an egg cell containing 24 chromosomes. A lab technician examining a karotype of fetal cells notices trisomy of chromosome pair 21.

28. **Sketch** the karotype.
DE

29. **Predict** how many chromosomes will be found in a muscle cell of the fetus.
DE

30. From the information provided, is it possible to predict the sex of the embryo? **Explain** your answer.
DE

31. Gene therapy is a technique in which defective genes are located and substituted by normally functioning genes. In the future, gene banks may likely be a common source of genes for treating genetic disorders. **List** two potential disadvantages to society of the use of gene banks.

Use the following information to answer questions 32 to 34.

Figure 3 shows the formation of sex cells in a mammal.

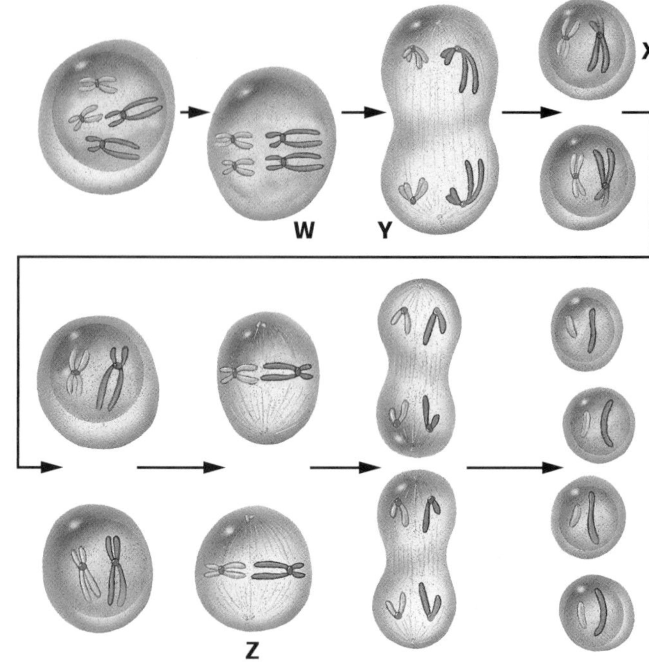

Figure 3

32. Use the diagrams and labels in **Figure 3** to help **explain** the process of crossing over.
DE

33. **Identify** correctly the letter label in **Figure 3** that marks the first haploid cells formed by meiosis. Explain your answer.
DE

34. **Identify** the correct letter label that marks metaphase II. What is happening during this phase?
DE

Use the following information to answer questions 35 and 36.

In guinea pigs, black hair is dominant to white hair, and short hair is dominant to long hair. A guinea pig that is homozygous for both white hair and for short hair is mated with a guinea pig that is homozygous for both black hair and for long hair.

35. **Predict** the phenotype(s) of the F_1 generation.
DE

36. Two members of the F_1 generation are mated. **Determine** the predicted phenotype ratio for the F_2 generation.
DE

37. In chickens, the allele for rose comb (*R*) is dominant over the allele for single comb (*r*), and the allele for feathered legs (*F*) is dominant to the allele for clean legs (*f*). A breeder mates four birds with feather legs and rose combs. The phenotypes of the offspring of these crosses are shown in **Table 2**. **Determine** the genotypes of the parents.

Table 2

Parents	Phenotype of F_1 offspring
rooster A → hen C	all have rose combs; some have feathered legs and some have clean legs
rooster A → hen D	all rose combs and feathered legs
rooster B → hen C	most have rose combs, some have single combs; all have feathered legs
rooster B → hen D	rose and single combs; all have feathered legs

38. In mice, coat colour is determined by more than one gene. For one gene, the allele *C* determines a coloured coat, and the allele *c* determines an albino phenotype. For a second gene, the *B* allele causes activation of a pigment that produces black coat colour. The recessive allele, *b*, causes incomplete activation of the pigment, producing brown coat colour. These two genes are located on separate chromosomes and segregate independently. **Determine** the predicted genotypic and phenotypic ratios of the F_1 generation from the cross *CcBb* × *CcBb*.

39. In your notebook, construct a table to **compare** replication, transcription, and translation. (A comparison includes similarities and differences.) Your table should include the following headings: Process name, Location in cell, Time during cell cycle, Product, Brief summary of process.

40. In actively dividing cells, DNA replication occurs during interphase. **Sketch** the process of replication, using the following segment of DNA as an example:

5′-AAAAATTTAATATATTACAATGGCCCCGCGAT AGTTCGTAGT-3′

3′-TTTTTAAATTATATAATGTTACCGGGGCGCTAT CAAGCATCA-5′

Label and annotate your diagram to describe the process. Clearly indicate the start codon on your diagram.

Use the following information to answer questions 41 to 44.

Tay Sach disease results from a mutation in the gene for the enzyme hexoseaminidase. This mutation is an autosomal recessive disorder. The absence of a correct gene for this enzyme results in an inability to break down fatty material called ganglioside, which causes eventual death as the ganglioside builds up in the brain. There is no effective treatment for this disease.

5′-AUGCAGGUGACCUCAGUG-3′
mRNA sequence for normal protein

5′-AUGCAGGUGACAUACCUCAGUG-3′
mRNA sequence for mutated protein

41. DE Give the amino acid sequence that would result from translation of the mRNA at the ribosome.

42. DE Write the sequence for the normal and mutated protein into your notebook. **Determine** the DNA sequence from which each sequence is transcribed.

43. DE Tay Sach disease is the result of a gene mutation. **Identify** the mutation by circling the changed sequence. Name the type of mutation that has occurred and **explain** the changes that would occur in the protein.

44. DE **Outline** the procedure that you would follow to attempt a gene therapy treatment for Tay Sach disease. Start from the assumption you already know the sequence of the normal gene.

45. **Describe** an advantage and disadvantage to treating individuals with Tay Sachs by applying gene therapy to somatic cells. **Describe** an advantage and disadvantage to treating individuals with Tay Sachs by applying gene therapy to sex cells.

46. The gene for growth hormone has been isolated from human chromosomes and cloned in bacteria. The bacteria produce human growth hormone, which can be harvested in large quantities. The hormone is invaluable to people with dwarfism. Before its development, people with dwarfism relied on costly pituitary extracts. Although the prospect of curing dwarfism has been met with approval, some concerns have been raised about the potentially vast supply of growth hormone. Should individuals who do not have dwarfism but who want to grow a few more centimetres have access to the growth hormone biotechnology? **Justify** your opinion.

47. Review the focusing questions on page 552. Using the knowledge you have gained from this unit, briefly **outline** a response to each of these questions.

unit

30 D

Population and Community Dynamics

Populations are the functioning units of individual species. Individuals within a population vary due to their genetic diversity and the demands of their environment, and interact with each other in many ways. Many populations together make up an ecological community, in which each population interacts with the others. These interactions, rather than the individuals or species themselves, provide both stability and the potential for dynamic change in the ecosystem. In many ecosystems, such as in the boreal forest shown here, the biotic and abiotic components of the environment vary with the seasons. Population ecologists document and interpret the interactions, quantifying the changes that occur over time.

In this unit, you will gain an understanding of the variety of interactions both within populations and among the populations in a community. You will use this understanding to examine the very successful growth of our own species and our changing relationships with the other organisms on Earth.

As you progress through the unit, think about these focusing questions:

- How does one determine if populations are changing over time?
- In what ways may individual members of a population interact with one another or with members of a different population?
- What quantitative measures indicate that populations change over time?

UNIT 30 D PERFORMANCE TASK

Changes in Human Population Size

The United Nations estimates that the global human population is greater than 6 billion people. About 100 000 years ago, only a few thousand people lived on Earth. What factors contributed to this growth? How did humans become such a successful species? At the end of this unit, you may apply your skills and knowledge to complete this Performance Task.

GENERAL OUTCOMES

In this unit, you will

- describe a community as a composite of populations in which individuals contribute to a gene pool that can change over time
- explain the interaction of individuals in populations with each other and with members of other populations, the basis of which is genetic variation
- explain, in quantitative terms, the changes in populations over time

Unit 30 D Population and Community Dynamics

ARE YOU READY?

These questions will help you find out what you already know, and what you need to review, before you continue with this unit.

Prerequisites

Concepts

- resource limits of an ecosystem
- roles of meiosis, mitosis, DNA, genes, alleles
- relationship between genotypes, phenotypes, and the environment
- types of mutations
- role of genetic recombination including crossing over

Skills

- analyze a population study using Punnett squares
- apply an understanding of inheritance
- relate an understanding of biological diversity to genetic diversity

You can review prerequisite concepts and skills on the Nelson Web site and in the Appendices.

A Unit Pre-Test is also available online.

www.science.nelson.com 

Knowledge

1. In your notebook, indicate whether the statement is true or false. Rewrite a false statement to make it true.
   (a) Mutations are changes in DNA that are harmful to the cell.
   (b) Sexual reproduction is disadvantageous because the offspring show little or no genetic diversity.
   (c) Through the process of genetic recombination, meiosis produces diploid cells and increases the potential diversity of offspring.
   (d) In species that reproduce asexually, offspring are always genetically identical to their parent.
   (e) Over time, dominant alleles will tend to become more common in a population, while recessive alleles will become more rare.
   (f) An organism's genotype refers to its genetic makeup, which is unaffected by the environment.
   (g) An organism's phenotype refers to traits that are expressed in the organism and affected by both its genotype and the environment.
   (h) A species is a population or populations of organisms that are able to interbreed under natural conditions and produce fertile offspring.
   (i) Harmful or lethal mutations have little or no effect on the health of large multicellular organisms.
   (j) Virtually all large populations exhibit genetic variation among individuals.
2. Define these terms:
   (a) exotic species
   (b) carrying capacity
   (c) food chain
   (d) food web
   (e) biotic factors
   (f) abiotic factors
3. **Figure 1** shows four steps in meiosis that contribute to genetic recombination. Explain what event is occurring in each step, and how each step contributes to increased genetic variation of gametes.

step 1

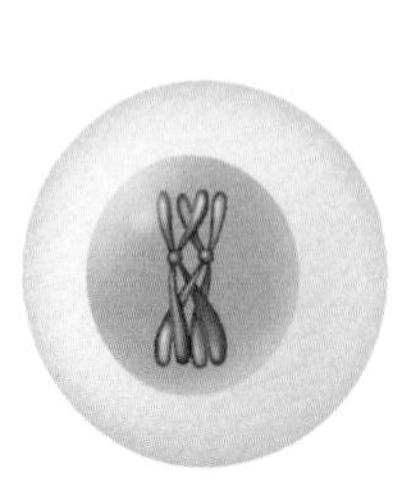

step 2

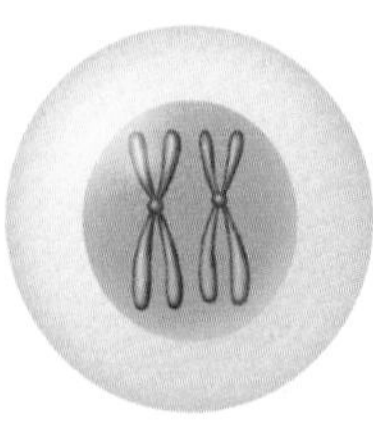

step 3

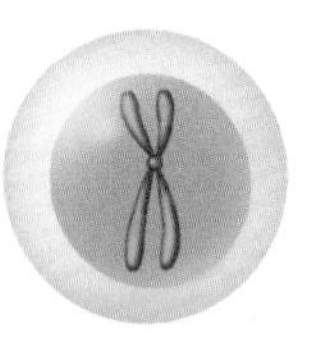
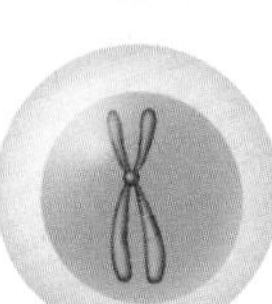

step 4

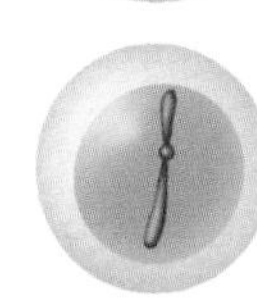
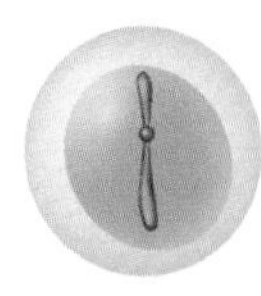
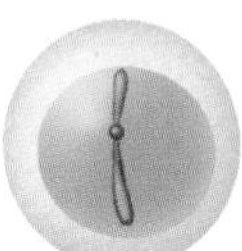

Figure 1
Some steps in meiosis, showing genetic recombination

Skills

4. Examine the Punnett square in **Figure 2**, which represents a cross between a male that is homozygous for two dominant alleles, *AA* and *HH*, and a female that is homozygous for two recessive alleles, *aa* and *hh*.
   (a) Have the variety and ratio of genotypes changed in the F_1 generation?
   (b) In the parent generation, state the ratio of the specific alleles for each gene (i.e., *A*:*a* and *H*:*h*).
   (c) Taking all F_1 individuals into consideration, do the allele ratios change in the F_1 generation? Explain your reasoning.
   (d) Draw a Punnett square and determine the allele ratios for the F_2 generation.

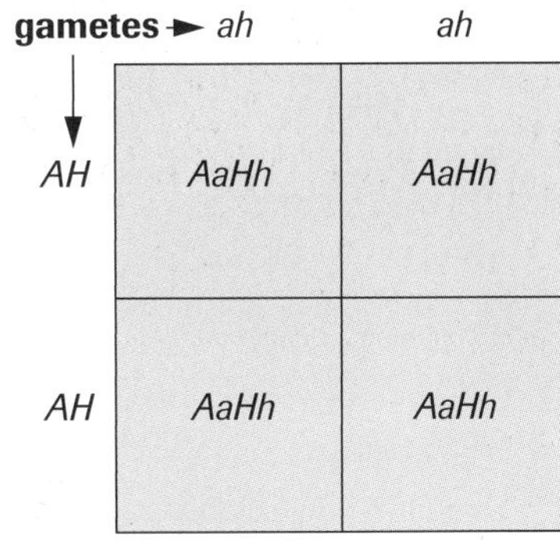

Figure 2
Punnett square analysis of a dihybid cross

5. Zebra mussels often grow in high concentrations on water intake pipes. Assume that **Table 1** represents the number of mussels per square metre of pipe surface sampled over a 10-year period.

Table 1 Zebra Mussel Population in a Small Water Body, 1991–2000

Year	1991	1992	1993	1994	1995	1996	1997	1998	1999	2000
Population (per m^2)	400	520	676	879	1142	1485	1930	2509	3262	4241

   (a) Draw a population curve for the zebra mussel population from 1991 to 2000. Label your axes, and give your graph an appropriate title.
   (b) Describe the growth illustrated by your graph.
   (c) Calculate the population growth rate of zebra mussels from 1996 to 2000.
   (d) If no measures are taken to control the zebra mussel population in this location, hypothesize what the population would be in 2010. Add these data to your graph.
   (e) What factors are likely to limit the growth of this zebra mussel population?

STS Connections

6. For each of the following, list two examples, one that is not genetically inherited and one that might have been genetically inherited:
   (a) physical characteristics
   (b) diseases and medical conditions
   (c) behaviours, and likes and dislikes

7. Zebra mussels clog pipelines and other underwater structures (**Figure 3**). What economic and other social impacts could this problem cause?

8. In January 2002, the North American Commission for Environmental Cooperation released a report that declared that North America is facing a "widespread crisis" because of its shrinking biodiversity.
   (a) How is the loss of biodiversity related to the loss of genetic diversity?
   (b) Why do so many scientists, government agencies, and members of the public consider it an important issue?

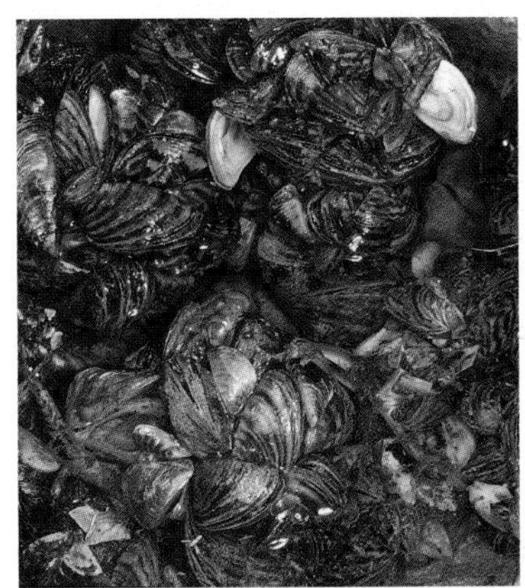

Figure 3
Zebra mussels

chapter 21

The Genetic Basis for Population Change

▶ In this chapter

- Exploration: Distinguishing Traits
- Web Activity: Global Variation in Blood Type
- Explore an Issue: Are Human "Races" Only Skin Deep?
- Web Activity: Hardy–Weinberg
- Mini Investigation: Quantifying Human Genetic Variation
- Mini Investigation: Demonstrating Chance
- Explore an Issue: Genetic Diversity at Risk
- Case Study: Antibiotic-Resistant Bacteria
- Web Activity: Hardy–Weinberg and the Colour of Guppies
- Investigation 21.1: Agents of Change
- Career Connections: University Professor; Anthropologist

We have all noticed that certain traits are inherited from generation to generation (**Figure 1**). In *On the Origin of Species,* Charles Darwin provided compelling evidence for evolution and natural selection. About 70 years after Darwin's work, scientists finally understood how parents' traits are inherited by offspring. Now, geneticists can distinguish the genetic code of one individual from those of a whole population. This powerful science is also being used to measure the genetic differences between entire species and to document changes in the genetic makeup of populations over surprisingly short periods of time.

STARTING Points

Answer these questions as best you can with your current knowledge. Then, using the concepts and skills you have learned, you will revise your answers at the end of the chapter.

1. Successful individuals of a species are able to reproduce and adapt to their environments. What role might their genetic makeup play in meeting these two demands?
2. The population size of marine green sea turtles (**Figure 2 (a)**) shows little change over time while the locust population in the Canadian prairies (**Figure 2 (b)**) varies widely from year to year. What might this suggest about the environments in which they live? Which environment is the most stable?

Figure 2
(a) green sea turtle
(b) locust

Figure 1
Although individuals in a population have some unique traits, other traits are common to all the members.

▶ Exploration Distinguishing Traits

Study the photo of the group of people in **Figure 1**. These individuals exhibit variations, but they also share such inherited physical features as limbs, internal organs, and paired eyes and ears. Yet pigeons, alligators, horses, and toads also possess these features.

(a) List inheritable features by which you can distinguish human beings from all other species.
(b) List inheritable features by which you can distinguish human individuals from one another.
(c) On each list, circle the two or three most significant distinguishing traits.
(d) Are the most distinguishing traits from parts (a) and (b) unique to each species and individual respectively, or do they represent variations of shared features?

21.1 The Hardy–Weinberg Principle

Figure 1
The genetic diversity of many populations, such as this one of long-nosed bats, may not be readily apparent.

Recall from Unit 30 C that all individuals of the same species possess a common genome, except for sex chromosomes (when present). However, each individual has a different genotype. Differences in genotypes and environmental influences account for differences among the phenotypes of individuals of the same species. These different phenotypes are then acted on by natural selection.

Traits that distinguish individuals from one another represent genetic diversity, which varies both within species and from species to species (**Figure 1**).

With techniques such as DNA sequencing, geneticists have begun to analyze and compare the genetic code of individuals, populations, and entire species. One finding is that the amount of DNA present in different species varies dramatically, as shown by the examples in **Table 1**. Organisms with larger genomes have the potential for greater genetic diversity and present more targets for mutation.

The size of genomes, however, does not provide an accurate comparison of a species' genetic diversity. Genomes of many eukaryotic organisms, for example, contain DNA that is not transcribed. Some noncoding sequences in the genome of humans, as well as other organisms, may be repeated as many as 500 000 times. Some species, such as maize or wheat, are polyploids. This means that the species has more than two copies of each chromosome, resulting in multiple, often identical, copies of the same genes.

Regardless of the total quantity of DNA present, most species (other than some microorganisms) have large numbers of different genes—usually numbering in the thousands. Species that possess a larger number of genes have the potential for increased genetic diversity. Similarly, the greater the number of different alleles for these genes, the more genetic variation there will be between individuals in a species. For species that undergo sexual reproduction, genetic diversity within a population increases enormously when the various alleles from two parents recombine at fertilization.

As you learned in Chapter 6, all of the genes that occur in a population are referred to as the gene pool. The gene pool maintains continuity of traits from generation to generation. Although some gene frequencies remain the same over many generations, others change quickly.

CAREER CONNECTION

University Professor

University professors conduct and publish new research, increasing the body of scientific knowledge in the world. They also teach post-secondary students and supervise and develop research programs. University professors are able to follow their passions and study whatever they find the most interesting. If you are interested in exploring new areas of scientific discovery and enjoy teaching, find out more information on becoming a university professor.

www.science.nelson.com 

Table 1 Total Amount of DNA in the Genomes of Selected Species

Species	Common name	DNA (kilobases)
Mycoplasma genetalium	bacterium	580
Saccharomyces cerevisiae	yeast	1200
Drosophila melanogaster	fruit fly	180 000
Xenopus laevis	toad	3 100 000
Macaca nigra	macaque	3 399 900
Homo sapiens	human	3 400 000
Necturus maculosus	mud puppy	81 300 000
Amphiuma means	newt	84 000 000
Trillium species	trillium	100 000 000
Amoeba dubia	amoeba	670 000 000

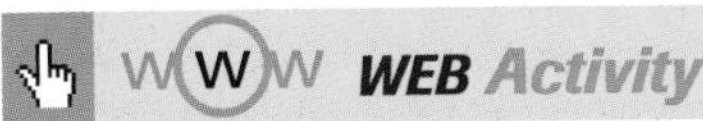

Case Study—Global Variation in Blood Type

Blood type is an inherited characteristic. Each individual has type A, B, AB, or O blood, and also either Rh negative (Rh−) or Rh positive (Rh+). The alleles responsible for these blood types are designated as I^A, I^B, I^O, *Rh+*, and *Rh−*.

Your ABO blood type was determined by the direct inheritance of one allele from each of your parents; it cannot be altered by any environmental factor. As a result, blood types are ideally suited for the study of human genetic variation and provide dramatic evidence of human genetic diversity at the population level.

In this activity, you will examine the geographic distribution of different blood types in humans. You will analyze these patterns and relate them to human genetic diversity, and use your understanding of genetics and populations to account for the distribution patterns.

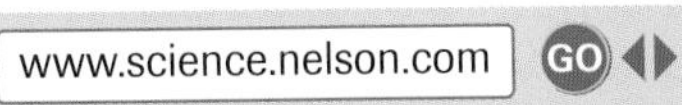

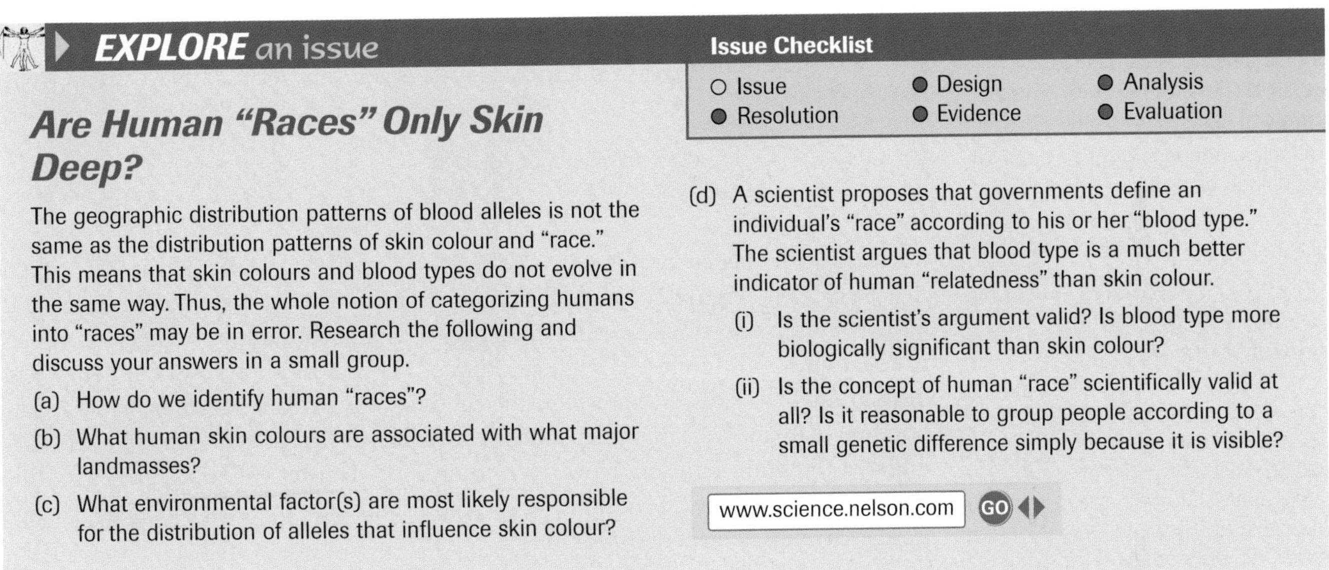

EXPLORE an issue

Issue Checklist

- ○ Issue
- ● Resolution
- ● Design
- ● Evidence
- ● Analysis
- ● Evaluation

Are Human "Races" Only Skin Deep?

The geographic distribution patterns of blood alleles is not the same as the distribution patterns of skin colour and "race." This means that skin colours and blood types do not evolve in the same way. Thus, the whole notion of categorizing humans into "races" may be in error. Research the following and discuss your answers in a small group.

(a) How do we identify human "races"?

(b) What human skin colours are associated with what major landmasses?

(c) What environmental factor(s) are most likely responsible for the distribution of alleles that influence skin colour?

(d) A scientist proposes that governments define an individual's "race" according to his or her "blood type." The scientist argues that blood type is a much better indicator of human "relatedness" than skin colour.

(i) Is the scientist's argument valid? Is blood type more biologically significant than skin colour?

(ii) Is the concept of human "race" scientifically valid at all? Is it reasonable to group people according to a small genetic difference simply because it is visible?

www.science.nelson.com GO

Hardy–Weinberg Principle and Population Equilibrium

Population geneticists have developed a method to quantify a gene pool—the genetic information of an entire population—by measuring each **allele frequency**. Thus, changes in populations can be measured in part by looking for changes in allele frequencies. Note that not all genes exhibit variation. Where only a single allele exists for a particular gene, that allele's frequency is 100 % and it is described as a **fixed frequency**.

allele frequency the proportion of gene copies in a population of a given allele

fixed frequency the frequency of an allele within a population when only a single allele is present for a particular gene (i.e., the allele's frequency is 100 %)

Consider a population of moths for which there are two alleles, *A* and *a*, where *A* represents the allele for dark brown wings, which is dominant, and *a* represents the allele for light brown wings, which is recessive. A population of 500 comprises 320 moths with *AA* homozygous dark wings, 160 moths with *Aa* heterozygous dark wings, and 20 moths with *aa* homozygous light brown wings. Each individual contributes two alleles to the gene pool, giving 640 *A* (from *AA* genotype), 160 *A* + 160 *a* (from *Aa* genotype), and 40 *a* (from *aa* genotype).

Learning Tip

An allele is one of several forms of the same gene. For example, the gene for wing colour in **Figure 2** has two alleles: dark brown and light brown.

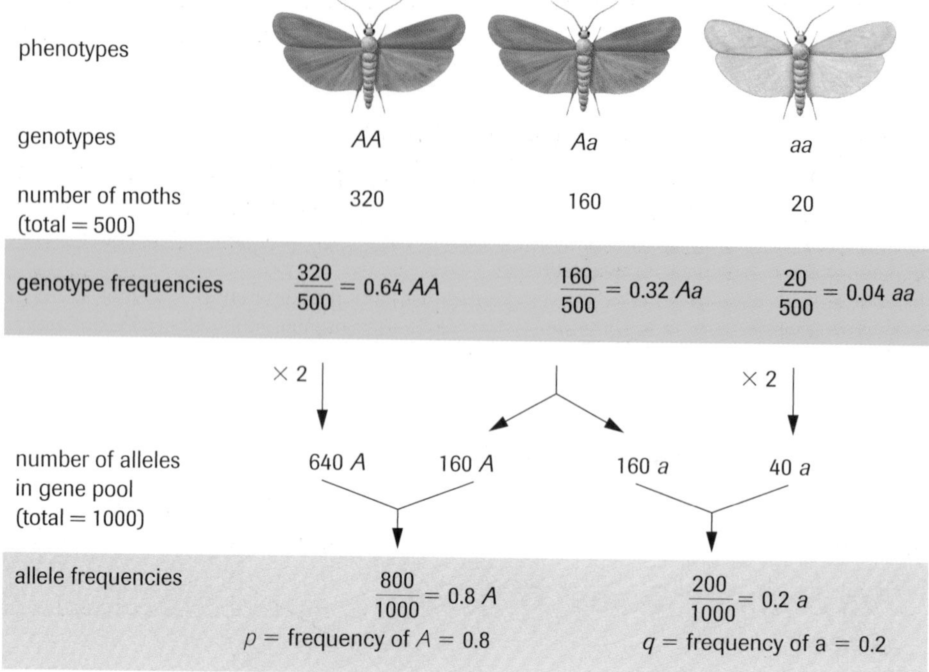

Figure 2
The allele frequencies of a population of moths

The allele frequency for A is $800 \div 1000 = 0.80$, or 80 %, and that of a is $200 \div 1000 = 0.20$, or 20 % (**Figure 2**). Would the dominant form of moth wing become more and more common over time? Do allele frequencies remain constant or change over time?

These questions interested Reginald Punnett. Over a meal in 1908, Punnett posed them to Godfrey Hardy, an eminent mathematician, who, without hesitation, wrote a solution on a napkin. Working independently, German physician Wilhelm Weinberg formulated the same solution. Now referred to as the Hardy–Weinberg Principle, this mathematical relationship, outlined below, shows that allele frequencies will not change from generation to generation, as long as certain conditions are met.

Conditions of the Hardy–Weinberg Principle

Allele frequencies in a population will not change if

- the population is infinitely large
- no migration occurs
- no mutations occur
- no natural selection occurs
- mating is random

For a gene with only two alleles (A and a), the Hardy–Weinberg Principle can be expressed using the following equation:

If p = frequency of allele A and q = frequency of allele a, then

$$p + q = 1$$
$$(p + q)^2 = 1^2$$

and so $$p^2 + 2pq + q^2 = 1$$

p^2 = frequency of genotype AA
$2pq$ = frequency of genotype Aa
q^2 = frequency of genotype aa

DID YOU KNOW?

Hardy's Reluctance

When Punnett first saw Hardy's now famous equation, he suggested that Hardy publish the idea immediately. Hardy was reluctant, apparently not wanting his name associated with so simple an idea.

This equation gives the expected genotype frequencies of the population, when all the conditions of the Hardy–Weinberg Principle are met. We will refer to it as the Hardy–Weinberg equation. Note that after a single generation of random mating, the genotype frequencies are given by p^2, $2pq$, and q^2.

Applying the Hardy–Weinberg Principle

For the moth population in **Figure 2**, on the previous page, the allele frequency of the *A* allele is 0.80, or 80 %, and the frequency of the *a* allele is 0.20, or 20 %. If mating is random, when the population reproduces, 80 % of all gametes will bear the *A* allele, while the remaining 20 % of gametes will bear the *a* allele. The genetic recombination that occurs in the next generation is shown in **Figure 3**. Substituting these values into the Hardy–Weinberg equation, we get the following:

$$(0.80)^2 + 2(0.80)(0.20) + (0.20)^2 = 1$$
$$0.64 + 0.32 + 0.04 = 1$$

Therefore, the frequency of the *AA* genotype is 0.64, or 64 %, the frequency of the *Aa* genotype is 0.32, or 32 %, and the frequency of the *aa* genotype is 0.04, or 4 %. The genotype frequency values of offspring generations are the same as those for the parent generation. If random mating continues to occur, allele frequencies are likely to remain constant from generation to generation.

Solving Problems Involving the Hardy–Weinberg Principle

Listen to this audio clip of some guiding principles for solving frequency calculations in problems dealing with the Hardy–Weinberg Principle.

www.science.nelson.com 

Genetic structure of second generation

Recombination of alleles from first generation (parents)

		ova: *A*, $p = 0.8$	ova: *a*, $q = 0.2$
sperm	*A*, $p = 0.8$	*AA* $p^2 = 0.64$	*Aa* $pq = 0.16$
sperm	*a*, $q = 0.2$	*Aa* $pq = 0.16$	*aa* $q^2 = 0.04$

Second generation:

genotype frequencies	$p^2 = 0.64$ *AA*	$2pq = 0.32$ *Aa*	$q^2 = 0.04$ *aa*
allele frequencies	$p = 0.8$ *A*	$q = 0.2$ *a*	

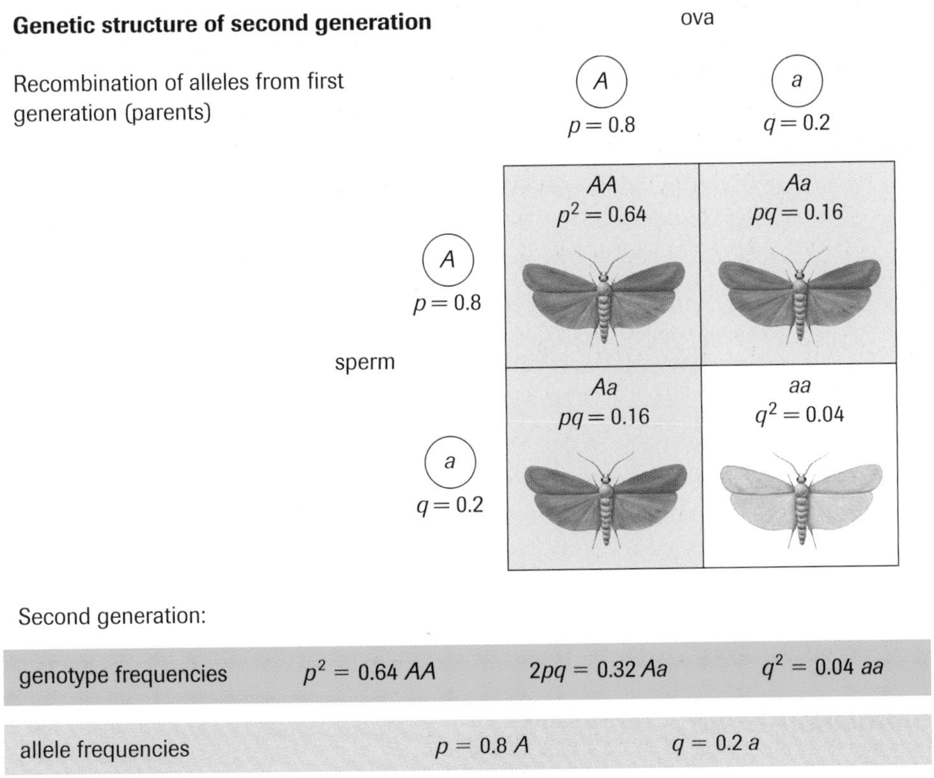

Figure 3
A typical Punnett square shows a cross between two individuals. This one depicts the allele frequencies of offspring within the moth population in **Figure 2** on the previous page.

SAMPLE exercise 1

Apply the Hardy–Weinberg equation to solve the following problem, assuming that all five of the Hardy–Weinberg conditions are met:

A population has only two alleles, *R* and *r*, for a particular gene. The allele frequency of *R* is 20 %. What are the frequencies of *RR*, *Rr*, and *rr* in the population?

Solution

If p represents the frequency of allele *R*, q the frequency of allele *r*, and $p = 0.20$, then $q = 0.80$. Using the equation for the Hardy–Weinberg Principle, we get the following:

$$(0.20)^2 + 2(0.20)(0.80) + (0.80)^2 = 1$$
$$0.04 + 0.32 + 0.64 = 1$$

frequency of *RR* genotype = 0.04, or 4 %

frequency of *Rr* genotype = 0.32, or 32 %

frequency of *rr* genotype = 0.64, or 64 %

Learning Tip

Turn to Appendix A7, Math Skills, for a review of how to correctly perform calculations using scientific notation.

Practice

For all questions, assume that the conditions for the Hardy–Weinberg Principle are being met.

1. A large population consists of 400 individuals, of which 289 are homozygous dominant (*MM*), 102 are heterozygous (*Mm*), and 9 are homozygous recessive (*mm*). Determine the allele frequencies of *M* and *m*.
2. The gene pool of a certain large population of fruit flies contains only two eye-colour alleles: the dominant red allele, *R*, and the recessive red allele, *r*. Only 1 % of the population has red eyes. Determine the allele and genotype frequencies of this population.
3. Manx cats have no tails (or have very short tails) and have large hind legs. The no-tail trait results from a heterozygous genotype, *Tt*. Interestingly, *TT* genotypes are normal cats, while the *tt* genotype is lethal and cat embryos that possess it do not survive. In a population of 1000 cats, only 1 % are Manx and 99 % are normal.
   (a) What are the allele frequencies in this population?
   (b) Determine the expected frequency of each genotype in the next generation.
   (c) Determine the allele frequencies of the population of cats from (b).
   (d) What influence do homozygous recessive genotypes have on allele frequencies in this generation?
   (e) Predict the long-term result of a lethal homozygous recessive trait in a wild population.

WWW WEB Activity

Simulation—Hardy–Weinberg

In this activity, you will visit links on the Nelson Web site to observe various simulation models of populations. These simulations allow you to manipulate the conditions necessary for maintaining Hardy–Weinberg equilibrium. Your tasks are to

- experimentally test the effect of altering each condition
- critique at least two different simulation models and assess their strengths and weaknesses

www.science.nelson.com

mini Investigation — Quantifying Human Genetic Variation

Humans possess several easily distinguishable traits, each of which is controlled by a single recessive and dominant allele combination.

- Select two of the following traits:
  - blue eyes
  - widow's peak
  - hitchhiker's thumb
  - attached earlobes
  - freckles
  - dimples
  - tongue rolling
  - long second toe (second toe extends beyond big toe)
- Research to determine if the trait is controlled by a dominant or a recessive allele.
- Survey at least 20 students in your class and record the presence or absence of the trait. If possible, share data with other classes to increase the sample size.
- Apply your understanding of genetics and the Hardy–Weinberg equation to estimate population allele frequencies.
- Conduct research to find the accepted allele frequency values.

www.science.nelson.com 

(a) How would your data have differed if you had surveyed your family members instead of students?

(b) Suggest methods you could use to determine if the alleles you studied were in Hardy-Weinberg equilibrium.

(c) Account for any differences between your findings and the accepted allele frequency values for the human population.

SUMMARY — The Hardy–Weinberg Principle

- The gene pool of a population is determined by the alleles possessed by the individuals in the population. A gene pool can be quantified by measuring the allele frequency.
- According to the Hardy–Weinberg Principle, the gene pool of a population will not change when the following conditions are met:
  - The population is infinitely large.
  - No migration occurs.
  - No mutations occur.
  - No natural selection occurs.
  - Mating is random.
- When the Hardy–Weinberg conditions are met, then, for a gene with two alleles (A and a), the allele frequency in the population will be

  $$p + q = 1$$

  where p = frequency of allele A and q = frequency of allele a
- When all the Hardy–Weinberg conditions are met, then, for a gene with two alleles (A and a), the genotype frequency in the population will be

  $$p^2 + 2pq + q^2 = 1$$

  where p^2 = frequency of genotype AA, $2pq$ = frequency of genotype Aa, and q^2 = frequency of genotype aa

Section 21.1 Questions

1. Describe how the genetic diversity of a population is influenced by recombination and heterozygosity.
2. Study **Table 1** on page 716.
   (a) Suggest possible reasons that might account for the widely varying amounts of DNA found in these species.
   (b) *Necturus* and *Amphiuma* have similar sized genomes. Why is this not surprising?
   (c) The size of the genome does not provide any information on the genetic variability within chromosomes. How might polyploidy, non-coding sequences, and multiple alleles contribute to the genetic diversity of species?
3. Describe how gene duplication and recombination during meiosis contribute to the overall genetic diversity of populations.
4. Use the Punnett square in **Figure 4** to briefly explain how sexual reproduction increases the potential for genetic variation.

♀ parent *RrTt* / ♂ parent *RrTt*	*RT*	*Rt*	*rT*	*rt*
RT	*RRTT*	*RRTt*	*RrTT*	*RrTt*
Rt	*RRTt*	*RRtt*	*RrTt*	*Rrtt*
rT	*RrTT*	*RrTt*	*rrTT*	*rrTt*
rt	*RrTt*	*Rrtt*	*rrTt*	*rrtt*

Figure 4
A Punnett square showing the offspring of parents with identical genotypes and phenotypes. The possible phenotypes are represented in different-coloured cells.

5. For each of the following, predict whether Hardy–Weinberg equilibrium would be maintained generation after generation:
   (a) a population of African violets maintained by a plant breeder
   (b) the population of mosquitoes in northern Alberta
   (c) an elk population living in Banff
   (d) a newly discovered bird population on a remote island off the coast of British Columbia
6. A population of 200 includes 32 individuals that are homozygous recessive (*bb*) for a given trait. Assuming the population meets the conditions for Hardy–Weinberg equilibrium, how many of the 200 individuals would you expect to be homozygous dominant (*BB*)?
7. Cystic fibrosis is a recessive condition that affects about 1 in 2500 people in the Caucasian population of Canada. Calculate the following:
   (a) the population frequencies for the dominant (*C*) and recessive (*c*) alleles
   (b) the percentage of the population that is a carrier of the recessive allele
   (c) the number of students in your school that are likely to be carriers of the cystic fibrosis allele
8. A recessive allele (*h*) codes for complete hair loss in chimpanzees. Homozygous recessive individuals lose all their hair by about six months of age. Chimpanzees with one or two dominant alleles (*H*) show no signs of this disorder. In a population of captive chimpanzees, 16 % of the chimpanzees lose all their hair.
   (a) Calculate the allele frequencies of *H* and *h*.
   (b) What percentage of the chimpanzees could *not* be the parents of chimpanzees with this condition.
   (c) Hairless chimpanzees have reduced survival rates and lower reproductive success. Predict how the allele frequencies will change over time. Explain your reasoning as it relates to the Hardy–Weinberg equilibrium assumptions.

Changes in Gene Pools 21.2

The Hardy–Weinberg Principle predicts that, under a set of specific conditions, a gene pool will remain unchanged from generation to generation. The underlying conditions are critically important. When the conditions of the Hardy–Weinberg Principle are not met, a gene pool is predicted to change in the following ways:

- When a population is small, chance fluctuations will cause changes in allele frequencies.
- When individuals migrate, they will remove alleles from one population and add them to another.
- When mutations occur, new alleles will arise or one allele will be changed into another, thereby changing the allele frequencies in the population.
- When natural selection occurs, individuals with certain alleles will have greater reproductive success than others do, thereby increasing the relative frequency of their alleles in the next generation.
- When mating is not random, individuals that are preferred as mates will pass on their alleles in greater numbers than less preferred mates.

Real populations can be affected by any of these conditions, resulting in changes to allele frequencies in the gene pool.

Genetic Drift

genetic drift changes to allele frequency as a result of chance

Genetic drift is a change in the genetic makeup of a population resulting from chance. When populations are small, chance can significantly alter allele frequencies. For example, assume that only 1 in 100 whooping cranes carries a particular allele, C_1 (**Figure 1**). If the whooping crane population had 10 000 individuals, you would expect 100 birds to carry the allele. If half the population died in a severe storm, for example, about 50 of the 5000 survivors would have the C_1 allele. Therefore, the allele frequency is not expected to change significantly. If the whooping crane population is only 200 individuals, only two birds would have the C_1 allele. If half of this population died, both the C_1 carriers could die, eliminating the C_1 allele entirely. If both survived, then the C_1 allele frequency would double.

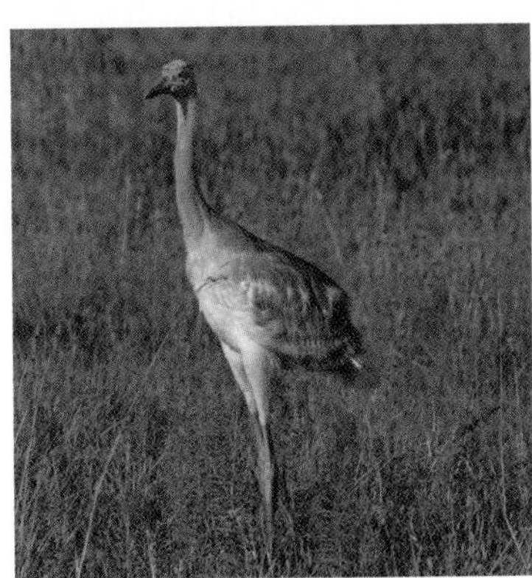

Figure 1
A young whooping crane. In 1941, there were only 22 individuals left in Alberta. Today, the breeding population in Wood Buffalo National Park remains very susceptible to the effects of genetic drift.

Figure 2, on the next page, shows how population size affects genetic drift. **Figure 2 (a)** illustrates genetic drift in a population of 25 stoneflies. The frequency of allele *A* fluctuates wildly from generation to generation. In five of the trials, the *A* allele frequency became fixed at 100 % in 22 generations or fewer. In the other four trials, the *A* allele was lost entirely in 36 generations or fewer. In a larger population of 500 stoneflies, shown in **Figure 2 (b)**, the allele frequency remained relatively stable even after 50 generations had passed. There was no trend toward fixing of the allele. In small populations, genetic drift can lead to fixation of alleles. This increases the percentage of homozygous individuals within a population and reduces its genetic diversity.

When a few individuals from a large population leave to establish a new population, the resulting genetic drift is called a **founder effect**. The allele frequencies of the new population will likely not be the same as those of the original population and may deviate further as the new population expands. Founder effects seem to be common in nature, such as when a few seeds carried by a bird or by winds to a distant volcanic island may germinate and rapidly establish a large population. With self-pollinating plants, an entire population can be established from a single fertile seed. Founder effects can also be seen in

founder effect genetic drift that results when a small number of individuals separate from their original population and find a new population

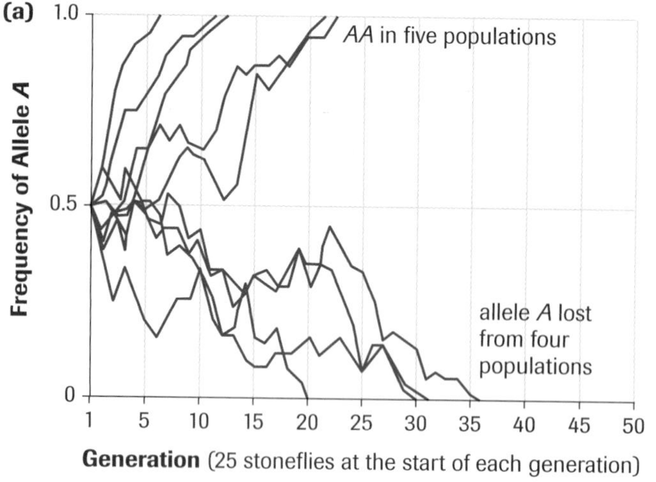

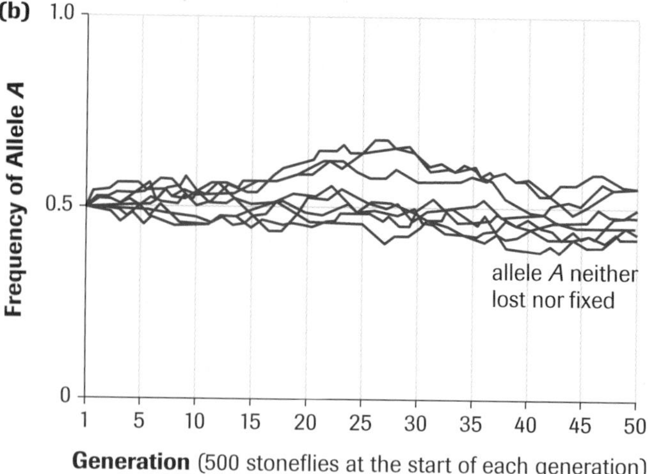

Figure 2
(a) In small populations, genetic drift can result in dramatic changes in allele frequencies.
(b) In larger populations, genetic drift is not usually significant.

human populations. Members of the Amish community in Pennsylvania are all descendants of about 30 people who emigrated from Switzerland in 1720. One of the founders had a rare recessive allele that causes unusually short limbs. The frequency of this allele in the current Amish population is about 7 %, compared to a frequency of 0.1 % in most populations.

bottleneck effect a dramatic, often temporary, reduction in population size, usually resulting in significant genetic drift

When a severe environmental event results in a drastic reduction in population size, a population may experience a **bottleneck effect** (**Figure 3**). With the bottleneck effect, the frequency of alleles in the survivors is very different from that in the original population. Additional genetic drift may result in further changes in the gene pool. This is known to have occurred with the northern elephant seal (**Figure 4**).

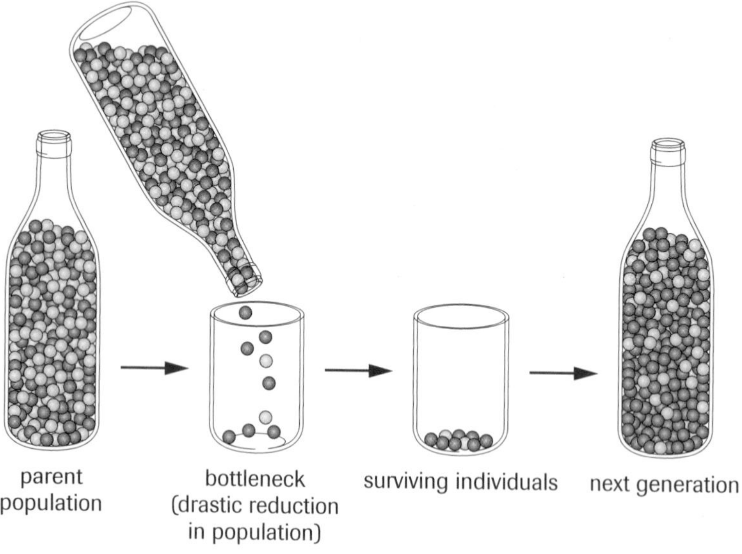

Figure 3
A dramatic, sometimes temporary, reduction in the size of a population can result in a bottleneck effect.

Figure 4
The northern elephant seal population was reduced by overhunting to 20 individuals in the 1890s. Although the population had rebounded to over 30 000 individuals by 1974, 24 gene loci were found to be homozygous by genetic testing.

mini Investigation — Demonstrating Chance

See for yourself how random chance works in small populations.

A large population of birds possesses six different alleles for a specific gene. All alleles are present in equal frequencies. Assume that 30 individuals are randomly separated from the original population and become established on a remote island. Let the alleles be represented by the numbers 1 to 6.

- Model the initial allele frequency of the new population by tossing a six-sided die 30 times. Record your results.
- Examine the results obtained by your classmates.

(a) How often did you roll a three? Did your response differ from the one-sixth you would expect by chance?

(b) How many times did you roll a three in your first six tosses? What ratio did this produce?

(c) Relate the variations in the frequencies of the number three to variations in allele frequencies that occur when small founder populations form.

Gene Flow

When organisms migrate, leaving one population and joining another, they alter the allele frequencies of both populations. Such **gene flow** occurs frequently in most wild populations. For example, prairie dogs live in dense colonies consisting of a few dozen members. For much of the year they prevent other prairie dogs from joining their colony. In late summer, however, mature male pups are permitted to enter new colonies, thereby affecting both gene pools. New alleles may be added or rare alleles lost during such events. Gene flow can also occur when individuals of adjacent populations mate without moving permanently. In these ways, genetic information is shared between populations. Unlike genetic drift, gene flow tends to reduce differences between populations.

gene flow the movement of alleles from one population to another through the movement of individuals or gametes

Mutations

As you have previously learned, mutations are randomly occurring events that alter the inheritable genetic material of an individual. Mutations are the source of new genetic diversity in a species as a whole. Mutations vary considerably in size. They range from the alteration of a single base pair in a DNA molecule to large-scale changes such as multi-base-pair deletions, insertions, or inversions.

Many mutations are neutral mutations, and have no effect on the individual or its reproductive success. Other mutations may be beneficial mutations (enhancing reproductive success) or harmful mutations (reducing reproductive success). You will find more information about mutations in Chapters 5 and 20. When a mutation arises in a population, it has the potential to alter the gene pool or allele frequencies of the population, and therefore the Hardy–Weinberg equilibrium. However, the mutation will not influence the entire population or species unless the resulting genetic change becomes relatively common. Genetic changes resulting from mutations become common when they are beneficial to the individuals that possess them. As you have learned, inheritable characteristics that are favoured by natural selection become more common over time. Since these traits are determined by specific alleles then, as a result of natural selection, the allele frequencies (or genetic makeup) of a population will change over time. Most natural populations are large and reproduce rapidly, with each new individual inheriting a very large number of alleles. Although the chances of a mutation arising in any specific allele are low, new mutations arise often and continuously in the population as a whole.

DID YOU KNOW?

Lots of Mutations

It has been estimated that each new human cell contains about 100 new mutations. Although this number seems high, most of the mutations occur in non-coding DNA sequences.

EXPLORE an issue

Genetic Diversity at Risk

Issue Checklist

○ Issue ○ Design ● Analysis
● Resolution ● Evidence ● Evaluation

In this activity, you will examine several significant threats to genetic diversity that face both wild and domesticated species, and learn how biologists and conservationists are addressing these threats. What do you already know about the Threats listed in **Table 1**? Are you familiar with any of the Actions that are being taken to preserve genetic diversity?

- Share your prior knowledge about these topics with members of your group.
- Choose one Threat and a related Action with your group. For example, you might choose the loss of crop-seed varieties (Threat) and the establishment of seed banks (Action).
- Conduct some preliminary research to determine the general nature of the Threat and the Action. During your research, document the global status of the Threat and the scope of the Action. Consider the factors that are driving the Action. What are the underlying causes of this Threat and what are the motivating concerns behind the Action? Consider both the short-term and long-term implications of the Threat and the Action. What is predicted to happen if the current Threat persists or if the Action is unsuccessful?

www.science.nelson.com 

- When research is completed, select examples you think best exemplify the Threat and Action you reviewed. Conduct more in-depth research on these examples and document your findings.

(a) Prepare a class presentation on your Threat and Action. Make sure that your presentation
   - provides an overview of the Threat and the Action
   - accounts for the root cause of the Threat
   - highlights examples in detail
   - relates the topic directly to the impact of human activities
   - includes a summary flowchart that relates the Threat to the Action

Table 1 Some Threats to Genetic Diversity and Actions to Reduce Its Effect

Threats to genetic diversity	Actions to protect genetic diversity
• habitat loss such as clearing of tropical rainforests, elimination of wild-grass prairies, and coral-reef bleaching • over-harvesting of individual species • fragmentation of wilderness, leading to small isolated populations • competition with exotic species • loss of traditional domesticated animal and plant crop varieties	• establishment of natural reserves and parks • international treaties to protect species and ecosystems • direct protection of endangered species and their primary habitat • creation of gene and seed "banks" • captive animal- and plant-breeding programs in zoos and botanical gardens

Natural Selection

Mutations provide a continuous supply of new genetic variations, which may be inherited and expressed as different phenotypes. Natural selection then acts on these mutations. Although mutations provide the source of variation, natural selection acts on individuals and their phenotypes. As a result, particular alleles are most successful and passed on when they enhance the phenotype of the individual and, thereby, contribute to their reproductive success. Selective forces can favour particular variations in the phenotype of individuals in a number of ways. Sickle-cell anemia, a potentially serious blood disorder, is a useful example of how mutation, genetic variation, and the environment result in different patterns of natural selection.

The allele for sickle-cell anemia differs from the normal hemoglobin gene by a single base-pair mutation. Individuals homozygous for the sickle-cell allele are severely afflicted with this disorder. Heterozygous individuals are only mildly affected by sickle-cell anemia; however, they are much more resistant to malaria than are people with normal hemoglobin. In regions where malaria is uncommon, individuals with the sickle-cell allele are at a disadvantage and their phenotypes are less likely to contribute alleles to the gene pool. But in regions where malaria is common (**Figure 5**), heterozygous individuals are strongly favoured; they are much more likely to survive and pass on their genes to the next generation. The environment selects the best-adapted phenotype and, in so doing, favours a particular set of alleles.

DID YOU KNOW ?

Selection of Another Hemoglobin Allele?

In November 2001, geneticists reported in the journal *Nature* about another mutated form of the hemoglobin gene that provides resistance to malaria. Unlike the sickle-cell allele (*HbS*), individuals with two copies of the *HbC* allele show no signs of disease and are very resistant to even the most serious form of malaria. Interestingly, the mutation in the β-hemoglobin gene that produced the *HbC* allele is in the identical location as the *HbS* allele.

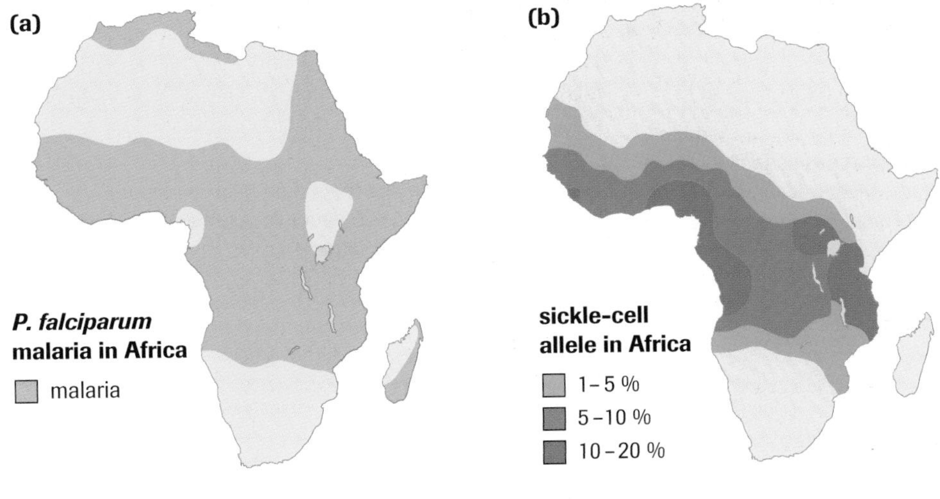

Figure 5
Of the 120 million new cases of malaria each year, about 1 million are fatal. The prevalence of malaria in Africa in **(a)** closely matches the distribution of the sickle-cell allele in **(b)**. The percentages are estimates of a distribution range.

The sickle-cell allele is only common where it provides an overall advantage to the individual. In populations where it has an overall harmful effect, it does not persist. This pattern demonstrates an important relationship between mutations and gene pool changes in a population:

- Harmful mutations occur frequently, but they are selected against and, therefore, these mutant alleles remain extremely rare.
- Beneficial mutations are rare, but they are selected for and, therefore, these mutant alleles may accumulate over time.

CAREER **CONNECTION**

Anthropologist

Anthropologists study changes in human physical characteristics and relate them to influences of heredity and environment. There are many different branches of anthropology, and the range of research interest is very broad. Are you interested in studying how human populations have changed over time?

www.science.nelson.com GO

Case Study

Antibiotic-Resistant Bacteria

An article in the *Canadian Medical Association Journal* (July 2001) reported an alarming six-fold increase in the rate of antibiotic resistance in Canada between 1995 and 1999. In addition to added health risks, fighting antibiotic resistance can be expensive. Across Canada, the cost is estimated at $50 to $60 million a year.

In 1996, doctors took samples of bacteria from a patient suffering from tuberculosis, a lung infection caused by the bacterium *Mycobacterium tuberculosis.* Cultures of the bacteria found it to be sensitive to a variety of antibiotics, including rifampin. The patient was treated with rifampin and initially responded so well that the lung infection seemed to be over. Soon after, however, the patient had a relapse and died. An autopsy revealed that bacteria had invaded the lungs again in large numbers. Cultures of these bacteria were found to be sensitive to many antibiotics, but resistant to rifampin. DNA sequencing revealed that a certain bacteria's gene had a single base-pair mutation that was known to confer resistance to rifampin. Doctors compared the new bacteria culture with the original culture and found that the sequences were identical except for this single mutation. Researchers then examined more than 100 strains of bacteria from other tuberculosis patients living in the same city at the same time. None of these bacteria had the same genetic code as the rifampin-resistant bacteria obtained in the autopsy. When doctors had begun administering rifampin, the bacteria in the patient had been subjected to a new environmental selective agent, one that gave the mutant strain a major adaptive advantage.

The pattern in this story is not uncommon, but evolution offers some hope as well as alarm. Many traits that provide antibiotic resistance are harmful to the bacteria. For example, a strain of *E. coli* bacteria possesses a plasmid with a gene that enables it to produce an enzyme called b-lactamase. This enzyme gives the bacterium resistance to the antibiotic ampicillin. However, there is a cost for this resistance: to maintain its antibiotic resistance, the bacterium must devote cellular resources to producing the enzyme and to making copies of the plasmid before cell division, slowing its growth rate. In another example, the bacterium *Mycobacterium tuberculosis* normally produces catalase, a beneficial but non-essential enzyme. This enzyme, however, activates the antibiotic isoniazid, which destroys the bacterium. Bacteria that have a defective catalase gene are, therefore, resistant to isoniazid–as it cannot be activated in the absence of catalase–but they lack the benefits normally provided by the enzyme. As a result of these costs of resistance, when an antibiotic is not present, natural selection often favours those bacteria that do not carry antibiotic-resistant alleles.

Case Study Questions

1. Did the rifampin-resistant bacteria found in the autopsy evolve within the patient's lungs or did they result from a brand new infection? Explain the evidence.
2. Most antibiotics are derived from microorganisms that do not occur naturally in the human body. Most infectious bacteria showed no resistance to these antibiotics when they were first used in the 1940s. Why?
3. Bacteria that are not resistant to antibiotics usually out-compete resistant strains in the absence of antibiotics. Account for this observation.
4. Tuberculosis patients are now routinely given two different antibiotics at the same time. Why might this approach be more effective than administering a different antibiotic only after bacteria develop resistance to the first?
5. Suggest some strategies that could help reduce the incidence of antibiotic resistance in your own home, your school, and in society at large.

Non-Random Mating

Individuals that mate and reproduce frequently make a substantial contribution to the gene pool of later generations. **Sexual selection** favours the selection of any trait that influences the mating success of the individual. The traits favoured in sexual selection include **sexual dimorphism** (i.e., striking differences in the physical appearance of males and females) and behavioural differences between the sexes. The most common forms of sexual selection result from female mate choice and from male-versus-male competition. In some species, females choose mates based on physical traits, such as bright coloration, or behavioural traits, such as courtship displays and song. In other species, males are equipped with physical features that assist them in establishing control of and defending their territory against other males (**Figure 6**). This territory provides an area to which they can attract, and sometimes forcibly detain, the females with which they mate. Such traits are not produced by selective pressures from environmental conditions; if they were, both sexes would be expected to possess them.

Many species have evolved features that are a compromise between different selective pressures. Sexual selection has produced traits that are beneficial for mating, but may otherwise be detrimental. Avoiding predators is not made easier, for instance, by brilliant plumage or a distinctive song.

sexual selection differential reproductive success that results from variation in the ability to obtain mates; results in sexual dimorphism and mating and courtship behaviours

sexual dimorphism striking differences in the physical appearance of males and females not usually applied to behavioural differences between sexes

EXTENSION

The Hardy-Weinberg Principle "Agents of Change"

This audio clip summarizes the "agents of change" predicted by the Hardy-Weinberg Principle and explains how each can change allele frequency and genotype frequency of a population.

www.science.nelson.com  

Figure 6
Sexual dimorphism may take the form of a physical feature. For example, female fiddler crabs lack the special enlarged right claw of the male as seen here.

Sexual diversity is not limited to animal populations. Most plants do not select mates, but they do need to attract or use various agents—such as insects, birds, and bats—to assist in pollination. Flowers and scents are the most obvious sexual features that have evolved through natural selection.

Not all species show obvious sexual dimorphism. In some species of penguin, males and females look so similar that even they have a hard time telling each other apart (**Figure 7**). A male picks up a stone and drops it at the feet of a would-be mate. If the other penguin happens to be a male, the gift is firmly rejected.

Figure 7
Penguin species that lack sexual dimorphism instead have behaviours that allow them to distinguish males from females.

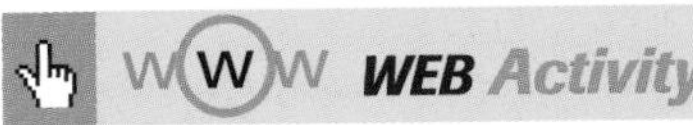

WEB Activity

Web Quest—Hardy–Weinberg and the Colour of Guppies

The use of computer models is very important in a lot of current scientific research. Many multi-disciplinary teams work together on common projects, and the use of models often allows these teams to share findings. In this Web Quest, you and the members of your class will form a research team exploring variation in coloration of a population of guppies. In groups, you will explore several computer models of the Hardy–Weinberg principle. Each group will then use one of these models to explain the colour variations, and then present the results to the rest of the research group. The entire multi-disciplinary research team will then reach a consensus explanation.

www.science.nelson.com GO

INVESTIGATION 21.1 ***Introduction***

Agents of Change

Population size, genetic drift, and natural selection all affect allele frequencies. Using coloured beads to model alleles in a population, you will design and conduct an investigation to explore how population size, genetic drift, and natural selection effect changes in allele frequency. How can the influence of these factors be predicted?

Report Checklist

○ Purpose	● Design	● Analysis
● Problem	○ Materials	● Evaluation
● Hypothesis	● Procedure	● Synthesis
○ Prediction	● Evidence	

To perform this investigation, turn to page 731. 

SUMMARY *Changes in Gene Pools*

- When Hardy–Weinberg conditions are not met, the gene pool of a population may change over time.
- In small populations, genetic drift (including the bottleneck and founder effects) and gene flow may change allele frequencies and genetic diversity.
- Migration may cause gene flow, in which alleles are removed from the gene pool of one population and added to another.
- Mutation may change the frequency of existing alleles and add new alleles to the gene pool.
- Natural selection may change allele frequencies in a gene pool by selecting against harmful alleles and selecting for beneficial alleles
- Non-random mating may cause some alleles to occur more or less frequently in the gene pool of the next generation.

Section 21.2 Questions

1. Define genetic drift and genetic flow, offering two examples to illustrate each definition.
2. Suggest three types of organisms that might produce founder populations. Explain the process that results in this effect.
3. The world's population of cheetahs is almost identical genetically. Male cheetahs are known to have low sperm counts and the species in general has a low resistance to many infectious diseases. All cheetahs are thought to be homozygous at over 99.9 % of their gene loci. Explain how a severe genetic bottleneck effect in the past could account for these observations.
4. If variation in species were solely a result of genetic recombination during sexual reproduction, how would that limit the evolution of species?
5. Relate two ways in which alleles can become fixed in a population.
6. It is thought that a billion prairie dogs once populated an area of more than 100 million ha. Their current territory has been reduced and fragmented to less than 1 % of this original space. Predict the impact of these changes in habitat on the prairie dog gene pool, as well as on the survival of the species.
7. The present population of whooping cranes suffers from low genetic diversity and susceptibility to a variety of diseases. Which of the founder effect, the bottleneck effect, and gene flow are likely to account for these observations?
8. Many insect species have evolved resistance very rapidly to a range of pesticides. Like other species, insects exhibit variation in physical, chemical, and behavioural traits.
   (a) Describe how an insect species would evolve resistance to a pesticide newly introduced into its environment.
   (b) How might high rates of reproduction and the short duration of insect generations affect their evolution?
   (c) How might an understanding of the evolution of pesticide resistance influence how you use pesticides or alternative methods of insect control?
9. In recent years, many Africans who are carriers of the allele for sickle-cell anemia have emigrated from malaria-stricken areas in Africa to North America. Has this influenced the biological role of the sickle-cell allele? Explain.
10. Suggest how large antlers or bright coloration could be a disadvantage for males of some species.
11. Although, in theory, an individual could mate at random with other members of a large population, this seldom occurs. Under most natural conditions, individuals tend to mate with nearby members of the same species, especially if they are not very mobile. Alternatively, individuals choose mates that share similar traits; for example, toads (and often humans) tend to pair according to size.
    (a) How might inbreeding (the mating of closely related individuals) lead to an increase in the number of sometimes harmful recessive phenotypes? Relate your answer to either a population of cheetahs in the wild or a population of golden retrievers in a breeding kennel.
    (b) Does nonrandom mating result in changes to population phenotype frequencies, genotype frequencies, or allele frequencies?
12. In many zoos, artificial insemination of female tigers is becoming common practice. Semen is collected from male tigers in various zoos around the world, frozen in liquid nitrogen, and shipped to zoos where it is used to inseminate female tigers in estrus.
    (a) Why do you think this is being done?
    (b) How might this affect the gene pool of tiger populations?
    (c) Do you think these efforts are enough to prevent a genetic bottleneck from occurring? Explain.
    (d) What conditions do you think are necessary to ensure the genetic diversity of zoo populations?
13. Insect resistance to pesticides is estimated to cost tens of millions of dollars per year in Canada. The Colorado potato beetle, for example, developed resistance to five different pesticides over a period of only 15 years. Predict how such evolutionary consequences might affect and concern consumers, ecologists, pesticide companies, organic farmers, and plant breeders.

INVESTIGATION 21.1

Agents of Change

Report Checklist

- ○ Purpose
- ● Problem
- ● Hypothesis
- ○ Prediction
- ● Design
- ○ Materials
- ● Procedure
- ● Evidence
- ● Analysis
- ● Evaluation
- ● Synthesis

In this investigation, you will design and conduct experiments to examine the influence of population size, genetic drift, and natural selection on the rate of evolution, by measuring changes in allele frequencies.

Work with your partner to develop a design and conduct experiments for Parts 1, 2, and 3, using or modifying the procedure below. Prepare data collection tables. Submit your modified experimental design to your teacher for approval before conducting each of your three experiments.

Problem

How do genetic drift and natural selection influence the allele frequency within a population?

Materials

80 or more beads in colour A (to represent allele *R*)
80 or more beads in colour B (to represent allele *r*)
large opaque container (to represent a gene pool)

Immediately pick up any beads that drop on the floor, as they might cause someone to slip.

Procedure

1. Place 40 beads of each colour (80 beads in total) in the large opaque container.
2. Thoroughly mix the "alleles" (beads) in the "gene pool" (container).
3. At random, reach into the gene pool and take out 20 pairs of alleles to represent offspring genotypes that contribute to the next generation.
4. Determine and record the number of each genotype (e.g., 5 *RR*, 7 *Rr*, 8 *rr*).
5. Record the F_1 allele frequencies as decimal values. For example, divide 17 *R* and 23 *r* by 40 to get the frequencies of 0.425 *R* and 0.575 *r*, respectively.
6. Place the next generation of 80 beads in the "gene pool" container in the same proportions of allele frequencies as the "offspring" (e.g., $0.425 \times 80 = 34$ *R*, $0.575 \times 80 = 46$ *r*).
7. Repeat steps 3 to 6 for four additional generations.

Part 1: Random Mating, No Selection

8. Run at least two trials in which you use large populations and meet the conditions of the Hardy–Weinberg Principle. These trials act as your control in Part 2 and Part 3.

Part 2: Genetic Drift

9. Run at least two trials in which you examine the influence of population size on the degree and rate of genetic drift. Choose two or more starting populations of different sizes. As an option, you may also wish to model a founder effect.

Part 3: Natural Selection

10. Run at least two trials in which natural selection occurs. You might model a favoured homozygous genotype in which, for example, *RR* offspring might be twice as successful as other genotypes. If so, you would need to allow for the increased ratio of offspring contributing to the next generation, while maintaining a stable, large population. As an option, you could investigate selection against a homozygous lethal allele by assuming that each time a specific homozygous allele pair is selected, it dies, and you have to keep adding pairs until you have 20 offspring. Another option is to investigate a selective advantage for a dominant phenotype.

Analysis and Evaluation

(a) Make a separate graph of the data you collected for each of Parts 1, 2, and 3, by plotting allele frequency versus generation. On each graph, use two different colours on the same set of axes to represent the *R* and *r* alleles.

(b) How did population size influence the degree and rate of evolutionary change? Did any alleles become fixed in a population? In what size populations might you expect it to be relatively common for alleles to become fixed? Why?

(c) What conditions occur in nature that result in small populations?

(d) How did natural selection influence the degree and rate of evolutionary change? Did any alleles become fixed in the population?

(e) Were your results unusual compared with similar conditions in other groups?

(f) For each of your experiments in which evolution did occur, which of the five conditions of the Hardy–Weinberg Principle was not met?

Synthesis

(g) Assume you introduced a single new mutant allele to your population. Explain what you expect would happen under each of the following conditions:

(i) The mutant is harmful and the population size is large.

(ii) The mutant is harmful and the population size is small.

(iii) The mutant is beneficial and the population size is large.

(iv) The mutant is beneficial and the population size is small.

(v) A beneficial mutant is introduced and the population is observed four generations later.

(vi) A beneficial mutant is introduced and the population is observed 400 generations later.

Chapter 21 SUMMARY

Outcomes

Knowledge

- describe the Hardy-Weinberg Principle and explain its importance to population gene-pool stability and the significance of non-equilibrium values (21.1)
- describe the factors that cause the gene pool diversity to change, i.e., genetic drift, gene flow, non-random mating, bottleneck effect, migration, mutation, natural selection, and founder effect (21.2)
- apply quantitatively the Hardy–Weinberg Principle to observed and published data to determine allele and genotype frequencies (21.1)
- describe the molecular basis of gene-pool change and the significance of these changes over time, i.e., mutations and natural selection (21.2)

STS

- explain that science and technology have both intended and unintended consequences for humans and the environment (21.2)
- explain how concepts, models, and theories are often used in interpreting and explaining phenomena (21.1)

Skills

- ask questions and plan investigations (21.2)
- conduct investigations and gather and record data and information by: designing and performing an investigation to demonstrate population growth and gene-pool change (21.2)
- analyze data and apply mathematical and conceptual models by: calculating and interpreting problem-solving exercises involving the Hardy–Weinberg Principle (21.2)
- work as members of a team and apply the skills and conventions of science (all)

Key Terms

21.1

allele frequency
fixed frequency

21.2

genetic drift
founder effect
bottleneck effect
gene flow
sexual selection
sexual dimorphism

Key Equation

Hardy–Weinberg Equation

If p = frequency of allele A and q = frequency of allele a, then

$$p + q = 1$$
$$(p + q)^2 = 1^2$$
$$p^2 + 2pq + q^2 = 1$$

where p^2 = frequency of genotype AA, $2pq$ = frequency of genotype Aa, and q^2 = frequency of genotype aa

MAKE a summary

1. Evolution in its simplest form is the change in the gene pool of a species over time. According to the Hardy–Weinberg Principle, gene pool changes do not occur in populations if certain conditions are met. Write a detailed article to address this apparent contradiction. Explain how each of the following may cause gene pool change:
   - random chance
   - gene flow
   - small population size
   - natural selection
   - mutation
   - sexual selection
2. Revisit your answers to the Starting Points questions at the start of the chapter. Would you answer the questions differently now? Why?

Go To

The following components are available on the Nelson Web site. Follow the links for *Nelson Biology Alberta 20–30*.

- an interactive Self Quiz for Chapter 21
- additional Diploma Exam-style Review Questions
- Illustrated Glossary
- additional IB-related material

There is more information on the Web site wherever you see the Go icon in the chapter.

EXTENSION

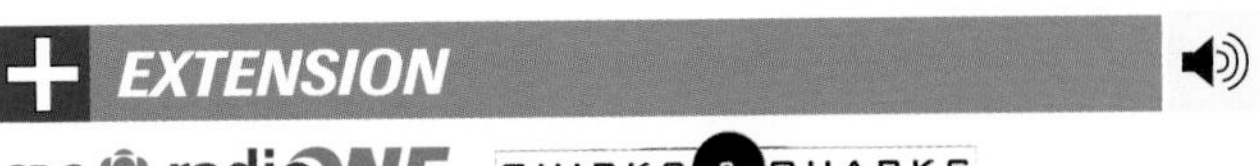

Fowl Play: Disappearing Diversity

Dr. Mary Delany (assistant professor at the University of California, Davis), Dr. Donald Shaver (former head of the Shaver group, one of Canada's largest poultry breeders), Dr. Frank Robinson (professor of poultry management and physiology at the University of Alberta), and Dr. David Notter (Virginia Tech) discuss their various viewpoints on the genetic issues of Canada's commercial poultry. The gene pool for these birds is very small, and outside stock to maintain the gene pool is disappearing.

www.science.nelson.com GO

▸ Chapter 21 REVIEW

Many of these questions are in the style of the Diploma Exam. You will find guidance for writing Diploma Exams in Appendix A5. Science Directing Words used in Diploma Exams are in bold type. Exam study tips and test-taking suggestions are on the Nelson Web site.

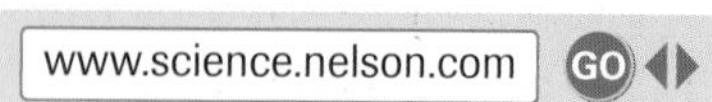

DO NOT WRITE IN THIS TEXTBOOK.

Part 1

1. Identify which of the following conditions is not necessary to maintain Hardy-Weinberg equilibrium in a population.
   A. Mating must be random.
   B. The population must be large.
   C. Initial allele frequencies must be equal.
   D. Immigration or emigration cannot occur.

2. A small number of individuals establish a new population with a distinct set of allele frequencies that is isolated from the parent population. This is referred to as
   A. evolution
   B. a bottleneck
   C. genetic drift
   D. the founder effect

3. When a population does not meet the conditions necessary for maintaining Hardy–Weinberg equilibrium, it will
   A. evolve
   B. increase rapidly in population size
   C. result in all allele frequencies becoming equal
   D. usually decline in numbers, leading to extinction

4. Four percent of an African population is born with a severe form of sickle-cell anemia (*ss*). The percentage of the population that will be heterozygous (*Ss*) for the sickle-cell gene is
   A. 4 %
   B. 16 %
   C. 32 %
   D. 96 %

5. The bottleneck effect is *not* associated with
   A. increases in mutation rate
   B. small populations
   C. increases in the risk of extinction
   D. enhancement of the influence of genetic drift

6. Which of the following traits is probably *not* associated with sexual selection?
   A. defending a nesting territory
   B. extreme running speed in pronghorn antelope
   C. the large, bright tail feathers of a male peacock
   D. differences in size between male and female wood buffalo adults

7. Antibiotic resistance is largely a result of
   A. genetic drift
   B. many random mutations
   C. an evolutionary response to a change in the environment
   D. the same individual bacterium being repeatedly exposed to antibiotics

8. A gene for which there exists only a single allele in the population are referred to as
   A. fixed
   B. recessive
   C. dominant
   D. homozygous

9. NR For each of the factors given below, determine the number that would be expected to increase the rate of genetic change over time. (Record all four digits of your answer in lowest-to-highest numerical order.)
   1. large population
   2. random breeding
   3. migration
   4. stable environment
   5. non-random breeding
   6. changing environment
   7. small population
   8. no migration

Part 2

10. **Outline** in a list the conditions that must be met to satisfy the Hardy–Weinberg equilibrium in a population. Clearly **explain** how the failure to meet any one of the conditions can lead to evolutionary change.

11. If beneficial mutations are much more rare than harmful ones, **how** can they have such an important role in evolution?

12. **Illustrate**, with an example, how random chance can have a greater effect on small populations than on larger populations.

13. Sketch **Figure 1** into your notebook, adding relevant labels. **Identify** and **describe** the effect that your sketch illustrates.

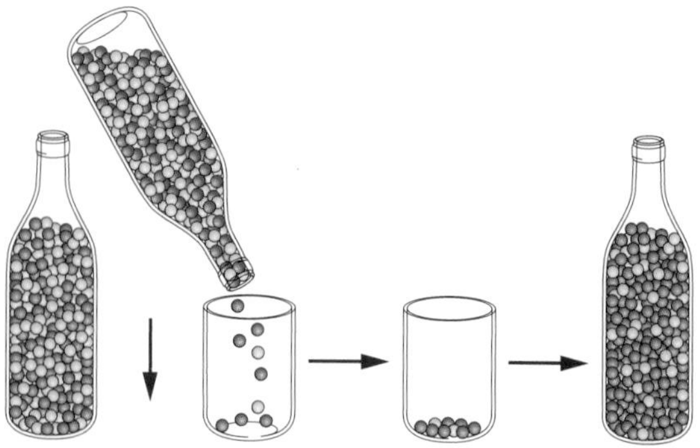

Figure 1

14. **Outline** in a list and **explain** some of the factors that have led to the rapid evolution of antibiotic resistance among many bacteria.

15. Would you expect bacteria occurring in wildlife, or in domesticated animals, to show signs of antibiotic resistance? **Explain** your answer.

16. A small population of pygmy mammoths measuring only DE 2 m in height once lived on a small island off the coast of California. Biologists believe this is an example of a population that descended from a few large mammoths that reached the island more than 50 000 years ago. In a unified response, **explain** how the following factors might have contributed to the formation of this unusual species:
    - the small founding population,
    - the remote location, and
    - natural selection on this island.

17. Before the large-scale movement of people around the world, including the slave trade, the sickle-cell allele was extremely rare except in regions where malaria occurs. Based on this distribution, is it accurate to describe the allele as harmful? **Explain**.

18. In a population of 40 000 bats, you have identified two distinct phenotypes that result from two alleles at a single gene locus. One allele (*C*) produces dark brown hair and the other (*c*) produces cinnamon-coloured hair. If only 16 bats are cinnamon-coloured, **determine** the allele frequencies in the population. Assume the population is in Hardy–Weinberg equilibrium.

19. Suppose that 1 in 400 people in a large population have a recessive disorder. Apply the Hardy–Weinberg Principle to **determine** the proportion of individuals who are carriers of (i.e., heterozygous for) this disorder.

20. **Predict** how the genetic diversity of a population of lake trout from a small lake in northern Alberta would compare with the genetic diversity of a population of lake trout in Lake Winnipeg. **How** might you investigate your prediction?

21. In order to mate, sage grouse males gather in "leks" and engage in unusual display behaviours in hopes of attracting females. **How** would this behaviour influence the Hardy–Weinberg equilibrium in such a population?

Use the following information to answer questions 22 to 24.

An unusual group of black bears live in the rainforests of British Columbia. The Kermode (spirit) bears are white, a trait coded for by a recessive allele (*k*). The more common black colour is coded for by a dominant allele (*K*). On Princess Royal Island, approximately 10 % of the bears are white in colour.

22. **Determine** the frequencies of both the recessive and DE dominant alleles in the population.

23. **Determine** the percentage of the population you would DE expect to be carriers of the *K* allele.

24. Assume that the bear population behaves according to the DE Hardy–Weinberg equation. **Predict** what would happen to the frequencies of *K* and *k*, if the entire population doubled in size.

Use the following informationto answer questions 25 to 27.

The wood buffalo population in Elk Island National Park began with the introduction of a small founder population of 11 animals whose parents lived in Wood Buffalo National Park. Recent DNA studies indicate that the genetic diversity of the Elk Island population is much lower than that of the Wood Buffalo National Park population.

25. **Explain** the lower genetic diversity in the Elk Island DE population.

26. **Identify** the population that would be most able to DE respond to environmental changes? **Justify** your choice.

27. A wildlife officer wants to establish a population of wood DE buffalo elsewhere, using animals from the Elk Island captive population. **Describe** what precautions might the officer take to increase the chances of success?

---

28. The majority of the Afrikaner population in South Africa is descended from a single shipload of Dutch immigrants in 1652. Compared to the Dutch population, these descendants have a much higher incidence of such rare genes as the ones that cause Huntington's disease and the enzyme defect *variegate porphyria*. **Describe** the most likely explanation for these observations.

chapter

22 Population Changes

In this chapter

- Exploration: Moving Populations
- Web Activity: Dr. Stephen Herrero
- Web Activity: Wildlife Tracking
- Mini Investigation: Blogs in a Bottle: Population Growth in a Finite Environment
- Investigation 22.1: Measuring Population Changes
- Explore an Issue: Carrying Capacity Changes in a Warm Arctic

Populations of organisms are dynamic (**Figure 1**). Some populations, such as those of the African black rhinoceros and the Vancouver Island marmot, are in serious decline and threatened with imminent extinction unless drastic action is taken. Other populations, such as those of the California sea lion along the west coast of North America and the cane toads in Australia, are experiencing unprecedented growth. While the number of chimpanzees, our closest living relative, has declined from about 2 million in 1900 to less than 150 000 at present, our own population has increased by more than 4 billion in the same time frame.

Can the extinction of entire species be avoided? What are the consequences of rapid population growth? To answer these questions, biologists must study populations carefully and observe and monitor changing environmental conditions. Changes in population numbers and in the patterns of distribution of individuals can have direct effects on the local ecosystem and may affect the well-being of other species within the ecological community.

Population ecologists use specialized methods to monitor, quantify, and model changes in populations. They also study the interrelationships between different species. In this way, they gather data necessary to predict future trends in the growth of populations. This information can be used to assess the health of individual species and entire ecosystems, to develop policies and plans of action to save species from extinction, and to address the impacts of rapidly growing populations.

STARTING Points

Answer these questions as best you can with your current knowledge. Then, using the concepts and skills you have learned, you will revise your answers at the end of the chapter.

Study **Figure 1** on the next page and reflect on the following:

1. What relationships might exist among these animals?
2. List and explain factors in this environment that might be responsible for the organisms present there.
3. What conditions in ecosystems and which activities by human and other animals might affect the number of individuals within each population?
4. How would you measure the change in each population over time?

Career Connections:
Ecologist; College, Technical, or Vocational Instructor

Figure 1
The size of the various populations in an area, such as those that come to this watering hole, changes over time. Population ecologists have developed a number of methods of quantifying these changes.

Exploration — Moving Populations

While the populations of many species remain in the same general area all the time, the populations of some species migrate. Each fall, 120 million red land crabs on Christmas Island migrate overland to the coast to mate and lay their eggs (**Figure 2**).

(a) What are the advantages of all the crabs migrating and breeding at precisely the same time each year?
(b) What are the disadvantages to such a strategy?
(c) Each female crab lays about 100 000 eggs, whereas many animal species produce far fewer young. What are the advantages and disadvantages of producing so many offspring? Do you think a high birth rate guarantees population growth?
(d) How might the size of the red crab population fluctuate during the course of a year? Would you expect this pattern to be typical or unusual for wild populations?
(e) If you were a biologist trying to determine if the population was increasing or decreasing over the long term, what challenges would you face?

Figure 2
Red land crabs

22.1 Characteristics of Populations

Figure 1
Greater snow geese are endangering their own survival by exceeding the carrying capacity of the natural marshes along the St. Lawrence River during their migration.

Canadian wildlife biologists have expressed concern over the increase in the greater snow goose population in the eastern Canadian Arctic from 50 000 in the late 1960s to about 950 000 in 2004 (**Figure 1**). The presence of increasing numbers of these snow geese has affected other species within the habitat. Overgrazing has caused widespread damage to the vegetation of Arctic coastal sites, resulting in a decline in the abundance of other bird and wildlife species that also depend on these habitats for resources. In the fall, the snow geese migrate south, stopping to feed on agricultural crops in central and eastern Canada and the United States, so many farmers regard the geese as pests. Members of the Arctic Goose Habitat Working Group, a consortium of Canadian and American wildlife biologists, have recommended that, to decrease damage to Arctic ecosystems, the total population of this species be reduced. How do biologists count huge populations of birds that migrate each fall, produce young each spring, and die at different times? How can they determine what population size might be ideal for a particular habitat and how can they tell when a population reaches this ideal size?

Population Size and Density

population size the number of individuals of a specific species occupying a given area/volume at a given time

population density the number of individuals of the same species that occur per unit area or volume

To study populations, scientists measure such characteristics as **population size**, or the estimated total number of organisms, as well as the density and dispersion of organisms within their habitat. The **population density** (D_p) of any population is calculated by dividing the total numbers counted (N) by the area (A) or volume (V) occupied by the population. For example, the population density of 480 bison living in a 600 hectare (ha) region of Wood Buffalo National Park would be calculated as follows:

$$D_p = \frac{N}{A} \quad \text{or} \quad D_p = \frac{N}{V}$$

$$D_p = \frac{480 \text{ bison}}{600 \text{ ha}}$$

$$= 0.800 \text{ bison/ha}$$

Populations vary widely among different species occupying different habitats. As shown in **Table 1**, small organisms usually have higher population densities than larger organisms. These widely ranging densities pose different challenges to biologists attempting to gather data on a particular species. Population density can be deceiving because of unused or unusable space within a habitat. For example, the bison in Wood Buffalo National Park do not use areas that are open lake water.

Learning Tip

You can calculate population density using either area or volume.

$$D_p = \frac{N}{A} \quad \text{or} \quad D_p = \frac{N}{V}$$

where D_p is population density, N is number of individuals, and A is area or V is volume

Table 1 Examples of Population Densities

Population	Density
jack pine	380/ha
field mice	250/ha
bison	0.800/ha
soil arthropods	500 000/m^2
phytoplankton (in a pond)	4 000 000/m^3

Practice

1. Calculate the density of a population of painted turtles (**Figure 2**) if 34 turtles were counted in a 200 ha park.

Figure 2
A painted turtle

2. Speculate about areas within the park that might not be used by the painted turtles.
3. Suggest a possible proportion (%) of the park that is not used by the turtle. Use the proportion that you think is used by the turtles to calculate a density value. This value is referred to as the **ecological density**.
4. A student counts 56 mosquito larvae in a 2 L sample of water from a local pond. Calculate the density of the mosquito population per litre and per cubic metre of pond water.

ecological density population density measured in terms of the number of individuals of the same species per unit area or volume actually used by the individuals

WEB Activity

Canadian Achievers—Dr. Stephen Herrero

Ecologists use many techniques to determine population size, density, and growth. One such ecologist is Dr. Stephen Herrero, a professor emeritus of environmental science at the University of Calgary (**Figure 3**). Dr. Herrero specializes in wildlife ecology and conservation biology with a special interest in the ecology of large predators—most notably grizzly bears. Learn more about Dr. Herrero and his research on grizzly bears in the eastern Rockies. Write a report or make a presentation that explains how Dr. Herrero uses knowledge of population size, density, and growth to improve grizzly bear management and conservation efforts.

www.science.nelson.com 

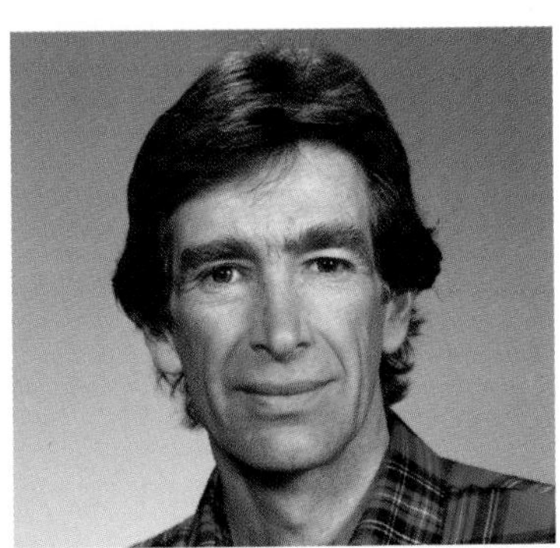

Figure 3
Dr. Stephen Herrero

Environmental conditions and suitable habitats differ throughout a population's geographic range. For this reason, the **population dispersion** of groups of organisms within a population varies throughout the range. Biologists have identified three main dispersion patterns among wild populations: clumped, uniform, and random. Most populations exhibit patchy or **clumped dispersion**, in which organisms are densely grouped in areas of the habitat with favourable conditions for survival. Cattails exhibit clumped dispersion. They are usually restricted to growing along the edges of ponds and lakes, or in other wet soils. Clumped dispersion may also be the result of social behaviour, such as fish swimming in large schools to gain protection from predators, as shown in **Figure 4** (a) on the next page.

population dispersion the general pattern in which individuals are distributed through a specified area

clumped dispersion the pattern in which individuals in a population are more concentrated in certain parts of a habitat

uniform dispersion the pattern in which individuals are equally spaced throughout a habitat

random dispersion the pattern in which individuals are spread throughout a habitat in an unpredictable and patternless manner

Other organisms exhibit **uniform dispersion** in which individuals are evenly distributed throughout the habitat. This pattern may result from competition between individuals that set up territories for feeding, breeding, or nesting. When King penguins nest on South Georgia Island in the South Atlantic Ocean, they often exhibit a nearly uniform dispersion pattern, as shown in **Figure 4 (b)**. Although wild species rarely exhibit uniform dispersion, the plants in crop fields, orchards, and tree plantations are often uniformly dispersed.

Individuals exhibit **random dispersion** when they are minimally influenced by interactions with other individuals and when habitat conditions are also virtually uniform. As shown in **Figure 4 (c)**, some species of trees in tropical rain forests exhibit random dispersion, although this pattern is also rare in nature.

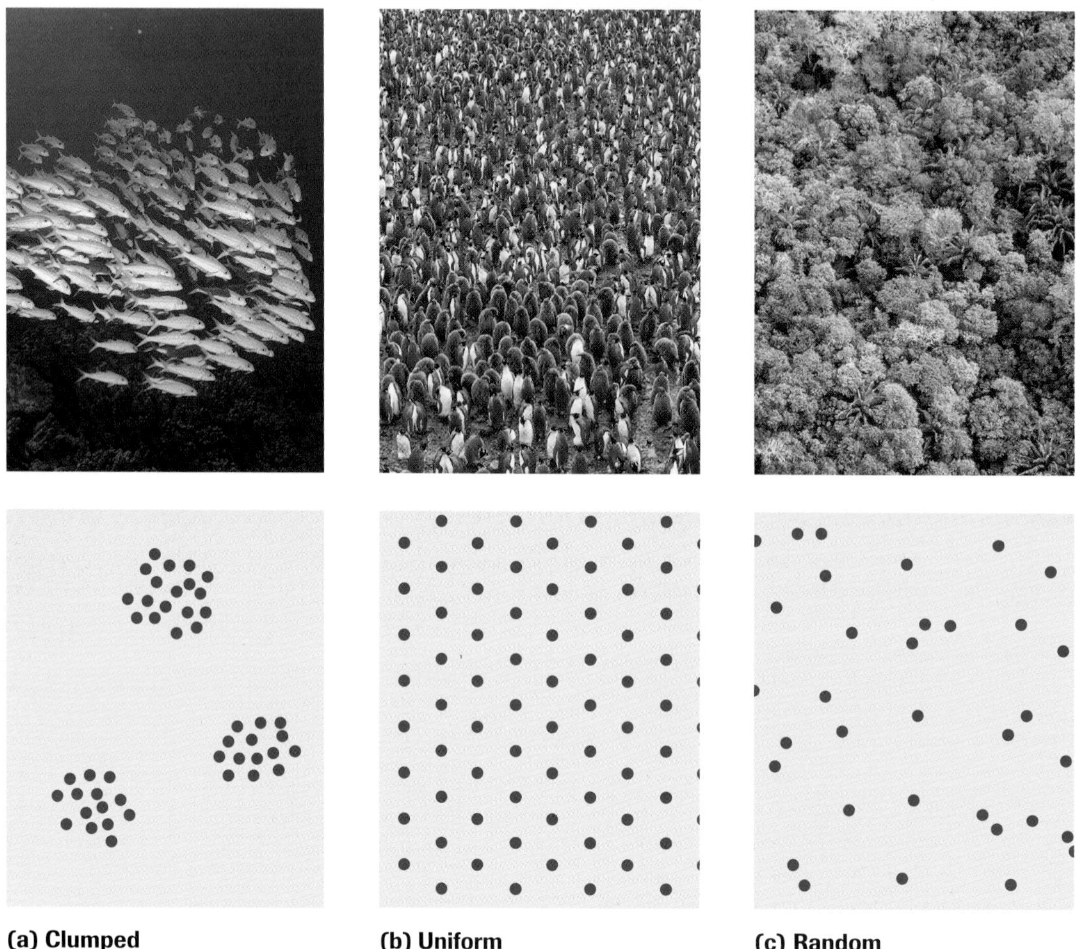

Figure 4
Populations generally exhibit one of three patterns of dispersion:
(a) Yellow goatfish are often found clumped in schools.
(b) Nesting King penguins exhibit a uniform pattern.
(c) In tropical rain forests, trees of the same species may be randomly dispersed.

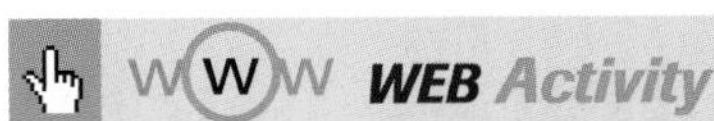

WEB Activity

Case Study—Wildlife Tracking

It is often difficult to determine the range and distribution of wildlife over long periods of time. While many organisms are easy to observe during parts of the year or parts of their life span, they may be very difficult to locate at other times. For example, it is easy to observe sea turtles when they come ashore to lay eggs, but harder to find where they travel and feed in the open ocean. It is easy to observe Alberta's breeding birds in the spring and summer, but much more difficult to determine their migration routes and winter range. Many species pose similar challenges. Beginning in 1937, researchers Fred and Norah Urquhart annually marked monarch butterflies in an attempt to discover the wintering location of this migratory species. In 1975, they finally discovered it.

In this activity, you will conduct research to explore the science of marking and releasing organisms.

www.science.nelson.com 

EXTENSION

Mark-Recapture Method

In this animation, you will apply this method of estimating population size to virtual butterflies.

www.science.nelson.com 

SUMMARY Characteristics of Populations

- Biologists use different measurements, such as population size and population density, to describe and monitor populations.
- Populations in a given geographical range exhibit one of three distinct dispersion patterns: clumped, uniform, or random.

Section 22.1 Questions

1. The Arctic Goose Habitat Working Group recommended that the eastern arctic greater snow goose population be held between 800 000 and 1 million birds by 2002. This reduced population would still be 15 to 20 times greater than the population in the late 1960s.
   (a) What are some consequences of the population remaining so large?
   (b) Discuss some ways in which reductions of geese populations may be achieved.
2. In a group, brainstorm and discuss challenges that biologists encounter in estimating population characteristics for wild populations of
   (a) whales that migrate along the western coasts of North and South America;
   (b) algae that live in water bodies receiving excess fertilizers in runoff from cropland;
   (c) caribou that inhabit an Arctic tundra environment; and
   (d) amphibians that live in marshes.
3. A 1998 study of grizzly bears in the Kananaskis area estimated the population size at 48 to 56 individuals. The study area encompassed 4000 hectares.
   (a) Use these values to determine maximum and minimum density estimates for the population.
   (b) Researchers examined the DNA of hair samples they collected during their field work. How might the analysis of DNA be of value in estimating the size of the bear population?
4. Biologists sometimes measure fish densities using the number of individuals per kilometre of stream. In a study of juvenile bull trout in Eunice Creek, Alberta, the density was observed to increase from less than 50/km in 1984 to over 600/km a year later. Approximately how many more fish were there in 1985 in a section of creek 0.5 km long?
5. The northern leopard frog is one of Alberta's species at risk. It has a highly clumped distribution and is restricted to isolated wetlands supporting very small populations. How might both the isolation and small population sizes of this species threaten its long-term viability?

22.2 Measuring and Modelling Population Change

An ecosystem has finite biotic and abiotic resources at any given time. Biotic resources, such as prey, vary in availability. Some abiotic resources, such as space and light, vary little, while others, such as temperature and water availability, vary greatly. There is, therefore, a limit to the number of individuals that an environment can support at any given time. The carrying capacity of an ecosystem is the maximum number of organisms that can be sustained by available resources over a period of time. You can review these concepts in Chapter 4.

Carrying capacity is dynamic, since environmental conditions are always changing. Two populations of the same species of fish, for example, might occupy quite different ecosystems with different carrying capacities, due to biotic and abiotic variations in the environment. A large, nutrient-poor, oligotrophic lake (**Figure 1 (a)**) could have a smaller carrying capacity per unit area than a much smaller, nutrient-rich eutrophic environment (**Figure 1 (b)**). In this case, the population density of fish in the oligotrophic lake would be much lower than that of the fish in the eutrophic lake.

Figure 1
Carrying capacity is determined by the environment in which a population lives. The population size in the oligotrophic lake **(a)** might be limited by available food, while the population size in the eutrophic lake **(b)** might be limited by available space.

When populations increase in size, the amount of resources available per individual decreases. When populations change in density, their new density may exceed the available supply of resources. A variety of factors influences how rapidly populations can grow before they meet or exceed the carrying capacity of their environment.

natality the number of births per unit of time

mortality the number of deaths per unit of time

immigration the number of individuals that move into an existing population per unit of time

emigration the number of individuals that move away from an existing population per unit of time

Factors That Affect Population Growth

Populations are always changing. Depending on the species and on environmental conditions, populations experience natural hourly, daily, seasonal, and annual fluctuations in numbers. Population size can change when individual organisms are added to the population through births or removed through deaths. Population size may also increase when individuals immigrate and decrease when individuals emigrate. The main factors that affect population growth, measured per unit of time, are **natality** (the number of births), **mortality** (the number of deaths), **immigration** (the number of individuals that move into an existing population), and **emigration** (the number of individuals that move away from an existing population). These factors may vary from species to species. For example, the females of some species have the potential to produce very large numbers of offspring in their lifetimes. Each female of many species of starfish, for example, can lay over 1 million eggs per year. In contrast, a female hippopotamus may have the potential to give birth to just 20 young in an entire lifetime of 45 years. For any organism, the maximum reproductive rate that could be achieved under ideal conditions is called the biotic potential. You can review the factors that determine biotic potential in Section 4.4 of this textbook. Biotic potential is an inherited trait, and so can be acted on by natural selection. Human actions can also affect birth, death, immigration, and emigration rates in populations.

DID YOU KNOW?

Biotic Potential

Consider the biotic potential of a single *Escherichia coli* (*E. coli*) bacterium on a hamburger patty. Under ideal conditions, *E. coli* can reproduce by binary fission every 12 min. After 12 min there are two bacterial cells, and after 24 min there are four cells. If this doubling continued unchecked for the next 24 h, there would be enough *E. coli* cells to cover the entire surface of Earth to a depth of more than 1 m!

Determining Changes in Population Size

Population ecologists often need to quantify changes in population growth in order to monitor and evaluate these changes. Mathematical models provide the underlying foundation for this science.

The number of individuals in a population is given by the variable ***N***. The change in the number of individuals in a population, **Δ*N***, can be calculated from natality, mortality, immigration, and emigration, using the following equation:

N a variable describing the number of individuals in a population

Δ*N* a variable describing the change in the number of individuals in a population

$$\Delta N = [\text{natality } (n) + \text{immigration } (i)] - [\text{mortality } (m) + \text{emigration } (e)]$$

If the number of births plus immigrants is higher than the number of deaths plus emigrants, the population will have positive growth, increasing in size. Conversely, if the number of deaths plus emigrants exceeds the number of births plus immigrants, the population will experience negative growth, decreasing in size. If the number of births plus immigrants equals the number of deaths plus emigrants, the population is said to have zero growth and will remain a constant size.

While measuring ΔN is of great value, population ecologists are often more interested in the **growth rate** (***gr***), which describes how quickly a population is increasing or decreasing—the change in population size per unit of time. The population growth rate is given by the formula:

growth rate (*gr*) the change in population size per unit of time

$$gr = \frac{\Delta N}{\Delta t}, \text{ where } \Delta t \text{ represents the change in time (often measured in years)}$$

The growth rate is often expressed as a **per capita growth rate** (***cgr***) and represents the change in population size, ΔN, relative to the initial population size, N.

per capita growth rate (*cgr*) the change in population size relative to the initial size of the population, per unit time

$$cgr = \frac{\Delta N}{N}$$

The usefulness of per capita growth rate is clear when comparing populations of different sizes. For example, a population of 2000 individuals that grows by 40 in 1 year has a growth rate of 0.020, while a smaller population of only 200 individuals, with the same increase in numbers (40), experiences a dramatic growth rate of 0.20. Per capita growth rate may also be expressed as a percentage, by multiplying it by 100 ($cgr \times 100$).

SAMPLE exercise 1

Over 2 years, a population of 900 experienced 66 births and 14 deaths. Five individuals left the population and 13 individuals joined the population. Using this information, determine

(a) the population change

(b) the new population size

(c) the growth rate

(d) the per capita growth rate

Solution

(a) We are given the following variables:

change in time, $\Delta t = 2$ years

initial population size, $N = 900$ individuals

natality, $n = 66$ individuals

immigration, $i = 13$ individuals

mortality, $m = 14$ indiviuals

emigration, $e = 5$ individuals

The required variable is population change, ΔN. It can be determined from equation

$$\begin{aligned}\Delta N &= [(n) + (i)] - [(m) + (e)] \\ &= [66 \text{ individuals} + 13 \text{ individuals}] - [14 \text{ individuals} + 5 \text{ individuals}] \\ &= 60 \text{ individuals}\end{aligned}$$

The population change, ΔN, is 60 individuals.

(b) From the given information, we know that the initial population size, N, was 900 individuals. We determined the change in population size, ΔN, in part (a). The new population size is the sum of these values.

$$\begin{aligned}N + \Delta N &= 900 \text{ individuals} + 60 \text{ individuals} \\ &= 960 \text{ individuals}\end{aligned}$$

The new population size is 960 individuals.

(c) The required variable is growth rate, gr. We know the change in time, Δt, from the given variables. We determined the change in population size, ΔN, in part (a). The growth rate is determined from the equation

$$\begin{aligned}gr &= \frac{\Delta N}{\Delta t} \\ &= \frac{60 \text{ individuals}}{2 \text{ years}} \\ &= 30 \text{ individuals/year}\end{aligned}$$

The growth rate is 30 individuals per year.

(d) The required variable is per capita growth rate, cgr. We were given the initial population size, N. We determined the change in population size, ΔN, in part (a). The per capita growth rate is determined from the equation

$$\begin{aligned}cgr &= \frac{\Delta N}{N} \\ &= \frac{60 \cancel{\text{ individuals}}}{900 \cancel{\text{ individuals}}} \\ &= 0.067\end{aligned}$$

Learning Tip

When solving a problem involving a calculation, a good strategy is to start by identifying the given variables and the required variable.

Learning Tip

Exact numbers, like the number of individuals in this question, are considered to have an infinite number of significant digits. You can review the rules for determining significant digits in Appendix A7, Math Skills.

Since the population change took place over 2 years, then the per capita growth rate is 0.067 per 2 years. To get the per capita growth rate per year, we therefore must divide 0.067 by 2.

$$\frac{0.067}{2 \text{ years}} = 0.0335 \text{ per year}$$

The per capita growth rate per year is 0.0335.

Practice

1. Complete **Table 1** by calculating the missing values.

Table 1 Measured and Calculated Factors Describing Four Different Populations

	Initial population (*N*)	Time period (Δt)	Births (*n*)	Deaths (*m*)	Immigrants (*i*)	Emigrants (*e*)	Population change (ΔN)	Growth rate (*gr*)	Per capita growth rate (*cgr*)
(a)	600	2	20	15	25	10			
(b)	200	4	40	60	10	0			
(c)	3000	1	450	350		100	150		
(d)	1000		180	160	30	40		5	

2. The human population has a per capita growth rate of approximately 0.012 per year. If the human population is 6 billion, determine
(a) the change in population per year
(b) the change in population per day

Population Growth Models

Scientists studying wild populations often use such mathematical models, based on data collected in the field. Models can provide a visual tool to help researchers see patterns in past population changes and predict future population change. For example, population ecologists may use plots of the past growth rate of a population over time to predict future increases or decreases in the population of a species at risk.

The growth of a population also depends on whether the population is open or closed. An **open population** refers to a population that is influenced by the factors of natality, mortality, emigration, and immigration. Most wild populations are open, since they have the ability to immigrate and emigrate between populations that exist in different locations. In a **closed population** immigration and emigration do not occur so only natality and mortality determine population growth. Closed animal populations are rare. Land-based populations on secluded islands, such as the Peary caribou herd that inhabits an Arctic Ocean island, can be thought of as closed because they have no easy means to travel to other populations. (The animals are able to move between islands in winter.)

We will explore two common models of population growth, exponential growth and logistic growth. For both these models, it is assumed that immigration is equal to emigration, so only natality and mortality are considered. This would be similar to a closed population.

When a population increases by **exponential growth**, the population size increases by a fixed rate over a fixed time period. This rate is denoted by the variable ***r***. A population will only grow exponentially when its ecosystem has an unlimited supply of the biotic and abiotic resources it needs, such as food, light, space, and water. Under these

open population a population in which change in number and density is determined by natality, mortality, immigration, and emigration

closed population a population in which change in size and density is determined by natality and mortality alone

exponential growth a pattern of population growth in which the population size increases by a fixed rate per a fixed unit of time

r a variable indicating the rate of increase of a population experiencing exponential growth; *r* is limited only by the biotic potential of the organisms in the population

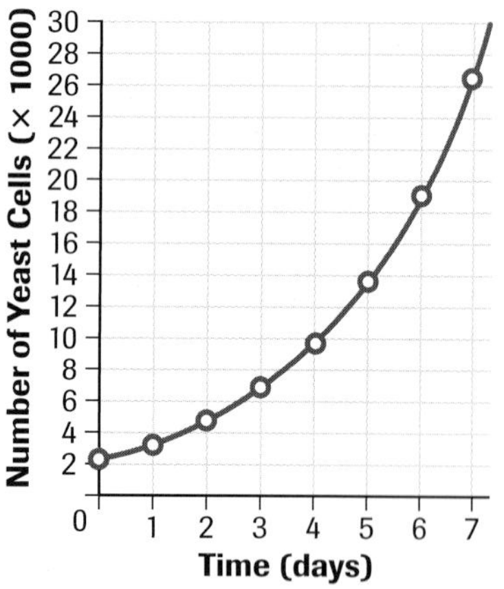

Figure 2 Exponential growth curves are always J-shaped.

conditions, the only limit on population growth is the biotic potential of the individuals making up the population.

During exponential growth, natality is always higher than mortality. Therefore, each successive generation of a population will have more individuals and more offspring than the previous generation. For example, let's assume that the initial size of a yeast cell population is 3000 yeast cells and that 10 % of the cells die each generation. The cells in the starting population divide to produce 6000 offspring, of which 600 die. Reproduction of the remaining 5400 cells gives 10 800 offspring, of which 1080 die. The next generation would then be 21 600 cells, of which 2160 would die, and so on. You can see how population size increases very rapidly during exponential growth. When population size versus time is plotted for a population undergoing exponential growth, the resulting graph is always J-shaped, as shown in **Figure 2**. Therefore, if a researcher has data that gives a J-shaped curve, she or he knows that the population is growing exponentially.

Notice that in **Figure 2**, the exponential growth curve is smooth. This is because yeast cells reproduce throughout the year, as do many other species (including humans). However, many species reproduce only at a particular time of the year. For example, harbour seals in northern British Columbia breed only between May and June. In these species, population size typically increases very quickly during the breeding season and then drops. Therefore, population size must be measured at the same time each year (such as June of each year) to accurately determine population size changes. If the ratio between natality and mortality remains constant, the size of the population will increase in steps over time (**Figure 3 (a)**).

Population biologists are often more interested in long-term growth patterns than in short-term seasonal fluctuations. Population growth graphs for species that reproduce only at specific times are therefore usually drawn as smooth curves, which show changes in average population size over time (**Figure 3 (b)**).

Population Growth Curves

Listen to this discussion of why population size increases gradually during the early stages of a population's growth.

www.science.nelson.com

(a)

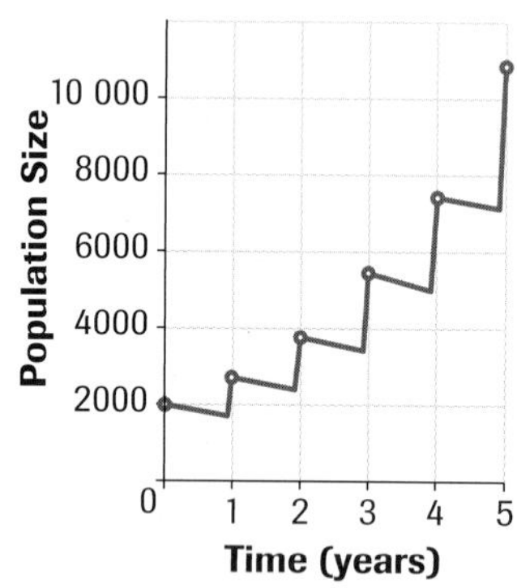

(b)

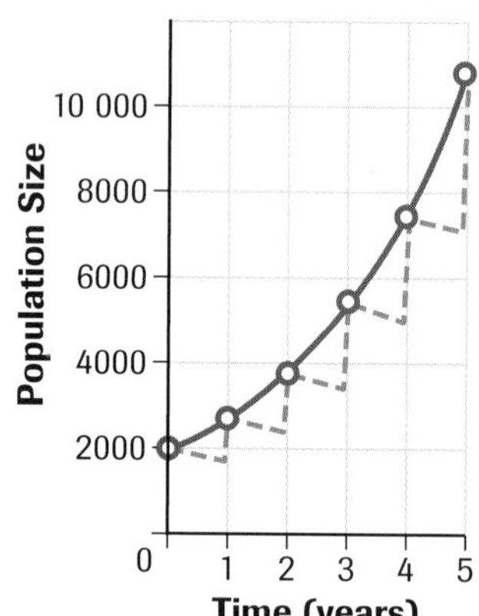

Figure 3
(a) The size of the seal population size was determined several times each year. There are sharp increases when reproduction occurred, followed by declines in numbers.
(b) Drawing the graph as a smooth curve shows the long-term trend in average population size.

doubling time (t_d) the time needed for a population that is growing exponentially to double

For any population growing exponentially, the time needed for the population to double in size is a constant. The **doubling time** (t_d) of the population can be estimated by the following formula:

$$t_d = \frac{0.69}{cgr}$$

The value 0.69 is a constant. For example, if a population has a per capita growth rate of 2.0 % per year (0.020), the approximate time needed for the population to double would be $\frac{0.69}{0.020}$, or 35 years (to two significant digits).

CAREER CONNECTION

Ecologist

Ecologists study a wide range of subjects, all of which involve the relationships of living organisms to each other and to their environments. Ecologists are often particularly interested in population size and population growth characteristics. Ecologists plan and conduct field research and long-term studies to find life history patterns, and develop recommendations on wildlife management. Are you interested in a career as an ecologist?

www.science.nelson.com 

SAMPLE exercise 2

A population of 2500 yeast cells in a culture tube is growing exponentially. If the per capita growth rate, *cgr*, is 3.0 % per hour, calculate

(a) the time it will take for the population to double in size

(b) the size of the population after each of four doubling times

Solution

(a) We are given the following variables:

number of individuals, N = 2500 individuals

per capita growth rate, cgr = 3.0 % or 0.030 per hour

The required variable is population change, t_d. It can be determined from equation

$$t_d = \frac{0.69}{cgr}$$

$$= \frac{0.69}{0.030 \times \frac{1}{\text{hour}}}$$

$$= 23 \text{ hours}$$

The yeast population will double in size every 23 hours.

(b) The size of the population after four doubling times can be determined using a table, as shown in **Table 2**.

t_d = 23 hours, initial population size is 2500

Table 2 Change in Yeast Cell Population Size

Doubling times	Time (hours)	Population size
0	0	2500
1	23	5000
2	46	10 000
3	69	20 000
4	92	40 000

Practice

3. After the rainy season begins in the tropics, a small population of mosquitoes exhibits exponential growth. The initial population size is 980 and the per capita growth rate is 34.5 % per day.

(a) Calculate the doubling time for the population.

(b) How many doubling times will have to pass in order for the population to exceed 2 000 000? How many days is this?

Learning Tip

Remember to follow the rules for significant digits in your answers. You can review these rules in Appendix A7.

environmental resistance any factor that limits a population's ability to realize its biotic potential when it nears or exceeds the environment's carrying capacity

logistic growth a model of population growth describing growth that levels off as the size of the population approaches its carrying capacity

lag phase the initial stage in which population growth rates are slow as a result of a small population size; characteristic of geometric, exponential, and logistic population growth

log phase the stage in which population growth rates are very rapid; characteristic of geometric, exponential, and logistic growth

stationary phase the phase in which population growth rates approach zero as the population size reaches the carrying capacity and stabilizes; the defining characteristic of logistic population growth

K a variable indicating the number of individuals in a population at the carrying capacity of an environment

The exponential model of population growth assumes that a population will continue to grow at the same rate indefinitely. This implies that the population has continuous access to an unlimited supply of resources. Of course, an unlimited resource supply is never the case in the real world. Any ecosystem has a limited supply of biotic and abiotic factors to support the organisms in it. Eventually, resources will become scarce.

However, when a population enters a new ecosystem, abiotic and biotic resources are often plentiful. Initially, there may be only a few individuals, so the initial growth rate may be slow. However, since population growth isn't limited by resources, the population size will increase exponentially. Eventually, however, the population size will approach the carrying capacity of the ecosystem, and resources such as food, water, light and space will begin to limit population growth.

The influence of biotic and abiotic factors that limit the size of a population is called **environmental resistance**. As environmental resistance increases, the growth rate of the population slows until natality and mortality become about equal. At this point, the size of the population stabilizes. This pattern of population growth is called **logistic growth**. This model of population growth fits most closely with population growth patterns seen in nature.

If you graph logistic growth, the curve resembles the letter S. As a result, it is referred to as an S-shaped or sigmoidal curve, which has three distinct phases (**Figure 4**). The first, called the **lag phase**, occurs when the population is small and is increasing slowly. The second phase, called the **log phase**, occurs when the population undergoes exponential growth. As available resources become limited, the population experiences increasing environmental resistance and cannot continue rapid growth; therefore, the population's reproduction slows and the number of deaths increases. This is the **stationary phase**, which occurs at or close to the carrying capacity of the environment. The size of the population when it has reached the carrying capacity is indicated by the variable ***K***. At the stationary phase, a population is said to be in dynamic equilibrium, because the number of births equals the number of deaths, resulting in no net increase in population size.

Logistic growth can be seen in a population of fur seals on St. Paul Island, Alaska. In 1911, fur seal hunting was banned since the population had become extremely low. Since their numbers were so low, the seals had many unused resources to support the recovering population. The population grew rapidly until it stabilized around its carrying capacity, as shown on **Figure 5** on the next page.

EXTENSION

Factors Contributing to the End of Exponential Growth

Why does exponential population growth end? Find out more by listening to this description of what happens as a population nears the carrying capacity and its rate of growth slows.

www.science.nelson.com GO

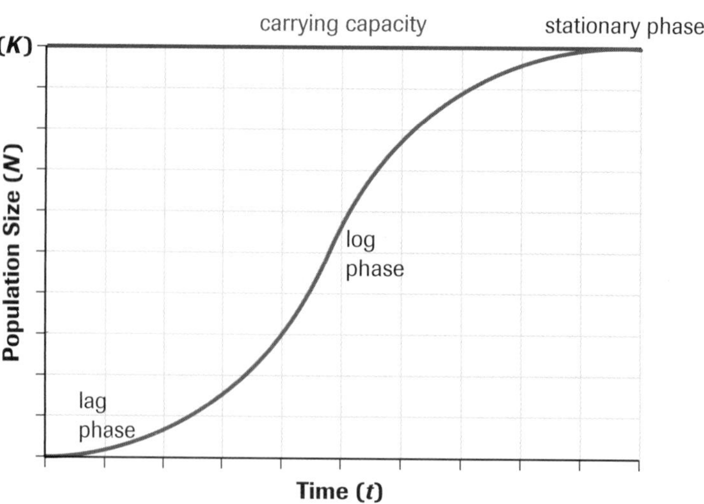

Figure 4
The logistic growth model results in a sigmoidal (S-shaped) curve.

The logistic growth model works for populations growing under suitable conditions, but fits few natural populations perfectly for two main reasons: no population exists by itself, and many interactions occur among the members of a single population.

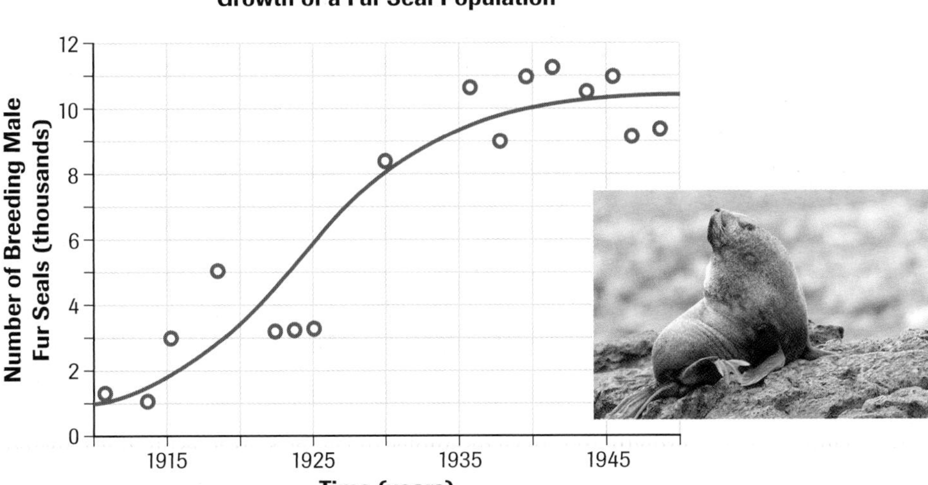

Figure 5
A population graph from 1910 to 1950 for fur seals on St. Paul Island, Alaska

mini *Investigation* — *Blogs in a Bottle: Population Growth in a Finite Environment*

The size of most populations fluctuates over short periods, but remain relatively stable over long periods of time. However, under certain environmental conditions, populations may be able to grow steadily and often rapidly. Such populations eventually reach or exceed the carrying capacity of their environments and their growth ceases.

In this activity, you will model the growth of an imaginary population that lives in a large but finite environment. The Blog population has a constant *cgr* and doubles in size every five days. Blogs can only live in a bottle.

Materials: water (Blogs), eye dropper, graduated cylinders (small and large), large bottle

Predict the number of doubling times it will take for the population of Blogs to completely fill their bottle (reach their maximum sustainable population size).

- Place the starting population (one drop of water) in the bottle. Record the population size in a data table.
- Add a second drop of water to represent the passing of five days. Record the time and total population size.
- Add enough water to again double the total size of the population. Record your values.
- Repeat the above step until the bottle is completely full or you have run out of time.

Note: When the total population size reaches 16 drops, you may convert your measurements to millilitres. One millilitre is roughly equivalent to 16 drops.

(a) Plot a graph of population size versus time. If you have access to a spreadsheet program, use it to tabulate your data and generate the graph.

(b) How many doubling times did it take for the Blogs to completely fill their bottle?

(c) Was your prediction/hypothesis correct? Were you surprised by the results?

(d) If the Blogs found three new environments—three similar empty bottles—how many more doubling times would it take to completely fill all four bottles?

(e) Examine your graph. During what span of time would the Blogs not have worried about running out of space? In other words, when do you think the Blog population might have first realized they had little time left at their current growth rate?

SUMMARY Measuring and Modelling Population Change

- Mathematical models are used to predict trends in population growth.
- Exponential growth demonstrates growth limited only by biotic potential.
- Logistic growth, limited by carrying capacity, is most like the population growth patterns seen in wild populations.

Section 22.2 Questions

1. Researchers studied a population of 34 peregrine falcons for one year to analyze the effect of pesticides on population growth. In the first three months, 57 eggs were laid. Owing to thin shells suspected to have resulted from pesticide damage, 28 eggs broke. Of the remainder, 20 hatched successfully (**Figure 6**). However, nine baby falcons died from severe birth defects. During the next 6 months, 11 birds died as a result of direct pesticide exposure, and 8 were captured and taken to a conservation area. During the last three months, four birds migrated into the area. Determine the population growth of peregrine falcons in this study.

Figure 6

2. The growth rate for a population of 90 field mice in 6 months was 429 %. If the number of births was 342, the number of deaths was 43, and there was no emigration, determine the number of mice that migrated into the field.
3. In practising both agriculture and forestry, humans attempt to maximize productivity of the plants they are harvesting. For example, the application of herbicides on crops and tree plantations helps reduce competition from other plant species. Describe additional ways in which farmers and foresters help domesticated and harvested species approach their biotic potential.
4. In many rural areas, stray cats are a problem as they may return to being wild (also known as feral). Feral cats that have not been spayed or neutered can reproduce, which may result in a population of feral cats. One pair of cats can produce 12 kittens in 1 year. If half these kittens are female, this increased population could potentially produce 84 kittens in the second year. In 5 years, the population could reach almost 33 000 feral cats.
   (a) Identify the kind of growth that is occurring.
   (b) Outline the conditions that would have to be in place for the population to achieve its biotic potential.
   (c) Describe various types of environmental resistance that might restrict the feral cats from reaching their biotic potential.
5. A biologist determines the growth rate of a population of 198 frogs in a marsh near Beaverhill Lake, Alberta, to evaluate the quality of the environment. The researcher finds that, in one year, 34 were born, 86 died, 12 migrated into the marsh, and there was no emigration.
   (a) Determine the growth rate, *gr*, and the per capita growth rate, *cgr*, of the population.
   (b) Do you think that tracking the population growth rate of one population of frogs over one year in this marsh is adequate to make a conclusion about the environment? Explain your reasoning.
6. Scientists monitored the population size of a species newly introduced to an ecosystem. Their data are in **Table 3**.

Table 3 Population Size of Species X

Year	Population size	Year	Population size
1999	44	2003	301
2000	56	2004	275
2001	132	2005	321
2002	224	2006	298

   (a) Sketch a graph of the data. Identify the form of growth curve of the species.
   (b) Predict the long-term impact on population size if a second group of 44 individuals were added to this population in 2007.
   (c) Use your graph to estimate the number of individuals in the whole population when it has reached the carrying capacity of the ecosystem (*K*).

Factors Affecting Population Change 22.3

In 1993, zebra mussel populations in the lower Illinois River, which had exploded to a density of nearly 100 000 per square metre, were causing significant harm to aquatic ecosystems. The zebra mussels were severely depleting the amount of dissolved oxygen available to the entire ecosystem, and increasing competition for food resources. The resulting conditions were stressful for other species, but also affected the survival of the zebra mussels. Scientists observed a dramatic decline in these populations. Researchers now believe that the increased density of the zebra mussel population led to increased competition among members of the population (**Figure 1**).

Figure 1
Competition for resources among zebra mussels will eventually limit growth in these populations.

Density-Dependent Factors

With an increase in population size—for example, after young are born—the population density of the species increases. High density results in adverse conditions. Some individuals may find it difficult to obtain food and may emigrate. Others may die. A factor that affects a population only when it has a particular density is called a **density-dependent factor**. Such a factor limits population growth. Charles Darwin recognized that the struggle for available resources within a growing population would inherently limit population size. This struggle for survival involves such factors as competition, predation, disease, and other biological effects.

When the individuals of the same species rely on the same resources for survival, **intraspecific competition** occurs. As population density increases, intraspecific competition increases, so the population's growth rate slows. This intraspecific competition can have a pronounced effect on the reproductive success of individuals, as shown in the example in **Figure 2**. As competition for food increases, the amount of food per individual often decreases. This decrease in nutrition results in a decrease in an individual's growth and reproductive success. Harp seals, for example, reach sexual maturity when they have grown to 87 % of their mature body weight. When the population density increases, each individual seal gets less to eat and gains weight more slowly than it would if the population density were lower. As a result, the seals reach sexual maturity at a slower rate, which decreases the potential number of offspring they might have.

density-dependent factor a factor that influences a population at a particular density

intraspecific competition an ecological interaction in which individuals of the same species compete for resources in their habitat

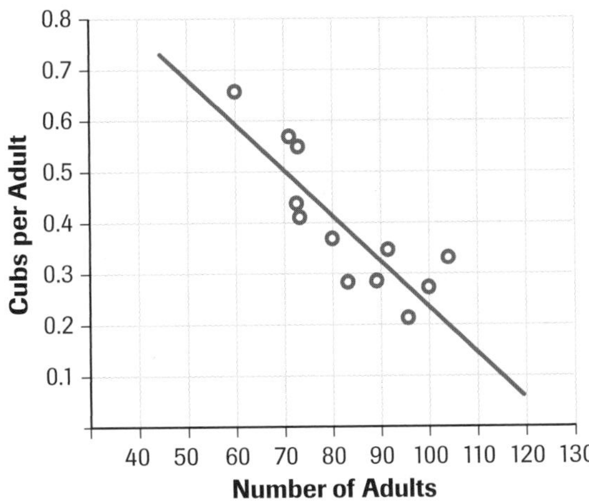

Figure 2
As population density increases in this grizzly bear population, the number of cubs per adult decreases.

predation an ecological interaction in which a predator (a member of one species) kills and consumes prey (usually a member of another species)

minimum viable population size the smallest number of individuals needed for a population to continue for a given period of time

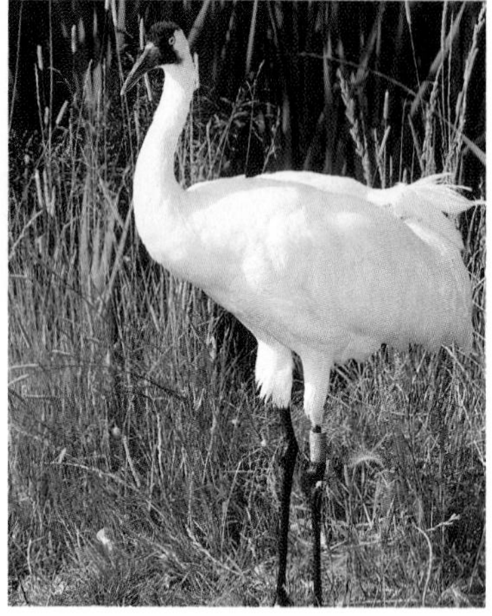

Figure 3
Minimum viable population size is only a prediction. The whooping crane did not become extinct, even when there were only 23 birds left.

density-independent factor a factor that has the same influence on a population at any population density

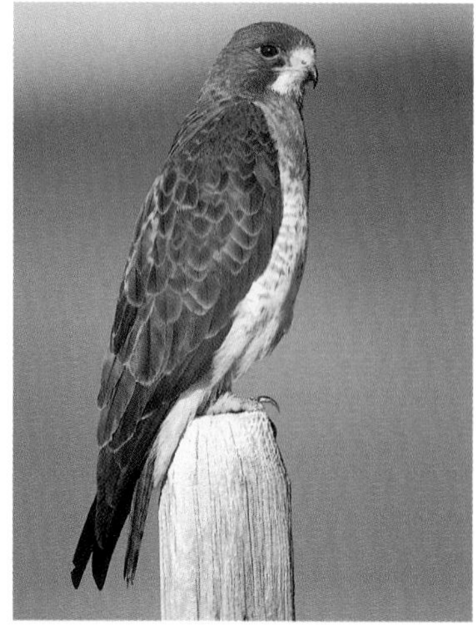

Figure 4
Swainson's hawks are decreasing in numbers as a result of pesticide use.

Another major density-dependent factor that limits population growth is **predation**, the consumption of prey by predators. If a prey species has a large, dense population, intense competition for limited food may result in individuals with poorer health. These individuals are easier for the predator species to catch.

Disease can also be a significant density-dependent factor that limits population size. In dense or overcrowded populations, pathogens are able to pass more easily from host to host. The population declines in size as a result of increased mortality. The overcrowding of farm animals can lead to the spread of disease, such as foot-and-mouth disease in cattle and avian flu in poultry. In 2000, in the *Proceedings of the National Academy of Science*, researchers Wesley M. Hochachka and André A. Dhondt reported the spread of a common poultry pathogen, *Mycoplasma gallisepticum*, in North America through the house finch, *Carpodacus mexicanus*. They showed a relationship between population size and the incidence of the disease, concluding that the spread of this disease was density-dependent.

Some density-dependent factors reduce population growth rates at low densities. A small population size can result in inbreeding and the loss of genetic variation, which can threaten a population's continued survival. The **minimum viable population size** is the smallest number of individuals that ensures the population can persist for a given amount of time. The minimum viable population size consists of enough individuals so that the population can cope with variations in natality and mortality as well as environmental change or disasters. The minimum viable population size varies among species. Scientists use it as a model to estimate the size at which a population would be considered at risk. In 1941, biologists were concerned that the whooping crane would become extinct, since the wild population worldwide had decreased to 21 birds, and only two birds were in captivity (**Figure 3**). Hunting of the birds for meat and eggs, as well as disturbance of their wetland habitats in Wood Buffalo National Park in Canada and along the Texas coast in the United States, had reduced the number of whooping cranes to well below the minimum viable population size predicted by biologists. An ambitious breeding program, along with legal protection of the whooping crane and its winter and summer habitats, have restored the population of wild and captive birds to nearly 300, although the species is still considered endangered.

Density-Independent Factors

Populations may also experience changes in size that are not related to population density. **Density-independent factors** can limit population growth through changes in environmental conditions. For example, certain species of thrips, a small insect considered a common plant pest, feed on so many plant species that food supply is rarely a limiting factor. Cooler temperatures, however, reduce the reproductive success of these species. With a reduced birth rate, the population size declines. With the return of warmer temperatures, reproductive success improves and populations expand once again.

Insecticide application is a density-independent factor caused by human actions. The lethal effects of the pesticide exist whether the population has two organisms or two million. Swainson's hawks migrate between the grasslands of the Canadian prairies and Argentina (**Figure 4**). Wildlife biologists noted a drastic decrease in the population of these birds throughout North America, but had not found the cause. It was suspected that many of these hawks hunted for insects, mostly grasshoppers, in farmers' fields. Argentinian fields were regularly sprayed with highly toxic pesticides to control the grasshopper population and preserve the crops for human food. These particular pesticides are banned in North America.

In 1996, 12 Swainson's hawks were captured in Alberta and tagged with satellite transmitters before they migrated to Argentina. Biologists flew to the migration destination to observe the tagged birds and counted more than 5000 dead hawks, killed from pesticide exposure either directly or through the food chain. Some of the pesticides have now been banned in Argentina, and the numbers of Swainson's hawk are beginning to recover.

Limiting Factors and Population Size

Any environmental factor, whether it is density-dependent or density-independent, can be the limiting factor of an ecosystem. Of all the resources that a population requires for growth, the resource in shortest supply is called the limiting factor, and it determines how much the population can grow. For example, a plant population requires nitrogen, carbon dioxide, and sunlight in order to grow (**Figure 5**). If it uses up all available nitrogen, it can no longer grow, even if there is still an abundance of sunlight and carbon dioxide. In this case, nitrogen is the limiting factor. Limiting factors prevent populations from achieving their biotic potential, and determine the carrying capacity of the populations.

EXTENSION

Population Biology

In this Virtual Biology Lab, you can manipulate variables to explore the relationships between population size, environmental carrying capacity, birth rate, and death rate in a population.

www.science.nelson.com GO

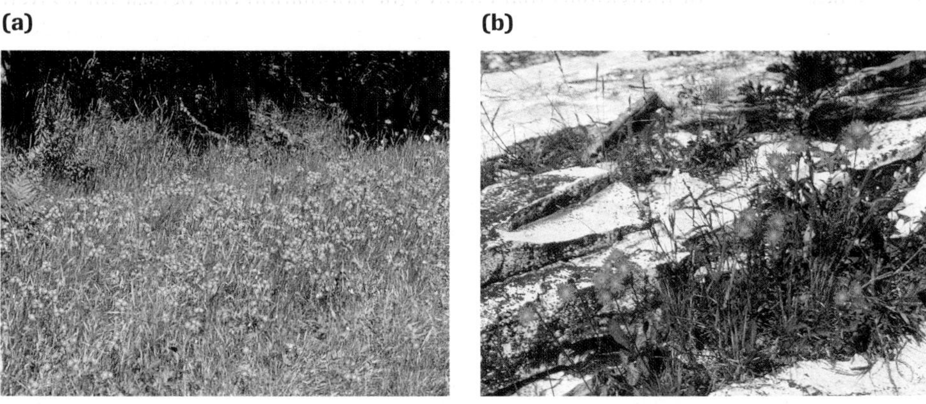

Figure 5
Plants need many different resources for growth and survival. The resource in shortest supply is considered the limiting factor to growth. The orange hawkweed plants in **(a)** are flourishing while the plants in **(b)** are limited by available space.

INVESTIGATION 22.1 *Introduction*

Measuring Population Changes

Duckweed is a tiny flowering plant that floats in clusters on the surface of freshwater ponds. In this investigation, you will design and conduct experiments to test the influence of environmental factors on the growth rate of a duckweed population. You will also estimate the carrying capacity of the environment.

Report Checklist

- Purpose
- Problem
- Hypothesis
- Prediction
- Design
- Materials
- Procedure
- Evidence
- Analysis
- Evaluation
- Synthesis

To perform this investigation, turn to page 758. 

EXPLORE an issue

Issue Checklist

○ Issue ○ Design ● Analysis
● Resolution ● Evidence ● Evaluation

Carrying Capacity Changes in a Warm Arctic

In February 2005, Alexander Wolfe and Neal Michelutti, researchers at the University of Alberta, published their findings on climate change. As part of a 16-member team of scientists from Canada, Norway, Finland, and Russia, the researchers studied changes to populations of microscopic algae and primary consumers in the High Arctic and came to the conclusion that "the biology is starting to change."

Canada's Arctic landscape is one of the most beautiful, pristine, and harsh environments on Earth. Species diversity is limited, many population sizes are small, and population densities are often low. The extremely cold winters, shifting pack ice, and permafrost have all been major limiting factors that have prevented the vast majority of species from inhabiting this vast ecosystem. Meanwhile, these same physical conditions have created an environment in which a very special group of species has evolved. Polar bears, arctic poppies, arctic char, and narwhals all call the Arctic their home. These species and many others survive the long harsh winters and reproduce successfully during the long summer days. The Arctic is also home to Inuit, who have flourished in this environment for thousands of years.

But this environment is changing: the Arctic is warming. Until recently, most of the attention regarding climate change and global warming has focused on physical data—temperature changes, pack ice and permafrost melting, sea-level changes, and changing weather patterns. Now, data and observations are emerging that highlight the impacts on living systems (**Table 1**).

1. Suggest one or more specific environmental limiting factors that may be responsible for each of the changes shown in **Table 1**.
2. When an environmental factor changes, is the result always detrimental to living organisms?
3. Why are major environmental changes more likely to benefit species that do not normally live in the region, and more likely to harm species that are native to the region?
4. Populations of many Arctic species are small and have low densities. How might these factors make them more vulnerable to change?
5. Conduct library and Internet research to become more aware of the impact of climate change on Inuit in Canada. How does climate change threaten their traditional way of life?

www.science.nelson.com 

Table 1 Observed Changes in Populations Living in Arctic Regions

Species	Changing population parameters
ivory gulls	Rapid and dramatic 80 % decline in populations nesting in the High Arctic.
various	Expanding home ranges. Insects such as the yellow jacket wasp, mammals including cougar and mule deer, and birds such as the rose grosbeak and dusky flycatcher are all appearing in northern communities for the first time.
insect pests	The spruce bark beetle has devastated 300 000 ha of forest in Canada's Kluane National Park, Yukon. The spruce budworm now appears only 400 km south of the Arctic circle.
trees	Trees are growing faster, as evidenced by thicker tree rings in trees sampled in the Mackenzie River delta.
polar bears	Reductions in pack ice are forcing polar bears to swim farther to reach their seal-hunting grounds. Some scientists predict that summer pack ice may be completely gone in a matter of decades.

Environmental Stability and Population Change

The amount of change in an ecosystem also affects the growth of populations. In a stable ecosystem, the amounts and types of abiotic and biotic factors remain very similar over time. Undisturbed boreal forests, such as can be found in Jasper National Park, are stable ecosystems. In unstable ecosystems, factors in the ecosystem undergo rapid, unpredictable change. A boreal forest that is being logged is an example of an unstable ecosystem. Different organisms have different reproductive strategies, and natural selection favours different strategies in these two types of ecosystems.

Recall from the previous section that *K* is the number of individuals in a population at the carrying capacity of its ecosystem. ***K*-selected organisms** have traits that adapt them to living in a population at or near to the carrying capacity of their ecosystem. They are most often found in a stable environment. The most significant trait of *K*-selected organisms is their reproductive strategy. They produce only a few offspring and devote large amounts of parental resources ensuring those offspring survive. *K*-selected organisms are usually large, with long life-spans. Their offspring tend to be slow-growing and require a lot of parental care. They have a low biotic potential, so the size of populations of *K*-selected organisms tends to change slowly. When the number of *K*-selected organisms in an ecosystem becomes too high, competition between individuals soon becomes intense, reducing the survival rate and limiting the number of adults available to breed. The overall population is therefore maintained close to the carrying capacity. Large mammals such as elk, bears, and humans are *K*-selected species (**Figure 6 (a)**).

***K*-selected organism** an organism that is adapted to survive at or near the carrying capacity of its environment

The variable *r* represents the rate of increase of a population experiencing exponential growth. The genetic traits of ***r*-selected organisms** allow them to increase their population size rapidly. These organisms are most often found in unstable environments. The reproductive strategy of *r*-selected organisms is to produce many offspring and devote very little parental resources to their survival. They are usually small in size, have a short life-span, and have a high biotic potential. When environmental conditions are favourable, a population of *r*-selected organisms can grow very quickly, with competition not usually being a significant factor. Conversely, a change to unfavourable environmental conditions can result in deaths. Many insect species are *r*-selected organisms (**Figure 6 (b)**).

***r*-selected organism** an organism that is adapted to increase population size rapidly

(a)

(b)

Figure 6
(a) Humans are *K*-selected organisms. Each individual is capable of producing relatively few offspring and invests a lot of time and resources in their care.
(b) Mosquitoes are *r*-selected organisms. Each individual is capable of producing hundreds of offspring, and invests little in their care.

 CAREER CONNECTION

College, Technical, or Vocational Instructor
Studying population change and community dynamics requires many technical skills. Much of this training can be gained at a college or a technical or vocational institution. Instructors at these schools teach various subjects, including hands-on laboratory and research techniques. If you enjoy the idea of combining skills in science with teaching and training, this may be a good career for you.

www.science.nelson.com 

The general characteristics of these two classes of organisms are summarized in **Table 2**.

Table 2 General Features of *K*-selected Species and *r*-selected Species

K-selected species	*r*-selected species
live in predictable, stable environments	exploit rapidly changing environments
long-lived	short-lived
population size stable	population size highly variable
density-dependent mortality	density-independent mortality
competition intense	competition low
multiple reproductive events beginning later in life	single reproductive event at a young age
prolonged parental care of young	little or no parental care of young
modest numbers of offspring	very high numbers of offspring
tend to have an S-shaped population growth curve	tend to have a J-shaped population growth curve
large body size	small body size

SUMMARY Population Change

- Density-dependent factors affect a population only at particular population densities.
- The influence of density-independent factors is the same regardless of population density.
- *K*-selected organisms tend to be found in stable environments. Their reproductive strategy is to produce fewer offspring and devote significant parental resources to ensure their survival.
- *r*-selected organisms tend to be found in unstable environments. Their reproductive strategy is to produce many offspring and devote few parental resources to them.

Section 22.3 Questions

1. Explain the difference between density-dependent and density-independent factors.
2. Classify the following scenarios as density-dependent or density-independent:
   (a) A forest fire destroys a great deal of habitat in Jasper National Park.
   (b) Many aquatic organisms die as a result of adverse weather conditions during the breeding season.
   (c) A young aggressive hawk invades the geographic range of established hawks, driving weaker birds from the geographic range.
3. Identify one density-dependent and one density-independent limiting factor that were not discussed in this section. Explain how they might affect the growth of a population.
4. Differentiate between *r* and *K* population growth strategies. Give at least two examples of each.

5. Study the graph in **Figure 7** which shows a population of the great tit, a European bird similar to the chickadee. The graph illustrates population density versus clutch size (the number of eggs to be hatched at one time).
   (a) Is this a case of density-dependent or density-independent regulation?
   (b) Draw a corresponding graph to illustrate population density versus food supply. Explain the reasoning behind the shape of your graph.
6. For each example in **Figure 8**, determine whether the population is made up of *r*-selected organisms or *K*-selected organisms. Justify your answer using the characteristics listed in **Table 2**.

Changes in Clutch Size with Population Density

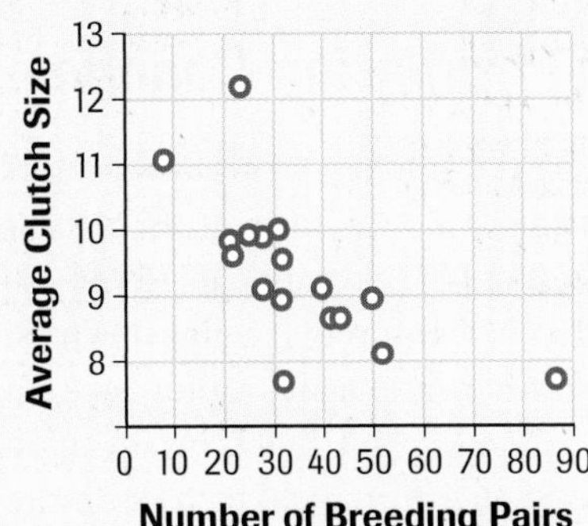

Figure 7

(a) Galapagos tortoise

(b) pioneer succession plant species or large insect swarm

(c) rabbit

(d) **Bacteria Growing in a Glass of Milk**

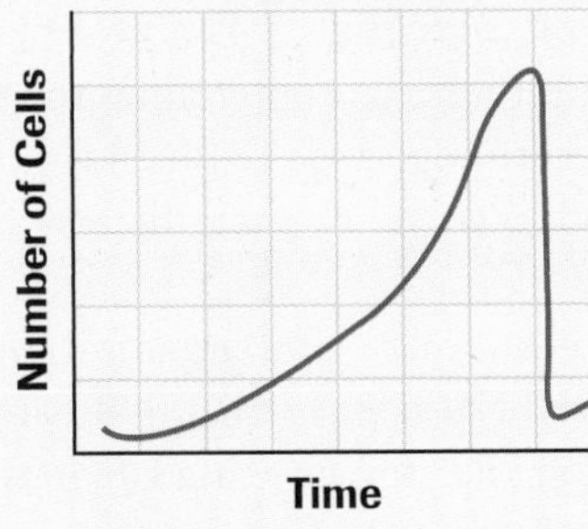

(e) **Population of Coyotes in a Large Parkland**

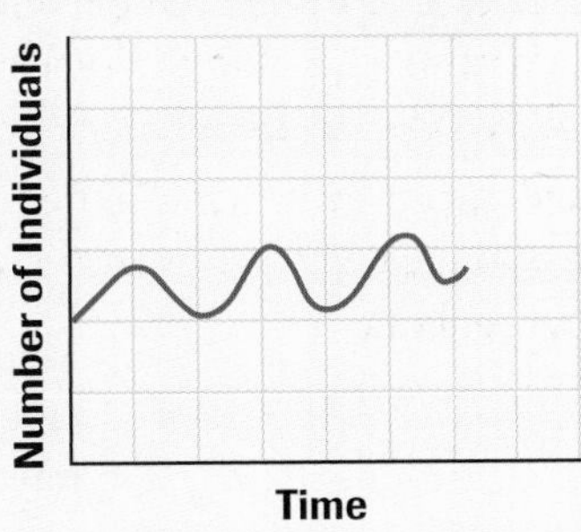

(f) **An Introduced Species in a New Environment**

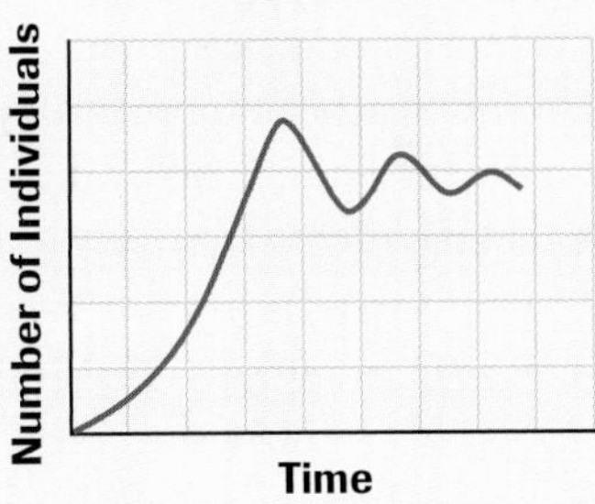

Figure 8

INVESTIGATION 22.1

Measuring Population Changes

Duckweeds, among the smallest of all flowering plants, are free-floating, aquatic plants that form green mats on the surfaces of freshwater ponds. One plant consists of a single leaf-like structure with a single tiny root hanging down. Duckweeds can grow and reproduce (asexually) rapidly as each new leaf breaks off and forms a new plant. In this investigation, you will test the influence of environmental factors on the population growth rate of duckweed. You will also estimate the carrying capacity of the environment.

Report Checklist

- Purpose
- Problem
- Hypothesis
- Prediction
- Design
- Materials
- Procedure
- Evidence
- Analysis
- Evaluation
- Synthesis

Materials

duckweed plants
plastic cups or 150 mL beakers
pond water
liquid fertilizer (optional)
artificial light source and timer (optional)
water bath or other suitable heat source

Design

With your group, design experiments to test the influence of an environmental variable on the growth rate of a duckweed population and to estimate the carrying capacity of the experimental environment. You may choose from a wide variety of variables such as temperature, nutrient availability, or light intensity. Base your estimate of carrying capacity on the size of population that can be sustained in one container. Be sure to obtain your teacher's approval of your selected variable(s) and experimental design before beginning the experiment.

Note that in order to measure the carrying capacity of the environment directly, the duckweed population must be allowed to grow for an extended period of time. However, it may be possible to generate a crude estimate of carrying capacity by extrapolating graphic data.

Your design must include one or more testable hypotheses; proper selection of independent and dependent variables as well as control(s); a set of procedures and data collection tables; and criteria for analyzing your data, including tracking the changes in population size, density, and growth rate.

Analysis and Evalution

(a) What effect, if any, did the environmental variable have on the growth of the duckweed population?

(b) Was the effect of the variable density-dependent or density-independent? Explain your reasoning.

(c) Describe the growth patterns of your duckweed populations. Did they follow a recognizable or predictable pattern?

(d) Would you describe the duckweed as having an "r" or "K" reproductive strategy? Explain.

(e) Would you expect your chosen variable to be a limiting factor in natural duckweed populations? Explain your reasoning.

Synthesis

(f) "Environmental factors can eventually limit the maximum size of any growing population." Explain why this statement is undeniable.

(g) No environment is infinite. How did the "cup environment" in your experiment model planet Earth?

(h) If nutrients and light were readily available, the duckweed population in a small container could probably continue to grow until it was limited by physical space. Do you think the same is true of the human population on Earth?
   (i) What do you think is/are the key factor(s) that will eventually limit human population growth?
   (ii) Estimate Earth's carrying capacity for the human population, which is currently more than six billion.
   (iii) Many scientists, economists, and organizations (such as the United Nations) predict that Earth's human population will stop growing late in this century. Conduct research to find out their predictions for the final stable population size.

www.science.nelson.com 

EXTENSION

Age Structure Diagrams

Age structure diagrams depict the number of individuals in a population in different age groups. The relative size of age groups can affect the population growth rate. If all other conditions are the same, the population with the highest number of individuals of reproductive age will grow the fastest. This animation shows age structure diagrams for various countries, including Canada.

www.science.nelson.com 

Chapter 22 SUMMARY

Outcomes

Knowledge

- describe and explain, quantitatively, factors that influence population growth (22.2)
- describe the growth of populations in terms of the mathematical relationship among carrying capacity, biotic potential, environmental resistance, and the number of individuals in the population (22.1, 22.2)
- explain the different population growth patterns (22.2)
- describe the characteristics and reproductive strategies of *r*-selected and *K*-selected organisms (22.3)

STS

- explain how concepts, models, and theories are often used in interpreting and explaining observations and in predicting future observations (22.2, 22.3)

Skills

- ask questions and plan investigations (22.2, 22.3)
- conduct investigations and gather and record data and information (22.3)
- analyze data and apply mathematical and conceptual models by: designing and performing an experiment or computer simulation to demonstrate the effect of environmental factors on population growth rate (22.2, 22.3)
- work as members of a team and apply the skills and conventions of science (all)

Key Terms

22.1

population size
population density
ecological density
population dispersion
clumped dispersion
uniform dispersion
random dispersion

22.2

natality
mortality
immigration
emigration
N
ΔN
growth rate (*gr*)
per capita growth rate (*cgr*)
open population
closed population
exponential growth
r
doubling time (t_d)
environmental resistance
logistic growth
lag phase
log phase
stationary phase
K

22.3

density-dependent factor
intraspecific competition
predation
minimum viable population size
density-independent factor
K-selected organism
r-selected organism

Key Equations

- population density: $D_p = \frac{N}{A}$ or $D_p = \frac{N}{V}$
- population change: $\Delta N = [\text{natality } (n) + \text{immigration } (i)] - [\text{mortality } (m) + \text{emigration } (e)]$
- population growth rate: $gr = \frac{\Delta N}{\Delta t}$
- per capita growth rate: $cgr = \frac{\Delta N}{N}$
- population doubling time: $t_d = \frac{0.69}{cgr}$

MAKE a summary

1. Select a microorganism, plant, or animal and consider its role and functions as an individual and as a part of a population. Describe its life in terms of
   - current population status
   - intraspecific interactions within the population
   - potential changes to population status and size
   - factors that might affect the population growth
2. Revisit your answers to the Starting Points questions at the start of the chapter. Would you answer the questions differently now? Why?

Go To www.science.nelson.com GO

The following components are available on the Nelson Web site. Follow the links for *Nelson Biology Alberta 20–30*.

- an interactive Self Quiz for Chapter 22
- additional Diploma Exam-style Review Questions
- Illustrated Glossary
- additional IB-related material

There is more information on the Web site wherever you see the Go icon in the chapter.

▸ Chapter 22 REVIEW

Many of these questions are in the style of the Diploma Exam. You will find guidance for writing Diploma Exams in Appendix D5. Science Directing Words used in Diploma Exams are in bold type. Exam study tips and test-taking suggestions are on the Nelson Web site.

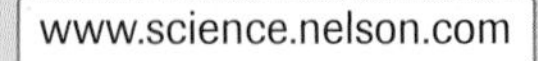

DO NOT WRITE IN THIS TEXTBOOK.

Part 1

1. Most wild populations exhibit
   A. random distribution patterns
   B. clumped distribution patterns
   C. uniform distribution patterns
   D. continuously changing distribution patterns

2. Researchers discovered that when populations are large, female arctic ground squirrels run low on food resources and stop reproducing. This is an example of
   A. an *r*-selected reproductive strategy
   B. a density-dependent factor
   C. a change in biotic potential
   D. a density-independent factor

3. NR Tree density was determined in a stand of aspen. The tree count was 6400 stems in 3.8 ha. Determine the density of the stand. (Record your answer to two significant digits.)

4. Which statement best describes carrying capacity?
   A. the maximum number of individuals of all species that can live in an area
   B. the maximum number of individuals of one species that can live in an area
   C. the maximum number of individuals of all species that can live continuously and sustainably in an area
   D. the maximum number of individuals of one species that can live continuously and sustainably in an area

5. A population of grouse was counted over the years. When graphed, the population size grew rapidly, peaked, and then fluctuated year over year. Which is true of the population?
   A. Grouse cannot increase exponentially.
   B. The population followed a typical logistic growth pattern.
   C. The population appeared to be made up of *r*-selected organisms.
   D. The population size fluctuates once it reaches the environment's carrying capacity.

6. Which of the following is *not* a density-dependent factor?
   A. predation
   B. disease
   C. drought
   D. intraspecific competition

7. NR A population is growing exponentially at a rate of 14 % per year. How many years will it take for the population to double in size? (Record all two digits of your answer.)

8. A sudden environmental change to a habitat generally favours
   A. *K*-selected organisms
   B. species that reproduce numerous times in their lives
   C. small organisms that are *r*-selected
   D. organisms that establish complex symbiotic relationships

9. Which statement is true, if the North American human population is growing at an annual rate of about 0.7 %?
   A. The population has effectively stopped growing.
   B. The population will soon begin to decline.
   C. The population will double in about 100 years.
   D. The population will double in about 1000 years.

10. Which of the following represents the correct pattern for a population undergoing logistic growth?
    A. lag phase, log phase, stationary phase
    B. stationary phase, log phase, lag phase
    C. log phase, lag phase, stationary phase
    D. lag phase, stationary phase, log phase

11. NR Determine the density of a population of southern flying squirrels, if 940 squirrels were counted in a 68 ha area. (Record your answer to two significant digits.)

Part 2

12. Using two examples, **explain** why it is important for scientists to track the population status of Canadian species.

13. **Identify** and **describe** ways in which the decline of resources in an ecosystem can affect the growth rate of a population in that ecosystem.

Use the following information to answer questions 14 to 18.

Scientists conducted a study into the competition between two species of rodents: the woodland jumping mouse, *Napaeozapus insignis,* and the meadow jumping mouse, *Zapus hudsonius.* The meadow jumping mouse is known to be able to exist in both field and forest habitats. Both species of mice are seed feeders. The experimental design included the selection of three approximately 100 ha plots with similar plant cover. Plot 1 (100 ha) supported a population of *N. insignis,* plot 2 (92 ha) supported a population of *Z. hudsonius,* while plot 3 (104 ha) supported populations of both *N. insignis* and *Z. hudsonius.* The populations of mice were monitored over a period of 4 years (**Table 1**, next page).

Table 1 Experimental Data of Mouse Populations

	Plot 1 (100 ha)	Plot 2 (92 ha)
Mouse species	*N. insignis*	*Z. hudsonius*
year 1	632	345
year 2	788	461
year 3	840	509
year 4	671	328
	Plot 3 (104 ha)	
Mouse species	*N. insignis*	*Z. hudsonius*
year 1	610	102
year 2	559	188
year 3	663	173
year 4	601	80

14. **Determine** the average population density for each population in each plot over the four-year study. DE

15. Based on these results, what can you **infer** regarding the interactions between these two rodent species? DE

16. **Identify** the type of interaction occurring in plot 3. DE

17. Some biologists might argue that the evidence from this study is inconclusive due to the assumptions being made by the researchers. **Identify** three such assumptions and criticize the acceptability of each. DE

18. **Describe** the improvements that could be made to the experimental design used in this study. DE

19. Six ground finches began nesting on an island in 1990. Biologists monitored numbers in this population for nine years, compiling their data as shown in **Table 2**.
    (a) **Graphically** show the changes in this population over the nine-year period. Label the various population growth phases on your graph.
    (b) **Determine** an estimate of the carrying capacity of the island. Label this value on your graph.

Table 2 Data on Ground Finch Population

Year	Population	Year	Population
1990	18	1995	477
1991	35	1996	359
1992	58	1997	296
1993	170	1998	283
1994	280		

20. **Outline** the elements of the prairie ecosystem that were affected by the depletion of the buffalo herds on the Great Plains of the U.S. and Canada. Consider flora, fauna, and humans as essential elements in your answer.

21. **Table 3** shows the population of Alberta from 1901 to 2003. Write a unified response addressing the following aspects of the population changes over this time: DE
    - **Graphically** present the population data for the province of Alberta shown in **Table 3**. Use a spreadsheet program or graphing calculator, if possible.
    - **Identify** the decade during which per capita growth rate appears to be greatest. Does this rate of growth appear to be sustainable? **Explain**.
    - Use your graph to **determine** an estimate of Alberta's population in 50 years. Do you think this population size will be reached? **Justify** your response.
    - During the past 100 years, Alberta's population increased in size by almost 70 times. **Determine** an estimate of the population size if it increased another 70 times in the next 100 years.

Table 3 Population of Alberta

Year	Population (thousands)	Year	Population (thousands)
1901	43	1960	841
1911	247	1965	910
1920	360	1970	1 046
1925	375	1975	1 227
1930	459	1980	2 179
1935	513	1983	2 345
1940	547	1994	2 705
1945	565	1997	2 838
1950	623	2001	2 975
1955	717	2003	3 164

chapter

23 Population Interactions

In this chapter

- Exploration: Effects and Consequences
- Investigation 23.1: Planting Opposition: Intraspecific and Interspecific Competition
- Web Activity: Gause's Principle
- Web Activity: Elk Management in Banff National Park
- Lab Exercise 23.A: Predator–Prey Cycles
- Mini Investigation: Finding a Host
- Web Activity: Zebra Mussels
- Web Activity: Wildfires and Succession
- Investigation 23.2: Microbial Succession

Individual species do not live and evolve in isolation. They are all members of ecological communities, which are made up of many interacting populations within a physical environment that may itself be changing. Just as individual species exhibit recognizable traits that have evolved over long periods of time, entire ecosystems exhibit clearly identifiable patterns and relationships that not only characterize the interactions of living things with their environment, but are also dynamic in time and space.

The relationships between the members of an ecological community are always changing. They may change gradually, as the ecosystem slowly matures, or abruptly, if it is suddenly disrupted by a significant event. Whatever the case, change is inevitable. While very few species can significantly modify their environment, most have adaptations that can help the organism thrive in a changing ecosystem.

Humans, an intelligent and successful species, are unique among all species. Our use of tools has allowed us to live in environments well outside our biological range of tolerances: we inhabit almost every terrestrial ecosystem on Earth (**Figure 1**). Even so, the human species experiences the same limitations as other species do. Like all populations, humans live in finite environments with limited carrying capacities. Today, the rapidly growing human population and its consumption of resources place significant stresses on those environments.

STARTING Points

Answer these questions as best you can with your current knowledge. Then, using the concepts and skills you have learned, you will revise your answers at the end of the chapter.

1. Study the images in **Figure 1 (a)–(c)** and reflect on the following questions:
   (a) What are some factors that enable the human species to live in different environments?
   (b) What are the key resources needed to support any human population? Where and how are these resources obtained?
2. Compare the ways in which urban populations differ from rural populations in how they obtain resources.
3. What are potential ecological effects on the environment of the activities of large human populations?

Career Connection: Interpretive Naturalist

Figure 1
Using our skills to adapt to the environmental conditions, humans now live almost everywhere on Earth.

Exploration — *Effects and Consequences*

With two or three other students, brainstorm some possible effects of the human population on each of the following:

- forests
- grain and livestock production
- wildlife
- water supply and water quality
- biodiversity
- the atmosphere
- harvesting of seafood

(a) Design a concept map to illustrate these effects.

(b) Present your concept map to the class.

23.1 Interactions within Communities

Populations do not live in isolation. Within a given ecosystem, populations of different species interact in a community. Within each community, each organism occupies its own ecological niche. Ecologist Eugene Odum describes an organism's ecological niche as its "occupation." For example, on the African savannah, a variety of interactions occur among organisms (**Figure 1**). While the lions, zebras, water buffalo, and antelope all occupy the same habitat, each member of this community uses different mechanisms to survive.

CAREER CONNECTION

Interpretive Naturalist
A career as an interpretive naturalist involves research in natural history and the environment, and also presenting that information to the general public. Most interpretive naturalists work for a park, botanical garden, or wilderness area. This career needs a sound understanding of populations and how they interact in an environment or ecosystem. What kind of training and experience is needed to enter this career?

www.science.nelson.com 

Figure 1
An African grassland community. The African lion's ecological niche includes what it eats, what eats it, the way it reproduces, the temperature range it tolerates, its habitat, its behavioural responses, and any other factors that describe its pattern of living.

Interactions among individuals of different species (interspecific) in a community have important influences on the population dynamics of individual species. Although species interact in various ways, interactions between two species and their effects on the population density can be classified into the five categories shown in **Table 1**. **Symbiosis** includes a variety of interactions in which two species live together in close, usually physical, association. Parasitism, mutualism, and commensalism are types of symbiotic interactions.

symbiosis various interactions in which two species maintain a close, usually physical, association; includes parasitism, mutualism, and commensalism

Table 1 Classification of Interactions between Two Species

Interaction		Effect on populations
interspecific competition		Interaction may be detrimental to one or both species.
predation		Interaction is beneficial to one species and usually lethal to individuals of the other.
symbiosis	• parasitism	Interaction is beneficial to one species and harmful, but not usually fatal, to the other.
	• mutualism	Interaction is beneficial to both species.
	• commensalism	Interaction is beneficial to one species and the other species is unaffected.

Interspecific Competition

Interspecific competition occurs between individuals of different species and restricts population growth. Interspecific competition can occur in two ways. Actual fighting over resources is called **interference competition**. An example of interference competition is the fighting that sometimes occurs between tree swallows and bluebirds over birdhouses. The consumption or use of shared resources is referred to as **exploitative competition**. An example of exploitative competition occurs when both Arctic foxes and snowy owls prey on the same population of Arctic hares.

The strongest competition occurs between populations of species with overlapping niches. The more that niches overlap, the greater the competition between species, as demonstrated by Russian ecologist G.F. Gause. Gause tested the theory that two species with similar requirements could not coexist in the same community. He predicted that one species would consume most of the resources, reproduce efficiently, and drive the other species to extinction. Gause's experiments led to the conclusion that, if resources are limited, no two species can remain in competition for exactly the same niche indefinitely. This became known as Gause's principle, or **competitive exclusion**. In nature, such severe competition is usually avoided by **resource partitioning**, in which different species with similar requirements use resources in different ways—for example at different times or in different places.

The results of interspecific competition take on several forms:

- the population size of the weaker competitor could decline;
- one species could change its behaviour so that it is able to survive using different resources;
- individuals in one population could migrate to another habitat where resources are more plentiful.

In any of these cases, competition would decline.

interspecific competition competition between individuals of different species

interference competition interspecific competition that involves aggression between individuals of different species who fight over the same resource(s)

exploitative competition interspecific competition that involves consumption of shared resources by individuals of different species, where consumption by one species may limit resource availability to other species

competitive exclusion the concept that, if resources are limited, no two species can remain in competition for exactly the same niche indefinitely; also know as Gause's Principle

resource partitioning avoidance of, or reduction in, competition for similar resources by individuals of different species occupying different non-overlapping ecological niches

INVESTIGATION 23.1 *Introduction*

Planting Opposition: Intraspecific and Interspecific Competition

Virtually all naturally occurring organisms are in competition—either with members of their own species (intraspecific competition) or with members of different species (interspecific competition). In this investigation you will design and conduct experiments to measure the effect of both intraspecific and interspecific competition on plant seedlings.

Report Checklist

- ● Purpose
- ○ Problem
- ● Hypothesis
- ● Prediction
- ● Design
- ● Materials
- ● Procedure
- ● Evidence
- ● Analysis
- ● Evaluation
- ● Synthesis

To perform this investigation, turn to page 776. 

Case Study—Gause's Principle

Ecologists describe the struggle for survival in terms of the competitive interactions between different species in nature. Gause was an ecologist who studied the effects of competition on two *Paramecium* species. He grew each species separately in culture tubes, and then put the two together in the same tube. In this Web Activity, you will compare the growth and population densities of the *Paramecium* populations, both separately and together.

www.science.nelson.com 

Changes in Population Size of a Predator and Prey

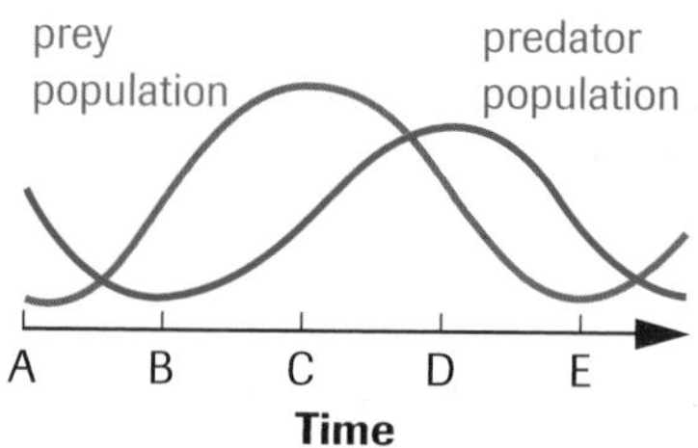

Figure 4
A model of the predator–prey cycle. Because of the oscillations in the populations, the line on this graph is referred to as a sinusoidal curve.

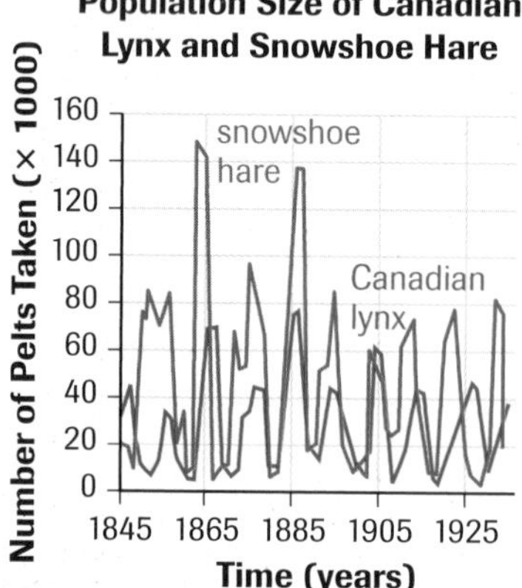

Figure 5
A 10-year cycling pattern in the population of Canadian lynx and the population of snowshoe hare

Predation

Predation is an example of an interspecific interaction in which the population density of one species—the predator—increases while the population density of the other species—the prey—declines. Predator–prey relationships can have significant effects on the size of both predator and prey populations. When the prey population increases, there is more food for predators. This abundance can result in an increase in the size of the predator population. As the predator population increases, however, the prey population decreases. The reduction of prey then results in a decline in the predator population, unless it has access to another food source. There are time lags between each of these responses as the predator population responds to changes in prey abundance.

Some predator–prey relationships coexist at steady levels and display a cyclical pattern. The two species tend to cycle slightly out of synchronization, with the predator patterns lagging behind the prey patterns (**Figure 4**). In this model of a predator–prey cycle, adjustments to population size can be seen during the time intervals from A to E. This graph is referred to as a sinusoidal curve. At time A, when the prey population density is low, the predators have little food and their population declines. A reduction in the predator population allows the prey population to recover and increase. The predator population does not increase again until they begin to reproduce (at time B). Prey and predator populations grow until the increase in the predator population causes the prey population to decline (from time C to time E). As the predator population increases, more of the prey population is devoured. The resulting low density in the prey population leads to starvation and lowered fecundity among predators, slowing its population growth rate (at time D).

In nature, many factors can influence this model of the sinusoidal predator–prey cycle. In 1831, the manager of the Hudson's Bay Company in northern Ontario reported that there was a scarcity of snowshoe hares and the local Ojibwa population was starving as a result. In the early 1900s, wildlife biologists began analyzing the fur-trading records of the Hudson's Bay Company. They discovered that the hares have a population cycle of 10 years. The population cycle of the Canadian lynx, a significant predator of snowshoe hares, mirrors, with a slight time lag, the changes in the snowshoe hare population (**Figure 5**).

WWW **WEB** *Activity*

Case Study—Elk Management in Banff National Park

Human activities such as agriculture and over-hunting often disrupt the natural balance of wildlife populations. This can lead to a loss or reduction in the home range of a particular species and an associated decline in its population size. Management programs may lead to a recovery of the species. An interesting case of the influence of humans on wildlife populations is the history of the elk that live in Banff National Park, Alberta.

In this activity, you will consider ecological and human/elk issues around elk in the park. You will also assess preliminary results of the Banff National Park Elk Management Strategy on elk population biology.

www.science.nelson.com GO

+ EXTENSION

Natural Selection and Predator/Prey Interactions
Find out about the concept of co-evolution and the role that predator-prey interactions play in the evolution of species.

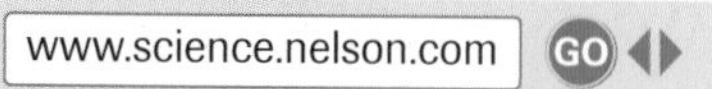

LAB EXERCISE 23.A

Report Checklist

- ○ Purpose
- ○ Problem
- ● Hypothesis
- ○ Prediction
- ○ Design
- ○ Materials
- ○ Procedure
- ○ Evidence
- ● Analysis
- ● Evaluation
- ● Synthesis

Predator–Prey Cycles

The large white-tailed deer population in a forest reserve in Alberta has caused concern about overgrazing that might lead to the extinction of plant and animal species found there. To manage this excessive deer population, forest personnel decided to introduce its natural predator, the wolf (**Figure 6**). In the year 1990, 2000 deer lived within the reserve, and 10 wolves were flown into this reserve. Population densities of white-tailed deer and wolves were monitored for a 10-year period.

Problem

What effect does the introduction of a natural predator, the wolf, into a habitat have on the white-tailed deer population?

Hypothesis

(a) Develop a hypothesis about the effect on the white-tailed deer population as a result of the introduction of wolves into their habitat.

Evidence

Table 2 Changes in White-tailed Deer and Wolf Populations

Year	White-tailed deer	Wolves
1990	2000	10
1991	2300	12
1992	2500	16
1993	2360	22
1994	2244	28
1995	2094	24
1996	1968	21
1997	1916	18
1998	1952	19
1999	1972	19

Analysis

(b) Plot the changes in the white-tailed deer and wolf population using the data in **Table 2**, including both sets of data on one graph and using an appropriate labelling method. Use two separate *y*-axes, one on the left-hand side of the graph for deer and the other on the right-hand side for wolves, each with an appropriate scale.

Evaluation

(c) Is wolf predation a limiting factor in this forest reserve? Explain your reasoning.

(d) What other factors might limit the deer population?

(e) Explain how the number of wolves in the reserve is influenced by the size of the deer population.

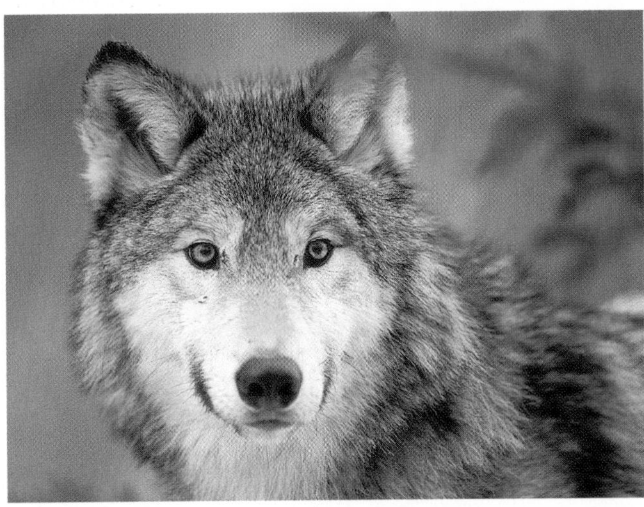

Figure 6

Synthesis

(f) The Atlantic cod population was an extremely abundant stock of primary economic importance to fishing communities throughout the Atlantic provinces. The Department of Fisheries and Oceans has stated that the collapse in Atlantic cod stocks can be attributed to overfishing. Others claim that the use of equipment that disturbs fish spawning sites on the ocean floor is primarily responsible, and still others argue that the harp seal, a predator of Atlantic cod, is responsible for this mass reduction in the cod population. One suggestion to help cod stocks recover is to kill large numbers of harp seals. Suggest some ways that marine biologists might study changes to the Atlantic cod population to determine whether reducing the harp seal population would be an effective solution.

DID YOU KNOW ?

A Twig or a Caterpillar?

Some prey species use this passive defence mechanism to hide from predators. For example, the inchworm in **Figure 7** is camouflaged, blending in with its surroundings. Camouflage is also called cryptic coloration.

Figure 7

Figure 9

This syrphid fly is less likely to be preyed upon because it mimics stinging bees and wasps.

mutualism a symbiotic relationship in which both organisms benefit; as neither is harmed, it is categorized as a +/+ relationship

commensalism a symbiotic relationship in which one organism benefits and the other organism is unaffected; it is categorized as a +/0 relationship

Defence Mechanisms

Predator–prey interactions have resulted in the evolution of various defence mechanisms in plant and animal species, through repeated encounters with predators over time. Plants use both morphological defences—such as thorns, hooks, spines, and needles—and chemical defences against herbivores. The mustard family of plants, for example, contains oils that give off a pungent odour and make them distasteful and toxic to some insects. Some plants, such as balsam fir, produce chemicals that mimic an insect growth hormone. When a young linden bug (*Pyrrhocoris apterus*) feeds on balsam fir, it remains in the juvenile stage and eventually dies.

Some insects use chemicals produced by their food as a defence against their own potential predators. For instance, the monarch butterfly uses potent plant toxins to make itself distasteful to its predators (**Figure 8**). Caterpillars of the monarch butterfly obtain these toxins by feeding on plants of the milkweed family. The toxins are stored in fatty tissues of the caterpillar, making both it and the adult butterfly unpalatable.

Figure 8

The monarch butterfly and its predator, the blue jay, provide an example of defence mechanisms by prey against predators. Blue jays have been known to regurgitate a monarch butterfly after swallowing it.

Animals sometimes employ passive defence mechanisms, such as hiding, or active defences, such as fleeing from their predators. Active defences are more costly to the prey in terms of energy use than are passive defences. Some species, such as Richardson's ground squirrels, use alarm calls to signal each other when a predator is near. Some animals give a visual warning to predators of their chemical defence mechanisms, such as poisons.

Both predator and prey species can protect themselves through mimicry. In one type of mimicry, a palatable or harmless species mimics an unpalatable or harmful organism, a phenomenon often observed in insects. Predators are often fooled by these mimics who, as a result, avoid predation. A typical example is the harmless syrphid fly that looks remarkably similar to bees and wasps (**Figure 9**).

Symbiosis

Symbiosis, meaning "living together," refers to a relationship in which organisms of two different species live in close, usually physical, contact. At least one of the two species benefits from the association. One type of symbiotic relationship is **mutualism**, which occurs when both species in the relationship benefit and neither is harmed. Most biologists also include as symbiotic relationships **commensalism**, which occurs when one organism benefits and the other neither benefits nor is harmed, and **parasitism**, which occurs when one organism benefits at the expense of another organism's well-being.

Mutualism

There are many common examples of mutualism in which both organisms benefit. Bacteria live in the guts of herbivores, such as cows, deer, and sheep. These animals do not produce the enzymes required to digest plant products such as cellulose and lignin. The bacteria secrete enzymes to break down these products into useable nutrients for the animals. In return, the bacteria are provided with nutrition themselves. Beneficial bacteria also live in the large intestines of humans, producing nutrients such as vitamins B and K, which our cells can use.

parasitism a symbiotic relationship in which one organism (the parasite) benefits at the expense of another organism (the host), which is often harmed but usually not killed; it is categorized as a +/− relationship

Commensalism

It can be difficult to classify a relationship as an example of commensalism. Some biologists argue that they do not exist at all, since it is very difficult to determine whether an individual of the unaffected species is, in fact, benefiting or being harmed. Caribou and Arctic foxes interact in a way that has been classified as commensalistic (**Figure 10**). The foxes follow the caribou herds when they forage for food in their wintering grounds. The caribou have shovel-like feet that can remove snow from lichens on the ground, which is the caribou's primary food source. The caribou expose many small mammals, which are eaten by the foxes. Thus, the foxes benefit from this interspecific interaction and the caribou neither benefit nor are harmed by it. In a similar way, tropical "ant birds" follow army ant colonies through the rainforest, feeding not on the ants but on the other insects and small animals that are disturbed by the ants.

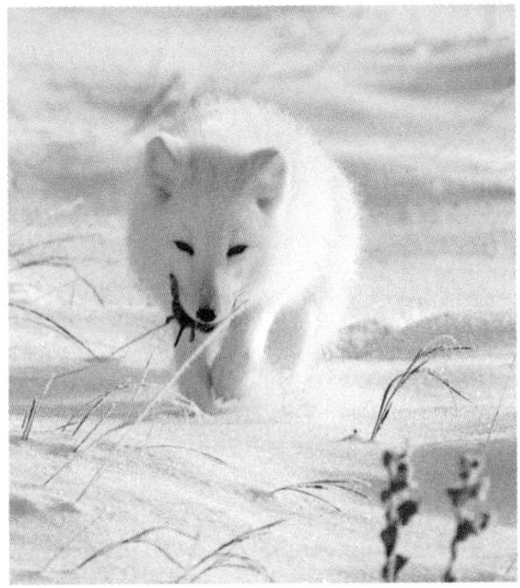

Figure 10
Caribou unknowingly help Arctic foxes by exposing snow-covered habitats of fox prey.

Parasitism

Most parasites live and feed on or in the bodies of other living organisms, and cannot complete their life cycle in the absence of their hosts. Parasitism is extremely common. Biologists estimate that as many as one in four animal species may be parasites. Virtually all species of plants and animals are hosts to one or more species of parasite. While the best-known parasites are responsible for serious human diseases—such as malaria, schistosomiasis, and African sleeping sickness—the vast majority of parasites cause little or no significant harm to their host. This makes sense, since they would be harming the environment on which their own survival relies.

Parasites do not always live on or in another organism. Some species are classified as **social parasites**. These organisms manipulate the behaviour of another species so that they can complete their life cycle. North American cowbirds are social parasites. They lay their eggs in the nests of other smaller birds and, therefore, do not have to expend energy building their own nests or feeding their own young. The cowbird eggs usually hatch earlier and the larger newborn cowbirds monopolize the food resources. The other newborn birds are usually killed, resulting in a very high survival rate for the young cowbirds.

Altruism: Why Can't We All Just Get Along?
Dr. Sigal Balshine, Dr. David Sloan Wilson, Dr. Joel Peck, and Dr. Troy Day, discuss their research into interspecific interactions, particularly altruism and co-operation.

www.science.nelson.com 

social parasite a parasite that completes its life cycle by manipulating the social behaviour of its hosts

mini *Investigation* — *Finding a Host*

Internal parasites live in hosts that eventually die, usually due to something other than the parasite. For this reason it is essential that parasites be able to find and invade new host individuals on a regular basis. This is particularly challenging for internal parasites and results in very complex life cycles for these species.

- Choose an internal parasite and research the ways it is able to get from one host to another. Common internal parasites include flukes, tapeworms, *Plasmodium*, and *Trypanosome* species.

(a) Draw the life cycle of your chosen parasite, indicating how it gets from one host to another.

Figure 11
Some African killer bees escaped from Brazilian beekeeping operations and have spread accidentally into North America.

Disruption of Community Equilibrium

Biological communities are stable when the resources necessary for survival are sustained, populations do not exceed their environment's carrying capacity, and interspecific interactions contribute to biodiversity. Interspecific interactions help to maintain the necessary equilibrium within the complex and dynamic natural systems that sustain communities. A variety of disturbances can affect this equilibrium in drastic ways. A natural disaster can disturb most populations within a community and can break down the intricate interactions among its organisms. The introduction of exotic species can have devastating biological and economic effects on the habitats they invade (**Figure 11**). These nonindigenous species, often with few predators, may reduce or eliminate indigenous species by outcompeting them for food and habitat, or by preying on them. Some recent examples of the harmful effects of introducing an exotic species into an ecological community are shown in **Table 3**.

Table 3 Selected Invading Species

Wild caraway (*Carum carvi*)	Grown in Western Canada as a spice crop, non-native "wild" caraway has escaped cultivation. In parts of Alberta this species is now invading pasture, rangeland, and natural habitats. It is not consumed by livestock and when left uncontrolled can quickly outcompete many other plant species.
African killer bees (Figure 11)	These aggressive bees are hybrids of the domesticated European bee and an African bee that was imported to Brazil by scientists. Large numbers of these bees attack much more readily than the common honeybee does. Aside from public safety, Africanized killer bees have a significant economic impact on commercial beekeepers and food production.
West Nile virus	The West Nile virus, detected in wildlife populations throughout North America, was first identified in the West Nile region of Uganda in 1937. It can be transmitted to humans by three species of mosquitoes: *Culex pipiens* (the common household mosquito), *Aedes vexans* (an indiscriminate feeder), and *A. japonicus*. It is responsible for serious wildlife population losses in many parts of the world. The virus is believed to have been accidentally introduced to North America in an exotic frog species.

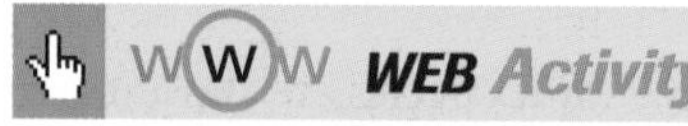

Web Quest—Zebra Mussels

Shipping is one of the most common methods of transporting goods long distances. Massive transportation networks depend on cutting-edge technology to stay organized and accident-free. Unfortunately, the sophisticated technology needed to run shipping companies has not been able to stop the transfer of unwanted guests from one part of the world to another. In this Web Quest, you will look at the impact of one of these stowaway organisms—the zebra mussel. This exotic species has had a huge impact in its new environment, and you are going to explore the effects of this little bivalve.

www.science.nelson.com 

Predator-Prey I
In this Virtual Biology Lab, you will explore the effect of changes in populations of predator and prey on population growth, through a series of activities. You can modify factors such as birth rate, death rate, and the level of predation.

www.science.nelson.com 

SUMMARY Interactions within Communities

- Predator–prey interactions are affected by a wide range of factors. Both predators and prey have evolved adaptations that enhance survival.
- Symbiosis may result in mutually beneficial relationships between species.
- Commensalism may result in one species indirectly benefiting another.
- Parasitism is an interaction in which one species feeds and lives in or on a host organism to the detriment of the host.
- Invasions by exotic species, human interference, and natural disasters can disrupt the stability of an ecological community.

Mosquitoes versus Malaria

Dr. Ken Vernick and his colleagues have discovered that a large proportion of *Anopheles* mosquitoes have a genetic resistance to the malaria parasite. They are able to kill the parasite as soon as it enters their body, so they can't pass the disease on to humans.

www.science.nelson.com 

Section 23.1 Questions

1. For each of the following examples, identify what type of interspecific competition is occurring and justify your answer.
   (a) Argentine ants can displace indigenous ants from a community by rapidly depleting resources.
   (b) Some plants release toxins that kill or inhibit the growth of other plants, thereby preventing them from growing in close proximity where they may compete for space, light, water, and food.
   (c) In the Kibale Forest in Uganda, mangabey monkeys, a large species, drive away the smaller blue monkeys.
   (d) Hawks and owls rely on similar prey, but hawks feed during full daylight while owls hunt and feed from dusk to dawn. What term is used to describe this method of avoiding competition?
2. A study was conducted of mussels and the starfish *Pisaster* in the intertidal area along the shore. Results showed that greater diversity of marine invertebrates was found in the area where *Pisaster* and mussels were present together, compared to where mussels were found alone. Explain this observation in terms of competition.
3. Identify the type of defence mechanism in each of the following examples:
   (a) Tiger moths have a highly detailed wing pattern that makes them virtually undetectable against tree bark.
   (b) When attacked by ants, ladybugs secrete a sticky fluid that entangles ant antennae long enough to allow the ladybug to escape.
4. Explain how predation differs from parasitism.
5. Termites eat wood but cannot digest it. They have unicellular, heterotrophic organisms called zoomastigotes living inside their digestive tract that do this for them. Identify the type of interspecific interaction between the termites and the zoomastigotes.
6. In the Great Smoky and Balsam Mountains, ecologists are studying two species of salamander. *Plethodon glutinosus* usually lives at lower elevations than its relative, *P. jordani*, shown in **Figure 12**, although the researchers have found some areas inhabited by both species. As part of the study, the scientists established different test plots from which one of the species was removed and control plots in which the populations remained untouched. After five years, no changes were observed in the control plots, but in the test plots, salamander populations were increasing in size. For instance, if one of the test plots was cleared of *P. jordani*, it had a greater population density of *P. glutinosus* and vice versa. What inferences or conclusions might be drawn from this investigation?

Figure 12
Salamander *Plethodon jordani*

7. Insects are sometimes used as biological control agents, replacing chemical herbicides to control agricultural weeds. For example, in an area near Edmonton, Alberta, the black dot spurge beetle (*Aphthona nigriscutis*) was released in an attempt to control the leafy spurge, an aggressive weed species. The results were dramatic: a 99 % reduction in spurge density and a 30-fold increase in grass biomass after four years. Research some costs and benefits of using insects as biological controls. Summarize your research on the societal, economic, ecological, and environmental impacts in a PMI chart.

www.science.nelson.com 

23.2 Succession

Figure 1
New life begins after a devastating forest fire.

succession the slow, progressive replacement of one community by another during the development of vegetation in any area

climax community the final, relatively stable community reached during successional stages

primary succession the occupation, by plant life, of an area not previously covered by vegetation

secondary succession succession in an area that was previously covered by vegetation and still has some soil

pioneer community the first species to appear during succession

Few things appear as devastating as the destruction of a mature forest by a severe fire. All that remains is a blackened landscape with a few solitary tree trunks starkly pointing to the sky. Within a few weeks, however, the ground will slowly turn green as annual and perennial plants, tolerant of the sunlight and the resulting high soil temperatures, begin to grow and reproduce in a soil made fertile by the mineral content of the ash (**Figure 1**). Within two or three years, shrubs and young trees are evident and growing rapidly. A few years later, an untrained observer would probably never know that the area had once been burned out. Over the long term, a forest will become established and reach maturity. When mature, the forest will remain until another disturbance, natural or human-caused, once again alters the abiotic environment and vegetation.

Along with the changing vegetation is a corresponding progression in the variety of animals (birds, mammals, insects) present. Populations enlarge and then decline as the habitat slowly but surely changes.

The pattern described is not limited to forest communities. Other terrestrial regions of the biosphere, such as prairie and tundra, also show regular regrowth following environmental change. This process is referred to as succession. **Succession** describes the gradual changes in the vegetation of an area as it develops toward a final stable community, called a **climax community**.

There are two types of succession. **Primary succession** occurs in an area in which no community existed previously, for example, after a volcanic eruption or when bare rock or mineral soil is exposed by human activity or from beneath a retreating glacier. Lichens and mosses, usually the first to colonize the bare rock surface, release chemicals that help break the rock into fine soil particles. Slowly, by this break-down and weathering, enough soil and dead organic matter accumulate to support small plants. These plants form a community that begins to support a growing diversity of organisms. Over time, the community changes as new species become established and former species are outcompeted. Eventually, a relatively stable plant community forms. **Figure 2** shows a hypothetical process of succession in a forest ecosystem.

Secondary succession occurs when a community is partially or completely destroyed and its dominant plant species have been eliminated. Such destruction may result from causes such as fire, severe flooding, landslides, or human disturbance. Regrowth after a forest fire is the best-known example of secondary succession. Since soil is already present, the lengthy process of soil formation (seen in primary succession) is not necessary. The first plant community to appear, along with its associated animal species, is referred to as the **pioneer community**. Small plants, such as grasses, are common pioneer species. These plants usually have small wind-borne or animal-borne seeds and can exist in full sun and fluctuating soil moisture and temperatures. Moisture levels often dictate which plants survive. As the vegetation develops, however, new ground-level abiotic conditions are set up. As larger plants grow and provide shade, the soil temperature becomes somewhat lower and evaporation is reduced. Decay processes increase the thickness and fertility of the soil layer. Small woody shrubs may then begin to grow, and a new community of plants begins to take over. These plants tend to be taller than the pioneer plants, effectively blocking out much of the solar radiation and contributing even more to the changing microclimate and soil conditions. Often, tree species displace smaller shrubs and form forest communities.

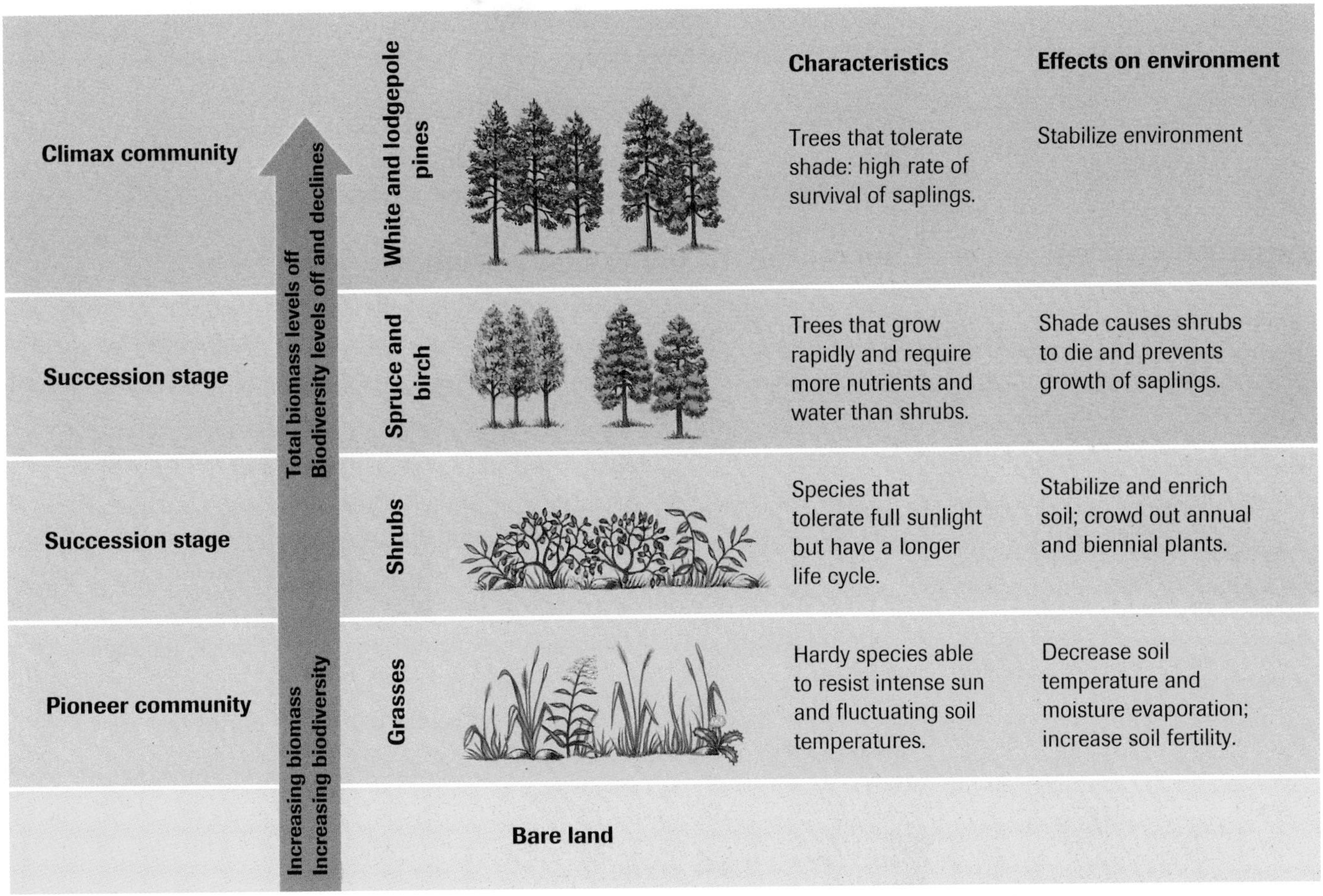

	Increasing biomass / Increasing biodiversity → Total biomass levels off / Biodiversity levels off and declines		**Characteristics**	**Effects on environment**
Climax community		**White and lodgepole pines**	Trees that tolerate shade: high rate of survival of saplings.	Stabilize environment
Succession stage		**Spruce and birch**	Trees that grow rapidly and require more nutrients and water than shrubs.	Shade causes shrubs to die and prevents growth of saplings.
Succession stage		**Shrubs**	Species that tolerate full sunlight but have a longer life cycle.	Stabilize and enrich soil; crowd out annual and biennial plants.
Pioneer community		**Grasses**	Hardy species able to resist intense sun and fluctuating soil temperatures.	Decrease soil temperature and moisture evaporation; increase soil fertility.
		Bare land		

Figure 2
Secondary succession

Just as the plant communities change, so do the ecological niches available to the other species in these communities. As a result, there is a parallel succession of animal, fungal, protist, and bacterial species. Their activities and wastes contribute to the community development. The community continues to change until a final community is reached that can self-perpetuate. This is called the climax community. The process of succession is closely linked to changes in species diversity, net productivity, and biomass. **Figure 3** illustrates the general trends in these factors over 160 years of succession.

While this traditional view of orderly succession provides a good theoretical model of how plant communities change and respond to disturbances, ecologists now recognize that gradual succession, leading directly to a stable climax community, is rare. Instead, successional changes are highly variable and often influenced by frequent and variable disturbances, which can prevent an area from ever reaching a climax community. For example, once they are established, many natural grasslands are maintained by routine fire disturbance—preventing succession to a forest community. Climax communities, if and when established, are in a state of dynamic equilibrium, dominated by the climax vegetation but usually containing extensive areas of vegetation representing earlier stages.

Changes in Net Productivity, Biomass, and Biodiversity over Time

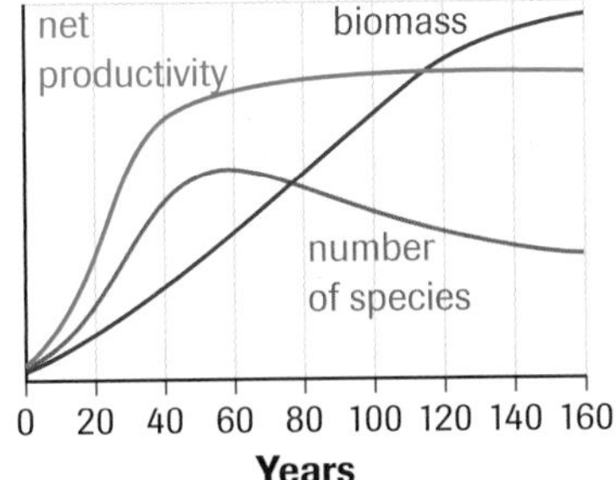

Figure 3
Successional changes in plant communities are accompanied by changes in the net productivity, biomass, and species diversity.

The pattern of succession can also vary between biomes. For example, following a forest fire in a boreal forest biome, the vegetation begins to grow rapidly, as secondary succession commences. The rich vegetation may attract large herbivores, such as deer and moose. However, in a taiga biome, the reverse is possible. Due to the cold climate, lichens, a major food source for the woodland caribou, are extremely slow growing. A fire in these regions may result in a massive decline in the caribou population.

+ EXTENSION 

Succession and *r* and *K* Reproductive Strategies

The dominant organisms at different stages of succession often have different reproductive strategies. This audio clip will highlight the different reproductive strategies commonly found in organisms in pioneer communities versus those in climax communities.

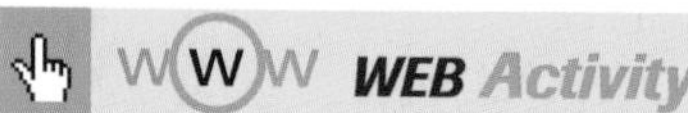

Generalizations about Succession

- Plant succession is triggered by one or both of these factors: disturbances that provide new habitats and removal of previously dominant plant species.
- Succession generally follows a pattern in which smaller pioneer species are replaced by larger species over time.
- Most plant communities exist in a state of flux, with disturbances producing a mosaic of patches in different stages of succession.
- The total number of species increases dramatically during the early stages of succession, begins to level off during the intermediary phases, and usually declines as the climax community becomes established.
- Net productivity generally increases rapidly during the early stages and then levels off.
- Biomass increases during succession and begins to level off during the establishment of the climax community.

 WWW **WEB** Activity

Case Study—Wildfires and Succession

In many terrestrial ecosystems, wildfires play an important ecological role as part of the natural cycle of renewal. Evidence of wildfires can be found in petrified wood dating back nearly 350 million years. A fossilized charcoal, called fusain, is found in the petrified trees once scarred by burning. In this Web-based Case Study, you will evaluate the role of wildfires in two types of ecosystems found in Alberta and elsewhere, forests and grasslands.

www.science.nelson.com GO

INVESTIGATION 23.2 *Introduction*

Microbial Succession

Ecological succession can describe any set of predictable changes that result in the transition of living communities over time. Successional changes can even occur in environments inhabited almost exclusively by microbes. In this investigation, you will document changes in microbial communities in a hay infusion.

To perform this investigation, turn to page 777. 

Report Checklist

- Purpose
- Problem
- Hypothesis
- Prediction
- Design
- Materials
- Procedure
- Evidence
- Analysis
- Evaluation
- Synthesis

SUMMARY Succession

- Succession is the series of predictable gradual stages as living communities change over time.
- Primary succession occurs on a barren landscape where no community existed previously.
- Secondary succession occurs after a previous community suffers complete or partial destruction.
- Each stage of succession may be recognized by the presence of one or more characteristic dominant species.

EXTENSION

Wildfires and Succession

You have read about the process of succession. Now, listen to this audio clip discussing why non-climax species "sow the seeds of their own destruction." What does this mean for climax species?

www.science.nelson.com 

Section 23.2 Questions

1. Distinguish between primary and secondary succession. Which of these processes would you expect to proceed more rapidly? Explain your reasoning.
2. What is meant by a climax community? How would you recognize a climax forest community?
3. Describe three ways in which pioneer plants alter the environment to make it more suitable for later-stage species. Describe two ways in which later-stage species alter the environment to make it less suitable for pioneer species.
4. Name two human activities that can result in secondary succession.
5. Why does succession proceed in a series of stages?
6. Aspen trees produce many extremely lightweight seeds that are carried long distances by the wind. In contrast, oak trees produce relatively small numbers of heavy seeds that fall to the ground and may be carried short distances by foraging animals.
   (a) Which species would you expect to be an early succession species and why?
   (b) What advantage might a large seed give to a plant that must germinate and survive in a late-stage mature forest with heavy shade?
   (c) Would you expect pioneer or late-stage plant species to be more tolerant of dry conditions? Explain.
7. Jack pines produce cones with a waxy outer coating that protects the seeds from extreme heat. After exposure to very high temperatures, the cones open and release their unharmed seeds.
   (a) How does such an adaptation make jack pine a secondary succession specialist?
   (b) How might human forest fire management programs alter the ecology of jack pine forests?
8. Over time, small shallow ponds and bogs can become filled in with sediment and organic matter, eventually becoming forested land. Research the formation of a peat bog and the process of succession in it.
   (a) Describe the mechanisms by which sphagnum moss is able to cover the bog.
   (b) Describe the process by which peat deposits accumulate over time.
   (c) Draw or obtain an image of a cross-sectional view of peat bog formation/succession.

   www.science.nelson.com 

9. Disturbances occur on many scales. In a forest, small disturbances include the deaths of individual trees that create openings or gaps in the canopy. Large-scale disturbances include forest fires. Modern forestry cutting practices can be used to mimic both of these disturbance scales. Obtain reference materials from the forestry industry and/or a government agency, and use the information you find to answer the following:
   (a) What is a shelter-wood cut? When is this cutting practice chosen and how does it mimic natural disturbances?
   (b) What is a clear-cut? When is this cutting practice chosen, and how does it mimic natural disturbances?
   (c) What are the similarities and differences between these forms of human disturbance and those that they are supposed to mimic in nature?

INVESTIGATION 23.1

Report Checklist

- ● Purpose
- ○ Problem
- ● Hypothesis
- ● Prediction
- ● Design
- ● Materials
- ● Procedure
- ● Evidence
- ● Analysis
- ● Evaluation
- ● Synthesis

Plant Opposition: Intraspecific and Interspecific Competition

Virtually all organisms are in competition, both with members of their own species (intraspecific) and with members of different species (interspecific). Unlike most animals, individual plants cannot move to new locations to avoid or reduce competition; they are constantly in direct competition with their immediate neighbours. Plants compete for a variety of resources, including physical space, soil nutrients, light, and water. In the short term, such competition may result in a reduction in the growth rate or health of individual plants, while in the long term, competition may result in reduced reproductive success or death of some of the plants.

In this investigation you will design and conduct experiments to measure the effect of both intraspecific and interspecific competition on plant seedlings.

Problem

Part 1: Intraspecific Competition

Does the presence of other plants from the same species affect the growth of individual plants?

Part 2: Interspecific Competition

Does the presence of plants from other species affect plant growth differently from the presence of plants from the same species?

Materials

small plant pots
soil mix
plant seeds (variety of species)

Design

Design an investigation and write a detailed procedure to address each problem. Consider coordinating your investigations with those of other groups to maximize the amount of data that you are able to include in your analysis. Groups that share data must use identical experimental designs.

Your design and procedure must include the following:

- clearly stated and testable hypotheses for both your intraspecific and interspecific competition experiments
- independent and dependent variables including a proper control
- careful monitoring of your experiments and gathering and recording of evidence (How will you determine if competition has taken place?)

Once your teacher has approved your design, carry out your procedure. Make sure you follow appropriate safety measures.

Analysis and Evaluation

(a) How did intraspecific competition influence plant growth rates in your trials? Was the effect the same for all species? Suggest explanations to account for any differences.

(b) In your interspecific competition trials, did both plant species suffer from competition equally or did one species appear to "out-compete" the other?

(c) Did you notice any differences between the competing plants and the controls? (For example, did they appear to grow taller?) Did this demonstrate an adaptive response to competition?

(d) Predict the long-term results of both forms of competition if you allowed your plants to continue growing for a year.

(e) The plant seedlings in your experiments may have competed for a variety of environmental resources.
   (i) What do you think were the direct causes of any observed effects? Identify which factor(s) had a role in the competition effects: limited access to light, nutrients, space, or water.
   (ii) Suggest a modification to your experimental design that could be used to test your answer in part (i) above.

Synthesis

(f) Most plants have obvious adaptations for seed dispersal. Explain how each of the following features enhances seed dispersal.
   (i) the seed head of a dandelion
   (ii) the colourful and tasty fruits of apples and strawberries
   (iii) the hooks on a burr
   (iv) the wing of a pine seed

INVESTIGATION 23.1 *continued*

(g) Do the adaptations in question (f) reduce intraspecific or interspecific competition? Explain.

(h) Most agricultural operations attempt to minimize the influence of competition. Plants that compete with crops are called "weeds" and are often destroyed using herbicide applications or by mechanical removal and cultivation. Conduct research to answer the following:

(i) What is the most widely used herbicide in Alberta? Approximately how many tonnes are applied each year?

(ii) List four important weed species in Alberta crops.

(iii) List the most important advantages and disadvantages of using herbicides to reduce competition with weeds.

www.science.nelson.com 

(i) The forestry industry also manages intraspecific and interspecific competition by using a variety of silviculture practices. Conduct research to determine how forestry companies reduce competition from non-commercial plant species and how they manage the competition between individuals of valuable species.

www.science.nelson.com GO

(j) Allelopathy, the equivalent of underground chemical warfare, is a strategy employed by many plant species to reduce competition. Research allelopathy and report your findings back to the class.

www.science.nelson.com GO

INVESTIGATION 23.2

Microbial Succession

Ecological successional changes occur in every inhabited environment on Earth: the surface of a rotting log, the lichens that colonize barren rock, and the development of large coral reefs. Among the least obvious are those that occur in environments inhabited almost exclusively by microbes.

Bacteria and protists fill a variety of ecological niches, including photosynthetic producers, gut symbionts, pathogens, and decomposers. In this investigation you will use a hay infusion to study succession in a microbial community.

Report Checklist

● Purpose	● Design	● Analysis
● Problem	● Materials	● Evaluation
● Hypothesis	● Procedure	● Synthesis
● Prediction	● Evidence	

Design

In this part of the Investigation, you will design an investigation to observe changes in the microbial populations of a hay infusion. Read the procedure for preparing the hay infusion. Then, generate a hypothesis concerning the relationship between factors such as rates of population growth, types of microorganisms, changes in microbe diversity over time, etc. Your design must enable you to judge the validity of your initial hypothesis.

- How can you test your hypothesis regarding population growth of microbes in the hay infusion?

Write a procedure that will allow you to test your hypothesis. Your procedure must include steps in which you monitor and record the changes that take place in the microbial community over a period of two to three weeks.

- How will you obtain samples of the infusion? Should you sample from different depths in the beaker?
- What equipment and references will you need in order to observe and identify different micro-organisms?
- What safety measures must be observed?
- Will you attempt to quantify the populations of each species, and if so, how?
- How will you record the evidence?

Write a prediction for your experiment.

Materials

2 beakers (250 mL)
water
scissors
hay
hotplate
stirring rod
sieve
distilled water
watch glass or Petri dish lid (to cover one beaker)

Procedure

1. Loosely fill a 250 mL beaker with coarsely chopped hay. Fill the beaker to the 200 mL mark with water.
2. Bring the hay and water to a boil, stirring occasionally, and allow to simmer for 10 minutes.
3. Let the mixture cool overnight.
4. Using the sieve and the second beaker, separate the yellowish infusion from the cooked hay. Discard the hay. Top up the infusion to 200 mL using distilled water.
5. Cut some fresh dry hay into tiny pieces, less than 5 mm in length. Add about 10 mL of this cut hay to your infusion.
6. Cover the beaker with a watch glass or the lid from a Petri dish.
7. Add distilled water as needed to replace water lost due to evaporation.

Analysis

(a) Which types of microbes, bacteria or protists, grew first in the infusion? Suggest an explanation for this observation.

(b) What was the source of the organisms in the infusion? From where did these species originate?

(c) How might a microbe's ability to form resistant spores or cysts enhance its biological success?

(d) How might the order of appearance of the microbes be related to their place in a food chain?

(e) Was there any evidence of photosynthesizing organisms?

(f) Even if no producers are present, an infusion will support a large community of micro-organisms. What is the primary energy source supporting the food chain in such a system?

Evaluation

(g) Modify your procedure so that you could observe microbial succession in an environment that
  (i) had a higher concentration of oxygen gas,
  (ii) had a higher (or lower) pH, and
  (iii) modelled the internal gut environment of a mammal.

Chapter 23 SUMMARY

Outcomes

Knowledge

- describe the basis of species interactions and symbiotic relationships and their influences on population changes (23.1)
- explain the role of defence mechanisms in predation and competition as caused by genetic variation (23.1)
- explain how mixtures of populations that define communities may change over time or remain as a climax community, i.e., primary succession, secondary succession (23.2)

STS

- explain why Canadian society supports scientific research and technological development that helps achieve a sustainable society, economy and environment (23.1)

Skills

- ask questions about observed relationships, and plan investigations (all)
- conduct investigations and gather and record data and information by designing and performing: an experiment or simulation to demonstrate interspecific and intraspecific competition (23.1); an experiment to demonstate succession in a microenvironment and recording its pattern of succession over time (23.2); and by performing simulations to investigate relationships between predators and their prey (23.1)
- analyze data and apply mathematical and conceptual models by summarizing and evaluating a symbiotic relationship (23.1)
- work as members of a team and apply the skills and conventions of science (all)

Key Terms

23.1

symbiosis
interspecific competition
interference competition
exploitative competition
resource partitioning
mutualism
commensalism
parasitism
social parasite

23.2

succession
climax community
primary succession
secondary succession
pioneer community

MAKE a summary

1. Relationships between populations in a community can harm, benefit, or have little or no effect on each population. For each pair, summarize how each species influences the actions of the other. Consider the impact on the entire population as well as on individual members.
   (a) lynx and snowshoe hare
   (b) pioneer plant species and later-stage plant species
   (c) internal parasites and their host species
   (d) Arctic fox and caribou
   (e) honey bees and flowering plants
   (f) monarch and viceroy butterflies
   (g) *Parmecium aurelia* and *Paramecium caudatum*
   (h) an invasive species and a native species sharing similar ecological niches
2. Revisit your answers to the Starting Points questions at the start of the chapter. Would you answer the questions differently now? Why?

Go To

The following components are available on the Nelson Web site. Follow the links for *Nelson Biology Alberta 20–30*.

- an interactive Self Quiz for Chapter 23
- additional Diploma Exam-style Review Questions
- Illustrated glossary
- additional IB-related material

There is more information on the Web site wherever you see the Go icon in the chapter.

EXTENSION

Issues and Impacts—Fire Ants in the Pants

Fire ants are an imported species that are out-competing native ant species in the southern United States. What strategies are being used to re-establish a more natural balance?

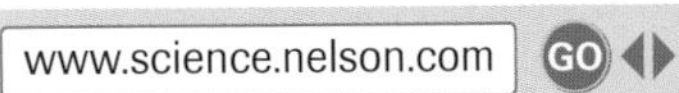

UNIT 30 D PERFORMANCE TASK

Changes in Human Population Size

The human population can be analyzed in the same way as the population of any other organism, using the tools and knowledge you acquired in this unit. In this Performance Task, you will work in a group to decide if you support or refute this statement: "The human population is growing at an alarming rate and is rapidly approaching Earth's carrying capacity."

www.science.nelson.com

Chapter 23 REVIEW

Many of these questions are in the style of the Diploma Exam. You will find guidance for writing Diploma Exams in Appendix A5. Science Directing Words used in Diploma Exams are in bold type. Exam study tips and test-taking suggestions are on the Nelson Web site.

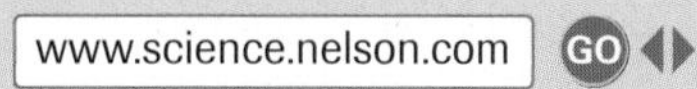

DO NOT WRITE IN THIS TEXTBOOK.

Part 1

1. Which of the following best describes a commensal relationship?
   A. One species benefits and the other is usually killed.
   B. One species feeds on a host species but the host is usually not seriously harmed.
   C. One species benefits and the other is usually unaffected.
   D. Both species benefit.

2. According to the concept of competitive exclusion
   A. no two species can successfully occupy the same habitat at the same time
   B. two members of the same species cannot share the same territory
   C. no two species can successfully occupy the same ecological niche in the same region
   D. using the same resources often leads to the establishment of a mutualistic relationship

3. Which of the following best describes predator–prey relationships?
   A. Predators out-number prey and their population growth lags behind that of their prey.
   B. Prey out-number predators and their population growth lags behind that of the predators.
   C. Predators out-number prey and their population growth precedes that of their prey.
   D. Prey out-number predators and their population growth precedes that of the predators.

4. NR Place the following successional events in the proper sequence. (Record all four digits of your answer.)
   1. Shade-tolerant species begin to become established.
   2. Taller, shade-intolerant species become dominant.
   3. Species that are resistant to high temperatures and dry conditions are abundant.
   4. A community of plants exhibits little change over long periods of time.

Part 2

5. For each of the photographs in **Figure 1**, **identify** the defence mechanism used by each species.

Figure 1
(a) white-tailed deer fawn
(b) venomous Eastern coral snake (top) and harmless Sinoloan milk snake (bottom)
(c) African killer bees
(d) rose

6. In one type of mimicry, several unrelated animal species, all of whom are poisonous or dangerous, resemble one another. For example, monarch and viceroy butterflies have evolved similar coloration (**Figure 2**). **Predict** how this similarity might affect bird species that prey on insects.

Figure 2
(a) a monarch butterfly
(b) a viceroy butterfly

7. **Explain** why it would be a mistake to eliminate a major predator from a community.

8. **Compare** predators and parasites.

9. In an Arctic ecosystem, a fox population begins to prey on small herbivores, such as mice and hares. Caribou are large herbivores that compete for many of the same plants as smaller herbivores. In a unified response, address the following aspects of the changes in this ecosystem:
DE
- **Predict** how the foxes' predation of herbivores will affect the population of plants.
- **Explain** the role of carrying capacity on the size of the population of plants.
- **Predict** how the caribou population will change.

Use the following information to answer questions 10 to 12.

Human activity over the past century extirpated wolves from northern Montana. Coyotes were occupying the habitat as the largest member of the canid family. As a growing wolf population from Alberta invaded the coyotes' territory, Canadian researchers documented the changes in coyote behaviour (**Table 1**).

Table 1 Coyote Behaviour

Before recolonization by wolves
• Coyotes usually were found alone or in pairs. • Coyotes fed on rabbits, hares, and some plants. • Coyotes were most active during the early morning and late evening. • The coyote population was relatively large.
After recolonization by wolves
• Coyotes tended to be found in pairs or small packs. • Coyotes relied on larger prey and scavenged wolf kills. • Coyotes avoided times when wolves were active during the winter months. • Coyotes maintained historic activity patterns during the summer months. • Coyote population decreased significantly but remained stable.

10. **Describe** the evidence that suggests that the niches of wolves and coyotes overlap.

11. Wolves are known as predators of coyotes. **Identify** the behavioural changes by the coyotes that are likely to reduce the number taken by wolves.

12 Wolves have a dramatically smaller home range in summer when they stay closer to their dens. Does the coyote behaviour seem to account for this change? **Explain**.

Use the following information to answer questions 13 and 14.

The cowbird, a social parasite, lays its eggs in the nests of other birds. The relationship between cowbirds and large grazing mammals is also an example of commensalism. The cowbirds follow migrating herds of mammals, feeding on insects disturbed by the movement of the mammals as they graze. Historically, adult cowbirds were associated with herds of plains bison.

13. **Predict** how the behaviour of cowbirds might have evolved differently if the herds of bison remained in the same small area for weeks at a time during the cowbirds' breeding season.

14. Cowbirds are an open-field species and rarely parasitize nests that are located deep in wooded areas. **Predict** how large-scale clear-cutting of forests might influence the success of this species.

15. Research the sea lamprey, a non-indigenous species, which has had a great impact on the fish communities of the Great Lakes, and then answer the following questions based on your finding:
(a) **Describe** the fundamental and realized niche of the sea lamprey.
(b) **Describe** how sea lampreys may have entered the Great Lake ecosystem.
(c) **Identify** the interspecific interactions of the sea lamprey and its effects on the Great Lakes.
(d) **Describe** some economic setbacks faced by Canadian fisheries as a result of sea lamprey invasion and outline any control efforts.

www.science.nelson.com 

16. In 1883, a massive volcanic eruption obliterated half of the island of Krakatau and covered the remainder in ash and pumice, 30 m thick. All previous life was wiped out. Conduct research to learn about the re-colonization of this island by plants and animals.
(a) **Identify** the length of time it took for plants and animals to become re-established on the island.
(b) **Explain** whether the process of succession was rapid or slow.
(c) Do you think the presence of a thick ash layer enhances or inhibits the rate of primary succession? **Explain**.

www.science.nelson.com 

Many of these questions are in the style of the Diploma Exam. You will find guidance for writing Diploma Exams in Appendix A5. Science Directing Words used in Diploma Exams are in bold type. Exam study tips and test-taking suggestions are on the Nelson Web site.

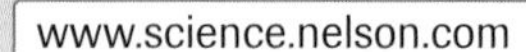
www.science.nelson.com

DO NOT WRITE IN THIS TEXTBOOK.

Part 1

1. The bottleneck effect
   A. increases genetic variability thus leading to evolutionary change
   B. results in lower genetic variation within the population resulting in lower viability
   C. refers to the movement of a small number of individuals into a new environment
   D. is an example of evolutionary change due to natural selection

2. Which of the following choices gives three types of symbiotic relationships?
   A. predator–prey, parasitism, commensalism
   B. mutualism, parasitism, commensalism
   C. predator-prey, mutualism, commensalism
   D. parasitism, mutualism, predator–prey

3. It was observed that as the number of night-time flying insects increases in a region, the population of insect-eating bats also increases. This is an example of
   A. density-dependent, intraspecific competition
   B. density-independent, intraspecific competition
   C. density-dependent, predator–prey relationship
   D. density-independent, predator–prey relationship

4. Which of the following is *not* a defence mechanism?
   A. camouflage
   B. leaf toxins
   C. interference competition
   D. mimicry

5. What is the change in population size if natality = 22, immigration = 6, emigration = 7, and mortality = 14?
   A. 7
   B. 9
   C. -5
   D. 23

6. It was estimated that an original population of 74 bull trout in a section of stream increased in number to 110 over three years. The annual population growth rate and per capita growth rate were
   A. 36 and 3
   B. 12 and 3
   C. 36 and 0.49
   D. 12 and 0.49
   (Note that units are intentionally omitted.)

7. NR In each of the following, a change in the ecosystems affects the size of a population in the ecosystem:
   1. Fertilizer run-off causes an increase in the algae population in a freshwater lake.
   2. The introduction of a predator causes a decline in a population size of snow geese.
   3. A fatal infectious disease spreads through a poultry farm and causes a decline in the number of chickens.
   4. Habitat loss due to urban expansion causes a decline in the population size of grizzlies.

   Identify the statements which describe change due to a density-independent factor. (Record all three digits of your answer.)

8. NR Place the following plants in proper sequence from earliest to latest in primary succession. (Record all four digits of your answer.)
   1. lichens
   2. shrubs
   3. trees
   4. grasses

9. NR Match the description with the term. (Record all four digits of your answer in the order of the descriptions.)
   ___ A small population is isolated on an island.
   ___ Bacteria are observed to become increasingly resistant to antibiotics.
   ___ Individuals from one population join another.
   ___ A new trait appears in the population.

   1. mutation
   2. sexual selection
   3. founder effect
   4. migration

10. Which of the following is *not* true regarding succession?
   A. Primary succession usually begins on bare rock or volcanic ash.
   B. Secondary succession is the second stage that follows primary succession species.
   C. Many climax species are shade-tolerant.
   D. Fires are a primary cause of secondary succession.

11. Which of the following are all characteristics of primary successional species?
   A. moisture-loving, sun-loving, long-lived
   B. moisture-loving, shade-loving, long-lived
   C. drought-resistant, shade-loving, long- lived
   D. drought-resistant, sun-loving, short-lived

12. NR A forest fire removes all vegetation from an area. Place the following species in the order in which you would expect them to appear during succession. (Record all four digits of your answer.)
   1. slow-growing pine trees
   2. grasses
   3. fast-growing spruce trees
   4. shrubs

Part 2

13. **Define** *evolution* in terms of gene frequencies.

14. **Outline** in a list the conditions that must be met to maintain Hardy–Weinberg equilibrium.

15. DE Genetic changes resulting from mutation can be harmful, beneficial, or neutral. Write a unified response that addresses the following aspects of the relationship between mutations and changes in the gene pool of a population.
    - **Explain** how harmful mutations have little or no influence on the gene pool of a population.
    - **Describe** how beneficial mutations, though more rare, can cause dramatic long-term changes on the gene pool.

Use this information to answer questions 16 and 17.

A recessive allele (*l*) codes for lactose intolerance in humans. As they get older, people who are lactose intolerant lose the ability to digest the lactose sugar in milk. Homozygous dominant (*LL*) and heterozygous individuals (*Ll*) do not have this problem. In Australians of European descent, the incidence of lactose intolerance is only 4 % while 85 % of Australian Aborigines are lactose intolerant.

16. **Determine** the *L* and *l* allele frequencies for these two groups of people.

17. Europeans have a long history of drinking milk from domesticated animals while Aboriginal peoples do not. **How** might this explain such a marked difference in these frequencies? **Relate** your answer to the assumptions required to maintain Hardy–Weinberg equilibrium.

18. Students sampled aquatic insect larvae living on a small section of river bottom measuring 2.0 m by 0.8 m. They found approximately 45 000 black fly larvae in the sample.
    (a) **Determine** the population density of this species.
    (b) **Determine** an estimate of the number of black fly larvae living in a similar habitat of river bottom measuring 50 m by 10 m.

19. According to the 2001 census, the population of Canada had reached 30 007 094 people.
    (a) **Determine** the population density of Canadians, if Canada's land area is 9 976 000 km^2.
    (b) Using our population as an example, **explain** why the ecological density of a species is usually greater than its crude density.

20. **Outline** in a list five environmental resources for which there might be intraspecific competition. **Illustrate** each with an example.

21. DE Natality, mortality, immigration, and emigration are all terms that may apply to any population. Write a unified response addressing the following aspects of these processes:
    - **Describe** briefly what each term means.
    - **Explain** briefly how each process affects a population.
    - **Identify** which of the terms do *not* relate to a closed population. **Explain** why not.
    - **Outline** in a list several examples of closed populations that occur naturally. **Outline** in a second list examples of closed populations produced by human intervention or other activities.

22. DE **Describe** the changes in population size that give rise to the zig-zag pattern visible in **Figure 1**. Explain why this population growth pattern is so common.

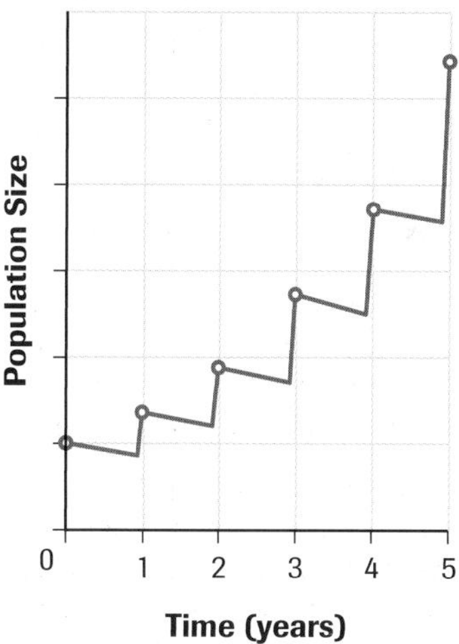

Figure 1

23. **Explain** why small populations often experience relatively slow growth for several generations. **Identify** the name given to this region of slow growth on a sigmoidal curve.

24. **Identify** the conditions that are necessary for a population to experience prolonged exponential growth.

25. **Explain** what happens once a population reaches a dynamic equilibrium.

26. Study the graphs of two different populations in **Figure 2**, on the next page. One graph shows a population of bacteria growing in a laboratory, and the other graph shows a population of owls living in a forest. **Identify** which graph represents which population. **Explain** your reasoning.

(a)

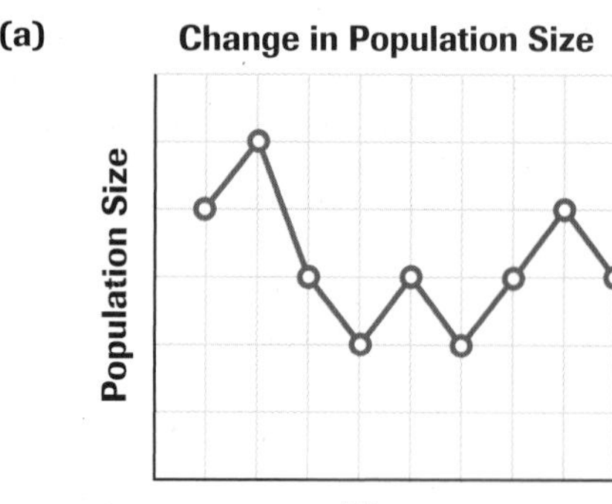

(b)

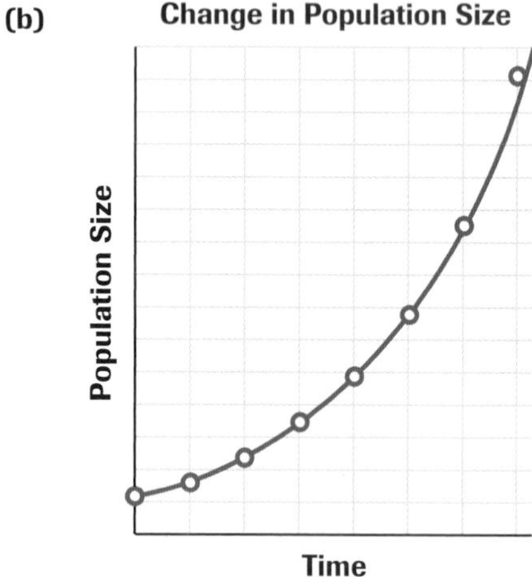

Figure 2

27. **Explain** and **illustrate** with an example the differences between intraspecific and interspecific interactions.

28. **Describe** the obvious defence mechanism utilized by the sea urchin, *Stronglyocentrotus franciacanus*, shown in **Figure 3**. **Infer** the possible adaptive benefit(s) of its bright coloration.

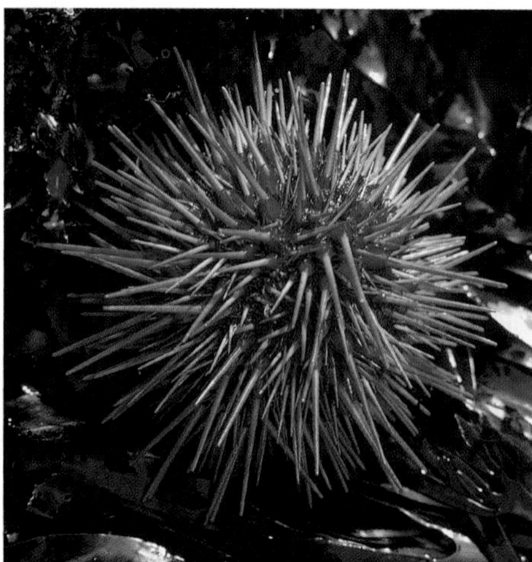

Figure 3
Sea urchin

29. **Describe** and **illustrate** with two examples, each of the following:
    (a) commensalism
    (b) mutualism
    (c) parasitism

30. In a laboratory, researchers placed a *Paramecium* species in a test tube with its predator protozoan. After time, predator–prey cycles became shortened and the system collapsed. The researchers now plan to repeat the experiment with new *Paramecium* being added to the test tube every few days. Write a unified response that addresses the following aspects of the interactions between these two species.
    - **Sketch** a graph that shows the changes in the predator and prey populations in the first experiment. Explain the shape of the curves on your graph.
    - **Why** did the system collapse in the first experiment?
    - **Predict** what the predator-prey cycle will be like in the second experiment. Provide reasoning for your answer. **Justify** your response.

Use the following information to answer questions 31 to 33.

Meadow voles, sometimes referred to as field mice, are extremely common small rodents that breed actively throughout the year with females becoming fertile at under two months of age. The data in **Table 1** represent the growth over time of a population of these voles living in a small grassland.

Table 1 Monthly Growth for a Population of Meadow Voles (Field Mice)

Month	Meadow vole population
December	3 920
January	5 488
February	7 683
March	10 756
April	15 058
May	21 081
June	29 513
July	41 318
August	57 845
September	80 983
October	113 376

31. Represent the data **graphically**.

32. DE Based on your graph, **infer** whether the meadow vole population is exhibiting logistic or exponential growth. **Explain**.

33. DE Using your graph, **determine** an estimate of the size of the vole population after three more months.

34. **Table 2** compares Canadian population statistics for the periods 1861–1871 and 1991–1996. In 2004, the number of immigrants was about 236 000 while the number of emigrants was approximately 61 000. Write a unified response that addresses the following aspects of these data.
DE
- **Determine** Canada's annual per capita birth and death rates between 1861 and 1871.
- **How** did these values change over the next 120 years? **Hypothesize** reasons for these changes.
- **Determine** the annual per capita growth rate for these two time intervals.
- **Conclude** whether the 2004 values follow the trend(s) in the previous values.

Table 2 Canadian Population Statistics

	1861–1871	1991–1996
starting population	3 229 000	27 852 000
births	1 370 000	1 936 000
deaths	760 000	1 024 000
immigrants	260 000	1 137 000
emigrants	410 000	229 000

35. Over the past few hundred years, humans have developed technologies that enable us to drastically alter Earth's environment and influence its carrying capacity for our species. Recently, humans have even placed rovers on the surface of Mars. The rovers have gathered extensive data on the physical characteristics of the "red planet." Data from these and other sources are compared with similar data from Earth in **Table 3**. Write a unified response that addresses the following aspects of the environments of Earth and Mars.
DE
- **Compare** the abiotic features of the two planets that influence their carrying capacity for human life.
- **Identify** the factors that will have to be altered in order to increase the carrying capacity of the planet, if humans are ever to inhabit Mars.
- **Outline** in a list the aspects of our own planet's abiotic and biotic features that we have altered to increase the short-term carrying capacity for the human population.
- **Describe** the impacts that humans are having on Earth that may be decreasing the long-term carrying capacity of Earth.
- Do you think that Mars could support as many humans as Earth in the future? **Justify** your answer.

Table 3 Abiotic and Biotic Factors on Earth and Mars

	Earth	Mars
atmosphere	thick, 78 % nitrogen gas, 21 % oxygen gas	less than 1 % as dense as that of Earth > 95 % carbon dioxide gas, 0.15 % oxygen gas
weather	highly variable, precipitation in the form of rain and snow	no precipitation, dust storms common
cosmic radiation	mostly shielded by magnetic field	bombardment strong due to weak magnetic field
temperature	highly variable, ranges from extremes of −50 °C to +50 °C	generally very cold with an average of −55 °C.
water	covers over 50 % of Earth's surface; extensive ice caps and cloud cover	present but frozen below the surface, none in liquid form.
life	estimates of 10–30 million species including humans	no known life; microbes remain a possibility
hours/day, days/year	24 h, 365 d	24.5 h, 670 d

Use the following information to answer questions 36 to 39.

Researchers recorded the number of individuals in two populations over 8 years. Their data are shown in **Table 4**.

Table 4 Changes in Size of Population A and B

Time (years)	0	1	2	3	4	5	6	7	8
Size of population A	40	60	85	120	170	235	340	330	70
Size of population B	20	25	30	50	115	160	145	155	150

36. **Sketch** a graph of the two sets of population data in **Table 4**. on Include the data for both populations on the same set of axes.
DE

37. **Identify** which population shows a J-shaped growth curve, and whether its growth pattern is logistic or exponential.
DE

38. Between years 5 and 8, both populations show quite different growth patterns. **Explain** the role of the environment in causing these changes.
DE

39. **Identify** the species that has a growth curve similar to that of a *K*-selected species. Add a labelled horizontal line to indicate **graphically** the approximate carrying capacity of environment for that species.
DE

40. Review the focusing questions on page 710. Using the knowledge you have gained from this unit, briefly **outline** a response to each of these questions.

Appendices

A1 Scientific Inquiry

Planning an Investigation

In our attempts to further our understanding of the natural world, we encounter questions, mysteries, or events that are not readily explainable. To develop explanations, we investigate using scientific inquiry. The methods used in scientific inquiry depend, to a large degree, on the purpose of the inquiry.

Controlled Experiments

A controlled experiment is an example of scientific inquiry in which a **manipulated variable** is purposefully changed to determine its effect on a second **responding variable**. All other variables are controlled or kept constant. Controlled experiments are performed when the purpose of the inquiry is to create, test, or use a scientific concept.

The common components of controlled experiments are outlined below. *Note that there are normally many cycles through the steps during an actual experiment.*

Stating the Purpose

Every investigation in science has a purpose; for example,

- to develop a scientific concept (a theory, law, generalization, or definition);
- to test a scientific concept;
- to perform a chemical analysis;
- to determine a scientific constant.

Defining the Problem

The problem is the purpose of your experiment, rewritten in the form of a question. The problem forms the basis for your investigation: the investigation is designed to answer the question. Controlled experiments are about relationships, so the problem could be about the effects on variable A when variable B is changed.

Hypothesizing/Predicting

A **hypothesis** is a tentative explanation of the relationships being investigated by the experiment. Hypotheses propose an explanation for specific observations. For example, it is generally observed that plants die when kept in darkness. A hypothesis to explain this observation could be "Plants require solar energy to carry out photosynthesis." Hypotheses refer to general principles or observations, and are often based on current scientific knowledge, such as a theory or a law. Most importantly, to be useful in scientific inquiry, a hypothesis must be testable. In the example given here, the hypothesis could be tested by looking for a relationship between solar energy and the products of photosynthesis

The prediction states what you expect to observe in your particular experiment. It is more specific than the hypothesis: a prediction is a tentative answer to the problem you are investigating. Although it refers to your experiment, the prediction is always based upon the hypothesis. For example, a prediction might be "When plants are kept in darkness, they will not produce carbohydrates such as starch."

Designing the Investigation

The design of a controlled experiment identifies how you plan to change the manipulated variable, measure the responding variable, and control all the other variables in pursuit of an answer to the problem. It is a summary of your plan for the experiment.

Carrying Out the Procedure

When you carry out the procedure of an investigation, you are gathering evidence to support or refute your prediction and the hypothesis. Make sure you have read the procedure first (or, if you have designed it yourself, that you have received approval), and that you follow all safety procedures. As you work, you will need to gather and record data and observations (the evidence). Plan ahead and think about what data you will need and how best to record them. This helps to clarify your thinking and helps you to organize your evidence for easier analysis

Analyzing the Evidence

Analysis of the evidence involves looking for patterns and trends. This may involve creating graphs or making calculations. After analyzing the evidence, you may be able to answer the problem posed at the beginning of the investigation.

Evaluating the Evidence and the Hypothesis/Prediction

At this stage of the investigation, you evaluate the processes that you followed to plan and perform the investigation.

You will also evaluate the outcome of the investigation, which includes any prediction you made and the hypothesis or more established concept on which the prediction was based. You must identify and take into account any sources of error and uncertainty in your measurements.

Finally, compare the answer you predicted with the answer generated by analyzing the evidence. Does the evidence you gathered support or refute the hypothesis?

Reporting on the Investigation

In your report, describe your planning process and procedure clearly and in sufficient detail that the reader could repeat the experiment exactly as you performed it. You also must clearly communicate the evidence, analysis, and evaluation of your experiment accurately and honestly.

Observational Studies

Often the purpose of inquiry is simply to study a natural phenomenon, with the intention of gaining scientifically significant information. Observational studies involve observing a subject or phenomenon in an unobtrusive or unstructured manner, often with no specific hypothesis or prediction. A hypothesis to describe or explain the observations may, however, be generated after repeated observations, and modified as new information is collected over time.

The stages and processes of scientific inquiry through observational studies are summarized below. *Note that there are normally many cycles through the steps during the actual study.*

Stating the Purpose

Choose a topic that interests you. For example, a purpose of an observational study might be "To observe the organs of a fetal pig." Determine whether you are going to replicate or revise a previous study, or create a new one.

Stating the Problem

In an observational study, the problem is usually very general. For the purpose given above, the problem might be "What are the organ systems in a fetal pig and how are they organized?" Stating a problem can help you to focus the scope of your observations. You may or may not follow the problem with the creation of a hypothesis and/or a prediction.

Hypothesizing/Predicting

Observational studies usually do not involve a hypothesis or a prediction. A hypothesis can be formed after observations have been made and information gathered on a topic. A hypothesis may be created in the analysis.

Designing the Investigation

The design of an observational study describes how you will make observations relevant to the problem.

Gathering, Recording, and Organizing Observations

There are many ways to gather and record observations during an investigation. During your observational study, you should quantify your observations where possible. All observations should be objective and unambiguous. Consider ways to organize your information for easier analysis.

Analyzing the Observations

After thoroughly analyzing your observations, you may have sufficient and appropriate evidence to enable you to answer the problem posed at the beginning of the investigation. You may also have enough observations and information to form a hypothesis.

Evaluating the Evidence and the Hypothesis

At this stage of the investigation, you will evaluate the processes used to plan and perform the investigation. Evaluating the processes includes evaluating the materials, the design, the procedure, and your skills. The results of most such investigations will suggest further studies, perhaps correlational studies or controlled experiments to explore tentative hypotheses you may have developed.

Reporting on the Investigation

In your report, describe your design and procedure accurately, and report your observations accurately and honestly.

A2 Decision Making

Modern life is filled with environmental and social issues that have scientific and technological dimensions. An issue is defined as a problem that has at least two possible solutions rather than a single answer. There can be many positions on a single issue, generally determined by the values that an individual or a society holds. Which solution is "best" is a matter of opinion. Ideally, the solution that is implemented is the one that is most appropriate for society as a whole.

The common processes involved in the decision-making process are outlined below. *Note that you may go through several cycles before deciding you are ready to defend a decision.*

Defining the Issue

The first step in understanding an issue is to explain why it is an issue, describe the problems associated with the issue, and identify the individuals or groups, called stakeholders, involved in the issue. You could brainstorm the following questions to research the issue: Who? What? Where? When? Why? How? Develop background information on the issue by clarifying facts and concepts, and identifying relevant attributes, features, or characteristics of the problem.

Identifying Alternatives/Positions

Examine the issue and think of as many alternative solutions as you can. At this point it does not matter if the solutions seem unrealistic. To analyze the alternatives, you should examine the issue from a variety of perspectives. Stakeholders may bring different viewpoints to an issue and these may influence their position on the issue. Brainstorm or hypothesize how different stakeholders would feel about your alternatives. Perspectives that stakeholders may adopt while approaching an issue are listed in **Table 1**.

Researching the Issue

Formulate a research question that helps to limit, narrow, or define the issue. Then, develop a plan to identify and find reliable and relevant sources of information. Outline the stages of your information search: gathering, sorting, evaluating, selecting, and integrating relevant information. You may consider using a flow chart, concept map, or other graphic organizer to outline the stages of your information search. Gather information from many sources, including newspapers, magazines, scientific journals, the Internet, and the library.

Analyzing the Issue

In this stage, you will analyze the issue in an attempt to clarify where you stand. First, you should establish criteria for evaluating your information to determine its relevance and significance. You can then evaluate your sources, determine what assumptions may have been made, and assess whether you have enough information to make your decision.

There are five steps that must be completed to effectively analyze the issue:

1. Establish criteria for determining the relevance and significance of the data you have gathered.
2. Evaluate the sources of information.
3. Identify and determine what assumptions have been made. Challenge unsupported evidence.
4. Determine any causal, sequential, or structural relationships associated with the issue.
5. Evaluate the alternative solutions, possibly by conducting a risk-benefit analysis.

Table 1 Some Possible Perspectives on an Issue

cultural	focused on customs and practices of a particular group
environmental	focused on effects on natural processes and other living things
economic	focused on the production, distribution, and consumption of wealth
educational	focused on the effects on learning
emotional	focused on feelings and emotions
aesthetic	focused on what is artistic, tasteful, beautiful
moral/ethical	focused on what is good/bad, right/wrong
legal	focused on rights and responsibilities
spiritual	focused on the effects on personal beliefs
political	focused on the aims of an identifiable group or party
scientific	focused on logic or the results of relevant inquiry
social	focused on effects on human relationships, the community
technological	focused on the use of machines and processes

Defending the Decision

After analyzing your information, you can answer your research question and take an informed position on the issue. You should be able to defend your preferred solution in an appropriate format—debate, class discussion, speech, position paper, multimedia presentation, video, brochure, poster, or other creative formats.

Your position on the issue must be justified using the supporting information that you have discovered in your research and tested in your analysis. You should be able to defend your position to people with different perspectives. In preparing for your defence, ask yourself the following questions:

- Do I have supporting evidence from a variety of sources?
- Can I state my position clearly?
- Do I have solid arguments (with solid evidence) supporting my position?
- Have I considered arguments against my position, and identified their faults?
- Have I analyzed the strong and weak points of each perspective?

Evaluating the Process

The final phase of decision making includes evaluating the decision the group reached, the process used to reach the decision, and the part you played in decision making. After a decision has been reached, carefully examine the thinking that led to the decision. Some questions to guide your evaluation follow:

- What was my initial perspective on the issue? How has my perspective changed since I first began to explore the issue?
- How did we make our decision? What process did we use? What steps did we follow?
- In what ways does our decision resolve the issue?
- What are the likely short- and long-term effects of our decision?
- To what extent am I satisfied with our decision?
- What reasons would I give to explain our decision?
- If we had to make this decision again, what would I do differently?

Using a Risk–Benefit Analysis Model

Risk–benefit analysis is a tool used to organize and analyze information gathered in research. A thorough analysis of the risks and benefits associated with each alternative solution can help you decide on the best alternative.

- Research as many aspects of the proposal as possible. Look at it from different perspectives.
- Collect as much evidence as you can, including reasonable projections of likely outcomes if the proposal is adopted.
- Classify every individual potential result as being either a benefit or a risk.
- Quantify the size of the potential benefit or risk (perhaps as a dollar figure, or a number of lives affected, or in severity on a scale of 1 to 5).
- Estimate the probability (percentage) of that event occurring.
- By multiplying the size of a benefit (or risk) by the probability of its happening, you can assign a significance value for each potential result.
- Total the significance values of all the potential risks and all the potential benefits, and compare the sums to help you decide whether to accept the proposed action.

Note that although you should try to be objective in your assessment, your beliefs will have an effect on the outcome—two people, even if using the same information and the same tools, could come to a different conclusion about the balance of risk and benefit for any proposed solution to an issue.

A3 Lab Reports

When carrying out investigations, it is important that scientists keep records of their plans and results, and share their findings. In order to have their investigations repeated (replicated) and accepted by the scientific community, scientists generally share their work by publishing papers in which details of their design, materials, procedure, evidence, analysis, and evaluation are given.

Lab reports are prepared after an investigation is completed. To ensure that you can accurately describe the investigation, it is important to keep thorough and accurate records of your activities as you carry out the investigation.

Investigators use a similar format in their final reports or lab books, although the headings and order may vary. Your lab book or report should reflect the type of scientific inquiry that you used in the investigation and should be based on the following headings, as appropriate.

Title

At the beginning of your report, write the number and title of your investigation. In this course the title is usually given, but if you are designing your own investigation, create a title that suggests what the investigation is about. Include the date the investigation was conducted and the names of all lab partners (if you worked as a team).

Purpose

State the purpose of the investigation. Why are you doing this investigation?

Problem

This is the problem that you attempted to answer in the investigation. If it is appropriate to do so, state the problem in terms of manipulated and responding variables.

Hypothesis/Prediction

Based on your reasoning or on a concept that you have studied, make a prediction—a statement of what you expect to observe—before carrying out the investigation. You may also write a hypothesis, which is a tentative explanation of the relationships being investigated by the experiment. Hypotheses propose an explanation for specific observations. A hypothesis must always be testable. Whether or not you have a hypothesis or a prediction will depend on the nature of your investigation.

Design

This is a brief general overview (one to three sentences) of what was done. If your investigation involved manipulated, responding, and controlled variables, list them. Identify any control or control group that was used in the investigation.

Materials

This is a detailed list of all materials used, including sizes and quantities where appropriate. Be sure to include safety equipment such as eye protection, lab apron, latex gloves, and tongs, where needed. Draw a diagram to show any complicated setup of apparatus.

Procedure

In detailed, numbered steps, describe the procedure you followed to carry out your investigation. Include steps to clean up and dispose of waste.

Evidence

This includes all qualitative and quantitative observations you made. Be as precise as possible when describing quantitative observations. Include any unexpected observations and present your information in a form that is easily understood. If you have only a few observations, this could be a list; for controlled experiments and for many observations, a table will be more appropriate.

Analysis

Interpret your observations and present the evidence in the form of tables, graphs, or illustrations, each with a title. Include any calculations, the results of which can be shown in a table. Make statements about any patterns or trends you observed. Conclude the analysis with a statement based only on the evidence you have gathered, answering the problem that initiated the investigation.

Evaluation

The evaluation is your judgment about the quality of evidence obtained and about the validity of the prediction and hypothesis (if present). This section can be divided into two parts:

- Did your observations provide reliable and valid evidence to enable you to address the problem? Are you confident enough in the evidence to use it to evaluate any prediction and/or hypothesis you made?
- Was the prediction you made before the investigation supported or falsified by the evidence? Based on your evaluation of the evidence and prediction, is the hypothesis you used to make your prediction supported, or should it be rejected?

The leading questions that follow should help you through the process of evaluation.

Evaluation of the Experiment

1. Were you able to address the problem using the chosen experimental design? Are there any obvious flaws in the design? What alternative designs (better or worse) are available? To your knowledge, is this design the best available in terms of controls, efficiency, and cost? How great is your confidence in the chosen design?

   You may sum up your conclusions about the design in a statement like: "The experimental design [name or describe in a few words] is judged to be adequate/inadequate because..."
2. Were the steps that you used in the laboratory correctly sequenced, and adequate to gather sufficient evidence? What improvements could be made to the procedure? What steps, if not done correctly, would have significantly affected the results?

   Sum up your conclusions about the procedure in a statement like: "The procedure is judged to be adequate/inadequate because..."
3. Which specialized skills, if any, might have the greatest effect on the experimental results? Was the evidence from repeated trials reasonably similar? Can the measurements be made more precise?

   Sum up your conclusions: "The technological skills are judged to be adequate/inadequate because..."
4. You should now be ready to sum up your evaluation of the experiment. Do you have enough confidence in your experimental results to proceed with your evaluation of the hypothesis being tested? Based on uncertainties and errors you have identified in the course of your evaluation, what would be an acceptable percent difference for this experiment (1 %, 5 %, or 10 %)?

   State your confidence level in a summary statement: "Based upon my evaluation of the experiment, I am not certain/I am moderately certain/I am very certain of my experimental results. The major sources of uncertainty or error are..."

Evaluation of the Prediction

1. Calculate the percent difference for your experiment. Recall that the notation $|x|$ means the absolute value of x.

$$\% \text{ difference} = \frac{|\text{experimental value}| - |\text{predicted value}|}{|\text{predicted value}|} \times 100\ \%$$

   How does the percent difference compare with your estimated total uncertainty (i.e. is the percent difference greater or smaller than the difference you've judged acceptable for this experiment)? Does the predicted answer clearly agree with the experimental answer in your analysis? Can the percent difference be accounted for by the sources of uncertainty listed earlier in the evaluation?

   Sum up your evaluation of the prediction: "The prediction is judged to be verified/inconclusive/falsified because..."
2. If the prediction was verified, the hypothesis behind it is supported by the experiment. If the results of the experiment were inconclusive or the prediction was falsified, then doubt is cast upon the hypothesis. How confident do you feel about any judgment you can make based on the experiment? Is there a need for a new or revised hypothesis, or to restrict, reverse, or replace the hypothesis being tested?

   Sum up your evaluation: "[The hypothesis] being tested is accepted/refuted because..."

Synthesis

When scientists publish their research, they often relate their observations to other research and to problems outside the laboratory. They may also describe additional research they plan to do, based on the results of their current experiments. In some Investigations in *Nelson Biology Alberta 20-30*, you will be guided in making these connections by a series of questions.

A4 Use of the Microscope

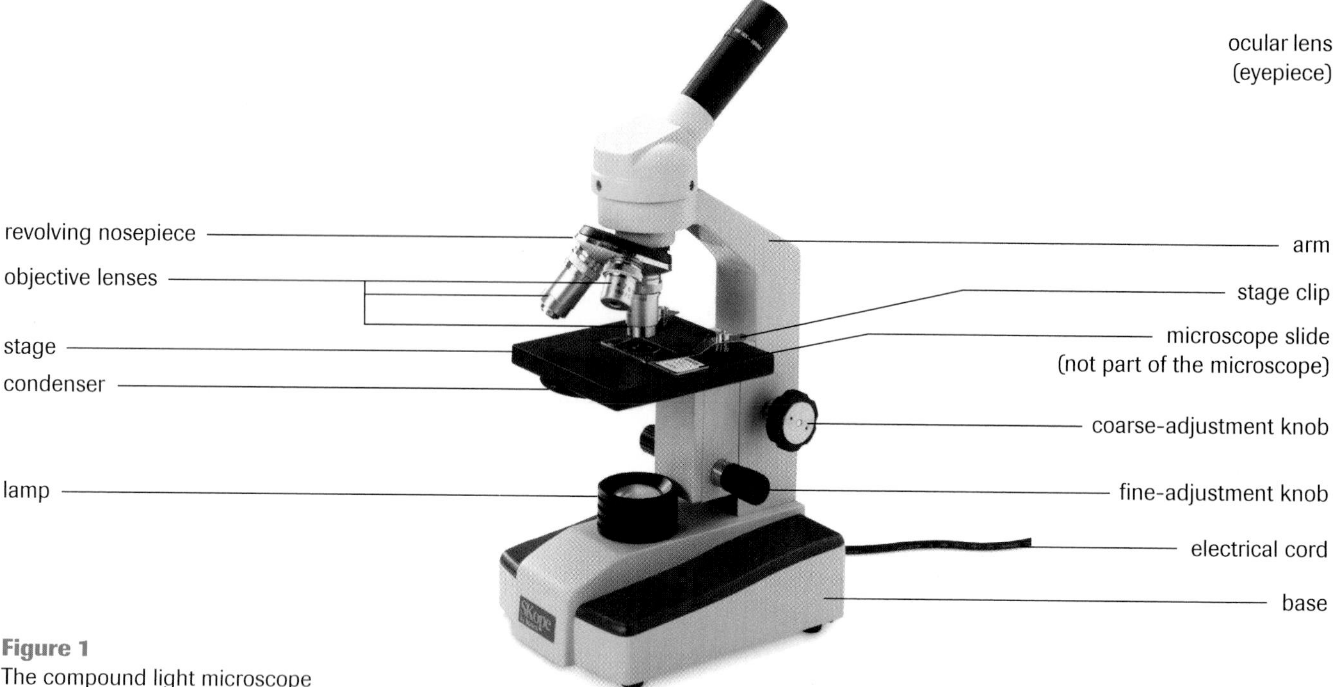

Figure 1
The compound light microscope

The microscope (**Figure 1**) is a useful tool in making observations and collecting data during scientific investigations in biology.

The eyepiece lens usually magnifies 10×. This information is printed on the side of the eyepiece.The microscopes that you will likely use have three objective lenses: low (magnifies 4×), medium (magnifies 10×), and high (magnifies 40×). To determine the total magnification, multiply the magnification of the eyepiece lens by the magnification of the objective lens. For example, the magnification obtained using the medium-power objective lens is 10× multiplied by 10×, or 100×.In other words, a specimen viewed under medium power will appear 100× larger than it actually is.

Use of the Compound Light Microscope

1. Obtain a microscope from the storage area. Grasp the arm with one hand and use the other to support the base of the microscope.
2. If the microscope has a built-in light supply, plug it in. Place the cord so that it will not be hooked accidentally.
3. Rotate the revolving nosepiece until the shortest (low-power) objective lens clicks into place.
4. Place a slide on the stage and centre it. Hold the slide in place with the stage clips.
5. Turn the coarse-adjustment knob away from you to lower the lens down as far as possible. Watch from the side to ensure that the lens does not contact the slide.
6. Keeping both eyes open, look through the eyepiece and turn the coarse-adjustment knob toward you until the specimen comes into view. Use the fine-adjustment knob to focus the image.
7. Adjust the condenser to control the amount of light and fix the contrast. If the microscope has a mirror in the base, adjust it to receive the appropriate amount of light.
8. With the image in focus and centred in the field of view, rotate the nosepiece until the next longer objective lens clicks into place.
9. Use the fine-adjustment knob to refocus the image, if necessary.
10. Readjust the condenser or the mirror to regulate the amount of light. The higher the lens power, the more light that is necessary.
11. Repeat the previous three steps with the high-power lens.

12. When you have finished viewing a specimen, always rotate the nosepiece so that the shortest (low-power) lens is centred before making any adjustments with the focusing knobs.
13. Remove and clean the slide and cover slip and return them to their appropriate location.
14. Return the microscope to the storage area.

Determining Field of View

It is often necessary to measure the size of objects viewed through the microscope. The field of view is the circle of light seen while looking through the eyepiece. Once the size of the field of view is determined, it is possible to estimate the size of a specimen by comparing it with the size of the field of view.

1. With the low-power objective lens in place, lay a microscope slide on the stage and place a transparent millimetre ruler on the slide.
2. Viewing the microscope stage from the side, position the millimetre marks on the ruler immediately below the objective lens.
3. Looking through the eyepiece, focus the marks on the ruler using the coarse- and fine-adjustment knobs.
4. Move the ruler so that one of the millimetre marks is at the edge of the field of view.
5. Use the following equations to calculate the diameter of the medium- and high-power fields of view. (*Note*: Magnification is shortened to mag. in the equations.)

   For medium power:

   $$\text{diameter} = \text{total mag.}_{\text{low power}} \times \frac{\text{diameter}_{\text{low power}}}{\text{total mag.}_{\text{medium power}}}$$

   For high power:

   $$\text{diameter} = \text{total mag.}_{\text{low power}} \times \frac{\text{diameter}_{\text{low power}}}{\text{total mag.}_{\text{high power}}}$$

6. Using a table similar to **Table 1**, determine the magnification of each of the lenses on your microscope, and record the diameter of the field of view.

Table 1 Characteristics of Microscope Lenses

Lens	Magnification	Eyepiece magnification	Total magnification	Diameter (mm)
low		10×		
medium		10×		
high		10×		

Estimating Size

- **Figure 2** shows the edge of a ruler under low power with the markings 1 mm apart. The diameter of the field of view is estimated to be 1.3 mm.

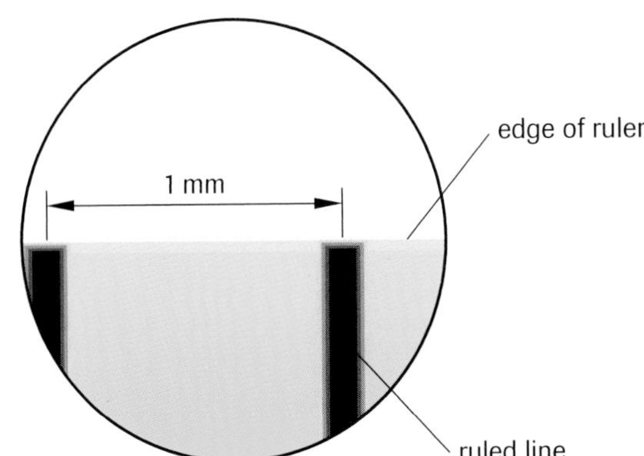

Figure 2
Markings of a ruler under low power

- Estimate the length and width of the specimen by comparing it to the diameter of the field of view.
- **Figure 3** shows a skin cell viewed under high power. One might estimate it to be 0.2 mm wide.

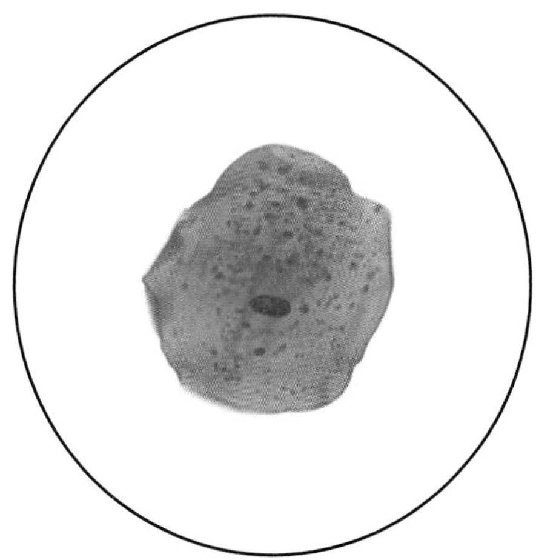

Figure 3
Skin cell viewed under high power

Preparing a Wet-Mount Slide

Specimens of all types can be mounted in a fluid medium before they are examined. Water is the most convenient, but 30 % glycerol can also be used. Glycerol helps make the material more transparent, and it does not dry out as fast as water does. A cover slip is used so that there are no reflecting surfaces.

1. Clean a slide and cover slip, holding them by the edges so that you do not leave fingerprints on them. Lay them on a clean, dry surface.

2. Place a drop of water or glycerol in the centre of the slide.
3. Transfer the specimen into the water or glycerol.
4. Hold the edges of the cover slip between thumb and forefinger. Place the cover slip in an almost vertical position on the slide so that the cover slip just touches the edge of the drop of water or glycerol (**Figure 4**).

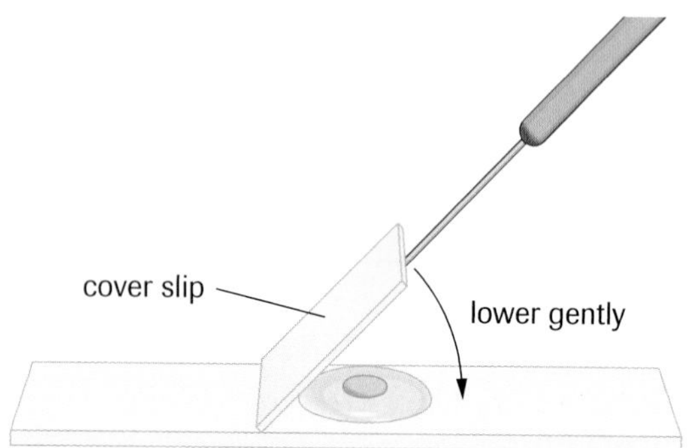

Figure 4
Preparing a wet mount

5. The water or glycerol will spread along the edge of the cover slip. Supporting the cover slip with the point of a needle, gently lower the cover slip onto the slide.
6. Use blotting paper to dry off any excess water or glycerol around the cover slip. Dry any water or glycerol that accidentally drops onto the stage of the microscope or onto the objective lenses.

Biological Drawings

Biological drawings are an essential part of recording your observations, both microscopic and macroscopic. These drawings are used to communicate, so it is very important that they are as accurate as possible, clear, well-labelled, and easy to understand. You will be required to make drawings of external features of whole specimens, parts of specimens, dissections, and prepared slides.

Preparation

- Use plain, white paper and a sharp, hard pencil (2H or 4H). Sharpen your pencil often to ensure clear, fine lines.
- Plan your drawing to fit on the page. Ensure that it is large enough to show the details.
- Leave space for labelling to the right of the drawing.

Drawing Tips

- Draw only what you see. Do not copy diagrams from books or draw what you think you should see.
- Use firm, clear lines. When recording microscope observations, use only the outline of structures for low-power observations; show details in high-power observations (**Figure 5**).

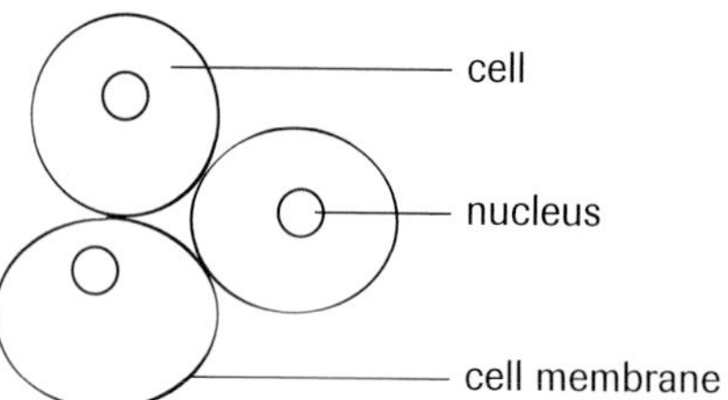

Figure 5
Clear, solid lines showing outlines of cells

- If important details are too small to be shown clearly, they should be shown in an enlarged drawing on the side.
- Don't use colouring or shading. To show darker areas, stippling (dots) may be used. Draw double lines to indicate thick structures (**Figure 6**).

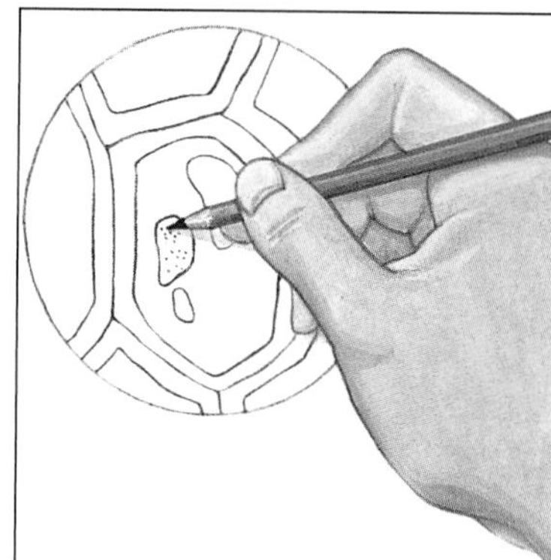

Figure 6
Use stippling to show darker areas and double lines to show thick structures.

- If a specimen shows repetitive structures, it is sufficient to draw only a representative section in detail (**Figure 7**).
- Don't draw on both sides of the paper.

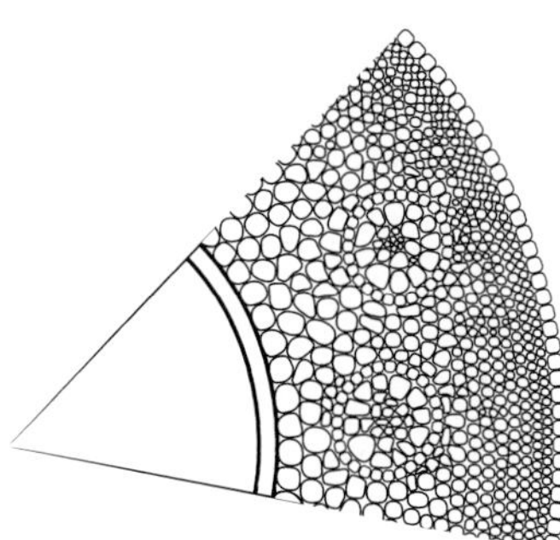

Figure 7
A representative drawing of a stem cross section.

Labelling

- All important structures should be labelled clearly. Always use the singular form for the labels (e.g., chloroplast, not chloroplasts).
- Connect labels to the appropriate parts using only horizontal lines if possible (**Figure 8**).

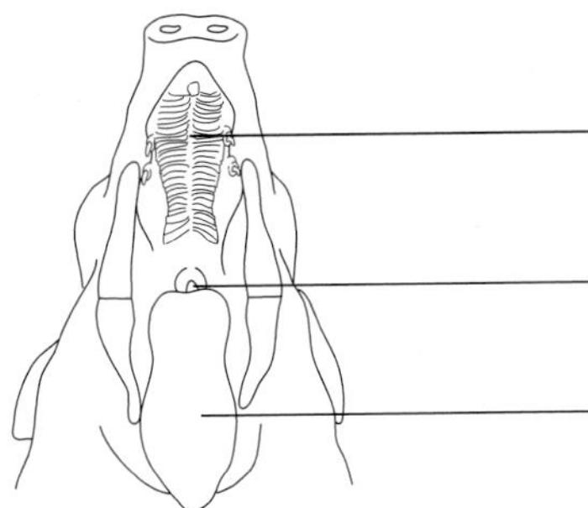

Figure 8
Connect your labels with horizontal lines.

- Don't label too close to the drawing, and never write on the drawing itself. It is preferable to list your labels in an even column down the right side (**Figure 9**).

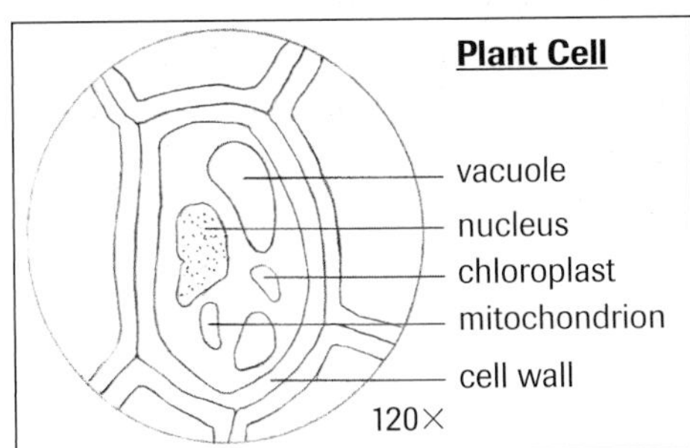

Figure 9
Neat labelling makes your drawing clear.

- For drawings of microscope observations, indicate the magnification.
- Title the drawing. Use the name of the specimen and any other information that will help identify the drawing. Underline the title.

A5 Preparing for the Biology 30 Diploma Exam

One goal of your studies is to prepare for the Biology 30 Diploma Exam. You have been provided opportunities to practice answering Diploma Exam-style questions in *Nelson Biology Alberta 20-30*. Part 1 of the Chapter and Unit Reviews contain multiple choice and numerical response questions. Part 2 of the Chapter and Unit Reviews contain written-response questions, which are marked by the icon "DE". The Case Studies also provide practice in answering closed-response written questions based on a scenario, and the Explore an Issue features help you to develop skills for answering open-response written questions. The **Additional Diploma Exam-style Review Questions** on the Nelson Web site are longer scenario-based questions, sometimes using published articles. Here are some general tips that will help you to answer Diploma Exam-style questions and to perform your best on the Diploma Exam.

- **Involve yourself in class**: Attend class regularly. Be active in your learning by asking questions and completing assignments. If you work steadily, you will not need to try to learn everything just before the exam.
- **Keep up-to-date with Biology 30 material:** Schedule a regular review time every week. Use this time to organize your notes, review the material, and ask yourself questions about what you have learned. Use the Self Quizzes, Chapter Summaries, and other study aids.
- **Read and understand the scoring criteria**: The scoring criteria for the different types of questions found in the Biology 30 Diploma Exam are available on the Nelson Web site. Read these criteria carefully and make sure you understand what they mean.

www.science.nelson.com GO

- **Practice writing old exams**: Use the old exams to simulate the conditions of the exam, including the time constraints. This will also help you practice answering the types of questions on the exam. Afterward, compare your answers to the scoring criteria to see where you can improve.
- **Read the instructions**: Make sure you read all instructions and questions very carefully.

Types of Questions on the Diploma Exam

There are three types of questions on the Diploma Exam: Multiple Choice, Numerical Response, and Written Response. Multiple choice and numerical response questions are found in Part 1 of the Diploma Exam, and written-response questions are found in Part 2.

Multiple Choice Questions

Multiple choice questions are a large part of the Diploma Exam. Most of the multiple choice questions on the Diploma Exam are context-dependent. The remainders are not context-dependent and are called discrete questions.

Context-dependent multiple choice questions use information provided in addition to the actual question. **Figure 1** and questions 1-4 are an example of this style.

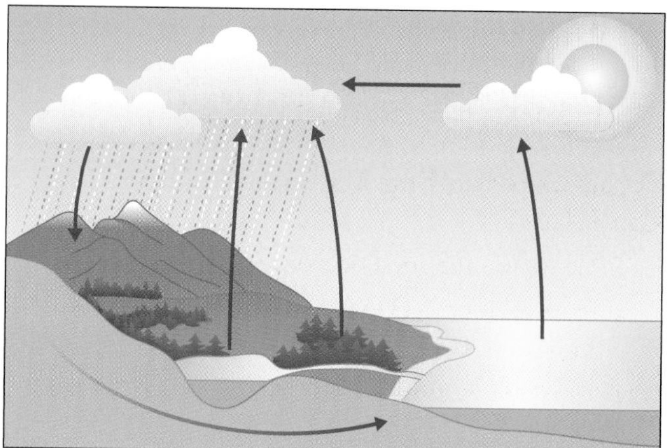

Figure 1

1. Identify three abiotic factors of the ecosystem shown in **Figure 1**.
   A. rain, sunlight, and soil quality
   B. water temperature, water lilies, and minnows
   C. poplars, grasses, and earthworms
   D. soil quality, bacteria, and earthworms
2. Explain how two members of the biotic community affect an abiotic factor.
   A. Pine trees and poplar trees affect the growth of grasses.
   B. Beavers and shrubs affect the number of poplar trees.
   C. Water temperature and pond oxygen levels affect the amount of plankton in the lake.
   D. Poplar trees and shrubs lose their leaves, which are decomposed and improve soil quality.

3. Identify the statement that lists two decomposers and correctly explains their role in the ecosystem.
   A. Clams and algae improve soil quality by returning organic nutrients to the soil.
   B. Bacteria and earthworms improve soil quality by returning organic nutrients to the soil.
   C. Pine trees and shrubs perform photosynthesis and add oxygen to the ecosystem.
   D. Algae and bacteria perform photosynthesis and add oxygen to the ecosystem.

4. What is the ultimate source of energy for the ecosystem shown in **Figure 1**?
   A. water
   B. sunlight
   C. producers
   D. consumers

Discrete multiple choice questions have no additional information or directions, such as in the following example.

5. The process of splitting water to release hydrogen ions, electrons, and oxygen occurs
   A. during the light-dependent reactions
   B. during the Calvin cycle
   C. during photorespiration
   D. during carbon fixation

Tips for Answering Multiple Choice Questions

- Try to answer the question before looking at the choices.
- Eliminate any choices that are incorrect by crossing them out.
- Stay alert for key words: *most, least, NOT one of the following*, etc. Negative terms ("Which of the following structures is *not* part of the respiratory system?) will be in italics.
- When writing the Diploma Exam, first mark the correct answer on the question sheet and then fill in the corresponding circle on the answer sheet at the end. Then, double-check to that you correctly marked your answer sheet. However, stay aware of time, so that you don't run out of time to transcribe your answers from the question sheet to the answer sheet.

Numerical Response Questions

There are three types of numerical response questions on the Diploma Exam. They are

- calculating of numerical values;
- selecting numerical responses from diagrams or lists; and
- determining the sequence of listed events.

Numerical response questions on the Diploma Exam are clearly indicated with the heading 'NUMERICAL RESPONSE'. The number of decimal places required is stated in the question. Examples of these types of questions are clearly marked with the icon 'NR' in this textbook.

Specific instructions for recording the answer to each type of numerical response are given in the instructions of the Diploma Exam, as well as with each question. Read the instructions CAREFULLY.

Tips for Answering Numerical Response Questions

For numerical calculations, use the provided data to determine an answer. The answer is a numerical response with a maximum of four digits (including the decimal point). The first digit of your answer goes in the left-hand box on the answer sheet. Depending on the number of digits in your answer, there may be unfilled boxes to the right. The decimal point, if there is one, occupies one of the boxes.

0	.	2	5

Numerical responses from diagrams or lists involves selecting numbers (usually representing a term or item from several provided) and writing them in the correct order.

Numerical responses that ask you to sequence numbered events or data require you to rearrange variables, events, or data into a specified order. Pay particular attention to the instructions, which might specify, for example, "in the order in which they occur during respiration."

Written-Response Questions

There are two written-response questions on the Biology 30 Diploma Exam. One written-response question is a closed-response question (which has only one correct response) and the other is an open-response question (to which there is more than one correct response). Learn to determine which type of question is being asked.

Closed-Response Questions

Closed-response questions have only one correct answer. In the Diploma Exam, these questions are presented as sections and subsections (question 1. a, b, c, etc.). They usually are based on current research or a scenario, and may provide data in graph or a table, as shown in the example on the next page.

Use the following information to answer question 34.

The data in **Table 2** compares Canadian population statistics for the periods 1861–1871 and 1991–1996. In 2004, the number of immigrants was about 236 000 while the number of emigrants was approximately 61 000.

Table 2 Canadian Population Statistics

	1861–1871	1991–1996
Population at beginning of period	3 229 000	27 852 000
Births	1 370 000	1 936 000
Deaths	760 000	1 024 000
Immigrants	260 000	1 137 000
Emigrants	410 000	229 000

Additional examples of closed-response questions can be found on the Nelson Web site.

www.science.nelson.com GO

Open-Response Questions

Open-response questions have more than one possible answer. They usually include the phrase 'write a unified response…'. The question is asked as a series of bullets, and the answers are to be written in full sentences. Each bullet must be addressed and combined or 'unified' into the answer.

40. Darwin recognized that natural selection by the environment could produce change in a way similar to the artificial selection used by plant and animal breeders. Write a unified response that addresses the following aspects of these two processes.
- **Compare** the source of new variation in each process. **Illustrate** your answer with an example.
- **Describe** any role of selection *for* certain characteristics in each process. **Illustrate** your answer with an example.
- **Describe** any role of selection *against* certain characteristics in each process. **Illustrate** your answer with an example.
- **Compare** the length of time needed before noticeable differences can be seen. **Illustrate** your answer with an example.

Additional examples of closed-response questions can be found on the Nelson Web site.

www.science.nelson.com GO

The questions are based on provided background information. Each bullet contains at least one directing word. Your final answer must address each bullet fully in order to get full credit. At least one of these bulleted questions usually requires you to make and defend a judgment or opinion. Two separate scoring scales are used. One is based on the scientific aspects of your answer and the other is based on addressing technological, societal, and/or environmental aspects of your answer.

Tips for Answering Written-Response Questions

- Carefully read the information box and make sure you fully understand the material *and* all of the question parts before beginning to answer.
- Identify each key piece of information and make notes about the meaning and implications of that information. If it helps, mark key words and phrases. Identify which unit of Biology 30 is being addressed, to help focus your attention to the correct material.
- Identify any irrelevant information.
- Identify the **directing words** in the question. These are highlighted in bold in the question. The directing words have specific meanings and are indicators of what the graders expect for an answer. Examples of directing words include **illustrate**, **analyze**, **explain**, and **predict**. A complete list of directing words and their meanings can be found online. The Glossary includes directing words used in this textbook. Make sure that you know what is expected for each directing word.

www.science.nelson.com GO

- Read the question carefully and ask yourself what you are being asked to do. Write the question out in your own words if there are any doubts. Remember, if you don't understand the question, you will probably not be able to answer it correctly!
- Summarize your answers on scrap paper before writing them on the test answer page.
- Once you have answered the question, review your answer and make sure you have addressed all parts of the question.

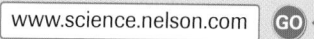

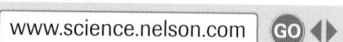

A

A6 Graphic Organizers

Graphic organizers such as those outlined in this section can help you to solidify your understanding of a topic, and assist you in formulating a clear, concise answer.

PMI Chart

A PMI chart is used to examine both sides of an issue. Positive aspects of a topic or issue are recorded in the P (plus) column. Negative aspects are recorded in the M (minus) column. Interesting or controversial questions are recorded in the I (interesting) column (**Table 1**).

Table 1: A PMI Chart

P	M	I

Table 2: A KWL Chart

K	W	L

KWL Chart

A KWL chart can help you identify prior knowledge and experience, decide what new information you want to learn about, and reflect on your learning. Before you begin a new concept, lesson, or unit, list what you know about a topic in the K column and what you want to know in the W column. After studying the new topic, list what you learned in the L column (**Table 2**).

Venn Diagram

A Venn diagram is used to show similarities and differences in two or more concepts. Write all similarities between the concepts in the overlapping section of the circles and all unique traits of each concept in the nonoverlapping parts of the appropriate circles (**Figure 1**).

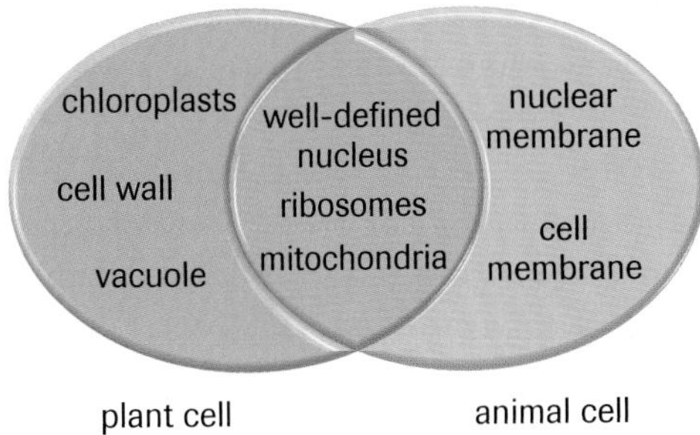

Figure 1
Venn diagram: plant and animal cells

Fishbone Diagram

A fishbone diagram is used to identify separate causes and effects. In the head of the fish, identify the effect, topic, or result. At the end of each major bone, identify the major subtopics or categories. On the minor bones that attach to each major bone, add details about the subtopics or possible causes of each effect or result (**Figure 2**).

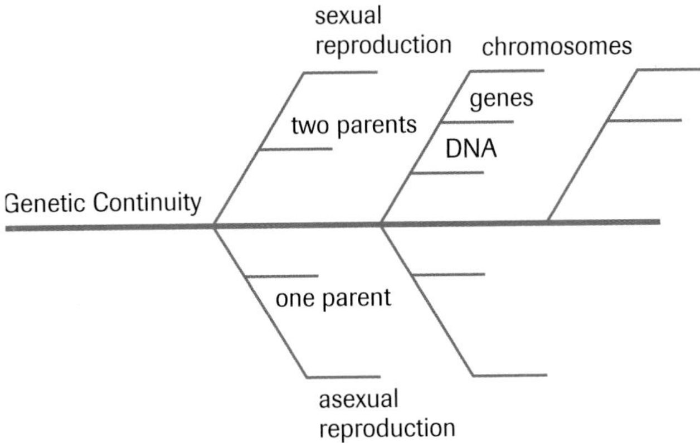

Figure 2
Fishbone diagram: genetic continuity

The Concept Map

Concept maps are used to show connections between ideas and concepts, using words or visuals. Put the central idea in the middle of a sheet of paper. Organize the ideas most closely related to each other around the centre. Draw arrows between the ideas that are related. On each arrow, write a short description of how the terms are related to each other (**Figure 3**).

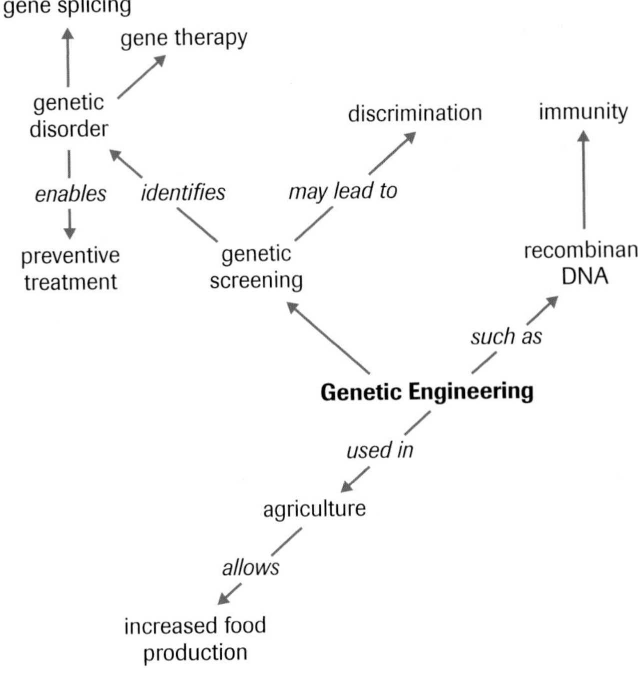

Figure 3
Concept map: genetic engineering

A7 Math Skills

Scientific Notation

It is difficult to work with very large or very small numbers when they are written in common decimal notation. Usually, it is possible to accommodate such numbers by changing the SI prefix so that the number falls between 0.1 and 1000. For example, 237 000 000 mm can be expressed as 237 km and 0.000 000 895 kg can be expressed as 0.895 mg. However, this prefix change is not always possible. An appropriate prefix may not exist or it may be essential to use a particular unit of measurement. In these cases, the best method of dealing with very large and very small numbers is to write them using scientific notation. Scientific notation expresses a number by writing it in the form $a \times 10^n$, where $1 < |a| < 10$ and the digits in the coefficient a are all significant. Recall that the notation $|x|$ means the absolute value of x. **Table 1** shows situations where scientific notation would be used.

Table 1 Examples of Scientific Notation

Expression	Common decimal notation	Scientific notation
124.5 million kilometres	124 500 000 km	1.245×10^8 km
154 thousand picometres	154 000 pm	1.54×10^{-5} pm
602 sextillion /mol	602 000 000 000 000 000 000 000 /mol	6.02×10^{23}/mol

To multiply numbers in scientific notation, multiply the coefficients and add the exponents; the answer is expressed in scientific notation. Note that when writing a number in scientific notation, the coefficient should be between 1 and 10 and should be rounded to the same certainty (number of significant digits) as the measurement with the least certainty (fewest number of significant digits). Look at the following examples:

$$(4.73 \times 10^5\ \text{m})(5.82 \times 10^7\ \text{m}) = 27.5 \times 10^{12}\ \text{m}^2 = 2.75 \times 10^{13}\ \text{m}^2$$

$$(3.9 \times 10^4\ \text{N})(5.3 \times 10^{-3}\ \text{m}) = 21 \times 10^1\ \text{N•m} = 2.1 \times 10^2\ \text{N•m}$$

On many calculators, scientific notation is entered using a special key, labelled EXP or EE. This key includes "$\times$ 10" from the scientific notation; you need to enter only the exponent. For example, to enter

7.5×10^4	press	7.5 EXP 4
3.6×10^{-3}	press	3.6 EXP +/−3

Logarithms

In the exponential equation $y = a^n$, a is the base and n is the exponent. $y = a^n$ can be written as $\log_a y = n$ ($a > 0$ and $a \neq 1$) and is read as "the logarithm of y with base a is equal to n." For example, $10^2 = 100$ can be written as $\log_{10}100 = 2$.

On many scientific calculators, the key "LOG" calculates the logarithm of a number with base 10. For example, to enter

$\log_{10}2$	press	LOG 2

Logarithm of a product is one of the logarithm laws. The law is as follows:

$$\log_a(mn) = \log_a m + \log_a n$$

This law is useful when calculating the pH of solutions. The definition of pH is the negative logarithm of the hydronium ion concentration, $-\log_{10}[H_3O^+{}_{(aq)}]$, where the concentration is measured in moles per litre of solution (mol/L).

In pure water at 25 °C, the $H_3O^+{}_{(aq)}$ is 1.0×10^{-7} mol/L.

$$\begin{aligned} \text{pH} &= -\log_{10}[H_3O^+{}_{(aq)}] \\ &= -\log_{10}(1.0 \times 10^{-7}) \\ &= -((\log_{10}1.0) + \log_{10}(10^{-7})) \\ &= -(0 + (-7)) \\ &= 7 \end{aligned}$$

Therefore, the pH of pure water is 7.

Uncertainty in Measurements

There are two types of quantities that are used in science: exact values and measurements. Exact values include defined quantities (1 m = 100 cm) and counted values (5 cars in a parking lot). Measurements, however, are not exact because there is some uncertainty or error associated with every measurement.

There are two types of measurement error. **Random error** results when an estimate is made to obtain the last significant figure for any measurement. The size of the random error is determined by the precision of the measuring instrument. For example, when measuring length, it is necessary to estimate between the marks on the measuring tape. If these marks are 1 cm apart, the random error will be greater and the precision will be less than if the marks are 1 mm apart.

Systematic error is associated with an inherent problem with the measuring system, such as the presence of an interfering substance, incorrect calibration, or room conditions. For example, if the balance is not zeroed at the beginning, all measurements will have a systematic error; if using a metre stick that has been worn slightly, all measurements will contain an error.

The precision of measurements depends upon the gradations of the measuring device. **Precision** is the place value of the last measurable digit. For example, a measurement of 12.74 cm is more precise than a measurement of 127.4 cm, because the first value was measured to hundredths of a centimetre, whereas the latter was measured to tenths of a centimetre.

When adding or subtracting measurements of different precision, the answer is rounded to the same precision as the least precise measurement. For example, using a calculator, add

$$11.7 \text{ cm} + 3.29 \text{ cm} + 0.542 \text{ cm} = 15.532 \text{ cm}$$

The answer must be rounded to 15.5 cm, because the first measurement limits the precision to a tenth of a centimetre.

No matter how precise a measurement is, it still may not be accurate. **Accuracy** refers to how close a value is to its true value. The comparison of the two values can be expressed as a percentage difference. The percentage difference is calculated as:

$$\% \text{ difference} = \frac{|\text{experimental value} - \text{predicted value}|}{\text{predicted value}} \times 100\ \%$$

Figure 1 shows an analogy between precision and accuracy, and the positions of darts thrown at a dartboard.

How certain you are about a measurement depends on two factors: the precision of the instrument used and the size of the measured quantity. More precise instruments give more certain values. For example, a mass measurement of 13 g is less precise than a measurement of 12.76 g; you are more certain about the second measurement than the first. Certainty also depends on the measurement. For example, consider the measurements 0.4 cm and 15.9 cm; both have the same precision. However, if the measuring instrument is precise to ± 0.1 cm, the first measurement is 0.4 ± 0.1 cm (0.3 cm or 0.5 cm) or an error of 25 %, whereas the second measurement could be 15.9 ± 0.1 cm (15.8 cm or 16.0 cm) for an error of 0.6 %. For both factors—the precision of the instrument used and the value of the measured quantity—the more digits there are in a measurement, the more certain you are about the measurement.

Significant Digits

The certainty of any measurement is communicated by the number of significant digits in the measurement. In a measured or calculated value, significant digits are the digits that are certain plus one estimated (uncertain) digit. Significant digits include all digits correctly reported from a measurement.

Follow these rules to decide if a digit is significant:

1. For any non-logarithmic value, zeros to the left of the first non-zero digit (leading zeros) are not significant.
2. Zeros to the right of the last non-zero digit (trailing zeros) of any value are significant.
3. All other digits are significant.
4. When a measurement is written in scientific notation, all digits in the coefficient are significant.
5. For all logarithmic values such as pH, any digit to the left of the decimal is not significant.
6. Counted and defined values have infinite significant digits.

Table 2 shows some examples of significant digits.

Table 2 Certainty in Significant Digits

Measurement	Number of significant digits
32.07 m	4
0.0041 g	2
5×10^5 kg	1
6400 s	4
pH 6.47	2

(a)

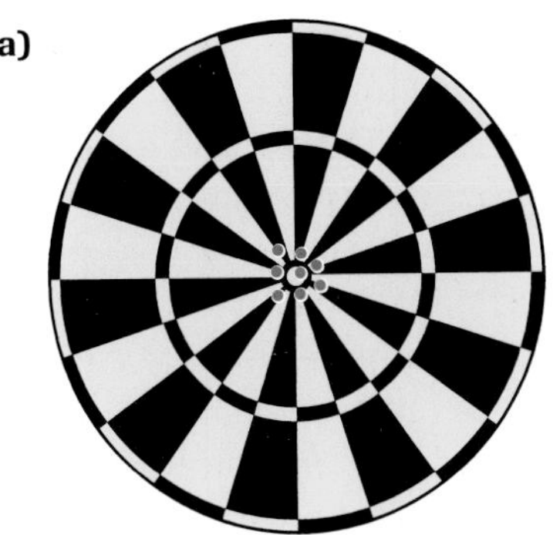

(b)

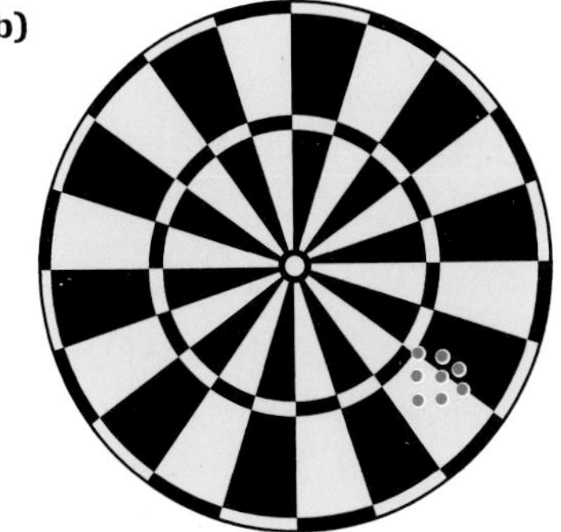

(c)

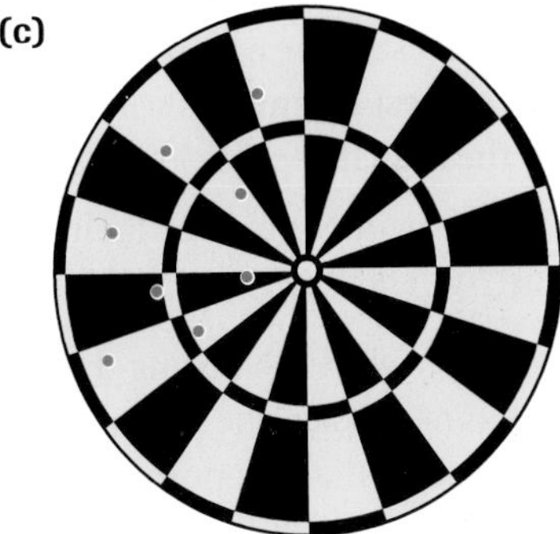

Figure 1
The positions of the darts in each of these figures are analogous to measured or calculated results in a laboratory setting. The results in **(a)** are precise and accurate, in **(b)** they are precise but not accurate, and in **(c)** they are neither precise nor accurate.

Rounding Off

An answer obtained by multiplying and/or dividing measurements is rounded to the same number of significant digits as the measurement with the fewest number of significant digits. For example, we could use a calculator to solve the following equation:

$$77.8 \text{ km/h} \times 0.8967 \text{ h} = 69.76326 \text{ km}$$

However, the certainty of the answer is limited to three significant digits, so the answer is rounded up to 69.8 km.

The following rules should be used when rounding answers to calculations.

1. When the first digit discarded is less than five, the last digit retained should not be changed.

   3.141 326 rounded to 4 digits is 3.141
2. When the first digit discarded is greater than five, or if it is a five followed by at least one digit other than zero, the last digit retained is increased by 1 unit.

   2.213 724 rounded to 4 digits is 2.214

   4.168 501 rounded to 4 digits is 4.169
3. When the first digit discarded is five followed by only zeros, the last digit retained is increased by 1 if it is odd, but not changed if it is even.

   2.35 rounded to 2 digits is 2.4

   2.45 rounded to 2 digits is 2.4

   −6.35 rounded to 2 digits is −6.4

Measuring and Estimating

Many people believe that all measurements are reliable (consistent over many trials), precise (to as many decimal places as possible), and accurate (representing the actual value). But there are many things that can go wrong when measuring.

- There may be limitations that make the instrument or its use unreliable (inconsistent).
- The investigator may make a mistake or fail to follow the correct techniques when reading the measurement to the available precision (number of decimal places).
- The instrument may be faulty or inaccurate; a similar instrument may give different readings.

For example, when measuring the temperature of a liquid, it is important to keep the thermometer at the proper depth and the bulb of the thermometer away from the bottom and sides of the container. If you sit a thermometer with its bulb at the bottom of a liquid-filled container, you will be measuring the temperature of the bottom of the container and not the temperature of the liquid. There are similar concerns with other measurements.

To be sure that you have measured correctly, you should repeat your measurements at least three times. If your measurements appear to be reliable, calculate the mean and use that value. To be more certain about the accuracy, repeat the measurements with a different instrument.

Every measurement is a best estimate of the actual value. The measuring instrument and the skill of the investigator determine the certainty and the precision of the measurement. The usual rule is to make a measurement that estimates between the smallest divisions on the scale of the instrument.

Probability

In scientific investigations, probability is a measure of the likelihood of a specific event occurring and is usually expressed as a number between 0 and 1. A probability of 0 means the event will not occur; a probability of 1 means the event will definitely occur. Probabilities may also be expressed as fractions or as percents.

There are two types of probability: theoretical probability and experimental probability. Theoretical probability is the likelihood of an event occurring based on the information known about certain conditions. This is an expectation.

$$\text{theoretical probability} = \frac{\text{number of desired outcomes}}{\text{total number of possible outcomes}}$$

Example

Black fur colour is a dominant trait in guinea pigs, while white fur colour is a recessive trait. What is the theoretical probability of a pair of heterozygous black guinea pigs (*Bb*) producing offspring with white fur (*bb*)?

Using a Punnett square (**Figure 2**), we show that if four offspring were produced, it is expected that three would have black fur and one would have white fur.

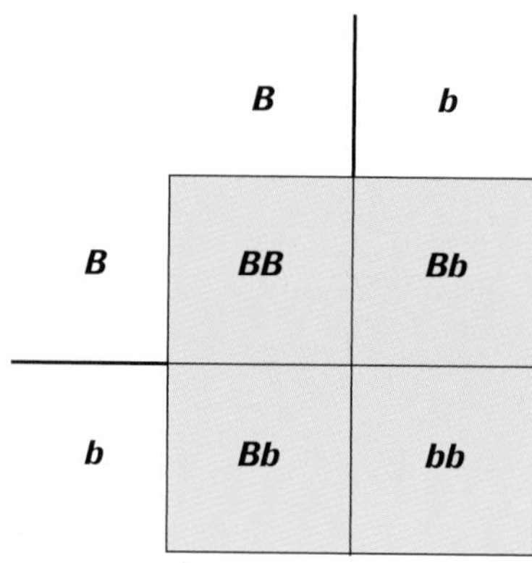

Figure 2
Punnett square showing a *Bb* × *Bb* cross

$$\text{theoretical probability} = \frac{\text{number of desired outcomes}}{\text{total number of possible outcomes}}$$

$$= \frac{\text{number of offspring with white fur}}{\text{total number of possible offspring}}$$

$$= \frac{1}{4}$$

$$= 0.25$$

$$= 25\ \%$$

The theoretical probability of producing white offspring is 1/4 or 25 %. So, if a litter had eight offspring, you could expect two to have white fur.

Experimental probability is based on the recorded outcomes or events of an investigation. The more often an experiment is repeated or the more observations made, the closer the experimental probability will be to the theoretical probability.

$$\text{experimental probability} = \frac{\text{number of desired outcomes observed}}{\text{total number of observations}}$$

Example

Black fur colour is a dominant trait in guinea pigs, while white fur colour is a recessive trait. Two heterozygous black guinea pigs (*Bb*) were crossed. The litter contained six offspring with black fur and one with white fur. What is the experimental probability of producing offspring with white fur?

$$\text{experimental probability} = \frac{\text{number of desired outcomes observed}}{\text{total number of observations}}$$

$$= \frac{\text{number of offspring with white fur}}{\text{total number of possible offspring}}$$

$$= \frac{1}{7}$$

$$\doteq 0.14$$

$$= 14\ \%$$

The experimental probability of having offspring with white fur is 14%. If you performed the same analysis on a large number of litters, you would expect the experimental probability to be the same as (or very close to) the theoretical probability.

Graphs

There are many types of graphs that you can use to organize your data. You need to identify which type of graph is best for your data before you begin graphing. Three of the most useful kinds are bar graphs, circle (pie) graphs, and point-and-line graphs.

Bar Graphs

When at least one of the variables is qualitative, use a bar graph to organize your data (**Figure 3**). For example, a bar graph would be a good way to present the data collected from a study of the number of plants (quantitative) and the type of plants found (qualitative) in a local nursery. In this graph, each bar stands for a different category, in this case a type of plant.

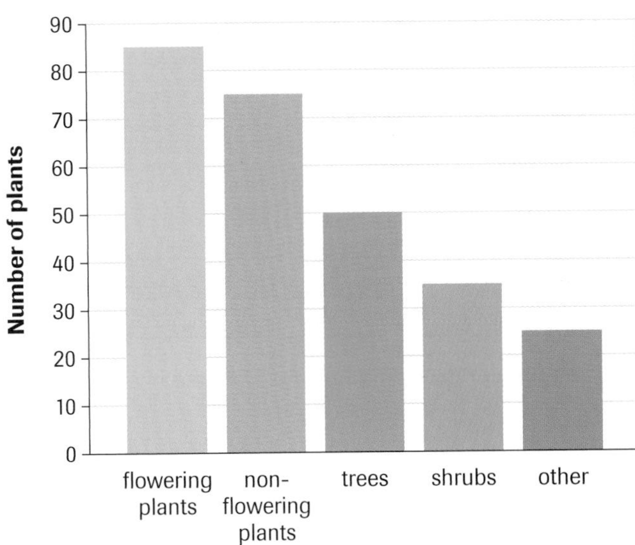

Figure 3
Bar graph

Circle Graphs

Circle graphs and bar graphs are used for similar types of data. A circle graph is used if the quantitative variable can be changed to a percentage of a total quantity (**Figure 4**). For example, if you surveyed a local nursery to determine the types of plants found and the number of each, you could make a circle graph. Each piece in the graph stands for a different category (e.g., the type of plant). The size of each piece is determined by the percentage of the total that belongs in each category (e.g., the percentage of plants of a particular type).

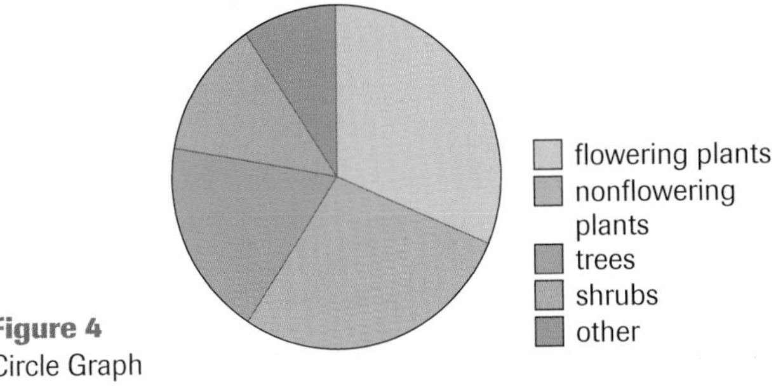

Figure 4
Circle Graph

Point-and-Line Graphs

When both variables are quantitative, use a point-and-line graph. For example, we can use the following guidelines and the data in **Table 3** to construct the point-and-line graph shown in **Figure 5**.

Table 3 Number of Brine Shrimp Eggs Hatched in Salt Solutions of Various Concentrations

Day	2 % salt	4 % salt	6 % salt	8 % salt
1	0	0	0	1
2	0	11	2	3
3	0	14	8	5
4	2	20	17	8
5	5	37	25	15
6	6	51	37	31

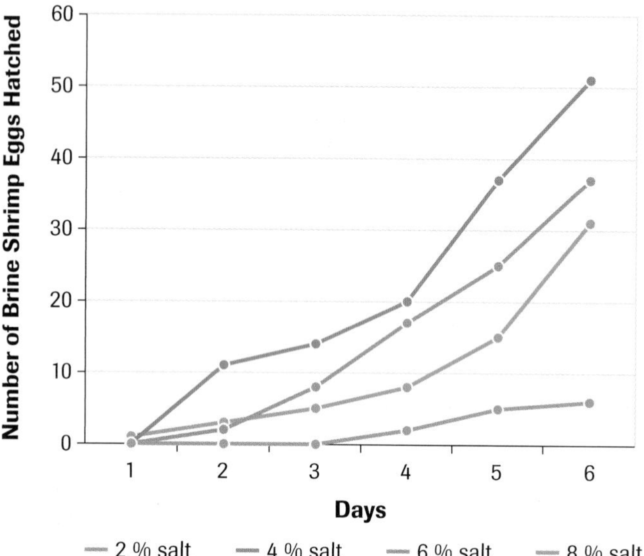

Figure 5
Point-and-line graph

1. Use graph paper and construct your graph on a grid. The horizontal edge on the bottom of this grid is the x-axis and the vertical edge on the left is the y-axis. Do not be too thrifty with graph paper—a larger graph is easier to interpret.
2. Decide which variable goes on which axis and label each axis, including the units of measurement. The manipulated variable is generally plotted along the x-axis and the responding variable along the y-axis. The exception to this is when you plot a variable against time: regardless of which is the manipulated or responding variable, always plot time on the x-axis. This convention ensures that the slope of the graph always represents a rate.
3. Title your graph. The title should be a concise description of the data contained in the graph.
4. Determine the range of values for each variable. The range is the difference between the largest and smallest values. Graphs often include a little extra length on each axis, to make them appear less cramped.
5. Choose a scale for each axis. This will depend on how much space you have and the range of values for each axis. Each line on the grid usually increases steadily in value by a convenient number, such as 1, 2, 5, 10, or 50.
6. Plot the points. Start with the first pair of values, which may or may not be at the origin of the graph.
7. After all the points are plotted, draw a line through the points to show the relationship between the variables, if possible. Not all points may lie exactly on a line; small errors in each measurement may have occurred and moved the points away from the perfect line. Draw a line that comes closest to most of the points. This is called the line of best fit—a smooth line that passes through or between the points so that there are about the same number of points on each side of the line. The line of best fit may be straight or curved.
8. If you are plotting more than one set of data on one graph, use different colours or symbols to indicate the different sets, and include a legend (**Figure 5**).

Spreadsheets

A spreadsheet is a useful tool for creating different graph types such as column, bar, line, and circle to display data.

The following steps show how the data for the plants in a local nursery can be used to create a column (or bar) graph.

Step 1
Enter the data in the spreadsheet.

Step 2
Select the graph type that will display the data in the most appropriate form.

Step 3
Select the data from the spreadsheet that will be plotted on the graph.

Step 4
Enter the remaining graph information, such as the graph title and axes titles.

Step 5
Indicate where the graph is to be located in the spreadsheet. It can be included on the same sheet as the data or on a new sheet.

B1 Safety Conventions and Symbols

Although every effort is undertaken to make the science experience a safe one, there are inherent risks associated with some scientific investigations. These risks are generally associated with the materials and equipment used, and the disregard of safety instructions that accompany investigations. However, there may also be risks associated with the location of the investigation, whether in the science laboratory, at home, or outdoors. Most of these risks pose no more danger than one would normally experience in everyday life. With an awareness of the possible hazards, knowledge of the rules, appropriate behaviour, and a little common sense, these risks can be practically eliminated.

Remember, you share the responsibility not only for your own safety, but also for the safety of those around you. Always alert the teacher in case of an accident.

In this text, chemicals, equipment, and procedures that are hazardous are highlighted in red and are preceded by the appropriate Workplace Hazardous Materials Information System (WHMIS) symbol or by .

WHMIS Symbols and HHPS

The Workplace Hazardous Materials Information System (WHMIS) provides workers and students with complete and accurate information regarding hazardous products. All chemical products supplied to schools, businesses, and industries must contain standardized labels and be accompanied by Material Safety Data sheets (MSDS) providing detailed information about the product. Clear and standardized labelling is an important component of WHMIS (**Table 1**). These labels must be present on the product's original container or be added to other containers if the product is transferred.

The Canadian Hazardous Products Act requires manufacturers of consumer products containing chemicals to include a symbol specifying both the nature of the primary hazard and the degree of this hazard. In addition, any secondary hazards, first aid treatment, storage, and disposal must be noted. Household Hazardous Product Symbols (HHPS) are used to show the hazard and the degree of the hazard by the type of border surrounding the illustration (**Figure 1**).

	Corrosive
	This material can burn your skin and eyes. If you swallow it, it will damage your throat and stomach.
	Flammable
	This product or the gas (or vapour) from it can catch fire quickly. Keep this product away from heat, flames, and sparks.
	Explosive
	Container will explode if it is heated or if a hole is punched in it. Metal or plastic can fly out and hurt your eyes and other parts of your body.
	Poisonous
	If you swallow or lick this product, you could become very sick or die. Some products with this symbol on the label can hurt you even if you breathe (or inhale) them.

Danger

Warning

Caution

Figure 1
Hazardous household product symbols

Table 1 The Workplace Hazardous Materials Information System (WHMIS)

Class and type of compounds	WHMIS symbol	Risks	Precautions
Class A: *Compressed Gas* Material that is normally gaseous and kept in a pressurized container		• could explode due to pressure • could explode if heated or dropped • possible hazard from both the force of explosion and the release of contents	• ensure container is always secured • store in designated areas • do not drop or allow to fall
Class B: *Flammable and Combustible Materials* Materials that will continue to burn after being exposed to a flame or other ignition source		• may ignite spontaneously • may release flammable products if allowed to degrade or when exposed to water	• store in properly designated areas • work in well-ventilated areas • avoid heating • avoid sparks and flames • ensure that electrical sources are safe
Class C: *Oxidizing Materials* Materials that can cause other materials to burn or support combustion		• can cause skin or eye burns • increase fire and explosion hazards • may cause combustibles to explode or react violently	• store away from combustibles • wear body, hand, face, and eye protection • store in proper container that will not rust or oxidize
Class D: *Toxic Materials Immediate and Severe* Poisons and potentially fatal materials that cause immediate and severe harm		• may be fatal if ingested or inhaled • may be absorbed through the skin • small volumes have a toxic effect	• avoid breathing dust or vapours • avoid contact with skin or eyes • wear protective clothing, and face and eye protection • work in well-ventilated areas and wear breathing protection
Class D: *Toxic Materials Long Term Concealed* Materials that have a harmful effect after repeated exposures or over a long period		• may cause death or permanent injury • may cause birth defects or sterility • may cause cancer • may be sensitizers causing allergies	• wear appropriate personal protection • work in a well-ventilated area • store in appropriate designated areas • avoid direct contact • use hand, body, face, and eye protection • ensure respiratory and body protection is appropriate for the specific hazard
Class D: *Biohazardous Infectious Materials* Infectious agents or a biological toxin causing a serious disease or death		• may cause anaphylactic shock • includes viruses, yeasts, moulds, bacteria, and parasites that affect humans • includes fluids containing toxic products • includes cellular components	• special training is required to handle materials • work in designated biological areas with appropriate engineering controls • avoid forming aerosols • avoid breathing vapours • avoid contamination of people and/or area • store in special designated areas
Class E: *Corrosive Materials* Materials that react with metals and living tissue		• eye and skin irritation on exposure • severe burns/tissue damage on longer exposure • lung damage if inhaled • may cause blindness if contacts eyes • environmental damage from fumes	• wear body, hand, face, and eye protection • use breathing apparatus • ensure protective equipment is appropriate • work in a well-ventilated area • avoid all direct body contact • use appropriate storage containers and ensure proper non-venting closures
Class F: *Dangerously Reactive Materials* Materials that may have unexpected reactions		• may react with water • may be chemically unstable • may explode if exposed to shock or heat • may release toxic or flammable vapours • may vigorously polymerize • may burn unexpectedly	• handle with care, avoiding vibration, shocks, and sudden temperature changes • store in appropriate containers • ensure storage containers are sealed • store and work in designated areas

B2 Safety in the Laboratory

General Safety Rules

Safety in the laboratory is an attitude and a habit more than it is a set of rules. It is easier to prevent accidents than to deal with the consequences of an accident. Most of the following rules are common sense:

- Do not enter a laboratory unless a teacher or other supervisor is present, or you have permission to do so.
- Familiarize yourself with your school's safety regulations.
- Make your teacher aware of any allergies and other health problems you may have.
- Wear eye protection, lab aprons or coats, and gloves when appropriate.
- Wear closed shoes (not sandals) when working in the laboratory.
- Place your books and bags away from the work area. Keep your work area clear of all materials except those that you will use in the investigation.
- Do not chew gum, eat, or drink in the laboratory. Food should not be stored in refrigerators in laboratories.
- Know the location of MSDS information, exits, and all safety equipment, such as the fire blanket, fire extinguisher, and eyewash station.
- Avoid sudden or rapid motion in the laboratory that may interfere with someone carrying or working with chemicals or using sharp instruments.
- Never engage in horseplay or practical jokes in the laboratory.
- Ask for assistance when you are not sure how to do a procedural step.
- Never attempt any unauthorized experiments.
- Never work in a crowded area or alone in the laboratory.
- Always wash your hands with soap and water before and after you leave the laboratory. Definitely wash your hands before you touch any food.
- Use stands, clamps, and holders to secure any potentially dangerous or fragile equipment that could be tipped over.
- Do not taste any substance in a laboratory.
- Never smell chemicals unless specifically instructed to do so by the teacher. Do not inhale the vapours, or gas, directly from the container. Take a deep breath to fill your lungs with air, then waft or fan the vapours toward your nose.
- Clean up all spills, even water spills, immediately.
- If you are using a microscope with a mirror, never direct the mirror to sunlight. The concentrated reflected light could hurt your eyes badly.
- Do not forget safety procedures when you leave the laboratory. Accidents can also occur outdoors, at home, and at work.

Eye and Face Safety

- Always wear approved eye protection in a laboratory, no matter how simple or safe the task appears to be. Keep the safety glasses over your eyes, not on top of your head. For certain experiments, full face protection may be necessary.
- If you must wear contact lenses in the laboratory, be extra careful; whether or not you wear contact lenses, do not touch your eyes without first washing your hands. If you do wear contact lenses, make sure that your teacher is aware of it. Carry your lens case and a pair of glasses with you.
- Do not stare directly at any bright source of light (e.g., a burning magnesium ribbon, lasers, the Sun). You will not feel any pain if your retina is being damaged by intense radiation. You cannot rely on the sensation of pain to protect you.
- Never look directly into the opening of flasks or test tubes.

Handling Glassware Safely

- Never use glassware that is cracked or chipped. Give such glassware to your teacher or dispose of it as directed. Do not put the item back into circulation.
- Never pick up broken glassware with your fingers. Use a broom and dustpan.
- Do not put broken glassware into garbage containers. Dispose of glass fragments in special containers marked "Broken Glass."
- Heat glassware only if it is approved for heating. Check with your teacher before heating any glassware.
- Be very careful when cleaning glassware. There is an increased risk of breakage from dropping when the glassware is wet and slippery.

- If you need to insert glass tubing or a thermometer into a rubber stopper, get a cork borer of a suitable size. Insert the borer in the hole of the rubber stopper, starting from the small end of the stopper. Once the borer is pushed all the way through the hole, insert the tubing or thermometer through the borer. Ease the borer out of the hole, leaving the tubing or thermometer inside. To remove the tubing or thermometer from the stopper, push the borer from the small end through the stopper until it shows at the other end. Ease the tubing or thermometer out of the borer.
- Protect your hands with heavy gloves or several layers of cloth before inserting glass into rubber stoppers.

Using Sharp Instruments Safely

- Make sure your instruments are sharp. Surprisingly, one of the main causes of accidents with cutting instruments is using a dull instrument. Dull cutting instruments require more pressure than sharp instruments and are, therefore, much more likely to slip.
- Always transport a scalpel in a dissection case or box. Never carry the scalpel from one area of the laboratory to another with an exposed blade.
- Select the appropriate instrument for the task. Never use a knife when scissors would work best.
- Always cut away from yourself and others.

Fire Safety

- Immediately inform your teacher of any fires. Very small fires in a container may be extinguished by covering the container with a wet paper towel or a ceramic square to cut off the supply of air. Alternatively, sand may be used to smother small fires. A bucket of sand with a scoop should be available in the laboratory.
- If anyone's clothes or hair catch fire, tell the person to drop to the floor and roll. Then use a fire blanket to help smother the flames. Never wrap the blanket around a person on fire; the chimney effect will burn the lungs. For larger fires, immediately evacuate the area. Call the office or sound the fire alarm if close by. Do not try to extinguish larger fires. Your prime concern is to save lives. As you leave the classroom, make sure that the windows and doors are closed.
- If you use a fire extinguisher, direct the extinguisher at the base of the fire and use a sweeping motion, moving the extinguisher nozzle back and forth across the front of the fire's base. Different extinguishers are effective for different classes of fires. The fire classes are outlined below. Fire extinguishers in the laboratory are 2A10BC. They extinguish classes A, B, and C fires.
- Class A fires involve ordinary combustible materials that leave coals or ashes, such as wood, paper, or cloth. Use water or dry chemical extinguishers on class A fires.
- Class B fires involve flammable liquids such as gasoline or solvents. Carbon dioxide or dry chemical extinguishers are effective on class B fires.
- Class C fires involve live electrical equipment, such as appliances, photocopiers, computers, or laboratory electrical apparatus. Carbon dioxide or dry chemical extinguishers are recommended for class C fires. Do not use water on live electrical devices as this can result in severe electrical shock.
- Class D fires involve burning metals, such as sodium, potassium, magnesium, or aluminum. Sand, salt, or graphite can be used to put out class D fires. Do not use water on a metal fire as this can cause a violent reaction.
- Class E fires involve a radioactive substance. These require special consideration at each site.

Heat Safety

- Keep a clear workplace when performing experiments with heat.
- Make sure that heating equipment, such as the burner, hot plate, or electric heater, is secure on the bench and clamped in place when necessary.
- Do not use a laboratory burner near wooden shelves, flammable liquids, or any other item that is combustible.
- Take care that the heat developed by the heat source does not cause any material close by to get hot enough to burst into flame. Do not allow overheating if you are performing an experiment in a closed area. For example, if you are using a light source in a large cardboard box, be sure you have enough holes at the top of the box and on the sides to dissipate heat.
- Before using a laboratory burner, make sure that long hair is always tied back. Do not wear loose clothing (wide long sleeves should be tied back or rolled up).

- Always assume that hot plates and electric heaters are hot and use protective gloves when handling.
- Do not touch a light source that has been on for some time. It may be hot and cause burns.
- In a laboratory where burners or hot plates are being used, never pick up a glass object without first checking the temperature by lightly and quickly touching the item, or by placing your hand near but not touching it. Glass items that have been heated stay hot for a long time, even if they do not appear to be hot. Metal items such as ring stands and hot plates can also cause burns; take care when touching them.
- Never look down the barrel of a laboratory burner.
- Always pick up a burner by the base, never by the barrel.
- Never leave a lighted burner unattended.
- Any metal powder can be explosive. Do not put these in a flame.
- When heating a test tube over a laboratory burner, use a test-tube holder and a spurt cap. Holding the test tube at an angle, with the open end pointed away from you and others, gently move the test tube back and forth through the flame.
- To heat a beaker, put it on the hot plate and secure with a ring support attached to a utility stand. (A wire gauze under the beaker is optional.)
- Remember to include a cooling time in your experiment plan; do not put away hot equipment.

To use a burner:

- Tie back long hair and tie back or roll up wide long sleeves.
- Secure the burner to a stand using a metal clamp.
- Check that the rubber hose is properly connected to the gas valve.
- Close the air vents on the burner. Use a sparker to light the burner.
- Open the air vents just enough to get a blue flame.
- Control the size of the flame using the gas valve.

Electrical Safety

- Water or wet hands should never be used near electrical equipment such as a hotplate, a light source, or a microscope.
- Do not use the equipment if the cord is frayed or if the third pin on the plug is missing. If the teacher allows this, then make sure the equipment has a double-insulated cord.
- Do not operate electrical equipment near running water or a large container of water.
- Check the condition of electrical equipment. Do not use if wires or plugs are damaged.
- If using a light source, check that the wires of the light fixture are not frayed, and that the bulb socket is in good shape and well secured to a stand.
- Make sure that electrical cords are not placed where someone could trip over them.
- When unplugging equipment, remove the plug gently from the socket. Do not pull on the cord.

Handling Chemicals Safely

Many chemicals are hazardous to some degree. When using chemicals, operate under the following principles:

- Never underestimate the risks associated with chemicals. Assume that any unknown chemicals are hazardous.
- Use a less hazardous chemical wherever possible.
- Reduce exposure to chemicals as much as possible. Avoid direct skin contact if possible.
- Ensure that there is adequate ventilation when using chemicals.

The following guidelines do not address every possible situation but, used with common sense, are appropriate for situations in the high school laboratory.

- Obtain an MSDS for each chemical and consult the MSDS before you use the chemical.
- Know the emergency procedures for the building, the department, and the chemicals being used.
- Wear a lab coat and/or other protective clothing (e.g., apron, gloves), as well as appropriate eye protection at all times in areas where chemicals are used or stored.
- Never use the contents from a bottle that has no label or has an illegible label. Give any containers with illegible labels to your teacher. When leaving chemicals in containers, ensure that the containers are labelled. Always double-check the label, once, when you pick it up, and a second time when you are about to use it.
- Carry chemicals carefully using two hands, one around the container and one underneath.
- Always pour from the side opposite the label on a reagent bottle; your hands and the label are protected

as previous drips are always on the side of the bottle opposite of the label.

- Do not let the chemicals touch your skin. Use a laboratory scoop or spatula for handling solids.
- Pour chemicals carefully (down the side of the receiving container or down a stirring rod) to ensure that they do not splash.
- Always pour volatile chemicals in a fume hood or in a well-ventilated area.
- Never pipet or start a siphon by mouth. Always use a pipet suction device (such as a bulb or a pump).
- If you spill a chemical, use a chemical spill kit to clean up.
- Return chemicals to their proper storage place according to your teacher's instructions.
- Do not return surplus chemicals to stock bottles. Dispose of excess chemicals in an appropriate manner as instructed by your teacher.
- Clean up your work area, the fume hood, and any other area where chemicals were used.
- Wash hands immediately after handling chemicals and before and after leaving the lab, even if you wore gloves. Definitely wash your hands before you touch any food.

Handling Animals, Plants, and Other Organisms Safely

- Do not perform any investigation on any animal that might cause suffering or pain, or that might pose a health hazard to you or anyone else in the school.
- Animals that live in the classroom should be treated with care and respect, and be kept in a clean, healthy environment.
- Ensure that your teacher is aware of any plant or animal allergies that you may have.
- Never bring a plant, animal, or other organism to school without receiving prior permission from the teacher.
- Keep cages and tanks clean—both for your health and the health of the organism. Most jurisdictions recommend no live mammals or birds in the laboratory. Reptiles often carry Salmonella.
- Wear gloves and wash your hands before and after feeding or handling an animal, touching materials from the animal's cage or tank, or handling bacterial cultures.
- Do not grow any microorganisms other than those that occur naturally on mouldy bread, cheese, and mildewed objects. Anaerobic bacteria should not be grown.
- Cultures should be grown at room temperature or in the range of 25 °C to 32 °C. Incubation at 37 °C may encourage the growth of microorganisms that are capable of living in the human body.
- Bacteria from soils should not be grown because of the possibility of culturing tetanus-causing organisms.
- Spores collected from household locations, such as telephones or bathrooms, should not be cultured in the laboratory. The body can destroy small numbers of these bacteria, but may not be able to cope with large numbers.
- All surfaces and equipment used in culturing microorganisms should be washed down with a disinfectant (e.g., a solution of bleach).
- Apparatus used in microbiology should be autoclaved because liquid disinfectants and germicidal agents generally cannot guarantee complete sterilization. The oven of an ordinary kitchen stove may be used.
- Wild or sick animals should never be brought into the lab. Dead animals, wild or tame, that have died from unknown causes should also not be brought into the lab.
- Preserved specimens should be removed from the preservative with gloves or tongs, and rinsed thoroughly in running water.
- Before going on field trips, become familiar with any dangerous plants and animals that may be common in the area (e.g., stinging nettles and poisonous plants).

Waste Disposal

Waste disposal at school, at home, and at work is a societal issue. To protect the environment, federal and provincial governments have regulations to control wastes, especially chemical wastes. For example, the WHMIS program applies to controlled products that are being handled. Most laboratory waste can be washed down the drain or, if it is in solid form, placed in ordinary garbage containers. However, some waste must be treated more carefully. It is your responsibility to follow procedures and to dispose of waste in the safest possible manner according to the teacher's instructions.

Flammable Substances

Flammable liquids should not be washed down the drain. Special fire-resistant containers are used to store flammable liquid waste. Waste solids that pose a fire hazard should be stored in fireproof containers. Care must be taken not to allow flammable waste to come into contact with any sparks, flames, other ignition sources, or oxidizing materials. The method of disposal depends on the nature of the substance.

Corrosive Solutions

Solutions that are corrosive but not toxic, such as acids, bases, and oxidizing agents, should be disposed of in a container provided by the teacher, preferably kept on the teacher's desk. Do not pour corrosive solutions down the drain.

Toxic Substances

Solutions of toxic substances should not be poured down the drain, in order to keep them out of the environment. A special container should be kept in the laboratory for toxic substances and disposed by a teacher, according to the regulations of your area.

Organic Material

Remains of plants and animals can generally be disposed of in school garbage containers. Before disposal, organic material should be rinsed thoroughly to rid it of any excess preservative. Fungi and bacterial cultures should be autoclaved or treated with a fungicide or antibacterial soap before disposal.

First Aid

The following guidelines apply in case of an injury, such as a burn, cut, chemical spill, ingestion, inhalation, or splash in the eyes.

- Always inform your teacher immediately of any injury.
- Know the location of the first-aid kit, fire blanket, eyewash station, and shower, and be familiar with the contents and operation of them.
- If the injury is a minor cut or abrasion, wash the area thoroughly. Using a compress, apply pressure to the cut to stop the bleeding. When bleeding has stopped, replace the compress with a sterile bandage. If the cut is serious, apply pressure and seek medical attention immediately.
- If the injury is the result of chemicals, drench the affected area with a continuous flow of water for 15 min. Clothing should be removed as necessary. Retrieve the Material Safety Data Sheet (MSDS) for the chemical; this sheet provides information about the first-aid requirements for the chemical.
- If you get a solution in your eye, quickly use the eyewash or nearest running water. Continue to rinse the eye with water for at least 15 min. This is a very long time—have someone time you. Unless you have a plumbed eyewash system, you will also need assistance in refilling the eyewash container. Have another student inform your teacher of the accident. The injured eye should be examined by a doctor.
- If you have ingested or inhaled a hazardous substance, inform your teacher immediately. The MSDS provides information about the first-aid requirements for the substance. Contact the Poison Control Centre in your area.
- If the injury is from a burn, immediately immerse the affected area in cold water or run cold water gently over the burned area. This will reduce the temperature and prevent further tissue damage.
- In case of electric shock, unplug the appliance and do not touch it or the victim. Inform your teacher immediately.
- If a classmate's injury has rendered him/her unconscious, notify the teacher immediately. The teacher will perform CPR if necessary. Do not administer CPR unless under specific instructions from the teacher. You can assist by keeping the person warm and by reassuring him/her once conscious.

Appendix C REFERENCE

C1 Numerical Prefixes and Units

Throughout *Nelson Biology Alberta 20-30* and in this reference section, we have attempted to be consistent in the presentation and usage of units. As far as possible, *Nelson Biology Alberta 20-30* uses the International System (SI) of Units. However, some other units have been included because of their practical importance, wide usage, or use in specialized fields. For example, Health Canada and the medical profession continue to use millimetres of mercury (mmHg) as the units for measurement of blood pressure, although the Metric Practice Guide indicates that this unit is not to be used with the SI.

The most recent *Canadian Metric Practice Guide* (CAN/CSA-Z234.1-89) was published in 1989 and reaffirmed in 1995 by the Canadian Standards Association.

Other data in this reference section has been taken largely from Lange's *Handbook of Chemistry*, Fifteenth Edition, McGraw-Hill, 1999.

Numerical Prefixes

Prefix	Power	Symbol
deca-	10^{1}	da
hecto-	10^{2}	h
kilo-	10^{3}	k*
mega-	10^{6}	M*
giga-	10^{9}	G*
tera-	10^{12}	T
peta-	10^{15}	P
exa-	10^{18}	E
deci-	10^{-1}	d
centi-	10^{-2}	c*
milli-	10^{-3}	m*
micro-	10^{-6}	m*
nano-	10^{-9}	n*
pico-	10^{-12}	p
femto-	10^{-15}	f
atto-	10^{-18}	a

* commonly used

Common Multiples

Multiple	Prefix
0.5	hemi–
1	mono–
1.5	sesqui–
2	bi–, di–
2.5	hemipenta–
3	tri–
4	tetra–
5	penta
6	hexa
7	hepta–
8	octa
9	nona–
10	deca–

Some Examples of Prefix Use

0.0034 mol = 3.4×10^{-3} mol = 3.4 **milli**moles or 3.4 mmol

1530 L = 1.53×10^{3} L = 1.53 **kilo**litres or 1.53 kL

C

SI Base Units

Quantity	Symbol	Unit name	Symbol
amount of substance	n	mole	mol
electric current	I	ampere	A
length	L, l, h, d, w	metre	m
luminous intensity	I_v	candela	cd
mass	m	kilogram	kg
temperature	T	kelvin	K
time	t	second	s

Some SI Derived Units

Quantity	Symbol	Unit	Unit Symbol	Expression in SI base unit
acceleration	$\vec{a}$	metre per second per second	m/s^2	m/s^2
area	A	square metre	m^2	m^2
density	ρ, D	kilogram per cubic metre	kg/m^3	kg/m^3
displacement	$\vec{d}$	metre	m	m
electric charge	Q, q, e	coulomb	C	A·s
electric potential	V	volt	V	$kg{\cdot}m^2/(A{\cdot}s^3)$
electric field	E	volt per metre	V/m	$kg{\cdot}m/(A{\cdot}s^3)$
electric field intensity	E	newton per coulomb	N/C	$kg/(A{\cdot}s^3)$
electric resistance	R	ohm	Ω	$kg{\cdot}m^2/(A^2{\cdot}s^3)$
energy	E, E_k, E_p	joule	J	$kg{\cdot}m^2/s^2$
force	F	newton	N	$kg{\cdot}m/s^2$
frequency	f	hertz	Hz	s^{-1}
heat	Q	joule	J	$kg{\cdot}m^2/s^2$
magnetic flux	Φ	weber	Wb	$kg{\cdot}m^2/(A{\cdot}s^2)$
magnetic field	B	weber per square metre Tesla	Wb/m^2 T	$kg/(A{\cdot}s^2)$
momentum	P, p	kilogram metre per second	kg·m/s	kg·m/s
period	T	second	s	s
power	P	watt	W	$kg{\cdot}m^2/s^3$
pressure	P p	pascal newton per square metre	Pa N/m^2	$kg/(m{\cdot}s^2)$
speed	v	metre per second	m/s	m/s
velocity	$\vec{v}$	metre per second	m/s	m/s
volume	V	cubic metre	m^3	m^3
wavelength	λ	metre	m	m
weight	W, w	newton	N	$kg{\cdot}m/s^2$
work	W	joule	J	$kg{\cdot}m^2/s^2$

C2 Greek and Latin Prefixes and Suffixes

Greek and Latin Prefixes

Prefix	Meaning	Prefix	Meaning	Prefix	Meaning
a-	not, without	em-	inside	micr-, micro-	small
ab-	away from	en-	in	mono-	one
abd-	led away	end-, endo-	within	morpho-	form, shape
acro-	end, tip	epi-	at, on, over	muc-, muco-	slime
adip-	fat	equi-	equal	multi-	many
aer-, aero-	air	erythro-	red	myo-	muscle
agg-	to clump	ex-, exo-	away, out	nas-	nose
agro-	land	flag-	whip	necro-	corpse
alb-	white	gamet-, gamo-	marriage, united	neo-	new
allo-	other	gastr-, gastro-	stomach	neur-, neuro-	nerve
ameb-	change	geo-	earth	noct-	night
amphi-	around, both	glyc-	sweet	odont-, odonto-	tooth
amyl-	starch	halo-	salt	oligo-	few
an-	without	haplo-	single	oo-	egg
ana-	up	hem-, hema-, hemato-	blood	orni-	bird
andro-	man	hemi-	half	oss-, osseo-, osteo-	bone
ant-, anti-	opposite	hepat-, hepa-	liver	ovi-	egg
anth-	flower	hetero-	different	pale-, paleo-	ancient
archae-, archaeo-	ancient	histo-	web	patho-	disease
archi-	primitive	holo-	whole	peri-	around
astr-, astro-	star	homeo-	same	petro-	rock
aut-, auto-	self	hydro-	water	phag-, phago-	eat
baro-	weight (pressure)	hyper-	above	pharmaco-	drug
bi-	twice	hypo-	below	phono-	sound
bio-	life	infra-	under	photo-	light
blast-, blasto-	sprout (budding)	inter-	between	pneum-	air
carcin-	cancer	intra-	inside of, within	pod-	foot
cardio-, cardia-	heart	intro-	inward	poly-	many
chlor-, chloro-	green	iso-	equal	pseud-, pseudo-	false
chrom-, chromo-	colour	lact-, lacti-, lacto-	milk	pyr-, pyro-	fire
co-	with	leuc-, leuco-	white	radio-	ray
cosmo-	order, world	lip-, lipo-	fat	ren-	kidney
cut-	skin	lymph-, lympho-	clear water	rhizo-	root
cyan-	blue	lys-, lyso-	break up	sacchar-, saccharo-	sugar
cyt-, cyto-	cell	macro-	large	sapr-, sapro-	rotten
dendr-, dendri-, dendro-	tree	mamm-	breast	soma-	body
dent-, denti-	tooth	meg-, mega-	great	spermato-	seed
derm-	skin	melan-	black	sporo-	seed
di-	two	meningo-	membrane	squam-	scale
dors-	back	mes-, meso-	middle	sub-	beneath
ec-, ecto-	outside	meta-	after, transition	super-, supra-	above

Greek and Latin Prefixes *(continued)*

Prefix	Meaning	Prefix	Meaning	Prefix	Meaning
sym-, syn-	with, together	ultra-	beyond	xanth-, xantho-	yellow
telo-	end	uro-	tail, urine	xer-, xero-	dry
therm-, thermo-	temperature, heat	vas-, vaso-	vessel	xyl-	wood
tox-	poison	vita-	life	zoo-	animal
trans-	across	vitro-	glass	zygo-	yoke
trich-	hair	vivi-	alive		

Greek and Latin Suffixes

Suffix	Meaning	Suffix	Meaning	Suffix	Meaning
-aceous	like	-lysis	loosening	-phyll	leaf
-blast	budding	-lyt	dissolvable	-phyte	plant
-cide	kill	-mere	share	-pod	foot
-crin	secrete	-metry	measure	-sis	a condition
-cut	skin	-mnesia	memory	-some	body
-cyte	cell	-oid	like	-stas, -stasis	halt
-emia	blood	-ol	alcohol	-stat	to stand, stabilize
-gen	born, agent	-ole	oil	-tone, -tonic	strength
-genesis	formation	-oma	tumour	-troph	nourishment
-graph, -graphy	to write	-osis	a condition	-ty	state of
-gynous	woman	-pathy	suffering	-vorous	eat
-itis	inflammation	-ped	foot	-yl	wood
-logy	the study of	-phage	eat	-zyme	ferment

C3 Data for Some Radioisotopes

Name	Symbol	Uses	Half-life
carbon-14	^{14}C	radiometric dating—effective dating range: 100 to 100 000 years	5730 years
fluorine-18	^{18}F	medical—to image tumours and localized infections (PET)	110 minutes
indium-111	^{111}In	medical—to study the brain, the colon, and sites of infection	2.8 days
iodine-125	^{125}I	medical—to evaluate the filtration rate of kidneys and to determine bone density measurements	42 days
iodine-131	^{131}I	medical—to view and treat thyroid, liver, kidney diseases, and various cancers	8.0 days
phosphorus-32	^{32}P	medical—to treat polycythemia vera (excess red blood cells)	14.3 days
potassium-40	^{40}K	radiometric dating—effective dating range: 100 000 to 4.6 billion years	1.3 billion years
strontium-89	^{89}Sr	medical—to relieve the pain of secondary cancers lodged in the bone	46.7 hours
technetium-99*	^{99}Tc	medical—to view the skeleton and heart muscle in particular; but also the brain, thyroid, lungs, liver, spleen, kidney, gall bladder, bone marrow, and salivary glands	6.02 hours
uranium-235	^{235}U	radiometric dating—effective dating range: 10 million to 4.6 billion years	713 million years

* the most commonly used isotope in medicine

C4 RNA Codons and Amino Acids

The codons in mRNA are nucleotide bases arranged in groups of three. There are 61 of these base triplets that correspond to 20 amino acids. In **Table 1**, read the first nucleotide from the first (left) column, the second from one of the middle columns, and the third from the last (right) column. For example, the triplet UGG represents tryptophan, and tyrosine is represented by both UAU and UAC. mRNA reads the arrangements of amino acids on the DNA and carries the information to the ribosomes for the synthesis of proteins.

Table 1: Messenger Ribonucleic Acid (mRNA) Codons and Their Corresponding Amino Acids

First Base	Second Base				Third Base
	U	C	A	G	
U	UUU phenylalanine UUC phenylalanine UUA leucine UUG leucine	UCU serine UCC serine UCA serine UCG serine	UAU tyrosine UAC tyrosine UAA STOP** UAG STOP**	UGU cysteine UGC cysteine UGA STOP** UGG tryptophan	U C A G
C	CUU leucine CUC leucine CUA leucine CUG leucine	CCU proline CCC proline CCA proline CCG proline	CAU histidine CAC histidine CAA glutamine CAG glutamine	CGU arginine CGC arginine CGA arginine CGG arginine	U C A G
A	AUU isoleucine AUC isoleucine AUA isoleucine AUG methionine*	ACU threonine ACC threonine ACA threonine ACG threonine	AAU asparagine AAC asparagine AAA lysine AAG lysine	AGU serine AGC serine AGA arginine AGG arginine	U C A G
G	GUU valine GUC valine GUA valine GUG valine	GCU alanine GCC alanine GCA alanine GCG alanine	GAU aspartate GAC aspartate GAA glutamate GAG glutamate	GGU glycine GGC glycine GGA glycine GGG glycine	U C A G

* AUG is an initiator codon and also codes for the amino acid methionine.
** UAA, UAG, and UGA are terminator codons.

Answers

Unit 20 A

Section 1.1, p. 10

1. both closed systems
2. no outside source of raw material
3. abiotic—non-living; biotic—living
4. community—all populations; ecosystem—community plus its environment
5. organism, population, community, ecosystem
7. (a) variety of species in an ecosystem
   (b) mitochondria
   (c) high–Grand Banks, north shore of Lake Erie; low–Arctic Ocean, taiga ecosystems

Section 1.2, p. 16

3. (a) lives in freshwater and forest ecosystems; skin vulnerable to pollutants
5. (b) preserve habitat for organisms at risk

Chapter 1 Review, pp. 18–19

9. (a) bounties—reduced wolf populations led to increased deer populations
   (b) hunting—reduced bison; overfishing reduced cod and salmon
   (c) increase in sea urchins led to reduction in kelp and fish
10. doubtful if the species will survive without intervention
11. (a) extinct, endangered, extirpated, threatened, vulnerable
12. (a) threatened
    (b) endangered
    (c) extirpated
15. (a) Cockroaches are scavengers that lives off garbage.

Section 2.1, p. 27

1. the position of a species on a food chain
2. eats primary consumers (meat)
3. food chain—single path; food web—multiple interwoven pathways
4. reactants—CO_2, H_2O, energy; products—O_2, glucose
5. reactants—O_2, glucose; products—CO_2, H_2O, energy
6. inorganic chemicals—hydrogen sulphide, ammonia, ferrous ions, sulfur
8. 90 % of energy required for processes such as, photosynthesis, growth, and reproduction

Practice, p. 31

1. 1st—10 cm^2 or 100cm^3; 2nd —980 cm^2 or 9800cm^3; 3rd—50 cm^2 or 500 mm^3; 4th—1 cm^2 or 10 cm^3; 5th—0.3 cm^2 or 3 cm^3

Practice, p. 32

2. plankton—200 cm^2; zooplankton—20 cm^2; herring—2 cm^2; salmon—0.2 cm^2
3. (a) 200 rabbits
   (b) 10 foxes
   (c) plants—100 cm^2 or 1000 cm^3; rabbits—20 cm^2 or 20 cm^3; foxes—1 cm^2 or 10 mm^3

Section 2.2. p. 34

1. population size of all organisms
2. does not show energy flow
5. energy flow in ecosystems obeys laws of thermodynamics; energy lost at each level
6. plant tissue
7. 150 000 kJ
8. (a) 1.5×10^6 kJ
   (b) 1st—200 cm^2; 2nd—20 cm^2; 3rd—2 cm^2; 4th—0.2cm^2

Chapter 2 Review, pp. 38–39

4. eats lower-order consumers; is not eaten by other organisms
10. 1, 2, 4—not sustainable; 3—is sustainable
14. energy assimilated by chemoautotrophs
16. (a) middle-latitude woodland ecosystem
    (b) middle-latitude woodland ecosystem
    (c) middle-latitude woodland ecosystem
19. pyramid of energy
20. 4th—100 kJ; 5th—10 kJ, insufficient to maintain a carnivore
22. producer—they convert light energy into chemical energy
24. (a) kelp → sea urchins → sea otters
    (b) reduce the kelp
    (c) decreased barnacles and mussels
25. introduced tropical fishes; chlorine leaking from swimming pool; beaver dam

Section 3.1, p. 48

1. (a) C and H
   (b) through breathing
   (c) food (in animals); roots (in plants)
   (d) breathing; excreting; decay after death
4. to determine if life has ever existed there
6. no bacteria to recycle the organic matter
7. most metabolic reactions require H_2O
9. highest level belowground that is saturated with H_2O

Section 3.2, p. 59

1. They release C from dead organisms.
3. releases C stored in peat, coal, natural gas, petroleum
4. (a) fewer plants; slower rate of photosynthesis; plants are dormant in winter
5. (a) entering—232 × 10^{13} kg; leaving—227 × 10^{13} kg.; increasing at 5 × 10^{13} kg per year
   (c) atmospheric O_2—photosynthesis produces O_2 as a by-product
6. (a) reduces atmospheric O_2—photosynthesis is reduced
   (b) more difficult for plants and animals to carry on respiration

D

Section 3.3, p. 66

1. Nutrients are stored in the crops.
3. (a) Spring runoff contains nitrates and nitrites.
5. green manure
6. used to produce proteins and nucleic acids
7. must be converted into nitrates before it can be used by organisms
8. consume dead organic matter
9. bacteria converts N to nitrates for plant; plant provide sugar to bacteria
11. exposes denitrifying bacteria to O_2
12. ADP, ATP, cell membranes, DNA molecules, bones
13. fix N improving soil quality
14. lack N-fixing bacteria and organism that aerate the soil
16. (a) 3—low soil nitrates, high biomass nitrates
    (b) 1 grassland—high soil temperature and biomass nitrates
    2 temperate rainforest—low soil temperature and high biomass nitrates
    3 tropical rainforest—high soil temperature and high biomass nitrates
    (c) low soil and biomass nitrate; low soil temperature
18. ammonia, nitrates, nitrites pollute groundwater

19. both water soluble; taken up by plant roots to enter the food chain

Chapter 3 Review, pp. 73–75

7. cycling of materials through the biosphere
16. May—70 %; August—20 %
17. willow
18. balsam poplar—47 % loss
19. temperature
20. arrival of insects; increase in bacteria
22. energy flows through an ecosystem; nutrients are recycled
24. manipulated—distance to light; responding—number O_2 bubbles
25. light, size and species of plant; amount and temperature of water
27. Fire returns nutrients and minerals to the soil.
29. (a) photosynthesis, respiration
32. O_2 solubility increases as temperatures decrease.

Unit 20 A Review, pp. 76–79

38. How can transpiration be measured?
39. leaf number, size; amount of sunlight
41. decrease
42. reduced surface area, leaf number, stomata number; cuticle; hairs

Unit 20 B

4.1 Practice, p. 86

1. study of all interactions in the biosphere
2. population—one species; community—many populations
3. ecosystem is the community plus biotic and abiotic components

Section 4.1, p. 93

2. ecotone—organisms from both ecosystems found there
4. organism's role in food web and abiotic and biotic requirements

4.2 Practice, p. 98

1. layer of frozen soil that doesn't melt in summer
2. muskeg—poor drainage, short growing season, cool temperatures; grassland—warm temperatures, rapid nutrient cycling
3. adapted to moist, acidic soils and cooler temperatures
4. too arid

Section 4.2, p. 100

2. waxy needles, pyramid shaped, flexible branches
3. (a) deciduous forest > taiga > muskeg > grassland
   (b) grassland > deciduous forest > taiga > muskeg
   (c) grassland > deciduous forest > taiga > muskeg
   (d) deciduous forest > grassland > taiga > muskeg

4.3 Practice, p. 104

2. depth and type of the bedrock, precipitation

Section 4.3, p. 107

1. fertilizers, sewage emissions, litter from plants, animal wastes, die-off

Section 4.4, pp. 111–112

1. biotic potential, limiting factors, carrying capacity, limits of tolerance
2. (a) increase carrying capacity
   (b) falcons are feeding the waxwings; falcon attracted to feeders
3. (a) increase in the moose population
   (b) wolf population should recover; population size will fluctuate
   (c) when biotic or abiotic conditions become favourable
5. (a) C—causes steady decline in beetles
   (b) D—beetle increases and D decreases
   (c) each predator eats many prey
   (d) population would crash; surviving beetles help population rebound

4.5 Practice, p. 115

1. recycle H_2O and CO_2; prevent soil erosion
2. slash and burn, clear-cutting, selective cutting
3. decrease biodiversity, wind and water erosion, deplete soil nutrients

4.5 Practice, p. 118

4. organic solid waste, thermal energy, organic chemicals
5. warm lake—more productive
6. fertilizer run off, run off of organic salts from roads

4.5 Practice, p. 120

7. removing plants, making a sandy beach, planting lawns
8. increase runoff of harmful substances, increase water temperature
9. positive—reduce economic and ecological costs; negative—affect water cycle

Section 4.5, p. 122

4. (a) decreases
   (b) deeper lakes are cooler
   (c) higher lake temperatures lead to greater littoral zone diversity
   (e) eat plants found in 2nd stage
5. (a) sewage-treatment plant
   (b) B—nitrate and phosphate levels are highest
   (c) more organisms live at B; they consume O_2
   (d) C—fewer nutrients; fewer organisms consuming O_2
   (e) no—drop in dissolved O_2; high nutrient load

Chapter 4 Review, pp. 130–133

9. algae, fescue grass
10. wet, muddy, and windy
11. both pond and grassland species present
12. likely effect both ecosystems

5.1 Practice, p. 137

2. naming organisms using genus and species
3. provides a common language
4. kingdom, phylum, class, order, family, genus, species

Section 5.1, p. 139

1. illustration showing relations among organisms
2. unified classification system
3. reduces confusion; shows evolutionary relationships
5. Archaebacteria—oldest form of life
6. (a) (vii)
   (b) (i)
   (c) (iv)
   (d) (iii)
   (e) (vi)
   (f) (v)
   (g) (viii)
   (h) (ii)
7. (a) mink, shorttailed weasel, ferret
   (b) muskrat
   (c) chipmunk
   (d) groundhog, chipmunk

5.2 Practice, p. 142

2. method to age rock

Section 5.2, p. 143

1. (a) older fossils—less complex, lower diversity
2. remote island—less gene flow

5.3 Practice, p. 145

1. analogous

Section 5.3, p. 149

4. evolutionary rate is quite fast

Section 5.4, p. 152

1. (a) selection against large males
   (b) rate is unchanged

Section 5.5, p. 156

1. unaware of the source of variation

Section 5.6, p. 161

4. distinct species often appear abruptly in fossil record; little further change

Chapter 5 Review, pp. 168–169

13. natural selection
14. all letters have an equal chance of "mutating" in each generation

15. not included in the next generation
16. yes—eventually
18. yes
19. yes
20. no
23. shows how related species differ
24. advantages—accuracy, quantitative; disadvantages—costly, time consuming

Unit 20 B Review, pp. 170–173

19. becomes shallower and warmer
20. sedimentation; lower water table; decreased rainfall; diverted stream
22. decrease O_2—loss of some species
23. lakes becoming colder; continued respiration under ice
24. changing O_2 levels
25. removal of shoreline plants; fertilizers; thermal pollution
26. most economical (short-term); reduces biodiversity, soil erosion, loss of soil nutrients
28. spring and autumn
29. spring—flush of nutrients; autumn—decomposing organic matter
35. sewage—increase BOD, decreased dissolved O_2
39. sexual reproducing species have greater variability

Unit 20 C

6.1 Practice, p. 181

1. plants, plantlike protists, cyanobacteria
2. (a) form of energy that travels at 3×10^8 m/s in the form of photons
   (b) EM wave packets of light

6.1 Practice, p. 182

3. chlorophyll
4. chlorophyll *a*—dark blue and orange; chlorophyll *b*—light blue and dark yellow

Section 6.1, p. 185

1. (a) As wavelength increases, the energy in a photon decreases.
   (b) green light—it has a shorter wavelength
   (c) A higher wavelength has lower energy. Red light is 750 nm; violet is 380 nm.
2. (a) chlorophyll *a*, chlorophyll *b*, carotenoids, xanthophylls, anthocyanins
3. contain the molecule chlorophyll to capture electromagnetic radiation
4. A—thylakoid; B—stroma; C—inner envelope membrane; D—outer envelope membrane

6.2 Practice, p. 187

1. ATP, NADPH, glucose
2. thylakoid membrane of a chloroplast
3. stroma of chloroplasts

6.2 Practice, p. 188

4. thylakoid membrane
5. Electrons gain energy or become excited.
6. replaced by photolysis of water

6.2 Practice, p. 190

7. enter the electron transport chain
9. oxidation—loss of electrons; reduction—gain of electrons
10. They release energy in small amounts.

6.2 Practice, p. 191

11. electrons from photosystem II
12. build up a positive charge inside the lumen
13. used to transfer high-energy electrons to the Calvin cycle
14. process for synthesizing ATP

6.2 Practice, p. 193

15. stroma
16. G3P—used to make glucose

Section 6.2, p. 194

1. adenosine triphosphate—a usable form of chemical energy
2. $6\ CO_2 + 6\ H_2O \rightarrow 6\ O_2 + C_6H_{12}O_6$
3. (a) capture electromagnetic radiation; convert it to chemical potential energy
   (b) thylakoid membranes
   (c) O_2, ATP, NADPH
   (d) Calvin cycle
4. (a) O_2
   (b) H_2O
6. (a) 12
   (b) 36
   (c) 24

Chapter 6 Review, pp. 200–201

11. (a) short wavelengths
    (b) 380 to 480 nm and 620 to 680 nm
14 purple, blue, orange, and red—they are most absorbed by the pigments
15 green—they are the least absorbed
16 chlorophyll *a*
17 Chlorophyll does not absorb green light, it reflects it.
18 chlorophyll *a*, chlorophyll *b*

7.1 Practice, p. 205

1. converts glucose into usable ATP

Section 7.1, p. 209

2. produces waste energy which heats our bodies
4. provides cells with energy for cellular processes
5. glycolysis, pyruvate oxidation, Krebs cycle, electron transport chain and chemiosmosis

Section 7.2, p. 212

1. 1 glucose + 2 ADP + 2 P_i + 2 $NAD^+ \rightarrow$ 2 pyruvate + 2 ATP + 2 NADH + 2 H^+
2. (a) splitting of a glucose molecule into two pyruvate molecules
   (b) 2 pyruvate, 2 NADH, 2 ADP, 4 ATP
3. NADH, 2 pyruvate molecules

7.3 Practice, p. 215

1. Krebs cycle, electron transport chain, chemiosmosis
2. gains 2 H^+ ions and 2 electrons to become NADH
3. joins to acetic acid group to form acetyl-coA

7.3 Practice, p. 219

5. 6 CO_2, 6 H_2O, 36 ATP
6. $FADH_2$, NADH.

Section 7.3, p. 220

2. (a) cytoplasm
   (b) pyruvate, NADH
5. (a) hydrogen
   (d) chemiosmosis
   (e) Peter Mitchell
6. (b) oxygen
7. does not show the formation of energy or that water is required

7.4 Practice, p. 222

2. CO_2
3. (a) 2
   (b) alcoholic fermentation—2; lactic acid fermentation—0
   (c) none

7.4 Practice, p. 226

4. alcohol fermentation—CO_2, ethanol; lactic acid fermentation—lactic acid
5. muscle stiffness, soreness, fatigue

Section 7.4, p. 228

2. build-up of lactic acid
6. (a) 3.0 mmol/L

Chapter 7 Review, pp. 232–233

11. (a) 36
    (b) 2
15. lactic acid
16. allow lactic acid to be converted into pyruvate
18. A—faster growth rate
22. 15 mL/kg/min
23. resting—1125 mL/min; highest VO_2 max—6750 mL/min

Unit 20 C Review, pp. 234–235

16. photosynthesis
17. cellular respiration
18. glucose—accumulate; CO_2—decrease
19. Biomass would increase.

Unit 20 D

8.1 Practice, p. 245

1. provide energy
2. glucose (many foods); fructose (fruit); galactose (milk)

D

4. They are converted to fat and stored.
5. Sugars end in "ose."
6. They are both polysaccharides; starch is a storage molecule, cellulose is a structural molecule.

8.1 Practice, p. 247

7. compounds of carbon, hydrogen, and oxygen that supply energy to cells
8. fatty acids and glycerol
9. saturated fats—contain no double bonds; unsaturated fats—contain double bonds
10. yes—they carry some important vitamins

Section 8.1, p. 253

1. glucose + fructose = sucrose + H_2O
2. excess of glucose in the blood is converted to glycogen in the liver and stored; can be used for energy
3. holds water and helps eliminate solid waste
4. (a) donkey and horse
   (b) very dissimilar; less similar

Section 8.2, p. 258

1. increase the rates of chemical reactions without high temperatures
2. bring reactants together in the proper configuration, reducing activation energy
3. temperature, pH, substrate concentration, inhibitor molecules
4. They help enzymes combine with substrates.
5. molecules that fit the active site of an enzyme and inhibit the reaction
7. feedback inhibition
11. (a) A—reactants; B—activation energy; C—products
    (b) reaction will slow down
    (c) curve would be flatter
12. (b) rate of reaction would decrease

8.3 Practice, p. 260

1. initiates carbohydrate breakdown (amylase); lubricates food passage; dissolves food particles; activates taste buds
2. breaks food into smaller pieces, increasing surface area for enzyme action
3. initiate the hydrolysis (breakdown) of carbohydrates
4. peristalsis

Section 8.3, p. 263

2. physical—breaks down large particles by chewing; chemical digestion—breaks chemical bonds with enzymes
3. only voluntary action is swallowing
4. (a) carnivores
   (b) herbivores
5. sphincter muscles
6. mucus, hydrochloric acid, pepsinogens
7. protects the cells of the stomach
8. instrument used to view the inside of the body
9. pH, temperature
10. amylase—initiates breakdown of carbohydrates; pepsin—initiates breakdown of protein
11. bacteria, stomach acid
12. They would digest proteins and long-chain peptides even in the absence of food.
13. pH 2.0—stomach; pH 7.0—mouth
14. pH of stomach changes shape of the amylase, making it inactive
15. more tooth decay; acids cause tooth decay

8.4 Practice, p. 266

1. bicarbonate ions buffer HCl
2. trypsinogen and erepsins, amylases, lipases
4. lipase, phospholipase acts on phospholipids; yes
5. bicarbonate ions neutralize HCl in the duodenum inactivating pepsin
6. less absorption; overall food energy intake is reduced
7. lined with villi and microvilli; they increase the surface area for absorption

8.4 Practice, p. 268

8. bile salts and pigments; produced in liver; stored in the gallbladder
9. emulsify fats, providing more surface area for fat-digesting enzymes
10. It is nonpolar.
12. water reabsorption
13. provides bulk

Section 8.4, p. 270

1. must be emulsified; occurs in small intestine; bile salts break up fat
3. both; carbohydrates and amino acids—capillary networks of villi; fats—lacteals
5. seeing or smelling food
7. crystals of precipitated bile salts in the gallbladder
8. yellowish discoloration of tissues caused by a buildup of bile pigments in the blood
9. reduce fat intake

Chapter 8 Review, pp. 278–279

10. soluble in fats (nonpolar solvents) and water (polar solvents) so they can penetrate cell membranes
12. reaction X
13. enzyme is being used at its maximum rate
14. reaction X—curve would rise; reaction Y—line would become steeper
15. reaction would be blocked between R and S

9.1 Practice, p. 283

1. Cells of the body obtain energy through oxidation.
2. breathing—movement of gases between the external environment and the lungs; cellular respiration—the oxidation of glucose in cells of the body, producing ATP
3. diffusion of oxygen and carbon dioxide between the cells and the external environment

9.1 Practice, p. 285

4. remove foreign particles trapped in the mucus that lines the respiratory tract

Section 9.1, p. 287

7. inhalation—ribs move upward, diaphragm moves downward; exhalation—ribs move downward, diaphragm moves upward
8. Narrower airways decrease airflow during inhalation and exhalation.
9. less blood flow, less oxygen to the cells of the body

9.2 Practice, p. 288

1. (a) atmospheric air; cells
   (b) oxygen diffuses from an area of high partial pressure to an area of low partial pressure
2. cells; atmospheric air

Section 9.2, p. 291

1. A gas diffuses from an area of high pressure in the alveoli to an area of low pressure in the blood.
4. atmosphere, alveoli, blood plasma, red blood cells, hemoglobin
5. speeds the conversion of carbon dioxide and water to carbonic acid

9.3 Practice, p. 295

1. inflammation of the bronchial tubes; tissue swelling, excess mucus production, narrowing of the bronchial tubes, reduced air flow

Section 9.3, p. 297

1. stimulate chemoreceptors in the medulla oblongata
5. dissolves in plasma; combines with hemoglobin to form carbamino-hemoglobin; combines with water from the plasma to form carbonic acid
7. allows a greater number of foreign particles to enter the lungs
10. air in lungs allows more X rays to pass through; tumour blocks more X rays

Section 9.4, p. 304

1. the sheath that surrounds muscle fibres
2. actin and myosin

3. thin actin filaments and thick myosin filaments overlap and produce a striped appearance
4. to provide energy
5. It ensures ATP supplies remain high by supplying a phosphate to ADP.
6. the state of constant muscle contraction due to repeated muscle stimulation
7. sprinting—athlete A; long-distance running—athlete B

Chapter 9 Review, pp. 308–309

9. W—alveolus; X—trachea; Y—bronchiole
10. X
11. Y
13. (a) approximately 2.2 s
    (b) approximately 1.0 s
    (c) approximately 3.0 s
17. fetal hemoglobin—fetus secures oxygen from the mother's blood

10.1 Practice, p. 316

1. change in the diameter of the arteries following heart contraction
2. vasodilation—widening of blood vessel; vasoconstriction—narrowing of the blood vessel
3. diffusion of gases, nutrients, and wastes between the blood and surrounding cells

Section 10.1, p. 318

1. Blood rushes into capillaries.
2. no—if open all the time, blood rushing into capillaries would cause a dramatic drop in blood pressure
3. advantage—small distance for diffusion of gases and nutrients; disadvantage—easily damaged
5. may rupture, causing hemorrhage
7. Skeletal muscles massage blood back to the heart; veins have one-way valves to prevent back flow of blood.
8. pooling of blood in veins; avoiding standing for long periods
9. (b) restricted blood flow to organs; high blood pressure
   (c) medication to reduce cholesterol; balloon angioplasty

10.2 Practice, p. 320

1. systemic—carries oxygenated blood to the tissues of the body and deoxygenated blood back to the heart; pulmonary—carries deoxygenated blood to the lungs and oxygenated blood back to the heart
2. AV valves—prevent the back flow of blood from the ventricles into the atria; semilunar valves—prevent the back flow of blood from the arteries into the ventricles
3. chest pain; too little oxygen reaching the heart due to narrowing of the coronary arteries
4. operation to divert blood flow around a blockage to maintain adequate oxygen for heart muscle

10.2 Practice, p. 323

5. muscle that contracts without external nerve stimulation
6. sympathetic—prepares the body for stress; parasympathetic—returns the body to normal following adjustments to stress

10.2 Practice, p. 325

7. diastole—relaxation of the heart during which the cavities of the heart fill with blood; systole—contraction of the heart during which blood is pushed out of the heart
8. closing of the heart valves
9. faulty heart valves

Section 10.2, p. 327

1. atria—thin-walled chambers of the heart that receive blood from veins; ventricles—thick-walled chambers of the heart that deliver blood to the arteries
2. Blood flows one way through arteries and veins.
5. stronger in carotid artery because it is closer to the heart
8. beats faster, contracts with more force, increases in mass
9. a recording of the electrical impulses of the heart
13. advantage—do not carry antigens therefore rejection is less likely, do not harbour viruses and other infectious diseases; disadvantage—do not work as well as real hearts
14. beta 1 blocker

10.3 Practice, p. 332

1. high blood pressure
2. increase it
4. different body mass, less effective respiratory system

Section 10.3, p. 335

1. Increased stroke volume increases cardiac output.
4. no
5. heart is at the same level as the blood pressure receptors; less pressure needed to get blood to the head
7. Erect hair traps warm, still air to help reduce heat loss.
8. wearing clothes to stay warm, being in the sun
9. Core body temperature (rectal) is usually higher than oral temperature, which is affected by movement of cooler air into mouth.
12. A—sweating; B—evaporation; C—adjustment; D—shivering; E—adjustment
13. reduce fat in diet; increase physical activity

10.4 Practice, p. 337

1. arterioles
2. greater
3. filtration

Section 10.4, p. 339

1. fluid pressure and osmotic pressure
4. open-ended vessels that transport lymph fluid; they join the venous system
5. fluid that contains some small proteins; transported in lymph vessels; the venous system
6. They produce antibodies.
7. a reservoir for blood and a filtering site for lymph

Chapter 10 Review, pp. 346–347

9. 1 and 2
10. 5
11. 4 and 7
13. false
14. It pumps blood a greater distance.
15. high blood pressure; heart attack
21. Constriction of arterioles reduces blood flow to placenta.

11.1 Practice, p. 352

1. plasma, cellular components
2. albumin—maintain osmotic pressure in capillaries; globulins—antibodies; fibrinogens—blood clotting
3. carry oxygen
4. high altitude, hemorrhage
5. reduction of blood oxygen levels
6. initiate blood clotting

Section 11.1, p. 356

1. red blood cells—transport oxygen
3. undetermined—they have no nucleus when they are mature
4. anemia, hemorrhage
5. have nuclei when mature; don't carry hemoglobin
6. destroy invading microbes; form antibodies
7. form a plug to stop bleeding; release substances to trap more platelets and cause clotting proteins to form
8. embolus—dislodged blood clot; thrombus—blood clot that blocks a blood vessel
9. advantages—long storage time, no need to match blood type, no viruses; disadvantages—no clotting or immunity function
10. B

11. bacterial or viral infection
12. C
13. A
14. to increase the amount of oxygen delivered to tissue
15. Rh+ red blood cells have Rhesus antigen
16. it has no A or B antigens; it has both A and B antigens
17. B, O: agglutination of blood; A, AB: no agglutination
18. Antibodies from mother destroy red blood cells of fetus.

Section 11.2, p. 366

1. destroys the cell walls of foreign bacteria
4. swelling—sign of the inflammatory response; pus—phagocytosis is occurring
9. low—autoimmune disease is destroying leukocytes; high—infection

Section 11.3, p. 370

1. overreaction by the immune system
3. increases heart rate, compensating for the drop in blood pressure
4. Immune system attacks cells of the body as if they were foreign.
6. to reduce rejection of the donated organ by the recipient

Chapter 11 Review, pp. 374–375

11. memory B cells quickly stimulate the antibody-producing B cells
12. T lymphocytes—processed by the thymus gland, do not produce antibodies; B lymphocytes—produce antibodies
13. Protein coat allows it to attach to cell.
15. chemical messenger between T cells and B cells
16. (a) puncture membranes of cells infected with foreign invaders
    (b) read a blueprint of the invader and pass it on to B cells, which produce antibodies
    (c) turn off the immune system
    (d) retain information about the shape of an antigen
17. they had no immunity
18. cells capable of differentiating into a number of different specialized cells
21. X
22. Z
23. Y
24. antibiotics might be used as treatment
25. they indicate the presence of a microbe

12.1 Practice, p. 380

1. elimination of wastes and regulation of pH and water balance
2. removal of an amino group from an organic compound

Section 12.1, p. 386

1. Two kidneys provide a backup if one kidney fails.
2. filter blood
3. (a) D—kidney
   (b) E—ureter
   (c) C—renal artery
   (d) F—bladder
5. (a) glucose in the blood exceeds threshold level
   (b) excess glucose in nephron creates strong osmotic force, drawing water into nephron

Section 12.2, p. 392

1. precipitation of mineral solutes from the blood
7. rejection of the donor kidney by the recipient
8. (a) D
   (b) decreased blood pressure would decrease filtration and urine output
   (c) glucose in nephron creates an osmotic force, drawing fluids from the extracellular fluid into the nephron, increasing urine production

Chapter 12 Review, pp. 396–397

7. (b), (c), (e), (f), (a), (d)
8. proteins
9. urea
10. glucose
11. diffusion; dialysis solution
13. mitochondria provide ATP
15. increase
18. reduce filtration, thereby decreasing the amount of urine
20. it decreases

Unit 20 D Review, pp. 398–401

15. (a) capillary
    (b) aorta
16. (a) 10—diaphragm
    (b) 5—left bronchus
    (c) 2—epiglottis
    (d) 9—lung
17. (a) flask 2
19. emphysema, cardiovascular disease (heart attack and stroke)
20. 1—pancreatin and bile salts are needed for the digestion of fats and proteins
21. Fats are digested to fatty acids and proteins are broken down to amino acids, which both lower pH.
22. Bile salts in test tube 4 cause emulsification allowing pancreatin to chemically digest more of lipids.
23. Only physical digestion has occurred.
24. myoglobin
25. approximately 55 mmHg
26. approximately 40 mmHg
37. the state of constant muscle contraction caused by sustained nerve impulses

Unit 30 A

Section 13.1, p. 414

3. III, II, I

13.2 Practice, p. 418

2. A nerve of muscle responds completely or not at all.

Section 13.2, p. 425

1. They are very large.
3. opens at A
4. at peak between B and C

13.3 Practice, p. 429

1. cerebrum, corpus callosum, thalamus, hypothalamus, olfactory bulbs
2. cerebellum, pons, medulla oblongata
3. corpus callosum
4. acts as a relay station between cerebellum and medulla

Section 13.3, p. 432

3. right and left hemispheres could not communicate
5. cerebrum—contains the area of memory

Section 13.4, p. 435

2. preganglionic neurons, postganglionic neurons
3. innervate the heart bronchi, liver, pancreas, digestive tract

Chapter 13 Review, p. 441–443

15. cerebellum
17. 20 mV.
18. Neuron B

Section 14.1, p. 448

1. chemical—taste buds, olfactory cells; mechanical—skin; heat—skin; light—eye; sound—ear

14.2 Practice, p. 541

1. sclera, choroid layer, retina

Section 14.2, p. 455

2. adjustment of lens to near and far
3. rods respond to low-intensity light

Chapter 14 Review, pp. 466–467

11. 25 °C
12. 42 °C
20. effect of age on near-point accommodation
21. As age increases, near-point accommodation decreases.
22. 50 years

15.1 Practice, p. 472

1. Internal environment is maintained despite changes in external environment.

15.1 Practice, p. 475

4. chemical produced by an endocrine
5. no

Section 15.1, p. 477

3. have specific receptor sites which bind with hormones

15.2 Practice, p. 482

6. stimulates liver to convert amino acids into glucose

Chapter 15 Review, pp. 501–502

12. thirst, tiredness
21. Does caffeine affect endurance of athletes or non-athletes?
23. both decaffeinated treatments
25. caffeine effects endurance of athletes only

Unit 30 B

16.1 Practice, p. 514

1. unable to produce viable sperm

16.1 Practice, p. 515

3. formation of sperm

16.2 Practice, p. 522

1. contains oocyte

16.2 Practice, p. 526

4. FSH and LH regulate production of estrogen and progesterone

Section 16.2, p. 529

4. Menstrual cycle would not be initiated.
5. test to diagnose cervical cancer
6. (a) ovum would not reach the uterus
   (b) yes—hormones that trigger menstruation and ovulation are produced

16.3 Practice, p. 532

1. amnion—protects embryo; allentois—provides blood vessels to placenta

Section 16.3, p. 544

1. mass of undifferentiated cells which implants in the endometrium
2. prevents corpus luteum degeneration; avoids menstruation

Unit 30 B Review, pp. 548–551

15. sperm not viable
17. reduces availability of testosterone receptor sites causing testes to atrophy
18. decreases secretion of GnRH
22. X
23. Z
32. Identical twins result in 1 corpus lutei; fraternal twins result in 2.
34. in vitro fertilization
35. genetic mother has blocked Fallopian tubes and is unable to carry fetus

Unit 30 C

17.1 Practice, p. 562

1. interphase, prophase, metaphase, anaphase; telophase
2. 10

Section 17.1, p. 564

1. Genetic material must replicate.
2. pro—prior to; meta—occurring later than; ana—backward; telo—end
3. genetically identical; daughter cells smaller, fewer organelles
4. microtubules—direct chromosomes
5. produces two distinct cells; single cell with two nuclei
6. divide or die
7. dead cells not replaced; organism would die
8. Both sister chromatids moved to the same pole.
10. regulates the number of cell divisions
12. (a) 36 h—dividing at slower rate
    (b) 24 h cell
13. blood, skin, digestive tract
14. cells divide too quickly to specialize
15. no—blood cells continually replaced

17.2 Practice, p. 569

2. developed from the same fertilized egg
3. no
4. a cell with no nucleus

Section 17.2, p. 571

1. nucleus from one cell removed and inserted into cytoplasm of another
2. cloned from an adult cell
3. Females would be able to produce females by cloning.

17.3 Practice, p. 575

1. the formation of gametes
2. Haploid cells have half the number of chromosomes.
3. a pair of homologous chromosomes, each with two chromatids
4. chromosomes similar in shape, size, genetic arrangement, information
5. yes
6. no

Section 17.3, p. 581

1. first—homologous chromosomes separate; second—chromatids separate
2. new combinations of genetic material due to crossing over
4. (a) 22
   (b) 11
   (c) 22
8. (a) B and C
   (b) 6
9. (a) Z
   (b) W and X
10. male determines sex of the child
11. female; genetically identical to the mother

17.4 Practice, p. 586

1. Klinefelter syndrome

Section 17.4, p. 586

1. Both homologous chromosomes move to the same pole.
2. monosomy—1 homologous chromosome; trisomy—3 homologous chromosomes
3. trisomy of chromosome 21
4. pictorial representation of homologous chromosomes
5. monosomy (XO) of sex chromosomes

Chapter 17 Review, pp. 593–595

14. Skin becomes thicker if cells are damaged due to abrasion.
15. nondisjunction

21A

22. D—9; E—8; F—7
23. fertilization
24. E
25. D—trisomy; F—monosomy

Section 18.1, p. 600

2. each allele located on a homologous chromosome
3. genotype—*RR*; phenotype—round seeds
4. (a) homozygous—*BB*; heterozygous—*Bb*
   (b) no—yellow dog must have two yellow alleles
5. (a) *Rr* and *rr*
   (b) *R* and *r*
   (c) both *r*
   (d) *Rr* and *rr*; 1/2 round, 1/2 wrinkled

18.2 Practice, p. 602

1. 100 % tall
2. 100 % red; 100 % *Rr*

18.2 Practice, p. 604

3. perform a test cross of red male and yellow female
4. both *Rr*

Section 18.2, p. 604

1. (b) *ss*; non-spotted
2. both *Hh*

18.3 Practice, p. 606

1. (a) 4
   (b) both *Dd*
   (c) both *dd*

Section 18.3, p. 607

1. (a) *Hh*
   (b) *hh*
   (c) 3
2. (a) 3
   (b) 5
   (c) 1—*Pp*; 2—*pp*
   (d) probability of inheriting *P* allele is 50 %
   (e) no

18.4 Practice, p. 609

1. 1:1 wild-type eyes:apricot eyes

Section 18.4, p. 612

1. (a) C^hC^a and C^aC^a; 50 % Himalayan, 50 % albino
   (b) full-colour—CC^a; light-grey—$C^{ch}C^a$
   (c) $C^{ch}C^{ch}$ and $C^{ch}C^a$; 50 % chinchilla, 50 % light grey

(d) $C^{ch}C^{h}$

2. 1:1 C^mC^m to C^mC^r; 1:1 cremello to palomino
3. skin colour

18.5 Practice, p. 616

1. (a)
   (b)
   (c)

Section 18.5, p. 619

1. (a) *BbSs* and *Bbss*; 1/2 black short, 1/2 black long
   (b) *BbSs*, *Bbss*, *bbSs*, *bbss*; 1/4 black short, 1/4 black long, 1/4/ white short, 1/4 white long
   (c) BBSs, *BbSs*, *BBss*, *Bbss*; 1/2 black short, 1/2 black long
2. male—*BbHh*; female A—*bbHH*; female B—*BbHh*; female C—*bbhh*
3. A, Rh+; A, Rh–; O, Rh+; O, Rh–

Chapter 18 Review, pp. 623–625

10. male—*Tt*; first female and her foal—*tt*; second female—*tt*; second foal—*Tt*; third female—*Tt*; third foal—*tt*
11. (a) A or B
    (b) AB—yes; O—no
13. codominance
14. 25 % T^mT^m, 50 % T^mT^n, 25 % T^nT^n
16. no
17. male—H^nH^n (normal) with female—H^nH^B
18. no—females must be H^BH^B to be bald

Section 19.1, p. 634

2. sex cells—haploid; somatic cells—diploid
4. hemophilia, colour blindness
6. (a) if mother heterozygous, hemophilic male offspring possible
   (b) father—hemophilic; mother—carrier or hemophilic
7. (a) X^CX^c and X^CY; all have colour vision
   (b) X^CX^C X^CX^c X^CY X^cY; 75 % normal colour vision, 25 % colour blind (male)

(c) father—X^cY; mother—X^CX^c or X^cX^c

19.2 Practice, p. 639

1. B → 4 → A → 10 → C

Section 19.2, p. 641

1. closer genes less likely to crossover
2. increases variability
3. (a) A → 12 → C → 11 → B
   (b) X → 6.25 → Y → 2.25 → Z

Chapter 19 Review, pp. 657–659

14. P_1—X^WX^w, X^WY; F_1—X^WX^W, X^WX^w, X^WY, X^wY
16. Y-linked trait
17. 1—normal female; 2—normal male
18. 25 %
19. 50 %
20. 4: X^HX^h; 5: X^HY
23. *C* and *S*
24. *FV* allele—between *C* and *B* alleles

20.1 Practice, p. 663

2. pairing does not allow for hydrogen bonding
3. 3'–TACGGAAT–5'

Section 20.1, p. 666

2. purine—double ringed; pyrimidine—single ring
4. thymine—20 %, adenine—20 %, guanine—30 %, cytosine—30 %
6. 2.2 x10^8

20.2 Practice, p. 669

1. AUGAUGCCAUCCAUAU
2. (b) ATAATAT

20.2 Practice, p. 671

3. AUGCCUAAAGAGGCUU UAAUCCC
4. Met-Pro-Ser-Ile-Pro-Gly-Arg-stop
5. 15

Section 20.2, p. 676

1. DNA to mRNA to protein
2. ribosomes—synthesize protein; mRNA—template for protein synthesis; tRNA—delivers amino acids to ribosome
4. CCUAGUCCAGGUCCGU UAAAUCGUACGGGGUU
5. Met-Gly-His-Tyr-Phe-Ala-Arg-Cys-Gly-Gly-Ala-stop
6. 15
7. (a) RNA polymerase will continue to transcribe and build mRNA beyond the gene.
   (b) Transcription will not take place.
10. D

20.3 Practice, p. 681

1. (a) 5'–AATTCGCCC GGG ATATTACGGATTATGC ATTATCCGCCC GGG ATATTTAGCA–3'
   3'–TTAAGCGGG CCC TATAATGCCTAATACG TAATAGGCGGG CCC TATAAAATCGA–5'
   (b) 3
   (c) blunt ends
2. sticky ends
4. GCGCTAAGGATAGCATTC GAATTCCCAATTAGGATC CTTTAAAGCTTATCC CGCGATTCCTATCGTAAG CTTAAGGGTTAATCCTAG GAAATTTCGAATAGG

Section 20.3, p. 686

2. (a) digest foreign DNA or DNA that is unmethylated
3. blunt ends—ends fully base-paired; sticky ends—possess single-stranded overhangs
4. recognition site—DNA sequence that a restriction endonuclease recognizes and cuts

Section 20.4, p. 694

2. can change the reading frame
3. nonsense
4. UV radiation, X rays, chemicals
5. (a) single-base substitution—no effect
   (b) nonsense mutation—UAA is a stop codon, protein is not fully translated
   (c) frameshift mutation—different amino acids
   (d) frameshift mutation—different amino acids
   (e) inversion—different protein is synthesized
6. (a), (c), (d)

Chapter 20 Review, pp. 702–704

11. TTAACGTAT
13. adenine—22.5 %; thymine—22.5 %; cytosine—27.5 %; guanine—27.5 %
16. lys–tyr–ser
20. CGTCATCGATCATGCAGC TC
24. valine
25. repeating valine amino acids—cause protein to have different function
29. mtDNA
31. PCR and gene sequencing

Unit 30 C Review, pp. 705–711

17. whitefish: I—81 %; P—10 %; M—5 %; A—1 %; T—3 %
    frog: I—88% ; P—6 %; M—5 %; A—0 %; T—1 %
18. prophase
21. interphase
22. prophase
24. X—meiosis I; Y—meiosis II
26. C
27. 22
29. 47
30. yes—XX girl, XY boy
32. Z
33. Z
35. all black short hair
36. 9:3:3:1
37. A—*RRFf*; B—*RrFF*; C—*RrFf*; D—*RrFF*
38. 9 black : 3 brown : 4 albino
41. normal—Met-Gln-Val-Thr-Ser-Val; mutated—Met-Gln-Val-Thr-Tyr-Leu-Ser
42. normal—TACGTCCACT GGAGTCAC; mutated—TACGTCCACTGTATGGAG TCAC
43. TACGTCCACTGTATGGAG TCAC; insertion mutation

Unit 30 D

21.1 Practice, p. 720

1. *M*—0.85; *m*—0.15
2. *WW*—0.81; *Ww*—0.18; *ww*—0.01
3. (a) *T*—0.995; *t*—0.005
   (b) *TT*—0.99; *Tt*—0.01; *tt*—0.000025 (embryos do not survive)
   (c) *T*—0.995: *t*—0.005

(d) no significant effect

Section 21.1, p. 722

5. (a) no
   (b) yes
   (c) no
   (d) no
7. (a) *c*—0.02; *C*—0.98
   (b) 3.92 %
   (c) 0.0392 × Caucasian population number
8. (a) *h*—0.4; *H*—0.6
   (b) 36 %

Chapter 21 Review, pp. 734–735

17. no
18. *C*—0.98
19. *A*—0.095
22. *k*—0.32; *K*—0.68
23. 44 %

22.1 Practice, p. 739

1. 0.17 turtles/ha
3. If unliveable space is 40 ha, then ecological density is 0.21 turtles/ha.
4. 28 mosquitoes/ha; 28 000 mosquitoes/m^3

Section 22.1, p. 741

3. (a) 0.012 to 0.014 bears/ha
4. 275

22.2 Practice, p. 745

2. (a) up 7.2×10^7
   (b) up 2.0×10^5

22.2 Practice, p. 747

3. (a) 2 days
   (b) 22 days; 11 doubling times

Section 22.2, p. 750

1. *gr*—4 /year
2. 87
4. (a) exponential growth
5. (a) *gr*—-40 individuals/year; *cgr*—-0.20
6. (a) S-shaped curve
   (c) about 300

Section 22.3, pp. 756–757

2. (a) density dependent
   (b) density independent
   (c) density independent
5. (a) density dependent
6. (a) *K*-selected
   (b) *r*-selected
   (c) *r*-selected
   (d) *r*-selected
   (e) *K*-selected
   (f) *K*-selected

Chapter 22 Review, pp. 760–761

14. *N. insignis*, Plot 1—7.3/ha; *Z. hudsonius*, Plot 2—4.6/ha; *N. insignis*, Plot 3—5.8/ha; *Z. hudsonius*, Plot 3—1.3/ha
16. intraspecific competition
19. (b) about 300
21. greatest growth—1975–1985; est. population 2055—5 000 000; est. population—221 480 000

Section 23.1, p. 771

1. (a) exploitative competition
   (b) interference competition
   (c) interference competition
   (d) resource partitioning
3. (a) camouflage
   (b) active chemical defence (toxins)
5. mutualism
6. Both populations increase in the absence of competition.

Section 23.2, p. 775

4. forest fires; harvesting of the forest

Chapter 23 Review, pp. 780–782

5. (a) camouflage
(b) mimicry
(c) toxic sting
   (d) thorn

Unit 30 D Review, pp. 782–786

16. European: *l*—0.2; *L*—0.8; Aboriginal: *l*—0.92; *L*—0.08
18. (a) 28 125/m^2
    (b) 1.4×10^7 black flies
19. (a) 3.0/km^2
32. exponential
33. 250 000 to 300 000

D

A

abiotic components the non-living components of the biosphere; includes chemical and physical factors

abiotic factor a non-living factor that influences an organism

accommodation adjustments made by the lens and pupil of the eye for near and distant objects

acetylcholine neurotransmitter released from vesicles in the end plates of neurons, which makes the postsynaptic membranes more permeable to Na^+ ions

acrosome the cap found on sperm cells, containing enzymes that permit the sperm cell to move through the outer layers that surround the egg

action potential the voltage difference across a nerve cell membrane when the nerve is excited

active transport movement of substances across cell membranes against a concentration gradient which uses energy

active site the area of an enzyme that combines with the substrate

ADP a molecule containing two high-energy phosphate bonds that may be formed by breaking one of the phosphate bonds in ATP; abbreviation of adenosine diphosphate

adrenal cortex outer region of the adrenal gland that produces glucocorticoids and mineralocorticoids

adrenal medulla found at the core of the adrenal gland, produces epinephrine and norepinephrine

adrenocorticotropic hormone (ACTH) pituitary hormone that promotes cortisol release by the adrenal cortex; also called corticotropin

aerobic cellular respiration the set of reactions that takes place in the cell in the presence of oxygen and releases energy stored in glucose

afferent arteriole a small branch of the renal artery that carries blood to the glomerulus

albedo a term used to describe the extent to which a surface can reflect light that strikes it; an albedo of 0.08 means that 8 % of the light is reflected

alcohol fermentation a form of fermentation occurring in yeast in which NADH passes its hydrogen atoms to acetaldehyde, generating carbon dioxide, ethanol, and NAD^+

aldosterone hormone produced by the adrenal cortex that helps regulate water balance by increasing sodium retention and water reabsorption by the kidneys

allantois extraembryonic structure that contributes to the blood vessels of the placenta

allele one of alternative forms of a gene

allele frequency the proportion of gene copies in a population of a given allele

allopatric speciation speciation by reproductive isolation

all-or-none response a nerve or muscle fibre responds completely or not at all to a stimulus

allosteric activity a change in an enzyme caused by the binding of a molecule

alveoli sacs of the lung in which gas exchange occurs

amino acid a chemical that contains nitrogen; can be linked together to form proteins

amnion a fluid-filled extraembryonic structure

amniotic cavity the fluid-filled cavity inside the amnion that contains the developing embryo

amylase an enzyme that breaks down complex carbohydrates

anabolic steroids substances that are designed to mimic many of the muscle-building traits of the sex hormone testosterone

anaerobic cellular respiration the set of reactions that takes place in the cell in the absence of oxygen and releases energy stored in glucose

analogous features features that are similar in appearance and function, but do not appear to have the same evolutionary origin

analyze make an examination of parts to determine the nature, proportion, function, interrelationship, etc. of the whole

anemia the reduction in blood oxygen due to low levels of hemoglobin or poor red blood cell production

aneurysm a bulge in the weakened wall of a blood vessel, usually an artery

antagonistic muscles a pair of skeletal muscles that are arranged in pairs and that work against each other to make a joint move

antibody a protein formed within the blood that reacts with an antigen

anticodon group of three complementary bases on tRNA that recognizes and pairs with a codon on the mRNA

antidiuretic hormone (ADH) a hormone that causes the kidneys to increase water reabsorption

antigen a substance, usually protein, that stimulates the formation of an antibody

antiparallel parallel but running in opposite directions; the 5′ end of one strand of DNA aligns with the 3′ end of the other strand in a double helix

aorta the largest artery in the body; carries oxygenated blood to the tissues

aqueous humour watery liquid that protects the lens of the eye and supplies the cornea with nutrients

Archaebacteria in a six-kingdom system, a kingdom consisting of prokaryotic microorganisms distinct from eubacteria that possess a cell wall not containing peptidoglycan and that live in harsh environments such as salt lakes and thermal vents

arteriosclerosis a group of disorders that cause the blood vessels to thicken, harden, and lose their elasticity

artery a blood vessel that carries blood away from the heart

artificial ecosystem an cosystem that is planned or maintained by humans

artificial selection the process of humans selecting and breeding individuals with the desired traits

asexual reproduction the production of offspring from a single parent; offspring inherit the genes of that parent only

astigmatism vision defect caused by abnormal curvature of surface of the lens or cornea

atherosclerosis a degeneration of blood vessels caused by the accumulation of fat deposits in the inner wall

ATP a molecule containing three high-energy phosphate bonds that acts as the primary energy-transferring molecule in living organisms; abbreviation of adenosine triphosphate

ATP synthase complex a specialized protein complex embedded in the thylakoid membrane that allows H^+ ions to escape from the lumen and uses the resulting energy to generate ATP

atrioventricular (AV) node a small mass of tissue in the right atrioventricular region through which impulses from the sinoatrial node are passed to the ventricles

atrioventricular (AV) valve a heart valve that prevents the backflow of blood from a ventricle into an atrium

atrium (plural atria) a thin-walled chamber of the heart that receives blood from veins

auditory canal carries sound waves to the eardrum

autonomic nervous system the part of the nervous system that controls the motor nerves that regulate equilibrium, and that is not under conscious control

autosome a chromosome not involved in sex determination

autotroph an organism that uses the Sun's energy and raw materials to make its own food; a producer

axon extension of cytoplasm that carries nerve impulses away from the cell body

B

B cell a lymphocyte, made and processed in the bone marrow, that produces antibodies

bacteriophage a virus that infects bacteria

Barr body a small, dark spot of chromatin located in the nucleus of a female mammalian cell

basilar membrane anchors the receptor hair cells in the organ of Corti

bedrock the layer beneath the soil, composed of rock

beneficial mutation a mutation that enhances an organism's fitness

bile salt a component of bile that breaks down large fat globules

binomial nomenclature a method of naming organisms by using two names—the genus name and the species name; scientific names are italicized

biodiversity the number of species in an ecosystem

biogeography the study of the geographic distribution of life on Earth

biological oxygen demand (BOD) the amount of dissolved oxygen needed by decomposers to completely break down the organic matter in a water sample at 20 °C over five days

biomass the total dry mass of all the living material in an ecosystem

biome a large geographical region with a specific range of temperatures and precipitation, and the organisms that are adapted to those conditions of temperature and precipitation

biosphere the narrow zone around Earth that harbours life

biotic components the biological or living components of the biosphere

biotic factor a living factor that influences an organism

biotic potential the maximum number of offspring that a species could produce with unlimited resources

blastocyst an early stage of embryo development

blunt ends fragment ends of a DNA molecule that are fully base paired, resulting from cleavage by a restriction enzyme

bottleneck effect a dramatic, often temporary, reduction in population size, usually resulting in significant genetic drift

Bowman's capsule the cuplike structure that surrounds the glomerulus

breathing the process of the exchange of air between the lungs and the environment, including inspiration and expiration

bronchi the passages from the trachea to the left and right lung

bronchial asthma a respiratory disorder characterized by reversible narrowing of the bronchial passages

bronchiole the smallest passageways of the respiratory tract

bronchitis an inflammation of the bronchial tubes

buffer a substance capable of neutralizing acids and bases, thus maintaining the original pH of the solution

C

calcitonin hormone produced by the thyroid gland that lowers calcium levels in the blood

Calvin cycle a cyclic set of reactions occurring in the stroma of chloroplasts that fixes the carbon of CO_2 into carbohydrate molecules and recycles coenzymes

canopy the upper layer of vegetation in a forest

capillary a blood vessel that connects arteries and veins; the site of fluid and gas exchange

carbohydrate a molecule composed of sugar subunits that contains carbon, hydrogen, and oxygen in a 1:2:1 ratio

carbon cycle the cycle of matter in which carbon atoms move from an inorganic form to an organic form and then back to an inorganic form

carbon fixation the process of incorporating CO_2 into carbohydrate molecules

carbonic anhydrase an enzyme found in red blood cells that speeds the conversion of carbon dioxide and water to carbonic acid

cardiac muscle the involuntary muscle of the heart

cardiac output the amount of blood pumped from the heart each minute

carnivore an animal that feeds only on other animals

carrying capacity the maximum number of individuals of a species that can be supported by an ecosystem

catalyst a chemical that regulates the rate of chemical reactions without being altered itself

cataract condition that occurs when the lens or cornea becomes opaque, preventing light from passing through

cell cycle the sequence of stages through which a cell passes from one cell division to the next

cellular respiration the process by which cells break down glucose into carbon dioxide and water, releasing energy

cellulose a plant polysaccharide that makes up plant cell walls

central nervous system (CNS) the body's coordinating centre for mechanical and chemical actions; made up of the brain and spinal cord

centriole small protein body found in the cytoplasm of animal cells that provide attachment for spindle fibres during cell division

centromere the structure that holds chromatids together

cerebellum part of the hindbrain that controls limb movements, balance, and muscle tone

cerebral cortex outer layer of the cerebral hemispheres

cerebrospinal fluid cushioning fluid that circulates between the innermost and middle membranes of the brain and spinal cord; it provides a connection between neural and endocrine systems

cerebrum largest and most highly developed part of the human brain, which stores sensory information and initiates voluntary motor activities

cervix a muscular band that separates the vagina from the uterus

chemiosmosis a process for synthesizing ATP using the energy of an electrochemical gradient and the ATP synthase enzyme

chemoautotroph an organism that can synthesize organic compounds from inorganic chemicals without using solar energy

chemoreceptor a specialized nerve receptor that is sensitive to specific chemicals

chemosynthesis the process by which non-photosynthetic organisms convert inorganic chemicals to organic compounds without solar energy

chlorophyll the light-absorbing green-coloured pigment that begins the process of photosynthesis

chloroplast a membrane-bound organelle in green plant and algal cells that carries out photosynthesis

cholecystokinin a hormone secreted by the small intestine that stimulates the release of bile salts

cholinesterase enzyme, which breaks down acetylcholine, that is released from presynaptic membranes in the end plates of neurons shortly after acetylcholine

chorion the outer extraembryonic structure of a developing embryo that will contribute to the placenta

chorionic villi vascular projections of the chorion

choroid layer middle layer of tissue in the eye that contains blood vessels that nourish the retina

chromatin the complex of DNA and protein that make up chromosomes

cilia tiny hairlike structures found on some cells that sweep away foreign debris

cirrhosis chronic inflammation of the liver tissue characterized by the growth of nonfunctioning fibrous tissue

clear-cutting the removal of all trees in an area

cleavage cell division of a zygote, in which the number of cells increases without any change in the size of the zygote

climax community the final, relatively stable community reached during successional stages

closed population a population in which change in size and density is determined by births and deaths alone

clumped dispersion the pattern in which individuals in a population are more concentrated in certain parts of a habitat

coagulation the process that occurs when the bonds of a protein molecule are disrupted, causing a permanent change in shape

cochlea coiled structure of the inner ear that responds to various sound waves and converts them into nerve impulses

codominance the expression of both forms of an allele in a heterozygous individual in different cells of the same organism

codon sequence of three bases in DNA or complementary mRNA that serves as a code for a particular amino acid

coenzyme an organic molecule synthesized from a vitamin that helps an enzyme to combine with a substrate molecule

cofactor an inorganic ion that helps an enzyme combine with a substrate molecule

coliform bacteria a type of bacteria that occurs naturally in the intestines of humans and other animals, and indicates the presence of fecal contamination in water

collecting duct a tube that carries urine from nephrons to the renal pelvis

colon the largest segment of the large intestine, where water reabsorption occurs

combustion the chemical reaction that occurs when a substance reacts very quickly with oxygen to release energy

commensalism a symbiotic relationship in which one organism benefits and the other organism is unaffected; it is categorized as a +/0 relationship

community all the organisms of various species that share a habitat or ecosystem

compare examine the character or qualities of two things by providing characteristics of both that point out their mutual similarities and differences

competitive exclusion the concept that, if resources are limited, no two species can remain in competition for exactly the same niche indefinitely; also know as Gause's Principle

competitive inhibitor a molecule with a shape complementary to a specific enzyme that competes with the substrate for access to the active site of the enzyme and blocks chemical reactions

complement protein a plasma protein that helps defend against invading microbes by tagging the microbe for phagocytosis, puncturing cell membranes, or triggering the formation of a mucous coating

complementary base pairing pairing of the nitrogenous base of one strand of DNA with the nitrogenous base of another strand

conclude state a logical end based on reasoning and/or evidence

cones photoreceptors that operate in bright light to identify colour

consumer a heterotroph; an organism that must eat producers or other consumers to survive

continuity of life a succession of offspring that share structural similarities with those of their parents

contrast point out the differences between two things that have similar or comparable natures

cornea transparent part of the sclera that protects the eye and refracts light toward the pupil of the eye

coronary artery an artery that supplies the cardiac muscle with oxygen and nutrients

corpus callosum nerve tract that joins the two cerebral hemispheres

corpus luteum a mass of follicle cells that forms within the ovary after ovulation; secretes estrogen and progesterone

cortex the outer layer of the kidney

cortisol hormone that stimulates the conversion of amino acids to glucose by the liver

Cowper's (bulbourethral) gland structure that contributes a mucus rich fluid to the seminal fluid (semen)

creatine phosphate a compound in muscle cells that releases a phosphate to ADP and helps regenerate ATP supplies in muscle cells

criticize point out the merits and demerits of an item or issue

crossing over the exchange of genetic material between two homologous chromosomes

cytokinesis the division of cytoplasm

D

deamination removal of an amino group from an organic compound

decomposer an organism that feeds on detritus

define provide the essential qualities or meaning of a word or a concept; make distinct and clear by marking out the limit

dehydration synthesis the process by which larger molecules are formed by the removal of water from two smaller molecules

deletion the elimination of a base pair or group of base pairs from a DNA sequence

ΔN a variable describing the change in the number of individuals in a population

denaturation the process that occurs when the bonds of a protein molecule are disrupted, causing a temporary change in shape

dendrite projection of cytoplasm that carries impulses toward the cell body

denitrification the process in which nitrates are converted to nitrites and then to nitrogen gas

density-dependent factor a factor in an ecosystem that affects members of a population because of the population density

density-independent factor a factor in an ecosystem that affects members of a population regardless of population density

deoxyribose sugar a sugar molecule containing five carbons that has lost the –OH (hydroxyl group) on its 2′ position

depolarization diffusion of sodium ions into the nerve cell resulting in a charge reversal

describe give a written account or represent the characteristics of something by a figure, model, or picture

design construct a plan, i.e., a detailed sequence of actions, for a specific purpose

determine find a solution, to a specific degree of accuracy, to a problem by showing appropriate formulas, procedures, and calculations

detoxify remove the effects of a poison

detritus waste from plants and animals, including their dead remains

diabetes chronic disease in which the body cannot produce any insulin or enough insulin, or is unable to use properly the insulin it does make

diaphragm a sheet of muscle that separates the organs of the thoracic cavity from those of the abdominal cavity

diastole relaxation (dilation) of the heart, during which the atria fill with blood

dichotomous key a two-part key used to identify living things; *di* means "two"

dihybrid cross a genetic cross involving two genes, each of which has more than one allele

diploid refers to twice the number of chromosomes in a gamete

disaccharide a sugar formed by the joining of two monosaccharide subunits

distal tubule conducts urine from the loop of Henle to the collecting duct

distinguish point out the differences between two things that have similar or comparable natures

divergent evolution evolution into many different species

DNA the molecule that makes up genetic material; abbreviation of deoxyribosenucleic acid

DNA helicase the enzyme that unwinds double-helical DNA by disrupting hydrogen bonds

DNA ligase an enzyme that joins DNA fragments together

DNA polymerase I an enzyme that removes RNA primers and replaces them with the appropriate nucleotides during DNA replication

DNA polymerase III the enzyme that synthesizes complementary strands of DNA during DNA replication

DNA replication the process whereby DNA makes exact copies of itself

dominant trait a characteristic that is expressed when one or both alleles in an individual are the dominant form

doubling time (t_d) the time needed for a population that is growing exponentially to double

duodenum the first segment of the small intestine

dynamic equilibrium describes any system with constant change in which the components can adjust to the changes without disturbing the entire system

E

ecological density population density measured in terms of the number of individuals of the same species per unit area or volume actually used by the individuals

ecological niche an organism's role in an ecosystem, consisting of its place in the food web, its habitat, its breeding area, and the time of day at which it is most active

ecological pyramid a representation of energy flow in food chains and webs

ecology the study of interactions between organisms and their living and non-living environment

ecosystem a community and its physical and chemical environment

ecotone a transition area between ecosystems

ectoderm the outer layer of cells in an embryo

effector a cell or organ that produces a physiological response when stimulated by a nerve impulse

efferent arteriole a small branch of the renal artery that carries blood away from the glomerulus to the peritubular capillaries

electron transport chain a cluster of photosynthetic pigments embedded in a thylakoid membrane of a chloroplast that absorbs light energy

embolus a blood clot that dislodges and is carried by the circulatory system to another part of the body

embryo the early stages of an animal's development

emigration the number of individuals that move away from an existing population per unit of time

emphysema a respiratory disorder characterized by an overinflation of the alveoli

endemic a term used to describe a species that is found in one location only

endocrine hormones chemicals secreted by endocrine glands directly into the blood

endoderm the inner layer of cells in an embryo

endometrium the glandular inner lining of the uterus

enterogastrone a hormone secreted by the small intestine that decreases gastric secretions and motility

enterokinase an enzyme of the small intestine that converts trypsinogen to trypsin

enucleated the condition where a cell does not contain a nucleus

environmental resistance any factor that limits a population's ability to realize its biotic potential when it nears or exceeds the environment's carrying capacity

enzyme a protein catalyst that permits chemical reactions to proceed at low temperatures

epididymis structure located along the posterior border of the testis, consisting of coiled tubules that store sperm cells

epiglottis the structure that covers the glottis (opening of the trachea) during swallowing

epilimnion the upper level of a lake, which warms up in summer

epinephrine (adrenaline) hormone, produced in the adrenal medulla that accelerates heart rate and body reactions during a crisis (the fight-or-flight response)

erepsin an enzyme that completes protein digestion by converting short-chain peptides to amino acids

erythrocyte a red blood cell that contains hemoglobin and carries oxygen

essential amino acid an amino acid that must be obtained from the diet

estrogen hormone that activates development of female secondary sex characteristics, and increased thickening of the endometrium during the menstrual cycle

Eubacteria in a six-kingdom system, a kingdom consisting of prokaryotic microorganisms that possess a peptidoglycan cell wall

eustachian tube air-filled tube of the middle ear that equalizes pressure between the external and internal ear

eutrophic having high nutrient levels

evaluate give the significance or worth of something by identifying the good and bad points or the advantages and disadvantages

explain make clear what is not immediately obvious or entirely known; give the cause of or reason for; make known in detail

exploitative competition interspecific competition that involves consumption of shared resources by individuals of different species, where consumption by one species may limit resource availability to other species

exponential growth a pattern of population growth in which the population size increases by a fixed rate per a fixed unit of time

extensor the muscle that must contract to straighten a joint

extracellular fluid (ECF) fluid that occupies the spaces between cells and tissues; includes plasma and interstitial fluid

extraembryonic coelom body cavity between the amnion and the chorion

F

facilitated diffusion transport of substances across cell membrane down a concentration gradient by a carrier in the membrane; does not use energy

FAD^+ an electron carrier, accepts electrons in cellular processes; abbreviated form of flavin adenine dinucleotide

$FADH_2$ an electron carrier, donates electrons in cellular processes; reduced form of FAD^+

Fallopian tube (oviduct) one of two tubes that connect the ovaries to the uterus

farsightedness condition that occurs when the image is focused behind the retina

fat a lipid composed of glycerol and saturated fatty acids; solid at room temperature

feedback inhibition the inhibition of an enzyme in a metabolic pathway by the final product of that pathway

fertilization fusion of a male and a female sex cell

fertilizer a material used to restore nutrients to plants

fetus the later stages of an unborn offspring's development

fibrium (plural fibria) a fingerlike projection at the end of a Fallopian tube

filtration the selective movement of materials through capillary walls by a pressure gradient

first trimester the period during pregnancy from conception until the end of the third month

fitness an organism's reproductive success

fixed frequency the frequency of an allele within a population when only a single allele is present for a particular gene (i.e., the allele's frequency is 100 %)

flexor the muscle that must contract to bend a joint

follicle structure in the ovary that contains the oocyte

follicle-stimulating hormone (FSH) a gonadotropic hormone that in females, promotes the development of the follicles in the ovary; in males, it increases sperm production

follicular phase phase marked by development of ovarian follicles before ovulation

food chain a sequence linking organisms that feed on each other, starting with a food source and continuing in order with each consumer

food web a representation of the feeding relationships among organisms in an ecosystem

founder effect genetic drift that results when a small number of individuals separate from their original population and find a new population

fovea centralis area at centre of retina where cones are most dense and vision is sharpest

frameshift mutation a mutation that causes the reading frame of codons to change

G

gallstone crystals of bile salts that form in the gallbladder

gametogenesis the formation of gametes (sex cells) in animals

ganglion (plural ganglia) collections of nerve cell bodies located outside the central nervous system

gastrin a hormone secreted by the stomach that stimulates the release of HCl

gastrula stage of embryonic development in which the embryo is composed of three layers: ectoderm, mesoderm, and endoderm

gastrulation process by which a gastrula is formed

gated ion channel a pore in the cell membrane that allows ions to move in and out of the cell by opening and closing

gene a segment of DNA that performs a specific function, such as coding for a particular protein

gene expression conversion of a gene into a specific trait through the production of a particular polypeptide

gene flow the movement of alleles from one population to another through the movement of individuals or gametes

gene mutation a mutation that changes the coding for amino acids

gene pool all the genes in a certain population

genetic drift changes to allele frequency as a result of chance

genetic transformation introduction and expression of foreign DNA in a living organism

genotype the genetic complement of an organism

genotypic ratio the ratio of offspring with each possible allele combination from a particular cross

genus the first part of a binomial name; a genus includes several species

glaucoma disease of the eye in which increased pressure within the eyeball causes a gradual loss of sight

glial cell nonconducting cell important for structural support and metabolism of the nerve cells

glomerulus the high-pressure capillary bed that is the site of filtration

glucagon hormone produced by the pancreas; when blood sugar levels are low, glucagon promotes conversion of glycogen to glucose

glucocorticoid any of the steroids produced by the adrenal cortex that help to regulate electrolyte and water balance

glycogen a plant carbohydrate used to store energy

glycolysis a process for harnessing energy in which a glucose molecule is broken into two pyruvate molecules in the cytoplasm of a cell

goiter disorder that causes an enlargement of the thyroid gland

gonadotropic hormones (gonadotropins) hormones produced by the pituitary gland that regulate the functions of the testes in males and the ovaries in females

gonadotropin-releasing hormone (GnRH) chemical messenger from the hypothalamus that stimulates secretions of FSH and LH from the pituitary

grana (singular granum) stacks of thylakoids

granulosa the layer of small cells that forms the wall of a follicle

graphically using a drawing that is produced electronically or by hand, and that shows a relationship between certain sets of n umbers

groundwater water in the soil or rock below Earth's surface

growth rate (*gr*) the change in population size per unit of time

H

habitat a place or type of environment with conditions suitable for the survival of an organism or population of organisms

haploid refers to the number of chromosomes in a gamete

harmful mutation a mutation that reduces an organism's fitness

helper T cell a T cell with receptors that bind to fragments of antigens

hemoglobin the oxygen-carrying molecule in red blood cells

herbivore an animal that eats only plants

heterotroph an organism that is incapable of making its own food, and so must feed on other organisms to gain energy

heterozygous having different alleles for the same gene

homeostasis the process by which a constant internal environment is maintained despite changes in the environment

homologous chromosomes paired chromosomes similar in shape, size, gene arrangement, and gene information

homologous features features with similar structures but different functions

homozygous having identical alleles for the same gene

hormones chemicals released by cells that affect cells in other parts of the body

how show in what manner or way, with what meaning

human chorionic gonadotropic hormone (HCG) an embryonic hormone that maintains the corpus luteum

human growth hormone (hGH) hormone produced by the pituitary gland that stimulates growth of the body; also known as somatotropin (STH)

humus decaying plant and animal matter

hydrogen bond the type of bond that is formed between the positive end of one water molecule and the negative end of another water molecule

hydrological cycle (water cycle) the movement of water through the environment from the atmosphere to Earth and back

hydrolysis the process by which larger molecules are split into smaller molecules by the addition of water

hyperpolarization condition in which the inside of the nerve cell membrane has a greater negative charge than the resting membrane; caused by excessive diffusion of potassium ions out of the cell

hypolimnion the lower level of a lake, which remains at a low temperature year round

hypothalamus area of the brain that coordinates many nerve and hormone functions

hypothesize from a tentative position intended as a possible explanation for an observed phenomenon; i.e., a possible cause for a special effect; the proposition should be testable logically and/or empirically

I

identify recognize and select as having the characteristics of something

illustrate make clear by giving an example; the form of the example must be specified in the question; i.e., word description, sketch, or diagram

immigration the number of individuals that move into an existing population per unit of time

implantation the attachment of the embryo to the endometrium

inbreeding the process whereby breeding stock is drawn from a limited number of individuals possessing desirable phenotypes

incomplete dominance the expression of both forms of an allele in a heterozygous individual in the cells of an organism, producing an intermediate phenotype

indicator species a species sensitive to small changes in environmental conditions

induced mutation a mutation caused by a chemical agent or radiation

infer form a generalization from sample data; arrive at a conclusion by reasoning from evidence

inflammatory response localized nonspecific response triggered when tissue cells are injured by bacteria or physical injury, characterized by swelling, heat, redness, and pain

inheritance of acquired characteristics the false concept of inheritance of features acquired during the life of an individual

inhibin a hormone produced by the Sertoli cells that inhibits production of FSH

inhibiting factor chemical that inhibits production of a hormone by the anterior pituitary gland

insertion the placement of an extra nucleotide in a DNA sequence

insulin hormone produced by the islets of Langerhans in the pancreas; insulin is secreted when blood sugar levels are high

intercostal muscle a muscle that raises and lowers the rib cage

interference competition interspecific competition that involves aggression between individuals of different species who fight over the same resource(s)

intermembrane space the fluid-filled space between the inner and outer mitochondrial membranes

interneuron a neuron of the central nervous system that connects with sensory, motor, and other interneurons to integrate sensory input with motor output; also known as association neuron

interphase the time interval between nuclear divisions when a cell increases in mass, roughly doubles the cytoplasmic components, and duplicates its chromosomes

interpret tell the meaning of something; present information in a new form that adds meaning to the original data

interspecific competition competition between individuals of different species

interstitial fluid the fluid that surrounds the body cells

intraspecific competition an ecological interaction in which individuals of the same species compete for resources in their habitat

inversion the reversal of a segment of DNA within a chromosome

iris opaque disk of tissue surrounding the pupil that regulates amount of light entering the eye

islets of Langerhans hormone producing cells of the pancreas; these cells are part of the endocrine system

isomer one of a group of chemicals that have the same chemical formula but different arrangements of the atoms

isotope one of two or more atoms of the same element containing the same number of protons but a different number of neutrons

J

jaundice the yellowish discoloration of the skin and other tissues brought about by the collection of bile pigments in the blood

juxtaglomerular apparatus (JGA) a functional unit near a kidney glomerulus that controls renin release in response to changes in blood pressure

justify show reasons for or give facts that support a position

K

K a variable indicating the number of individuals in a population at the carrying capacity of an environment

***K*-selected organism** an organism that is adapted to survive at or near the carrying capacity of its environment

karyotype chart a picture of chromosomes arranged in homologous pairs

killer T cell a T cell that destroys microbes, body cells infected with viruses, and mutated cells by puncturing cell membranes

Krebs cycle a cyclic series of reactions that transfers energy from organic molecules to ATP, NADH, and $FADH_2$, and removes carbon atoms as CO_2

L

lacteal a small vessel that transports the products of fat digestion to the circulatory system

lactic acid fermentation a form of fermentation occurring in animal cells in which NADH transfers its hydrogen atoms to pyruvate, regenerating NAD^+ and lactic acid

lactic acid threshold the value of exercise intensity at which lactic acid production increases

lag phase the initial stage in which population growth rates are slow as a result of a small population size; characteristic of geometric, exponential, and logistic population growth

lagging strand the new strand of DNA that is synthesized away from the replication fork and in short fragments, which are later joined together

lamellae (singular lamella) groups of unstacked thylakoids between grana

larynx the voice box

law of the minimum states that the nutrient in the least supply is the one that limits growth

law of tolerance states that an organism can survive within a particular range of an abiotic factor

leaching the removal of soluble minerals by percolation

leading strand the new strand of DNA that is synthesized towards the replication fork and continuously during DNA replication

leukocyte a white blood cell

light-dependent reactions the first set of reactions of photosynthesis in which light energy excites electrons in chlorophyll molecules, powers chemiosmotic ATP synthesis, and results in the reduction of $NADP^+$ to NADPH

light-independent reactions The second set of reactions in photosynthesis (the Calvin cycle); these reactions do not require solar energy

limnetic zone the area of a lake or pond in which there is open water and sufficient light for photosynthesis to occur

LINEs repeated DNA sequences 5000 to 7000 base pairs long that alternate with lengths of DNA sequences found in the genomes of higher organisms

linkage group a group of linked genes on a chromosome

linked genes genes that are located on the same chromosome

lipase a lipid-digesting enzyme

litter the upper layer of soil, composed mainly of partially decomposed leaves or grasses

littoral zone the area from the shore of a lake or pond to the point where no more plants grow in the lake bottom

locus (plural loci) a specific location along a chromosome where a particular gene is found

log phase the stage in which population growth rates are very rapid; characteristic of exponential and logistic growth

logistic growth a model of population growth describing growth that levels off as the size of the population approaches its carrying capacity

loop of Henle the section of the tubule that carries filtrate from the proximal tubule to the distal tubule

luteal phase phase of the menstrual cycle characterized by the formation of the corpus luteum following ovulation

luteinizing hormone (LH) a gonadotropin, in females, promotes ovulation and the formation of the corpus luteum; in males, it regulates the production of testosterone

lymph the fluid found in lymph vessels that contains some proteins that have leaked through capillary walls

lymph node a mass of tissue that stores lymphocytes and removes bacteria and foreign particles from the lymph

lymphocyte a white blood cell that produces antibodies

lymphokine a protein produced by the T cells that acts as a chemical messenger between other T cells and B cells

M

macrophage a phagocytic white blood cells found in lymph nodes, bone marrow, and the spleen and liver

marker gene a gene that confers an easily identifiable phenotype and is used to trace the inheritance of other genes that are difficult to identify; the marker gene must be located on the same chromosome, and ideally, at a very small distance from the gene being followed

maximum oxygen consumption (VO_2 max) the maximum volume of oxygen, in millilitres, that the cells of the body can remove from the bloodstream in one minute per kilogram of body mass while the body experiences maximal exertion

medulla oblongata region of the hindbrain that joins the spinal cord to the cerebellum; one of the most important sites of autonomic nerve control

medulla the area inside of the cortex

meiosis two-stage cell division in which the chromosome number of the parental cell is reduced by half

memory B cell a B cell that retains information about the shape of an antigen

meninges protective membranes that surround the brain and spinal cord

menopause the termination of the female reproductive years

menstrual cycle an almost-monthly cycle in which the endometrial lining of the uterus prepares for pregnancy; if pregnancy does not occur the lining is shed at menstruation

menstruation (flow phase) the shedding of the endometrium during the menstrual cycle

mesoderm the middle layer of cells in an embryo

messenger RNA (mRNA) the product of transcription of a gene; mRNA is translated by ribosomes into protein

methylase an enzyme that adds a methyl group to one of the nucleotides found in a restriction endonuclease recognition site

microvilli microscopic, fingerlike projections of the cell membrane

mineralocorticoid any of the steroids produced by the adrenal cortex that regulate carbohydrate, lipid, and protein metabolism and inhibit the release of corticotrophin

minimum viable population size the smallest number of individuals needed for a population to continue for a given period of time

missense mutation a mutation that results in the single substitution of one amino acid in the resulting polypeptide

mitochondrial matrix the fluid that fills the interior space of the mitochondrion

mitochondrion a eukaryotic cell organelle in which aerobic cellular respiration occurs

mitosis a type of cell division in which a daughter cell receives the same number of chromosomes as the parent cell

Monera in a five-kingdom system, a kingdom that includes organisms that lack a true nucleus

monoculture cultivation of a single species

monosaccharide a single sugar unit

monosomy the condition in which there is a single chromosome in place of a homologous pair

mortality the number of deaths per unit of time

motor neuron neuron that carries impulses from the central nervous system to an effector; also known as efferent neuron

mucus a protective lubricating substance composed mostly of protein

multiple-cloning site a region in a vector that is engineered to contain the recognition site of a number of restriction enzymes

muskeg soil above the permafrost that is swampy or boggy in summer

mutagenic agent an agent that can cause a mutation

mutant any allele of a gene other than the wild type allele

mutation a change in the DNA sequence in a chromosome

mutualism a symbiotic relationship in which both organisms benefit; as neither is harmed, it is categorized as a +/+ relationship

myelin sheath insulated covering over the axon of a nerve cell

myofilament a thread of contractile proteins found within muscle fibres

myogenic muscle muscle that contracts without external nerve stimulation

N

N a variable describing the number of individuals in a population

NAD^+ an electron carrier, accepts electrons in cellular processes; abbreviation of nicotinamide adenine dinucleotide

NADH an electron carrier, donates electrons in cellular processes; reduced form of NAD^+

NADP$^+$ a compound that accepts one hydrogen atom and two electrons, forming NADPH; is an electron acceptor; abbreviation of nicotinamide adenine dinucleotide phosphate

NADPH a compound that donates one hydrogen atom and two electrons to another molecule, to reform NADP$^+$; is an electron donor

natality the number of births per unit of time

natural ecosystem an ecosystem in which the interactions are not changed purposely by human actions

natural selection the result of differential reproductive success of individuals caused by variations in their inherited characteristics

nearsightedness condition that occurs when the image is focused in front of the retina

negative feedback the process by which a mechanism is activated to restore conditions to their original state

nephron a functional unit of the kidney

neurilemma delicate membrane that surrounds the axon of some nerve cells

neuron nerve cell that conducts nerve impulses

neurotransmitter chemical messenger released by the presynaptic neuron that binds to receptors on the postsynaptic neuron

neutral mutation a mutation that has no effect on the organism

nitrogen cycle a cycle of matter in which nitrogen atoms move from nitrogen gas in the atmosphere, to inorganic forms in the soil, to organic forms in living things, and then back to inorganic forms in the soil and nitrogen gas in the atmosphere

nitrogen fixation two processes in which atmospheric or dissolved nitrogen is converted into nitrate ions

nitrogenous base an alkaline, cyclic molecule containing nitrogen

nodes of Ranvier regularly occurring gaps between sections of myelin sheath along the axon

nondisjunction the failure of a pair of homologous chromosomes to separate properly during meiosis

nonsense mutation a mutation that converts a codon for an amino acid into a stop codon

norephinephrine also known as noradrenaline, it initiates the fight-or-flight response by increasing heart rate and blood sugar

nucleotide a molecule having a five-carbon sugar with a nitrogenous base attached to its 1′ carbon and a phosphate group attached to its 5′ carbon

nutrient a substance that provides the raw materials required for cell metabolism and growth

O

oil a lipid composed of glycerol and unsaturated fatty acids; liquid at room temperature

olfactory bulb area of the brain that processes information about smell; one bulb in each hemisphere

oligotrophic having low nutrient levels

omnivore an animal that eats both plants and other animals

oocyte an immature ovum

oogenesis the formation and development of mature ova

ootid an unfertilized ovum

open population a population in which change in number and density is determined by births, deaths, immigration, and emigration

organ of Corti primary sound receptor in the cochlea

osmoreceptors sensory receptors in the hypothalamus that detect changes in the osmotic pressure of the blood and surrounding extracellular fluids (ECF)

ossicles tiny bones that amplify and carry sound in the middle ear

otoliths tiny stones of calcium carbonate embedded in a gelatinous coating within the saccule and utricle

outline give, in an organized fashion, the essential parts of something; the form of the outline must be specified in the question; i.e., lists, flow charts, concept maps

oval window oval-shaped hole in the vestibule of the inner ear, covered by a thin layer of tissue

ovaries (singular ovary) the female gonads, or reproductive organs; female sex hormones and egg cells are produced in the ovaries

ovulation release of the secondary oocyte from the follicle held within the ovary

ovulatory phase phase in which ovulation occurs

ovum (plural ova) egg cell

oxidation a reaction in which an atom or molecule loses electrons

oxidative ATP synthesis the production of ATP from a series of oxidation reactions

oxyhemoglobin hemoglobin that is bound to oxygen

oxytocin a hormone from the pituitary gland; causes strong uterine contractions

ozone (O_3) an inorganic molecule; a layer of ozone found in the stratosphere helps to screen out ultraviolet radiation

P

paleontology the study of fossils

palindromic reading the same backwards and forwards

parasitism a symbiotic relationship in which one organism (the parasite) benefits at the expense of another organism (the host), which is often harmed but usually not killed; it is categorized as a +/-

parasympathetic nervous system a division of the autonomic nervous system that returns the body to normal resting levels following adjustments to stress

parathyroid glands four pea-sized glands in the thyroid gland that produce parathyroid hormone to regulate blood calcium and phosphate levels

parathyroid hormone (PTH) hormone produced by the parathyroid glands, which will increase calcium levels in the blood and lower the levels of phosphates

parturition the act of giving birth; labour

peat slowly decomposing plant matter produced in low-oxygen environments such as bogs

pedigree chart a chart used to record the transmission of a particular trait or traits over several generations

pepsin a protein-digesting enzyme produced in the stomach

peptide bond the bond that joins amino acids

per capita growth rate (*cgr*) the change in population size relative to the initial size of the population, per unit time

percolation the movement of a liquid through a porous material, such as soil particles

peripheral nervous system (PNS) all parts of the nervous system, excluding brain and spinal cord, that relay information between the central nervous system and other parts of the body

peristalsis rhythmic, wavelike contractions of muscle that move food along the gastrointestinal tract

peritubular capillary a member of the network of small blood vessels that surround the tubule of the nephron

permafrost permanently frozen soil

phagocytosis the process by which a white blood cell engulfs and chemically destroys a microbe

phenotype the observable characteristics of an organism

phenotypic ratio the ratio of offspring with a dominant trait to the alternative, recessive trait

phosphate group a group of four oxygen atoms surrounding a central phosphorus atom; found in the backbone of DNA

phospholipid a lipid with a phosphate molecule attached to the glycerol backbone, making the molecule polar; the major components of cell membranes

phosphorus cycle the cycling of phosphorus between the biotic and abiotic components of the environment; consists of a biological and geochemical cycle

photolysis a chemical reaction in which a compound is broken down by light; in photosynthesis, water molecules are split by photolysis

photon a packet of light

photosynthesis the process by which green plants and some other organisms use solar energy, carbon dioxide, and water to produce carbohydrates

photosystem a cluster of photosynthetic pigments embedded in a thylakoid membrane of a chloroplast that absorbs light energy

phylogeny proposed evolutionary history of a species or group of organisms

pinna outer part of the ear that acts like a funnel, taking sound from a large area and channelling it into a small canal

pioneer community the first species to appear during succession

pituitary gland gland at the base of the brain that, together with the hypothalamus, functions as a control centre, coordinating the endocrine and nervous systems

placenta the site for the exchange of nutrients and wastes between mother and fetus

plan construct a plan, i.e., a detailed sequence of actions, for a specific purpose

plankton autotrophic and heterotrophic microorganisms found in the limnetic zone of a lake or pond

plasma the fluid portion of the blood

plasmid a small double-stranded circular DNA molecule found in some bacteria

platelet a component of blood responsible for initiating blood clotting

pleural membrane a thin membrane that surrounds the outer surface of the lungs and lines the inner wall of the chest cavity

pluripotent cell a cell that is capable of developing into a number of specialized cells, such as a neuron or muscle cell

point mutation a mutation at a specific base pair

polar body cell that contains all the genetic information of a haploid ovum, but lacks sufficient cytoplasm to survive; formed during meiosis in females

polar molecule a molecule that has a positive and a negative end

polarized membrane membrane charged by unequal distribution of positively charged ions inside and outside the nerve cell

polymer a molecule composed of three or more subunits

polymerase chain reaction (PCR) a technique for amplifying a DNA sequence by repeated cycles of strand separation and replication

polypeptide a chain of three or more amino acids

polyploidy a condition in which an organism has more than two complete sets of chromosomes

polysaccharide a carbohydrate composed of many single sugar subunits

pons region of the brain that acts as a relay station by sending nerve messages between the cerebellum and the medulla

population a group of organisms of the same species that live in the same habitat or ecosystem at the same time

population density the number of individuals of the same species that occur per unit area or volume

population dispersion the general pattern in which individuals are distributed through a specified area

population size the number of individuals of a specific species occupying a given area/volume at a given time

positive feedback the process by which a small effect is amplified

postsynaptic neuron neuron that carries impulses away from the synapse

precursor activity the activation of the last enzyme in a metabolic pathway by the initial substrate

predation an ecological interaction in which a predator (a member of one species) kills and consumes prey (usually a member of another species)

predict tell in advance on the basis of empirical evidence and/or logic

prescribed burn a controlled fire set intentionally in a designated area

presynaptic neuron neuron that carries impulses to the synapse

primary sexual characteristics physical characteristics of an organisms that are directly involved in reproduction

primary succession the occupation, by plant life, of an area not previously covered by vegetation

primary consumer in a food chain or food web, an organism that relies directly on autotrophs for its source of energy; organisms at the second trophic level

producer an autotroph; an organism that makes its own food

profundal zone the region of a lake beneath the limnetic zone, in which there is insufficient light for photosynthesis to occur

progeny new individuals that result from reproduction; offspring

progesterone hormone produced primarily by the corpus luteum, that induces changes in the endometrium during the menstrual cycle

prolactin a hormone produced by the pituitary gland and associated with milk production

promoter sequence of DNA in front of a gene that binds RNA polymerase

prostaglandins a group of hormones that act on the cells that produce them in response to cell damage; produced by most cells

prostate gland structure that contributes to the seminal fluid (semen), a secretion containing buffers that protect sperm cells from the acidic environment of the vagina

protein a chain of amino acids that form the structural parts of cells or act as antibodies or enzymes

Protista a kingdom originally proposed for all unicellular organisms such as the amoeba; more recently, multicellular algae have been added to the kingdom

prove establish the truth or validity of a statement for the general case by giving factual evidence or logical argument

proximal tubule the section of the nephron joining the Bowman's capsule with the loop of Henle

pulmonary circulatory system the system of blood vessels that carries deoxygenated blood to the lungs and oxygenated blood back to the heart

pulse change in the diameter of the arteries following heart contractions

Punnett square a chart used to determine the predicted outcome of a genetic cross

Purkinje fibre a nerve fibre that branches and carries electrical impulses throughout the ventricles

pus a thick liquid composed of protein fragments from digested leukocytes and microbes

R

r a variable indicating the rate of increase of a population experiencing exponential growth; *r* is limited only by the biotic potential of the organisms in the population

***r*-selected organism** an organism that is adapted to increase population size rapidly

radioisotope an unstable isotope that decays spontaneously by emitting radiation

radiometric dating a technique used to determine the age of a rock or fossil

random dispersion the pattern in which individuals are spread throughout a habitat in an unpredictable and patternless manner

receptor sites a port along a cell membrane into which hormones, nutrients, and other needed materials fit

recessive lethal a trait that, when both recessive alleles are present, results in death or severe malformation of the offspring; usually, recessive traits occur more frequently in males

recessive trait a characteristic that is expressed only when both alleles in an individual are the recessive form

recognition site a specific sequence within double-stranded DNA that a restriction endonuclease recognizes and cuts

recombinant DNA fragment of DNA composed of sequences originating from at least two different sources

reduction a reaction in which an atom or molecule gains electrons

reflex arc neural circuit through the spinal cord that provides a framework for a reflex action

refractory period recovery time required before a neuron can produce another action potential

relate show logical or casual connection between things

relaxin a hormone produced by the placenta prior to labour; causes the ligaments within the pelvis to loosen

releasing hormone a peptide produced by the hypothalamus that stimulates the anterior pituitary gland to release a stored hormone; also called a releasing factor

renal pelvis the hollow area where the kidney joins the ureter

repolarization process of restoring the original polarity of the nerve membrane

resource partitioning avoidance of, or reduction in, competition for similar resources by individuals of different species occupying different non-overlapping ecological niches

respiration all processes involved in the exchange of oxygen and carbon dioxide between cells and the environment, including breathing, gas exchange, and cellular respiration

respiratory membrane the membrane where the diffusion of oxygen and other gases occurs between the living cells of the body and the external environment (the atmosphere or water)

resting potential voltage difference across a nerve cell membrane when it is not transmitting a nerve impulse (usually negative)

restriction endonuclease an enzyme that cuts double-stranded DNA into fragments at a specific sequence; also known as a restriction enzyme

retina innermost layer of tissue at the back of the eye containing photoreceptors

rhodopsin the pigment found in the rods of the eye

ribonucleic acid (RNA) a nucleic acid consisting of nucleotides comprised of the sugar ribose and nitrogenous bases

ribosome an organelle composed of RNA and protein and located in the cytoplasm that carries out protein synthesis

RNA polymerase enzyme that transcribes DNA

rods photoreceptors that operate in dim light to detect light in black and white

S

saltatory conduction generation of action potentials only at nodes of Ranvier in myelinated axons, resulting in rapid transmission of nerve impulses

sarcolemma the delicate sheath that surrounds muscle fibres

Schwann cell special type of glial cell that produces the myelin sheath

sclera outer covering of the eye that supports and protects the eye's inner layers; usually referred to as the white of the eye

scrotum the sac that contains the testes

second trimester the period during pregnancy from the fourth month to the end of the sixth month

secondary sexual characteristics external features of an organism that are indicative of its gender (male or female), but are not the reproductive organs themselves

secondary succession succession in an area that was previously covered by vegetation and still has some soil

secondary consumer in a food chain or food web, an organism that relies on primary consumers for its principal source of energy; organisms at the third trophic level

secretin a hormone released from the duodenum that stimulates pancreatic and bile secretions

segregation the separation of alleles during meiosis

selective breeding the crossing of desired traits from plants or animals to produce offspring with both characteristics

selective cutting the harvesting of only certain trees from an area

semen (seminal fluid) a secretion of the male reproductive organs that is composed of sperm and fluids

semicircular canals fluid-filled structures within the inner ear that provide information about dynamic equilibrium

semiconservative replication process of replication in which each DNA molecule is composed of one parent strand and one newly synthesized strand

semilunar valves a valve that prevents the backflow of blood from an artery into a ventricle

seminal vesicles structure that contributes to the seminal fluid (semen), a secretion that contains fructose and prostaglandins

seminiferous tubules coiled ducts found within the testes, where immature sperm cells divide and differentiate

sensory adaptation occurs once you have adjusted to a change in the environment; sensory receptors become less sensitive when stimulated repeatedly

sensory neuron neuron that carries impulses to the central nervous system; also known as afferent neuron

sensory receptor highly modified dendrites of a sensory neuron that are activated by an environmental stimulus

septum a wall of muscle that separates the right and left sides of the heart

Sertoli cell a cell that provides metabolic and mechanical support to developing sperm cells

sex hormone any hormone that affects the development and growth of sex organs

sex-linked trait trait that is determined by genes located on the sex chromosomes

sexual dimorphism striking differences in the physical appearance of males and females not usually applied to behavioural differences between sexes

sexual selection differential reproductive success that results from variation in the ability to obtain mates; results in sexual dimorphism and mating and courtship behaviours

sexual reproduction the production of offspring by the union of sex cells from two different parents; the offspring inherit a combination of genes from both parents

show how show reasons for or give facts that support a position

siblings offspring from the same parent (in asexual reproduction) or parents (in sexual reproduction)

silent mutation a mutation that does not result in a change in the amino acid coded for

SINEs repeated DNA sequences 300 base pairs long that alternate with lengths of DNA sequences found in the genomes of higher organisms

sinoatrial (SA) node a small mass of tissue in the right atrium that originates the impulses stimulating the heartbeat

sister chromatids a chromosome and its duplicate, attached to one another by a centromere until separated during mitosis

skeletal muscle the voluntary muscle that makes the bones of the skeleton move

sketch provide a drawing that represents the key features of an object or graph

slash-and-burn the complete clearing of a forest by felling and burning the trees

smooth muscle the involuntary muscle found in the lining of many organs

social parasite a parasite that completes its life cycle by manipulating the social behaviour of its hosts

sodium-potassium pump a transporter in the cell membrane that moves potassium ions into the cytoplasm while simultaneously removing sodium ions from the cytoplasm to the extracellular fluid

somatic cell any cell in a multicellular organism that is not a reproductive cell

speciation the formation of new species

species a group of organisms that look alike and can interbreed under natural conditions to produce fertile offspring

spermatid an immature sperm cell that arises from division of a spermatocyte

spermatocyte a cell that arises from division of spermatogonia during spermatogenesis

spermatogenesis process by which spermatogonia divide and differentiate into mature sperm cells

spermatogonia sperm-producing cells found in the seminiferous tubules

sphincter a constrictor muscle that regulates the opening and closing of a tubelike structure

sphygmomanometer a device used to measure blood pressure

spindle fibre protein structure that guides chromosomes during cell division

spleen a lymphoid organ that acts as a reservoir for blood and a filtering site for lymph

spontaneous mutation a mutation occurring as a result of errors made in DNA replication

spontaneous generation the belief that living things arose from non-living matter

starch a plant carbohydrate used to store energy

start codon specific codon (AUG) that signals the start of translation

stationary phase the phase in which population growth rates approach zero as the population size reaches the carrying capacity and stabilizes; the defining characteristic of logistic population growth

stem cell a cell from which any other type of cell can arise; any precursor cell

sticky ends fragment ends of a DNA molecule with short single stranded overhangs, resulting from cleavage by a restriction enzyme

stop codon specific codon that signals the end of translation

stroke volume the quantity of blood pumped with each beat of the heart

stroma the protein-rich semiliquid material in the interior of a chloroplast

stromatolite a banded limestone structure containing fossilized bacteria

subsoil the soil layer beneath the topsoil, usually containing more rock particles and less organic matter than the topsoil

substrate a molecule on which an enzyme works

succession the slow, progressive replacement of one community by another during the development of vegetation in any area

summarize give a brief account of the main points

summation increased muscle contraction produced by the accumulation of neurotransmitters from two or more neurons

suppressor T cell a T cell that turns off the immune system

symbiosis various interactions in which two species maintain a close, usually physical, association; includes parasitism, mutualism, and commensalism

sympathetic nervous system a division of the autonomic nervous system that prepares the body for stress

synapse a region between neurons, or between neurons and effectors; also known as the synaptic cleft

synapsis the pairing of homologous chromosomes

systemic circulatory system the system of blood vessels that carries oxygenated blood to the tissues of the body and deoxygenated blood back to the heart

systole contraction of the heart, during which blood is pushed out of the heart

T

T cell a lymphocyte, manufactured in the bone marrow and processed by the thymus gland, that identifies and attacks foreign substances

taxon (plural taxa) categories used to classify organisms

taxonomy the science of classification according to the inferred (presumed) relationships among organisms

telomere the cap at the end of a chromosome

template a single-stranded DNA sequence that acts as the guiding pattern for producing a complementary DNA strand

template strand the strand of DNA that the RNA polymerase uses as a guide to build complementary mRNA

tendon a band of connective tissue that joins muscle to bone

teratogen any medication, chemical, infectious disease, or environmental agent that might interfere with the normal development of a fetus or embryo

termination sequence sequence of bases at the end of a gene that signals the RNA polymerase to stop transcribing

test cross the cross of an individual of unknown genotype to an individual that is fully recessive

testes the male gonads, or primary reproductive organs; male sex hormones and sperm are produced in the testes

testosterone male sex hormone produced by the interstitial cells of the testes

tetanus the state of constant muscle contraction caused by sustained nerve impulses

tetrad a pair of homologous chromosomes, each with two chromatids

thalamus area of brain that coordinates and interprets sensory information and directs it to the cerebrum

theory of gradualism the idea that speciation takes place slowly

theory of punctuated equilibrium the idea that species evolve rapidly, followed by a period of little or no change

thermocline the zone between the epilimnion and hypolimnion, in which temperature changes rapidly

thermodynamics a scientific study of energy transformations, described by laws

thermoregulation maintenance of body temperature within a range that enables cells to function efficiently

third trimester the period during pregnancy from the seventh month until birth

threshold level minimum level of a stimulus required to produce a response; the maximum amount of a substance that can be moved across the nephron in the kidney

thrombus a blood clot that forms within a blood vessel and blocks it

thylakoid a system of interconnected flattened membrane sacs forming a separate compartment within the stroma of a chloroplast

thylakoid lumen the fluid-filled space inside a thylakoid

thylakoid membrane the photosynthetic membrane within a chloroplast that contains light-gathering pigment molecules and electron transport chains

thymus gland a lymphoid organ in which T lymphocytes mature

thyroid gland a two-lobed gland at the base of the neck that regulates metabolic processes

thyroxine (T4) hormone produced by the thyroid gland that increases metabolism and regulates growth

topsoil the soil layer beneath the litter, composed of small particles of rock mixed with humus

trachea the windpipe

transcription the process of converting DNA into messenger RNA

transfer RNA (tRNA) the form of RNA that delivers amino acids to a ribosome during translation

transgenic a cell or an organism that is transformed by DNA from another species

translation the process of synthesizing a specific polypeptide as coded for by messenger RNA

translocation the transfer of a fragment of DNA from one site in the genome to another location

transpiration the loss of water through plant leaves

triglyceride a lipid composed of glycerol and three fatty acids

triiodothyronine (T3) hormone produced by the thyroid gland that increases metabolism and regulates growth; contains three iodine atoms

trisomy the condition in which there are three homologous chromosomes in place of a homologous pair

trophic hormone hormone that stimulates a specific target gland to secrete other hormones

trophic level a category of living things defined by how it gains its energy; the first trophic level contains autotrophs, and each higher level contains heterotrophs

trypsin a protein-digesting enzyme

tympanic membrane thin layer of tissue that receives sound vibrations, also known as the eardrum

U

ulcer a lesion on the surface of an organ

ultraviolet radiation electromagnetic radiation from the Sun that can cause burning of the skin (sunburn) and cellular mutations

umbilical cord structure that connects the fetus to the placenta

understorey below the canopy layer; usually shrubs and smaller trees

uniform dispersion the pattern in which individuals are equally spaced throughout a habitat

urea nitrogen waste formed from two molecules of ammonia and one molecule of carbon dioxide

ureter a tube that conducts urine from the kidney to the bladder

urethra the tube that carries urine from the bladder to the exterior of the body

uric acid a waste product formed from the breakdown of nucleic acids

uterus (womb) the hollow, pear-shaped organ located between the bladder and the anus in females

V

vagina the muscular canal extending from the cervix to the outer environment; the birth canal

vagus nerve major cranial nerve that is part of the parasympathetic nervous system

vas deferens tube that conducts sperm toward the urethra

vasoconstriction the narrowing of blood vessels, allowing less blood to the tissues

vasodilation the widening of blood vessels, allowing more blood to the tissues

vector a vehicle by which foreign DNA may be introduced into a cell

vein a blood vessel that carries blood toward the heart

ventricle a muscular, thick-walled chamber of the heart that delivers blood to the arteries

vestibule chamber found at the base of the semicircular canals that provides information about static equilibrium

vestigial features rudimentary structures with no useful function

villi small, fingerlike projections that extend into the small intestine to increase surface area for absorption

W

water table the boundary between the layer of soil that is saturated with water, and the unsaturated soil above it

watershed the land that drains toward a lake or other body of water

wax a long-chain lipid that is insoluble in water

why show the cause, reason, or purpose

wild type the most common allele of a gene with multiple alleles

Y

yolk sac a membranous sac that forms during embryo development of most vertebrates; in humans, it does not contain yolk

Z

zygote the cell resulting from the union of a male and female sex cell

Index

C

D

O

P

T

U

V

W

X

Y

Z

R

S

Greek and Latin Prefixes and Suffixes

Greek and Latin Prefixes

Prefix	Meaning	Prefix	Meaning	Prefix	Meaning
a-	not, without	em-	inside	micr-, micro-	small
ab-	away from	en-	in	mono-	one
abd-	led away	end-, endo-	within	morpho-	form, shape
acro-	end, tip	epi-	at, on, over	muc-, muco-	slime
adip-	fat	equi-	equal	multi-	many
aer-, aero-	air	erythro-	red	myo-	muscle
agg-	to clump	ex-, exo-	away, out	nas-	nose
agro-	land	flag-	whip	necro-	corpse
alb-	white	gamet-, gamo-	marriage, united	neo-	new
allo-	other	gastr-, gastro-	stomach	neur-, neuro-	nerve
ameb-	change	geo-	earth	noct-	night
amphi-	around, both	glyc-	sweet	odont-, odonto-	tooth
amyl-	starch	halo-	salt	oligo-	few
an-	without	haplo-	single	oo-	egg
ana-	up	hem-, hema-, hemato-	blood	orni-	bird
andro-	man	hemi-	half	oss-, osseo-, osteo-	bone
ant-, anti-	opposite	hepat-, hepa-	liver	ovi-	egg
anth-	flower	hetero-	different	pale-, paleo-	ancient
archae-, archaeo-	ancient	histo-	web	patho-	disease
archi-	primitive	holo-	whole	peri-	around
astr-, astro-	star	homeo-	same	petro-	rock
aut-, auto-	self	hydro-	water	phag-, phago-	eat
baro-	weight (pressure)	hyper-	above	pharmaco-	drug
bi-	twice	hypo-	below	phono-	sound
bio-	life	infra-	under	photo-	light
blast-, blasto-	sprout (budding)	inter-	between	pneum-	air
carcin-	cancer	intra-	inside of, within	pod-	foot
cardio-, cardia-	heart	intro-	inward	poly-	many
chlor-, chloro-	green	iso-	equal	pseud-, pseudo-	false
chrom-, chromo-	colour	lact-, lacti-, lacto-	milk	pyr-, pyro-	fire
co-	with	leuc-, leuco-	white	radio-	ray
cosmo-	order, world	lip-, lipo-	fat	ren-	kidney
cut-	skin	lymph-, lympho-	clear water	rhizo-	root
cyan-	blue	lys-, lyso-	break up	sacchar-, saccharo-	sugar
cyt-, cyto-	cell	macro-	large	sapr-, sapro-	rotten
dendr-, dendri-, dendro-	tree	mamm-	breast	soma-	body
dent-, denti-	tooth	meg-, mega-	great	spermato-	seed
derm-	skin	melan-	black	sporo-	seed
di-	two	meningo-	membrane	squam-	scale
dors-	back	mes-, meso-	middle	sub-	beneath
ec-, ecto-	outside	meta-	after, transition	super-, supra-	above

Credits

CHAPTER 1: p. 3: Science VU/GSFC/Visuals Unlimited; p. 7: CP PHOTO/ Edmonton Sun/ Walter Tychnowicz; p. 8: (t) Photodisc, (m) Corbis, (b) Photodisc; p. 9: CP/Jim Wells; p. 10: CP PHOTO/Larry MacDougal; p. 11: (wolverine) Esther Schmidt/Valan Photos, (salamander) Zig Leszczynski/Animals Animals, (whooping crane) John Cancalosi/Valan Photos, (Atlantic cod) Rick Price/CORBIS, (Fowler's toad) John Mitchell/Valan Photos, (eastern mountain avens) Nova Scotia Museum of Natural History, (pitcher's thistle) Susan Middleton & David Littscwater/CORBIS, (Kirtland's warbler) Dan Roby & K. Fri/Academy of Natural Science Philadelphia (c) Vireo; p. 12: (l) Gary Meszaros/ Visuals Unlimited, (r) J.A. Wilkinson/Valan Photos; p. 15: Wayne Lankinen/Valan

CHAPTER 2: p. 21: © Alec Pytlowany/Masterfile; p. 33: © Roy Ooms/Masterfile; p. 34: Dr. Morley Read/Science Photo Library

CHAPTER 3: p. 41: Charles McCrae/Visuals Unlimited; p. 47: (t) 4x5/Superstock, (b) Will McIntyre/Photo Researchers; p. 52: Sir Ghillian Prance/Visuals Unlimited; p. 53: Jack Zehrt; p. 61: (t) J.D. Cunningham/ Visuals Unlimited, (m) E. Weber/Visuals Unlimited, (b) Jana R. Jirak/ Visuals Unlimited; p. 62: Sally A. Morgan/Ecoscene/CORBIS; p. 67: Dave Starrett

CHAPTER 4: p. 80: © Bill Beatty/Visuals Unlimited; p. 81: John Marriott; p. 82: (a) Gary W. Carter/Visuals Unlimited, (b) Charles Philip/Visuals Unlimited, (c) Gerald & Buff Coris/Visuals Unlimited, (d) Gerald & Buff Coris/Visuals Unlimited, (e) Bill Banaszewski/Visuals Unlimited, (f) Barbara Gerlach/Visuals Unlimited; p. 85: (tl) © R. Ian Lloyd/Masterfile, (tm) © Sherman Hines/Masterfile, (tr) © Garry Black/Masterfile, (bl) © Miles Ertman/Masterfile, (bm) © DiMaggio/ Kalish/CORBIS, (br) © Steve Craft/Masterfile; p . 87: Courtesy of Mary Thomas. Photo by Bert Crowfoot; p. 90: (l) Maslowski/Visuals Unlimited, (r) © Werner H. Müller/CORBIS; p. 91: (l) Shutterstock (m) © Pat Anderson/Visuals Unlimited, (tr) Tom J. Ulrich/Visuals Unlimited, (mr) Shutterstock, (br) © Charles Melton/Visuals Unlimited; p. 94: (t) Harold V. Green/Valan, (b) © Christopher Morris/Corbis; p. 95 (t) Wayne Lankinen/Valan, (m) Shutterstock, (b) J.R. Page/Valan; p. 96: Joel W. Rogers/Corbis; p. 101: Richard Nowitz/Valan Photos; p. 104: John Marriott; p. 108: (l) Corel, (ml) Photodisc, (mr) Photodisc, (r) Corel; p. 109: Herman H. Guethoorn/Valan Photos; p. 115: © Bettmann/CORBIS; p. 118: Courtesy of Bill Donahue

CHAPTER 5: p. 133: (t) Auscape International Photo Library, (bottom, a) Doug Fraser, (b) Doug Fraser, (c) Christopher J. Crowel/Visuals Unlimited; p. 134: (tl) Mack Henly/Visuals Unlimited, (tm) Hal Beral/ Visuals Unlimited, (tr) Daniel W. Gotshall/ Visuals Unlimited, (bl) Daniel W. Gotshall/ Visuals Unlimited, (bm) Gerald & Buff Corsi/ Visuals Unlimited, (br) David Fleetham/Visuals Unlimited; p. 141: (l) Michale Maslan Historic Photographs/CORBIS/MAGMA, (m) Inga Spence/Visuals Unlimited, (tr) Ken Lucas/Visuals Unlimited, (br) Ken Lucas/Visuals Unlimited; p. 142: © Carolina Biological Supply/Visuals Unlimited; p. 150 (t) Visuals Unlimited (b) Erwin Bud Nielsen/Index Stock; p. 152: © Tom Brakefield/CORBIS; p. 156: Doug Fraser; p. 157: (l) Royal BC Museum, (tr) © Raymond Gehman/CORBIS, (mr) G&R. Grambo/First Light, (br) © Ken Lucas/Visuals Unlimited; p. 161: (l) Gary Meszaros/Visuals Unlimited, (r) Ray Coleman/Visuals Unlimited; p. 163: (fig 2) Gerard Lacz/Peter Arnold, (fig 3) C. Allan Morgan/Peter Arnold, (fig 4) David Fleetham/Visuals Unlimited, (fig 5) Science VU/Visuals Unlimited, (fig 6) Shane Moore/Animals Animals, (fig 7) Still Pictures/Peter Arnold, (fig 8) David Barron / Animals Animals; p. 168: Kay Coleman/Visuals Unlimited

CHAPTER 6: p. 175: Tom Ellison/First Light; p. 177: (b) Boreal; p. 179: (t) David Nunuk/First Light; (b) NASA; p. 182: Lynne Ledbetter/Visuals Unlimited; p. 183: Gerald Van Dyke/Visuals Unlimited; p. 184: Canada Centre for Remote Sensing ; p. 192: © Markowitz Jeffrey/CORBIS SYGMA; p. 196: © Canadian Museum of Civilization/CORBIS

CHAPTER 7: p. 203: © J.P. Moczulski/Reuters/Corbis; p. 214: D. Fawcett/ Visuals Unlimited; p. 222: (t) Photodisc, (b) Bettman/CORBIS; p. 223: Dick Hemingway; p. 224: AP Photo/Amy Sancetta; p. 225: UIC Photo Services, University of Illinois at Chicago

CHAPTER 8: p. 237: CP/Frank Gunn; p. 239: Meckes Ottawa/Photo Researchers, Inc.; p. 241: (tl) Jeff Greenberg/Visuals Unlimited, (tr) Malcolm S. Kirk/Peter Arnold Inc., (bl) Steve Callahan /Visuals Unlimited, (br) D.S. Kerr/Visuals Unlimited; p. 245: Thomson Nelson; p. 248: Alfred Pasieka/Science Photo Library; p. 252: U.S. Department of Energy/Photo Researchers, Inc.; p. 262: (t) Dr. R.F.R. Schiller/Science Photo Library, (b) Dr. R.F.R. Schiller/Science Photo Library; p. 264: Manfred Cage/Science Photo Library

CHAPTER 9: p. 281: CP/Jeff deBooy; p. 291: Lyle Stafford/Reuters /Landov; p. 294: Courtesy of Dr. Malcolm King; p. 295: (all) James Stevenson/Science Photo Library; p. 297: Canadian Cancer Society; p. 298: (l) Alfred Pasieka/Science Photo Library, (m) Prof. P.M. Motta & E. Vizza/Science Photo Library, (r) Prof. P.M. Motta & E. Vizza/Science Photo Library; p. 304: Peter Skinner / Photo Researchers, Inc.

CHAPTER 10: p. 311: (t) Cardio-Thoracic Centre/ Freeman Hospital/ Science Photo Library, (b) Z&B Barran/Stone/Getty Images; p. 312: SPL / Photo Researchers, Inc.; p. 314: (r) Cabisco/Visuals Unlimited; p. 315: (tl) Cabisco/Visuals Unlimited, (tr) Alfred Pasieka/Peter Arnold, (b) Nelson Thomson; p. 316: Ed Reschke/Peter Arnold; p. 321: Courtesy of Dr. Michael Sefton; p. 322: Cardio-Thoracic Centre/ Freeman Hospital/ Science Photo Library; p. 329: Sheila Terry/ Science Photo Library; p. 333: (l) CP/Andrew Vaughn, (r) Photodisc

CHAPTER 11: p. 349: Photodisc; p. 353: Manfred Kage/Peter Arnold; p. 357: RMF/Visuals Unlimited; p. 358: Juergen Berger/Max-Planck Institute/SPL/Photo Researchers, Inc.; p. 365: Science V.U./B.Ingelheim/Visuals Unlimited

CHAPTER 12: p. 377: Mark Oleskyn; p. 378: SIU Biomed/Custom Medical Stock Photo; p. 388: David M Phillips/Photo Researchers Inc.; p. 390: B. Nelson/Custom Medical Stock Photo; p. 391: AP Photo/PPL Therapeutics

CHAPTER 13: p. 403: © Dr. Dennis Kunkel/Visuals Unlimited; p. 407: (t) CP Photo/Kevork Djansezian, (b) City of Edmonton Archives, EA-10-2072; p. 411: CP Photo/Clifford Skarstdt; p. 430: (t) CP Photo, (b) University of Iowa; p. 431: (t) Science Photo Library/Photo Researchers, (b) Dr. M. Goedert / Photo Researchers, Inc.

CHAPTER 14: p. 445: (t) © Daryl Benson/Masterfile, (b) Janice Palmer; p. 446: © Lester Lefkowitz/CORBIS; p. 450: Ralph C. Eagle/Photo Researchers, Inc.; p. 455: Bill Kamin/Visuals Unlimited

CHAPTER 15: p. 469: CP Photo/Paul Chiasson; p. 473: C.O.R.E. Digital Pictures Inc.; p. 479: Dick Hemingway; p. 480: Banting House National Historic Site; p. 481: Courtesy of the Clinical Islet Transplant Program; p. 486: Ken Greer/Visuals Unlimited; p. 488: Biophoto Associates/Science Source/Photo Researchers, Inc.; p. 494: Bettman/CORBIS

CHAPTER 16: p. 507: Tracy Frankel/Image Bank/Getty Images; p. 508: (tl) Dr. Dennis Kunkel/Visuals Unlimited, (tr) Dr. Dennis Kunkel/Visuals Unlimited, (bl) Dr. Fred Hossler/Visuals Unlimited, (br) Dr. Fred Hossler/Visuals Unlimited; p. 509: (tl) Photodisc/Getty Images, (tm) Corel, (tr) © H. Reinhard/zefa/Corbis, (b) Pascal Goetgheluck / Photo Researchers, Inc.; p. 511: Francois Gohier/Photo Researchers, Inc.;

p. 514: G.Shih-R. Kessel/Visuals Unlimited; p. 521: David M. Phillips/ Visuals Unlimited; p. 530: (l) From Lennart Nilsson, A Child Is Born © 1966, 1977, Dell Publishing Company Inc., (m) Andy Walker, Midland Fertility Services/Science Photo Library, (r) Andy Walker, Midland Fertility Services/Science Photo Library; p. 533: (all) From Lennart Nilsson, A Child Is Born © 1966, 1977, Dell Publishing Company Inc.; p. 536: Courtesy of Dr. Keith Bagnall; p. 538: Oxford Scientific Films

CHAPTER 17: p. 553: © Dr. Gopal Murti/Visuals Unlimited; p. 555: (tl) K. Calentine/ Visuals Unlimited, (tr) Visuals Unlimited, (bl) David M. Phillips/Visuals Unlimited, (br) David M. Phillips/Visuals Unlimited; p. 557: John D. Cunningham/Visuals Unlimited; p. 560: Ed Reschke/ Peter Arnold; p. 561 (all) Ed Reschke/ Peter Arnold; p. 565: (l) J.A.L. Cooke/ Oxford Scientific Films, (ml) Kevin & Betty Collins/Visuals Unlimited, (mr) Mark E. Gibson/Visuals Unlimited, (r) Andre Gallant/ The Image Bank/Getty Images; p. 567: Science VU /Visuals Unlimited; p. 568: AP/Paul Clements; p. 575: A. Morris/ Visuals Unlimited; p. 582: Courtesy of Dr. Renee Martin; p. 583: (t) CP/Don Janisse, (b) CP/Frank Gunn; p. 584: (l) Scott Camazine/Oxford Scientific Films, (r) Valerie Lindgren/ Visuals Unlimited; p. 589: © Biodisc/Visuals Unlimited

CHAPTER 18: p. 597: (tl) CP/Ryan Remiorz, (tr) Doug MacLellan/Hockey Hall of Fame, (bl) CP/Shaney Komulainen; (br) Kurt Kreiger/CORBIS; p. 598: CORBIS; p. 608: Dr. Jeremy Burgess/Science Photo Library; p. 609: E.R. Degginger; p. 615: (all) Richard Siemens; p. 618: Photos.com; p. 620: Carolina Biological Supply Co.

CHAPTER 19: p. 627: © John McAnulty/CORBIS; p. 628: Royal Windsor Library; p. 629: Dr. D.R. Degginger; p. 633: Custom Medical Stock; p. 641: B. Ritter; p. 642: Getty Images; p. 646: (t) © Bettmann/CORBIS, (m) Courtesy of the National Library of Medicine, (b) Oliver Meckes/ E.O.S./MPI-Tubingen/Photo Researchers, Inc.; p. 648: Barrigton Brown/ Photo Researchers, Inc.; p. 649: Omikron/Photo Researchers, Inc.; p. 650: Bromide print by Vittoro Luzzati/National Portrait Gallery, London

CHAPTER 20: p. 661: Nelson Thomson; p. 668: 2313 R.C. Williams, Proc. Nat. Academy of Science 74 (1977); p. 678: Courtesy of Dr. Judith Hall

CHAPTER 21: p. 711: © Gunter Marx Photography/CORBIS; p. 713: Gary Meszaros/Visuals Unlimited; p. 714: (l) © Hal Beral/Visuals Unlimited, (r) Photos.com; p. 715: Will & Deni McIntyre/Photo Researchers, Inc.; p. 716: Merlin Tuttle/Bat Conservation International; p. 723: © John Cornell/Visuals Unlimited; p. 724: © Joe McDonald/ Visuals Unlimited; p. 728: © Joe McDonald/Visuals Unlimited; p. 729: © Gerald & Buff Coris/Visuals Unlimited

CHAPTER 22: p. 737: (t) A.B.P.L./Photo Researchers, Inc., (b) © Roger Garwood & Trish Ainslie/CORBIS; p. 738: Arthur Morris/Visuals Unlimited; p. 739: (t) Gary Meszaros/Visuals Unlimited, (b) Courtesy of Dr. Stephen Herrero; p. 740: (l) Frederick R. McConnaughey/Photo Researchers, Inc., (m) Fritz Polking/Visuals Unlimited, (r) Will & Deni McIntyre/Photo Researchers, Inc.; p. 742: (l) Janice Palmer, (r) Janice Palmer; p. 749: Arthur Morris/Visuals Unlimited; p. 750: Feltcher & Baylis/Photo Researchers, Inc.; p. 751: Gary Meszaros/Visuals Unlimited; p. 752: (t) Ken Lucas/Visuals Unlimited, (b) John Gerlach/Visuals Unlimited; p. 753: (l) Palmer SciEd Services, (r) Palmer SciEd Services; p. 755: (l) Alison Barnes Martin/Masterfile, (r) © Greg Dimijian/Photo Researchers, Inc.; p. 757: (l) Doug Fraser, (m) © Jim Hughes/Visuals Unlimited, (r) Shutterstock

CHAPTER 23: p. 763: (a) © Jacques Langevin/CORBIS SYGMA, (b) Bill Kamin/Visuals Unlimited, (c) B&C Alexander/First Light; p. 764: Mitch Reardon/Photo Researchers, Inc.; p. 767: Joe McDonald/Visuals Unlimited; p. 768: (tl) Bill Beatty/Visuals Unlimited, (bl) Gary Meszaros/ Visuals Unlimited, (m) Lincoln P. Brower, Sweet Briar College, (r) Lincoln P. Brower, Sweet Briar College; p. 769: Stephen J. Kraserman/ Photo Researchers; p. 770: D.M. Caron BES/Visuals Unlimited; p. 771: Larry Miller/Photo Researchers, Inc.; p. 772: Barbara Von Hoffman/Tom Stack & Associates; p. 780: top (a) Cheryl A. Ertelt/Visuals Umlimited, (b – top) William J. Weber/Visuals Unlimited, (b – bottom) Joe McDonald/ Visuals Unlimited, (c) S. Camazine/P.K.Visschers/Photo Researchers, Inc., (d) Doug Fraser; (bl) John Gerlach/Visuals Unlimited, (br) John Gerlach/Visuals Unlimited; p. 784: Doug Fraser